D1253263

# A GERMAN-ENGLISH DICTIONARY FOR CHEMISTS

Books by The Late Austin M. Patterson

A GERMAN-ENGLISH DICTIONARY FOR CHEMISTS
*Third edition*

A FRENCH-ENGLISH DICTIONARY FOR CHEMISTS
*Second edition*

TO

WILLIAM ALBERT NOYES

1857–1941

# PREFACE TO THE THIRD EDITION

Although this book is designed primarily for chemists and chemical engineers it contains a large number of terms from related fields of science and hence has proved useful also to physicists, biologists, geologists, etc. It was the first technical dictionary, as far as the author knows, to include a vocabulary of *general* words (see the Introduction). Special attention has been paid to prefixes, suffixes, and abbreviations. All the parts of speech are indicated by the customary marks. Labels are freely used to indicate the field in which a German word has a particular English meaning. Many obsolete or antiquated chemical terms are defined as a help to reading the older literature; where they might be confused with modern meanings they are distinguished by the label "*Old Chem.*" or in some other way. (It should be remembered that some terms that have been replaced in chemistry are still in use in pharmacy or industry.) Words that have the same, or practically the same, spelling in German and English have in general been omitted in order to economize space.

The Introduction furnishes hints for using the book and devotes special attention to the peculiarities of German chemical nomenclature.

The vocabulary in this edition contains an estimated total of 59,000 terms, some of the larger additions being in the fields of chemical technology, electronics, and warfare. Additional meanings are given for many terms that were listed in the earlier editions. The latest decisions in nomenclature are followed; in particular, the Stock valence names for inorganic compounds are freely given, as well as the older names.

The German-English vocabularies chiefly consulted are as follows: *General:* Duden, *Orthographisches Wörterbuch;* Flügel-Schmidt-Tanger, *Deutsch-Englisches Wörterbuch;* Hebert-Hirsch, *New German-English Dictionary;* Muret-Sanders, *Encyclopädisches Deutsch-Englisches Wörterbuch. Technical:* Allied Control Commission for Germany, *Glossary of Technical Terms of the Oil Industry;* Artschwager, *Dictionary of Biological Equivalents;* Bading, *Wörterbuch der Landwirtschaft;* Cissarz-Jones, *German-English Geological Terminology;* De Vries, *German-English Science Dictionary;* Eger, *Technologisches Wörterbuch;* Freeman, *Das Englische Fachwort;* Freeman, *Deutsch-Englisches Spezial-Wörterbuch für das Maschinenwesen;* Freeman, *Elektrotechnisches Englisch;* Freeman, *Fachwörterbuch der Metallurgie;* Harras, *Technologisches Wörterbuch;* Hinnerichs, *Deutsch-Englisches Fachwörterbuch;* Hoyer-Kreuter-Schlomann, *Technologisches Wörterbuch* (6th edition); I. G. Farbenindustrie,

*Fachwörterbuch für die Farbstoffe und Textilhilfsmittel verbrauchenden Industrien;* King-Fromherz, *German-English Chemical Terminology;* König-Bohrisch, *Warenlexikon für den Verkehr mit Drogen und Chemikalien;* Lang-Meyers, *German-English Medical Dictionary;* Lingen, *Deutsch-Englisch Fachwörterbuch Papier und Druck;* Mayer, *Chemisches Fachwörterbuch;* Partridge, *Dictionary of Bacteriological Equivalents;* Pietzsch, *Fremdsprachliches Optisches Wörterbuch;* Regen-Regen, *German-English Dictionary for Electronics Engineers and Physicists;* Ruis, *Bergbau Fachwörterbuch;* v. Seebach, *Fachwörterbuch für Bergbautechnik und Bergbauwirtschaft;* Singer, *German-English Dictionary of Metallurgy;* Slater, *Pitman's Technical Dictionary of Engineering and Industrial Science;* U. S. Air Force *German-English Technical Dictionary* (ed. Leidecker); Webel, *German-English Technical and Scientific Dictionary;* Wittfoht, *Kunststofftechnisches Wörterbuch;* and various glossaries. Textbooks, journals, and dealers' catalogs have also been examined for words.

The author is grateful to the many friends and correspondents who have coöperated in improving the dictionary. He is specially indebted to Prof. William T. Hall, Prof. C. W. Foulk, Prof. Paul Rothemund and Miss Janet D. Scott for assistance in proofreading and for suggestions; to Dr. E. J. Crane and the *Chemical Abstracts* corps for general help; to Prof. H. V. Knorr for coöperation on terms in atomic structure; and to Mr. T. E. R. Singer for aid in procuring German books after World War II. Others who deserve special mention are: Dr. Nicolas W. Baklanoff, Dr. D. D. Berolzheimer, Dr. C. C. Davis, Dr. Francis C. Frary, Miss Mildred W. Grafflin and associates, Dr. Geo. C. O. Haas, and Prof. Kurt F. Leidecker.

As in the past, corrections and suggestions for additions are welcomed.

AUSTIN M. PATTERSON

XENIA, OHIO
February, 1950

# GERMAN LETTERS

## With Their Roman Equivalents

| 𝔄 𝔞 | A a | 𝔒 𝔬 | O o |
|---|---|---|---|
| 𝔄̈ 𝔞̈ | Ä ä | 𝔒̈ 𝔬̈ | Ö ö |
| 𝔅 𝔟 | B b | 𝔓 𝔭 | P p |
| ℭ 𝔠 | C c | 𝔔 𝔮 | Q q |
| 𝔇 𝔡 | D d | ℜ 𝔯 | R r |
| 𝔈 𝔢 | E e | 𝔖 ſ 𝔰 | S s |
| 𝔉 𝔣 | F f | 𝔗 𝔱 | T t |
| 𝔊 𝔤 | G g | 𝔘 𝔲 | U u |
| ℌ 𝔥 | H h | 𝔘̈ 𝔲̈ | Ü ü |
| ℑ 𝔦 | I i | 𝔙 𝔳 | V v |
| 𝔍 𝔧 | J j | 𝔚 𝔴 | W w |
| 𝔎 𝔨 | K k | 𝔛 𝔵 | X x |
| 𝔏 𝔩 | L l | 𝔜 𝔶 | Y y |
| 𝔐 𝔪 | M m | ℨ 𝔷 | Z z |
| 𝔑 𝔫 | N n | ß | ss |

# ABBREVIATIONS

| | |
|---|---|
| *a.* | adjective. |
| *abbrev.* | abbreviation. |
| *adv.* | adverb. |
| *Aero.* | Aeronautics. |
| *Agric.* | Agriculture. |
| *Anat.* | Anatomy. |
| *Arith.* | Arithmetic. |
| *Astron.* | Astronomy. |
| *Bact.* | Bacteriology. |
| *Biol.* | Biology, Biological. |
| *Bot.* | Botany. |
| *Calico* | Calico Printing. |
| *Ceram.* | Ceramics. |
| *cf.* | compare. |
| *Chem.* | Chemistry. |
| *Com.* | Commerce. |
| *conj.* | conjunction. |
| *Cryst.* | Crystallography. |
| *Elec.* | Electricity. |
| *esp.* | especially. |
| *Expl.* | Explosives. |
| *f.* | feminine noun. |
| *fig.* | figuratively. |
| *gen.* | genitive. |
| *Geol.* | Geology. |
| *Geom.* | Geometry. |
| *interj.* | interjection. |
| *lit.* | literally, literatim. |
| *m.* | masculine noun. |
| *Mach.* | Machinery. |
| *Manuf.* | Manufacture. |
| *Math.* | Mathematics. |
| *Mech.* | Mechanics. |
| *Med.* | Medicine. |
| *Metal.* | Metallurgy. |
| *Micros.* | Microscopy. |
| *Mil.* | Military. |
| *Min.* | Mineralogy. |
| *n.* | neuter noun. |
| *Obs.* | obsolete. |
| *Org.* | Organic. |
| *p.a.* | participial adjective. |
| *Petrog.* | Petrography. |
| *Pharm.* | Pharmacy. |
| *Photog.* | Photography. |
| *Physiol.* | Physiology. |
| *pl.* | plural. |
| *p.p.* | past participle. |
| *pr.* | present. |
| *prep.* | preposition. |
| *pret.* | preterit. |
| *pron.* | pronoun. |
| *Pyro.* | Pyrotechnics. |
| *sing.* | singular. |
| *sp.* | species |
| *sp. gr.* | specific gravity. |
| *specif.* | specifically. |
| *Spect.* | Spectrography, Spectroscopy. |
| *subj.* | subjunctive. |
| *Tech.* | Technical, Technology. |
| *Teleg.* | Telegraphy. |
| *Thermochem.* | Thermochemistry. |
| *T.N.* | Trade Name. |
| *v.aux.* | auxiliary verb. |
| *v.i.* | intransitive verb. |
| *v.r.* | reflexive verb (with sich). |
| *v.t.* | transitive verb. |
| *Zoöl.* | Zoölogy. |

# INTRODUCTION

To the advanced worker in chemistry a knowledge of German is almost indispensable, since a very large proportion of chemical literature is published in that language. Even if he has had a good general course in German (which is too often not the case), he must become familiar with an immense special vocabulary which no dictionary can give completely. It is hoped, therefore, that the following hints as to the use of this dictionary will be found helpful.

**General Words.** A general vocabulary which is superior to many pocket dictionaries has been included, for two reasons: first, to save the user the trouble of looking up the more common German words in a separate dictionary; and secondly, because many general words have one or more technical meanings. In a general work these meanings are often either absent or buried among other senses. In this dictionary the special chemical meaning is put first or indicated in some way, the aim being in all cases to give the user immediately the meaning he is most likely to be seeking.

**Self-evident Words.** Words which are common to English and German (even with a slight variation in spelling), and which are therefore so readily recognized that they are not likely to be looked up, are omitted from the vocabulary, unless there is a special reason for inserting them.

**Spelling.** Owing to official German spelling reforms, many variant spellings appear in the current literature. In this book both old and new forms are freely given, or what seems to be the prevailing chemical usage is followed, though in doubtful cases the official form is preferred. Those who wish to know the correct official spellings should consult Duden's "Orthographisches Wörterbuch" (inexpensive) or some similar book. For ordinary purposes it will suffice to know the following changes, which are not all invariable, but which apply to many words:

**c** (hard) becomes **k,** as in Kohäsion.

**c** (with sound of ts) becomes **z,** as in Zylinder.

**fff** and similar triplets lose one member, as Schiffahrt for Schifffahrt.

**i** becomes **ie** in the verb ending -ieren (formerly -iren).

**ph** becomes **f,** as in Efeu (formerly Epheu).

**th** becomes **t,** as in Ton (formerly Thon).

**ti** becomes **zi** in certain cases, as in Reagenzien.

Umlauts are represented by two dots (never by e), as Ä instead of Ae. In this dictionary the only effect of an umlaut on the vocabulary order is to make the word follow a word of the same spelling without the umlaut. Thus fällen immediately follows fallen and is not placed under fae-. Similarly Äther is found under At-, not under Aet-.

In the vocabulary s is used to represent both ſ and 𝔰, and ss for ß (and sometimes for SZ when the word is spelled in capitals; thus STRASZE would be found as Strasse).

**Noun Endings.** Since the case endings of nouns are occasionally puzzling, a résumé of the ways in which German nouns may form nominative plurals from nominative singulars may be of assistance (note specially 7):

1. No change, as Kasten from Kasten.
2. Umlaut, as Vögel from Vogel.
3. Ending *-e*, as Jahre from Jahr.
4. Umlaut and *-e*, Bäume from Baum.
5. Ending *-er* and umlaut if possible, Männer from Mann, Kinder from Kind.
6. Ending *-n*, *-en*, or *-nen*, Blumen from Blume, Doktoren from Doktor, Wirtinnen from Wirtin.
7. Plurals from Latin and Greek neuters: Studien from Studium, Materialien from Material, Dramen from Drama.

The other cases are either the same as the corresponding nominative or formed from it, as follows: genitive singular, *-en*, *-ens*, *-es*, *-n*, *-ns*, or *-s;* dative and accusative singular and dative plural, *-n* or *-en*.

**Irregular Verbs.** The preterit, past participle, and present third singular (indicative) of *simple* verbs are given in all cases where the student might miss finding the meaning. In the case of compound verbs, if the irregular parts are not given one can easily find them by going back to the simple form; thus, if *verschob* is not found, *schob* is looked for and found to be the preterit of *schieben*, whence *verschob* is the preterit of *verschieben*. Again, if *zerrissen* were not found, the form *gerissen* would be looked up, because it is the corresponding part of the simple verb; it is the past participle of *reissen*, and accordingly *zerrissen* is from *zerreissen*. Regularly formed "strong" past participles like *gebacken* are not systematically entered because they merely prefix *ge-* to the infinitive. Participles used as adjectives are "run in" after the verbs from which they are derived. For the inflection of verbs, adjectives, etc., a grammar must be consulted.

**Adverbs.** Since in German nearly any adjective may be used adverbially without change of form, the user of the dictionary is ordinarily left to form these adverbial meanings for himself.

**Prefixes and Suffixes.** Combining forms are given plentifully in the vocabuiary in the hope that the reader may often be able to determine the meaning of words that are not found in the dictionary. He is earnestly urged to make use of them, especially the suffixes, which are likely to be overlooked. Some of those defined are: -ähnlich, -artig, -bar, -de, -el, -en, -er, -erlei, -ern, -fach, -falt, -faltig, -förmig, -haft, -haltig, -heit, -icht, -ieren, -ig, -in, -isch, -keit, -lich, -ling, -los, -mässig, -nis, -ös, -sam, -schaft, -ung, -ür, -wärts, -weise.

**Abbreviations.** Many abbreviations found in German chemical literature but not in English are entered in the vocabulary in their proper places, as if the letters composing them spelled a word. An abbreviation is often converted from singular to plural by doubling the final letter; as, *Lsg.*, Lösung; *Lsgg.*, Lösungen.

**Inorganic Nomenclature.** Compounds may be named in German merely by compounding the names of the elements; as, *Jodkalium* (potassium iodide), *Siliziumfluorwasserstoff* (hydrogen silicofluoride, fluosilicic acid). Words formed from the names of two elements are usually to be translated by giving the *-ide* ending to the first part (Jodkalium, potassium iod*ide*).

Compounds are also named in a manner more like the English method; as, *Strontiumchlorid* (strontium chloride), *Kaliumsulfid* (potassium sulfide). To indicate a lower compound the ending *-ür* is used where *-ous* or *sub-* would occur in English; as, *Kupferchlorür* (cuprous chloride), *Silberchlorür* (silver subchloride). In corresponding names *-id* and *-ür* are contrasted like *-ic* and *-ous* in English; thus, *Kupferchlorid*, in addition to its general sense of "copper chloride," is used particularly to designate cupric chloride. Another way of distinguishing between two compounds of the same elements is by the use of Latin combining forms; as, *Cuprochlorid*, cuprous chloride; *Cuprichlorid*, cupric chloride; or by the use of di-, tri-, etc., as in English. For the old prefixes zweifach, dreifach, etc., see the Vocabulary.

Higher and lower oxides are distinguished as *-oxyd* and *-oxydul* (*Eisenoxyd*, ferric oxide; *Eisenoxydul*, ferrous oxide) or by Latin forms (*Ferrioxyd*, ferric oxide; *Ferrooxyd*, ferrous oxide).

Names of acids in German are formed very simply by attaching the word Säure to some other word; as, *Salzsäure* (literally "salt acid"), hydrochloric acid; *Osmiumsäure*, osmic acid. These names are translated into English by attaching the ending *-ic acid* to a suitable combining form; as, *Zinnsäure* (literally "tin acid"), stannic acid, from *stannum*, Latin for tin. Hydracids are designated in German by the ending *-wasserstoffsäure;* as, *Bromwasserstoffsäure*, hydrobromic acid. The German equivalent of *-ous* in naming acids is *-ig;* as, *schweflige Säure*, or, less commonly, *Schwefligsäure*, sulfurous acid. Similarly, *unter-* corresponds to *hypo-* and *über-* to *per-* (*unterchlorige Säure*, hypochlorous acid; *Übermangansäure*, permanganic acid). Any acid name may form an adjective ending in *-sauer;* as, *salpetersaure Lösung*, nitric acid solution; *man-*

*gansaures Blei*, manganate of lead; *mangansaures Salz*, salt of manganic acid, manganate. Latin names for salts are also used; as, *Manganat*, manganate; and these occur in combination; as, *Bleimanganat*, lead manganate; *Chromisulfat*, chromic sulfate.

Words ending in *-it* in German, as, for instance, the names of a great many minerals, should as a rule be translated with the ending *-ite;* as, *Kainit*, kainite (not kainit). If it seems best to retain the original spelling of a trade name it should be placed in quotation marks or its initial letter should be capitalized; as, *Permutit*, permutite or "permutit" or Permutit.

**Organic Nomenclature.** There has been much carelessness in translating German organic names, and as a result many uncouth forms are seen in English articles. The following rules represent the usage of the American Chemical Society as embodied in the "Directions to Abstractors," and this harmonizes well with the best usage in Great Britain:

(1) Translate *oxy-* by *hydroxy-* when it designates hydroxyl, as is commonly the case. When *oxy-* designates the ketonic group it is preferably translated *oxo-*.

(2) Translate names of compounds the chief function of which is alcoholic (or phenolic) so that the name ends in *-ol;* as, glycerol, resorcinol, mannitol, pinacol (not pinacone).

(3) When the German ending *-ol* does not indicate hydroxyl it should be translated *-ole* (as, anisole, indole), or in the case of a few hydrocarbons *-ene* (as, *Benzol*, benzene; *Toluol*, toluene; *Styrol*, styrene).

(4) The ending *-in* should be translated *-ine* in the case of basic substances and *-in* elsewhere; as, aniline, glycine, palmitin, albumin. (But for names of alcohols see (2)).

(5) The form *amido-* should be so translated only when it is in combination with an acid group. Usually it is to be translated *amino-;* as, *Amidopropionsäure*, aminopropionic acid; *Amidophenol*, aminophenol. The same holds for imido-, anilido-, etc.

(6) In such combining forms as bromo-, cyano-, chloro-, nitro-, the connective *o* is to be used invariably (with the exception of a few well-established words such as acetamide, cyanamide); as, *Chlorbenzol*, chlorobenzene; *Chloressigsäure*, chloroacetic acid. This usage is by no means universal, but those who can not reconcile themselves to such spellings as "bromoacetic" should at least avoid the German forms bromphenol, acetphenetidine, etc., and use the connecting *o* before consonants.

(7) The German ending *-an* should be translated *-ane* if it is the name of a hydrocarbon (or parent heterocyclic compound) which is *fully saturated;* otherwise, *-an*. Examples: methane, menthane, tolan, furan, pentosan.

(8) Most German simple names of organic acids are correctly translated by

substituting *-ic acid* for *-säure.* Some of the exceptions are old-established names such as Milchsäure (lactic acid) and Valeriansäure (valeric acid). Elements coming before *-säure* that are likely to be dropped in translating are: vowels (*Syringasäure,* syringic acid; *Benzoesäure,* benzoic acid), *us* (*Cheiranthussäure,* cheiranthic acid), *um* or *ium* (*Cnidiumsäure,* cnidic acid). An *o* should be *inserted* in translating German Geneva names of acids (hydrocarbon name plus -säure), as, *Pentensäure,* pentenoic acid (not pentenic acid).

When the name ends in *-insäure* the translator *may* substitute *-ic acid* for this unless another acid already bears the resulting name; thus *Akridinsäure* is often called acridic acid instead of the longer acridinic acid, but *Mekoninsäure* should be translated meconinic acid because *Mekonsäure* has preëmpted the translation meconic acid. Such exceptions are given in the dictionary as far as possible, but in doubtful cases the longer form "-inic acid" would be the safer.

Names ending in *-carbonsäure* are translated *-carboxylic acid,* not -carbonic acid (but -carbonyl chloride is preferred to -carboxylyl chloride).

The student should be warned against confusing chemical endings and case endings; for example, *-en* may be equivalent to the English *-ene* or only a plural sign: *Terpenen* means not terpenene but terpenes; *Ketone* means not ketone but ketones; *Terpene,* not terpene but terpenes.

**How to Handle Difficulties.** If the word sought is not in the vocabulary, or if its meaning is not clear, the experienced dictionary user still has many resources. He is often able to "puzzle out" an obscure word, and the student should practise the art, using the context to guide him. A few possibilities are suggested:

1. The word may be a variant spelling. See *Spelling,* above, and look up other possible forms.

2. It may be an inflected form of a word given in the dictionary. See *Noun Endings* and *Irregular Verbs,* above. A thoro knowledge of German grammar is of course the best assistance here.

3. The word may be a verb with a separated prefix, such as *ab, an,* or *zu.* Look for this in the part of the sentence that follows, and hunt the meaning under the compound verb, or, if necessary, deduce what meaning you can from the meanings of the prefix and the simple verb. For example, in the sentence *es fängt an zu sieden,* the meaning of *fängt an* is found under *anfangen.* Such compound verbs are very numerous, and if not found in the vocabulary their meanings can often be guessed, for the prefixes are in reality merely adverbs attached to the verb.

4. The word may be formed from some word which is in the vocabulary by the addition of one or more prefixes or suffixes (see the paragraph on these, above). A number of these combining forms are common in chemical writings, as *ent-*, *-frei*, *-los*, *-widrig,* and their meanings should be familiar. So also verbal

nouns are freely formed from verbs by capitalizing the infinitive or by substituting *-ung* for *-en,* as Schmelzen or Schmelzung from schmelzen, and these cannot all be given.

5. The word may be a *compound* of two or more words. The capacity of German to form such compounds is much greater than that of English, and although a large number are found in this dictionary they are only a small part of those in the literature. Many words drop or add letters in combining. The general meaning of many such combining forms is given in the vocabulary. Occasionally the beginner may make a wrong division of a compound word, and he should bear this in mind; for instance, Gastrolle is from Gast and Rolle, not from Gas and Trolle. See also the rule for dropping one member of a triplet letter (under *Spelling,* above). In deciphering the meaning of compound words the student who is able will frequently find it helpful to think of the Latin or Greek equivalents; thus, Überführung means trans-ference; Königswasser means aqua regia; Lichtmesser, photo-meter.

Persistent practice is the great essential to acquiring a foreign language vocabulary and sensing its word order and idioms. At the outset the chemical student will find it very helpful to read in German elementary chemical textbooks with the subject matter of which he is familiar. This will serve the double purpose of review and German practice.

# GERMAN-ENGLISH DICTIONARY FOR CHEMISTS

## A

**a.,** *abbrev.* (aus) of; (an, am) on; (asymmetrisch) asymmetric(al); ana-.

**A,** *abbrev.* (Arbeit) work; (Atomgewicht) atomic weight.

**A.,** *abbrev.* Alkohol; Annalen der Chemie; ampere(s).

**Ä.,** *abbrev.* (Äther) ether.

**Aal,** *m.* eel.

**a.a.O.,** *abbrev.* (an anderen Orten) elsewhere; (an angeführten, or angegebenen, Orte) in the place cited.

**Aar,** *m.* eagle.

**Aas,** *n.* fleshings, scrapings (from hides); carrion, carcass; groats.

**aasen,** *v.t.* flesh (hides).

**Aas-geruch,** *m.* carrion odor. **-schmiere,** *f.* (*Leather*) flesh-side dubbing. **-seite,** *f.* (*Leather*) flesh side.

**ab,** *adv.* off, away, down. — *prep.* from, since. — **— und zu,** to and fro; off and on.

**Abakafaser,** *f.* abacá (Manila hemp) fiber.

**abänderlich,** *a.* alterable, modifiable.

**abändern,** *v.t.* modify, change, alter, vary, amend.

**Abänderung,** *f.* modification; alteration; variation; amendment; variant.

**Abänderungspatent,** *n.* reissue patent.

**abarbeiten,** *v.t.* work off; rough-work; tire out. — *v.r.* overwork.

**Abart,** *f.* variety, modification, variant.

**abarten,** *v.i.* vary; deviate; degenerate.

**abätmen, abatmen,** *v.t.* glow (a cupel); cupel; anneal.

**abätzen,** *v.t.* corrode, corrode off, eat away. — **abätzend,** *p.a.* corrosive, corroding.

**Abb.,** *abbrev.* (Abbildung) cut, illustration.

**Abbau,** *m.* decomposition, disintegration, analysis (as opposed to synthesis), degradation; demolishing; dismounting, disassembly, dismantling; (*Mining*) working; (*Physiol.*) catabolism.

**abbauen,** *v.t.* decompose, disintegrate, analyze, degrade, etc. (see Abbau).

**Abbau-mittel,** *n.* decomposing or disintegrating agent. **-produkt,** *n.* decomposition product, degradation product. **-stufe,** *f.* step or stage in decomposition or degradation.

**abbauverhindernd,** *a.* antidisintegrant, stabilizing.

**abbeissen,** *v.i.* bite off; nip off.

**Abbeizdruck,** *m.* (*Calico*) discharge printing.

**abbeizen,** *v.t.* remove with corrosives; scour; (*Metal.*) dip, pickle; (*Calico*) discharge; (*Leather*) dress. — **abbeizend,** *p.a.* corrosive.

**Abbeizmittel,** *n.* corrosive; pickling agent; paint remover.

**Abbeizung,** *f.* scouring, etc. (see abbeizen).

**abbersten,** *v.i.* burst off, crack off, fly off.

**abberufen,** *v.t.* call away, recall.

**abbestellen,** *v.t.* revoke, countermand.

**abbiegen, abbeugen,** *v.t.* bend off, bend aside, turn off, deflect; diffract; snap off; (*Grammar*) inflect.

**Abbiegung, Abbeugung,** *f.* deflection, etc. (see abbiegen).

**Abbild,** *n.* copy, image, likeness.

**abbilden,** *v.t.* portray, copy, model; focus; describe, represent. — **abbildend,** *p.a.* portraying, etc.; (*Optics*) image-forming.

**Abbildung,** *f.* illustration, cut; representation, portrait, copy; (*Optics*) image formation, also image.

**Abbildungsvermögen,** *n.* resolving power (of a microscope).

**abbimsen,** *v.t.* rub with pumice; (*Leather*) friz, fluff, buff.

**abbinden,** *v.t.* unbind, untie, loosen; tie off; remove (by chemical combination); castrate; frame. — *v.i.* (of cement, etc.) set.

**Abbindezeit,** *f.* setting time (of cement, etc.).

**Abbitte,** *f.* apology; deprecation.

**abbitten,** *v.t.* apologize for; beg. — **abbittend,** *p.a.* deprecatory.

**Abblasehahn,** *m.* blowoff cock.

**abblasen,** *v.t.* blow away, blow off, blow; blast (castings); distil off. — *v.i.* (of gases) expand.

**Abblaseventil,** *n.* blowoff valve.

**abblassen,** *v.i.* fade, lose color, grow pale.

**abblättern,** *v.r. & i.* scale off, exfoliate; desquamate; shed the leaves. — *v.t.* descale; strip of leaves.

**Abblätterung,** *f.* scaling off, exfoliation; stripping of leaves.

**Abblätterungsmittel,** *n.* exfoliative.

**abbläuen,** *v.t.* blue (fabrics). — *v.i.* lose blue color.

**abbleichen,** *v.t.* bleach, bleach out. — *v.i.* fade; finish bleaching; pale.

**abblenden,** *v.t.* screen off; (*Photog.*) stop down; black out.

**abblicken,** *v.i.* (*Metal.*) grow dull after the flash or "blick."

**abblitzen,** *v.i.* miss fire; cease lightening.

**abblühen,** *v.i.* cease blooming; fade, wither.

**abborken,** *v.t.* strip (of bark), bark, debark.

**abböschen,** *v.t.* slope, slant.

**Abbrand,** *m.* burnt or roasted ore; waste (in forging, etc.); loss by burning, consumption; calcination.

**abbrauchen,** *v.t.* use up, wear out.

**abbrauen,** *v.t.* brew (thoroly). — *v.i.* finish brewing.

**abbraunen,** *v.i.* lose brown color.

**abbräunen,** *v.t.* brown, dye brown (thoroly). — *v.i.* lose brown color.

**abbrausen,** *v.t.* rinse off; drench. — *v.i.* cease effervescing; cease roaring; go off with a roar.

**abbrechen,** *v.t.* break off, break up, interrupt, discontinue, remove; deduct. — *v.i.* break off; leave off.

**abbreiten,** *v.t.* stretch out, flatten.

**abbremsen,** *v.t.* check, retard, brake, decelerate.

**abbrennbar,** *a.* combustible, deflagrable.

**Abbrennbarkeit,** *f.* combustibility, deflagrability.

**abbrennen,** *v.i.* burn off, away, or down; deflagrate; miss fire. — *v.t.* burn off, away, or down; deflagrate; calcine; fire off; temper: distil off; dip, pickle; cauterize; sear, singe; (*Ceram.*) finish firing.

**Abbrenner,** *m.* deflagrator.

**Abbrenn-glocke,** *f.* deflagrating jar. **-löffel,** *m.* deflagrating spoon.

**Abbrennung,** *f.* burning off, etc. (see abbrennen).

**abbreviieren,** *v.t.* abbreviate.

**abbringen,** *v.t.* bring off, get off, remove; turn off; dissuade; lead astray.

**abbröckeln,** *v.i.* scale off, chip off; crumble away. — *v.t.* break off in bits.

**Abbruch,** *m.* breaking off or down; discontinuance; fragment; damage; breach; demolition.

**abbrüchig,** *a.* crumbly, friable, brittle; detrimental.

**abbrühen,** *v.t.* scald, seethe, parboil.

**Abbrühkessel,** *m.* scalding kettle.

**abbuffen,** *v.t.* buff.

**abbürsten,** *v.t.* brush off, brush.

**Abdachung,** *f.* slope, declivity; unroofing.

**abdämmen,** *v.t.* dam off, dam up.

**Abdampf,** *m.* exhaust steam, waste steam.

**Abdampf-.** evaporating; exhaust-steam. **-apparat,** *m.* evaporating apparatus.

**abdampfen,** *v.t.* & *i.* evaporate; volatilize (solids); vaporize; boil down; (of steam) exhaust.

**Abdampfen,** *n.* evaporation, etc. (see abdampfen).

**abdämpfen,** *v.t.* evaporate; volatilize; steam; scald; stew; quench (charcoal); damp.

**Abdampf-gefäss,** *n.* evaporating vessel. **-heizung,** *f.* waste-steam heating. **-kapelle,** *f.* evaporating capsule. **-kasserole,** *f.* evaporating pan. **-kessel,** *m.* evaporating kettle or pan. **-kolben,** *m.* evaporating flask. **-leitung,** *f.* exhaust-steam line. **-maschine,** *f.* evaporator; (*Ceram.*) slip kiln. **-ofen,** *m.* (*Ceram.*) slip kiln. **-pfanne,** *f.* evaporating pan. **-rückstand,** *m.* residue on evaporation. **-schale,** *f.* evaporating dish or basin. **-temperatur,** *f.* temperature of evaporation. **-trichter,** *m.* evaporating funnel.

**Abdampfung,** *f.* evaporation; volatilization.

**Abdampfungs-gefäss,** *n.* evaporating vessel. **-kessel,** *m.* evaporating kettle or pan. **-pfanne,** *f.* evaporating pan. **-rückstand,** *m.* residue on evaporation.

**Abdampfvorrichtung,** *f.* evaporating apparatus, evaporator.

**abdanken,** *v.t.* dismiss, retire. — *v.i.* resign, retire.

**abdarren,** *v.t.* dry, kiln-dry, desiccate, cure (by drying); (*Metal.*) liquate.

**Abdarrtemperatur,** *f.* (*Brewing*) finishing temperature.

**abdecken,** *v.t.* uncover, unroof; skin, flay; cover; screen off (rays).

**Abdeckereifett, Abdeckerfett,** *n.* fat from flaying.

**Abdeckerhaut,** *f.* (*Leather*) morkin.

**Abdeckplatte,** *f.* cover plate.

**Abdeckung,** *f.* uncovering; flaying; covering.

**Abdeckvorrichtung,** *f.* covering device.

**abdekantieren,** *v.t.* decant.

**abdestillieren,** *v.t.* distil off, distil.

**abdichten,** *v.t.* make tight, calk, lute, seal, pack.

**Abdichtung,** *f.* making tight, calking, luting, sealing, packing.

**abdicken,** *v.t.* boil down, evaporate down, thicken (by boiling), inspissate.

**Abdickung,** *f.* boiling down, etc. (see abdicken).

**abdissoziieren,** *v.t.* & *i.* dissociate (off).

**abdörren,** *v.t.* dry up, dry thoroly, parch, roast.

**Abdörrofen,** *m.* refining furnace.

**Abdraht,** *m.* turnings.

**abdrehen,** *v.t.* turn off (gas, etc.); turn (on a lathe); dress; twist off; unscrew.

**Abdreh-maschine,** *f.* lathe; (*Ceram.*) finishing machine. **-späne,** *m.pl.* turnings. **-spindel,** *f.* (*Ceram.*) finishing machine.

**abdringen,** *v.t.* extort (from).
**Abd. Rk.,** *abbrev.* (Abderhalden'sche Reaktion) Abderhalden reaction.
**abdrosseln,** *v.t.* throttle, choke, shut off.
**Abdruck,** *m.* copy, impression, print; transfer; cast; printing, copying; counterpart.
**abdrucken,** *v.t.* print; stamp; copy (by pressure), mold (by pressure).
**abdrücken,** *v.t.* press off; force out; fire (a gun).
**Abdruckmasse,** *f.* molding material.
**abduften,** *v.i.* lose aroma or smell; fade, grow dim.
**abdunkeln,** *v.t.* darken, sadden (colors). — *v.i.* grow darker.
**Abdunklungsmittel,** *n.* (*Dyeing*) saddening agent.
**abdunsten,** *v.i.* evaporate; vaporize.
**Abdunsten,** *n.* evaporation.
**abdünsten,** *v.t.* evaporate; vaporize; graduate (brine).
**Abdunstung, Abdünstung,** *f.* evaporation.
**Abdünstungshaus,** *n.* (*Salt*) graduation house.
**abecelich,** *a.* alphabetic.
**abeichen,** *v.t.* gage, adjust (measures).
**Abelmoschkorn, Abelmoschuskorn,** *n.* abelmosk seed.
**Abel-prüfer,** *m.* Abel tester. **-test,** *m.* Abel test.
**Abend,** *m.* evening, night. **-brot, -essen,** *n.* supper. **-land,** *n.* western country, West, Occident.
**abendländisch,** *a.* western, occidental.
**Abendmahl,** *n.* evening meal, supper.
**abends,** *adv.* in the evening.
**abendwärts,** *adv.* westward.
**Abenteuer,** *n.* adventure.
**aber,** *conj.* but, however.
**Aberglaube,** *m.* superstition.
**aberkennen,** *v.t.* dispossess; abrogate; deprive. — *v.i.* pass sentence.
**abermalig,** *a.* repeated, further, new.
**abermals,** *adv.* again.
**Aberraute,** *f.* = Eberraute.
**aberregen,** *v.t.* deactivate, de-energize.
**aberwitzig,** *a.* crazy, foolish.
**Abessinien,** *n.* Abyssinia.
**abfachen,** *v.t.* classify; partition.
**abfahrbar,** *a.* removable.
**abfahren,** *v.i.* depart, leave. — *v.t.* carry off, cart off; take off, remove.
**Abfahrt,** *f.* departure; emigration.
**Abfall,** *m.* falling off; decrease, drop, deterioration, decline, loss; slope, declivity; desertion; contrast; (also *pl.* **Abfälle**) waste, refuse, by-product, chips, parings, cuttings, scrap, tailings, garbage, etc.
**Abfall-.** waste, refuse; descending. **-baumwolle,** *f.* cotton waste. **-brennstoff,** *m.* refuse fuel. **-eimer,** *m.* waste bucket, waste pail. **-eisen,** *n.* scrap iron.
**abfallen,** *v.i.* fall off; descend; diminish, drop, decrease; decay; be lost or wasted; lose flesh; slope; deviate; desert; be rebuffed; contrast badly. —**abfallend,** *p.a.* falling off; deciduous; sloping.
**Abfallerzeugnis,** *n.* waste product.
**Abfälleverwertung,** *f.* utilization of waste.
**Abfall-fett,** *n.* waste fat or grease. **-gummi,** *n.* waste rubber, scrap rubber. **-gut,** *n.* waste material (to be treated for recovery). **-hefe,** *f.* waste yeast. **-holz,** *n.* waste wood.
**abfällig,** *a.* falling off, sloping, etc. (see abfallen); deciduous; adverse.
**Abfall-kohle,** *f.* waste coal or charcoal. **-koks,** *m.* coke breeze, refuse coke. **-lauge,** *f.* spent lye. **-marke,** *f.* (*Dyeing*) off shade. **-öl,** *n.* waste oil. **-papier,** *n.* waste paper. **-produkt,** *n.* by-product; waste product. **-salz,** *n.* waste salt. **-säure,** *f.* waste acid, spent acid. **-seife,** *f.* waste soap, soap waste. **-stoff,** *m.* waste material, specif. sewage. **-strom,** *m.* (*Elec.*) waste current. **-tonne,** *f.* refuse barrel (or keg, cask, tun). **-topf,** *m.* waste jar. **-vernichtung,** *f.* destruction of waste. **-ware,** *f.* rejected ware, culls. **-wasser,** *n.* waste water, sewage.
**abfangen,** *v.t.* catch, capture, intercept; tap (molten metal).
**Abfangverfahren,** *n.* interception process.
**abfärben,** *v.t.* dye (thoroly); finish dyeing. — *v.i.* lose color, bleed, crock, rub off; (*Min.*) give a colored streak; (*Paper*) rub off.
**abfärbig,** *a.* liable to crock or rub off.
**abfasern,** *v.i.* & *r.* lose fibers, fuzz; unravel.
**abfassen,** *v.t.* write, word, compose, draw up; catch, seize; bend (iron).
**Abfasser,** *m.* writer.
**abfedern,** *v.t.* provide with springs; (*Expl.*) cushion; free from feathers.
**Abfegemittel,** *n.* detergent.
**abfegen,** *v.t.* sweep away or off; clean. —**abfegend,** *p.a.* detergent.
**abfeilen,** *v.t.* file off.
**Abfeilicht,** *n.* filings.
**abfertigen,** *v.t.* send off, dispatch; finish.
**Abfett,** *m.* fat taken off, skimmings.
**abfetten,** *v.t.* take fat or grease from, degrease.
**abfeuern,** *v.t.* fire off.
**abfiedeln,** *v.t.* (*Metal.*) skim off.
**abfiltrieren, abfiltern,** *v.t.* filter off.
**Abfiltrierung,** *f.* filtering off, filtration.
**abfinden,** *v.t.* pay off, satisfy. — *v.r.* settle, reach an agreement; reckon (with); put up (with).
**Abfindung,** *f.* indemnification, satisfaction.
**abflachen,** *v.t.* make flat, level; bevel. — **abgeflacht,** *p.a.* flattened, flat; oblate; shallow.
**Abflachung,** *f.* flattening, leveling; beveling, bevel; (of a curve) rounding off.
**abflammen,** *v.t* singe, gas; grease, tallow (hides).

**abflauen,** *v.t.* wash, scour (ore), buddle. — *v.i.* decrease, diminish.

**abfleckecht,** *a.* fast to rubbing, not spotting.

**abflecken,** *v.i.* stain, make stains. — *v.t.* remove spots from.

**abfleischen,** *v.t.* flesh (hides).

**abfliegen,** *v.i.* fly away, fly off.

**abfliessen,** *v.i.* flow away or off or down, discharge, drain.

**abfluchten,** *v.t.* line out, mark out, align.

**Abfluss,** *m.* flowing off, efflux, discharge; outlet; drain pipe; effluent; waste water. **-geschwindigkeit,** *f.* velocity of discharge. **-hahn,** *m.* discharge cock. **-kühler,** *m.* a condenser which leads the condensate away, efflux condenser (contrasted with Rückflusskühler). **-leitung,** *f.* outlet pipe, drain pipe.

**abflusslos,** *a.* having no outlet.

**Abfluss-menge,** *f.* amount of discharge. **-öffnung,** *f.* discharge opening, outlet. **-rinne,** *f.* outlet trough, discharge gutter. **-rohr, -röhrchen,** *n.* discharge tube, outlet tube, waste pipe, escape pipe. **-ventil,** *n.* discharge valve. **-wasser,** *n.* waste water.

**Abfolge,** *f.* series, sequence; conclusion, inference.

**abfordern,** *v.t.* demand; recall (a person).

**abformen,** *v.t.* form, shape, mold; copy, imitate.

**abfragen,** *v.t.* question; elicit (by questions).

**abfräsen,** *v.t.* mill off or away.

**abfressen,** *v.t.* eat away or up; corrode (off); remove by caustics; consume.

**abfrieren,** *v.i.* freeze off, freeze.

**Abfrischen,** *n.* (*Brewing*) changing of steep water.

**Abfuhr,** *f.* removal; outlet; transport, carriage. **-dünger,** *m.* night soil.

**abführen,** *v.t.* lead off, draw off, carry away, remove; send (goods); draw (wire); exhaust (steam); (*Med.*) evacuate, purge. — **abführend,** *p.a.* (*Med.*) purgative, laxative, aperient, efferent, excretory. — **abführendes Brausepulver,** Seidlitz powder.

**Abführ-gang,** *m.* (*Physiol.*) efferent duct. **-mittel,** *n.* purgative, aperient. **-pille,** *f.* cathartic pill, purgative pill. **-salz,** *n.* aperient salt.

**Abführung,** *f.* leading off, etc. (see abführen); outlet; discharge.

**Abführungs-gang, -kanal,** *m.* excretory passage or duct; efferent duct. **-rohr,** *n.* discharge tube or pipe.

**Abfüll-apparat,** *m.* emptying apparatus, etc. (see abfüllen); (*Brewing*) racker. **-bütte,** *f.* (*Brewing*) racking square.

**abfüllen,** *v.t.* empty, draw off (wine, etc.), drain off; rack, decant; take off, skim off (scum or dross).

**Abfüll-flasche,** *f.* bottle or jar into which something is emptied or drawn off. **-pipette,** *f.* delivery pipet(te). **-schlauch,** *m.* (*Brewing*) racking hose. **-trichter,** *m.* filling funnel. **-vorrichtung,** *f.* emptying contrivance or apparatus.

**Abfurchung,** *f.* division, segmentation.

**abfüttern, abfuttern,** *v.t.* case, line; feed.

**Abgabe,** *f.* delivery; giving off, emission, evolution, escape (of gases, etc.); tax, duty; (*Com.*) draft; royalty. **-rohr,** *n.*, **-röhre,** *f.* delivery tube, outlet tube, escape tube.

**Abgang,** *m.* waste; loss; decrease, decline; going off, leaving; escape (of gases, etc.); miscarriage; sale, market. — **Abgänge,** *pl.* (*Metal.*) tailings.

**abgängig,** *a.* waste; wanting; salable; decrepit.

**Abgangpapier,** *n.* waste paper.

**Abgangs-dampf,** *m.* exhaust steam. **-rohr,** *n.* waste pipe. **-säure,** *f.* waste acid, spent acid.

**abgären,** *v.i.* ferment; cease fermenting.

**Abgas,** *n.* waste gas; flue gas; exhaust gas. **-vorwärmer,** *m.* forewarmer.

**abgäschen,** *v.i.* cease foaming or fermenting.

**abgautschen,** *v.t.* (*Paper*) couch.

**abgeben,** *v.t.* give up or off, part with; deliver; yield; serve as, act as. — *v.r.* occupy oneself.

**abgebrochen,** *p.p.* of abbrechen.

**abgebunden,** *p.p.* of abbinden.

**abgedroschen,** *p.a.* trite, hackneyed.

**abgeflacht,** *p.a.* see abflachen.

**abgegriffen,** *p.a.* worn, worn-out.

**abgehen,** *v.i.* pass off, come off, go away, pass away.

**abgehoben,** *p.p.* of abheben.

**abgekürzt,** *p.a.* see abkürzen.

**abgelegen,** *p.a.* see abliegen.

**abgeleitet,** *p.p.* (of ableiten), derived, etc.

**Abgeltung,** *f.* remuneration, compensation.

**abgemessen,** *p.a.* see abmessen.

**abgeneigt,** *p.a.* disinclined.

**Abgeordnete,** *m.* deputy, delegate.

**abgeplattet,** *p.a.* see abplatten.

**abgerben,** *v.t.* tan (thoroly).

**abgerundet,** *p.a.* see abrunden.

**Abgesandte,** *m.* envoy, delegate.

**Abgeschäumtes,** *n.* skimmings.

**abgeschieden,** *p.a.* see abscheiden.

**abgeschliffen,** *p.p.* of abschleifen.

**Abgeschliffenheit,** *f.* polish.

**abgeschlossen,** *p.p.* of abschliessen.

**abgeschmackt,** *p.a.* tasteless, insipid; absurd.

**abgeschmolzen,** *p.p.* of abschmelzen.

**abgeschwefelt,** *p.a.* desulfurized, etc. (see abschwefeln).

**abgesehen,** *p.a.* see absehen.

**abgespannt,** *p.a.* see abspannen.

**abgestanden,** *p.a.* see abstehen.

**abgestellt,** *p.p.* (of abstellen) turned off, etc.

**abgestrichen,** *p.p.* of abstreichen.

**abgestumpft,** *p.a.* see abstumpfen.
**abgetan,** *p.p.* of abtun.
**abgetrieben,** *p.p.* of abtreiben.
**abgewinnen,** *v.t.* win, win away.
**abgewogen,** *p.p.* of abwägen.
**abgewöhnen,** *v.t.* wean, break of a habit.
**abgezogen,** *p.p.* of abziehen.
**abgiessen,** *v.t.* pour off, decant; (*Founding*) cast; (*Metal.*) pour, teem.
**Abglanz,** *m.* reflection.
**abglätten,** *v.t.* polish, polish off.
**abgleichen,** *v.t.* make equal, equalize; level; smooth; justify (coins); balance (accounts).
**abgleiten,** *v.i.* glide off, slide off, glance.
**abgliedern,** *v.t.* dismember.
**abglühen,** *v.t.* heat thoroly, make red-hot, anneal; mull (wine). — *v.r.* cease glowing, cool gradually.
**abgraten,** *v.t.* trim, burr.
**Abgratschrott,** *m.* trimmings.
**abgreifen,** *v.t.* read off; wear out.
**abgrenzbar,** *a.* definable, limitable.
**abgrenzen,** *v.t.* mark off; bound; define.
**Abgrenzung,** *f.* demarcation, boundary.
**Abgriff,** *m.* reading off; recording.
**Abgrund,** *m.* abyss, chasm, precipice.
**Abguss,** *m.* pouring off, decanting; casting, cast; sink.
**abh.,** *abbrev.* (abhängig) dependent.
**Abh.,** *abbrev.* (Abhandlung) treatise, paper; transactions (of a society)
**abhaaren,** *v.t.* remove hair from, depilate, unhair.
**abhalten,** *v.t.* keep off or back, detain, deter, hinder; endure; hold (a meeting).
**Abhaltung,** *f.* hindrance, impediment; holding, celebration.
**abhandeln,** *v.t.* treat (of), discuss, examine into; buy; bargain for.
**abhanden,** *adv.* missing, lost.
**Abhandlung,** *f.* treatise, paper, article, dissertation, discourse; transaction.
**Abhang,** *m.* slope, declivity.
**abhangen,** *v.i.* depend; slope; hang down.
**abhängen,** *v.t.* take off or down, disconnect.
**abhängig,** *a.* dependent; sloping, inclined.
**Abhängigkeit,** *f.* dependence; slope.
**abhären,** *v.t.* = abhaaren.
**abhärten,** *v.t.* harden; temper (iron or steel); (*Med.*) strengthen.
**abharzen,** *v.t.* take resin from, tap.
**abhäuten,** *v.t.* skin; peel; abrade; (*Founding*) free of scum.
**abhebbar,** *a.* removable.
**abheben,** *v.t.* lift off, take off; skim off.
**abhebern,** *v.t.* siphon off.
**abhelfen,** *v.t.* help, remedy, correct.
**abhellen,** *v.t.* clarify, clear; fine (wine). — *v.r.* become clear.
**abhetzen,** *v.t.* overwork, harass.
**Abhilfe,** *f.* remedy, redress.
**Abhitze,** *f.* waste heat. **-kessel,** *m.* waste-heat boiler. **-verwertung,** *f.* waste-heat utilization.
**abhobeln,** *v.t.* plane off, plane, smooth.
**abhold,** *a.* unfavorable, averse.
**abholen,** *v.t.* fetch off, call for.
**abholzen,** *v.t.* cut off, clear (of timber).
**abhören,** *v.t.* hear; examine; audit.
**Abhub,** *m.* matter lifted off: scum, waste, dross, etc.
**abhülsen,** *v.t.* shell, hull, husk, peel.
**Abiesöl,** *n.* fir oil, abies oil.
**Abietinsäure,** *f.* abietic acid. **-äthylester,** *m.* ethyl abietate.
**Abirrung,** *f.* deviation, aberration.
**Abk.,** *abbrev.* (Abkürzung) abbreviation.
**abkalken,** *v.t.* unlime.
**abkälten,** *v.t.* cool, cool down.
**abkanten,** *v.t.* bevel; trim; fold.
**abkapseln,** *v.t.* encapsulate, encyst.
**abkarten,** *v.t.* prearrange, plot.
**abkehren,** *v.t.* turn away or aside, avert, divert; sweep, brush (off).
**abkeltern,** *v.t.* press (wine).
**abkippen,** *v.t.* dump, tip; pour out.
**abklappen,** *v.t.* swing aside or out; move the flaps of; open.
**abklären,** *v.t.* clarify, clear, defecate, fine; (according to method) filter, decant, elutriate, etc.; decolor (sugar); brighten (a color); strip off, boil off (a dye). — *v.r.* clear, clear up.
**Abklär-flasche,** *f.* decanting bottle (or flask). **-gefäss,** *n.* decanting vessel. **-topf,** *m.* decanting jar.
**Abklärung,** *f.* clarification, etc. (see abklären).
**Abklärungs-flasche,** *f.* = Abklärflasche. **-gefäss,** *n.* decanting vessel. **-methode,** *f.* method of clarification. **-mittel,** *n.* clarifying agent.
**Abklatsch,** *m.* print, copy; proof (sheet).
**abklatschen,** *v.t.* knock off; strike off, print; impress; transfer (a design).
**abklemmen,** *v.t.* pinch off, squeeze off.
**abklingen,** *v.i.* die away, die out, fade, damp; lose radioactivity, decay.
**Abkling(ungs)kurve,** *f.* curve of (radioactive) decay.
**Abklingzeit,** *f.* decay period.
**abklopfen,** *v.t.* beat; beat off, knock off; scale off; (*Med.*) percuss.
**abklören,** *v.t.* boil out (for redyeing).
**abknallen,** *v.i.* go off, explode. — *v.t.* fire off.
**abkneifen,** *v.t.* pinch off, nip off.
**abknicken,** *v.t.* bend (sharply); crack or snap off.
**abknistern,** *v.i.* decrepitate.
**Abknisterung,** *f.* decrepitation.
**abkochecht,** *a.* fast to boiling.
**abkochen,** *v.t.* boil, decoct; boil off; reboil.

**Abkochmittel,** *n.* decoction medium.
**Abkochung,** *f.* decoction; boiling.
**abkommen,** *v.i.* get off; be spared; grow out of use.
**Abkommen,** *n.* agreement; disuse.
**Abkommen,** *n.* agreement; (*Optics*) graticule; disuse.
**Abkömmling,** *m.* derivative; descendant.
**abkratzen,** *v.t.* scrape off, scrape.
**abkreiden,** *v.i.* (of paint, etc.) chalk.
**abkrücken,** *v.t.* rake off.
**Abkühlapparat,** *m.* cooler, refrigerator.
**abkühlen,** *v.t. & i.* cool, cool down, chill, refrigerate; anneal.
**Abkühler,** *m.* cooler.
**Abkühl-fass,** *n.* cooler, cooling vat; (*Glass*) annealing oven. **-gefäss,** *n.* cooling vessel. **-mittel,** *n.* cooling agent, refrigerant.
**Abkühlung,** *f.* cooling, refrigeration; chilling; annealing.
**Abkühlungs-dauer,** *f.* duration of cooling. **-fläche,** *f.* cooling surface. **-geschwindigkeit,** *f.* rate of cooling. **-gesetz,** *n.* law of cooling. **-kurve,** *f.* cooling curve. **-mittel,** *n.* refrigerant. **-oberfläche,** *f.* cooling surface. **-spannung,** *f.* cooling strain. **-zeit,** *f.* time of cooling, cooling period.
**Abkühlverlust,** *m.* loss from cooling.
**Abkunft,** *f.* origin, descent; breed, stock.
**abkuppeln,** *v.t.* uncouple, disconnect.
**abkürzen,** *v.t.* shorten, abbreviate; truncate. — **abgekürzt,** *p.a.* shortened; truncated; concise.
**Abkürzung,** *f.* abbreviation.
**abladen,** *v.t.* unload, discharge.
**Ablage,** *f.* laying down; storage place, depot.
**ablagern,** *v.t. & i.* deposit; store; age, mellow, mature, season. — *v.r.* deposit, settle, subside.
**Ablagerung,** *f.* deposit; deposition; sediment; sedimentation; storage.
**Ablagerungsmenge,** *f.* amount of deposit.
**ablaktieren,** *v.t.* wean, ablactate; inarch.
**ablängen,** *v.t.* cut to length; cut in lengths.
**Ablass,** *m.* draining, discharge; cessation; discount; drain, outlet.
**ablassen,** *v.t.* let off, draw off, siphon off, discharge, decant, drain; anneal (steel); deduct. — *v.i.* leave off, cease; (of colors) fade or come off.
**Ablass-hahn,** *m.* delivery cock, discharge cock, drain cock. **-leitung,** *f.* delivery pipe, discharge pipe. **-öffnung,** *f.* outlet, vent. **-rohr,** *n.*, **-röhre,** *f.* outlet tube or pipe. **-ventil,** *n.* outlet valve, drain valve.
**Ablauf,** *m.* running off, discharge, outlet, drain; sink; effluent; filtrate; slope; expiration (of time); result, event. **-brett,** *n.* drain board.
**ablaufen,** *v.i.* run off or down, drain; expire; turn out, come out.
**Ablauf-flüssigkeit,** *f.* discharge liquid, drainage liquid. **-hahn,** *m.* = Ablasshahn. **-öl,** *n.* expressed oil; run oil. **-rohr,** *n.*, **-röhre,** *f.* outlet tube, waste pipe. **-trichter,** *m.* draining funnel, condensing funnel (inverted funnel with tubulated rim for carrying off condensed vapors).
**Ablauge,** *f.* spent lye, spent liquor, waste liquor; washing out.
**ablaugen,** *v.t.* lixiviate; wash out lye from; steep in lye.
**abläutern,** *v.t.* clarify, purify, refine, fine; strain; draw off; wash (ore).
**Abläuterung,** *f.* clarification, etc. (see abläutern).
**Abläuterungsvorrichtung,** *f.* clarifying apparatus.
**Ableben,** *n.* death.
**ablecken,** *v.i.* drip down, trickle down.
**ablegen,** *v.t.* lay aside or off; take off; deposit; unwind, unroll.
**Ableger,** *m.* (of plants) layer, slip, scion.
**ablehnen,** *v.t.* decline, challenge, reject, refuse; turn aside.
**ablehren,** *v.t.* gage; dress, trim.
**ableitbar,** *a.* derivable, etc. (see ableiten).
**ableiten,** *v.t.* derive; turn aside, lead off, carry off; (*Elec.*) ground. — *v.r.* be derived (from).
**Ableiter,** *m.* conductor.
**Ableiterohr,** *n.* delivery tube or pipe.
**Ableitung,** *f.* derivation; derivative; deduction; carrying off; drainage; channel; turning aside; (*Elec.*) leakage, stray current, also grounding.
**Ableitungs-kanal,** *m.* drain. **-mittel,** *n.* revulsive; derivative. **-rinne,** *f.* drain pipe. **-rohr,** *n.*, **-röhre,** *f.* delivery tube, delivery pipe; drain conduit.
**ablenken,** *v.t.* turn off, deflect; diffract; distract. — *v.i.* turn aside, deviate.
**Ablenkung,** *f.* deflection; diffraction; diversion; deviation.
**Ablenkungs-kraft,** *f.* deflecting force. **-winkel,** *m.* angle of deflection.
**ablesbar,** *a.* readable.
**Ablese-.** reading. **-fehler,** *m.* error in reading. **-fernrohr,** *n.* reading telescope **-lupe,** *f.* reading lens.
**ablesen,** *v.t.* read off; pluck off, pick, gather.
**Ablese-schärfe,** *f.* sharpness of reading. **-vorrichtung,** *f.* reading device.
**Ablesung,** *f.* reading (off), observation; gathering, harvest, crop.
**Ablesungs-fehler,** *m.* error in reading. **-genauigkeit,** *f.* accuracy of reading. **-verfeinerung,** *f.* refinement of reading.
**ablichten,** *v.t.* (*Dyeing*) reduce, shade, strip.
**abliefern,** *v.t.* deliver.
**Ablieferung,** *f.* delivery.

**abliegen,** *v.i. & r.* ripen, mature; deteriorate from nonuse; be remote. — **abgelegen,** *p.a.* ripe, mature; remote, retired.
**ablohnen,** *v.t.* pay off.
**ablöschbar,** *a.* slakable (lime); temperable.
**ablöschen,** *v.t.* quench; slake (lime); temper (steel); smother, extinguish (fire); blot.
**Ablöschflüssigkeit,** *f.* quenching or tempering liquid.
**ablösen,** *v.t.* loosen; detach; split off; separate; dissolve; relieve, replace. — *v.r.* come loose, come off. — **ablösend,** *p.a.* loosening, etc.; alternate; (*Med.*) resolvent.
**Ablösung,** *f.* loosening, etc. (see ablösen).
**Ablösungs-fläche,** *f.* cleavage surface; (*Geol.*) jointing plane, joint. **-richtung,** *f.* (*Cryst.*) cleavage plane.
**ablöten,** *v.t.* unsolder.
**Abluft,** *f.* outgoing air.
**ablüften,** *v.t.* expose to the air, air.
**Abluftrohr,** *n.* air outlet tube (or pipe).
**ablutieren,** *v.t.* unlute.
**abmachen,** *v.t.* loosen, detach; settle, arrange.
**Abmachung,** *f.* taking off; arrangement, settlement, agreement; stipulation.
**abmagern,** *v.i.* lose flesh, grow thin. — *v.t.* emaciate.
**abmahnen,** *v.t.* dissuade, warn.
**abmaischen,** *v.t. & i.* finish mashing.
**Abmaischtemperatur,** *f.* final temperature (of mashing).
**abmarken,** *v.t.* mark off, mark out.
**Abmass,** *n.* off size; measure; (*Mach.*) tolerance.
**abmatten,** *v.t.* fatigue, exhaust; deaden (gold).
**abmessbar,** *a.* measurable, mensurable.
**abmessen,** *v.t.* measure off. — **abgemessen,** *p.a.* measured, precise.
**Abmessung,** *f.* measurement; adjustment; dimension.
**abmindern,** *v.t.* lessen, diminish.
**abmontieren,** *v.t.* dismount, demount, dismantle, disassemble, disconnect.
**abmustern,** *v.t.* muster; sample; evaluate.
**abnagen,** *v.t.* gnaw (off); erode.
**Abnahme,** *f.* decrease, decline, drop, diminution; taking off or away; acceptance; sale. **-versuch,** *m.* acceptance test.
**abnarben,** *v.t.* buff; scrape.
**abnehmbar** *a.* removable, detachable.
**abnehmen,** *v.t.* take off, take away, remove; accept; infer. — *v.i.* decrease, decline, diminish, wane.
**Abnehmer,** *m.* buyer, purchaser; customer.
**Abneigung,** *f.* deviation, slope; disinclination.
**abnorm,** *a.* abnormal, anomalous, irregular.
**Abnormität,** *f.* abnormality, anomaly, irregularity.
**abnutschen,** *v.t.* = absaugen.
**abnutzbar,** *a.* consumable, wearable.
**Abnutzbarkeit,** *f.* consumability; wearing quality.
**abnutzen, abnützen,** *v.t.* use up, wear out.
**Abnutzung, Abnützung,** *f.* wear, wear and tear, wasting, abrasion, attrition.
**Aböl,** *n.* waste oil.
**abölen,** *v.t.* oil off; remove oil from; oil thoroly.
**Abonnement,** *n.* subscription.
**Abonnent,** *m.* subscriber.
**abonnieren,** *v.i.* subscribe.
**Abort,** *m.* toilet, lavatory; = Abortus.
**Abortivmittel,** *n.* abortive agent, abortifacient.
**Abortöl,** *n.* lavatory oil.
**Abortus,** *m.* abortion; miscarriage; premature birth.
**aboxydieren,** *v.t.* oxidize off, remove by oxidation.
**abpälen,** *v.t.* unhair, depilate.
**abpassen,** *v.t.* measure, fit, adjust.
**Abperleffekt,** *m.* water-repellent effect.
**abpflücken,** *v.t.* pick, pluck, gather.
**abplatten,** *v.t.* flatten. — **abgeplattet,** *p.a.* flattened, oblate.
**abplatzen,** *v.i.* crack off, scale off, chip off, spall.
**abprallen,** *v.i.* rebound, recoil; be reflected.
**Abprallung,** *f.* rebound, resiliency, reverberation; (*Optics*) reflection.
**Abprallungswinkel** *m.* angle of rebound or reflection.
**abpressen,** *v.t.* press or squeeze off; separate by pressing; express.
**Abprodukt,** *n.* waste product, by-product.
**abpuffern,** *v.t.* buffer off, prevent by buffering.
**abpumpen,** *v.t.* pump off; drain by pumping.
**Abputz,** *m.* plaster, plastering.
**abputzen,** *v.t.* plaster; clean off, trim, dress; cut off.
**abquetschen,** *v.t.* squeeze off, squeeze out.
**abquicken,** *v.t.* purify; refine with mercury; separate (gold or silver) from amalgam.
**abrahmen,** *v.t.* take the cream from, skim.
**Abrahmer,** *m.* skimmer.
**Abrandkraut,** *n.* southernwood (*Artemisia abrotanum*).
**abraspeln,** *v.t.* rasp off, scrape off.
**abraten,** *v.t.* dissuade, warn.
**abrauchen,** *v.t. & i.* evaporate (with fuming).
**abräuchern,** *v.t* fumigate thoroly.
**Abrauch-raum,** *m.* evaporating space or chamber. **-schale,** *f.* evaporating dish or vessel.
**Abraum,** *m.* rubbish, trash, rubble.
**abräumen,** *v.t.* take away, clear away, remove; clear (of something); empty.
**Abräumen,** *n.* (*Brewing*) clearing the kiln.
**Abraum-salze,** *n. pl.* abraum salts (saline deposits overlying the rock salt at Stassfurt and elsewhere). **-sprengung,** *f.* stripping with explosives. **-stoff,** *m.* waste.

**abrechnen,** *v.t.* deduct; reckon off. — *v.i.* settle.
**Abrechnung,** *f.* deduction, discount; settlement; calculation; account.
**Abrede,** *f.* agreement; denial.
**abreiben,** *v.t.* rub off, scrape, scour, rub smooth, abrade; grind (colors).
**Abreibfestigkeit,** *f.* resistance to abrasion.
**Abreibung,** *f.* rubbing off or down; abrasion; attrition.
**abreisen,** *v.i.* depart.
**abreissen,** *v.t.* tear off, pull off, remove; pull down; draw. — *v.i.* break.
**Abreiss-funken,** *m.* (contact) breaking spark. **-zünder,** *m.* friction igniter; (*Elec.*) make-and-break igniter.
**abresten,** *v.t.* (*Brewing*) decant.
**Abrichtelauge,** *f.* (*Soap*) weak caustic liquor.
**abrichten,** *v.t.* fit, adjust, true; train.
**Abrieb,** *m.* rubbings, grindings, dust, fines.
**abrinden,** *v.t.* peel, strip, scale, bark, decorticate.
**Abriss,** *m.* outline, sketch, design.
**Abrohr,** *n.* outlet pipe, discharge pipe.
**abrollen,** *v.t.* roll off, unroll, unfold, uncoil.
**abröschen,** *v.t.* air (paper).
**abrosten,** *v.i.* rust off or away, corrode.
**abrösten,** *v.t.* roast thoroly.
**Abrostung,** *f.* rusting, corrosion.
**Abröstung,** *f.* thoro roasting.
**abröten,** *v.t.* dye red, color red. — *v.i.* lose red color.
**abrunden,** *v.t.* round off, round, finish off. — **abgerundet,** *p.a.* rounded off; (of glass edges) fire-polished; round (numbers).
**Abrundung,** *f.* rounding, rounding off; roundness, curvature.
**Abrusbohne,** *f.* jequirity bean.
**abrussecht,** *a.* fast to rubbing, not crocking.
**abrussen,** *v.i.* (of colored goods) rub off, crock.
**abrüsten,** *v.i.* disarm. — *v.t.* dismount.
**abrutschen,** *v.i.* slip, slide (off or down). — *v.t.* wear off or out.
**abs.,** *abbrev.* (absolut) absolute.
**absacken,** *v.t.* sack; unload; encyst. — *v.i.* sink down; shrink.
**absagen,** *v.t.* countermand, renounce.
**absägen,** *v.t.* saw off.
**absalzen,** *v.t.* salt (thoroly).
**absättigen,** *v.t.* saturate, neutralize.
**Absättigung,** *f.* saturation, neutralization.
**Absatz,** *m.* deposit, sediment; pause; offset; wear and tear; paragraph; sale; heel (of a shoe). **-bassin,** *n.* settling tank. **-bottich,** *m.* settling vat. **-gefäss,** *n.* sedimentation vessel, settling tank. **-gestein,** *n.* sedimentary rock.
**absätzig,** *a.* interrupted; (of wool) inferior, faulty.
**absatzweise,** *adv.* interruptedly, intermittently, fractionally; gradually.

**absäuern,** *v.t.* acidify, sour.
**Absaug(e)-flasche,** *f.* suction flask, filtering flask. **-haube,** *f.* suction hood. **-kolben,** *m.* suction flask, filter flask. **-leitung,** *f.* suction piping, suction line.
**absaugen,** *v.t.* suck off; filter with suction; draw off by suction, exhaust, aspirate; squeegee; (*Dyeing*) hydro-extract.
**Absaugentfeuchter,** *m.* vacuum desiccator.
**Absaug(e)-öffnung,** *f.* suction outlet. **-pumpe,** *f.* suction pump, vacuum pump.
**Absauger,** *m.* (*Paper*) suction box; (*Dyeing*) hydro-extractor; exhauster.
**Absaug(e)trockenofen,** *m.* vacuum drying oven.
**Absaugflasche,** etc. see Absaug(e)flasche, etc.
**Absaugung,** *f.* sucking off, suction, etc. (see absaugen).
**Absaugungsanlage,** *f.* suction installation.
**abschaben,** *v.t.* scrape off; clean; scrape, abrade.
**Abschabsel,** *n.* scrapings, shavings.
**abschaffen,** *v.t.* do away with, abolish.
**abschälen,** *v.t.* shell, peel, pare, bark, decorticate. — *v.r.* peel off, scale off, come off.
**abschalten,** *v.t.* disconnect, switch off.
**Abschälung,** *f.* shelling, etc. (see abschälen).
**abschattieren,** *v.t. & i.* shade off.
**abschätzen,** *v.t.* estimate, value, appraise.
**Abschaum,** *m.* scum, skimmings, dross.
**abschäumen,** *v.t.* skim off, skim.
**Abschäumer,** *m.* skimming apparatus; skimmer.
**Abschaum-löffel,** *m.* skimmer, skimming ladle. **-sieb,** *n.* skimming sieve.
**Abschäumung,** *f.* skimming off, skimming.
**abscheidbar,** *a.* separable.
**Abscheide-gefäss,** *n.* separating vessel. **-kammer,** *f.* separating chamber; condensation chamber.
**abscheiden,** *v.t.* separate; part, disengage, eliminate; refine (metals); secrete. — *v.r.* separate, be precipitated, be deposited; be separated. — *v.i.* depart. — **abgeschieden,** *p.a.* departed, deceased.
**Abscheider,** *m.* separator; trap; refiner.
**Abscheidung,** *f.* separation; elimination; refining; deposit; secretion; departure.
**Abscheidungs-mittel,** *n.* means of separation; precipitant. **-produkt,** *n.* secretion. **-verfahren,** *n.* separation process. **-vorrichtung,** *f.* separator.
**abschelfern,** *v.t., r. & i.* scale off, scale.
**abscheren,** *v.t.* shear off, cut off.
**Abscherfestigkeit,** *f.* shearing strength.
**Abscherung,** *f.* shearing (off), shear.
**Abscheu,** *m.* abhorrence, aversion.
**abscheuern,** *v.t.* scour (off), rub off; cleanse. — *v.r.* wear off.
**Abscheuerung,** *f.* scouring; attrition.
**abscheulich,** *a.* horrible, detestable.

**abschichten,** *v.t.* separate into layers.
**abschicken,** *v.t.* send, send off, forward.
**Abschied,** *m.* parting, departure; dismissal, discharge; farewell.
**abschiefern,** *v.i.* flake or scale off; exfoliate.
**abschiessen,** *v.t.* shoot off, set off. — *v.i.* shoot off or down; (of colors) fade, lose color.
**abschirmen,** *v.t.* screen off, screen, shield.
**Abschirmungszahl,** *f.* screening number, screening constant.
**abschlacken,** *v.t.* remove slag from, slag off.
**Abschlacköffnung,** *f.* cinder notch, cinder tap.
**Abschlag,** *m.* fragments, chips, etc.; rebound; outlet; deduction, reduction; instalment; refusal.
**abschlagen,** *v.t.* beat or knock off or back; take to pieces; refuse; turn off; drain; (*Founding*) stop (molten metal); (*Pharm.*) sieve. — *v.i.* abate; fall (in price).
**abschlämmen, abschlammen,** *v.t.* wash, elutriate; decant.
**Abschlämmung,** *f.* washing; decantation.
**abschleifen,** *v.t.* grind off, grind, rub off, abrade; polish; sharpen. — *v.r.* wear, wear off, wear smooth.
**Abschleifung,** *f.* grinding off, attrition; polishing; sharpening.
**Abschleifversuch,** *m.* abrasion test.
**abschleimen,** *v.t.* rid of slime, slime, clarify (sugar).
**abschlemmen,** *v.t.* wash, elutriate; decant.
**abschleppen,** *v.t.* draw off, carry away.
**Abschleudermaschine,** *f.* centrifugal, centrifuge; hydro-extractor.
**abschleudern,** *v.t.* centrifuge; hydro-extract (yarn, etc.); separate in a centrifugal; fling off.
**abschlichten,** *v.t.* smooth, plane.
**abschliessen,** *v.t.* occlude; close, shut off; seal off; seclude; separate; conclude. — **abgeschlossenes System,** closed system. — **abschliessend,** *p.a.* conclusive, final, positive.
**Abschliessung,** *f.* occlusion, etc. (see abschliessen).
**Abschluss,** *m.* = Abschliessung; closing device, shutoff; cutoff, seal. **-dichtung,** *f.* seal. **-hahn,** *m.* stopcock. **-schieber,** *m.* slide valve. **-ventil,** *n.* shutoff (or cutoff) valve. **-vorrichtung,** *f.* closing device.
**abschmeckend, abschmeckig,** *a.* of unpleasant flavor, unsavory; insipid.
**Abschmelzdraht,** *m.* fuse wire, fusible wire.
**abschmelzen,** *v.t.* melt off, melt, fuse, separate by melting; seal off, seal. — *v.i.* melt off.
**Abschmelz-konstante,** *f.* fusion coefficient. **-schweissung,** *f.* flash welding. **-sicherung,** *f.* (*Elec.*) safety fuse.
**Abschmelzung,** *f.* melting off, etc. (see abschmelzen); (*Metal.*) liquation.
**abschmieren,** *v.t.* grease (thoroly). — *v.i.* smear.
**abschmirgeln,** *v.t.* grind or polish with emery.
**abschmutzen,** *v.i.* rub off, soil.
**Abschn.,** *abbrev.* (Abschnitt) section.
**Abschneideapparat,** *m.* (*Mach.*) cutter.
**abschneiden,** *v.t.* cut off, cut away, cut; (*Math.*) truncate. — *v.i.* be cut off, end.
**Abschnitt,** *m.* cutting, trimming, scrap, chip; segment; intercept; portion, section, division; period (of time).
**Abschnitzel,** *n.* shred, chip, paring.
**abschnüren,** *v.t.* untie; tie off; mark off; enclose.
**abschöpfen,** *v.t.* skim off, skim; ladle out.
**abschrägen,** *v.t.* slope, slant, bevel, taper.
**Abschrägung,** *f.* sloping, slope, bevel, taper.
**abschrauben,** *v.t.* screw off, unscrew.
**Abschreck-bad,** *n.* (*Metal.*) quenching bath. **-bottich,** *m.* (*Metal.*) quenching tank.
**abschrecken,** *v.t.* chill, cool; (*Metal.*) chill (as cast iron), quench (as steel); render (water) lukewarm; scare off, deter.
**Abschreck-mittel,** *n.* cooling agent; (*Metal.*) quenching medium. **-temperatur,** *f.* (*Steel*) quenching temperature (from which the metal is quenched).
**Abschreckung,** *f.* chilling, etc. (see abschrecken).
**Abschreckzeit,** *f.* chilling time, quenching time, etc. (see abschrecken).
**abschreiben,** *v.t.* write off; copy; revoke.
**Abschreibung,** *f.* amortization, depreciation.
**abschreiten,** *v.t.* step off; pace off.
**Abschrift,** *f.* copy; duplicate.
**abschülfern,** *v.i.* scale off, flake off.
**abschülpen,** *v.i.* shell off, scale off, spall.
**abschuppen,** *v.i.* scale off, flake off.
**abschüssig,** *a.* steep.
**abschütteln,** *v.t.* shake off; shake hard; scold.
**abschütten,** *v.t.* pour off, run off.
**abschützen,** *v.t.* shield off, screen off.
**abschwächen,** *v.t.* & *r.* weaken; diminish, decrease, reduce, dilute; soften; mellow (leather); (*Photog.*) clear, reduce.
**Abschwächer,** *m.* (*Photog.*) clearing agent.
**Abschwächung,** *f.* weakening, etc. (see abschwächen).
**Abschwächungs-lösung,** *f.* (*Photog.*) clearing solution. **-mittel,** *n.* thinner, diluent, reducer.
**abschwärzen,** *v.t.* blacken. — *v.i.* lose black color, come off black.
**abschweelen,** *v.t.* = abschwelen.
**abschwefeln,** *v.t.* free of sulfur, desulfurize; coke (coal); less commonly, impregnate with sulfur.
**Abschwefelung,** *f.* desulfurization.
**Abschweifung,** *f.* deviation; digression.
**abschwelen, abschweelen,** *v.t.* calcine, roast.
**abschwemmen,** *v.t.* wash, rinse; wash away.
**abschwenken,** *v.t.* wash off, rinse; wash away.

**abschwingen,** *v.t.* centrifuge, hydro-extract; fan, winnow.
**abschwirren,** *v.t.* whiz, centrifuge.
**abschwitzen,** *v.t.* depilate (leather).
**Abscisse,** *f.* abscissa.
**absedimentieren,** *v.i.* deposit as sediment
**absehbar,** *a.* perceivable, observable. — **in absehbarer Zeit,** within any predeterminable time.
**absehen,** *v.t.* see, perceive; aim at. — *v.i.* (with von) disregard, let alone. — **abgesehen,** *p.a.* (with von) not mentioning, apart from.
**Abseide,** *f.* floss silk.
**abseifen,** *v.t.* clean with soap; wash out the soap from; test (welds) with soap solution.
**abseigern,** *v.t.* separate by fusion; (*Metal.*) liquate.
**Abseihbier,** *n.* drawings; residue beer in chip cask.
**Abseihebeutel,** *m.* filtering bag.
**abseihen,** *v.t.* filter, filter off, strain, decant, percolate.
**Abseihung,** *f.* filtration, etc. (see abseihen).
**abseits,** *adv.* aside, apart.
**absenden,** *v.t.* send off or away; forward.
**Absender,** *m.* sender, forwarder, shipper.
**absengen,** *v.t.* singe off, singe, flame.
**absenken,** *v.t.* lower.
**Absenkung,** *f.* lowering; (*Geol.*) downthrow.
**Absetz-bassin,** *n.* settling tank. **-behälter,** *m.* settling vessel, settler. **-bottich,** *m.* settling tub or vat.
**absetzen,** *v.t.* deposit; put down or off; remove; offset; lay off, plot; interrupt; put in type; depose; sell; wean. — *v.r.* settle, subside, deposit.
**Absetzenlassen,** *n.* deposition, sedimentation.
**Absetzung,** *f.* deposition, etc. (see absetzen); sedimentation; sediment.
**Absetz-zeit,** *f.* settling time. **-zisterne,** *f.* settling cistern.
**Absicht,** *f.* intention, purpose, view.
**absichtlich,** *a.* intentional.
**absieben,** *v.t.* sieve, screen.
**absieden,** *v.t.* decoct, extract by boiling, boil.
**absinken,** *v.i.* sink away, sink down.
**Absinth,** *m.* wormwood; absinth.
**absinthan, absinthartig,** *a.* absinthine.
**absiphonieren,** *v.t.* siphon off.
**Absitz-behälter,** *m.* settling vessel, settler. **-bütte,** *f.* (*Brewing*) settling tub. **-dauer,** *f.* settling time.
**absitzen,** *v.i.* deposit, settle; dismount.
**absol.,** *abbrev.* (absolut) absolute.
**absolut,** *a.* absolute; (of oils) essential.
**Absolutschwarz,** *n.* (*Dyes*) absolute black.
**absoluttrocken,** *a.* absolutely dry, bone-dry.
**Absoluttrockengewicht,** *n.* absolute dry weight (all moisture having been expelled).
**absondern,** *v.t.* separate, detach, isolate; insulate; abstract; extract, segregate; (*Physiol.*) secrete, excrete. — **absondernd,** *p.a.* (*Physiol.*) secretory, secreting, excreting.
**Absonderung,** *f.* separation, etc. (see absondern); (*Geol.*) jointing.
**Absonderungs-drüse,** *f.* secretory gland. **-flüssigkeit,** *f.* secretory fluid, secretion. **-stoff,** *m.* secreted material. **-vermögen,** *n.* (*Physiol.*) secretory power. **-vorgang,** *m.* process of secretion. **-werkzeug,** *n.* secretory organ.
**Absorbens,** *n.* absorbent.
**Absorbentia,** *n.pl.* absorbents.
**absorbierbar,** *a.* absorbable.
**Absorbierbarkeit,** *f.* absorbability.
**absorbieren,** *v.t.* absorb. — **absorbierend,** *p.a.* absorbent, absorptive. — **absorbierendes Mittel,** absorbent, absorptive.
**Absorbierung,** *f.* absorbing, absorption.
**absorptiometrisch,** *a.* absorptiometric.
**Absorptions-anlage,** *f.* absorption equipment or plant. **-apparat,** *m.* absorption apparatus.
**absorptionsfähig,** *a.* absorptive, absorbent.
**Absorptions-fähigkeit,** *f.* capability of absorbing, absorptive power. **-farbe,** *f.* absorption color. **-flasche,** *f.* absorption bottle, absorption flask. **-flüssigkeit,** *f.* absorption liquid. **-gefäss,** *n.* absorption vessel. **-geschwindigkeit,** *f.* absorption velocity. **-gesetz,** *n.* law of absorption. **-gewebe,** *n.* absorbent tissue. **-kohle,** *f.* absorption charcoal, absorptive charcoal. **-kolonne,** *f.* absorption column. **-kraft,** *f.* absorptive power. **-küvette,** *f.* absorption bulb or cell. **-messung,** *f.* absorption measurement. **-mittel,** *n.* absorbent. **-öl,** *n.* absorbent oil. **-rohr,** *n.*, **-röhre,** *f.* absorption tube. **-schlange,** *f.* absorption coil. **-streifen,** *m.* absorption band. **-turm,** *m.* absorption tower. **-verbindung,** *f.* absorption compound. **-verfahren,** *n.* absorption process. **-verlust,** *m.* absorption loss. **-vermögen,** *n.* absorptive power, absorption capacity. **-wärme,** *f.* heat of absorption.
**abspaltbar,** *a.* capable of being split off, cleavable, separable.
**abspalten,** *v.t. & i.* split off, cleave off, separate; crack (chemically).
**Abspaltung,** *f.* splitting off, cleavage, separation.
**abspannen,** *v.t.* relieve from tension, release (a spring, etc.); relax; (allow to) expand; cut off (steam). — **abgespannt,** *p.a.* released, etc.; unstrung, unnerved.
**Abspannung,** *f.* release (from tension); relaxation; expansion; lassitude.
**abspateln,** *v.t.* scrape off (with a spatula).
**absperrbar,** *a.* capable of being shut off, etc. (see absperren).
**absperren,** *v.t.* shut off, seal off, cut off, confine, stop, block.

**Absperr-flüssigkeit,** *f.* confining liquid, sealing liquid. **-glied,** *n.* shutoff. **-hahn,** *m.* stopcock. **-schieber,** *m.* slide valve. **-ventil,** *n.* cutoff valve, stop valve, check valve.
**abspiegeln,** *v.t.* reflect.
**abspielen,** *v.t.* play. — *v.r.* take place.
**Abspielnadel,** *f.* phonograph needle.
**abspitzen,** *v.t.* sharpen to a point, point.
**absplittern,** *v.t., i & r.* splinter off.
**absprechen,** *v.t.* deny; discuss; arrange. — *v.i.* pass judgment. — **absprechend,** *p.a.* peremptory, positive.
**abspreizen,** *v.t.* brace, prop, support.
**absprengen,** *v.t.* break, spring or burst off; drive off; blast.
**Absprenger,** *m.* (for glass tubes) cutter.
**abspringen,** *v.i.* spring off, fly off; burst off, crack off; rebound; (of wood) warp, start; (of iron) be red-short. — **abspringend,** *p.a.* in contrast; desultory.
**abspritzen,** *v.t.* wash off or down (with a jet); spray; spatter.
**absprudeln,** *v.i.* bubble away.
**Absprung,** *m.* leaping off or rebounding; contrast; fragment; (*Physics*) reflection.
**Abspülbad,** *n.* rinsing bath.
**abspülen,** *v.t.* wash off, wash, cleanse, rinse; wash away.
**Abspülung,** *f.* washing off, etc. (see abspülen).
**abstammen,** *v.i.* descend, come; be derived.
**Abstammung,** *f.* origin, descent, derivation.
**Abstand,** *m.* distance, interval; clearance; difference; desisting, renouncement. — **Abstand nehmen,** desist (from).
**abständig,** *a.* deteriorated; flat, stale.
**abstatten,** *v.t.* render, give.
**abstäubecht,** *a.* not crocking.
**abstäuben, abstauben,** *v.t.* dust off, dust. — *v.i.* (of colors) crock.
**abstechen,** *v.t.* tap, draw, run off; drain; etch (a picture); cut off; cut up; trim off. — *v.i.* contrast (with).
**Abstecher,** *m.* (*Metal.*) tapper; excursion.
**abstecken,** *v.t.* mark out.
**abstehen,** *v.i.* grow stale, decay, decompose; stand off; stand; be distant; desist. — **abgestanden,** *p.a.* stale, flat, dead; decayed. — **abstehen lassen,** let stand. — **abstehend,** *p.a.* distant; deteriorating; spreading.
**absteifen,** *v.t.* stiffen; thicken; prop, brace, reinforce.
**absteigen,** *v.i.* descend; decrease; alight.
**Abstellbrett,** *n.* storage board or shelf.
**abstellen,** *v.t.* turn off, shut off, stop; put off, put away; aim at, focus on; annul.
**Abstell-hahn,** *m.* stopcock. **-vorrichtung,** *f.* cutoff device.
**absterben,** *v.i.* die, fade, wither, decay; (of lime) air-slack; (*Sugar*) change from transparent to opaque crystalline mass.
**abstergieren,** *v.t.* cleanse.
**Abstich,** *m.* tapping, drawing; running; tapped metal; contrast. **-loch,** *n.*, **-öffnung,** *f.* tap hole. **-pfanne,** *f.* (*Metal.*) tap ladle.
**abstimmen,** *v.i.* disagree; vote. — *v.t.* tune; formulate (mixtures).
**abstoppen,** *v.t.* stop off, stop up, stop.
**abstöpseln,** *v.t.* unstop, uncork.
**abstossen,** *v.t.* repel; push off, rub off, scrape off. **-abstossend,** *p.a.* repelling, repulsive.
**Abstossung,** *f.* repulsion; pushing off.
**Abstossungskraft,** *f.* repulsive force or power.
**abstrahieren,** *v.t.* abstract.
**Abstrahl,** *m.* reflected ray.
**abstrahlen,** *v.t.* reflect; blast (as with sand). — *v.i.* be reflected; radiate.
**Abstrahlung,** *f.* reflection; radiation.
**Abstrebekraft,** *f.* centrifugal force.
**Abstreicheisen,** *n.* scraper; skimmer.
**abstreichen,** *v.t.* wipe or scrape off; skim; strike out; deduct.
**Abstreicher,** *m.* scraper; skimmer.
**Abstreich-löffel,** *n.* skimming ladle, skimmer. **-messer,** *n.* (literally, scraping-off knife) scraper; (*Calico*, etc.) doctor.
**abstreifen,** *v.t.* strip off, strip; skin.
**Abstreifmesser,** *n.* (*Mach.*) doctor blade, doctor; flaying knife.
**abstreiten,** *v.t.* dispute, contest.
**Abstrich,** *m.* skim, scum, dross, specif. a scum of arsenates, etc., on molten lead; down stroke; deduction. **-blei,** *n.* lead skim (see Abstrich).
**abströmen,** *v.i.* flow away, flow off.
**abstufen,** *v.t.* gradate; graduate. — *v.r.* grade, grade off.
**Abstufung,** *f.* gradation; graduation.
**abstumpfen,** *v.t.* neutralize, saturate (acids); truncate; blunt, dull, deaden. **-abgestumpft,** *p.a.* neutralized, etc.; blunt, dull.
**Abstumpfung,** *f.* neutralization, etc. (see abstumpfen).
**Abstumpfungsfläche,** *f.* (*Cryst.*) truncating face.
**abstürzen,** *v.t.* throw down, dump; remove the lid from. — *v.i.* fall down; fall off.
**absuchen,** *v.t.* search, examine, scan; pick off, clear off.
**Absud,** *m.* decoction, extract; (*Dyeing*) specif., iron or chrome mordant.
**Absüssbottich,** *m.* edulcorating vat.
**absüssen,** *v.t.* sweeten, purify by washing, edulcorate; wash out, wash (a precipitate).
**Absüss-kessel,** *m.* edulcorating vessel. **-spindel,** *f.* (*Sugar*) sweet-water spindle (or hydrometer).
**Absüssung,** *f.* sweetening, etc. (see absüssen).
**Absüsswasser,** *n.* (*Sugar*) sweet water.
**Absynt,** *m.* = Absinth.

**Abszisse,** *f.* abscissa.
**Abszissenachse,** *f.* axis of abscissas.
**Abt.,** *abbrev.* (Abteilung) division; section.
**abtasten,** *v.t.* feel out; make contact with; (*Physics*) scan; (*Med.*) palpate.
**Abtaster,** *m.* (*Physics*) scanner.
**abtauen,** *v.t.* thaw off, thaw, melt.
**Abteil,** *m.* compartment.
**abteilen,** *v.t.* separate, divide, divide off; graduate; classify.
**Abteilung,** *f.* division; graduation; part, section, class, lot.
**abteilungsweise,** *adv.* part by part, piece by piece.
**abteufen,** *v.t.* sink (a shaft or well); deepen.
**abthun,** *v.t.* = abtun.
**abtitrieren,** *v.t.* titrate (to the end point).
**Abtitrierungspunkt,** *m.* end point.
**abtönen,** *v.t.* tone down, shade off.
**abtöten,** *v.t.* destroy, kill.
**Abtrag,** *m.* removed material; excavation; payment.
**abtragen,** *v.t.* carry off, clear off; excavate; erode; pay off; wear away; wear out; disintegrate.
**Abtragung,** *f.* carrying off, etc. (see abtragen).
**Abtränkbrühe,** *f.* (*Leather*) tan liquor.
**abtränken,** *v.t.* saturate, impregnate; (*Leather*) fill up with tan liquor.
**Abtreib(e)-apparat,** *m.* distilling apparatus, still. **-herd,** *m.* refining hearth. **-kapelle,** *f.* refining cupel. **-kolonne,** *f.* separating column, distilling column. **-mittel,** *n.* expulsive agent; abortifacient.
**abtreiben,** *v.t.* drive off, expel; separate (by distillation); refine (by cupellation), cupel; clear (woods); (*Med.*) abort. **-abtreibend,** *p.a.* (*Med.*) abortifacient.
**Abtreibeofen,** *m.* cupel furnace.
**Abtreibgas,** *n.* expelled gas.
**Abtreibschmelze,** *f.* refining melt.
**Abtreibung,** *f.* driving off, etc. (see abtreiben).
**abtrennbar,** *a.* separable.
**abtrennen,** *v.t.* separate; dissociate; dissever; detach; disconnect.
**Abtrenner,** *m.* separator; disconnecter.
**Abtrennung,** *f.* separation, etc. (see abtrennen).
**Abtrennungsarbeit,** *f.* work of separation.
**abtreten,** *v.t.* tread, tread down, tread off; transfer, convey, assign; yield, cede. — *v.i.* retire, yield; alight.
**Abtretung,** *f.* treading, etc. (see abtreten); transfer, assignment, cession; retirement.
**Abtrieb,** *m.* driving off, etc. (see abtreiben); distillation; slack (of a cable); felling.
**Abtriebssäule,** *f.* separating column, distilling column.
**abtriefen,** *v.i.* trickle down, drip.
**Abtritt,** *m.* retirement, withdrawal; water closet.
**Abtritts-dünger,** *m.* cesspool fertilizer. **-grube,** *f.* cesspool.
**abtrocknen,** *v.t.* dry off, dry; wipe dry.
**Abtropf-blech,** *n.* drip pan. **-brett,** *n.* draining board or shelf.
**abtröpfeln,** *v.i.* drop, drip, drain, trickle.
**abtropfen,** *v.i.* drop (off), drip, drain, dry.
**Abtropfer,** *m.* drainer, drip board, etc.
**Abtropf-gefäss,** *n.* drainer. **-gestell,** *n.* draining stand, dropping horse. **-kasten,** *m.* (*Paper*) drain chest; (*Metal.*) drain table. **-pfanne,** *f.* drain pan, drainer; (in tin plating) list pot. **-platte,** *f.* draining plate. **-schale,** *f.* draining dish or basin, drainer (with perforated bottom). **-ständer,** *m.* draining stand.
**abtrüben,** *v.t.* dull, darken, sadden (colors).
**Abtrübungsfarbstoff,** *m.* saddening dye.
**abtun,** *v.t.* put or take off; settle.
**abwägen,** *v.t.* weigh off, weigh, weigh out; level; ponder.
**abwällen,** *v.t.* boil gently, simmer.
**abwalzen,** *v.t.* roll off, smooth off.
**abwälzen,** *v.t.* roll off, roll away.
**abwandelbar,** *a.* modifiable.
**abwandeln,** *v.r.* change, alter, vary.
**Abwanderung,** *f.* wandering off; migration.
**Abwandlung,** *f.* modification, variation.
**Abwärme,** *f.* waste heat, lost heat.
**abwärmen,** *v.t.* heat, warm.
**Abwärmeverlust,** *m.* waste-heat loss.
**abwarten,** *v.t.* wait for, wait on.
**abwärts,** *adv.* downward, down; off, away.
**Abwärts-bewegung,** *f.* downward motion. **-transformator,** *m.* (*Elec.*) step-down transformer.
**abwaschbar,** *a.* washable.
**abwaschen,** *v.t.* wash, wash off, wash out, rinse, cleanse.
**Abwaschmittel,** *n.* cleansing agent, cleanser.
**Abwaschung,** *f.* washing, etc. (see abwaschen); lotion.
**Abwasser,** *n.* waste water, waste liquor; specif., sewage. **-anlage,** *f.* sewage disposal plant. **-leitung,** *f.* drain.
**abwässern,** *v.t.* wash; free from water, drain, dry.
**Abwasser-reinigung,** *f.* waste-water purification. **-rohr,** *n.* waste pipe, drain pipe.
**abwechseln,** *v.t.* & *i.* alternate, vary. — **abwechselnd,** *p.a.* alternating, alternate, intermittent; variable.
**Abwechselung,** *f.* change, variation, alternation.
**Abweg,** *m.* byway; wrong way.
**abwegig,** *adv.* aberrantly, wrongly.
**Abwehr,** *f.* warding off, defense.
**abwehren,** *v.t.* ward off, prevent.
**Abwehr-ferment,** *n.* protective ferment (or enzyme), defensive ferment (or enzyme). **-mittel,** *n.* preventive, prophylactic.

**abweichen,** *v.t. & i.* soak, soak off, soften (by steeping), macerate. — *v.i.* deviate, diverge, depart, vary. **-abweichend,** *p.a.* deviating, divergent, irregular.

**Abweichung,** *f.* deviation; variation; declination (of the needle); (*Opt.*) aberration; anomaly; soaking, etc. (see abweichen, *v.t. & i.*).

**abweisen,** *v.t.* send away; refuse, reject.

**abweissen,** *v.t.* whiten. — *v.i.* lose whiteness.

**abwelken,** *v.t.* wilt, wither, dry; (*Leather*) sammy.

**abwenden,** *v.t.* turn off, avert.

**abwerfen,** *v.t.* throw off or out; throw down; break down (rock); run off (slag); give off; discharge; reject; (*Com.*) yield.

**Abwerf-ofen,** *m.* refining furnace. **-pfanne,** *f.* refining pan; (*Tinning*) list pot.

**Abwerg,** *n.* waste tow, waste oakum.

**abwerten,** *v.t.* devalue.

**abwesend,** *a.* absent.

**Abwesenheit,** *f.* absence.

**abwickeln,** *v.t.* wind off, unwind; wind up; evolve, develop; (*Math.*) rectify.

**abwiegen,** *v.t.* = abwägen.

**abwinden,** *v.t. & r.* unwind.

**abwischen,** *v.t.* wipe off, wipe.

**abwittern,** *v.i.* = verwittern.

**Abwurf.** *m.* throwing off; something thrown off, offal; coarse plaster, roughcast.

**abzählbar,** *a.* (*Math.*) enumerable.

**abzahlen,** *v.t.* pay, pay off.

**abzählen,** *v.t.* count, count off.

**abzapfen,** *v.t.* draw off, tap.

**abzehren,** *v.i., r. & t.* waste (away); corrode.

**Abzehrung,** *f.* wasting (away); corrosion.

**Abzeichen,** *n.* mark, sign, label; (*pl.*) insignia.

**abzeichnen,** *v.t.* draw, copy, trace; mark off.

**Abzieh-bad,** *n.* (*Dyeing*) stripping bath. **-bild,** *n.* transfer picture or design, decalcomania. **-blase,** *f.* retort, alembic.

**abziehen,** *v.t.* draw off, take away, remove; rack, decant (liquids); siphon off; bottle; distil, rectify; tap; skim; skin; sharpen; subtract; abstract; transfer (designs); print, copy; degum (silk); (*Dyeing*) strip, boil off (color); (*Leather*) strip, clear; (*Photog.*) print. — *v.i.* depart, leave, (of gases) escape. — **abgezogene Wasser,** distilled liquor(s).

**Abzieh-farbe,** *f.* transfer color. **-flotte,** *f.* (*Dyeing*) stripping bath. **-halle,** *f.* (*Brewing*) racking room. **-kolben,** *m.* retort, alembic. **-mittel,** *n.* (*Dyeing*) stripping agent. **-zünder,** *m.* friction igniter.

**Abzug,** *m.* hood, fume cupboard; scum, dross, specif. a scum on molten lead, sharp slag; outlet, discharge, drainage, drain; vent; drawing off; deduction; proof sheet, proof; copy; (*Photog.*) print.

**abzüglich,** *adv.* with deduction (of), less.

**Abzugs-blei,** *n.* lead obtained from dross. **-bogen,** *m.* proof sheet, proof; (*Expl.*) firing spring. **-dampf,** *m.* drawn-off vapor; specif., exhaust steam. **-gas,** *n.* chimney gas, flue gas; waste gas. **-haube,** *f.* hood (for fumes). **-kanal,** *m.* sewer, drain; discharge duct. **-kupfer,** *n.* copper obtained from dross (cf. Abzug). **-öffnung,** *f.* outlet, vent. **-raum,** *m.* hood. **-rohr,** *n.*, **-röhre,** *f.* waste pipe, drain tube, drain pipe, outlet tube or pipe. **-schacht,** *m.* hood flue; ventilating shaft. **-schrank,** *m.* hood, fume cupboard. **-ventil,** *n.* outlet valve. **-vorrichtung,** *f.* escape device; constant-level apparatus (for water baths); ventilator. **-wärme,** *f.* waste heat. **-werke,** *n.pl.* (*Metal.*) scum, dross.

**abzündern,** *v.i.* scale, scale off.

**Abzweig,** *m.* branching, branch.

**abzweigen,** *v.t.* trim off, detach. — *v.r.* branch off.

**Abzweig-leitung,** *f.* branch line. **-rohr,** *n.*, **-röhre,** *f.* branch tube or pipe. **-stromkreis,** *m.* (*Elec.*) derived circuit, shunt.

**Abzweigung,** *f.* branching, branch, (*Elec.*) shunt.

**Abzweig(ungs)widerstand,** *m.* (*Elec.*) shunt resistance.

**Ac-.** for words beginning Ac- see also Ak- and Az-.

**Acajou,** *m.* acajou (see Akajou).

**Acapuholz,** *n.* acapu wood (from *Andira americana*).

**Ac Blei.** actinium lead.

**Accaroidharz,** *n.* acaroid resin.

**Acceleren,** *pl.* accelerators.

**acceptieren,** *v.t.* accept.

**accessorisch,** *a.* accessory.

**Accise,** *f.* excise.

**Accracopalinsäure,** *f.* accracopalinic acid.

**Accracopalsäure,** *f.* accracopalic acid.

**Aceanthrenchinon,** *n.* aceanthrenequinone.

**Acenaphten,** *n.* acenaphthene. **-chinon,** *n.* acenaphthenequinone.

**Acenaphtylen,** *n.* acenaphthylene.

**Acet-.** acet-, aceto-, acetic. **-anhydrid,** *n.* acetic anhydride.

**Acetat-kunstseide,** *f.* = Acetatseide. **-lösung,** *f.* acetate solution. **-seide,** *f.* acetate silk (acetate rayon). **-zellwolle,** *f.* acetate spun rayon.

**Acetessig-äther, -ester,** *m.* acetoacetic ester. **-säure,** *f.* acetoacetic acid.

**Acetin-blau,** *n.* (*Dyes*) acetin blue. **-druck,** *m.* acetin printing.

**Acetolyse,** *f.* acetolysis.

**acetometrisch,** *a.* acetometric.

**Aceton-lösung,** *f.* acetone solution. **-öl,** *n.* acetone oil. **-säure,** *f.* acetonic ($\alpha$-hydroxyisobutyric) acid.

**Acetopersäure, Acetpersäure,** *f.* peroxyacetic acid, peracetic acid.

**Acetsäure,** *f.* acetic acid.

**Acetylen-anstalt,** *f.* acetylene plant. **-bindung,** *f.* acetylene linkage, triple bond. **-brenner,** *m.* acetylene burner. **-erzeuger,** *m.* acetylene generator. **-gebläse,** *n.* oxyacetylene blowpipe or torch. **-kohlenwasserstoff,** *m.* acetylene hydrocarbon. **-kupfer,** *n.* copper acetylide. **-reihe,** *f.* acetylene series. **-russ,** *m.* acetylene black. **-sauerstoffbrenner,** *m.* oxyacetylene blowpipe. **-sauerstoffschweissung,** *f.* oxyacetylene welding. **-schweissung,** *f.* acetylene welding.

**Acetylessigsäure,** *f.* acetoacetic acid.

**acetylierbar,** *a.* capable of being acetylated.

**acetylieren,** *v.t.* acetylate.

**Acetylierkolben,** *m.* acetylating flask.

**Acetylierung,** *f.* acetylation.

**Acetylierungs-kolben,** *m.* acetylation flask. **-mittel,** *n.* acetylating agent.

**Acetyl-säure,** *f.* acetic acid. **-schwefelsäure,** *f.* acetylsulfuric acid. **-senföl,** *n.* acetyl mustard oil. **-zahl,** *f.* acetyl number.

**Achat,** *m.* agate.

**achat-ähnlich, -artig,** *a.* agate-like, agatine. **-haltig,** *a.* containing agate, agatiferous.

**Achat-mörser,** *m.* agate mortar. **-porzellan,** *n.* agate ware. **-schale,** *f.* agate dish. **-schellack,** *m.* a shellac substitute. **-schneide,** *f.* agate knife edge.

**Achema,** *abbrev.* of *A*usstellung für *chem*isches *A*pparatewesen.

**Achillenöl,** *n.* achillea oil.

**Achmit,** *m.* (*Min.*) acmite.

**Achromasie,** *f.* (*Optics*) achromatism.

**Achromat,** *m.* achromatic lens, achromat.

**achromatisch,** *a.* achromatic.

**achromatisieren,** *v.t.* achromatize.

**Achromatismus,** *m.* achromatism.

**Achse,** *f.* axis; axle, shaft.

**Achsel,** *f.* shoulder; (*Physiol.*) axilla.

**Achsel-.** shoulder, axillary. **-drüse,** *f.* (*Physiol.*) axillary gland. **-grube, -höhle,** *f.* armpit, axilla.

**Achsen-.** axis, axial, axle. **-abschnitt,** *m.* axial intercept. **-drehung,** *f.* rotation. **-ebene,** *f.* axial plane. **-kreuz,** *n.* system of coördinates; (*Opt*) cross hairs. **-lager,** *n.* axle bearing.

**achsenlos,** *a.* having no axis, anaxial.

**Achsen-neigung,** *f.* inclination of an axis. **-öl,** *n.* axle oil. **-schmiere,** *f.* axle grease.

**achsensymmetrisch,** *a.* axially symmetrical.

**Achsen-verhältnis,** *n.* axial ratio. **-winkel,** *m.* axial angle.

**Achsfett,** *n.* axle grease.

**achsig, achsial,** *a.* axial.

**Achslager,** *n.* axle bearing.

**achsrecht,** *a.* axial. — *adv.* axially.

**acht,** *a.* eight.

**Acht,** *f.* attention, care. — **ausser — lassen,** disregard, neglect.

**achtbar,** *a.* respectable, honorable.

**achtbasisch,** *a.* octabasic.

**achte,** *a.* eighth.

**Achteck,** *n.* octagon.

**achteckig,** *a.* octagonal, eight-angled.

**Achtel,** *n.* eighth.

**Achtel-.** (in old names) octo-, octa-; as, **Achtelkohleneisen,** octoferric carbide, and **Achtelschwefeleisen,** octoferric sulfide.

**Achtelkreis,** *m.* (*Geom.*) octant.

**achten,** *v.t.* regard, respect, esteem. — *v.i.* pay attention, see (to).

**ächten,** *v.t.* outlaw.

**Achter,** *m.*, **Achter-figur,** *f.* figure-of-eight, figure 8. **-schale,** *f.* shell of eight electrons, octet shell.

**achtfach, achtfältig,** *a.* eightfold.

**Achtflach,** *n.* octahedron.

**achtflächig,** *a.* octahedral.

**Achtflächner,** *m.* octahedron.

**acht-gliedrig,** *a.* eight-membered. **-kantig,** *a.* octagonal. **-los,** *a.* inattentive, negligent. **-mal,** *adv.* eight times.

**Achtring,** *m.* eight-membered ring.

**achtsam,** *a.* careful, heedful.

**achtseitig,** *a.* eight-sided.

**Achtung,** *f.* attention, notice; esteem, respect.

**achtungsvoll,** *adv.* respectfully.

**achtwertig,** *a.* octavalent.

**Achtwertigkeit,** *f.* octavalence.

**achtzehn,** *a.* eighteen.

**Achtzehner-periode,** *f.* period of eighteen. **-schale,** *f.* shell of eighteen (electrons).

**achtzig,** *a.* eighty.

**ächzen,** *v.i.* groan.

**acidifizieren,** *v.t.* acidify.

**Acidifizierung,** *f.* acidification.

**Acidimetrie,** *f.* acidimetry.

**acidimetrisch,** *a.* acidimetric(al).

**Acidität,** *f.* acidity.

**acidylieren,** *v.t.* acylate.

**Acker,** *m.* field, land; acre. **-bau,** *m.* agriculture, farming. **-bauchemie,** *f.* agricultural chemistry. **-bauwissenschaft,** *f.* science of agriculture. **-beere,** *f.* dewberry (esp. *Rubus caesius*). **-boden,** *m.* arable soil, surface soil. **-bohne,** *f.* field bean, broad bean (*Vicia faba*). **-doppen,** *f.pl.* valonia.

**Ackerei,** *f.* tillage.

**Acker-erde,** *f.* (arable) soil. **-günsel,** *m.* ground pine (*Ayuga chamaepitys*). **-kamille,** *f.* wild camomile (*Matricaria*); field camomile (*Anthemis arvensis*). **-krume,** *f.* (arable) soil. **-mennig,** *m.* agrimony. **-minze,** *f.* corn mint (*Mentha arvensis*).

**ackern,** *v.t.* till, cultivate.

**Acon-.** see Akon-.
**Acrylharz,** *n.* acrylic resin.
**activieren,** *v.t.* activate.
**acyclisch, acyklisch,** *a.* acyclic.
**acylieren,** *v.t.* acylate.
**a.d.,** *abbrev.* (an der, an dem, etc.) at the, on, on the, to the.
**ad,** *prep.* (Latin) to, up to.
**adaptieren,** *v.t.* adapt.
**adäquat,** *a.* adequate.
**Addend,** *n.* something to be added, addendum.
**addieren,** *v.t.* add. — **addierend,** *p.a.* additive. — *adv.* additively.
**additionell,** *a.* additional, addition.
**additionsfähig,** *a.* capable of addition.
**Additions-fähigkeit,** *f.* additive power. **-reaktion,** *f.* addition reaction, additive reaction. **-verbindung,** *f.* addition compound.
**Additivität,** *f.* additivity.
**Additivitätsbeziehung,** *f.* additivity relation.
**Address-.** see Adress-.
**Adel,** *m.* nobility.
**adelig,** *a.* noble.
**adeln,** *v.t.* ennoble; dignify.
**Ader,** *f.* vein (in various senses); (*Elec.*) wire, strand. **-chen, Äderchen,** *n.* little vein, veinlet. **-haut,** *f.* choroid. **-häutchen,** *n.* chorion. **-holz,** *n.* wood cut with the grain.
**aderig, äderig,** *a.* veiny, veined, streaked; venous, vascular.
**Ader-knoten, -kropf,** *m.* varicose vein, varix. **-lass,** *m.* venesection.
**adern, ädern,** *v.t.* vein; grain, marble.
**Ader-schlag,** *m.* pulse, pulse beat. **-ung,** *f.* veining, marbling; (*Biol.*) venation. **-wasser,** *n.* blood serum.
**adhärieren,** *v.i.* adhere.
**Adhäsion,** *f.* adhesion.
**Adhäsions-fähigkeit,** *f.* adhesiveness. **-fett,** *n.* adhesive grease. **-kraft,** *f.* adhesive power; force of adhesion. **-masse,** *f.* adhesive substance, adhesive. **-vermögen,** *n.* adhesive power.
**adhäsiv,** *a.* adhesive.
**Adiabate,** *f.* adiabatic curve.
**adiabatisch,** *a.* adiabatic.
**adiaktinisch,** *a.* adiactinic.
**adiatherman,** *a.* adiathermanous, athermanous.
**Adiowan-öl,** *n.* ajowan oil. **-samen,** *m.* ajowan (fruit of *Carum copticum*).
**adipid,** *a.* fat, fatty.
**adipidieren,** *v.t.* grease.
**Adipinsäure,** *f.* adipic acid.
**Adipo-cire,** *n.* adipocere. **-malsäure,** *f.* adipomalic acid ($\alpha$-hydroxy-$\alpha$-methylglutaric acid).
**adipös,** *a.* adipose.
**Adipoweinsäure,** *f.* adipotartaric acid (dihydroxyadipic acid).
**adjungieren,** *v.t.* adjoin.
**Adjustage,** *f.* adjustment.
**adjustieren,** *v.t.* adjust, regulate.
**Adler,** *m.* eagle. **-holz,** *n.* eaglewood, agalloch **-stein,** *m.* eaglestone, aetites. **-vitriol,** *m.* Salzburg vitriol (mixed cupric and ferrous sulfate).
**adlig,** *a.* noble.
**Admiralitätsmetall,** *n.* admiralty brass (Cu 70, Zn 29, Sn 1).
**Admissions-druck,** *m.* admission pressure. **-spannung,** *f.* admission pressure.
**adoptieren,** *v.t.* adopt.
**adoucieren,** *v.t* sweeten; wash, edulcorate; temper, anneal; decarbonize (iron).
**Adoucier-gefäss,** *n.* annealing pot; edulcorating vessel. **-ofen,** *m.* tempering furnace, annealing furnace.
**Adr.,** *abbrev.* (Adresse) address.
**Adressant,** *m.* writer; sender.
**Adressat,** *m.* person addressed; consignee.
**Adressbuch,** *n.* directory.
**Adresse,** *f.* address, direction.
**adressieren,** *v.t.* address; forward.
**Adriabindung,** *f.* (*Textiles*) diagonal rib.
**adrig,** *a.* = aderig.
**Adsorbat, Adsorbend, Adsorbendum,** *n.* adsorbed substance, adsorbate.
**Adsorbens,** *m.* (*pl.* **Adsorbentien**) adsorbing substance, adsorbent.
**adsorbierbar,** *a.* adsorbable.
**Adsorbierbarkeit,** *f.* adsorbability.
**adsorbieren,** *v.t.* adsorb.
**Adsorptions-erscheinung,** *f.* adsorption phenomenon. **-fähigkeit,** *f.* adsorptive capacity, adsorptiveness. **-haut,** *f.*, **-häutchen,** *n.* adsorbed film, adsorption film. **-hülle,** *f.* adsorption shell or sheath. **-kohle,** *f.* activated charcoal. **-kraft,** *f* adsorption force; adsorptive power. **-schicht,** *f.* adsorption layer, adsorbed layer. **-verbindung,** *f.* adsorption compound. **-verdrängung,** *f.* adsorption displacement. **-vermögen,** *n.* adsorptive power. **-vorgang,** *m.* adsorption process. **-wärme,** *f.* heat of adsorption.
**Adstringens,** *n.* astringent.
**Adstringenz,** *f.* astringency.
**adstringierend,** *a.* astringent. — **adstringierendes Mittel,** astringent.
**Adular,** *m.* adularia.
**adventiv,** *a.* adventitious.
**Advokat,** *m.* lawyer.
**Ae.,** *abbrev.* (Äther) ether.
**Å.E.,** *abbrev.* (Ångströmeinheit) Ångström unit.
**Ae-.** for words beginning Ae- see also Ä-.
**AEF,** *abbrev.* (*A*usschuss für *E*inheiten und *F*ormeln) Committee on Units and Formulas.
**Aerob,** (*pl.*) **Aeroben.** (*Bact.*) aërobe(s).
**aerobisch, aerobiontisch,** *a.* aërobic.

**aerogen,** *a.* aërogenic.
**Aerogengas,** *n.* aërogene gas.
**aerostatisch,** *a.* aërostatic.
**Aetz-.** see Ätz-.
**Affe,** *m.* ape, monkey.
**Affekt,** *m.* emotion, ardor, passion.
**affektieren,** *v.t.* affect, feign.
**äffen,** *v.t.* ape, mock.
**Affenbrotbaum,** *m.* baobab tree.
**Affiche,** *f.* poster, bill.
**Affinade,** *f.* washed raw sugar.
**affinähnlich,** *a.* similar in affinity.
**Affination,** *f.* refining (esp. of gold by treating with sulfuric acid and of sugar by washing from mother liquor).
**affinieren,** *v.t.* refine.
**Affinierung,** *f.* refining.
**Affinität,** *f.* affinity.
**Affinitäts-einheit,** *f.* unit of affinity. **-kraft,** *f.* affinity force. **-lehre,** *f.* doctrine of affinity. **-rest,** *m.* affinity residue, residual affinity. **-richtung,** *f.* direction of affinity.
**Affinivalenz,** *f.* atomicity, valence.
**affizieren,** *v.t.* affect, move.
**After,** *m.* anus; bottom; refuse, offal.
**After-.** pseudo-, false, secondary, neo-, after-, back-, hind-; anal, rectal. **-bildung,** *f.* malformation, false formation. **-blatt, -blättchen,** *n.* (*Bot.*) stipule. **-darm,** *m.* (*Anat.*) rectum. **-drüse,** *f.* anal gland. **-geburt,** *f.* afterbirth. **-gewebe,** *n.* heteroplastic tissue. **-holz,** *n.* deadwood. **-kegel,** *m.* (*Geom.*) conoid. **-kohle,** *f.* slack coal, slack. **-kristall,** *m.* pseudomorph. **-kugel,** *f.* (*Geom.*) spheroid. **-mehl,** *n.* coarse flour, seconds; pollard. **-moos,** *n.* alga, algae. **-schörl,** *m.* axinite. **-silber,** *n.* silver containing dross.
**a.G.,** *abbrev.* (auf Gegenseitigkeit) mutual.
**A.G., A.-G.,** *abbrev.* (Atomgewicht) atomic weight; (Aktiengesellschaft) joint-stock company; (Amtsgericht) local court.
**Agaricinsäure,** *f.* agaric acid, agaricic acid.
**Agarizin,** *n.* (*Pharm.*) agaricin.
**Agathendisäure,** *f.* agathenedioic acid.
**Agave-faser,** *f.* agave fiber, sisal. **-hanf,** *m.* agave hemp, aloe hemp.
**Agens,** *n.* agent.
**Agentur,** *f.* agency.
**Agenzien,** *m.pl.* agents.
**Agfa,** *abbrev.* *A*ktien-*G*esellschaft *f*ür *A*nilinfarbenfabrikation.
**Agglomerat,** *n.* agglomerate; sinter cake.
**agglomerieren,** *v.t.* & *i.* agglomerate.
**agglutinieren,** *v.t.* & *i.* agglutinate.
**Aggregat,** *n.* aggregate; outfit; (*Mil.*) missile. **-zustand,** *m.* state of aggregation.
**aggregieren,** *v.t.* & *r.* aggregate.
**aggressiv,** *a.* aggressive, offensive; corrosive.
**Aggressivität,** *f.* aggressiveness.
**Agio,** *n.* premium, agio.
**Agitakel,** *n.* stirrer.
**agitatorisch,** *a.* agitative.
**agitieren,** *v.t.* & *i.* agitate.
**Agrikultur,** *f.* agriculture. **-chemie,** *f.* agricultural chemistry.
**Agtstein,** *m.* amber.
**Ägypten,** *n.* Egypt.
**Ägypterblau,** *n.* Egyptian blue.
**ägyptisch,** *a.* Egyptian. —**ägyptische Seifenwurzel,** Levant soaproot (*Gypsophila struthium*).
**Ahlbeere,** *f.* currant, *esp.* black currant (*Ribes nigrum*).
**Ahle,** *f.* awl, punch; black cherry.
**Ahn,** *m.* grandfather; ancestor.
**Ahne,** *f.* awn, chaff; grandmother.
**ähneln,** *v.i.* & *r.* resemble.
**ahnen,** *v.t.* anticipate; surmise.
**ähnlich,** *a.* similar; analogous, resembling, like.
**-ähnlich.** similar to, resembling, -like, -oid.
**Ähnlichkeit,** *f.* similarity, resemblance, likeness.
**Ahnung,** *f.* presentiment, anticipation.
**Ahorn,** *m.* maple. **-holz,** *n.* maple(wood). **-melasse,** *f.* maple sirup. **-saft,** *m.* maple sap. **-säure,** *f.* aceric acid. **-zucker,** *m.* maple sugar.
**Ähre,** *f.* ear, spike.
**Ähren-früchte,** *f.pl.* grains, cereals. **-gras,** *n.* cereal (grass). **-spitze,** *f.* (*Bot.*) awn, beard, glume.
**Aichamt,** *n.,* **aichen,** *v.t.,* etc., see Eichamt, eichen, etc.
**Aichmetall,** *n.* Aich('s) metal (Cu-Zn-Fe alloy).
**Ajowanöl, Ajoranöl,** *n.* ajowan oil.
**ajustieren,** *v.t.* adjust.
**Ajustiertisch,** *m.* adjusting table.
**Akajou,** *m.* acajou (either cashew or mahogany tree). **-harz,** *n.* acajou resin. **-nuss,** *f.* cashew nut. **-öl,** *n.* cashew (nut) oil.
**Akaridentod,** *m.* acaricide.
**Akaroidharz,** *n.* acaroid resin.
**Akaschu,** *m.* = Akajou.
**Akazie,** *f.* acacia.
**Akazien-gummi,** *n.* acacia gum, gum arabic. **-holz,** *n.* acacia wood. **-öl,** *n.* acacia oil. **-rinde,** *f.* wattle bark.
**Akazin, Akazingummi,** *n.* gum arabic.
**Akeeöl,** *n.* akee oil.
**Akkaroidharz,** *n.* acaroid resin.
**akklimatisieren,** *v.t.* acclimate.
**akkommodieren,** *v.t.* accommodate.
**Akkord,** *m.* agreement, accord; contract. **-arbeit,** *f.* piece work, job work.
**akkordieren,** *v.t.* & *i.* accord; arrange; agree.
**Akkordionbalg,** *m.* accordion bellows.
**Akkumulator,** *m.* accumulator, storage battery. **-säure,** *f.* battery acid, electrolyte. **-zelle,** *f.* storage-battery cell.

**akkumulieren,** *v.t.* accumulate.
**Akmegelb,** *n.* Acme yellow, chrysoidine.
**Akoninsäure,** *f.* aconinic acid.
**Akonitinsäure,** aconitic acid ($C_6H_6O_4$); (more recently) aconitinic acid ($C_{31}H_{35}NO_{10}$?).
**Akonit-knollen,** *f.pl.* aconite root, aconite. **-säure,** *f.* aconitic acid.
**Akonsäure,** *f.* aconic acid.
**Akridin-gelb,** *n.* acridine yellow. **-säure,** *f.* acridic acid, acridinic acid.
**Akrylsäure,** *f.* acrylic acid.
**Akt,** *m.* act, action, deed.
**Akte,** *f.* act, deed, document, file, record.
**Akten-papier,** *n.* deed paper, record paper. **-schrank,** *m.* filing cabinet. **-zeichen,** *n.* file number.
**Akt.-Ges.,** *abbrev.* of Aktiengesellschaft.
**Aktie,** *f.* share.
**Aktien-besitzer,** *m.* shareholder, stockholder. **-gesellschaft,** *f.* joint-stock company.
**aktinisch,** *a.* actinic.
**Aktinismus,** *m.* actinism.
**Aktinochemie,** *f.* actinochemistry.
**aktinometrisch,** *a.* actinometric.
**Aktionär,** *m.* shareholder, stockholder.
**aktiv,** *a.* active.
**Aktiva, Aktiven,** *n.pl.* assets.
**Aktivator,** *m.* activator.
**aktivieren,** *v.t.* activate.
**Aktivierung,** *f.* activation.
**Aktivierungs-energie,** *f.* energy of activation. **-mittel,** *n.* activating agent, activator. **-wärme,** *f.* heat of activation. **-zahl,** *f.* activation number.
**Aktivität,** *f.* activity.
**Aktivkohle,** *f.* active carbon or charcoal.
**aktuell,** *a.* actual; present; important; effective.
**Akustik,** *f.* acoustics.
**akustisch,** *a.* acoustic.
**Akzelerator,** *m.* accelerator.
**akzentuieren,** *v.t.* accentuate.
**Akzept,** *n.* acceptance.
**akzeptieren,** *v.t.* accept.
**Akzeptor,** *m.* acceptor.
**akzessorisch,** *a.* accessory.
**Akzidenzdruck,** *m.* display printing.
**Akzise,** *f.* excise.
**Alabastergips,** *m.* plaster of Paris (best grade).
**Alakreatin,** *n.* alacreatine.
**Alakreatinin,** *n.* alacreatinine.
**Alant,** *m.* elecampane. **-beere,** *f.* black currant. **-kampher,** *m.* helenin. **-öl,** *n.* elecampane oil. **-wurzel,** *f.* (*Pharm.*) inula, elecampane.
**Alarmglocke,** *f.* alarm bell.
**alarmieren,** *v.t.* alarm.
**Alarmvorrichtung,** *f.* alarm device, alarm.
**Alaun,** *m.* alum. — **— von Rocca,** roche alum, Roman alum.
**alaunartig,** *a.* alumish, aluminous.
**Alaun-bad,** *n.* alum bath. **-beize,** *f.* (*Dyeing*) aluminous mordant; alum bath; (*Leather*) aluming, also alum steep. **-brühe,** *f.* (*Leather*) alum steep, alum pickle.
**alaunen,** *v.t.* alum.
**Alaunerde,** *f.* alumina.
**alaunerdehaltig,** *a.* aluminiferous.
**Alaun-erdesulfat,** *n.* sulfate of alumina (aluminum sulfate). **-erz,** *n.* alunite. **-fass,** *n.* (*Leather*) alum vat. **-fels,** *m.* alunite. **-festigkeit,** *f.* (*Paper*) alum resistance.
**alaun-förmig,** *a.* aluminiform. **-gar,** *a.* dressed with alum, alumed, tawed.
**Alaun-gerber,** *m.* tawer. **-gerberei,** *f.* tawing; tawery. **-gips,** *m.* artificial marble (made with alum and gypsum).
**alaunhaltig,** *a.* containing alum, aluminous, aluminiferous.
**Alaunhütte,** *f.* alum works.
**alaunieren,** *v.t.* alum.
**alaunig,** *a.* aluminous.
**Alaun-karmin,** *m.* (*Micros.*) alum carmine. **-kies,** *m.* aluminous pyrites. **-kuchen,** *m.* alum cake. **-lauge,** *f.* alum liquor. **-leder,** *n.* alum leather. **-lösung,** *f.* alum solution. **-mehl, -pulver,** *n.* powdered alum, precipitated alum.
**alaunsauer,** *a.* aluminate of. — **alaunsaures Salz,** aluminate.
**Alaun-schiefer,** *m.*, **-schiefererz,** *n.* alum slate, alum shale. **-seife,** *f.* aluminous soap. **-sieden,** *n.* alum boiling, alum making. **-sieder,** *m.* alum boiler. **-siederei,** *f.* alum works. **-stein, -spat,** *m.* alum stone, alunite.
**alaunt,** *p.a.* alumed.
**Alaun-ton,** *m.* alum clay. **-ung,** *f.* aluming. **-wasser,** *n.* alum water. **-wurzel,** *f.* alumroot.
**Albinismus,** *m.* albinism, albinoism.
**albuminartig,** *a.* albuminoid.
**Albumingehalt,** *m.* albumin content.
**albuminisieren,** *v.t.* albuminize.
**Albuminisierung,** *f.* albuminization.
**Albumin-kupfer,** *m.* copper albuminate. **-stoff,** *m.* albuminous substance, protein. **-substanz,** *f.* albuminoid substance. **-urie,** *f.* albuminuria.
**Alchimie, Alchemie,** *f.* alchemy.
**alchimistisch,** *a.* alchemistic(al).
**Aldehydgrün,** *n.* aldehyde green.
**aldehydhaltig,** *a.* containing aldehyde.
**Aldehydharz,** *n.* aldehyde resin.
**aldehydisch,** *a.* aldehydic.
**Aldehydsäure,** *f.* aldehyde acid, aldehydic acid.
**Alembrothsalz,** *n.* alembroth, salt of alembroth ($2NH_4Cl \cdot HgCl_2 \cdot H_2O$).
**alepisch,** *a.* Aleppo. — **alepischer Gallapfel,** Aleppo gall.
**Aleuron-korn,** *m.* (*Bot.*) aleurone grain **-schicht,** *f.* (*Bot.*) aleurone layer.

**Alfa,** *f.* esparto (*Stipa tenacissima*).
**Algarot(t)pulver,** *n.* powder of Algaroth, algarot, algaroth (SbOCl).
**Alge,** *f.* alga, seaweed.
**algebraisch,** *a.* algebraic.
**Algenpilz,** *m.* algal fungus, phycomycete.
**Algerien,** *n.* Algeria.
**Algol-blau,** *n.* algol blue. **-farbe,** *f.*, **-farbstoff,** *m.* algol dye. **-rot,** *n.* algol red.
**Alhidade,** *f.* (*Optics*) alidade.
**alicyclisch,** *a.* alicyclic.
**aliphatisch,** *a.* aliphatic.
**Alit,** *n.*, **Alith,** *m.* (*Cement*) alite.
**alitieren,** *v.t.* (*Steel*) aluminize, calorize.
**Alizarin-altrot,** *n.* alizarin old red, Turkey red. **-blau,** *n.* alizarin blue. **-chinon,** *n.* alizarinquinone. **-farbe,** *f.* alizarin color or dye. **-färberei,** *f.* alizarin dyeing. **-gelb,** *n.* alizarin yellow. **-neurot,** *n.* alizarin new red. **-rot,** *n.* alizarin red. **-schwarz,** *n.* alizarin black. **-sulfosäure,** *f.* alizarinsulfonic acid. **-tinte,** *f.* alizarin ink.
**alizyklisch,** *a.* alicyclic.
**Alk.,** *abbrev.* (Alkohol) alcohol.
**alkal.,** *abbrev.* (alkalisch) alkaline.
**Alkaleszenz,** *f.* alkalescence.
**alkali-arm,** *a.* poor in alkali. **-artig,** *a.* alkaloidal, alkaloid. **-beständig,** *a.* resistant to alkalies. **-bildend,** *a.* alkaligenous.
**Alkali-blau,** *n.* alkali blue. **-chlorid,** *n.* alkali chloride.
**alkaliecht,** *a.* fast to alkali.
**Alkaliecht-farbe,** *f.* alkali-fast color or dye. **-rot,** *n.* alkali-fast red.
**alkaliempfindlich,** *a.* sensitive to alkali.
**Alkalien,** *n.pl.* alkalies.
**alkali-enthaltend,** *a.* = alkalihaltig. **-fest,** *a.* alkali-proof.
**Alkali-gehalt,** *m.* alkali content. **-gelb,** *n.* alkali yellow. **-gestein,** *n.* alkali rock. **-halogenid,** *n.* alkali halide.
**alkalihaltig,** *a.* containing alkali.
**Alkali-hydrat,** *n.* alkali hydrate (hydroxide). **-lauge,** *f.* alkali liquor, lye.
**alkalilöslich,** *a.* soluble in alkali, alkali-soluble.
**Alkali-lösung,** *f.* solution of alkali, alkaline liquor. **-menge,** *f.* amount of alkali. **-messer,** *m.* alkalimeter. **-messung,** *f.* alkalimetry. **-metrie,** *f.* alkalimetry.
**alkalimetrisch,** *a.* alkalimetric
**alkalinisch,** *a.* alkaline. — **alkalinische Erde,** alkaline earth.
**Alkalinität** *f.* alkalinity.
**Alkali-rückstand,** *m.* alkali residue. **-salz,** *n.* alkali (metal) salt.
**Alkalisator,** *m.* alkalizer.
**alkalisch,** *a.* alkaline. — **alkalische Erde,** alkaline earth. — **alkalische Erdmetalle,** alkaline-earth metals. — **alkalische Luft,** alkaline air (Priestley's name for ammonia). — **alkalisch machen,** render alkaline, alkalize. — **alkalisch reagierend,** giving an alkaline reaction.
**alkalisierbar,** *a.* alkalizable.
**alkalisieren,** *v.t.* render alkaline, alkalize.
**Alkalisierung,** *f.* alkalization.
**Alkalität,** *f.* alkalinity.
**Alkali-zelle,** *f.* (*Elec.*) alkaline cell; alkali-metal (photo)cell. **-zellstoff,** *m.* alkali cellulose.
**Alkalizität,** *f.* alkalinity.
**Alkalizyanid,** *n.* alkali cyanide.
**alkaloidartig,** *a.* alkaloid-like, alkaloidal.
**alkaloidisch,** *a.* alkaloidal.
**Alkaloid-lösung,** *f.* alkaloidal solution. **-vergiftung,** *f.* alkaloid poisoning.
**Alkamin,** *n.* alcamine.
**Alkan,** *n.* alkane.
**Alkanna-rot,** *n.* alkanna red, anchusin. **-wurzel,** *f.* alkanet (root).
**Alken,** *n.* alkene.
**Alkogel,** *n.* alcogel.
**alkoh.,** *abbrev.* (alkoholisch) alcoholic.
**alkoholartig,** *a.* alcohol-like, alcoholic.
**Alkohol-artigkeit,** *f.* alcoholicity. **-auszug,** *m.* alcoholic extract. **-bestimmung,** *f.* determination of alcohol. **-dampf.** *m.* alcohol vapor.
**alkohol-enthaltend,** *a.* containing alcohol, alcoholic. **-fest,** *a.* alcoholproof. **-frei,** *a.* alcohol-free, non-alcoholic.
**Alkohol-gärung,** *f.* alcoholic fermentation. **-gehalt,** *m.* alcohol content.
**alkoholhaltig,** *a.* containing alcohol, alcoholic.
**alkoholisch,** *a.* alcoholic. — **alkoholische Getränke,** alcoholic beverages.
**alkoholischwässerig,** *a.* aqueous-alcoholic.
**alkoholisierbar,** *a.* alcoholizable.
**alkoholisieren,** *v.t.* alcoholize.
**Alkoholisierung,** *f.* alcoholization.
**alkohollöslich,** *a.* soluble in alcohol.
**Alkohol-lösung,** *f.* alcohol(ic) solution. **-messer,** *m.* alcoholometer.
**alkoholometrisch,** *a.* alcoholometric.
**Alkoholpräparat,** *n.* alcoholic preparation.
**alkoholreich,** *a.* containing much alcohol.
**Alkohol-säure,** *f.* alcohol acid. **-stärke,** *f.* alcoholic strength. **-tafel,** *f.* alcohol table.
**alkoholunlöslich,** *a.* insoluble in alcohol.
**Alkohol-vergällung,** *f.* denaturing of alcohol. **-vergärung,** *f.* alcohol(ic) fermentation. **-vergiftung,** *f.* alcoholic poisoning.
**Alkoholyse,** *f.* alcoholysis.
**Alkoholzusatz,** *m.* addition of alcohol.
**Alkosol,** *n.* alcosol.
**Alkoven,** *m.* alcove, recess.
**alkoxyalkylieren,** *v.t.* convert into an alkoxy compound by alkylation.
**Alkydharz,** *n.* alkyd resin. **-lack,** *m.* alkyd resin varnish.

**Alkyl-derivat,** *n.* alkyl derivative. **-haloid,** *n.* alkyl halide.
**alkylieren,** *v.t.* introduce alkyl into, alkylate.
**Alkylierung,** *f.* alkylation.
**Alkylierungsmittel,** *n.* alkylating agent.
**Alkyl-rest,** *n.* alkyl residue, alkyl group. **-sulfosäure,** *f.* alkyl sulfonic acid. **-verbindung,** *f.* alkyl compound.
**all,** *a.* all, whole, every. — **vor allem,** above all.
**all.,** *abbrev.* (allgemein) general; generally.
**allantoisch,** *a.* allantoic.
**Allantosäure, Allantoissäure,** *f.* allantoic acid (allantoin).
**allbekannt,** *a.* well known, notorious.
**allda,** *adv.* there.
**alledem,** all that. — **bei alledem,** for all that, after all.
**Allee,** *f.* avenue, alley.
**allein,** *a.* alone, single, sole. — *adv.* only, merely. — *conj.* but, still.
**Allein-gerbstoff,** *m.* self-tannin. **-gerbung,** *f.* self-tannage. **-handel,** *m.* monopoly. **-hersteller,** *m.* sole producer.
**alleinig,** *a.* sole, unique.
**alleinstehend,** *p.a.* isolated, insulated; unmarried.
**allelotrop,** *a.* allelotropic.
**allemal,** *adv.* always, every time.
**allenfalls,** *adv.* at all events; if necessary; perhaps.
**allenthalben,** *adv.* everywhere.
**aller-best,** *a.* best (of all), very best. **-dings,** *adv.* to be sure, it is true, of course. **-erst,** *a.* first of all. **-feinst,** *a.* finest (of all), very fine. **-grösst,** *a.* greatest (of all), very greatest. **-hand,** *a.* of all kinds, all sorts of.
**Allerheiligenholz,** *n.* logwood.
**aller-höchst,** *a.* highest of all, utmost. **-jüngst,** *a.* very recent. **-lei,** *a.* all kinds of.
**Allerleigewürz,** *n.* allspice; mixed spice.
**aller-letzt,** *a.* very last, ultimate; very recent. **-neuest,** *a.* very newest or latest. **-wärts,** *adv.* everywhere. **-wesentlichst,** *a.* most essential. **-wichtigst,** *a.* most important.
**alles,** *n.* all, everything. — **vor allem,** before all, above all, in the first place.
**allfällig,** *a.* eventual. — *adv.* eventually.
**allg.,** *abbrev.* (allgemein) general; generally.
**allgemach,** *adv.* gradually, by degrees.
**allgemein,** *a.* general; common; (*Med.*) constitutional; epidemic.—*adv.* generally, commonly. **-giltig, -gültig,** *a.* of universal validity.
**Allgemein-giltigkeit, -gültigkeit,** *f.* universal validity. **-heit,** *f.* generality, universality. **-kosten,** *f.pl.* general expenses. **-reaktion,** *f.* general reaction. **-wirkung,** *f.* general action or effect.
**Allheilmittel,** *n.* universal remedy, panacea.
**alliieren,** *v.t. & r.* ally.
**alljährlich,** *a.* yearly, annual.
**allmählich,** *a.* gradual. — *adv.* gradually, by degrees.
**allmonatlich,** *a.* every month, monthly.
**allochromatisch,** *a.* allochromatic.
**Alloisomerie,** *f.* alloisomerism.
**Allomerie,** *f.* allomerism.
**allomerisch,** *a.* allomeric.
**Allomerismus,** *m.* allomerism.
**allomorph,** *a.* allomorphic.
**Allomorphismus,** *m.* allomorphism.
**Allonge,** *f.* adapter; (*Zinc*) prolong; fly leaf.
**Alloschleimsäure,** *f.* allomucic acid.
**allotrop,** *a.* allotropic.
**Allotropie,** *f.* allotropy, allotropism.
**allotropisch,** *a.* allotropic.
**Allotropismus,** *m.* allotropism.
**Alloxur-basen,** *f.pl.* alloxuric bases (purine bases). **-körper,** *m.pl.* alloxuric substances (purine substances).
**Allozimtsäure,** *f.* allocinnamic acid.
**allseitig,** *a.* on all sides; universal; versatile.
**Alltag,** *m.* every day; work day, weekday.
**all-täglich,** *a.* daily; commonplace; (*Med.*) quotidian. **-wöchentlich,** *a.* every week, weekly.
**Allyl-jodid,** *n.* allyl iodide. **-rhodanid,** *n.* allyl thiocyanate. **-senföl,** *n.* allyl mustard oil. **-verbindung,** *f.* allyl compound.
**allzu,** *adv.* too much, altogether too. **-weit,** *adv.* too far.
**Alm,** *f.* alpine pasture. —, *n.* (proposed term for) aluminum.
**Almeroder Tiegel.** Hessian crucible.
**Aloe,** *f.* aloes.
**aloehaltig,** *a.* aloetic.
**Aloe-hanf,** *m.* aloe hemp (agave). **-holz,** *n.* agalloch. **-mittel,** *n.* (*Med.*) aloetic. **-saft,** *m.* aloe juice, aloes.
**Aloetinsäure, Aloesäure,** *f.* aloetic acid.
**aloetisch,** *a.* aloetic.
**Alpen-mehl,** *n.* lycopodium powder. **-ranken,** *f.pl.* = Alpranken.
**alphabetisch,** *a.* alphabetic(al).
**Alpha-gras,** *n.* alfa grass, esparto. **-milchsäure,** *f.* ($\alpha$-)lactic acid **-naphtol,** *n.* alpha naphthol, $\alpha$-naphthol (1-naphthol). **-strahlen,** *m.pl.* alpha rays. **-zellstoff,** *m.* alpha cellulose.
**Alpranken,** *f.pl.* bittersweet (*Solanum dulcamara*).
**Alquifoux,** *n.* alquifou, potter's lead.
**Alraun,** *m.*, **Alraune, Alrune,** *f.* mandrake.
**Alraunwurzel,** *f.* (*Pharm.*) mandragora.
**als,** *conj.* as, like; than, except; when; as if.
**als-bald,** *adv.* at once. **-dann,** *adv.* then.
**also,** *adv. & conj.* accordingly, therefore, so, thus, then, i.e.
**alt,** *a.* old, aged, ancient. **-backen,** *p.a.* stale. **-bekannt,** *p.a.* long known, well known.
**Alteisen,** *n.* old iron, scrap iron.

**älter,** *a.* older; elder.
**Alter,** *n.* age, old age. **—,** *m.* old man.
**Alterantia,** *n.pl.* alteratives.
**altern,** *v.i.* age, grow old; deteriorate; decline. — *v.t.* age.
**alternieren,** *v.i.* alternate. — **alternierend,** *p.a.* alternating, alternate.
**Alters-.** old-age, senile, age, of age. **-rang,** *m.* seniority, priority.
**Altertum,** *n.* antiquity.
**Altertums-forscher,** *m.* archeologist. **-kunde,** *f.* archeology.
**Alterung,** *f.* aging, etc. (see altern).
**Alterungs-härtung,** *f.* age-hardening. **-schutzmittel,** *n.* age resister, antiager. **-verfahren,** *n.* aging process. **-vorgang,** *m.* aging process.
**ältest,** *a.* oldest, eldest.
**Alt-gesell,** *m.* foreman. **-gold,** *n.* old gold. **-grad,** *m.* (*Math.*) old (or conventional) degree, $\frac{1}{360}$ circle. **-gummi,** *n.* old rubber, used rubber, scrap rubber.
**Althee,** *f.* marsh mallow (*Althaea officinalis*); (*Pharm.*) althaea. **-wurzel,** *f.* (*Pharm.*) althaea.
**Altholz,** *n.* mature timber.
**altklug,** *a.* precocious.
**Alt-malz,** *n.* stored malt. **-messing,** *n.* old brass. **-metall,** *n.* old metal, scrap metal. **-papier,** *n.* old paper, used paper, waste paper. **-rotgrundierung,** *f.* (*Dyeing*) old red ground. **-rotverfahren,** *n.* old red process, Turkey-red dyeing. **-schadenwasser,** *n.* (*Pharm.*) yellow mercurial lotion. **-stoff,** *m.* old material, waste.
**altvulkanisch,** *a.* (*Geol.*) old volcanic.
**Aluchiharz,** *n.* acouchi resin, aluchi resin.
**Aludelofen,** *m.* aludel furnace.
**alumetieren,** *v.t.* plate with aluminum.
**Aluminatlauge,** *f.* aluminate liquor.
**Aluminium,** *n.* aluminum, aluminium. **-blech,** *n.* sheet aluminum. **-bor,** *n.* aluminum boride. **-draht,** *m.* aluminum wire. **-eisen,** *n.* ferroaluminum. **-erz,** *n.* aluminum ore. **-feilspäne,** *m.pl.* aluminum filings. **-fluorwasserstoffsäure,** *f.* fluoaluminic acid. **-folie,** *f.* aluminum foil. **-formiat,** *n.* aluminum formate. **-giesserei,** *f.* aluminum foundry or founding. **-griess,** *m.* (coarse) aluminum powder; aluminum shot. **-guss,** *m.* aluminum casting(s), cast aluminum.
**aluminiumhaltig,** *a.* containing aluminum.
**Aluminium-hydrat,** *n.* aluminum hydroxide. **-jodat,** *n.* aluminum iodate. **-jodid,** *n.* aluminum iodide. **-kaliumsulfat,** *n.* aluminum potassium sulfate. **-legierung,** *f.* aluminum alloy. **-messing,** *n.* aluminum brass. **-oxydhydrat,** *n.* aluminum hydroxide. **-pulver,** *n.* aluminum powder. **-rhodanid,** *n.* aluminum thiocyanate. **-rohr,** *n.*, **-röhre,** *f.* aluminum pipe or tube. **-salz,** *n.* aluminum salt. **-seife,** *f.* aluminum soap. **-stange,** *f* aluminum rod or bar. **-staub,** *m.* aluminum dust or powder.
**aluminothermisch,** *a.* aluminothermic.
**Aluminoxyd,** *n.* aluminum oxide.
**Alundumziegel,** *m.* alundum brick.
**Alunitisierung,** *f.* alunitization.
**am,** *abbrev.* (an dem) at the, to the, etc.
**amalgamierbar,** *a.* amalgamable.
**amalgamieren,** *v.t.* amalgamate.
**Amalgamierpfanne,** *f.* amalgamating pan,
**Amalgamierung,** *f.* amalgamation.
**Amalgamverfahren** *n.* amalgamation process.
**Amarant,** *m.* amaranth. **-holz,** *n.* purpleheart purplewood.
**Amause,** *f.* enamel.
**Amazonenstein,** *m.* Amazon stone, amazonite.
**Amber,** *m.* amber; (**grauer**) ambergris.
**amberartig,** *a.* amber-like, amber.
**Amber-fett, -harz,** *n.* ambrain. **-kraut,** *n.* cat thyme (*Teucrium marum*). **-öl,** *n.* oil of amber, amber oil. **-stoff,** *m.* ambrain.
**Amboss,** *m.* anvil; (*Anat.*) incus.
**Ambra,** *m., f. & n.* amber. — **gelber —,** yellow or ordinary amber. — **grauer —,** ambergris. — **flüssiger —,** liquidambar. **-baum,** *m.* amber tree. **-fett,** *n.* ambrain. **-holz,** *n.* yellow sandalwood. **-öl,** *n.* oil of amber.
**Ambretteöl,** *n.* ambrette oil (from amber seeds).
**ambulant,** *a.* moving about, traveling, ambulant.
**Ameise,** *f.* ant.
**Ameisen-.** formic. **-aldehyd,** *n.* formaldehyde. **-amyläther, -amylester,** *m.* amyl formate. **-äther,** *m.* formic ether (ethyl formate). **-geist,** *m.* (*Pharm.*) spirit of ants (a mixture of formic acid, alcohol and water). **-naphta,** *n.* = Ameisenäther. **-persäure,** *f.* peroxyformic acid, performic acid.
**ameisensauer,** *a.* of or combined with formic acid, formate of. — **ameisensaures Salz,** formate.
**Ameisensäure,** *f.* formic acid. **-nitril,** *n.* formonitrile (HCN). **-salz,** *n.* salt of formic acid, formate. **-sulfonsäure,** *f.* sulfoformic acid.
**Ameisen-spiritus,** *m.* = Ameisengeist. **-weinäther,** *m.* ethyl formate.
**Amerikaner,** *m.* American.
**amerikanisch,** *a.* American. — **amerikanischer Nussbaum,** black walnut (*Juglans nigra*).
**Ametall,** *n.* nonmetal.
**Amethystfarbe,** *f.* amethyst color.
**Amiant, Amianth,** *m.* amianthus (silky asbestos).
**amiantartig,** *a.* amianthine.
**Amidgruppe,** *f.* amido (or amino) group, amidogen.
**amidieren,** *v.t.* amidate, convert into an amide.

**Amidierung,** *f.* amidation.

**Amido-.** amino-, amido- (should be translated amido- only when the compound is of amide nature, otherwise amino-). **-azobenzol,** *n.* aminoazobenzene. **-benzol,** *n.* aminobenzene. **-essigsäure,** *f.* aminoacetic acid. **-kohlensäure,** *f.* amidocarbonic acid (carbamic acid). **-säure,** *f.* amino acid. **-schwefelsäure,** *f.* amidosulfuric acid (sulfamic acid, $NH_2SO_3H$). **-sulfosäure, -sulfonsäure,** *f.* amidosulfuric (sulfamic) acid; aminosulfonic acid. **-toluol,** *n.* aminotoluene.

**Amid-säure,** *f.* amide acid, amic acid. **-stickstoff,** *m.* amide nitrogen.

**-amidsäure,** *f.* -amic acid.

**amikroskopisch,** *a.* amicroscopic, submicroscopic.

**aminartig,** *a.* amine-like.

**aminieren,** *v.t.* aminate, convert into an amine.

**Amino-benzol,** *n.* aminobenzene, aniline. **-essigsäure,** *f.* aminoacetic acid, glycine. **-kohlensäure,** *f.* amidocarbonic acid, carbamic acid. **-säure,** *f.* amino acid. **-säurerest,** *m.* amino acid residue. **-verbindung,** *f.* amino compound. **-zucker,** *m.* amino sugar.

**Aminsäure,** *f.* amino acid; amic acid.

**-aminsäure,** *f.* -amic acid.

**Ammenzeugung,** *f.* (*Biol.*) asexual reproduction.

**Ammiak,** *n.* ammine.

**Ammon,** *m.* ammonia. — **oxalsauer —,** oxalate of ammonia, ammonium oxalate.

**Ammon-.** ammonium; ammonia. **-alaun,** *m.* ammonia alum, ammonium alum. **-chlorid,** *n.* ammonium chloride. **-eisenalaun,** *m.* ammonium iron alum. **-formiat,** *n.* ammonium formate.

**Ammoniak,** *n.* ammonia (in old names of salts equivalent to ammonium, as **salzsaures —,** ammonium chloride); ammoniac. **-alaun,** *m.* ammonia alum.

**ammoniakalisch,** *a.* ammoniacal.

**ammoniakarm,** *a.* poor in ammonia.

**Ammoniakbestimmung,** *f.* determination of ammonia.

**ammoniakbindend,** *a.* combining with ammonia.

**Ammoniak-dampf,** *m.* ammonia vapor. **-entwicklung,** *f.* evolution of ammonia. **-flasche,** *f.* ammonia bottle, flask or cylinder. **-flüssigkeit,** *f.* ammonia water, aqueous ammonia; (*Tech.*) ammoniacal liquor. **-gas,** *n.* ammonia gas. **-gummi,** *m.* gum ammoniac, ammoniac.

**ammoniakhaltig,** *a.* containing ammonia, ammoniacal.

**Ammoniak-harz,** *n.* = Ammoniakgummi. **-kupferchlorür,** *n.* ammoniacal cuprous chloride. **-laugung,** *f.* ammonia leaching. **-leitung,** *f.* conduction of ammonia; ammonia piping or line. **-lösung,** *f.* ammonia solution. **-messer,** *m.* ammonia meter. **-pflanze,** *f.* ammoniac plant. **-pflaster,** *n.* ammoniac plaster. **-prüfer,** *m.* ammonia tester.

**ammoniakreich,** *a.* rich in ammonia.

**Ammoniak-rest,** *m.* ammonia residue (amidogen, $NH_2$). **-rohr,** *n.* ammonia tube or pipe. **-salpeter,** *m.* ammonia saltpeter (ammonium nitrate). **-salz,** *n.* ammonium salt. **-seife,** *f.* ammonia soap. **-soda,** *f.* ammonia soda, Solvay soda. **-stickstoff,** *m.* ammonia nitrogen. **-verbindung,** *f.* ammonia compound; ammonium compound. **-verfahren,** *n.* ammonia process. **-wäsche,** *f.* ammonia scrubbing; ammonia recovery plant. **-wäscher,** *m.* ammonia scrubber, ammonia washer. **-wasser,** *n.* ammonia water; (*Tech.*) ammoniacal liquor. **-weinstein,** *m.* ammonium potassium tartrate. **-zusatz,** *m.* addition of ammonia.

**Ammonium bromatum.** (*Pharm.*) ammonium bromide.

**Ammonium chloratum.** (*Pharm.*) ammonium chloride.

**Ammonium jodatum.** (*Pharm.*) ammonium iodide.

**Ammonium-ferrisulfat,** *n.* ammonium iron(III) sulfate, ferric ammonium sulfate. **-ferrosulfat,** *n.* ammonium iron(II) sulfate, ferrous ammonium sulfate. **-jodat,** *n.* ammonium iodate. **-jodid,** *n.* ammonium iodide. **-platinchlorid,** *n.* ammonium platinichloride (chloroplatinate). **-rest,** *m.* ammonium radical. **-rhodanid, -rhodanür,** *n.* ammonium thiocyanate. **-salpeter,** *m.* ammonium nitrate. **-salz,** *n.* ammonium salt. **-seife,** *f.* ammonia soap. **-sulfhydrat,** *n.* ammonium hydrosulfide. **-sulfocyanid,** *n.* ammonium thiocyanate. **-verbindung,** *f.* ammonium compound. **-zinnchlorid,** *n.* ammonium chlorostannate, pink salt.

**Ammon-jodid,** *n.* ammonium iodide. **-karbonat,** *n.* carbonate of ammonia. **-karbonit,** *n.* ammoncarbonite (trade name of an explosive). **-nitrat,** *n.* ammonium nitrate. **-persulfat,** *n.* ammonium persulfate. **-platinchlorid,** *n.* ammonium platinichloride (chloroplatinate). **-pulver,** *n.* an explosive made by evaporating ammonium nitrate solution with powdered charcoal. **-rest,** *m.* ammonium radical ($NH_4$). **-rhodanid,** *n.* ammonium thiocyanate. **-salpeter,** *m.* ammonium nitrate. **-salpetersprengstoff,** *m.* ammonium nitrate explosive. **-salz,** *n.* ammonium salt. **-seife,** *f.* ammonia soap. **-sulfat,** *n.* ammonium sulfate. **-sulfatsalpeter,** *m.* a mixture or compound of ammonium sulfate and nitrate. **-sulfhydrat,** *n.* ammonium hydrosulfide. **-sulfit,** *n.* ammonium sulfite. **-verbindung,** *f.* ammonium com-

pound. **-zinnchlorid,** *n.* ammonium chlorostannate, pink salt.
**Amnion-flüssigkeit,** *f.* amniotic fluid. **-säure,** *f.* amniotic acid (allantoin). **-wasser,** *n.* amniotic fluid.
**Amnios-.** = Amnion-.
**Amöbe,** *f.* (*Zoöl.*) amoeba, ameba.
**amorph, amorphisch,** *a.* amorphous.
**amortisieren,** *v.t.* amortize.
**am. P.,** *abbrev.* (amerikanisches Patent) American patent.
**Amp.,** *abbrev.* (Ampere) ampere.
**Ampel,** *f.* = Ampulla.
**Ampere-stunde,** *f.* (*Elec.*) ampere-hour. **-zahl,** *f.* amperage.
**Ampfer,** *m.* sorrel, dock (*Rumex*).
**amphichroitisch,** *a.* amphichroic.
**amphoter, amphoterisch,** *a.* amphoteric.
**Ampulle, Ampulla,** *f.* ampulla; (*Pharm.*) ampoule.
**Ampullenfabrikation,** *f.* manufacture of ampoules.
**ampullenförmig,** *a.* ampulliform.
**Amt,** *n.* office, post, employment, business; board, court, council.
**amtlich,** *a.* official.
**Amtmann,** *m.* magistrate.
**Amts-bericht,** *m.* official report. **-blatt,** *n.* official gazette.
**Amyl-äther,** *m.* amyl ether. **-jodid,** *n.* amyl iodide.
**Amylobrennerei,** *f.* distilling with the amylo process.
**amyloklastisch,** *a.* amyloclastic.
**Amylolyse,** *f.* amylolysis.
**Amyloverfahren,** *n.* (*Alcohol*) amylo process (of saccharification).
**Amyl-oxydhydrat,** *n.* amyl alcohol. **-verbindung,** *f.* amyl compound.
**an,** *prep.* at, by, along, against, to; in, on; near to, about; in respect to, by way of. — *adv.* on, onward, along, up. — **an sich,** in itself, in themselves, *per se*, intrinsically.
**an-.** (with verbs) at, toward, on, commence to, continue to.
**-an.** (*Org. Chem.*), in the names of *saturated* hydrocarbons and heterocyclic parent compounds, -ane; in other cases, -an; as. *Methan*, methane; *Menthan*, menthane: *Pyran*, pyran; *Urethan*, urethan.
**An.,** *abbrev.* (Anmerkung) note, remark.
**anaerob,** *a.* anaërobic.
**Anaeroben,** *pl.* anaërobes, anaërobic bacteria **-kolben,** *m.* anaërobic flask.
**anaerobisch,** *a.* anaërobic.
**anal.,** *abbrev.* (analytisch) analytical.
**Analdrüse,** *f.* anal gland.
**analeptisch,** *a.* (*Med.*) analeptic, restorative.
**analog,** *a.* analogous.
**Analogon,** *n.* analog.
**Analysator,** *m.* analyzer.
**Analyse,** *f.* analysis.
**Analysen-.** analytical. **-befund,** *m.* analytical finding or result. **-bericht,** *m.* report of analyses, analytical report. **-einwa(a)ge,** *f.* weighed portion for analysis. **-fehler,** *m.* analytical error.
**analysenfertig,** *a.* ready for analysis.
**Analysen-formel,** *f.* analysis formula, empirical formula. **-gang,** *m.* course or process of analysis. **-gewicht,** *n.* analytical weight. **-material,** *n.* analytical material. **-methode,** *f.* analytical method. **-probe,** *f.* analytical sample or test.
**analysenrein,** *a.* analytically pure, for analyses.
**Analysen-substanz,** *f.* substance to be analyzed. **-trichter,** *m.* analytical funnel. **-wage,** *f.* analytical balance.
**analysierbar,** *a.* analyzable.
**analysieren,** *v.t.* analyze.
**Analytiker,** *m.* analyst.
**analytisch,** *a.* analytical, analytic.
**Anämie,** *f.* anemia.
**Ananas,** *f.* pineapple. **-äther,** *m.*, **-essenz,** *f.* pineapple essence (ethyl butyrate). **-frucht,** *f.* pineapple (the fruit). **-öl,** *n.* banana oil (amyl acetate). **-saft,** *m.* pineapple juice.
**anaphylaktisch,** *a.* anaphylactic.
**Anaphylaxe, Anaphylaxie,** *f.* anaphylaxis.
**anarbeiten,** *v.t.* join, attach.
**Anästhesie,** *f.* anesthesia.
**Anästhetikum,** *n.* anesthetic.
**anästhetisch,** *a.* anesthetic. — **anästhetisches Mittel,** anesthetic.
**Anatas,** *m.* anatase.
**anatomisch,** *a.* anatomical.
**anätzen,** *v.t.* cauterize; begin to etch, begin to corrode; etch on.
**Anätzung,** *f.* cauterization.
**anbacken,** *v.t.* & *i.* bake on, burn on; bake slightly; stick on.
**anbahnen,** *v.t.* pave the way for.
**Anbau,** *m.* cultivation, culture; addition, annex, wing; colony.
**anbauen,** *v.t.* grow, cultivate; build on, add.
**Anbaustoffwechsel,** *m.* anabolism.
**anbei,** *adv.* herewith.
**anbeizen,** *v.t.* mordant.
**anbelangen,** *v.t.* relate to; concern.
**anbequemen,** *v.t.* accommodate, adapt.
**anberaumen,** *v.t.* appoint.
**anbeten,** *v.t.* adore.
**Anbetracht,** *m.* consideration.
**anbetreffen,** *v.t.* concern.
**anbieten,** *v.t.* offer, hold out, tender.
**anbinden,** *v.t.* tie, bind.
**Anbindezettel,** *m.* tag.
**anblaken,** *v.t.* blacken, smoke.

**anblassen,** *v.t.* blow in (a blast furnace); blow on; seal on (with the blast).
**anbläuen,** *v.t.* blue, tinge with blue.
**Anblick,** *m.* sight, aspect, view.
**anblicken,** *v.t.* look at.
**anbluten,** *v.i.* (of colors) bleed, run.
**anbohren,** *v.t.* bore, drill, tap; perforate.
**anbräunen,** *v.t.* brown.
**anbrechen,** *v.t.* begin on. — *v.i.* begin, appear; begin to spoil.
**anbrennen,** *v.t.* set fire to, light; scorch; calcine. — *v.i.* catch fire, begin to burn; calcine.
**anbringen,** *v.t.* place, put, put in, put on; mount, install; dispose of, sell; lodge (a complaint). — **angebracht,** *p.a.* fitting, suitable. applicable, timely.
**Anbruch,** *m.* decay; fracture; first ore; opening (of a mine); daybreak.
**anbrüchig,** *a.* decaying, putrescent, spoiled, rotten, moldy.
**Anbrüchigkeit,** *f.* putrescence, putridity, rottenness, moldiness.
**anbrühen,** *v.t.* scald, infuse, steep (in hot water).
**Anchovisöl,** *n.* anchovy oil.
**Anchusasäure,** *f.* anchusic acid (anchusin).
**Andacht,** *f.* devotion; devotions.
**andampfen,** *v.t. & i.* deposit by evaporation.
**Andaöl,** *n.* anda oil.
**andauern,** *v.i.* last, continue, persist. — **andauernd,** *p.a.* lasting, continual, steady.
**Andenken,** *m.* remembrance, memory.
**ander,** *a.* other, another, else.
**anderartig,** *a.* different, of another kind.
**änderbar,** *a.* alterable, changeable.
**Änderbarkeit,** *f.* alterability, changeability.
**ändern,** *v.t.* alter, change.
**andernfalls,** *adv.* else, otherwise.
**anders,** *adv.* otherwise, differently. — **wenn —,** if indeed, provided.
**anderseits,** *adv.* on the other hand, on the other side.
**anderswertig,** *a.* of another valence.
**anderswo,** *adv.* elsewhere.
**anderthalb,** *a.* sesqui-; one and a half. **-basisch,** *a.* sesquibasic. **-fach,** *a.* one and a half times; sesqui-. **-faches Chlorid,** sesquichloride. **-faches Oxyd,** sesquioxide. **-fachkohlensauer, -kohlensauer,** *a.* sesquicarbonate of.
**Änderung,** *f.* change, alteration, variation.
**anderwärts,** *adv.* elsewhere.
**anderweitig,** *a. & adv.* in another place or way otherwise, further.
**andeuten,** *v.t.* indicate, signify; intimate, hint.
**Andeutung,** *f.* indication, etc. (see andeuten).
**Andorn,** *m.*, **-kraut,** *n.* horehound.
**andorren,** *v.i.* dry on, adhere by drying.
**Andrang,** *m.* rush, crowd, congestion; urgency.
**andrehen,** *v.t.* twist on, screw on, turn on.
**andringen,** *v.i.* press, rush. — *v.t.* press, push.
**Andruck,** *m.* pressure.
**andrücken,** *v.t.* press on, press close.
**andunkeln,** *v.i.* darken.
**andunsten, andünsten,** *v.i.* be deposited by evaporation.
**aneignen,** *v.t.* assimilate; adapt; appropriate, acquire.
**aneinander,** *adv.* together. **-fügen,** *v.t.* join. **-grenzen,** *v.i.* come into contact, be in contact.
**Aneinanderlagerung,** *f.* juxtaposition.
**aneinanderschliessen,** *v.t.* close together, connect, join.
**anekeln,** *v.t.* disgust.
**Anelland,** *n.* a ring joined to another by "ortho fusion," anellated ring (see anellieren).
**anellieren,** *v.t.* (*Org. Chem.*) join by "ortho fusion" (as the two rings in naphthalene), anellate.
**Anellierung,** *f.* anellation (see anellieren).
**Anemoninsäure,** *f.* anemoninic acid.
**Anemon-kampher,** *m.* anemonin. **-säure,** *f.* anemonic acid.
**anerbieten,** *v.t.* offer, proffer, tender.
**anerk.,** *abbrev.* (anerkannt) recognized.
**anerkannt,** *p.p.* of anerkennen.
**anerkennbar,** *a.* recognizable.
**anerkennen,** *v.t.* recognize; acknowledge; honor; admit; appreciate.
**anerkennenswert,** *a.* worthy of recognition.
**Anerkennung,** *f.* recognizing, recognition, etc. (see anerkennen).
**Aneth,** *n.* dill.
**Anethol,** *n.* anethole.
**anfächeln,** *v.t.* fan.
**anfachen,** *v.t.* fan, blow; kindle; excite.
**Anfachung,** *f.* fanning, kindling.
**anfahren,** *v.t.* carry near, bring up; start (machinery); attack, snub. — *v.i.* approach, arrive.
**Anfall,** *m.* amount formed or collected, yield; attack; fit; stay, prop.
**anfallen,** *v.i.* fall on, fall; accumulate, accrue, yield, result; (of dyes) go on. — *v.t.* attack. — **anfallend,** *p.a.* resulting; aggressive.
**anfällig,** *a.* susceptible.
**Anfälligkeit,** *f.* susceptibility.
**Anfang,** *m.* beginning, start; origin.
**anfangen,** *v.t. & i.* begin, commence.
**Anfänger,** *m.* beginner.
**anfänglich,** *a.* original, initial, incipient. — *adv.* at first, originally.
**anfangs,** *adv.* at first, originally.
**Anfangs-.** initial, beginning, first, primary; original. **-bad,** *n.* starting bath. **-bahn,** *f.* initial orbit or path. **-buchstabe,** *m.* initial; capital (letter). **-druck,** *m.* initial pressure. **-ergebnis,** *n.* initial product or yield. **-erzeugnis,** *f.* initial product, first product. **-ge-**

**schwindigkeit,** *f.* initial velocity. **-glied,** *n.* initial member, first member (of a series). **-lage,** *f.* initial position. **-lösung,** *f.* initial or original solution. **-niveau,** *n.* initial level. **-phase,** *f.* initial phase. **-produkt,** *m.* initial product, first product. **-punkt,** *m.* initial point, starting point; origin; zero. **-spannung,** *f.* initial tension; (*Elec.*) initial voltage. **-stadium,** *n.* initial stage or phase. **-temperatur,** *f.* initial temperature. **-wert,** *m.* initial value. **-zustand,** *m.* initial state or condition.

**anfärbbar,** *a.* colorable, dyeable, etc. (see anfärben).

**Anfärbbarkeit,** *f.* colorability, dyeability.

**anfärben,** *v.t.* color, dye, paint, tint, tinge; bleed, stain; start dyeing.

**Anfärbevermögen,** *n.* colorability, dyeability; coloring or dyeing power.

**anfassen,** *v.t.* seize, handle; undertake. — *v.r.* feel.

**anfaulen,** *v.i.* begin to rot. — **anfaulend,** *p.a.* putrescent. — **angefault,** *p.a.* rotten, decayed.

**anfechten,** *v.t.* combat, attack, contest; trouble, concern.

**anfertigen,** *v.t.* make ready, prepare, make, manufacture.

**Anfertigung,** *f.* making, manufacture; production; composition.

**anfetten,** *v.t.* grease; lubricate, oil.

**anfeuchten,** *v.t.* moisten, damp, wet.

**Anfeuchter,** *m.* moistener; (*Brewing*) sparger.

**Anfeuchtung,** *f.* moistening, damping, wetting.

**anfeuern,** *v.t.* light, fire; prime; inflame, excite.

**Anfeuerung,** *f.* priming; lighting; inflaming.

**anfirnissen,** *v.t.* varnish (over).

**anflehen,** *v.t.* implore, supplicate.

**anfliegen,** *v.i.* effloresce; grow spontaneously; (of dyes) rush on; fly on, fly; occur. — **angeflogen,** *p.a.* incrusted.

**Anflug,** *m.* incrustation, coating, efflorescence; tinge, tint, slight admixture; smattering; flying (against), flight; onset; young wood; copse.

**Anfluss,** *m.* alluvium; onflow, afflux.

**anfordern,** *v.t.* demand, require.

**Anforderung,** *f.* demand, requirement, claim.

**Anfr.,** *abbrev.* (Anfrage) inquiry.

**Anfrage,** *f.* inquiry; demand.

**anfragen,** *v.i.* inquire.

**Anfrass,** *m.* corrosion; erosion.

**anfressen,** *v.t.* corrode; erode; eat at; attack.

**Anfressung,** *f.* corrosion, etc. (see anfressen).

**anfressungsbeständig,** *a.* resistant to corrosion or erosion.

**anfrieren,** *v.i.* freeze on.

**anfrischen,** *v.t.* freshen, refresh, revive; reduce or refine (metals); varnish (paintings).

**Anfrisch-herd, -ofen,** *m.* refining furnace.

**Anfrischung,** *f.* freshening, etc. (see anfrischen).

**anfügen,** *v.t.* join, attach, affix, annex, add.

**anfühlen,** *v.t.* feel, touch, handle.

**Anfühlen,** *n.* feel, touch.

**Anfuhr,** *f.* carrying, carriage; importation.

**anführen,** *v.t.* lead; adduce; quote; mention, cite; impose on.

**Anführungszeichen,** *n.pl.* quotation marks.

**anfüllen,** *v.t.* fill, fill up; prime; charge.

**ang.,** *abbrev.* (angewandt) applied.

**Ang.,** *abbrev.* (Angebot) offer.

**Angabe,** *f.* statement; specification, estimate; report; information; indication (of an instrument); instruction; plan. — **Angaben,** *pl.* statements, etc.; data; particulars.

**angängig, angänglich,** *a.* feasible, admissible.

**angeätzt,** *p.p.* of anätzen.

**Angeb.,** *abbrev.* (Angebot) offer.

**angeben,** *v.t.* state, declare, tell; specify; accuse; indicate; devise.

**angeblich,** *a.* stated; alleged; pretended; nominal.

**angeboren,** *p.a.* inborn, innate, congenital.

**Angebot,** *n.* offer, bid, quotation.

**angebracht,** *p.a.* see anbringen.

**angebrannt,** *p.p.* of anbrennen.

**angebunden,** *p.p.* (of anbinden) tied, bound.

**angefault,** *p.a.* rotten, decayed.

**angefeuchtet,** *p.p.* of anfeuchten.

**angeflogen,** *p.a.* see anfliegen.

**angefressen,** *p.p.* of anfressen.

**angeführt,** *p.p.* of anführen; mentioned, cited.

**angegangen,** *p.p.* of angehen; decaying, tainted.

**angeglüht,** *p.p.* of anglühen; red-hot.

**angegriffen,** *p.p.* of angreifen.

**Angehäufe,** *n.* conglomerate; heap, aggregate.

**angehen,** *v.i.* begin (to grow, burn, decay, etc.); go on, (of dyes) be absorbed; be feasible; be passable. — *v.t.* approach; concern.

**angehören,** *v.i.* belong (to); pertain (to); be related (to).

**angehörig,** *a.* belonging, related.

**Angehörige,** *pl.* relatives, relations; adherents; inhabitants.

**Angel,** *f.* hinge; hook; pivot; axis.

**angelaufen,** *p.p.* of anlaufen; coated, tarnished.

**angelegen,** *p.a.* see anliegen.

**Angelegenheit,** *f.* concern; affair, matter.

**angelegentlich,** *a.* earnest, urgent.

**Angelikasäure, Angelicasäure,** *f.* angelic acid.

**Angelikawurzel,** *f.* angelica root.

**angeln,** *v.i.* angle, fish; strive. — *v.t.* trap, catch.

**Angelpunkt,** *m.* pivot; turning point.

**angelsächsisch,** *a.* Anglo-Saxon.

**Angelschnur,** *f.* fishing line.

**angem.,** *abbrev.* (angemeldet) (of a patent) applied for.

**angemessen,** *p.a.* suitable, adequate.

**angenähert,** *p.a.* see annähern.

**angenehm,** *a.* pleasant, agreeable.
**angenommen,** *p.a.* see annehmen.
**angepasst,** *p.a.* see anpassen.
**angeregt,** *p.a.* see anregen.
**angereichert,** *p.p.* of anreichern.
**angesäuert,** *p.p.* of ansäuern.
**angeschimmelt,** *p.a.* moldy.
**angeschmolzen,** *p.p.* of anschmelzen.
**angeschwemmt,** *p.a.* see anschwemmen.
**angesehen,** *p.a.* see ansehen.
**angesessen,** *p.a.* resident; settled.
**Angesicht,** *n.* face, countenance; look.
**angesichts,** *adv.* in face of, in view of.
**angestammt,** *a.* hereditary; inborn.
**Angestellte,** *m.* employee; appointee; official.
**angestrengt,** *p.a.* intense, forced.
**angew.,** *abbrev.* (angewandt) applied; employed.
**angewandt,** *p.a.* see anwenden.
**angewärmt,** *p.a.* warm, lukewarm, tepid.
**angewöhnen,** *v.t.* accustom.
**angezeigt,** *p.a.* see anzeigen.
**angezogen,** *p.a.* see anziehen.
**angiessen,** *v.t.* pour on; water; (*Founding*) cast on; (*Ceramics*) color by a coat of clay.
**angilben,** *v.i.* turn yellowish.
**angleichen,** *v.t.* synchronize; rectify, correct; adjust, adapt; assimilate; match (colors).
**Angleichung,** *f.* synchronizing, etc. (see angleichen).
**angliedern,** *v.t.* join on, link on, attach.
**Angliederung,** *f.* union; affiliation; linkage.
**anglühen,** *v.t.* heat to glowing, glow; mull (wine). — *v.r.* begin to glow.
**angreifbar,** *a.* capable of being attacked or affected.
**Angreifbarkeit,** *f.* attackability.
**angreifen,** *v.t.* attack, act on, affect; corrode (metals); lay hold of; fatigue; undertake.
**angrenzen,** *v.t.* border on, adjoin. — *v.i.* border (on). — **angrenzend,** *p.a.* adjacent, adjoining, contiguous.
**Angriff,** *m.* attack; handling; undertaking. — **in — nehmen,** take in hand, take up.
**Angriffs-geschwindigkeit,** *f.* rate of attack. **-mittel,** *n.* attacking agent; corrosive. **-punkt,** *m.* point of attack; point of application.
**Angst,** *f.* anxiety, fright, agony.
**ängstigen,** *v.t.* alarm, frighten, worry.
**ängstlich,** *a.* anxious; scrupulous; alarming.
**Anguss,** *m.* pouring on, etc. (see angiessen); (*Founding*) feedhead; lug; (*Ceram.*) engobe. **-farbe,** *f.* colored coating clay.
**anhaften,** *v.i.* adhere, stick, cling, be attached (to). — **anhaftend,** *p.a.* adhering; adhesive; inherent.
**Anhaftung,** *f.* adhering, adhesion; attachment.
**anhaken,** *v.t.* & *r.* hook to, hook on.
**Anhalt,** *m.* support; hold; stop, pause.
**Anhaltelager,** *n.* concentration camp.
**anhalten,** *v.t.* stop, stay, halt, arrest. — *v.i.* stop; hold on, persist; solicit. — **anhaltend,** *p.a.* continuous, persistent, lasting; astringent.
**Anhaltpunkt, Anhaltspunkt,** *m.* stopping point. station; criterion; essential point; reference point; (*Mech.*) fulcrum.
**Anhaltungsmittel,** *n.* astringent.
**Anhang,** *m.* addition, addendum, appendix, appendage, supplement; attachment; followers; (*Anat.*) appendix.
**anhangen,** *v.i.* adhere, hang on. — **anhangend, anhängend,** *p.a.* adhering, adhesive.
**Anhänger,** *m.* follower, adherent; appendage; tag; trailer.
**Anhängezettel,** *m.* label, tag.
**anhängig,** *a.* adhering; appended, annexed; pending.
**anhänglich,** *a.* attached; faithful.
**Anhängsel,** *n.* appendage; amulet.
**Anhangskraft,** *f.* adhesive force, adhesion.
**Anhauch,** *m.* tinge; breathing on.
**anhauchen,** *v.t.* breathe upon; tinge.
**anhäufen,** *v.t.* aggregate; accumulate; heap up. — *v.r.* accumulate.
**Anhäufung,** *f.* aggregation; accumulation; agglomeration; agglomerate.
**anheben,** *v.t., i.* & *r.* begin. — *v.t.* lift, raise; emphasize, accentuate.
**anheften,** *v.t.* fasten to, attach.
**Anheftungspunkt,** *m.* point of attachment.
**anheimfallen,** *v.i.* (with dative) fall into, undergo, suffer; fall (to), devolve (on).
**anheimstellen,** *v.t.* commit, submit.
**anheischig,** *a.* bound, pledged.
**anheizen,** *v.t.* heat (a little), begin to heat.
**Anheizperiode,** *f.* heating-up period.
**anher,** *adv.* hither. — **bis —,** hitherto.
**Anhöhe,** *f.* elevation, hill; rising ground.
**anhören,** *v.t.* listen to, hear. — *v.r.* sound.
**Anhydrämie,** *f.* anhydremia.
**anhydrieren,** *v.* = anhydrisieren.
**anhydrisch,** *a.* anhydrous.
**anhydrisieren,** *v.t.* render anhydrous, dehydrate. — *v.r.* become anhydrous.
**Anhydrisierungsmittel,** *n.* dehydrating agent.
**Anhydrosäure,** *f.* anhydro acid (an acid, such as pyrosulfuric, which is formed from a polyacid by elimination of water).
**Anhydroxyd,** *n.* anhydrous oxide, anhydride.
**Anilido-.** anilino-, anilido- (cf. Amido-).
**Anilin-blau,** *n.* aniline blue. **-braun,** *n.* aniline brown. **-chlorhydrat,** *n.* aniline hydrochloride. **-dampf,** *m.* aniline vapor. **-einbadschwarz,** *n.* one-dip aniline black. **-fabrik,** *f.* aniline works. **-farbe,** *f.* aniline color. **-farbstoff,** *m.* aniline dye. **-gelb,** *n.* aniline yellow. **-grün,** *n.* aniline green. **-klotz-**

**schwarz,** *n.* slop-padded aniline black. **-öl,** *n.* aniline oil. **-rot,** *n.* aniline red. **-salz,** *n.* aniline salt. **-schwarz,** *n.* aniline black. **-sulfosäure,** *f.* anilinesulfonic acid (aminobenzenesulfonic acid). **-tinte,** *f.* aniline ink. **-vergiftung,** *f.* aniline poisoning.

**Anilismus,** *m.* anilinism, anilism.

**animalisch,** *a.* animal.

**animalisieren,** *v.t.* animalize.

**Anime-gummi, -harz,** *n.* animé, gum animé.

**Anis,** *m.* anise; aniseed.

**anisähnlich,** *a.* like anise.

**Anis-branntwein,** *m.* anisette. **-geist,** *m.* (*Pharm.*) spirit of anise; anisette. **-kampher,** *m.* anise camphor, anethole. **-likör,** *m.* anisette.

**Anisol,** *n.* anisole.

**Anisöl,** *n.* aniseed oil, anise oil.

**anisometrisch,** *a.* anisometric.

**anisotrop, anisotropisch,** *a.* anisotropic.

**Anis-same, -samen,** *m.* aniseed, (*Pharm.*) anise. **-säure,** *f.* anisic acid. **-wasser,** *n.* anisette.

**ankalken,** *v.t.* limewash, whitewash.

**Ankauf,** *m.* buying, purchasing, purchase. **-preis,** *m.* purchase price, cost.

**Anker,** *m.* anchor; (*Elec.*) armature, rotor. **-spannung,** *f.* (*Elec.*) armature voltage. **-spule,** *f.* (*Elec.*) armature coil. **-strom,** *m.* (*Elec.*) armature current. **-wicklung,** *f.* armature winding.

**ankitten,** *v.t.* fasten with cement, cement.

**anklagen,** *v.t.* accuse, charge.

**Anklang,** *m.* concord, accord; approval; sympathy.

**ankleben,** *v.t.* stick on, glue on, paste on, agglutinate, attach. — *v.i.* stick, adhere. — **anklebend,** *p.a.* adhesive, agglutinative.

**ankleiden,** *v.t. & r.* dress.

**ankleistern,** *v.t.* paste on.

**anklingen,** *v.i.* grow stronger, increase.

**anknüpfen,** *v.t.* fasten (by tying), join, connect; enter upon, engage in. — *v.i.* start (at or from), refer (to).

**Anknüpfungspunkt,** *m.* point of contact.

**ankochen,** *v.t.* bring to the boil, begin to boil.

**ankohlen,** *v.t.* char partially.

**Ankohlung,** *f.* partial charring.

**ankommen,** *v.i.* arrive; approach; succeed; be important; depend; (*Brewing*) start fermenting.

**Ankömmling,** *m.* newcomer, novice; new product, novelty.

**ankreiden,** *v.t.* chalk; chalk up.

**Ankultur,** *f.* young culture.

**ankündigen, ankünden,** *v.t.* announce, publish.

**Ankündigung,** *f.* announcement, notice; prospectus.

**Ankunft,** *f.* arrival.

**ankuppeln,** *v.t.* couple (on), attach.

**Anküpung,** *f.* beginning of vatting.

**Anl.,** *abbrev.* of Anlage.

**Anlage,** *f.* laying on, etc. (see anlegen); establishment, plant; unit; installation, equipment; construction; design; outline; arrangement; (*Biol.*) rudiment, "anlage"; investment; tax; attached paper; tendency; talent.

**anlagern,** *v.t.* add (on), take up; accumulate.

**Anlagerung,** *f.* addition, etc. (see anlagern).

**Anlagerungs-erzeugnis,** *n.* addition product. **-reaktion,** *f.* addition reaction. **-verbindung,** *f.* addition compound.

**Anlagetypus,** *m.* (*Biol.*) genotype.

**anlangen,** *v.i.* arrive. — *v.t.* concern. — **anlangend,** *prep.* concerning, as for.

**Anlass,** *m.* occasion, motive, reason; occurrence; letting in; starting; (*Metal.*) temper.

**Anlassdauer,** *f.* (*Metal.*) duration of tempering or drawing.

**anlassen,** *v.t.* (*Metal.*) temper, draw; anneal (glass or metals); let in, turn on, start (going). — *v.r.* appear, look.

**Anlassen,** *n.* tempering, etc. (see anlassen).

**Anlasser,** *m.* starting device, starter.

**Anlass-farbe,** *f.* (*Steel*) temper color; (*Leather*) graining color. **-härte,** *f.* tempering hardness. **-härtung,** *f.* temper hardening.

**anlässlich,** *adv.* occasionally; apropos (of).

**Anlass-mittel,** *n.* (*Metal.*) tempering medium. **-ofen,** *m.* tempering furnace; annealing oven. **-öl,** *n.* tempering oil, drawing oil. **-wirkung,** *f.* tempering effect; annealing effect.

**Anlauf,** *m.* tarnish; tarnishing; swelling; slope; starting (of machinery), start; (*Mach.*) catch, tappet, shoulder, etc.; onset, run, attack; concourse, crowd.

**anlaufen,** *v.i.* become coated (with oxide, moisture, mold, etc.), tarnish, become dull or dim; (of dyed goods) recolor; swell, intumesce; increase; (*Mach.*) start; amount; run; approach; crowd.

**Anlauf-farbe,** *f.* (*Metal.*) tempering color. **-temperatur,** *f.* tempering temperature. **-zeit,** *f.* filling time (of a pipeline); (*Mach.*) starting period.

**anlegen,** *v.t.* lay or put on, apply, fix; invest; found; lay out; plan; plot (as a curve). — *v.r.* deposit, settle.

**Anlehen,** *m.* loan.

**anlehnen,** *v.t. & r.* lean (against or on), rest, be supported (by); (of a door) nearly close.

**Anlehnung,** *f.* leaning; dependence; support.

**Anleihe,** *f.* loan.

**anleimen,** *v.t.* glue on, glue.

**anleiten,** *v.t.* lead, guide, conduct; instruct.

**Anleitung,** *f.* leading, conducting; instruction (of books) introduction, guide, key.

**anliefern,** *v.t.* deliver, supply.

**Anlieferung,** *f.* delivery, supply.
**Anlieferungszustand,** *m.* state as received.
**anliegen,** *v.i.* be adjacent, lie near; join; fit; concern; entreat. — **angelegen,** *p.a.* interesting; important. — **anliegend,** *p.a.* adjacent, adjoining; attached, enclosed.
**Anliegen,** *n.* proximity; request.
**Anlockungsmittel,** *n.* lure, bait.
**anlöten,** *v.t.* solder, solder on; cause to adhere.
**Anlötung,** *f.* soldering, etc. (see anlöten).
**Anm.,** *abbrev.* (Anmerkung) note, remark.
**anmachen,** *v.t.* slack (lime or gypsum); mix, temper, dilute, wet, treat, prepare, flavor, adulterate; fasten on, attach; light (a fire).
**Anmachwasser,** *n.* mixing water; water of plasticity.
**anmalen,** *v.t.* paint.
**anmassen,** *v.t.* assume; usurp.
**anmelden,** *v.t.* announce, advertise, declare; apply for (a patent); register, enter.
**Anmeldung,** *f.* announcement, etc. (see anmelden).
**anmengen,** *v.t.* mix, blend, temper, dilute.
**anmerken,** *v.t.* note, mark; annotate.
**Anmerkung,** *f.* note, remark, comment.
**anmischen,** *v.t.* mix.
**Anmut,** *f.* grace, charm.
**anmuten,** *v.t.* expect, ask; please.
**Ann.,** *abbrev.* Annalen der Chemie.
**annähern,** *v.t.* & *r.* approach, approximate, bring or draw near. — **annähernd,** *p.a.* approximate; approaching. — **angenähert,** *p.a.* approximate.
**Annäherung,** *f.* approximation, approach.
**Annäherungsgrad,** *m.* degree of approximation.
**annäherungsweise,** *adv.* approximately.
**Annäherungswert,** *m.* approximate value.
**Annahme,** *f.* assumption, hypothesis; acceptance.
**Annalin,** *n.* annaline (a prepared calcium sulfate).
**annässen,** *v.t.* moisten a little, damp.
**annehmbar,** *a.* acceptable.
**annehmen,** *v.t.* assume, suppose; take, accept; adopt; take, take up (colors). — **angenommen,** *p.a.* assuming; false, fictitious.
**Annehmung,** *f.* assumption, etc. (see annehmen).
**annektieren,** *v.t.* annex.
**annetzen,** *v.t.* moisten, dampen.
**annieten,** *v.t.* rivet, rivet on.
**Anno.** in the year.
**Annonce,** *f.* advertisement.
**annoncieren,** *v.t.* advertise, announce.
**annullieren,** *v.t.* annul, cancel, strike out.
**Anoden-batterie,** *f.* anode battery, B battery. **-dichte,** *f.* anode density, anodic density. **-raum,** *m.* anode region, space around the anode. **-schlamm,** *m.* anode slime, anode mud **-spannung,** *f.* anode potential. **-strahl,** *m.* anode ray, positive ray.
**anodisch,** *a.* anodic.
**anölen,** *v.t.* oil, coat with oil.
**Anolyt,** *m.* (*Elec.*) anolyte.
**anomal, anomalisch,** *a.* anomalous.
**Anon,** *n.* Anon (cyclohexanone). *T.N.*
**anordnen,** *v.t.* arrange, regulate, order.
**Anordnung,** *f.* arrangement, disposition, regulation.
**anorg.,** *abbrev.* (anorganisch) inorganic.
**Anorganiker,** *m.* inorganic chemist.
**anorganisch,** *a.* inorganic.
**anormal,** *a.* abnormal.
**anoxydieren,** *v.t.* oxidize.
**anpassen,** *v.t.* adapt, adjust, align, fit, suit. — **anpassend,** *p.a.* suitable, fit. — **angepasst,** *p.a.* adapted, adjusted, suited, appropriate.
**Anpassung,** *f.* adaptation, adjustment.
**Anpassungsfähigkeit,** *f.* adaptability.
**anpflanzen,** *v.t.* plant; cultivate.
**anpinseln,** *v.t.* paint, paint on, daub.
**Anprall,** *m.* impact; contusion.
**anprallen,** *v.i.* strike, impinge (forcibly).
**anpreisen,** *v.t.* commend, recommend.
**anpudern,** *v.t.* powder.
**anputzen,** *v.t.* dress up, adorn, decorate.
**anquicken,** *v.t.* amalgamate.
**Anquick-fass,** *n.* amalgamating tub. **-silber,** *n.* silver amalgam.
**Anquickung,** *f.* amalgamation.
**Anrat,** *m.* advice, counsel.
**anraten,** *v.t.* advise, recommend.
**anrauchen,** *v.t.* smoke.
**anräuchern,** *v.t.* fumigate; perfume
**Anräucherung,** *f.* fumigation; perfuming.
**anrechnen,** *v.t.* charge; ascribe; count.
**Anrecht,** *n.* claim, title, right.
**Anrede,** *f.* address.
**anreden,** *v.t.* address, speak to.
**anregbar,** *a.* capable of being excited.
**anregen,** *v.t.* excite; stimulate; incite; activate; set going; interest; suggest, mention. — **anregend,** *p.a.* exciting; stimulating, stimulant; interesting. — **angeregter Zustand,** excited state; activated state.
**Anregung,** *f.* excitation; stimulation; stimulus, impulse; suggestion.
**Anregungs-energie,** *f.* excitation energy. **-grenze,** *f.* excitation limit. **-mittel,** *n.* (*Med.*) stimulant. **-potential,** *n.*, **-spannung,** *f.* excitation potential. **-stärke,** *f.* strength of excitation. **-wahrscheinlichkeit,** *f.* probability of excitation.
**anreiben,** *v.t.* rub, rub on; grind (colors).
**anreichern,** *v.t.* enrich, strengthen, concentrate.
**Anreicherung,** *f.* enrichment, concentration.
**Anreichlech,** *m.* enriched mat(te).

**anreihen,** *v.t.* arrange in a series; attach to a series, add.
**Anreiz,** *m.* stimulus; impulse; incitement.
**anreizen,** *v.t.* stimulate; instigate.
**anrichten,** *v.t.* prepare, dress; perform, produce; serve; mix (colors).
**Anrichter,** *m.* assayer; (ore) dresser.
**Anriss,** *m.* initial tear or break; surface crack.
**anrosten,** *v.i.* begin to rust; become fixed by rust.
**Anrostung,** *f.* rusting (on); corrosion.
**Anruf,** *m.* call; appeal.
**anrufen,** *v.t.* call; call up; call upon.
**anrühren,** *v.t.* touch, handle; stir; mix, temper; touch on, refer to.
**anrussen,** *v.t.* smoke, soot.
**ans,** *abbrev.* (an das) to the.
**ansagen,** *v.t.* announce, state.
**ansalzen,** *v.t.* salt lightly.
**ansammeln,** *v.t.* collect, gather, accumulate, amass; (*Physics*) focus.
**Ansammlung,** *f.* collection, etc. (see ansammeln); aggregation, heap, mass; throng.
**Ansatz,** *m.* deposit, sediment; incrustation; attachment, added piece, lug, shoulder, etc.; appendage; insertion; preparing, mixture; ingredients; rate; item; charge; statement; onset; tendency; (*Dyeing*) standard; extension, annex; starting material, start (as yeast). **-bad,** *n.* (*Dyeing*) first bath, initial bath. **-bottich,** *m.* preparing vessel. **-lösung,** *f.* starting solution. **-punkt,** *m.* point of attachment or insertion. **-rohr,** *n.* attached tube (or pipe), insert tube, connecting tube; nozzle. **-stück,** *n.* attached piece or part, attachment.
**ansäuern,** *v.t.* acidify, acidulate; sour; (*Baking*) add yeast to.
**Ansäuerung,** *f.* acidification; souring.
**Ansaugehub,** *m.* suction stroke.
**ansaugen,** *v.t. & i.* suck, suck in, suck up, (sometimes) adsorb.
**Ansaug-heber,** *m.* siphon. **-rohr,** *n.* suction tube, suction pipe.
**Ansaugung,** *f.* suction; (sometimes) adsorption; absorption.
**-ansäure.** -anoic acid (Geneva system); -anic acid.
**anschaffen,** *v.t.* provide, supply; purchase.
**anschärfen,** *v.t.* sharpen; strengthen (as a bath).
**anschauen,** *v.t.* look at, view, consider.
**anschaulich,** *a.* clear, plain, obvious.
**Anschauung,** *f.* mode of viewing, view, idea; observation; perception; intuition.
**Anschauungsweise,** *f.* point of view, standpoint.
**Anschein,** *m.* appearance; likelihood.
**anscheinen,** *v.i.* appear. — *v.t.* shine on. — **anscheinend,** *p.a.* apparent. — *adv.* apparently.
**anschichten,** *v.t.* pile in layers, stratify.
**anschicken,** *v.r.* prepare.
**Anschieber,** *m.* lengthening piece; (*Brewing*) workman; (*Baking*) kissing crust.
**anschiessen,** *v.i.* shoot into crystals, crystallize; shoot; rush; be adjacent.
**Anschiessgefäss,** *n.* crystallizing vessel, crystallizer.
**anschimmeln,** *v.i.* begin to mold.
**Anschlag,** *m.* stroke, impact; posting up, placard; estimate; plan, attempt; projection, stop, buffer.
**anschlagen,** *v.t.* strike at; fasten, affix; aim; estimate.
**anschlägig,** *a.* ingenious; estimated.
**Anschlag-wert,** *m.* estimated value. **-zettel,** *m.* placard, poster, bill.
**anschlämmen,** *v.t.* suspend; elutriate, wash; deposit (mud, etc.); make into a paste; smear with mud or slime.
**anschleifen,** *v.t.* grind, polish.
**anschliessen,** *v.t.* fasten (on), attach, annex, connect; join; fit. — *v.r.* join; concur (in), agree (with).
**Anschliff,** *m.* (*Min.*, etc.) section, ground surface.
**Anschluss,** *m.* joining; junction, connection; contact; coupling; enclosure, something annexed. **-klemme,** *f.* terminal clamp, terminal. **-rohr,** *n.* connecting tube or pipe. **-stück,** *n.* connecting piece.
**anschmauchen,** *v.t.* smoke, soot.
**anschmelzen,** *v.t.* melt or fuse on (to), join by fusion; solder; weld. — *v.i.* begin to melt; adhere by fusion.
**Anschmelzherd,** *m.* melting furnace, smelting furnace.
**anschmiegen,** *v.t.* cause to cling (to), press (to). — *v.r.* cling (to).
**anschmieren,** *v.t.* smear; adulterate; cheat.
**anschmutzen,** *v.t.* soil, stain.
**anschneiden,** *v.t.* cut, cut into; begin, broach; tally.
**Anschove, Anschovis,** *f.* anchovy.
**anschrauben,** *v.t.* screw on.
**anschreiben,** *v.t.* write down, note down.
**Anschrift,** *f.* address.
**anschüren,** *v.t.* stir up, stir, keep going (fire).
**Anschuss,** *m.* crystallization; crop (of crystals); shooting; rush. **-gefäss,** *n.* crystallizing vessel, crystallizer.
**anschütten,** *v.t.* pour on, discharge on; fill up.
**anschwängern,** *v.t.* saturate, impregnate.
**Anschwänzapparat,** *m.* sprinkler, sparger.
**anschwänzen,** *v.t.* sprinkle, sparge.
**anschwärzen,** *v.t.* blacken; slander.
**anschwefeln,** *v.t.* treat or fumigate with sulfur.
**anschweissen,** *v.t.* weld on, weld together.
**anschwellen,** *v.i.* swell, swell out; increase.
**Anschwellung,** *f.* swelling, intumescence; tumor.

**anschwemmen,** *v.t.* deposit (from a liquid). — **angeschwemmt,** *p.a.* deposited, settled; alluvial.
**Anschwemmfilter,** *n.* settling filter.
**Anschwödebrei,** *m.* (*Leather*) liming paste.
**anschwöden,** *v.t.* paint (the flesh side of hides) with lime.
**ansehen,** *v.t.* look at, see, regard; esteem. — **angesehen,** *p.a.* important, prominent.
**Ansehen,** *n.* appearance; standing, reputation.
**ansehnlich,** *a.* considerable; handsome.
**ansetzbar,** *a.* attachable, etc. (see ansetzen, *v.t.*).
**ansetzen,** *v.r.* crystallize; effloresce; be deposited. — *v.t.* set on, apply, attach; prepare, mix; charge (a furnace); form, produce; establish. — *v.i.* make a start, try.
**Ansetzung,** *f.* crystallization, etc. (see ansetzen).
**Ansicht,** *f.* view; inspection; opinion.
**ansichtig,** *a.* cognizant.
**ansieden,** *v.t.* boil, boil on; scorify; blanch; mordant (by boiling). — **Ansieden und Abdunkeln,** stuffing and saddening.
**Ansiede-probe,** *f.* scorification assay. **-scherbe,** *f.*, **-scherben,** *m.* scorifier.
**Ansiedung,** *f.* boiling, etc. (see ansieden).
**ansinnen,** *v.t.* expect, require; attribute.
**ansintern,** *v.i.* sinter; form sinter.
**anspalten,** *v.t.* & *i.* begin to cleave or split, cleave or split a little.
**anspannen,** *v.t.* subject to tension or stress; stress, strain, stretch, bend.
**Anspannung,** *f.* (*Mech.*) stress; tension, strain.
**anspielen,** *v.i.* hint, allude; begin to play.
**anspitzen,** *v.t.* point, sharpen.
**Anspr.,** *abbrev.* (Anspruch) claim, demand.
**ansprechen,** *v.t.* address; claim; ask; please; (with für) declare to be, pronounce, consider to be. — *v.i.* emit a sound, sound; respond (to).
**ansprengen,** *v.t.* blow up, blast; sprinkle; urge on.
**Anspruch,** *m.* claim; demand; requirement. — **in — nehmen,** engage, engross, tax; use.
**anspruchslos,** *a.* unassuming, unpretending.
**anstählen,** *v.t.* steel.
**Anstalt,** *f.* institution, establishment, plant, station; preparation, arrangement.
**Anstand,** *m.* delay; hesitation; objection; behavior, propriety, grace.
**anständig,** *a.* suitable, fit, proper; decent.
**anstandslos,** *a.* unhesitating.
**anstatt,** *prep.* instead of.
**anstäuben,** *v.t.* dust, powder.
**anstechen,** *v.t.* pierce, tap, open.
**anstecken,** *v.t.* stick on, fasten; infect, contaminate; light (a fire). — **ansteckend,** *p.a.* infectious; contagious.
**Ansteckung,** *f.* infection; contagion.
**Ansteckungs-quelle,** *f.* source of infection. **-stoff,** *m.* infectious matter.
**anstehen,** *v.i.* be near or next; be becoming; be pleasing; be deferred; hesitate; (of rocks) crop out.
**ansteigen,** *v.i.* rise, ascend, mount; increase.
**anstellbar,** *a.* adjustable; employable.
**Anstellbottich,** *m.* (*Brewing*) starting tub.
**anstelle,** *adv.* instead. — *prep.* instead of.
**anstellen,** *v.t.* institute, make; install, set going, start; prepare; pitch (wort); appoint, employ; plan. — *v.r.* behave; pretend.
**Ansteller,** *m.* employer.
**Anstellhefe,** *f.* (*Brewing*) pitching yeast.
**anstellig,** *a.* skilful, handy; suitable.
**Anstelltemperatur,** *f.* (*Brewing*) pitching temperature.
**Anstellung,** *f.* instituting, etc. (see anstellen); situation, employment.
**Anstichmethode,** *f.* puncture method.
**Anstieg,** *m.* rise, ascent; increase.
**anstiften,** *v.t.* contrive, cause.
**anstocken,** *v.i.* become moldy.
**Anstoss,** *m.* collision; impulse, impetus; shock; offense; butt joint; (*Calico*) overlapping.
**anstossen,** *v.t.* crush, prepare by crushing; strike against, impinge upon; stir into a paste; offend. — *v.i.* strike, impinge; be adjacent; stumble; stammer; offend. — **anstossend,** *p.a.* adjacent, contiguous.
**anstrahlen,** *v.t.* irradiate.
**Anstrebekraft,** *f.* centripetal force.
**anstreben,** *v.i.* strive toward; oppose. — *v.t.* strive for.
**Anstreiche,** *f.* paint, color.
**anstreichen,** *v.t.* paint, coat, color, varnish; mark; underscore.
**anstrengen,** *v.t.* stretch, strain, exert.
**Anstrich,** *m.* paint, painting, coat; varnish; dye; tint, color; appearance. **-bindemittel,** *n.* (*Painting*) binder. **-farbe,** *f.* painting color, pigment; priming.
**anstrichfertig,** *a.* (of paint) ready-mixed.
**Anstrich-masse,** *f.* coating compound, priming. **-stoff,** *m.* paint, varnish, lacquer.
**anstücken, anstückeln,** *v.t.* add, join, unite.
**ansuchen,** *v.t.* apply, request.
**Ansud,** *m.* boiling, etc. (see ansieden).
**ansüssen,** *v.t.* edulcorate; sweeten slightly.
**antaphrodisisch,** *a.* anaphrodisiac.
**anteeren,** *v.t.* tar.
**anteigen,** *v.t.* stir into a paste, make a paste of.
**Anteigmittel,** *n.* pasting agent.
**Anteil, Antheil,** *m.* constituent; portion, share; quota; interest, sympathy.
**anteilig,** *a.* proportionate, pro rata.
**antemetisch,** *a.* antiemetic.
**Antenne,** *f.* antenna.
**Anthocyan,** *n.* anthocyanin, anthocyan.
**Anthrac-.** see also Anthraz-, Antraz-.

**Anthracen-blau,** *n.* anthracene blue. **-farbstoff,** *m.* anthracene dye. **-öl,** *n.* anthracene oil. **-pech,** *n.* anthracene pitch.

**Anthrachinolin,** *n.* anthraquinoline.

**Anthrachinon,** *n.* anthraquinone. **-azin,** *n.* anthraquinonazine.

**Anthradichinon,** *n.* anthradiquinone.

**Anthrahydrochinon,** *n.* anthrahydroquinone.

**Anthrazen,** *n.* anthracene. **-farbstoff,** *m.*, **-farbe,** *f.* dye. **-öl,** *n.* anthracene oil.

**Anthrazit,** *n.* anthracite. **-bildung,** *f.* anthracitization.

**anthrazit-artig,** *a.* anthracitic. **-isch,** *a.* anthracitic.

**Anthrazitkohle,** *f.* anthracite coal, anthracite.

**Anthrazyl,** *n.* anthracyl.

**Anthroesäure,** *f.* anthroic acid.

**Antianaphylaxie,** *f.* antianaphylaxis.

**Antichlor,** *n.* antichlor, antichlorine.

**anticipieren,** *v.t.* anticipate.

**Antifäulnis,** *f.* antifouling.

**antik,** *a.* antique; old.

**Antikatalysator,** *m.* anticatalyst.

**antikatalytisch,** *a.* anticatalytic.

**Antiklopf-eigenschaft,** *f.* antiknock property. **-mittel,** *n.* antiknock agent.

**Antikörper,** *m.* antisubstance, antibody (cf. Körper).

**Antikrackmittel,** *n.* anticracking agent.

**antimetrisch,** *a.* (*Math.*) antimetric.

**Antimon,** *n.* antimony. **-arsen,** *n.* (*Min.*) allemontite. **-arsenfahlerz,** *n.* tetrahedrite.

**antimonartig,** *a.* like antimony; antimonial.

**Antimon-blei,** *n.* (*Metal.*) lead containing antimony, antimonial lead. **-bleiblende,** *f.* boulangerite. **-blende,** *f.* kermesite. **-blüte,** *f.* antimony bloom, valentinite. **-butter,** *f.* butter of antimony ($SbCl_3$). **-chlorid,** *n.* antimony chloride, specif. antimony pentachloride, antimony(V) chloride. **-chlorür,** *n.* antimony trichloride, antimony(III) chloride. **-erz,** *n.* antimony ore. **-fahlerz,** *n.* tetrahedrite. **-gehalt,** *m.* antimony content. **-gelb,** *n.* antimony yellow. **-glanz,** *m.* antimony glance, antimonite. **-goldschwefel,** *m.* golden antimony sulfide ($Sb_2S_5$). **-halogen,** *n.* antimony halide.

**antimonhaltig,** *a.* containing antimony; antimonial.

**antimonig, antimonicht,** *a.* antimonious. — **antimonige Säure,** antimonious acid.

**antimonigsauer,** *a.* of or combined with antimonious acid, antimonite of.

**Antimonigsäureanhydrid,** *n.* antimony trioxide, antimony(III) oxide.

**Antimonin,** *n.* antimony lactate.

**antimonisch,** *a.* antimonial, antimonic.

**Antimonium,** *n.* antimony.

**Antimon-jodür,** *n.* antimony triiodide. **-kaliumtartrat,** *n.* antimonyl potassium tartrate, tarter emetic.

**Antimon-kermes,** *m.* & *n.* kermes mineral. **-kupferglanz,** *m.* antimonial copper glance (bournonite or chalcostibite). **-legierung,** *f.* antimony alloy. **-metall,** *n.* antimony metal, metallic antimony. **-nickel,** *n.* (*Min.*) breithauptite. **-nickelglanz,** *m.* ullmannite. **-ocker,** *m.* antimony ocher (usually cervantite). **-oxychlorür,** *n.* antimony oxychloride ($SbOCl$). **-oxyd,** *n.* antimony oxide, specif. antimony trioxide, antimony(III) oxide.

**antimonreich,** *a.* rich in antimony.

**Antimon-safran,** *m.* antimonial saffron, crocus of antimony. **-salz,** *n.* antimony salt, specif. a double compound of antimony trifluoride and ammonium sulfate.

**antimonsauer,** *a.* of or combined with antimonic acid, antimonate of.

**Antimon-säure,** *f.* antimonic acid. **-säureanhydrid,** *n.* antimonic anhydride, antimony pentoxide. **-silber,** *n.* antimonial silver, dyscrasite. **-silberblende,** *f.* pyrargyrite. **-silberglanz,** *m.* stephanite. **-spiegel,** *m.* antimony mirror. **-sulfid,** *n.* antimony sulfide, specif. antimony pentasulfide, antimony(V) sulfide. **-sulfür,** *n.* antimony trisulfide, antimony(III) sulfide. **-verbindung,** *f.* antimony compound. **-wasser-stoff,** *m.* antimony hydride, stibine. **-weiss,** *n.* antimony white ($Sb_2O_3$). **-zinnober,** *m.* kermes mineral.

**Antioxydationsmittel,** *n.* antioxidizing agent, antioxidant.

**antiphlogistisch,** *a.* antiphlogistic.

**antipodisch,** *a.* antipodal, opposite.

**antipyretisch,** *a.* antipyretic.

**Antiquariat,** *n.* second-hand bookstore.

**antiquarisch,** *a.* (of books) second-hand.

**Antiquität,** *f.* antiquity.

**Antisepticum, Antiseptikum,** *n.* antiseptic.

**antiseptisch,** *a.* antiseptic.

**antiskorbutisch,** *a.* antiscorbutic.

**antistokes'sche Linien.** (*Physics*) antistokes lines.

**Antiweinsäure,** *f.* antitartaric acid.

**Antlitz,** *n.* countenance, face.

**antönen,** *v.t.* (*Dyeing*) stain, tint; begin to sound.

**Antoniusfeuer,** *n.* St. Anthony's fire (erysipelas).

**Antonskraut,** *n.* willow herb (*Chamaenerion angustifolium*).

**Antrag,** *m.* proposal, proposition.

**antragen,** *v.t.* lay on, apply; propose, offer.

**anträufeln,** *v.i.* drip (on).

**Antrazen,** *n.* anthracene. **-öl,** *n.* anthracene oil.

**antreffen,** *v.t.* hit upon, meet with; find.

**antreiben,** *v.t.* drive, drive on, drive against, drive in; hoop (casks); start (a fire); operate, actuate; incite, urge on.

**antreten,** *v.t.* enter on, set out on; approach; accost; tread down.
**Antrieb,** *m.* impulse, impulsion; propulsion; (*Mach.*) drive; motive.
**Antriebs-kraft,** *f.* driving force, motive power. **-strahl,** *m.* propulsive jet.
**Antritt,** *m.* beginning, entrance, first step.
**Antrittsvorlesung,** *f.* inaugural lecture.
**antrocknen,** *v.i.* dry on; begin to dry; dry on the surface.
**antun,** *v.t.* put on; do to; do violence to.
**Antwerpenerblau,** *n.* Antwerp blue.
**Antwort,** *f.* answer, reply.
**antworten,** *v.t. & i.* answer, reply.
**anvertrauen,** *v.t.* trust, confide.
**anverwandt,** *p.a.* related.
**anvisieren,** *v.t.* sight at, sight.
**Anvulkanisation,** *f.* prevulcanization, pre-cure.
**anvulkanisieren,** *v.t.* prevulcanize, pre-cure.
**Anw.,** *abbrev.* (Anwendung) employment, use.
**Anwachs,** *m.* increase; swelling; growth.
**anwachsen,** *v.i.* grow, increase; adhere; grow on, grow together; grow up; take root.
**Anwalt,** *m.* attorney; deputy.
**Anwandlung,** *f.* fit, attack.
**anwärmen,** *v.t.* warm, heat (moderately); dry (by heating). — *v.i.* warm, begin to heat.
**Anwärmer,** *m.* preheater, economizer.
**Anwärmzeit,** *f.* time of warming or moderate heating.
**Anwartschaft,** *f.* expectancy.
**anwässern,** *v.t.* moisten slightly.
**anweichen,** *v.t.* soften; soak slightly.
**anweisen,** *v.t.* point out, show; assign; direct; instruct.
**anweissen,** *v.t.* whitewash, whiten.
**Anweisung,** *f.* direction, instruction; indication; money order, check, draft; assignment.
**anwendbar,** *a.* usable, applicable, adaptable, practicable, available.
**Anwendbarkeit,** *f.* applicability, practicability, availability.
**anwenden,** *v.t.* apply, employ, use. — **angewandt,** *p.a.* applied, practical; employed.
**Anwendung,** *f.* application, employment, use, utilization.
**Anwendungs-bereich,** *m.*, **-gebiet,** *n.* field (or range) of application. **-weise,** *f.* mode of application.
**anwerfen,** *v.t.* throw, throw on, roughcast; (*Mach.*) throw into gear, start.
**Anwesen,** *n.* property, premises, estate.
**anwesend,** *a.* present.
**Anwesenheit,** *f.* presence.
**anwidern,** *v.t.* disgust, offend.
**Anwuchs,** *m.* growth, increase, increment.
**Anwurf,** *m.* roughcast; priming; deposit; first draft.
**anwürgen,** *v.t.* grip, crimp.

**Anz.,** *abbrev.* (Anzahl) number; Anzeiger (Advertiser).
**Anzahl,** *f.* number.
**anzahlen,** *v.t.* pay on account.
**anzapfen,** *v.t.* tap.
**Anzapfventil,** *n.* bleeder valve.
**Anzeichen,** *n.* sign, indication, symptom, omen.
**anzeichnen,** *v.t.* mark, indicate, note.
**Anzeige,** *f.* information; indication; (of an instrument) reading; notice, report, circular, advertisement, dispatch; sign, mark. **-instrument,** *n.* indicating instrument, indicator.
**anzeigen,** *v.t.* inform, announce, advertise; indicate; show. — **angezeigt,** *p.a.* advisable, proper, fit.
**Anzeigengebühren,** *f.pl.* advertising rates.
**Anzeiger,** *m.* indicator; gage; pointer; (*Math.*) exponent; informer, advertiser.
**Anzeigevorrichtung,** *f.* indicating device.
**anzementieren,** *v.t.* cement on.
**anzetteln,** *v.t.* plot; (*Weaving*) warp.
**anziehen,** *v.t.* draw, pull, attract; absorb; tighten; stretch; raise, grow; put on (clothes); quote. — *v.i.* take effect, hold well; set (as cement), harden; attract moisture; approach; advance. — **anziehend,** *p.a.* attractive; astringent. — **angezogen,** *p.a.* (of malt) slack.
**Anziehung,** *f.* attraction, etc. (see anziehen); adhesion; (*Physiol.*) adduction.
**Anziehungskraft,** *f.* attractive force or power, attraction; adhesive power.
**anzinnen,** *v.t.* coat with tin, tin.
**Anzucht,** *f.* raising, cultivation, culture.
**anzuckern,** *v.t.* sprinkle with sugar.
**Anzug,** *m.* clothes, clothing, suit; approach; entrance; taper, slope.
**Anzugskraft,** *f.* initial power or force.
**anzünden,** *v.t.* ignite, kindle, light.
**Anzünder,** *m.* igniter, lighter.
**Anzündung,** *f.* ignition, lighting.
**äolisch,** *a.* aeolian.
**Aorte,** *f.* aorta.
**Aorten-.** aortic.
**Aouaraöl,** *n.* African palm oil.
**A.P.,** *abbrev.* (amerikanisches Patent) American patent.
**Ap.,** *abbrev.* (Apotheker) druggist.
**apart,** *a.* odd, singular.
**aperiodisch,** *a.* aperiodic.
**Apfel,** *m.* apple.
**Apfeläther, Äpfeläther,** *m.* malic ether (ethyl malate); essence of apple (genuine or artificial).
**Apfelbranntwein,** *m.* apple brandy, apple jack.
**Äpfeleisenextrakt,** *n.* (*Pharm.*) ferrated extract of apples.
**Apfel-frucht,** *f.* (*Bot.*) pome. **-most,** *m.* sweet cider. **-mus,** *m.* apple sauce.

**Apfelöl, Äpfelöl,** *n.* apple oil.
**Apfelsalbe,** *f.* pomatum.
**apfelsauer, äpfelsauer,** *a.* of or combined with malic acid, malate of.
**Apfelsäure, Äpfelsäure,** *f.* malic acid.
**Apfel-schorf,** *m.* apple scab. **-sine,** *f.* (sweet) orange.
**Apfelsinen-saft,** *m.* orange juice. **-schalen-effekt,** *m.*, **-schalenerscheinung,** *f.* orange-peel effect (of lacquers, etc.). **-schalenöl,** *n.* orange-peel oil, essence of orange.
**Apfelwein, Äpfelwein,** *m.* cider.
**Aphel,** *n.* aphelion. **-abstand,** *m.* aphelion distance.
**aphlogistisch,** *a.* aphlogistic.
**aphoristisch,** *a.* aphoristic(al).
**Apiol,** *n.* apiole.
**aplanatisch,** *a.* aplanatic.
**aplitisch,** *a.* aplitic.
**Apocampher,** *m.* apocamphor. **-säure,** *f.* apocamphoric acid.
**Apochinen,** *n.* apoquinene.
**Apochinin,** *n.* apoquinine.
**apochromatisch,** *a.* apochromatic.
**Apogluzinsäure,** *f.* apoglucic acid.
**Apohydrochinin,** *n.* apohydroquinine.
**Apokaffein,** *n.* apocaffeine.
**Apokamphersäure,** *f.* apocamphoric acid.
**Apokodein,** *n.* apocodeine.
**aposteriorisch,** *a.* *a posteriori.*
**Apotheke,** *f.* drugstore, chemist's shop, apothecary's shop.
**Apotheker,** *m.* pharmacist, druggist, (in England) pharmaceutical chemist, apothecary. **-buch,** *n.* dispensatory; pharmacopeia. **-farbe,** *f.* drug color, pharmacist's color. **-gewicht,** *n.* apothecary's weight. **-kunst,** *f.* apothecary's art, pharmacy. **-ordnung,** *f.* dispensatory. **-verein,** *m.* pharmaceutical society, organization of druggists. **-wa(a)ge,** *f.* druggist's scales, apothecary's scales. **-waren,** *f.pl.* drugs. **-warenhändler,** *m.* druggist. **-wesen,** *n.* pharmaceutical matters. **-wissenschaft,** *f.* pharmacology.
**App.,** *abbrev.* Apparat.
**Apparat,** *m.* apparatus.
**Apparate-bau,** *m.* construction of apparatus. **-brett,** *n.* apparatus board; instrument board.
**Apparatenkunde,** *f.* knowledge relating to apparatus.
**Apparate-teil,** *m.* apparatus part or piece. **-tisch,** *m.* apparatus table; working table. **-wesen,** *n.* matters relating to apparatus.
**Apparatfärberei,** *f.* machine dyeing.
**apparativ,** *a.* pertaining to apparatus.
**Apparatur,** *f.* apparatus (collectively), equipment; machinery.
**appellieren,** *v.i.* appeal.
**appetitlich,** *a.* appetizing, delicious.
**applizieren,** *v.t.* apply.
**Applizierung,** *f.* application.
**Appret,** *n.* (*Textiles*) dressing, finishing, sizing.
**appretieren,** *v.t.* dress, finish (cloth).
**Appretiermasse,** *f.* finishing material, size.
**Appretkocher,** *m.* (*Textiles*) finish boiler.
**Appretur,** *f.* finishing, dressing; finish, dressing, size; (*Leather*) seasoning.
**appreturecht,** *a.* unaffected by finishing.
**Appretur-leim,** *m.* dressing size. **-masse,** *f.* dressing, sizing, size. **-mittel,** *n.* finishing agent, dressing material, dressing. **-öl,** *n.* dressing oil, finishing oil. **-präparat,** *n.* dressing. **-pulver,** *n.* dressing powder. **-seife,** *f.* dressing soap. **-verfahren,** *n.* finishing process.
**approbieren,** *v.t.* approve.
**Aprikose,** *f.* apricot.
**Aprikosen-kernöl,** *n.* apricot kernel oil. **-pfirsich,** *m.* nectarine.
**aptieren,** *v.t.* adapt, adjust, fit, arrange.
**apyrisch,** *a.* apyrous, incombustible.
**Aquarellfarbe,** *f.* aquarelle color, water color.
**Äquator,** *m.* equator.
**Aquavit,** *m.* aqua vitae, whisky; *pl.* spirits.
**äqui-.** equi-.
**äquimolekular,** *a.* equimolecular.
**Äquipartition,** *f.* equipartition.
**äquipotential, äquipotentiell,** *a.* equipotential.
**äquivalent,** *a.* equivalent.
**Äquivalent,** *n.* equivalent. **-gesetz,** *n.* law of equivalents. **-gewicht,** *n.* equivalent weight, combining weight. **-leitfähigkeit,** *f.* equivalent conductivity. **-verhältnis,** *n.* equivalent proportion; ratio of equivalents.
**Äquivalenz,** *f.* equivalence. **-punkt,** *m.* (*Analysis*) end point.
**Aquoverbindung,** *f.* aquo compound.
**Ära,** *f.* era.
**Araber,** *m.* Arab, Arabian.
**Arabien,** *n.* Arabia.
**Arabin-gummi,** *n.* gum arabic. **-säure,** *f.* arabic acid, arabin.
**arabisch,** *a.* Arabic, Arabian. — **arabischer Balsam,** balsam of Mecca, balm of Gilead. — **arabisches Gummi,** gum arabic.
**Arachinsäure,** *f.* arachic (or arachidic) acid.
**Arachisöl,** *n.* arachis oil, peanut oil.
**Aräometer,** *n.*, **Aräomesser,** *m.* hydrometer, areometer.
**Aräometrie,** *f.* hydrometry, areometry.
**aräometrisch,** *a.* hydrometric, areometric.
**Arb.,** *abbrev.* (Arbeit, Arbeiten) work(s), piece(s) of work.
**Arbeit,** *f.* work, labor; working; fermentation; task, job; workmanship; piece of work, (scientific) investigation; paper, article.
**arbeiten,** *v.i.* work; operate; ferment; (of wood) warp. — *v.t.* work, operate; perform, make. — **arbeitend,** *p.a.* working, active.

**Arbeiter,** *m.* worker, laborer, workman. **-stoff,** *m.* a coarse cloth, fustian.

**Arbeit-geber,** *m.* employer. **-nehmer,** *m.* workman, employee.

**Arbeits-.** working, work, of work or labor, operating.

**arbeitsam,** *a.* industrious; laborious.

**Arbeitsamkeit,** *f.* industriousness, industry.

**Arbeits-änderung,** *f.* change in work. **-äquivalent,** *n.* mechanical equivalent. **-aufwand,** *m.* expenditure of work. **-ausschuss,** *m.* working committee, executive committee. **-belastung,** *f.* working load. **-druck,** *m.* working pressure. **-einheit,** *f.* unit of work. **-einstellung,** *f.* strike.

**arbeitsfähig,** *a.* capable of work; able-bodied.

**Arbeits-fähigkeit,** *f.* capacity for performing work. **-fläche,** *f.* bearing surface; working surface. **-gang,** *m.* working state, operation; working process; course of manufacture. **-grösse,** *f.* quantity or amount of work; quantity having the dimensions of work. **-hub,** *m.* working stroke. **-kammer,** *f.* laboratory; work room. **-körper,** *m.* working substance, working medium. **-kraft,** *f.* working power, working faculty. **-kräfte,** *f.pl.* labor. **-leistung,** *f.* performance of work; efficiency; output. **-lohn,** *m.* wages, pay.

**arbeitslos,** *a. & adv.* without work, unemployed.

**Arbeits-methode,** *f.* method of work (or working). **-ordnung,** *f.* working regulation.

**arbeitsparend,** *a.* labor-saving.

**Arbeits-raum,** *m.* laboratory; work room. **-strom,** *m.* (*Elec.*) working current, open-circuit current (cf. Ruhestrom). **-stube,** *f.* = Arbeitszimmer. **-stufe,** *f.* stage of operation. **-teilung,** *f.* division of labor. **-tisch,** *m.* work table; laboratory table. **-tür,** *f.* (*Metal.*) charging door. **-vermögen,** *n.* (*Physics*) energy. **-verrichtung,** *f.* performance of work. **-vorgang,** *m.* operation. **-weise,** *f.* method of working, procedure; workmanship.

**Arbeitswert,** *m.* value in work. **— der Wärme,** mechanical equivalent of heat.

**Arbeitszimmer,** *n.* work room; laboratory; workshop; office; study.

**Arbitrium,** *n.* arbitrament.

**Arbuse,** *f.* watermelon.

**Arch.,** *abbrev.* Archiv, Archive.

**archäisch,** *a.* archaic; (*Geol.*) Archean.

**Archiv,** *n.* record office; *pl.* records, archives (often used in names of periodicals). **-tinte,** *f.* record ink.

**Arcus-cosinus,** *m.* (*Math.*) inverse cosine, arc cos, $\cos^{-1}$. **-sinus,** *m.* (*Math.*) inverse sine, arc sin, $\sin^{-1}$.

**Areal,** *n.* area.

**Arecanuss, Arekanuss,** *f.* areca nut.

**arg,** *a.* bad; strong, hard, severe, enormous.

**Arg,** *n.* harm, mischief.

**Argentindruck,** *m.* metal printing.

**Argentinien,** *m.* Argentina.

**ärgerlich,** *a.* angry; vexatious.

**arglistig,** *a.* artful, deceitful, fraudulent.

**arglos,** *a.* harmless; unsuspecting.

**argumentieren,** *v.i.* argue.

**Argwohn,** *n.* suspicion.

**Arier,** *m.* Aryan.

**arithmetisch,** *a.* arithmetical.

**arktisch,** *a.* arctic.

**arm,** *a.* poor; low, weak; (of gas, etc.) lean.

**Arm,** *m.* arm (in various senses); branch; cross bar (of a balance).

**-arm.** poor (in), low (in).

**Armatur,** *f.* fitting, mounting; armature; reinforcement (of concrete).

**Arm-binde,** *m.* sling. **-blei,** *n.* refined lead (from which the silver has been removed).

**Armee,** *f.* army.

**Ärmel,** *m.* sleeve.

**armenisch,** *a.* Armenian. **— armenische Erde,** Armenian bole.

**ärmer,** *a.* poorer.

**Armgas,** *n.* lean gas.

**armieren,** *v.t.* arm, equip; reinforce (concrete).

**Armierung,** *f.* arming, etc. (see armieren); fitting, mounting.

**ärmlich,** *a.* poor.

**Armoxyde,** *n.pl.* (*Lead*) skimmings.

**armselig,** *a.* poor, wretched, paltry.

**armtreiben,** *v.t.* (*Metal.*) concentrate.

**Armut,** *f.* poorness, poverty.

**Arnika-blüten,** *f.pl.* arnica flowers, (*Pharm.*) arnica. **-wurzel,** *f.* arnica rhizome, arnica root.

**Arom,** *n.* aroma.

**Aromaten,** *pl.* aromatic substances.

**aromatisch,** *a.* aromatic. **— aromatisches Mittel,** (*Pharm.*) aromatic. **— aromatische Reihe,** aromatic series.

**aromatisieren,** *v.t.* aromatize, scent, perfume.

**Aromatisierung,** *f.* aromatization.

**Aron,** *m.* arum. **-gewächse,** *n.pl.* (*Bot.*) Araceae.

**Aronsstärke,** *f.* arum starch.

**Aronwurzel,** *f.* arum root.

**Arrak,** *m.* arrack.

**arretieren,** *v.t.* arrest; stop, lock.

**Arretierung,** *f.* arrest; stop, detent.

**arrodieren,** *v.t.* erode.

**Arrosion,** *f.* erosion.

**Arrowmehl,** *n.* arrowroot flour, (*Pharm.*) arrowroot, maranta.

**Arsen,** *n.* arsenic. **-abstrich,** *m.* arsenic skimmings. **-antimon,** *n.* antimony arsenide. **-antimonnickelglanz,** *m.* corynite. **-bestimmung,** *f.* arsenic determination. **-blende,** *f.* arsenic blend (**gelbe,** orpiment; **rote,** realgar).

**-blüte,** *f.* arsenic bloom, arsenolite ($As_2O_3$). **-chlorid,** *n.* (any) arsenic chloride. **-dampf,** *m.* arsenic vapor, arsenical vapor. **-eisen,** *n.* iron arsenide; arsenical iron; (*Min.*) löllingite. **-eisensinter,** *m.* pitticite. **-erz,** *n.* arsenic ore. **-fahlerz,** *n.* tennantite. **-fleck,** *m.* arsenic spot or stain.

**arsen-frei,** *a.* free from arsenic, arsenic-free. **-führend,** *a.* arseniferous.

**Arsen-gehalt,** *m.* arsenic content. **-glas,** *n.* = Arsenikglas. **-halogen,** *n.* arsenic halide.

**arsenhaltig,** *a.* arsenical, containing arsenic.

**arsenig,** *a.* arsenious. — **arsenige Säure,** arsenious acid.

**arsenigsauer,** *a.* of or combined with arsenious acid, arsenite of.

**Arsenigsäure,** *f.* arsenious acid. **-salz,** *n.* arsenite.

**Arsenik,** *m.* & *n.* arsenic. — **gelber —,** orpiment. — **roter —,** realgar. — **weisser —,** white arsenic, arsenic trioxide.

**Arsenikalfahlerz,** *n.* tennantite.

**Arsenikalien,** *f.pl.* arsenicals, arsenical compounds or preparations.

**arsenikalisch,** *a.* arsenical.

**Arsenikalkies,** *m.* löllingite, esp. leucopyrite.

**Arsenik-antimon,** *a.* antimony arsenite. **-äscher,** *m.* (*Leather*) arsenic lime. **-blei,** *n.* lead arsenide. **-bleispat,** *m.* mimetite. **-blumen,** *f.pl.*, **-blüte,** *f.* = Arsenblüte. **-eisen,** *n.* = Arseneisen. **-erz,** *n.* arsenic ore. **-fahlerz,** *n.* tennantite. **-gegengift,** *n.* arsenic antidote. **-glas,** *n.* arsenic glass, vitreous arsenic trioxide; **(gelbes)** orpiment; **(rotes)** realgar.

**arsenikhaltig,** *a.* arsenical, containing arsenic.

**Arsenik-hütte,** *f.* arsenic works. **-jodür,** *n.* = Arsenjodür. **-kies,** *m.* arsenical pyrites (either arsenopyrite or löllingite). **-kobalt,** *m.* cobalt arsenide; (*Min.*) skutterudite. **-kobaltkies,** *m.* skutterudite. **-könig,** *m.* arsenic regulus. **-kupfer,** *n.* copper arsenide. **-metall,** *n.* = Arsenmetall. **-nickel,** *n.* nickel arsenide. **-öl, (ätzendes),** caustic oil of arsenic ($AsCl_3$). **-präparat,** *n.* = Arsenpräparat. **-probe,** *f.* arsenic test. **-rubin,** *m.* realgar. **-salz,** *n.* salt of arsenic, arsenate or arsenite.

**arseniksauer,** *a.* = arsensauer.

**Arseniksäure,** *f.* arsenic acid. — **unvollkommene —,** *f.* arsenious acid.

**Arsenik-schwarz,** *n.* arsenic black. **-silber,** *n.* arsenical silver. **-silberblende,** *f.* (*Min.*) proustite. **-sinter,** *m.* scorodite. **-spiegel,** *m.* arsenic mirror. **-spiessglanz,** *m.* allemontite. **-verbindung,** *f.* arsenic compound. **-vitriol,** *m.* arsenic sulfate. **-wasserstoff,** *m.* ≠ Arsenwasserstoff.

**Arsen-jodid,** *n.* arsenic iodide, specif. arsenic triiodide, arsenic(III) iodide. **-jodür,** *n.* arsenic diiodide, arsenic(II) iodide ($AsI_2$). **-kies,** *m.* = Arsenikkies. **-kobalt,** *m.* cobalt arsenide. **-kupfer,** *n.* copper arsenide; (*Min.*) domeykite. **-legierung,** *f.* arsenic alloy. **-lösung,** *f.* arsenic solution. **-metall,** *n.* metallic arsenide; metallic arsenic. **-nickel,** *m.* nickel arsenide; (*Min.*) niccolite. **-nickelglanz,** *m.* gersdorffite. **-nickelkies,** *m.* niccolite; chloanthite.

**Arsenobenzol,** *n.* arsenobenzene.

**Arsen-oxyd,** *n.* arsenic oxide, specif. arsenic trioxide, arsenic(III) oxide. **-präparat,** *n.* arsenical preparation, arsenical. **-probe,** *f.* arsenic test or sample. **-rohr,** *n.*, **-röhre,** *f.* arsenic tube. **-rotgültigerz,** *n.* proustite. **-rubin,** *m.* realgar. **-salz,** *n.* arsenic salt.

**arsensauer,** *a.* of or combined with arsenic acid, arsenate of.

**Arsen-säure,** *f.* arsenic acid. **-silber,** *n.* silver arsenide. **-silberblende,** *f.* proustite. **-spiegel,** *m.* arsenic mirror. **-sulfid,** *n.* arsenic sulfide, esp. the pentasulfide. **-sulfür,** *n.* arsenic trisulfide, arsenic(III) sulfide. **-ür,** *n.* (-ous) arsenide. **-verbindung,** *f.* arsenic compound. **-vergiftung,** *f.* arsenic poisoning. **-wasserstoff,** *m.* arsenic hydride, arseniuretted hydrogen (specif. arsine, $AsH_3$). **-zink,** *n.* zinc arsenide.

**Arsinigsäure,** *f.* arsinous acid, arsinic acid (better translated arsinic acid when referring to compounds of the formula RR′AsO·OH).

**Arsinoverbindung,** *f.* arsino compound. ("Arsino" preferably denotes the group $—AsH_2$ but has also been used to denote $>AsO \cdot OH$ and $—AsO(OH)_2$.)

**Arsinsäure,** *f.* arsonic acid, arsinic acid (better translated arsonic acid when referring to compounds of the formula $RAsO(OH)_2$).

**Art,** *f.* kind, sort, type, species, variety; nature; manner, way; race, breed; *pl.* manners; (*Biol.*) species. (Used as a suffix to give a generic meaning; as, *Pecharten,* pitches, *i.e.*, kinds of pitch.)

**Art-.** specific, species; typical.

**arteigen,** *a.* of the same kind, of like kind; (*Biol.*) characteristic of the species.

**Arteigenschaft,** *f.* (*Biol.*) species characteristic.

**arten,** *v.i.* be of a (certain) kind, be like, thrive. — *v.t.* form, modify. — **geartet,** disposed, -natured.

**arteriell,** *a.* arterial.

**Arterien-.** arterial.

**arteriös,** *a.* arterial.

**artesisch,** *a.* artesian.

**art-fremd,** *a.* of a different kind; alien; (*Biol.*) foreign to the species. **-gemäss,** *a.* true to type. **-gleich,** *a.* of the same kind, of like kind; (*Biol.*) of the same species.

**Artgleichheit,** *f.* (*Biol.*) identity of species.

**artificiell**, *a.* artificial.
**artig**, *a.* good, polite, agreeable.
**-artig.** A suffix attached to nouns and adjectives to form adjectives, and signifying "of the kind or nature of," "resembling," "like"; as *schwefelartig*, like sulfur, sulfurous.
**Artikel**, *m.* article; goods, commodity, material; entry, item; (*Calico*) style.
**Artischocke**, *f.* artichoke.
**Artkreuzung**, *f.* (*Biol.*) crossing of species.
**artlich**, *a.* qualitative.
**Artwärme**, *f.* specific heat.
**arylieren**, *v.t.* arylate.
**Arylierung**, *f.* arylation.
**Arznei, Arzenei**, *f.* medicine; *pl.* drugs.
**Arznei-.** medicinal, medical, medicated. **-bereiter**, *m.* pharmacist. **-bereitung**, *f.* preparing of medicines, pharmacy. **-buch**, *n.* pharmacopeia; dispensatory. **-essig**, *m.* medicated vinegar. **-fläschchen**, *n.* small medicine bottle. **-flasche**, *f.* medicine bottle. **-form**, *f.* medicinal form. **-formel**, *f.* medical formula. **-gabe**, *f.* dose (of medicine). **-gemisch**, *n.* medicinal mixture. **-geruch**, *m.* medicinal smell. **-geschmack**, *m.* medicinal taste. **-gewicht**, *n.* officinal weight. **-handel**, *m.* drug trade. **-händler**, *m.* druggist. **-kapsel**, *f.* medicinal capsule. **-körper**, *m.* medicinal substance.
**arzneikräftig**, *a.* medicinal, curative, therapeutic.
**Arznei-kraut**, *n.* medicinal plant, medicinal herb. **-kugel**, *f.* (*Pharm.*) bolus. **-kunde**, **-kunst**, *f.* medicine; pharmacy. **-lehre**, *f.* pharmacology.
**arzneilich**, *a.* medicinal, medical, pharmaceutical.
**Arznei-mass**, *n.* officinal measure. **-mischung**, *f.* medicinal mixture.
**Arzneimittel**, *n.* medicine, remedy. **-kunde**, **-lehre**, *f.* pharmacology. **-träger**, *m.* (*Pharm.*) carrier, excipient, menstruum.
**Arznei-pflanze**, *f.* medicinal plant. **-präparat**, *n.* medicinal preparation. **-seife**, *f.* medicinal soap. **-sirup**, *m.* medicated sirup. **-stoff**, *m.* medicinal substance, pharmaceutical. **-verordnung**, **-verschreibung**, *f.* (medical) prescription. **-ware**, *f.* drug. **-warenkunde**, *f.* pharmacology. **-wein**, *m.* medicinal (or medicated) wine. **-wesen**, *n.* pharmaceutical affairs. **-wissenschaft**, *f.* pharmacology; medical science.
**Arzt**, *m.* physician, doctor.
**Ärzte-schaft**, *f.* medical profession, medicine. **-verein**, *m.* medical society.
**ärztlich**, *a.* medical.
**A.S.**, *abbrev.* (Ampère-Stunde) ampere-hour.
**Asant, Asand**, *m.* — **stinkender —**, asafetida. — **wohlriechender —**, gum benzoin.
**Asantöl**, *n.* asafetida oil.
**Asarumkampher**, *m.* asarum camphor, asaron
**Asbest**, *m.* asbestos.
**asbestartig**, *a.* asbestoid, asbestine, asbestiform, amianthine.
**Asbest-aufschlämmung**, *f.* asbestos suspension **-drahtnetz**, *n.* asbestos wire gauze. **-faser**, *f.* asbestos fiber. **-filz**, *m.* asbestos felt. **-flocken**, *f.pl.* asbestos flocks, asbestos wool. **-gewebe**, *n.* asbestos cloth. **-handschuh**, *m.* asbestos glove. **-holz**, *n.* asbestos lumber. **-luftbad**, *n.* asbestos air bath. **-olith**, *n.* short-fibered asbestos. **-papier**, *n.* asbestos paper. **-pappe**, *f.* asbestos board. **-platte**, *f.* asbestos plate or board. **-schale**, *f.* asbestos dish. **-schicht**, *f.* asbestos layer or bed. **-schiefer**, *m.* asbestos slate. **-schirm**, *m.* asbestos screen. **-schnur**, *f.* asbestos twine or cord. **-schurz**, *m.*, **-schurze**, *f.* asbestos apron. **-wolle**, *f.* asbestos wool.
**Asch-blau**, *n.* zaffer. **-blei**, *n.* native bismuth.
**Asche**, *f.* ash, ashes.
**asche-bildend**, *a.* ash-forming. **-frei**, *a.* free from ash, ash-free.
**Äschel, Aschel**, *m.* (*Metal.*) sullage.
**aschen**, *v.t.* ash. **-arm**, *a.* poor in ash, low in ash.
**Aschen-bad**, *n.* ash bath. **-bestandteil**, *m.* ash constituent. **-bestimmung**, *f.* ash determination. **-dünger**, *m.* cinereal manure, cinereal. **-entfernung**, *f.* removal of ash(es). **-ermittelung**, *f.* determination of ash. **-fall**, *m.* ash pit, ash pan.
**aschen-fleckig**, *a.* (*Metal.*) specked with sullage. **-frei**, *a.* ash-free, ashless.
**Aschen-gehalt**, *m.* ash content. **-grube**, *f.* ash pit, cinder pit. **-halde**, *f.* ash heap, slag heap, dump. **-lauge**, *f.* lye from ashes. **-ofen**, *m.* calcining oven. **-raum**, *m.* ash pit. **-salz**, *n.* potash (potassium carbonate). **-schwefel**, *m.* sulfur in the ash(es). **-trecker**, *m.* tourmaline (old name). **-verflüssigung**, *f.* fusing of the ash(es), clinkering. **-zieher**, *m.* = Aschentrecker.
**Äscher**, *m.* (*Leather*) tanner's pit, lime pit; (*Soap*) ash cistern (also, ashes); (*Masonry*) slaked lime; (*Ceram.*) tin ashes. **-brühe**, *f.* (*Leather*) lime liquor.
**aschereich**, *a.* rich in ash, high in ash.
**Äscher-fass**, *n.* (*Leather*) liming tub. **-flüssigkeit**, *f.* = Äscherbrühe. **-grube**, *f.* (*Leather*) lime pit. **-kalk**, *m.* (*Leather*) lime.
**äschern**, *v.t.* ash; (*Leather*) lime.
**Äscherofen**, *m.* (*Ceram.*) frit kiln.
**Äscherung**, *f.* ashing; (*Leather*) liming.
**Aschfall**, *m.* ashpit, cinder pit.
**asch-farben**, *a.* ash-colored, ashy. **-grau**, *a.* ash-gray.
**äschig, äschicht**, *a.* ashy.
**aschist**, *a.* (*Petrog.*) aschistic.

**Asch-lauch,** *m.* shallot, eschalot (*Allium ascalonicum*). **-raum,** *m.* ash box, ash pit.
**Ascorbinsäure,** *f.* ascorbic acid.
**Äsculetin,** *n.* esculetin, aesculetin.
**Äsculin,** *n.* esculin, aesculin.
**aseptisch,** *a.* aseptic.
**asiatisch,** *a.* Asiatic.
**Askomyzeten,** *pl.* (*Bot.*) Ascomycetes.
**Äskuletin,** *n.* esculetin, aesculetin.
**Äskulin,** *n.* esculin, aesculin.
**Asordin,** *n.* Asordin (a chlorinated hydrocarbon).
**Asparaginsäure,** *f.* aspartic acid.
**Aspe,** *f.* aspen (tree).
**asphaltartig,** *a.* like asphalt, asphaltic, bituminous.
**Asphalt-beton,** *m.* asphalt(ic) concrete. **-firnis,** *m.* asphalt varnish.
**asphaltfrei,** *a.* asphalt-free.
**Asphaltgestein,** *n.* native asphalt.
**asphalthaltig,** *a.* containing asphalt, asphaltic, bituminiferous.
**asphaltieren,** *v.t.* asphalt.
**asphaltisch,** *a.* asphaltic.
**Asphalt-kitt,** *m.* asphalt cement, asphalt mastic. **-lack,** *m.* asphalt varnish. **-mastix,** *m.* = Asphaltkitt. **-mehl,** *n.* asphalt powder. **-papier,** *n.* asphalt paper. **-pappe,** *f.* asphalt board. **-pech,** *n.* bituminous pitch. **-pflaster,** *n.* asphalt pavement.
**asphaltreich,** *a.* rich in asphalt.
**Asphalt-stein,** *m.* native asphalt. **-überzug,** *m.* asphalt coat(ing). **-verfahren,** *n.* asphalt process, bitumen process.
**Aspirateur,** *m.* aspirator.
**aspirieren,** *v.i.* aspire. — *v.t.* aspirate.
**ass,** *pret.* (of essen) ate.
**Assamkautschuk,** *m.* & *n.* Assam rubber.
**Assanierung,** *f.* sanitation.
**Assekuranz,** *f.* insurance.
**assekurieren,** *v.t.* insure.
**assimilatorisch,** *a.* assimilatory, assimilative.
**assimilierbar,** *a.* assimilable.
**Assimilierbarkeit,** *f.* assimilability.
**assimilieren,** *v.t.* assimilate.
**Assistent,** *m.* assistant.
**Association,** *f.* association; (*Org. Chem.*) coupling.
**associieren,** *v.t.* associate.
**assortieren,** *v.t.* assort, sort.
**assouplieren,** *v.t.* render pliable, supple; half-boil (silk).
**Assoziationsgrad,** *m.* degree of association.
**assoziieren,** *v.t.* associate.
**Ast,** *m.* branch, bough; leg (of a tube); knot (in wood).
**astatisch,** *a.* astatic.
**astatisieren,** *v.t.* astatize, render astatic.
**Asterismus,** *m.* asterism.
**ästhetisch,** *a.* esthetic.
**ästig,** *a.* branched, branchy; knotted, gnarled.
**Astronom,** *m.* astronomer.
**astronomisch,** *a.* astronomical.
**astrophysikalisch,** *a.* astrophysical.
**asymmetrisch,** *a.* asymmetric, asymmetrical.
**asymptotisch,** *a.* asymptotic.
**asynchron,** *a.* asynchronous.
**aszendent,** *a.* (*Min.*) primary.
**At.,** *abbrev.* (Atom) atom; (Atmosphäre) atmosphere.
**-at.** (in names of salts, etc.) -ate.
**Ata, ata,** *abbrev.* atmosphere(s) absolute ($kg/cm^2$).
**Atem,** *m.* breath, breathing, respiration; spirit.
**Atem-.** of breathing, respiratory.
**atembar,** *a.* respirable.
**Atem-einsatz,** *m.* drum (of a German mask). **-gerät,** *n.* = Atmungsgerät. **-maske,** *f.* gas mask, respirator. **-rohr,** *n.*, **-röhre,** *f.* breathing tube, respiratory tube. **-zug,** *m.* breath.
**äterisch,** *a.* ethereal.
**At.-Gew.,** *abbrev.* (Atomgewicht) atomic weight.
**äth.,** *abbrev.* (ätherisch) ethereal.
**Äthal,** *n.* ethal (cetyl alcohol).
**Äthan,** *n.* ethane; *pl.* paraffins, hydrocarbons of the ethane series. **-al,** *n.* ethanal (acetaldehyde). **-oyl,** *n.* ethanoyl (acetyl). **-säure,** *f.* ethanoic acid (acetic acid).
**Äthebenin,** *n.* ethebenine.
**Äthebenol,** *n.* ethebenol.
**Äthen,** *n.* ethene (ethylene). **-yl,** *n.* ethenyl.
**Äther,** *m.* ether (in older names frequently equivalent to *ester*).
**ätherähnlich,** *a.* ether-like, ethereal.
**Ätherart,** *f.* kind of ether; *pl.* ethers.
**ätherartig,** *a.* ethereal.
**Äther-auszug,** *m.* ethereal extract, ether extract. **-bildung,** *f.* ether formation, etherification. **-dampf,** *m.* ether vapor.
**äther-förmig,** *a.* etheriform. **-haltig,** *a.* containing ether, ethereal.
**ätherifizieren,** *v.t.* etherify.
**Ätherifizierung,** *f.* etherification.
**Ätherin,** *n.* etherin.
**ätherisch,** *a.* ethereal; essential, volatile (oils). **-riechend,** *a.* of ethereal odor.
**ätherisierbar,** *a.* etherizable.
**ätherisieren,** *v.t.* etherize.
**Ätherisierung,** *f.* etherization.
**ätherlöslich,** *a.* ether-soluble.
**atherman,** *a.* athermanous.
**äthern,** *v.t.* etherize.
**Äther-prober,** *m.* ether tester. **-säure,** *f.* ether acid (compound which is both an ether and an acid); lampic acid (*Obs.*). **-schicht,** *f.* ether layer. **-schwefelsäure,** *f.* alkylsulfuric acid, specif. ethylsulfuric acid. **-schwingung,** *f.* vibration of the ether, ethereal vibration.

**-verlust,** *m.* loss or waste of ether. **-weingeist,** *m.* (*Pharm.*) spirit of ether (solution of ether in alcohol). **-welle,** *f.* ether wave.

**Äthiden,** *n.* ethidene, ethylidene.

**Äthin,** *n.* ethyne, ethine (acetylene).

**Äthionsäure,** *f.* ethionic acid.

**athmen,** *v.* = atmen.

**Äthoxalyl,** *n.* ethoxalyl.

**Äthoxy-.** ethoxy-.

**Äthoxyl,** *n.* ethoxyl.

**Äthyl,** *n.* ethyl. **-al,** *n.* ethylal.

**äthylalkoholisch,** *a.* ethyl-alcoholic.

**Äthyl-at,** *n.* ethylate. **-äther,** *m.* ethyl ether. **-azetat,** *n.* ethyl acetate. **-blau,** *n.* ethyl blue.

**Äthylen,** *n.* ethylene. **-bindung,** *f.* ethylene linkage, double bond. **-jodid,** *n.* ethylene iodide. **-oxyd,** *n.* ethylene oxide. **-reihe,** *f.* ethylene series. **-verbindung,** *f.* ethylene compound.

**Äthyl-formiat,** *n.* ethyl formate. **-grün,** *n.* ethyl green. **-gruppe,** *f.* ethyl group. **-gummi,** *n.* ethyl rubber.

**Äthyliden,** *n.* ethylidene. **-milchsäure,** *f.* ethylidene lactic acid.

**äthylieren,** *v.t.* ethylate.

**Äthylierung,** *f.* ethylation.

**Äthyl-jodid,** *n.* ethyl iodide, iodoethane. **-rhodanid,** *n.* ethyl thiocyanate. **-rot,** *n.* ethyl red. **-schwefelsäure,** *f.* ethylsulfuric acid. **-senföl,** *n.* ethyl mustard oil ($C_2H_5NCS$). **-sulfhydrat,** *n.* ethyl hydrosulfide. **-verbindung,** *f.* ethyl compound. **-wasserstoff,** *m.* ethyl hydride (ethane). **-zinnsäure,** *f.* ethylstannic acid.

**Ätio-.** etio-, aetio-.

**Ätiologie,** *f.* etiology, aetiology.

**Atlas,** *m.* satin; atlas.

**atlasartig,** *a.* satiny, satined.

**Atlas-erz,** *n.*, fibrous malachite. **-gips,** *m.* fibrous gypsum.

**atlasglänzend,** *a.* of satiny luster, satiny.

**Atlas-holz,** *n.* satinwood. **-kies,** *m.* = Atlaserz. **-papier,** *n.* glazed paper. **-spat, -stein,** *m.* satin spar (fibrous calcium carbonate). **-vitriol,** *m.* white vitriol, (hydrous) zinc sulfate.

**Atm.,** *abbrev.* (Atmosphäre) atmosphere(s).

**atmen,** *v.i.* breathe, respire. — *v.t.* breathe.

**Atmolyse,** *f.* atmolysis.

**Atmosphäre,** *f.* atmosphere.

**Atmosphären-druck,** *m.* atmospheric pressure. **-überdruck,** *m.* atmospheric excess pressure.

**Atmosphärilien,** *pl.* substances in the atmosphere; atmospheric influences.

**atmosphärisch,** *a.* atmospheric.

**Atmung,** *f.* breathing, respiration.

**Atmungs-.** of breathing, respiratory. **-apparat,** *m.* breathing apparatus, respirator. **-ferment,** *n.* respiratory enzyme. **-gerät,** *n.* breathing apparatus, respirator. **-gift,** *n.* respiratory poison. **-grösse,** *f.* respiration quotient. **-kohlensäure,** *f.* carbon dioxide of respiration. **-nahrungsmittel,** *n.* respiratory food. **-stoffwechsel,** *m.* respiratory metabolism. **-weg,** *m.* respiratory passage.

**atomähnlich,** *a.* atom-like.

**atomar,** *a.* atomic.

**atomartig,** *a.* atomic; atom-like.

**Atom-bau,** *n.* atomic structure. **-begriff,** *m.* conception of the atom. **-bewegung,** *f.* atomic motion. **-bindung,** *f.* atomic linkage or bond. **-bindungskraft,** *f.*, **-bindungsvermögen,** *n.*, **atombindende Kraft.** atomic combining power, valence. **-gewicht,** *n.* atomic weight. **-gewichtsbestimmung,** *f.* atomic-weight determination. **-gewichtstabelle, -gewichtstafel,** *f.* table of atomic weights. **-gitter,** *n.* atomic lattice. **-gramm,** *n.* gram atom. **-gruppe,** *f.* group of atoms, atomic group. **-gruppierung,** *f.* atomic grouping.

**atomhaltig,** *a.* atomic.

**Atom-hülle,** *f.* atomic envelope or sheath (total electrons surrounding the nucleus). **-hypothese,** *f.* atomic hypothesis.

**Atomigkeit,** *f.* atomicity.

**atomisch,** *a.* atomic.

**Atomismus,** *m.* atomism.

**Atomistik,** *f.* atomistics.

**atomistisch,** *a.* atomistic, atomic.

**Atomizität,** *f.* atomicity.

**Atom-kern,** *m.* atomic nucleus. **-kette,** *f.* chain of atoms, atomic chain. **-lage,** *f.* atomic layer; atomic position. **-lehre,** *f.* doctrine of atoms, atomic theory. **-mechanik,** *f.* mechanics of the atom. **-modell,** *n.* atomic model. **-nummer,** *f.* atomic number. **-ordnung,** *f.* atomic arrangement. **-refraktion,** *f.* atomic refraction. **-rest,** *m.* atomic residue (= Atomrumpf). **-ring,** *m.* ring of atoms. **-rumpf,** *m.* atomic residue or core (remainder of an atom, as after removal of some electrons). **-schale,** *f.* atomic shell. **-strahl,** *m.* atomic ray. **-tafel,** *f.* atomic table.

**atomtheoretisch,** *a.* of or according to the atomic theory.

**Atom-theorie,** *f.* atomic theory. **-verband,** *m.*, **-verbindung,** *f.* union of atoms, atomic union. **-verhältnis,** *n.* atomic relation or ratio. **-verkettung,** *f.* linking of atoms, atomic linkage. **-verschiebung,** *f.* atomic displacement. **-volum, -volumen,** *n.* atomic volume. **-wärme,** *f.* atomic heat. **-wertigkeit,** *f.* atomic valence. **-zahl,** *f.* atomic number; number of atoms. **-zeichen,** *n.* atomic symbol. **-zerfall,** *m.* atomic disintegration. **-zertrümmerung,** *f.* atom smashing. **-ziffer,** *f.* atomic number.

**atoxisch,** *a.* atoxic, nontoxic.

**Atramentstein,** *m.* inkstone, native copperas.

**Atranorinsäure,** *f.* atranorinic acid.
**Atranorsäure,** *f.* atranoric acid.
**atro,** *abbrev.* (absoluttrocken) bone-dry.
**Atrolaktinsäure,** *f.* atrolactic acid.
**Atropasäure,** *f.* atropic acid.
**attenuieren,** *v.t.* attenuate.
**Attest,** *n.* certificate.
**Attich,** *m.* dwarf elder, danewort.
**Attrappe,** *f.* dummy, mock-up, model.
**Atü.,** *abbrev.* (Atmosphärenüberdruck) atmospheres excess pressure.
**atypisch,** *a.* atypic, atypical.
**Ätz-.** caustic, corrosive; (*Calico*) discharging, discharge. **-alkali,** *n.* caustic alkali. **-alkalilösung,** *f.* caustic alkaline solution.
**ätzalkalisch,** *a.* caustic alkaline.
**Ätz-ammoniak,** *n.* caustic ammonia (ammonium hydroxide), ammonia water. **-artikel,** *m.* (*Calico*) discharge style. **-bad,** *n.* etching bath.
**ätzbar,** *a.* corrodible; (*Calico*) dischargeable.
**Ätz-barkeit,** *f.* corrodibility; (*Calico*) dischargeability. **-baryt,** *m.* caustic baryta (barium hydroxide). **-beizdruck,** *n.* discharge printing. **-beize,** *f.* chemical discharge, discharge mordant.
**ätzbeständig,** *a.* resisting caustic; (*Calico*) discharge-resisting.
**Ätz-bild,** *n.*, etching figure, etched figure. **-boden,** *m.* (*Calico*) discharge ground. **-druck,** *n.* discharge printing.
**Ätze,** *f.* corrosion; etching; cauterization; etching liquid, esp. aqua fortis; (*Calico*) discharge.
**ätzen,** *v.t.* corrode; etch, bite; cauterize; (*Calico*) discharge. — **ätzend,** *p.a.* caustic, corrosive. — **ätzend machen,** render caustic, causticize. — **ätzender Kalk** = Ätzkalk.
**Ätz-farbe,** *f.* etching ink; (*Calico*) discharge paste. **-figur,** *f.* etching figure, etched figure. **-flüssigkeit,** *f.* caustic liquid; etching acid. **-gift,** *n.* caustic poison. **-grübchen,** *n.* pit due to etching, etched pit. **-grund,** *m.* etching ground; (*Calico*) discharge ground.
**Ätzkali,** *n.* caustic potash. **-lauge,** *f.* caustic potash lye, caustic potash solution. **-lösung,** *f.* caustic potash solution. **-stück,** *n.* piece of caustic potash.
**Ätzkalk,** *m.* caustic lime (**gebrannter,** quicklime; **gelöschter,** slaked lime). **-lösung,** *f.* lime water.
**Ätz-kraft,** *f.* causticity; corrosiveness. **-kunst,** *f.* (art of) etching. **-lack,** *m.* discharge lake. **-lauge,** *f.* caustic lye, caustic liquor. **-lösung,** *f.* caustic solution; etching solution. **-magnesia,** *f.* caustic magnesia (magnesium hydroxide). **-methode,** *f.* etching method. **-mittel,** *n.* corrosive, caustic; etching medium; (*Calico*) chemical discharge, discharging agent.
**Ätznatron,** *n.* caustic soda. **-lauge,** *f.* caustic soda lye, caustic soda solution. **-lösung,** *f.* caustic soda solution. **-stück,** *n.* piece of caustic soda.
**Ätz-papp,** *m.* (*Calico*) resist. **-paste,** *f.* corrosive paste, etching paste.
**ätzpolieren,** *v.t.* polish with acid or other etching agent, etch-polish.
**Ätz-probe,** *f.* etching test or sample. **-pulver,** *n.* caustic powder; etching powder. **-salz,** *n.* corrosive salt. **-schliff,** *m.* ground section for etching (as of metals). **-silber,** *n.* lunar caustic (silver nitrate). **-stein,** *m.* lapis causticus, (fused) caustic potash; lunar caustic (silver nitrate). **-stoff,** *m.* caustic, corrosive. **-strontian,** *m.* caustic strontia (strontium oxide or hydroxide). **-sublimat,** *n.* corrosive sublimate (mercuric chloride). **-tinte,** *f.* etching ink.
**Ätzung,** *f.* corrosion; etching; cauterization.
**Ätz-verfahren,** *n.* caustic process, corrosive process, etching process. **-verhalten,** *n.* behavior to etching. **-wasser,** *n.* caustic water; etching liquid, specif. aqua fortis; mordant. **-weiss,** *n.* (*Calico*) white discharge. **-wirkung,** *f.* corrosive action; (*Calico*) action of the discharge.
**a.u.a.,** *abbrev.* (auch unter andern) also among others.
**auch,** *adv. & conj.* also, too; indeed, even. — **— nicht,** neither, not . . . either.
**Audienz,** *f.* hearing; reception (of sound).
**Aue,** *f.* islet; meadow.
**Auer-brenner,** *m.* Welsbach burner. **-licht,** *n.* Welsbach light. **-metall,** *n.* Welsbach metal (pyrophoric cerium alloy).
**auf,** *prep.* on, upon, in, at; about; into, to. — *adv. & prefix.* up, upward; open. — **— dass,** in order that. — **— einmal,** at once. — **— und ab,** up and down; to and fro.
**aufarbeiten,** *v.t.* work up; use up; finish (work); force open.
**aufatmen,** *v.i.* breathe hard, breathe again.
**aufätzen,** *v.t.* corrode or etch upon, etch; (*Med.*) open with caustic.
**Aufbau,** *m.* building up, synthesis; structure; mounting; building, construction, erection; superstructure; display.
**aufbauchen,** *v.t., i. & r.* swell up, puff up.
**aufbauen,** *v.t.* build up, synthesize; erect. — **aufbauend,** *p.a.* synthetic; constructive.
**aufbäumen,** *v.i.* show (metallic) luster. — *v.r.* bear up, struggle.
**Aufbauprinzip,** *n.* construction principle (governing the structure of atoms).
**aufbauschen,** *v.t., i. & r.* puff (up), swell.
**aufbeizen,** *v.t.* = aufätzen.
**aufbereiten,** *v.t.* prepare; dress (ores).
**Aufbereitung,** *f.* preparation; dressing (of ores).

**Aufbereitungsverlust,** *m.* loss from preparation or (of ores) dressing.
**aufbersten,** *v.i.* burst, crack.
**aufbessern,** *v.t.* improve, ameliorate, freshen.
**aufbeulen,** *v.i.* buckle.
**aufbewahren,** *v.t.* keep, store, preserve.
**Aufbewahrung,** *f.* keeping, storage, preservation.
**Aufbewahrungs-dauer,** *f.* length of storage. **-ort, -raum,** *m.* storage place, storehouse, depository.
**aufbiegen,** *v.t.* bend up, turn up; open, unfold.
**aufbieten,** *v.t.* call out, summon; exert; abuse.
**aufbinden,** *v.t.* tie up, fasten; untie, loosen.
**aufblähen,** *v.t., i. & r.* swell, swell up, bulge out, expand.
**aufblasen,** *v.t.* blow up, inflate.
**aufblättern,** *v.i.* (*Min. & Med.*) exfoliate.
**Aufblick,** *m.* (*Assaying*) fulguration, blick; look upward.
**aufblicken,** *v.i.* (*Assaying*) brighten, give the "blick"; look up.
**aufblitzen,** *v.i.* flash, flash up.
**aufblühen,** *v.i.* blossom, unfold; form a flower-like mass (before the blowpipe); develop.
**aufbohren,** *v.t.* bore open, bore.
**aufbrauchen,** *v.t.* use up, consume.
**aufbrausen,** *v.i.* effervesce; ferment; roar; fly into a passion. — **aufbrausend,** *p.a.* effervescent; fermenting.
**aufbrechen,** *v.t.* break up, break open. — *v.i.* open, break, burst.
**aufbrennen,** *v.t.* burn up, consume; refine (metals); brand; burn on; treat by burning, specif. sulfur (wine).
**aufbringen** *v.t.* bring (up), lift (up); put (up), set (up); raise; anger, provoke.
**aufbrodeln,** *v.i.* bubble up, boil up.
**aufbrühen,** *v.t.* boil up, boil.
**aufdampfen,** *v.i.* evaporate; smoke.
**aufdämpfen,** *v.t.* deposit by vaporization, vaporize on, distil on.
**aufdarren,** *v.t.* dry, desiccate.
**aufdecken,** *v.t.* uncover, disclose.
**aufdocken,** *v.t.* wind up, roll up; bundle, shock.
**aufdörren,** *v.t.* dry, desiccate.
**aufdrängen,** *v.t.* press open; force upon.
**aufdrehen,** *v.t.* screw open, untwist; turn on (as gas); turn up; (*Ceram.*) throw.
**aufdringen,** *v.t.* press upon, obtrude upon.
**aufdringlich,** *a.* (of odors) penetrating; obtrusive.
**Aufdringlichkeit,** *f.* penetrating quality; obtrusiveness, importunity.
**Aufdruck,** *m.* printing; print; imprint, stamp.
**aufdrucken,** *v.t.* imprint, print (as colors).
**aufdrücken,** *v.t.* impress, imprint, stamp.
**aufduften,** *v.i.* give off an odor or fragrance.
**aufdunsten,** *v.i.* evaporate.
**aufdünsten,** *v.t.* evaporate.
**aufeinander,** *adv.* one upon (or after) another.
**Aufeinanderfolge,** *f.* succession, series.
**aufeinander-folgend,** *p.a.* consecutive, successive. **-häufen,** *v.t.* heap up, pile up, stack. **-passen,** *v.i.* match, fit.
**Aufelektron,** *n.* outer electron, valence electron.
**Aufenthalt,** *m.* stay, stop; abode, residence.
**auferlegen,** *v.t.* impose (on or upon); punish.
**auffahren,** *v.i.* rise up, drive up, fly up, start up.
**auffallen,** *v.i.* fall (on); strike; astonish. — **auffallend,** *p.a.* incident; striking, remarkable, conspicuous.
**auffallenderweise,** *adv.* strikingly, remarkably.
**auffällig,** *a.* = auffallend.
**auffalten,** *v.t.* unfold, open; fold up, fold.
**Auffangbehälter,** *m.* collecting vessel, receiver.
**Auffange-.** collecting. **-gefäss,** *n.* collecting vessel, receiver. **-glas,** *n.* (*Optics*) object glass, objective.
**auffangen,** *v.t.* collect; intercept; catch, capture.
**Auffänger,** *m.* collector; collecting vessel, receiver; catcher.
**Auffang-gefäss,** *n.* collecting vessel, receiver. **-kolben,** *m.* receiving flask. **-rohr,** *n.*, **-röhre,** *f.* collecting tube, pipe or cylinder. **-schale,** *f.* collecting dish or basin; drip pan.
**auffärben,** *v.t.* dye anew, redye.
**Auffärber,** *m.* job dyer.
**auffasern,** *v.t.* separate into fibers, unravel.
**auffassen,** *v.t.* conceive, perceive, comprehend; interpret; catch up.
**Auffassung,** *f.* conception; perception; comprehension.
**auffeuchten,** *v.t.* moisten, wet.
**auffinden,** *v.t.* detect, discover, find, find out.
**aufflackern,** *v.i.* flare up; deflagrate.
**aufflammen,** *v.i.* flame up, blaze, deflagrate.
**auffliegen,** *v.i.* blow up, explode; fly up, rise.
**auffliessen,** *v.i.* flow on, run on.
**auffordern,** *v.t.* ask, request, summon.
**Aufforderung,** *f.* request; appeal; demand.
**auffressen,** *v.t.* corrode; eat up.
**auffrischen,** *v.t.* freshen (up), revive, restore, renew; regenerate; (*Brewing*) change (steep water), refresh (yeast).
**Aufrischung,** *f.* freshening, etc. (see auffrischen).
**aufführen,** *v.t.* erect, raise; perform; charge (in an account), enter, note; register; adduce, bring in (as evidence).
**auffüllen,** *v.t.* fill up, make up, fill.
**Auffüllung,** *f.* filling up, filling.
**Aufg.,** *abbrev.* (Aufgabe) problem.
**Aufgabe,** *f.* task, problem; function; giving up; delivery; order; lesson; theme.
**Aufgabe-.** charging, feeding; issuing, sending.
**Aufgabensammlung,** *f.* collection of problems.

**Aufgabe-trichter,** *m.* feed hopper, feed funnel. **-vorrichtung,** *f.* charging device, feeder.
**Aufgang,** *m.* rising, going up, ascent; disappearance.
**aufgären,** *v.i.* ferment, effervesce.
**aufgeben,** *v.t.* give up, give, deliver; abandon, relinquish; charge, feed (a furnace or the like); propose.
**aufgebläht,** *p.p.* of aufblähen; swollen, swelled.
**Aufgebot,** *n.* summons; levy; bans.
**aufgebracht,** *p.p.* of aufbringen.
**aufgedunsen,** *p.a.* swollen.
**aufgehen,** *v.i.* go up, rise, swell; ferment; appear; open, come open; unfold; be spent or consumed; evaporate; be merged; (of dyes) go on, be absorbed; (of plants) come up, shoot; (*Arith.*) leave no remainder.
**Aufgeld,** *n.* premium; extra charge.
**aufgelegt,** *p.a.* see auflegen.
**aufgeschliffen,** *p.p.* of aufschleifen.
**aufgeschlossen,** *p.p.* of aufschliessen.
**aufgeschmolzen,** *p.p.* of aufschmelzen.
**aufgesogen,** *p.p.* of aufsaugen.
**aufgeweckt,** *p.a.* lively, clever.
**aufgichten,** *v.t.* (*Metal.*) charge.
**aufgiessen,** *v.t.* infuse; pour on, pour upon.
**aufgischen,** *v.i.* foam up, boil up; ferment.
**aufglühen,** *v.i.* flame (up), flare (up), blaze.
**Aufguss,** *m.* infusion. **-apparat,** *m.* sparger. **-gefäss,** *n.* infusion vessel, digester. **-probe,** *f.* pour test. **-tierchen,** *n.pl.* Infusoria. **-verfahren,** *n.* infusion process or method; mashing process.
**aufhacken,** *v.t.* cut up, stir up.
**aufhalten,** *v.t.* hold up, support; stop, detain, obstruct. — *v.r.* stop, stay; find fault.
**aufhängen,** *v.t.* hang up, hang, suspend.
**Aufhänger,** *m.* hanger; rack.
**Aufhängung,** *f.* hanging (up), suspension; mounting.
**aufhäufen,** *v.t.* heap up, pile up, store up.
**aufheben,** *v.t.* lift up, raise; pick up; lay up, preserve; break up, abolish; annul, invalidate, cancel, destroy, neutralize; seize; counterbalance; (of colors) compensate, be complementary to; reduce (a fraction) to lowest terms.
**Aufhebung,** *f.* lifting up, etc. (see aufheben).
**aufheitern,** *v.t. & r.* clear up, brighten up.
**aufheizen,** *v.t.* heat up.
**aufhellen,** *v.t. & r.* clear up, clarify, brighten, make lighter (in color); illuminate.
**Aufhellungs-lage,** *f.* (*Min.*) position of maximum illumination, light position. **-mittel,** *n.* clearing agent. **-pigment,** *n.* brightening pigment.
**aufholen,** *v.t.* draw up, haul up, raise.
**aufhören,** *v.i.* stop, cease, discontinue, end; desist.
**aufkeimen,** *v.i.* germinate, sprout, bud.
**aufkippen,** *v.t.* tilt up, tip up.
**aufkitten,** *v.t.* cement on.
**aufklappbar,** *a.* capable of opening, hinged.
**aufklappen,** *v.t.* open (something leaved, as a book).
**aufklären,** *v.t.* clear up; explain; enlighten. — *v.r.* clear up, clear.
**Aufklärung,** *f.* clearing up, elucidation; information; explanation; enlightenment.
**aufkleben, aufkleistern,** *v.t.* paste on; paste up.
**aufklotzen,** *v.t.* (*Calico*) pad.
**aufkochen,** *v.t. & i.* boil up, boil; boil again warm up (food); prime (boilers).
**Aufkochgefäss,** *n.* boiler; reboiler.
**aufkohlen,** *v.t.* (*Metal.*) recarburize, carburize, cement.
**Aufkohlungsmittel,** *n.* (re)carburizing agent.
**aufkommen,** *v.i.* advance; come into use; come up, get up.
**Aufkosten,** *f.pl.* overhead, oncost.
**aufkratzen,** *v.t.* scratch up, scratch; rake, stir (a fire); dress, nap (fabrics); card (wool).
**aufkräusen,** *v.i.* (*Brewing*) form a head, esp. curly head.
**aufkühlen,** *v.t.* cool, (*Brewing*) aerate.
**aufkündigen,** *v.t.* give notice or warning of; recall.
**aufkupfern,** *v.t.* coat with copper, copper.
**Aufl.,** *abbrev.* (Auflage) edition.
**Aufladegeschwindigkeit,** *f.* loading or charging rate.
**aufladen,** *v.t.* load; (*Elec.*) charge.
**Aufladung,** *f.* loading; (*Elec.*) charge; (*Expl.*) top charge.
**Auflage,** *f.* edition, impression (of a book); duty, tax; (*Mech.*) rest, support; overlayer, superimposed layer. **-fläche,** *f.* bearing surface.
**Auflager,** *n.* support, bearing, seat.
**auflagern,** *v.t.* store up, store; superpose; support, bed. — *v.i.* form a layer, aggregate.
**auflassen,** *v.t.* leave open or blank; give up.
**Auflauf,** *m.* swelling; puff; mob, crowd.
**auflaufen,** *v.i.* run up, come up, rise, swell. — *v.t.* feed, supply to a furnace, etc.); beam, wind up.
**aufleben,** *v.i.* revive.
**auflegen,** *v.t.* lay on or up; apply; impose; print, publish. — **aufgelegt,** *p.a.* disposed, inclined.
**Auflegeschuss,** *m.* (*Mining*) mudcap, mud capping.
**auflehnen,** *v.r.* lean (upon); rebel (against).
**aufleimen,** *v.t.* glue on.
**auflesen,** *v.t.* pick up, gather.
**aufleuchten,** *v.i.* light up, shine, glow.
**aufliegen,** *v.i.* lie (on), rest (on); weigh (on); be incumbent (on).

**auflockern,** *v.t.* & *i.* loosen up, loosen; disintegrate; relax.

**Auflockerung,** *f.* loosening; disintegration; relaxation.

**Auflockerungs-mittel,** *n.* loosening agent. **-sprengung,** *f.* (*Expl.*) breaking-in shot.

**auflodern,** *v.i.* flame(up), flare(up), blaze.

**auflösbar,** *a.* soluble; resolvable.

**Auflösbarkeit,** *f.* solubility; resolvability.

**auflösen,** *v.t.* dissolve; loosen, untie, undo; resolve, decompose, dissipate; solve; cancel. — *v.r.* dissolve; deliquesce; decompose. — **auflösend,** *p.a.* solvent, dissolvent.

**Auflöser,** *m.* dissolver, etc. (see auflösen); (*Paper*, etc.) mixer.

**auflöslich,** *a.* soluble.

**Auflöslich-blau,** *n.* soluble blue. **-keit,** *f.* solubility.

**Auflösung,** *f.* solution; dissolving; unloosening, undoing; resolution, decomposition, dissolution, analysis (as opposed to synthesis); (of malt) mellowness, friability.

**auflösungsfähig,** *a.* capable of solution, soluble.

**Auflösungs-gefäss,** *n.* dissolving vessel, dissolver. **-geschwindigkeit,** *f.* velocity of solution, resolution, etc. **-grenze,** *f.* (*Micros.*) limit of resolution. **-kraft,** *f.* dissolving power; resolving power. **-mittel,** *n.* solvent. **-nafta, -naphta,** *f.* solvent naphtha. **-pfanne,** *f.* (*Sugar*) blow-up pan, clarifier. **-vermögen,** *n.* solvent power; (of a microscope) resolving power. **-wärme,** *f.* heat of solution.

**auflöten,** *v.t.* solder on; unsolder.

**aufmachen,** *v.t.* open, undo; put up; make up. — *v.r.* prepare; get up, rise.

**Aufmaischen,** *n.* second mashing.

**aufmerken,** *v.t.* mark, note. — *v.i.* pay attention.

**aufmerksam,** *a.* attentive, observing. — — **machen,** call (one's) attention (to).

**Aufmerksamkeit,** *f.* attention, attentiveness.

**aufmischen,** *v.t.* mix up.

**aufmuntern,** *v.t.* rouse, incite; encourage.

**Aufnahme,** *f.* taking up; absorbing, absorption; dissolving; admission; reception; fashion; survey, sketch; taking (as of photographs), exposure; plotting (of curves); (photographic) picture, photograph.

**aufnahmefähig,** *a.* absorbable; absorptive; receptive; admissible.

**Aufnahme-fähigkeit,** *f.* absorbability, absorptivity, absorbing power; capacity. **-geschwindigkeit,** *f.* absorption rate. **-kolben,** *m.* absorption flask. **-pipette,** *f.* a pipet calibrated to take up a definite volume. Cf. Ausflusspipette. **-vermögen,** *n.* absorptive power.

**aufnehmen,** *v.t.* take up; absorb; dissolve; admit, receive; trace, plot; draw, survey; take (a photograph); borrow. — **aufnehmend,** *p.a.* absorbing, absorptive.

**Aufnehmer,** *m.* receiver; absorber; etc. (see aufnehmen).

**aufnötigen,** *v.t.* force upon.

**aufopfern,** *v.t.* sacrifice.

**aufpassen,** *v.t.* fit on. — *v.i.* be watching.

**aufperlen,** *v.i.* bubble up, bubble.

**aufplatzen,** *v.i.* burst, blow up, explode, break open.

**aufprägen,** *v.t.* imprint, impress on, stamp on.

**Aufprall,** *m.* bound, rebound; impact; shock.

**aufprallen,** *v.i.* bound, rebound, strike (on).

**aufpressen,** *v.t.* press on, impress; imprint.

**aufpumpen,** *v.t.* pump up.

**aufputzen,** *v.t.* trim up, clean up, decorate.

**aufquellen,** *v.i.* swell, swell up; well up. — *v.t.* cause to swell, swell; soak, steep.

**Aufquellung,** *f.* swelling, etc. (see aufquellen).

**aufraffen,** *v.t.* rake up, collect.

**aufrahmen,** *v.t.* cream, cream up; stretch.

**aufrauhen,** *v.t.* roughen.

**aufräumen,** *v.t.* clear up, clear away, clear, open. — **aufgeräumt,** *p.a.* in good spirits.

**aufrechnen,** *v.t.* count up, count.

**aufrecht,** *a.* & *adv.* upright, erect.

**Aufrecht(er)haltung,** *f.* maintenance, support.

**aufregen,** *v.t.* excite, stimulate, irritate; agitate, rouse, alarm. — **aufregend,** *p.a.* irritant, stimulant; alarming.

**Aufregungsmittel,** *n.* irritant; stimulant.

**aufreihen,** *v.t.* arrange in a series; file.

**aufreissen,** *v.t.* tear up, tear open; crack, split; design, plot. — *v.i.* crack, split.

**aufreizen,** *v.t.* stimulate, irritate, incite.

**aufrichten,** *v.t.* set up, raise, erect; comfort.

**aufrichtig,** *a.* sincere, genuine.

**Aufriss,** *m.* elevation; sketch, design.

**aufrollen,** *v.t.* roll up; unroll.

**aufrücken,** *v.t.* & *i.* move up, advance.

**Aufruf,** *m.* call, summons.

**aufrühren,** *v.t.* stir, stir up.

**Aufrührer,** *m.* stirrer; agitator, rebel.

**aufrunden,** *v.t.* (*Math.*) round off.

**aufrütteln,** *v.t.* shake up, shake.

**aufsagen,** *v.t.* recite; revoke; give warning.

**aufsammeln,** *v.t.* collect; gather.

**Aufsatz,** *m.* something set on; attachment; fixture; head, headpiece; neck; top; dome; set (of china); essay, treatise, article, paper; (*Dyeing*) topping; (*Calico*) cover print. **-farbe,** *f.* (*Dyeing*) topping color. **-farbstoff,** *m.* topping dye. **-teil,** *m.* supplement (to a periodical).

**aufsäuern,** *v.t.* acidify (again).

**aufsaugbar,** *a.* absorbable.

**Aufsaugbarkeit,** *f.* absorbability.

**Aufsauge-fähigkeit,** *f.* absorptivity. **-flüssigkeit,** *f.* absorbing liquid, absorption liquid.

**aufsaugen,** *v.t.* suck up, absorb; aspirate. — **aufsaugend,** *p.a.* absorbent, absorptive. — **aufsaugendes Mittel,** absorbent.

**Aufsauger,** *m.* absorber.

**Aufsaugung,** *f.* absorption; suction.

**Aufsaugungs-fähigkeit,** *f.* absorptive ability or capacity. **-verfahren,** *n.* absorption process or method. **-vermögen,** *n.* absorptive power. **-wärme,** *f.* heat of absorption.

**aufschärfen,** *v.t.* sharpen; (*Dyeing*) strengthen.

**aufschaukeln,** *v.t.* amplify (waves).

**aufschäumen,** *v.i.* foam up, froth.

**aufschichten,** *v.t.* pile (up), stack; arrange in layers, stratify.

**Aufschichtung,** *f.* piling up; stratification.

**aufschieben,** *v.t.* put off, postpone, suspend; push open; push on.

**Aufschlag,** *m.* impact; percussion; increase, extra (in price or tax); cuff, facing; warp; bound (of a ball); (*Med.*) application.

**Aufschlagebuch,** *n.* reference book.

**aufschlagen,** *v.t.* strike up or open; open, unfold; unbung (casks); handle (hides); set up, erect; raise; apply (as a poultice). — *v.r.* spring up; strike; rise (in price). — *v.i.* strike, impinge.

**Aufschlagzünder,** *m.* percussion fuse; impact detonator.

**aufschlämmen,** *v.t.* suspend, make into a paste, reduce to slime.

**Aufschlämmung,** *f.* suspension; reduction to paste or slime; slime; sludge; paste.

**Aufschlämmverfahren,** *n.* flotation process.

**aufschleifen,** *v.t.* grind on; engrave on.

**aufschlemmen,** *v.* = aufschlämmen.

**Aufschliessarbeit,** *f.* work, task or operation of decomposition.

**aufschliessbar,** *a.* capable of being decomposed, etc. (see aufschliessen).

**aufschliessen,** *v.t.* decompose, open up, convert into nonrefractory form (as silicates by fusion with alkali carbonates); hydrolyze (as starch); break up, disintegrate; solubilize; unlock, open; disclose, explain.

**Aufschliess-maschine,** *f.* (*Ores*) crusher. **-mischung,** *f.* decomposition mixture.

**Aufschliessung,** *f.* decomposition, etc. (see aufschliessen).

**Aufschliessungsvermögen,** *n.* decomposing power (see aufschliessen).

**aufschlitzen,** *v.t.* slit, slash, split, rip.

**Aufschluss,** *m.* decomposition, etc. (see aufschliessen); information, explanation. **-grad,** *m.* degree of decomposition. **-mischung,** *f.* decomposition mixture. **-mittel,** *n.* decomposing agent. **-verfahren,** *n.* decomposition process, disintegration process.

**aufschmelzen,** *v.t.* melt on; fuse on; melt down; melt away; melt open or apart.

**aufschneiden,** *v.t.* cut open, dissect. — *v.i.* brag.

**Aufschnitt,** *m.* cutting open; cut, incision; sliced meat.

**aufschöpfen,** *v.t.* scoop up, dip up.

**aufschraubbar,** *a.* capable of being unscrewed; capable of being screwed on or up.

**aufschrauben,** *v.t.* unscrew; screw on, screw up; turn up (as gas).

**aufschrecken,** *v.t.* startle.

**aufschreiben,** *v.t.* write down, record.

**Aufschrift,** *f.* label, inscription; address.

**aufschrumpfen,** *v.t.* shrink on.

**Aufschub,** *m.* putting off, delay, postponement.

**aufschüren,** *v.t.* stir up, poke up, stoke.

**Aufschüttdichte,** *f.* apparent density.

**aufschütteln,** *v.t.* shake up, shake.

**aufschütten,** *v.t.* put on, pour on; charge; lay up, store up.

**Aufschütt-fass,** *n.* (*Dyeing*) settling vat. **-trichter,** *m.* feed hopper.

**Aufschüttung,** *f.* putting on, pouring on; charging; stoking; storing; dike, bank.

**aufschwefeln,** *v.t.* treat with sulfur, sulfur.

**aufschweissen,** *v.t.* weld on or together.

**aufschwellen,** *v.i.* swell up, tumefy.

**aufschwemmen,** *v.t.* deposit (silt, etc.); float or wash upon; swell up, bloat; soak.

**Aufschwemmung,** *f.* depositing; deposit; suspension; swelling, bloating; soaking.

**Aufschwung,** *m.* rising, rise; advance; growth.

**Aufsehen,** *n.* looking up; sensation.

**Aufseher,** *m.* overseer, inspector, superintendent, foreman.

**aufsetzbar,** *a.* capable of being put on (set up, or drawn up), attachable.

**aufsetzen,** *v.t.* set up, put up, erect; put on; draw up (writings); (*Dyeing*) top; (*Calico*) cover-print. — *v.i.* sit up; mount.

**Aufsetz-gewicht,** *n.* fractional weight. **-kasten,** *m.* (*Dyeing*) jig, jigger.

**Aufsicht,** *f.* inspection; superintendence, supervision, control; top view, (of drawings) plan; (*Dyeing*) underhand appearance, undertone. — **in der —,** in reflected light.

**Aufsichtsfarbe,** *f.* reflected color, surface color.

**aufsieden,** *v.t.* boil; boil again; boil out; blanch (silver). — *v.i.* boil up.

**Aufsieden,** *n.* boiling up, ebullition.

**aufspalten,** *v.t.* split (up), cleave; slit, slot. — *v.i.* split (up); burst.

**Aufspaltung,** *f.* splitting up, cleavage (of compounds); bursting.

**aufspannen,** *v.t.* stretch, spread; tighten, clamp; unfold, spread out.

**aufspeichern,** *v.t.* lay up, store, accumulate.

**Aufspeicherung,** *f.* storage, accumulation.

**aufsperren,** *v.t.* open wide, spread apart.

**aufsplittern,** *v.t. & i.* split up, divide.

**aufsprengen,** *v.t.* blow up, blast; force open.

**aufspriessen,** *v.i.* spring up, sprout, germinate.
**aufspringen,** *v.i.* crack, split; burst open; spring up.
**aufspritzen,** *v.t. & i.* squirt up; spray on.
**aufsprudeln,** *v.i.* boil up, bubble up, effervesce.
**aufspunden, aufspünden,** *v.t.* unbung.
**Aufst.,** *abbrev.* of Aufstellung.
**aufstampfen,** *v.t.* stamp, tamp, ram.
**aufstapeln,** *v.t.* pile, stack, store, store up.
**aufstäuben,** *v.t.* spray on, dust on, atomize on.
**aufstechen,** *v.t.* pick or pierce open puncture, lance; stir up.
**aufsteckbar,** *a.* attachable.
**Aufsteckblende,** *f.* (*Optics*) slip-on diaphragm; lens cover.
**aufstecken,** *v.t.* put (up), set up, stick up; put on, attach.
**Aufsteckglas,** *n.* (*Optics*) slip-on lens.
**aufstehen,** *v.i.* stand up, rise; stand open.
**aufsteigen,** *v.i.* rise, ascend; swell; boil; spit.
**aufstellen,** *v.t.* set up, put up; erect; assemble; install; advance, adduce; draw up; formulate (an equation).
**Aufstellung,** *f.* erection; assembly; arrangement, setup; formulation; statement; curve, graph.
**Aufstieg,** *m.* rise, ascent; swelling up; boiling up.
**aufstobern,** *v.t.* ferret out, discover.
**aufstossen,** *v.i.* ferment anew; become acid (wine); chance (upon). — *v.t.* push up, push open.
**aufstrahlen,** *v.i.* fluoresce; shine, beam.
**Aufstrahler, Aufstrahlstoff,** *m.* fluorescent substance.
**aufstreichen,** *v.t.* spread on, brush on; coat; stain (paper).
**aufstreuen,** *v.t.* sprinkle, strew.
**Aufstreupulver,** *n.* sprinkling powder.
**Aufstrich,** *m.* spreading or brushing on; coat; stain; up stroke; auction.
**aufstützen,** *v.t.* prop, prop up, support.
**aufsuchen,** *v.t.* seek out, search for.
**aufsummen, -summieren,** *v.t. & r.* sum up.
**auftauchen,** *v.i.* emerge, spring up.
**auftauen,** *v.i. & t.* thaw, melt, defrost.
**Auftaupunkt,** *m.* thawing point.
**aufteilen,** *v.t.* distribute, allot.
**Auftrag,** *m.* putting on, coating, coat (of color); order; commission, charge.
**auftragen,** *v.t.* lay on, apply; charge (a furnace); draw, plot, protract; order; serve up.
**aufträufeln, auftraufen,** *v.t.* drop on, pour on drop by drop. — *v.i.* drop, fall in drops.
**Auftreff-.** impact, collision.
**auftreffen,** *v.i.* strike (against), impinge (on).
**auftreiben,** *v.t.* sublime; blow, blow up (glass); distend, inflate; enlarge; drive up; drive on; beat out; procure. — *v.i.* swell; mount up, rise.
**Auftreiber,** *m.* (*Glassblowing*) flanger, reamer.
**Auftreibung,** *f.* sublimation, etc. (see auftreiben); bulge; (*Ceram.*) bubble.
**auftrennen,** *v.t.* sever, rip up, rip open.
**auftreten,** *v.i.* enter, appear, occur, come forth; be evolved; step; proceed.
**Auftreten,** *n.* appearance; occurrence; behavior.
**Auftrieb,** *m.* buoyancy; upward thrust; lift; plankton. **-mittel,** *n.* buoying agent; swelling agent.
**Auftriebskraft,** *f.* buoyant (or buoying) force, lifting force.
**Auftritt,** *m.* entrance, appearance; step; scene.
**auftrocknen,** *v.t.* dry up, dry. — *v.i.* dry up, dry on.
**auftun,** *v.t.* open, disclose. — *v.r.* become visible.
**auftürmen,** *v.t.* heap up, pile up. — *v.r.* tower.
**aufvulkanisieren,** *v.t.* vulcanize (on).
**aufwallen,** *v.i.* bubble up, bubble, boil up, boil.
**Aufwallung,** *f.* bubbling, ebullition, effervescence; (*Metal.*) wildness.
**Aufwand,** *m.* expenditure; expense; display.
**aufwärmen,** *v.t.* warm up, warm (again).
**aufwarten,** *v.t.* wait on, pay respects to.
**aufwärts,** *adv.* upward.
**Aufwärts-bewegung,** *f.* upward motion. **-strömung,** *f.* upward flow. **-transformator,** *m.* (*Elec.*) step-up transformer.
**aufwaschen,** *v.t.* wash, cleanse, scour.
**aufweichen,** *v.t.* moisten, wet, soak; soften; temper (colors). — *v.i.* soak; soften. — **aufweichend,** *p.a.* emollient.
**aufweisen,** *v.t.* show, exhibit, display.
**aufweiten,** *v.t.* widen, stretch, expand.
**aufwenden,** *v.t.* employ, devote, spend.
**Aufwendung,** *f.* employment; expenditure, outlay.
**aufwerfen,** *v.t.* throw up; throw open; throw on, pile up; dig; propose, put.
**aufwickeln,** *v.t.* wind up, wrap up; unwind, unwrap.
**aufwiegen,** *v.t.* counterbalance, compensate.
**aufwischen,** *v.t.* wipe up, wipe off, wipe.
**Aufwuchs,** *m.* growing up; growth.
**aufzählen,** *v.t.* count up, count, enumerate; list, itemize; pay down.
**Aufzählung,** *f.* counting; enumeration; summarization; payment.
**Aufzählungsreihe,** *f.* series of summations; frequency distribution.
**aufzehren,** *v.t.* absorb; eat up, consume.
**Aufzehrgrad,** *m.* (degree of) absorption.
**Aufzehrung,** *f.* absorption; consumption.
**aufzeichnen,** *v.t.* record; draw, trace, plot; note.
**Aufzeichner,** *m.* recorder; tracer, plotter.
**Aufzeichnung,** *f.* record; design; note; item.
**aufziehen,** *v.t.* draw up, raise up; wind up; open; loosen; raise, cultivate; mature;

rouse, agitate (yeast); educate; mount. — *v.i.* appear; (of dyes) go on, become attached, be absorbed.

**Aufzieh-geschwindigkeit,** *f.* (*Dyeing*) absorption rate. **-krücke,** *f.* (*Brewing*) rouser. **-vermögen,** *n.* (*Dyeing*) absorptive power, substantivity.

**aufzischen,** *v.i.* rush up with hissing, fizz.

**Aufzug,** *m.* elevator, crane, hoist; pump; drawing up; parade; act (of a play).

**aufzwingen, aufzwängen,** *v.t.* force on, press on; force open.

**Augapfel,** *m.* eyeball, "apple of the eye." **-bindehaut,** *f.* ocular conjunctiva. **-gefässhaut,** *f.* chorioid membrane, chorioid. **-haut,** *f.* sclerotic coat, sclera.

**Augbolzen,** *m.* eyebolt.

**Auge,** *n.* eye; bubble (in liquids, bread, etc.); luster (on fabrics); (*Bot.*) bud, eye. — **ins — fassen,** have in view; gaze at.

**Augen-.** eye, visual, ocular, optic. **-achat,** *m.* (*Min.*) cat's-eye. **-arzt,** *m.* oculist. **-bindehaut,** *f.* ocular conjunctiva. **-blick,** *m.* moment, instant.

**augenblicklich,** *a.* instantaneous; immediate; momentary, temporary; present. — *adv.* for the moment; at present; instantly.

**Augenblicks-.** instantaneous. **-bild,** *n.* instantaneous photograph, snapshot.

**Augen-bogen,** *m.* iris. **-bolzen,** *m.* eyebolt. **-braue,** *f.* eyebrow. **-deckel,** *m.* eyelid. **-drüse,** *f.* lacrimal gland. **-entzündung,** *f.* inflammation of the eye.

**augenfällig,** *a.* conspicuous, evident.

**Augen-farbe,** *f.* color of the eye(s). **-fehler,** *m.* visual error. **-feld,** *n.* field of vision. **-fleck,** *m.* eyespot. **-flüssigkeit,** *f.* (**glasartige**) vitreous humor; (**wasserartige**) aqueous humor. **-gefässhaut,** *f.* chorioid. **-heilkunde,** *f.* ophthalmology. **-höhle,** *f.* eye socket, orbit.

**Augenhöhlen-.** orbital.

**Augen-hornhaut,** *f.* cornea. **-kammerwasser,** *n.* aqueous humor. **-licht,** *n.* eyesight. **-lid,** *n.* eyelid. **-linse,** *f.* crystalline lens; eye lens, eyepiece. **-marmor,** *m.* eye-spotted marble. **-mass,** *n.* measure by eye. **-merk,** *n.* object in view, aim. **-nerv,** *m.* optic nerve. **-nichts,** *n.* nihil album (zinc oxide). **-pinsel,** *m.* eye brush (a small, soft camel's-hair brush). **-punkt,** *m.* point of sight, visual point. **-ring,** *m.* iris. **-schein,** *m.* appearance; inspection.

**augenscheinlich,** *a.* apparent, evident.

**Augen-schützer,** *m.* protecting spectacles, goggles. **-schwarz,** *n.* retinal pigment. **-stein,** *m.* white vitriol, zinc sulfate; a variety of chalcedony; lacrimal calculus. **-stern,** *m.* pupil (of the eye). **-täuschung,** *f.* optical illusion. **-trost,** *m.* eyebright (*Euphrasia officinalis*). **-wasser,** *n.* eyewater. **-wimper,** *f.* eyelash. **-wurzel, -wurz,** *f.* dandelion; wood anemone; mountain parsley.

**augitartig, augithaltig, augitisch,** *a.* augitic.

**Augitspat,** *m.* (*Min.*) any of several silicates, as acmite, augite, amphibole, wollastonite.

**Aureole,** *f.* aureole; arc flame.

**Auri-.** auric, auri-, gold(III). **-chlorid,** *n.* auric chloride, gold(III) chloride. **-chlorwasserstoffsäure,** *f.* chloroauric acid. **-cyanid,** *n.* auric cyanide, gold(III) cyanide; auricyanide, cyanoaurate(III). **-cyanwasserstoffsäure,** *f.* cyanoauric acid. **-hydroxyd,** *n.* auric hydroxide, gold(III) hydroxide. **-oxyd,** *n.* auric oxide, gold(III) oxide. **-pigment,** *n.* orpiment. **-rhodanwasserstoffsäure,** *f.* aurithiocyanic acid, thiocyanatoauric(III) acid. **-sulfid,** *n.* auric sulfide, gold(III) sulfide. **-verbindung,** *f.* auric compound, gold(III) compound.

**Auro-.** aurous, auro-, gold(I). **-chlorid,** *n.* aurous chloride, gold(I) chloride. **-chlorwasserstoffsäure,** *f.* chloroaurous acid, $HAuCl_2$. **-cyanid,** *n.* aurous cyanide, gold(I) cyanide; aurocyanide, cyanoaurate(I). **-cyanwasserstoffsäure,** *f.* aurocyanic acid, cyanoauric(I) acid. **-kaliumcyanid,** *n.* potassium aurocyanide, potassium cyanoaurate(I). **-oxyd,** *n.* aurous oxide, gold(I) oxide. **-rhodanwasserstoffsäure,** *f.* aurothiocyanic acid. **-verbindung,** *f.* aurous compound, gold(I) compound.

**aus,** *prep.* out of, from, away from. — *adv.* & *prefix.* out, forth; over, done; in front.

**ausarbeiten,** *v.t.* work out, prepare, finish off, finish, perfect, elaborate.

**ausarten,** *v.i.* degenerate; develop (adversely).

**ausäthern,** *v.t.* extract with ether.

**ausatmen,** *v.t.* breathe out, exhale.

**Ausatmungsluft,** *f.* exhaled air.

**ausätzen,** *v.t.* cauterize; destroy by caustics; discharge (colors).

**ausbalancieren,** *v.t.* counterbalance, balance.

**Ausbau,** *m.* completion; development; extension; dismantling, disassembly.

**ausbauchen,** *v.t.* swell, hollow out; emboss. — *v.i.* bulge, swell.

**Ausbauchung,** *f.* bulging, swelling; enlargement, protuberance, bulb.

**ausbauen,** *v.t.* complete; improve; equip; exhaust; dismantle, disassemble.

**ausbedingen,** *v.t.* stipulate, reserve.

**ausbeizen,** *v.t.* remove with corrosive.

**ausbessern,** *v.t.* mend, repair; reline (a furnace); correct.

**Ausbesserungsarbeit,** *f.* repair work.

**ausbeulen,** *v.t.* swell out, round out; flatten.

**Ausbeute,** *f* yield; crop; output; gain, profit.

**ausbeuten,** *v.t.* make the best of, turn to ac-

count; exploit; (*Agric.*) cultivate; (*Mining*) work, win.
**ausbiegen,** *v.t. & i.* turn out, bend out, deflect.
**ausbilden,** *v.t. & i.* form; develop, improve, perfect; educate, train.
**Ausbildung,** *f.* formation, etc. (see ausbilden).
**Ausbiss,** *m.* (*Mining*) outcrop.
**ausbitten,** *v.t.* request, insist upon, invite.
**Ausblase-dampf,** *m.* exhaust steam. **-hahn,** *m.* blow-off cock; drain cock.
**ausblasen,** *v.t.* blow out; blow off; blow out, shut down (a blast furnace); exhaust (steam). — **ausgeblasen,** *p.a.* blown out, etc.; exhaust (steam).
**Ausblaseventil,** *n.* blow-off valve.
**ausblassen,** *v.i.* pale (out), lose color.
**ausbleiben,** *v.i.* be absent; be missing, be omitted, fail to appear or occur.
**Ausbleiben,** *n.* absence, nonappearance, nonoccurrence, nonarrival.
**ausbleichen,** *v.t.* bleach out. — *v.i.* fade.
**Ausbleichung,** *f.* fading; bleaching out, bleaching.
**Ausbleichverfahren,** *n.* bleaching-out process.
**ausbleien,** *v.t.* line with lead.
**ausblenden,** *v.t.* (*Optics*) stop out, stop down; shield (from rays); scatter (rays).
**Ausblendung,** *f.* (*Optics*) stopping out, etc. (see ausblenden).
**Ausblick,** *m.* outlook, prospect.
**ausblühen,** *v.i.* effloresce; cease blooming.
**Ausblühung,** *f.* efflorescence; bloom.
**ausbohren,** *v.t.* bore out, drill.
**Ausbohrung,** *f.* boring out, drilling; bore.
**Ausbrand,** *m.* burning out; thoro combustion.
**ausbraten,** *v.t.* roast out; roast well; heat.
**ausbrechen,** *v.t.* break out, take out; clear (a furnace); work (a lode); quarry (stone); cut off, prune; vomit. — *v.i.* break out, break off; occur.
**ausbreiten,** *v.t. & r.* spread out, spread, extend; flatten; expand; diffuse; floor (grain, etc.); display.
**Ausbreiteprobe,** *f.* (*Metal.*) flattening test, hammering test.
**Ausbreitung,** *f.* spreading out, etc. (see ausbreiten); propagation (of wave motion).
**ausbrennen,** *v.t.* burn out; burn (thoroly); anneal (metals); frit (glass); (*Med.*) cauterize. — *v.i.* burn out; (*Expl.*) blow out.
**ausbringen,** *v.t.* yield, produce; get out, obtain; bring out, take away.
**Ausbruch,** *m.* wine of the first press; outburst, outbreak, explosion, eruption; excavation.
**ausbrühen,** *v.t.* scald, parboil.
**ausbrüten,** *v.t.* incubate.
**ausbuchten,** *v.t., i. & r.* bend out, blow out, bulge.
**ausdampfen,** *v.i.* evaporate; cease steaming.
**ausdämpfen,** *v.t.* steam, clean with steam; evaporate; smoke out.
**Ausdampfung,** *f.* evaporation.
**Ausdauer,** *f.* endurance, continuance, perseverance.
**ausdauernd,** *p.a.* enduring; persevering; (of plants) perennial.
**ausdecken,** *v.t.* cleanse, wash.
**ausdehnbar,** *a.* expansible; extensible, ductile.
**Ausdehnbarkeit,** *f.* expansibility; extensibility.
**ausdehnen,** *v.t., r. & i.* expand; stretch, extend, distend, dilate; spread (gold). — **ausgedehnt,** *p.a.* expanded, etc.; extensive.
**ausdehnsam,** *a.* = ausdehnbar.
**Ausdehnsamkeit,** *f.* = Ausdehnbarkeit.
**Ausdehnung,** *f.* expansion; spread, extent; extension, dilatation, distention; (*Math.*) dimension.
**Ausdehnungs-arbeit,** *f.* work done in expanding. **-koeffizient,** *m.* expansion coefficient. **-messer,** *m.* dilatometer; extensometer. **-vermögen,** *n.* expansibility; extensibility; dilatability. **-zahl,** *f.* expansion coefficient.
**ausdenken,** *v.t.* think out, devise, conceive.
**ausdeuten,** *v.t.* interpret, explain.
**ausdörren,** *v.t.* dry up, desiccate; season (timber).
**ausdrehen,** *v.t.* turn out or off; strip (a screw).
**Ausdruck,** *m.* expression.
**ausdrucken,** *v.t.* finish printing; print in full; use up in printing.
**ausdrücken,** *v.t.* express; press out, squeeze out.
**ausdrücklich,** *a.* express, explicit; intentional. — *adv.* expressly.
**ausdruckslos,** *a.* inexpressive; indefinable.
**Ausdrucksmittel,** *n.* means of expression.
**ausdrucksvoll,** *a.* expressive; impressive, striking.
**ausdünnen,** *v.t.* thin out, thin.
**Ausdunst,** *m.* = Ausdünstung.
**ausdünstbar, ausdunstbar,** *a.* evaporable.
**Ausdünstbarkeit,** *f.* evaporability.
**ausdünsten, ausdunsten,** *v.i.* evaporate; transpire; perspire. — *v.t.* exhale.
**Ausdünstung, Ausdunstung,** *f.* evaporation; exhalation; transpiration; perspiration; emanation, vapor.
**Ausdünstungs-apparat,** *m.* evaporating apparatus. **-messer,** *m.* atmometer, evaporimeter.
**ausegalisieren,** *v.t.* equalize, level up.
**auseinander,** *adv.* apart, asunder, separately. **-bringen,** *v.t.* separate; disarrange. **-fahren,** *v.i.* diverge, go apart; break up. **-fallen,** *v.i.* fall to pieces, crumble. **-falten,** *v.t.* unfold, open out. **-gehen,** *v.i.* fall apart, break up; separate, diverge. **-halten,** *v.t.* keep apart; distinguish. **-nehmen,** *v.t.* take apart, disconnect, dismount, dismantle. **-reissen,** *v.t.* tear apart, disrupt. **-setzen,** *v.t.* explain, set

forth; put or set apart. **-ziehen,** *v.t.* draw apart, spread apart; stretch out.
**ausentwickeln,** *v.t.* develop fully.
**auserkoren,** *p.a.* chosen, selected.
**auserlesen,** *p.a.* select; exquisite.
**ausersehen,** *v.t.* mark out, choose.
**ausexponieren,** *v.t.* expose fully.
**ausfahren,** *v.i.* drive out; go out; break out. — *v.t.* export.
**Ausfall,** *m.* precipitation, precipitate; falling out or off; deficiency, deficit, loss; breakdown, stoppage; result; sortie, attack; (electric) shock.
**Ausfällapparat,** *m.* precipitating apparatus, precipitator.
**ausfällbar,** *a.* precipitable.
**Ausfalleisen,** *n.* off-grade iron.
**ausfallen,** *v.i.* precipitate, deposit; fall or come out; result; be omitted. — **ausfallender Strahl,** emergent ray; reflected ray.
**ausfällen,** *v.t.* precipitate.
**Ausfall-öffnung,** *f.* discharge opening, outlet. **-schmelzung,** *f.* (*Metal.*) off-heat.
**Ausfällung,** *f.* precipitation, deposition.
**Ausfallwinkel,** *m.* angle of reflection or emergence.
**ausfärben,** *v.t.* finish dyeing, dye (completely); extract the color from, exhaust.
**Ausfärbvorrichtung,** *f.* color extractor.
**ausfasern,** *v.t.* & *i.* ravel out, unravel.
**ausfaulen,** *v.i.* rot out; (of sewage) digest.
**ausfertigen,** *v.t.* make out, draw up, make ready, dispatch.
**ausfetten,** *v.t.* deprive of fat or grease, scour (wool).
**ausfeuern,** *v.t.* burn out (casks); warm (a room).
**ausfiltern,** *v.t.* filter out.
**ausfinden,** *v.t.*, **ausfindig machen,** find out, discover, ascertain.
**ausfleischen,** *v.t.* flesh (hides).
**ausflicken,** *v.t.* patch, repair.
**ausfliessen,** *v.i.* flow or issue out; discharge; emanate.
**ausflocken,** *v.i.* separate in flakes or flocks, flocculate.
**Ausflockung,** *f.* separation in flocks, flocculation.
**Ausflucht,** *f.* evasion; subterfuge; flight.
**Ausflug,** *m.* flight; excursion.
**Ausfluss,** *m.* outflow, efflux; effluent; discharge; emanation; secretion; outlet, mouth; result. **-geschwindigkeit,** *f.* velocity of outflow; efflux velocity, rate of discharge. **-hahn,** *m.* outflow cock, discharge cock. **-loch,** *n.*, **-öffnung,** *f.* outlet, exit, discharge opening. **-pipette,** *f.* a pipet calibrated to deliver a definite volume. Cf. Aufnahmepipette. **-rohr,** *n.*, **-röhre,** *f.* outflow tube or pipe, discharge pipe. **-zeit,** *f.* time of outflow or discharge.
**ausfolgen,** *v.t.* deliver up.
**ausformen,** *v.t.* shape out, perfect; form; develop, improve.
**ausforschen,** *v.t.* search out, investigate.
**ausfragen,** *v.t.* question, examine.
**ausfräsen,** *v.t.* countersink; (*Mach.*) shape.
**ausfressen,** *v.t.* corrode (out), eat out.
**ausfrieren,** *v.t.* freeze out; concentrate by freezing; freeze thoroly. — *v.i.* freeze up; deteriorate thru freezing; cease freezing.
**Ausfriertasche,** *f.* cold trap, freezing trap (as for removing moisture).
**Ausfuhr,** *f.* export(ation); elimination.
**ausführbar,** *a.* practicable, feasible; exportable.
**Ausfuhrbewilligung,** *f.* export license.
**ausführen,** *v.t.* carry out, perform, execute; amplify, explain; clean, purge; evacuate; excrete; export; lead out; erect; (*Metal.*) assay.
**Ausführgang,** *m.* excretory duct.
**Ausfuhrhandel,** *m.* export trade
**ausführlich,** *a.* full, complete, detailed. — *adv.* in full, *in extenso*, amply.
**Ausführung,** *f.* carrying out, etc. (see ausführen); excretion; model, pattern, specimen; detailed statement; construction, make, style, finish.
**Ausführungs-gang,** *m.* excretory duct. **-mittel,** *n.* purgative. **-rohr,** *n.*, **-röhre,** *f.* discharge pipe or tube, outlet pipe or tube.
**Ausfuhrzoll,** *m.* export duty.
**ausfüllen,** *v.t.* fill, fill up, fill out; empty.
**Ausfüllmasse, Ausfüllungsmasse,** *f.* filling; packing; stuffing.
**Ausfüllstoff,** *m.* filling or packing material.
**ausfuttern, ausfüttern,** *v.t.* line; coat; feed, fatten.
**Ausfütterung,** *f.* lining.
**ausg.,** *abbrev.* (ausgegeben) published, issued, produced.
**Ausgabe,** *f.* expense, expenditure; edition; issue; distribution.
**ausgähren,** *v.i.* = ausgären.
**Ausgang,** *m.* starting out, going out, departure; outlet, egress; ending, end; outcome, result; exportation.
**Ausgangs-.** starting, initial; outlet; export. **-basis,** *f.* starting point. **-erzeugnis,** *n.* starting product, initial product. **-gestein,** *n.* parent rock. **-gleichung,** *f.* initial equation, starting equation. **-lösung,** *f.* initial solution, original solution, parent solution. **-material,** *n.* initial material, starting material, base material, raw material. **-niveau,** *n.* initial level. **-produkt,** *n.* starting product, initial product; raw product. **-punkt,** *m.* starting point, origin. **-rohr,** *n.*, **-röhre,** *f.* outlet pipe or tube, waste pipe, eduction pipe. **-spannung,** *f.* (*Elec.*) output voltage. **-stellung,** *f.*

initial position. **-stoff,** *m.* initial substance or material, starting material, parent material, primary material; raw material. **-zustand,** *m.* initial state or condition.

**ausgären,** *v.i.* ferment sufficiently; cease fermenting; rise (from fermentation). — *v.t.* throw off (by fermentation); weld (steel).

**Ausgarzeit,** *f.* (*Steel*) quiescent period.

**ausgeartet,** *p.a.* (from ausarten) degenerate.

**ausgeben,** *v.t.* yield, produce; give out; spend; publish; issue. — *v.i.* (of slaking lime) swell.

**ausgeblasen,** *p.a.* see ausblasen.

**ausgedehnt,** *p.a.* see ausdehnen.

**ausgeglichen,** *p.p.* of ausgleichen.

**Ausgeglichenheit,** *f.* compensated state.

**ausgehen,** *v.i.* go out; proceed, emanate; come off or out, fade; fail; stop; (*Baking*) ferment; (*Mining*) crop out. — **ausgehend,** *p.a.* outgoing; export.

**ausgekocht,** *p.a.* see auskochen.

**ausgelassen,** *p.a.* see auslassen.

**ausgemacht,** *p.a.* see ausmachen.

**ausgenommen,** *prep.* except.

**ausgeprägt,** *p.a.* marked, decided.

**ausgerben,** *v.t.* tan fully; weld (steel).

**ausgeschieden,** *p.p.* of ausscheiden.

**ausgeschlossen,** *p.a.* see ausschliessen.

**ausgeschmolzen,** *p.p.* of ausschmelzen.

**ausgesprochen,** *p.a.* see aussprechen.

**ausgestalten,** *v.t.* work out, develop; shape, model; fit out, equip.

**Ausgestaltung,** *f.* working out, development; conformation; equipment.

**ausgesucht,** *p.a.* see aussuchen.

**ausgewachsen,** *p.a.* see auswachsen.

**ausgewogen,** *p.p.* of auswägen.

**ausgezackt, ausgezahnt,** *a.* jagged, serrated, indented, notched.

**ausgezeichnet,** *p.a.* see auszeichnen.

**ausgezogen,** *p.a.* see ausziehen.

**ausgiebig,** *a.* productive, fertile, abundant; (of a dye) strong.

**Ausgiebigkeit,** *f.* productiveness, fertility, abundance; (of a dye) yield, strength; (of paint, etc.) spreading or covering power.

**ausgiessen,** *v.t.* pour out, run out; discharge; fill up by pouring; put out (fire); stereotype.

**Ausgiessung,** *f.* effusion; pouring out, etc. (see ausgiessen).

**ausgischen,** *v.i.* cease frothing.

**ausglätten,** *v.t.* smooth out, smooth.

**Ausgleich,** *m.* = Ausgleichung.

**ausgleichen,** *v.t.* equalize, adjust; compensate; balance; level; settle. — **ausgleichende Farbe,** compensation or complementary color.

**Ausgleicher,** *m.* equalizer, compensator.

**Ausgleich(s)-filter,** *n.* balanced filter; (*Photog.*) equalizing filter. **-gewicht,** *n.* counterweight. **-grube,** *f.* (*Metal.*) soaking pit. **-punkt,** *m.* equalization point. **-rechnung,** *f.* calculation to adjust for errors, specif. method of least squares. **-spannung,** *f.* (*Elec.*) compensating voltage.

**Ausgleichung,** *f.* equalization, etc. (see ausgleichen); equilibrium.

**Ausgleichungsstrom,** *m.*, **-strömung,** *f.* compensating (or equalizing) current.

**ausgleiten,** *v.i.* slip; glide out.

**ausglühen,** *v.t.* glow (thoroly), ignite; anneal; calcine; roast. — *v.i.* cease glowing; burn out.

**Ausglühtopf,** *m.* (*Glass*) annealing pot.

**Ausglühung,** *f.* glowing, etc. (see ausglühen).

**ausgraben,** *v.t.* dig out, dig, excavate, exhume; engrave.

**Ausguss,** *m.* lip; spout; outlet, drain, sink; pouring out, delivery; casting; effusion; stereo(type). **-leitung,** *f.* outlet piping, discharge piping. **-masse,** *f.* casting composition, filling compound. **-mörser,** *m.* lipped mortar. **-pfanne,** *f.* mold (for ingots). **-rinne,** *f.* pouring spout. **-röhre,** *f.* drain tube or pipe, waste pipe; delivery pipe. **-schnauze,** *f.* pouring spout or lip; nozzle. **-ventil,** *n.* discharge valve; escape valve. **-wasser,** *n.* waste water.

**aushalten,** *v.t.* endure, stand; (*Mining*) pick out, sort. — *v.i.* hold out, last.

**aushämmern,** *v.t.* hammer out, beat out.

**aushändigen,** *v.t.* hand over.

**Aushang,** *m.* placard, poster.

**Aushängeschild,** *n.* signboard, sign.

**ausharren,** *v.i.* persist; persevere. — **ausharrend,** *p.a.* persistent.

**aushärten,** *v.t.* harden; (*Metal.*) temper.

**Aushärten,** *n.* (*Metal.*) age hardening.

**ausharzen,** *v.i.* exude resinous matter; (*Leather*) spew.

**aushauchen,** *v.t. & i.* breathe out, exhale.

**Aushauchung,** *f.* exhalation.

**ausheben,** *v.t.* draw out, lift out, select; levy; dislocate.

**aushebern,** *v.t.* siphon out.

**aushecken,** *v.t.* hatch.

**ausheizen,** *v.t.* heat (thoroly); anneal.

**aushelfen,** *v.i. with dative.* help out, assist.

**Aushilfe,** *f.* help, assistance; stand-by, reserve, spare.

**Aushilfs-.** supplementary, auxiliary, emergency. **-mittel,** *n.* expedient, supplement.

**aushilfsweise,** *adv.* temporarily, as an expedient, in an emergency.

**aushöhlen,** *v.t.* hollow out, excavate.

**aushülsen,** *v.t.* husk, hull, shell, peel.

**auskalten,** *v.t. & i.* cool (thoroly), chill.

**auskehlen,** *v.t.* channel, groove, flute.

**auskeilen,** *v.i. & r.* taper off, thin out, pinch out.

**auskeimen,** *v.i.* germinate; cease germinating.

**auskellen,** *v.t.* ladle out.

**auskippen,** *v.t.* dump out, pour out.
**auskitten,** *v.t.* fill with cement, cement.
**ausklappbar,** *a.* (capable of) swinging out.
**auskleiden,** *v.t.* coat, line (as an oven); cover; disguise; undress, strip.
**Auskleidung,** *f.* coating, covering, lining; disguise.
**ausklingen,** *v.i.* die away. — *v.t.* release, disengage.
**ausklinken,** *v.t.* release, disengage, unlock.
**auskoagulieren,** *v.t.* coagulate.
**auskochen,** *v.t.* boil out, boil, decoct; extract by boiling; clean by boiling, scour, buck. — *v.i.* boil out, over or away; (*Expl.*) blow out. — **ausgekocht,** *p.a.* extracted, etc.; spent (hops). — **auskochender Sprengschuss,** blown-out shot.
**Auskocher,** *m.* boiler; bucking keir.
**Auskochung,** *f.* boiling out, etc. (see auskochen); decoction.
**Auskohlbad,** *n.* carbonizing bath.
**auskohlen,** *v.t.* carbonize (as wool).
**Auskohlung,** *f.* carbonization.
**Auskohlungsverfahren,** *n.* carbonizing process.
**auskommen,** *v.i.* come out, get out; manage, get on.
**auskopieren,** *v.t.* copy (out); (*Photog.*) print out.
**Auskopierpapier,** *n.* (*Photog.*) printing-out paper.
**auskörnen,** *v.t.* free from grains; thresh (grain); gin (cotton).
**auskratzen,** *v.t.* scratch out, scrape out, rake out; erase.
**auskristallisieren,** *v.t.* & *i.* crystallize out, crystallize.
**Auskristallisierung,** *f.* crystallization.
**auskrücken,** *v.t.* rake out.
**auskrystallisieren.** = auskristallisieren.
**auskühlen,** *v.i.* cool thoroly.
**Auskunft,** *f.* information; report; resource.
**Auskunfts-buch,** *n.* information book. **-mittel,** *n.* expedient, resort.
**auskuppeln,** *v.t.* disconnect, disengage.
**ausl.,** *abbrev.* (ausländisch) foreign.
**ausladen,** *v.t.* unload, discharge.
**Ausladung,** *f.* unloading, discharge; reach, range (of a crane); overhang.
**Auslage,** *f.* outlay, expense; display; show window.
**Ausland,** *n.* foreign country. — **im —, ins —, nach dem —,** abroad.
**Ausländer,** *m.* foreigner, alien.
**ausländisch,** *a.* foreign, alien; exotic.
**Auslass,** *m.* outlet, vent; exhaust; delivery; discharge.
**auslassen,** *v.t.* let out, emit, discharge; exhaust (steam); melt, render; leave out. — *v.r.* express oneself. — **ausgelassen,** *p.a.* let out, etc.; extravagant, wanton.
**Auslass-röhre,** *f.* outlet tube or pipe, discharge pipe. **-ventil,** *n.* escape valve, delivery valve.
**Auslauf,** *m.* outlet, mouth; running out; outflow, discharge; leaking, leak; outrun, outspread; start; projection.
**auslaufen,** *v.i.* run out; leak out, leak; blot; (of colors) run, bleed; project; wear out, play out; stop running; set out.
**Ausläufer,** *m.* runner; offshoot, branch; process; (*Bot.*) stolon; (*Spect.*) attendant line, satellite.
**Auslauf-flasche,** *f.* overflow flask. **-pipette,** *f.* delivery pipet(te). **-probe,** *f.* (*Metal.,* etc.) pouring test. **-rohr,** *n.*, **röhre,** *f.* outlet tube (or pipe), discharge tube (or pipe). **-spitze,** *f.* discharge tip (as of a buret). **-zeit,** *f.* time of outflow.
**Auslauge-.** lixiviating, leaching, extraction. **-behälter,** *m.* lixiviating tank. **-hülse,** *f.* extraction thimble. **-kasten,** *m.* lixiviating vat, leaching vat.
**auslaugen,** *v.t.* leach out, leach, lixiviate, extract; wash out, wash; steep or wash in lye, buck; (*Sugar*) diffuse.
**Auslauger,** *m.* leacher, extracter.
**Auslaugerei,** *f.* leaching out, lixiviation; **leaching** plant.
**Auslaugetrichter,** *m.* extraction funnel.
**Auslaugung,** *f.* leaching out, etc. (see auslaugen.)
**ausleeren,** *v.t.* empty out, empty, evacuate, drain; purge.
**Ausleerungsmittel,** *n.* (*Med.*) evacuant, esp. a purgative.
**auslegen,** *v.t.* lay out; exhibit; inlay, veneer; line, coat; interpret; explain.
**Ausleger,** *m.* (*Mach.*) arm, bracket, jib, (crane) beam.
**auslenken,** *v.t.* deflect.
**Auslenkhärte,** *f.* deflection hardness.
**Auslese,** *f.* selection; choice wine. **-fähigkeit,** *f.* selectivity.
**auslesen,** *v.t.* pick out, select, sort; read thru.
**Ausleser,** *m.* selecter, sorter, separator.
**ausleuchten,** *v.t.* extinguish; illuminate. — *v.i.* & *r.* cease giving light.
**Ausleuchtung,** *f.* extinguishment, extinction; illumination.
**Auslieferung,** *f.* delivery, giving up.
**auslöffeln,** *v.t.* spoon out, ladle out.
**auslösbar,** *a.* capable of being dissolved out, etc. (see auslösen).
**auslöschen,** *v.t.* extinguish; blot out, wipe out.
**Auslöschung,** *f.* extinction, extinguishment.
**auslösen,** *v.t.* dissolve out; release; liberate; give off, emit; loosen; relieve; uncouple, disengage.
**Auslösung,** *f.* dissolving out, etc. (see auslösen); release (of a balance).
**auslüften,** *v.t.* ventilate, air.

**ausmachen,** *v.t.* take out, put out; shell; gut; end, settle; find out; matter, amount to; constitute. — **ausmachend,** *p.a.* constituent, essential. — **ausgemacht,** *p.a.* certain; thoro.

**ausmahlen,** *v.t.* grind up, grind (thoroly).

**ausmalen,** *v.t.* paint, color; describe.

**Ausmass,** *m.* delivery; measure; extent; over-all dimension.

**ausmauern,** *v.t.* (*Masonry*) line, wall.

**ausmergeln,** *v.t.* exhaust.

**ausmerzen,** *v.t.* pick out, sort out, eliminate, reject.

**ausmessen,** *v.t.* measure out, gage.

**ausmitteln,** *v.t.* ascertain; approximate.

**ausmittig,** *a.* eccentric.

**ausmultiplizieren,** *v.t.* multiply out.

**Ausmündung,** *f.* orifice, outlet, mouth.

**Ausnahme,** *f.* exception.

**ausnahmelos, ausnahmslos,** *a.* without exception.

**ausnahmsweise,** *adv.* exceptionally.

**ausnehmen,** *v.t.* take out, draw; except, exclude; choose. — *v.r.* look, appear. — **ausnehmend,** *p.a.* exceptional, uncommon, exceeding. — *adv.* exceedingly.

**ausnutzbar,** *a.* exhaustible; utilizable.

**ausnutzen,** *v.t.* use up, exhaust, work out; utilize, make the most of, turn to profit.

**Ausnutzung,** *f.* using up, etc. (see ausnutzen); efficiency.

**Ausnutzungskoeffizient,** *m.* utilization coefficient.

**ausölen,** *v.t.* oil.

**auspacken,** *v.t.* unpack.

**auspflanzen,** *v.t.* transplant.

**ausphotometrieren,** *v.t.* investigate photometrically.

**auspichen,** *v.t.* pitch.

**auspinseln,** *v.t.* paint; brush out; paint out.

**ausplatten,** *v.t.* flatten out, hammer flat; pave with slabs or tiles.

**auspressen,** *v.t.* press out, press, express; squeeze; force (out).

**ausproben, ausprobieren,** *v.t.* try, try out, test (thoroly).

**Auspuff,** *m.* (*Mach.*) exhaust, escape. **-dampf,** *m.* exhaust steam; exhaust vapor. **-gas,** *n.* exhaust gas, burnt gas. **-hub,** *m.* exhaust stroke. **-rohr,** *n.*, **-röhre,** *f.* exhaust pipe. **-ventil,** *n.* exhaust valve.

**auspumpen,** *v.t.* pump out, exhaust.

**ausputzen,** *v.t.* clean out, clean, polish; dress out.

**ausquetschen,** *v.t.* squeeze out, crush out, wring out.

**ausradieren,** *v.t.* erase.

**ausräuchern,** *v.t.* fumigate; smoke, smoke out.

**Ausräucherung,** *f.* fumigation; smoking.

**ausräumen,** *v.t.* clear out, clean out, remove.

**ausrechnen,** *v.t.* calculate, compute.

**Ausrede,** *f.* evasion, excuse; utterance.

**ausreden,** *v.t.* utter; dissuade. — *v.i.* finish speaking. — *v.r.* excuse oneself.

**ausreiben,** *v.t.* rub out, scrape, scour, cleanse.

**ausreichen,** *v.i.* suffice. — *v.t.* seize. — **ausreichend,** *p.a.* sufficient, adequate.

**ausreichern,** *v.t.* enrich, strengthen.

**ausreifen,** *v.i.* ripen, mature.

**ausreinigen,** *v.t.* clean out, clean thoroly, purge.

**ausreissen,** *v.t.* pull out, tear out. — *v.i.* run away.

**ausrenken,** *v.t.* sprain; dislocate.

**ausrichten,** *v.t.* straighten; align; orient; adjust; give; perform, do; (*Mining*) discover, explore.

**Ausrichtung,** *f.* straightening, etc. (see ausrichten).

**ausringen,** *v.t.* wring out, squeeze out.

**ausrotten,** *v.t.* root up, exterminate.

**ausrücken,** *v.t.* disengage, ungear. — *v.i.* march out.

**Ausrücker,** *m.* disengaging gear.

**ausrufen,** *v.t. & i.* cry out, call out.

**Ausrufung,** *f.* crying out, exclamation; proclamation.

**ausrunden, ausründen,** *v.t.* round off; hollow out.

**ausrüsten,** *v.t.* fit out, equip, supply; finish (cloth).

**Ausrüstung,** *f.* equipment, outfit; finish.

**Aussaat,** *f.* sowing; inoculation; seed.

**aussäen,** *v.t.* seed, inoculate (with crystals); disseminate.

**Aussage,** *f.* statement, assertion, declaration.

**aussagen,** *v.t.* express, assert, affirm, state; indicate; testify, depose.

**aussaigern,** *v.t.* = ausseigern.

**aussalzbar,** *a.* capable of being salted out.

**aussalzen,** *v.t.* salt out, separate by addition of salt; (*Soap*) grain.

**Aussalzung,** *f.* salting out; (*Soap*) graining.

**Aussatz,** *m.* display (of wares); leprosy; scurf.

**aussäuern,** *v.t.* deprive of acid, deacidify; treat with acid.

**aussaugen,** *v.t.* suck out, suck dry, drain, exhaust.

**Aussaugpumpe,** *f.* suction pump (for gases), vacuum pump.

**ausschaltbar,** *a.* capable of being cut out or switched off.

**ausschalten,** *v.t.* cut out, switch out or off, disengage; take out, remove, eliminate, exclude.

**Ausschalter,** *m.* (*Elec.*) cut-out, circuit breaker.

**Ausschaltstellung,** *f.* "off" position.

**Ausschank,** *m.* retailing (of liquor); public house.

**ausschärfen,** *v.t.* neutralize, deaden, dull (colors); bevel; (*Dyeing*) sharpen, strengthen.

**ausschaufeln,** *v.t.* shovel out, scoop out.
**ausscheiden,** *v.t.* separate; set free, liberate, eliminate, precipitate, extract; secrete, excrete; sort out, sort. — *v.r.* separate (out), precipitate, deposit. — *v.i.* withdraw, retire.
**Ausscheidung,** *f.* separation, etc. (see ausscheiden); separated material.
**Ausscheidungs-mittel,** *n.* separating agent; precipitant. **-produkt,** *n.* separation product; by-product. **-punkt,** *m.* separation point; precipitation point.
**ausschenken,** *v.t.* pour out; sell (liquors) by retail.
**ausschiessen,** *v.t.* cast out, reject; discharge; shoot out. — *v.i.* shoot up.
**ausschirren,** *v.t.* ungear; unharness.
**ausschl.,** *abbrev.* (ausschliesslich) exclusive(ly).
**ausschlacken,** *v.t.* clear of dross or slag.
**Ausschlag,** *m.* throwing out, removal; throw, deflection (as of a galvanometer); amplitude (of vibration); exudation, scum, efflorescence; sprout, shoot; breaking out, eruption; rash; lining, trimming; turning of the scale, result; (*Brewing*) run of wort from the kettle. **-bütte,** *f.* (*Brewing*) underback. **-eisen,** *n.* punch; piercer; tool for pounding ore.
**ausschlagen,** *v.t.* knock, throw, or punch out, remove; express (oils, etc.); turn out (wort) from the kettle; flatten, planish; line, cover, coat; stretch; refuse. — *v.i.* break out; effloresce; (of a balance beam) turn; bud; sprout; strike out; turn out, prove; (*Leather*) spew.
**ausschlaggebend,** *a.* decisive, determining.
**Ausschlag-winkel,** *m.* angle of deflection. **-würze,** *f.* finished wort.
**ausschlämmen,** *v.t.* wash out, cleanse (from slime).
**ausschleifen,** *v.t.* grind, whet; (*Soap*) grain.
**Ausschleudermaschine,** *f.* centrifuse.
**ausschleudern,** *v.t.* expel by centrifugal force, centrifuge, spin out; (in atomic disintegration) eject, expel, emit; hydro-extract (yarns, etc.).
**ausschliessen,** *v.t.* shut out, exclude; except. — **ausgeschlossen,** *p.a.* out of the question.
**ausschliesslich,** *a.* exclusive; exceptional. — *prep.* exclusive of, except.
**Ausschliessungsprinzip,** *n.* exclusion principle.
**Ausschluss,** *m.* exclusion; exception.
**ausschmelzen,** *v.t.* melt out, render; (of metals) liquate; melt, fuse; purify by melting. — *v.i.* melt out; cease melting.
**Ausschmelzung,** *f.* melting out, etc. (see ausschmelzen).
**ausschmieren,** *v.t.* smear; copy; cheat.
**ausschneiden,** *v.t.* cut out, excise; prune; retail.
**Ausschnitt,** *m.* cutting out, cut; notch; hole (cut out), opening; sector; retail.
**ausschöpfen,** *v.t.* scoop out, ladle out; drain.
**Ausschöpfkelle,** *f.* ladle; scoop.
**ausschrauben,** *v.t.* screw out, unscrew.
**ausschreiben,** *v.t.* write out, write in full; copy; announce; summon; appoint, impose.
**Ausschreitung,** *f.* excess.
**Ausschuss,** *m.* refuse, scrap, waste; (*Paper*) broke; culls; committee; shooting out, emission.
**ausschütteln,** *v.t.* shake out, shake, agitate; extract by shaking.
**ausschütten,** *v.t.* pour out, dump out.
**ausschwefeln,** *v.t.* fumigate with sulfur.
**ausschweifend,** *p.a.* excessive; dissolute.
**ausschweissen,** *v.t.* weld out, cleanse (iron) by welding; bleed.
**ausschwemmen,** *v.t.* wash out, flush; rinse.
**ausschwenken,** *v.t.* whirl, centrifuge, hydroextract.
**Ausschwenkmaschine,** *f.* centrifugal, hydroextractor.
**ausschwingen,** *v.i.* swing out; cease swinging; (of oscillations) die out, decay. — *v.t.* swing out.
**Ausschwing-maschine,** *f.* centrifuge. **-stɩom,** *m.* decay current.
**ausschwirren,** *v.t.* whiz, centrifuge, hydro-extract.
**ausschwitzen,** *v.t.* & *i.* exude; sweat.
**Ausschwitzung,** *f.* exudation; sweating; sweat.
**aussedimentieren,** *v.i.* deposit sediment.
**aussehen,** *v.i.* look, appear; look out.
**Aussehen,** *n.* appearance, look, aspect.
**ausseigern,** *v.t.* liquate, separate by liquation.
**Ausseigerung,** *f.* liquation, eliquation.
**aussen,** *adv.* out, outside, outward; abroad.
**Aussen-.** outside, external, exterior, outer. **-anstrich,** *m.* exterior painting.
**aussenden,** *v.t.* emit, send out.
**Aussen-druck,** *m.* external pressure. **-drüse,** *f.* external gland.
**Aussendung,** *f.* emitting, emission, sending out.
**Aussen-durchmesser,** *m.* outside diameter. **-elektron,** *n.* outer electron. **-fläche,** *f.* outer surface. **-handel,** *m.* foreign trade. **-haut,** *f.* outer skin or membrane. **-korrosion,** *f.* external corrosion. **-iack,** *m.* outside varnish. **-leitung,** *f.* outside line or supply; (*Brewing & Elec.*) outer circuit. **-luft,** *f.* external air, atmosphere. **-lunker,** *n.* (*Metal.*) surface cavity. **-mass,** *n.* outside measurement.
**aussenmittig,** *a.* off-center, eccentric.
**Aussen-rinde,** *f.* (*Bot.*) outer bark, periderm. **-schicht,** *f.* outer layer. **-seite,** *f.* outer side, outside. **-taster,** *m.* outside calipers. **-wand,** *f.* outer wall, outside wall. **-welt,** *f.* external world.
**ausser,** *prep.* out of, outside of; except; besides, in addition to. — *conȷ.* except, unless.

**äusser,** *a.* outer, outward, exterior, external.

**ausser-achsig,** *a.* eccentric. **-achtlassen,** *v.t.* leave out of consideration, disregard.

**Ausserbetriebsetzung,** *f.* shutting down, putting out of operation.

**ausserdem,** *adv.* besides, moreover.

**Äussere, Äusseres,** *n.* exterior, outside; external appearance.

**aussergewöhnlich,** *a.* extraordinary, unusual.

**ausserhalb,** *adv. & prep.* outside, beyond.

**ausserirdisch,** *a.* extraterrestrial.

**äusserlich,** *a.* outer, outward, external, exterior; apparent; superficial; extrinsic. — *adv.* outwardly, apparently.

**aussermittig,** *a.* eccentric.

**äussern,** *v.t.* utter, express, manifest.

**ausserordentlich,** *a.* extraordinary, unusual. — *adv.* exceedingly, unusually.

**äusserst,** *a.* utmost, extreme; outmost. — *adv.* extremely, utterly.

**Äusserung,** *f.* manifestation, expression, utterance.

**ausserwesentlich,** *a.* nonessential.

**aussetzen,** *v.t.* set out, put out, expose; suspend, put off, postpone; line, face; censure. — *v.i.* crop out; stop, pause. — **aussetzend,** *p.a.* intermittent, discontinuous.

**Aussetzung,** *f.* setting out, etc. (see aussetzen); intermission.

**Aussicht,** *f.* outlook, view, prospect, chance. — **in — nehmen,** contemplate.

**aussichts-los,** *a.* hopeless. **-reich,** *a.* promising.

**aussickern,** *v.i.* trickle (or ooze) out, percolate; cease trickling.

**aussieben,** *v.t.* screen (out), sieve (out), filter (out).

**aussieden,** *v.t.* boil out, boil; blanch (silver).

**aussinnen,** *v.t.* contrive, invent.

**aussintern,** *v.i.* trickle out, ooze out.

**aussoggen,** *v.t. & i.* = soggen.

**aussöhnen,** *v.t.* reconcile; expiate.

**aussondern,** *v.t.* separate; secrete, excrete; sort; reject.

**aussortieren,** *v.t.* sort (out), pick out.

**ausspannen,** *v.t.* stretch, spread, extend; tenter; slacken; relax; unharness; carry off.

**Aussparung,** *f.* opening; clearance; saving (up).

**Aussprache,** *f.* pronunciation; discussion.

**aussprechen,** *v.t.* pronounce; express, declare; speak out. — **ausgesprochen,** *p.a.* pronounced, decided, outspoken.

**aussprengen,** *v.t.* blast; sprinkle (water); noise abroad.

**ausspringen,** *v.i.* spring out, spring off, fly off, crack; project. — **ausspringend,** *p.a.* salient.

**ausspritzen,** *v.t.* spurt out, squirt out; wash by squirting; inject.

**Ausspruch,** *m.* utterance, saying; decision.

**aussprühen,** *v.t.* throw out, eject, emit. — *v.i.* be thrown out, dart out, fly out.

**Aussprungswinkel,** *m.* angle of reflection.

**ausspülen,** *v.t.* wash out, wash, rinse out, rinse; flush.

**ausstaffieren,** *v.t.* furnish, provide, equip.

**ausstampfen,** *v.t.* stamp (out), ram, beat (out).

**Ausstand,** *m.* strike; (*pl.*) arrears.

**ausständig,** *a.* outstanding; wanting.

**ausstatten,** *v.t.* furnish, supply; get up, fit out; endow.

**Ausstattung,** *f.* fitting, equipment, outfit; setting; get-up; dowry.

**ausstäuben,** *v.t.* dust, winnow.

**ausstechen,** *v.t.* dig out, cut out, pierce; engrave.

**ausstehen,** *v.t.* stand, endure. — *v.i.* stand out; be owing; strike.

**aussteifen,** *v.t.* stiffen, stay, reinforce.

**ausstellen,** *v.t.* put out; lay out, exhibit; draw up; censure.

**Aussteller,** *m.* exhibitor; drawer, giver (of a bill, etc.), undersigner.

**Ausstellung,** *f.* putting out; exhibition, show; display; censure.

**Ausstellungsglas,** *n.* display glass, specimen jar (or tube).

**Aussteuerung,** *f.* equipment, provision, supply (as of energy).

**Ausstich,** *m.* choicest wine.

**ausstöpfeln,** *v.t.* unstopper, unstop, unplug.

**ausstopfen,** *v.t.* stuff; stop up, plug up.

**Ausstoss,** *m.* expulsion, etc. (see ausstossen); retailing (of liquors); (*Brewing*) output.

**ausstossen,** *v.t.* throw out, thrust out; expel, eject, extrude, eliminate, discharge, emit; flesh (hides); utter. — *v.i.* burst forth; froth out; (of liquids) work out.

**Ausstoss-ladung,** *f.* bursting charge. **-system,** *n.* (*Brewing*) cleansing system.

**Ausstossung,** *f.* expulsion, etc. (see ausstossen).

**Ausstrahl,** *m.* emission.

**ausstrahlen,** *v.t. & i.* radiate, emit or be emitted. — **ausstrahlend,** *p.a.* radiant.

**Ausstrahlung,** *f.* radiation; emission.

**Ausstrahlungs-fläche,** *f.* radiation surface. **-verlust,** *m.* radiation loss. **-vermögen,** *n.* radiating power, emissivity.

**ausstrecken,** *v.t.* stretch, spread, extend.

**ausstreichen,** *v.t.* strike out, erase; smooth out, level; spread out, smear. — *v.i.* crop out.

**Ausstrich,** *m.* striking out, etc. (see austreichen); smear; streak; (*Mining*) stream tin. **-präparat,** *n.* smear preparation.

**ausströmen,** *v.i.* emanate, escape, stream out, flow out.

**Ausströmung,** *f.* emanation, effusion, escape, outflow, efflux, effluence, flow.

**Ausströmungsrohr,** *n.* delivery pipe or tube.

**Ausstülpung,** *f.* protuberance; protrusion.
**ausstürzen,** *v.t.* pour out, empty, discharge.
**aussuchen,** *v.t.* search out, select, choose, sort. — **ausgesucht,** *p.a.* picked, select.
**Aussucher,** *m.* sorter.
**aussüssen,** *v.t.* wash (a precipitate), edulcorate; sweeten; (*Brewing*) sparge.
**Aussüss-glas,** *n.* wash bottle (for washing precipitates). **-pumpe,** *f.* leaching pump. **-rohr,** *n.*, **-röhre,** *f.* washing tube. **-vorrichtung,** *f.* wash bottle (for precipitates); sparger.
**austarieren,** *v.t.* tare.
**austauchen,** *v.i.* emerge; appear.
**Austausch,** *m.* exchange, interchange; (*Biol.*) crossing over, crossover; barter. **-azidität,** *f.* exchange acidity.
**austauschbar,** *a.* exchangeable, interchangeable.
**Austauschbarkeit,** *f.* exchangeability, interchangeability.
**austauschen,** *v.t.* exchange, interchange; barter.
**Austauschreaktion,** *f.* exchange reaction.
**austauschsauer,** *a.* (rendered) acid by exchange of ions.
**Austausch-stoff,** *m.* substitute. **-werkstoff,** *m.* substitute material.
**austeeren,** *v.t.* tar.
**austeilen,** *v.t.* distribute.
**austenitisch,** *a.* (*Metal.*) austenitic.
**Auster,** *f.* oyster.
**Austernschale,** *f.* oyster shell.
**austilgen,** *v.t.* destroy, efface, obliterate.
**Austonen,** *n.* change in (color) tone.
**Aust. P.,** *abbrev.* (australisches Patent) Australian patent.
**Austrag,** *m.* decision, issue; discharge.
**austragen,** *v.t.* deliver; discharge; distribute; carry out; wear out; decide; report. — *v.i.* amount; cease bearing.
**Austragsöffnung,** *f.* discharge opening.
**Australien,** *n.* Australia.
**australisch,** *a.* Australian.
**austreibbar,** *a.* capable of being driven out or expelled.
**austreiben,** *v.t.* expel, drive out, drive off; separate, set free; eject.
**Austreibung,** *f.* expulsion, etc. (see austreiben).
**austreten,** *v.i.* step out, go out, pass out, issue; leave, retire; project; (*Optics*) emerge; (*Physiol.*) extravasate. — **austretend,** *p.a.* (*Optics*) emergent.
**Austritt,** *m.* stepping out, etc. (see austreten); outlet, exit; escape; efflux; effusion (of blood); emergence (of rays); landing, balcony, antechamber.
**Austritts-arbeit,** *f.* (of electrons) work function. **-geschwindigkeit,** *f.* velocity of exit or discharge; rate of escape. **-öffnung,** *f.* outlet, exit; discharge opening; steam port (of a boiler); exhaust port (for steam). **-ventil,** *n.* outlet valve.
**austrocknen,** *v.t.* & *i.* dry up, dry, desiccate, exsiccate; drain; season (wood). — **austrocknendes Mittel,** drying agent.
**Austrockner,** *m.* desiccator, drier.
**Austrocknung** *f.* drying up, etc. (see austrocknen).
**Austrocknungsrinde,** *f.* crust due to drying.
**auströpfeln, austropfen,** *v.i.* drop out, drip out; cease dropping or dripping.
**ausüben,** *v.t.* exert; practise, carry on; execute.
**auswachsen,** *v.i.* grow out; germinate, sprout; grow up; grow together. — **ausgewachsen,** *p.a.* grown out, etc.; full-grown.
**auswägbar,** *a.* capable of being weighed out, weighable.
**auswägen,** *v.t.* weigh out; calibrate by weighing.
**Auswahl,** *f.* choice, selection.
**auswählen,** *v.t.* choose, select. — **auswählend,** *p.a.* selective.
**Auswahl-prinzip,** *n.* selection principle. **-regel,** *f.* selection rule.
**auswalzen,** *v.t.* roll out.
**auswandern,** *v.i.* emigrate; shift.
**auswärmen,** *v.t.* anneal; warm, heat; roast.
**Auswärm(e)ofen,** *m.* annealing furnace.
**auswärtig,** *a.* outward; foreign.
**auswärts,** *adv.* outward, without, abroad.
**auswaschbar,** *a.* capable of being washed out.
**auswaschen,** *v.t.* wash out, wash, rinse; edulcorate; scour (fabrics); scrub (gases).
**Auswaschflasche,** *f.* wash bottle.
**Auswaschung,** *f.* washing out, etc. (see auswaschen); erosion.
**Auswaschungsverlust,** *m.* loss from washing.
**auswässern,** *v.t.* soak; water. — *v.i.* be soaked.
**auswechselbar,** *a.* exchangeable; interchangeable.
**auswechseln,** *v.t.* exchange; interchange.
**Auswechs(e)lung,** *f.* exchange, interchange; replacement.
**Ausweg,** *m.* way out, outlet, vent; expedient, shift.
**ausweichen,** *v.i.* turn out or aside; give, give way; deviate; escape. — *v.t.* soften out, detach by soaking; soak; evade. — **ausweichend,** *p.a.* evasive, elusive.
**Ausweichung,** *f.* deviation; deflection; evasion; escape; soaking.
**ausweiden,** *v.t.* eviscerate, draw.
**Ausweis,** *m.* proof; evidence; report; credentials.
**ausweisen,** *v.t.* prove; turn out, expel; banish.
**ausweiten,** *v.t.* widen, extend, expand.
**auswendig,** *a.* outer, exterior. — *adv.* by heart.
**auswerfen,** *v.t.* throw out, eject, discharge; reject.

**Auswertung,** *f.* evaluation, valuation, value; interpretation.
**auswettern,** *v.t.* weather.
**auswiegen,** *v.t.* = auswägen.
**auswinden,** *v.t.* wring out, wrench out; unscrew.
**auswintern,** *v.t.* weather; winter-season.
**auswirken,** *v.t.* work out; take out (salt from the pans); knead (dough); procure; effect.
**Auswirkung,** *f.* working out, etc. (see auswirken); effect, result, consequence.
**auswischen,** *v.t.* wipe out.
**auswittern,** *v.i.* effloresce; weather; (of timber) season. — *v.t.* weather, season; get scent of.
**Auswitterung,** *f.* efflorescence; weathering; seasoning (of timber).
**Auswuchs,** *m.* outgrowth, excrescence; germination.
**auswuchten,** *v.t.* counterbalance, balance.
**Auswurf,** *m.* throwing out, discharge; expectoration; excretion; sputum; excrement; refuse, trash. **-leitung,** *f.* discharge piping. **-rohr,** *n.*, **-röhre,** *f.* discharge pipe or tube. **-stoffe,** *m.pl.* excretions, excrement.
**auswurfsbefördernd,** *a.* (*Med.*) expectorant.
**auszacken,** *v.t.* indent, notch, jag.
**Auszehrung,** *f.* consumption.
**auszeichnen,** *v.t.* mark out, distinguish. — **ausgezeichnet,** *p.a.* excellent, distinguished.
**Auszeichnung,** *f.* distinction; label, mark.
**ausziehbar,** *a.* capable of being extracted, etc. (see ausziehen); ductile; telescopic.
**ausziehen,** *v.t.* extract; exhaust (drugs, etc.); draw out, draw, pull out; fade (colors); abstract; pull off, undress; stretch, extend. — *v.r.* stretch, extend. — *v.i.* move. — **ausgezogen,** *p.a.* extracted, etc.; (of a line) solid (not broken or dotted), continuous.
**Auszieh-rohr,** *n.*, **-röhre,** *f.* telescopic tube. **-tisch,** *m.* extension table. **-tubus,** *m.* (*Micros.*) drawtube. **-tusch,** *m.*, **-tusche,** *f.* drawing ink.
**Ausziehung,** *f.* extraction, etc. (see ausziehen).
**Auszug,** *m.* extract; essence, tincture, infusion, decoction (according to circumstances); extraction; extension; removal, exodus; drawer; abstract; bill, note; (*Milling*) superfine flour. **-mehl,** *n.* superfine flour.
**authentisch,** *a.* authentic.
**Auto-bahn,** *f.* motor highway. **-benzin,** *n.* motor gasoline, motor spirit.
**autogen,** *a.* autogenic, autogenous.
**Autogenschweissung,** *f.* autogenous welding.
**Autokatalysator,** *m.* autocatalyst.
**Autokatalyse,** *f.* autocatalysis.
**autokatalytisch,** *a.* autocatalytic.
**Autoklav,** *m.* autoclave.
**Autolack,** *m.* automobile lacquer.
**Autolyse,** *f.* autolysis.
**automatisch,** *a.* automatic.
**autonom,** *a.* autonomous.
**Autopoliermittel,** *n.* automobile polish.
**Autor,** *m.* author.
**Autoracemisierung,** *f.* autoracemization.
**Autoren-recht,** *n.* copyright. **-register,** *n.* author index.
**autorisieren,** *v.t.* authorize.
**Autorität,** *f.* authority.
**Auto-schlauch,** *m.* (*Rubber*) inner tube. **-schmieröl,** *n.* automobile lubricant.
**autoxydabel,** *a.* autoxidizable.
**auxochrom,** *a.* auxochrome, -chromic, -chromous.
**Avanturin,** *m.* (*Min.*) aventurine.
**aventurisieren,** *v.t.* aventurize.
**Avidität,** *f.* avidity.
**avisieren,** *v.t.* inform, notify.
**Avivage,** *f.* reviving, etc. (see avivieren).
**avivierecht,** *a.* unaffected by brightening.
**avivieren,** *v.t.* revive, restore; (*Dyeing*) brighten, clear (also tone, top); scroop (silk).
**Aviviermittel,** *n.* (*Dyeing*) brightening agent.
**ä.W., Ä.W.,** *abbrev.* (äussere Weite) outside diameter.
**Axe,** *f.* axis.
**axialsymmetrisch,** *a.* axisymmetric(al).
**Axt,** *f.* ax; hatchet.
**AZ., A.Z.,** *abbrev.* (Acetylzahl) acetyl number.
**Aze-.** see also Ace-.
**Azelainsäure,** *f.* azelaic acid.
**Azenaphten,** *n.* acenaphthene.
**Azenaphtylen,** *n.* acenaphthylene.
**azeotropisch,** *a.* azeotropic.
**Azetal,** *n.* acetal.
**Azetat,** *n.* acetate.
**Azetessigäther,** *m.* acetoacetic ester.
**Azetil,** *n.* acetyl.
**Azeto-.** aceto-.
**Azetolyse,** *f.* acetolysis.
**Azeton,** *n.* acetone.
**Azetyl,** *n.* acetyl.
**Azetylen,** *n.* acetylene. **-entwickler,** *m.* acetylene generator.
**azetylieren,** *v.t.* acetylate.
**Azi-, azi-.** see also Aci-, aci-.
**Aziäthan,** *n.* aziethane.
**Azid,** *n.* azide; (sometimes, in combination) acid. **-cellulose,** *f.* acid cellulose.
**Azidimetrie,** *f.* acidimetry.
**Azidität,** *f.* acidity.
**Aziditätsgrad,** *m.* degree of acidity.
**Azido-.** azido-; (sometimes) acido-. **-essigsäure,** *f.* azidoacetic acid (diazoacetic acid).
**azidolitisch,** *a.* acidolytic.

**Azinfarbstoff,** *m.* azine dye.
**Azo-benzol,** *n.* azobenzene. **-blau,** *n.* azo blue.
**azocyclisch,** *a.* azocyclic.
**Azo-echtfarbe,** *f.* fast azo dye. **-farbe,** *f.* azo dye, azo color. **-farbstoff,** *m.* azo dye. **-gelb,** *n.* azo yellow. **-gruppe,** *f.* azo group.
**azoisch,** *a.* (*Geol.*) azoic.
**Azo-körper,** *m.* azo compound. **-rot,** *n.* azo red. **-säureblau,** *n.* azo acid blue. **-säurefarbstoff,** *m.* acid azo dye.
**Azot,** *n.* nitrogen.
**Azo-toluol,** *m.* azotoluene. **-verbindung,** *f.* azo compound. **-walkrot,** *n.* fulling azo red.
**Azoxy-benzol,** *n.* azoxybenzene. **-verbindung,** *f.* azoxy compound.
**Azulminsäure,** *f.* azulmic acid.
**azur, azurblau, azurn,** *a.* azure, sky-blue.
**Azurstein,** *m.* lapis lazuli.
**azyklisch,** *a.* acyclic.
**Azyl,** *n.* acyl.
**azylieren,** *v.t.* acylate.

# B

**b.,** *abbrev.* (bei) at, with; (beim) at the, with the.
**B.,** *abbrev.* Berichte der deutschen chemischen Gesellschaft; (Bildung) formation; (Blatt) leaf.
**Bach,** *m.* brook, stream. **-kresse,** *f.* watercress.
**bacillär,** *a.* bacillary.
**Bacille,** *f.* bacillus.
**Bacillen-.** of or pertaining to bacilli. **-art,** *f.* kind of bacillus. **-färbung,** *f.* staining of bacilli. **-lehre,** *f.* bacteriology.
**bacillenvernichtend,** *a.* bacillicide, -cidal.
**Back-.** baking; coking; dried. **-apfel,** *m.* dried apple; baking apple.
**Backe,** *f.*, **Backen,** *m.* cheek; (of a clamp) jaw.
**backen,** *v.t.* bake; (in a pan) fry; dry (fruits); roast (ores); burn (tile, etc.); cement (steel). — *v.i.* bake; cake, coke (of coal); stick (of pottery in the kiln).
**Backen-.** cheek, buccal. **-brecher,** *m.* jawbreaker, jaw crusher. **-drüse,** *f.* buccal gland. **-zahn,** *m.* molar tooth.
**Bäcker,** *m.* baker.
**Backerei,** *f.* baking.
**Bäckerei,** *f.* bakery; baker's trade.
**Bäckerhefe,** *f.* baker's yeast.
**backfähig,** *a.* capable of baking; capable of caking.
**Back-fähigkeit,** *f.* capacity for baking (or for caking, coking, etc.; see backen); coking property or quality. **-kohle,** *f.* caking coal, coking coal; (rarely) fat coal. **-masse,** *f.* baking dough; a kind of confection (as of nuts and sugar). **-obst,** *n.* dried fruit. **-ofen,** *m.* baking oven, oven. **-pfanne,** *f.* baking pan, frying pan. **-pflaume,** *f.* prune. **-probe,** *f.* baking test. **-pulver,** *n.* baking powder. **-stein,** *m.* (burnt) brick.
**backsteinartig,** *a.* brick-like.
**Backsteinofen,** *m.* brick kiln.
**bäckt,** *pr. 3 sing.* (of backen) bakes, etc.
**Back-vermögen,** *n.* baking ability, coking property, etc. (see backen). **-werk,** *n.* pastry. **-wert,** *m.* baking value. **-zahn,** *m.* molar tooth, molar.
**Bad,** *n.* bath; (*Tech.*) dip, steep; (*Elec.*) cell, tank; watering place.
**Badamöl,** *n.* badam oil.
**Bade-.** bath, bathing.
**baden,** *v.t.* bathe.
**Bade-salz,** *n.* bath salt. **-schwamm,** *m.* bath sponge. **-seife** *f.* bath soap. **-wanne,** *f.* bath tub.
**Badflüssigkeit,** *f.* bath liquid, bath solution.
**Badian,** *m.* Chinese anise, star anise, badian (*Illicium verum*). **-öl,** *n.* star anise oil.
**badisch,** *a.* of Baden. — **badische Säure,** badische acid, 2-naphthylamine-8-sulfonic acid.
**Bad-kasten,** *m.* (electrolytic) cell. **-nitrieren,** *n.* (*Metal.*) fused-salt nitriding. **-patentieren,** *n.* (*Wire*) patenting with cooling in a lead or salt bath. **-spannung,** *f.* bath tension, cell voltage. **-spiegel,** *m.* bath level, bath surface. **-zementieren,** *n.* (*Metal.*) bath cementation, liquid carburizing.
**Bael,** *f.* (*Bot.*) bel (*Aegle marmelos*).
**Bagassefeuerung,** *f.* bagasse furnace.
**Bagger,** *m.* dredger, excavator.
**baggern,** *v.t.* dredge, excavate.
**Baggertorf,** *m.* dredged peat.
**Bahamaholz,** *n.* brazilwood.
**bähen,** *v.t.* foment; toast (bread); warm, heat; force (plants).
**Bahia-gummi,** *n.* Bahia rubber (mangabeira rubber from Bahia). **-holz,** *n.* brazilwood. **-pulver,** *n.* Bahia powder, Goa powder.
**Bahn,** *f.* way, road, track; path; orbit; trajectory; railway; breadth (of cloth).
**bahnbrechend,** *p.a.* pioneer, epoch-making.
**Bahn-brecher,** *m.* pioneer. **-durchmesser,** *m.* orbital diameter. **-ebene,** *f.* orbital plane. **-elektron,** *n.* orbital electron.
**bahnen,** *v.t.* beat, smooth, clear (a way).
**Bahn-hof,** *m.* (railway) station. **-impuls,** *m.* linear momentum; orbital moment. **-schleife,** -**schlinge,** *f.*, orbital loop. **-spur,** *f.* track. **-übergang,** *m.* orbital transition. **-zug,** *m.* railway train.
**Bahre,** *f.* barrow, stretcher; bier.
**Bähungsmittel,** *n.* (*Med.*) fomentation agent.
**Bai,** *f.* bay. **-salz,** *n.* bay salt, sea salt.
**Bajonett,** *n.* bayonet. **-rohr,** *n.*, **-röhre,** *f.* bayonet tube (a combustion tube with bayonet-like end). **-verschluss,** *m.* bayonet seal; bayonet catch.
**Bakelitlack,** *m.* bakelite varnish or lacquer.
**Bakteriämie,** *f.* bacteriemia.
**bakteriämisch,** *a.* bacteriemic.
**Bakterie,** *f.* bacterium.
**bakteriell,** *a.* bacterial.
**Bakterien,** *f.pl.* bacteria. **-arten,** *f.pl.* kinds of bacteria.
**bakterienartig,** *a.* bacteroid, bacterial.
**Bakterien-faden,** *m.* thread or chain of bacteria.

**-farbe,** *f.* bacterial stain. **-färbung,** *f.* staining of bacteria. **-fäule,** *f.* bacterial rot, soft rot.
**bakterienfeindlich,** *a.* antibacterial.
**bakterienförmig,** *a.* bacteriform.
**Bakterien-forscher,** *m.* bacteriologic investigator. **-forschung,** *f.* bacteriologic research. **-gehalt,** *m.* bacterial content. **-gift,** *n.* bacterial toxin; bactericide.
**bakterienhaltig,** *a.* containing bacteria.
**Bakterien-kunde, -lehre,** *f.* bacteriology. **-nährlösung,** *f.* nutrient solution for bacteria. **-stamm,** *m.* bacterial strain.
**bakterien-tötend, -vernichtend,** *p.a.* bactericidal.
**Bakterien-wachstum,** *n.* bacterial growth. **-zählung,** *f.* bacterial count. **-züchtung,** *f.* bacterial culture.
**Bakteriolog, -loge,** *m.* bacteriologist.
**Bakteriologie,** *f.* bacteriology.
**bakteriologisch,** *a.* bacteriologic(al).
**Bakteriolyse,** *f.* bacteriolysis.
**bakteriolytisch,** *a.* bacteriolytic.
**Bakteriurie,** *f.* bacteriuria.
**bakterizid,** *a.* bactericidal.
**Bakterizidie,** *f.* bactericidal action.
**Balancier,** *m.* beam.
**balancieren,** *v.t. & i.* balance.
**Balatagummi,** *m.* balata gum.
**bald,** *adv.* soon, presently; almost. — *conj.* — . . . —, now . . . then; **so — als,** as soon as.
**baldig,** *a.* quick, early.
**baldigst,** *adv.* very soon, as early as possible.
**baldmöglichst,** *adv.* as soon as possible.
**Baldrian,** *m.* valerian. **-äther,** *m.* valeric ester, specif. ethyl valerate. **-öl,** *n.* valerian oil. **-salz,** *n.* valerate. **-säure,** *f.* valeric acid. **-wurzel,** *f.* valerian root, valerian.
**Balg,** *m.* skin; bellows; husk, pod, shell; chaff; (*Med.*) cyst; follicle. **-auszug,** *m.* bellows extension. **-frucht,** *f.* (*Bot.*) follicle. **-geschwulst,** *n.* (*Med.*) cystic tumor.
**Balken,** *m.* beam; girder; band; (*Anat.*) corpus callosum. **-mikrowage,** *f.* beam microbalance. **-wage,** *f.* beam balance.
**Ball,** *m.* ball; globe; bulb; (*Soda*) ball soda, black ash.
**Ballast-stoff,** *m.* ballast material (as a substance that does not take part in a reaction). **-widerstand,** *m.* (*Elec.*) fixed resistance.
**Ballaufnahme,** *f.* (*Photog.*) bulb exposure.
**ballen,** *v.t. & i.* ball (together), form into balls, conglomerate.
**Ballen,** *m.* bale; pack, packet, bundle; ball. **-presse,** *f.* baling press.
**ballförmig,** *a.* spherical, globular.
**ballig,** *a.* convex, bulged, crowned.
**ballistisch,** *a.* ballistic.
**Ballofen,** *m.* balling furnace.
**Ballon,** *m.* carboy; balloon flask (spherical flask with short neck); balloon; (rubber) bulb. **-abfüller,** *m.* balloon flask for drawing off liquid. **-entleerer,** *m.* carboy emptier. **-filter,** *m.* filtering flask (of porous porcelain). **-gas,** *n.* balloon gas. **-gestell,** *n.* carboy holder. **-kipper,** *m.* carboy tilter or inclinator. **-reifen,** *m.* balloon tire.
**ballotieren,** *v.i.* ballot.
**Ballung,** *f.* balling; agglomerate.
**Ballungsfähigkeit,** *f.* balling property.
**Balsam,** *m.* balsam, balm. **-apfel,** *m.* balsam apple, balm apple (*Momordica*). **-baum,** *m.* balsam tree (any of various balsameaceous trees).
**balsamerzeugend,** *a.* balsamiferous.
**Balsam-flasche,** *f.* balsam bottle. **-harz,** *n.* balsamic resin. **-holz,** *n.* xylobalsamum, balm-of-Gilead wood.
**balsamieren,** *v.t.* embalm; perfume.
**balsamisch,** *a.* balsamic, balmy. — **balsamisches Mittel,** balsamic.
**Balsam-kraut,** *n.* costmary; moschatel. **-pappel,** *f.* balsam poplar, tacamahac. **-tanne,** *f.* balsam fir (*Abies balsamea*); spruce (esp. Norway spruce, *Picea abies*).
**Balyrohr,** *n.* (*Spect.*) Baly tube.
**Bambus,** *m.* bamboo. **-rohr,** *n.* bamboo. **-zucker,** *m.* bamboo sugar, tabasheer.
**Banane,** *f.* banana.
**Bananenwachs,** *n.* pisang wax.
**Bancazinn,** *n.* Banca tin.
**band,** *pret.* bound, fixed, etc. (see binden).
**Band,** *m.* volume; binding. — *n.* band; ribbon, tape, strap, strip, belt, hoop; hinge; bond, tie, ligament. **-achat,** *m.* banded agate, ribbon agate.
**bandagieren,** *v.t.* bandage; fit with tires.
**bandähnlich, bandartig,** *a.* ribbon-like, striped, streaked; ligamentous.
**Bandarbeit,** *f.* moving-belt production.
**Bande,** *f.* edge, border; band; gang.
**Bandeisen,** *n.* hoop iron, band iron.
**Bandenlinie,** *f.* band line.
**Band-feder,** *f.* flat spring. **-förderer,** *m.* belt conveyor. **-kante,** *f.* edge of a band, band head. **-mass,** *n.* tape measure. **-stahl,** *m.* band steel, strip steel.
**bandstreifig,** *a.* banded, streaked, striped.
**Band-trockner,** *m.* belt drier. **-wurm,** *m.* tapeworm.
**Baniane,** *m.* banyan, banyan tree.
**Bank,** *f.* bench; bank; bed, layer, stratum. — **Banken,** *f.pl.* bank.
**Bankanweisung,** *f.* check, bank note.
**Bankazinn,** *n.* Banca tin.
**Bankbruch,** *m.* bankruptcy.
**bankerott,** *a.* bankrupt.
**Bankett,** *n.* banquet.
**Bankier,** *m.* banker.

**bankig,** *a.* (*Geol.*) bedding, bedded.
**bankrott,** *a.* bankrupt.
**Bankulnuss,** *f.* candlenut. **-öl,** *n.* candlenut oil.
**Bankwesen,** *n.* banking.
**Bann,** *m.* ban; jurisdiction; spell.
**bannen,** *v.t.* banish; confine; enchant.
**bar,** *a.* bare; pure, sheer; cash; destitute (of). — **für —, gegen —,** for cash.
**-bar.** An adjective suffix usually attached to verb roots and equivalent to -able, -ible; as, *haltbar*, stable (keepable), durable, tenable.
**Bär,** *m.* bear; debt; (*Mech.*) ram, monkey.
**Barbar,** *m.* barbarian.
**Barbier,** *m.* barber.
**barbieren,** *v.t.* shave; cheat.
**Barchent,** *m.* fustian.
**Bären-klau,** *f.* bear's-breech (*Acanthus mollis* or, incorrectly, the cow parsnip, *Heracleum sphondylium*). **-traube,** *f.* bearberry (*Arctostaphylos uva-ursi*). **-wurzel,** *f.* saxifrage.
**Bärfett,** *n.* bear fat.
**barg,** *pret.* (of bergen) saved, sheltered, etc.
**Barium-.** see Baryum-.
**Barke,** *f.* shallow vat, back, beck; bark, barge.
**Bärlapp,** *m.*, **-kraut,** *n.* lycopodium, club moss. **-mehl,** *n.*, **-samen,** *m.*, **-staub,** *n.* lycopodium (powder).
**Bärlauch,** *m.* ramson (*Allium ursinum*).
**Bärme,** *f.* yeast, barm.
**barmherzig,** *a.* merciful.
**Barnstein,** *m.* brick.
**Barockperlen,** *f.pl.* baroque pearls.
**Barometer-druck,** *m.* barometric pressure. **-rohr,** *n.*, **-röhre,** *f.* barometer tube. **-säule,** *f.* barometric column. **-stand,** *m.* height of the barometer, barometric height.
**barometrisch,** *a.* barometric.
**Barpreis,** *m.* cash price.
**Barre,** *f.*, **Barren,** *m.* bar; ingot.
**Barren-einguss,** *m.*, **-form,** *f.* ingot mold.
**Barsch,** *m.* perch (fish).
**Barschaft,** *f.* cash; property.
**barst,** *pret.* (of bersten) burst, exploded, etc.
**Bart,** *m.* beard; bur, seam; barb.
**bärtig,** *a.* bearded.
**bartlos,** *a.* beardless.
**Bartseife,** *f.* shaving soap.
**Bärwurzel,** *f.* saxifrage; spicknel.
**Baryt,** *m.* baryta ($BaO$ or $Ba(OH)_2$); (*Min.*) barite ($BaSO_4$).
**barytartig,** *a.* barytic.
**Baryt-erde,** *f.* barium oxide, baryta. **-filter,** *m.* & *n.* barium sulfate filter. **-flussspat,** *m.* fluorite containing barium.
**barytführend,** *a.* barytic.
**Barytgelb,** *n.* barium yellow ($BaCrO_4$).
**barythaltig,** *a.* containing barium.
**Baryt-hydrat,** *n.* barium hydroxide. **-lauge,** *f.* barium hydroxide solution. **-lösung,** *f.* baryta ($Ba(OH)_2$) solution. **-papier,** *n.* baryta paper. **-salpeter,** *m.* barium nitrate, (*Min.*) nitrobarite. **-spat, -stein,** *m.* (*Min.*) barite. **-wasser,** *n.* baryta water. **-weiss,** *n.* permanent white, blanc fixe ($BaSO_4$). **-zinkweiss,** *n.* lithopone.
**Baryum,** *n.* barium. **-chlorhydrat,** *n.* barium chloride. **-hydrat,** *n.* barium hydroxide. **-hyperoxyd,** *n.* barium peroxide, barium dioxide. **-jodid,** *n.* barium iodide. **-lack,** *m.* barium lake. **-oxydhydrat,** *n.* barium hydroxide. **-platincyanür,** *n.* barium cyanoplatinite, barium cyanoplatinate(II). **-rhodanid,** *n.* barium thiocyanate. **-salz,** *n.* barium salt.
**Barzahlung,** *f.* cash payment.
**bas.,** *abbrev.* (basisch) basic.
**basaltähnlich,** *a.* basaltoid, basaltic.
**Basalt-eisenerz,** *n.* basaltic iron ore. **-felsen,** *m.* basaltic rock.
**basaltförmig,** *a.* basaltiform.
**Basaltgestein,** *n.* basaltic rock.
**basalthaltig,** *a.* containing basalt.
**basaltieren,** *v.t.* convert (slag) into a material resembling basalt.
**basaltisch,** *a.* basaltic.
**Basaltsteingut,** *n.* (*Ceram.*) basalt (ware).
**Base,** *f.* base; basis; aunt; cousin.
**Baseler Grün.** Basle green, Paris green.
**Basenaustausch,** *m.* base exchange.
**basenbildend,** *a.* base-forming, basifying.
**Basen-bildner,** *m.* base former, basifier. **-druck,** *m.* (*Calico*) base printing. **-wert,** *m.* base value.
**Basicität,** *f.* basicity.
**Basicitätszahl,** *f.* basicity value or number.
**Basidie,** *f.*, **Basidium,** *n.* basidium.
**Basidienpilze,** *m.pl.* Basidiomycetes.
**basieren,** *v.t.* base. — *v.i.* be based.
**Basilicum, Basilicumkraut,** *n.* (sweet) basil.
**Basilicumsalbe,** *f.* (*Med.*) basilicon.
**Basilie,** *f.*, **Basilienkraut, Basilikum, Basilikumkraut,** *n.* (sweet) basil.
**Basis,** *f.* base; basis.
**basisch,** *a.* basic. — **basisch zugestellt,** (*Metal.*) basic-lined.
**basisch-chromsauer,** *a.* basic chromate of. **-essigsauer,** *a.* basic acetate of, subacetate of. **-salpetersauer,** *a.* basic nitrate of, subnitrate of. **-schwefelsauer,** *a.* basic sulfate of.
**Basis-ecke,** *f.*, **-eck,** *n.* base angle. **-fläche,** *f.* basal surface. **-ion,** *n.* basic ion.
**Basizität, Basität,** *f.* basicity.
**Basler Blau, Baslerblau,** *n.* Basel blue.
**Bassin,** *n.* tank, cistern, reservoir; basin; bowl.
**Bassoragummi,** *n.* Bassora gum.
**Bast,** *m.* & *n.* bast; gum (of silk), sericin.
**Bastand.,** *abbrev.* (Barometerstand) height of barometer.

**Bastard,** *m.* hybrid; bastard. **-bestäubung,** *f.* cross-pollination. **-erzeugung,** *f.* production of hybrids, hybridization. **-ierung,** *f.* hybridization. **-klee,** *m.* alsike clover, alsike. **-kräftigkeit,** *f.* hybrid vigor. **-küpe,** *f.* bastard vat.

**Bastern,** *m.* raw sugar.

**Basterzucker,** *m.* bastard sugar, raw sugar.

**Bast-faser,** *f.* bast fiber. **-körper,** *m.* (*Bot.*) bast tissue, phloëm. **-papier,** *n.* Manila paper. **-seide,** *f.* raw silk. **-seife,** *f.* (*Silk*) degumming liquor, degumming soap.

**bat,** *pret.* (of bitten) asked, begged.

**Batate,** *f.* sweet potato.

**batavisch,** *a.* Batavian.

**Batist,** *m.* cambric; batiste.

**batschen,** *v.t.* ret (flax, etc.); batch (jute).

**Batschöl,** *n.* batching oil (for jute).

**Batterie-entladung,** *f.* battery discharge. **-glas,** *n.* (glass) battery jar. **-spannung,** *f.* battery voltage. **-strom,** *m.* battery current. **-zündung,** *f.* battery ignition.

**Batzen,** *m.* large soft lump; large amount.

**Bau,** *m.* structure; constitution; construction; building; make; cultivation. **-art,** *f.* construction, design, style. **-breite,** *f.* over-all breadth.

**Bauch,** *m.* belly, abdomen, venter; stomach; swelling, bulge; bulb (of a retort).

**Bauch-.** abdominal, ventral.

**Bauchdecken-.** epigastric, abdominal.

**Bäuche, bäuchen,** etc. = Beuche, beuchen, etc.

**bauchen,** *v.i.* & *r.* belly, bulge, swell.

**Bauch-fell,** *n.* peritoneum. **-fellentzündung,** *f.* peritonitis. **-fluss,** *m.* diarrhea.

**bauchförmig,** *a.* bulged, inflated, ventricose.

**Bauch-füssler,** *m.* gastropod. **-gegend,** *f.* abdominal region. **-haut,** *f.* peritoneum. **-höhle,** *f.* abdominal cavity.

**bauchig,** *a.* bellied, convex, bulged.

**Bauchspeichel,** *m.* pancreatic juice. **-drüse,** *f.* pancreas.

**Bauchweh,** *n.* colic, abdominal pain.

**Baueisen,** *n.* structural iron.

**bauen,** *v.t.* build, construct; work, cultivate.

**Bauer,** *m.* builder; farmer, peasant; jack; cage.

**Bauerde,** *f.* (tillable) soil.

**Bauer-gut,** *n.* farm. **-hof,** *m.* farm; country house.

**Bauernsand,** *m.* molding sand.

**Bauerstand,** *m.* peasantry.

**bau-fähig,** *a.* (of land) arable; (of mines) workable. **-fällig,** *a.* out of repair; decaying.

**Baufehler,** *m.* structural defect.

**baufest,** *a.* well-built, solid, firm.

**Bau-form,** *f.* style of construction, design. **-holz,** *n.* timber. **-ingenieur,** *m.* structural engineer. **-kunst,** *f.* architecture, (art of) building or construction. **-länge,** *f.* over-all length.

**baulich,** *a.* structural, constructional.

**Baulichkeit,** *f.* structure, building, edifice.

**Baum** *m.* tree; (*Mech.*) beam, bar, arbor **-achat,** *m.* dendritic agate, moss agate.

**baum-ähnlich, -artig,** *a.* arborescent, tree-like

**Baumaterial,** *n.* building material.

**Baumégrad,** *m.* degree Baumé.

**Baumeister,** *m.* architect, builder.

**baumeln,** *v.i.* dangle.

**baumförmig,** *a.* dendritic, arborescent.

**Baum-garten,** *m.* orchard; nursery. **-harz,** *n.* tree resin; specif., rosin, esp. wood rosin. **-öl,** *n.* olive oil, sweet oil (esp. a second grade). **-ölseife,** *f.* olive oil soap, Venetian soap.

**Baumörtel,** *m.* building mortar, common mortar.

**Baum-rinde,** *f.* bark, rind. **-schlag,** *m.* foliage. **-schule,** *f.* nursery. **-schwamm,** *m.* agaric. **-senf,** *m.* candytuft. **-stamm,** *m.* tree trunk.

**baumstark,** *a.* robust.

**Baum-stein,** *m.* (*Min.*) dendrite. **-wachs,** *n.* grafting wax. **-wollabfall,** *m.* cotton waste. **-wolle,** *f.* cotton.

**baumwollen,** *a.* cotton.

**Baumwollen-abfall,** *m.* cotton waste. **-blau,** *n.* cotton blue. **-samen,** *m.* cottonseed.

**Baumwoll-faden,** *m.* cotton fiber; cotton thread; cotton twine. **-farbstoff,** *m.* cotton dye. **-garn,** *m.* cotton yarn. **-gelb,** *n.* cotton yellow. **-gewebe,** *n.* cotton fabric, cotton goods. **-kernöl,** *n.* cottonseed oil. **-pfropfen,** *m.* cotton plug, cotton stopper. **-putzwolle,** *f.* cotton waste. **-rot,** *n.* cotton red. **-samen,** *m.*, **-saat,** *f.* cottonseed. **-samenöl,** *n.* cottonseed oil. **-scharlach,** *n.* cotton scarlet. **-stoff,** *m.* cotton material. **-wachs,** *n.* cotton wax. **-waren,** *f.pl.* cotton goods. **-watte,** *f.* cotton wadding; cotton padding or pad. **-wurzelrinde,** *f.* cotton root bark. **-zwirn,** *m.* cotton thread.

**Bau-pappe,** *f.* building (paper) board. **-riss,** *m.* building plan. **-sand,** *m.* building sand, mortar sand.

**Bausch,** *m.* pad, compress; bundle; lump; plug, wad.

**Bäuschchen,** *n.* little pad, plug.

**bauschen,** *v.i.* swell out, bag, bulge. — *v.t.* puff up; refine (tin).

**Bauschung,** *f.* swelling, etc. (see bauschen); protuberance; bulge; crease (in fabrics).

**Bau-stahl,** *m.* structural steel. **-stein,** *m.* building stone; brick; (*fig.*) unit. **-stoff,** *m.* building material, structural material; (*Physiol.*) nutrient. **-stoffwechsel,** *m.* constructive metabolism, anabolism.

**Baute,** *f.* structure, building.

**Bau-werk,** *n.* building, structure, edifice. **-wesen,** *n.* construction, building (affairs).

**bauwürdig,** *a.* (*Mining*) workable, profitable.

**Bauxitziegel,** *m.* bauxite brick.

**Bauzwecke,** *m.pl.* building purposes.
**Baybeerenbaum,** *m.* bebeeru, greenheart tree.
**bayerisch,** *a.* Bavarian.
**Bayern,** *n.* Bavaria.
**Bayersche Säure.** Bayer's acid (2-naphthol-8-sulfonic acid).
**Bayöl,** *n.* oil of bay.
**bayrisch,** *a.* Bavarian.
**Bayrischblau,** *n.* Bavarian blue.
**bazillär,** *a.* bacillary.
**Bazille,** *f.*, **Bazillus,** *m.*, bacillus.
**Bazillen-.** see Bacillen-.
**Bd.,** *abbrev.* (Band) volume.
**Bde.,** *abbrev.* (Bände) volumes.
**Bdellion, Bdellium,** *n.* bdellium.
**be-.** A verbal prefix which, when prefixed to verbs, usually denotes completeness or thoroness; as *bedenken,* consider. With nouns it signifies "to provide with," as *bekalken,* to lime; with adjectives, "to make . . .," as *bereichern,* enrich.
**beabsichtigen,** *v.t.* intend, have in view, plan.
**beachten,** *v.t.* consider; notice, observe.
**beachtenswert,** *a.* worth attention; noteworthy, remarkable.
**Beamte, Beamter,** *m.* official; officer.
**beanspruchen,** *v.t.* stress, strain, load; require; claim.
**Beanspruchung,** *f.* stress, strain, load; tension; wear and tear; requirement; claim.
**beanstanden,** *v.t.* object to; reject, refuse.
**beantragen,** *v.t.* propose; apply for.
**beantworten,** *v.t.* answer, reply to.
**Beantwortung,** *f.* answer, reply.
**bearbeitbar,** *a.* workable, etc. (see bearbeiten).
**Bearbeitbarkeit,** *f.* workability, machining property, etc. (see bearbeiten).
**bearbeiten,** *v.t.* work; manipulate; make, dress, machine, roll, draw, till, etc.; treat; edit.
**Bearbeitung,** *f.* working, etc. (see bearbeiten); manufacture; workmanship.
**Beaufschlagung,** *f.* impact, pressure, stress; admission (of steam).
**beaufsichtigen,** *v.t.* superintend, inspect.
**beauftragen,** *v.t.* charge; authorize.
**beben,** *v.i.* quake, tremble; (*Physics*) vibrate.
**beblättert,** *a.* having leaves, leafy.
**bebrüten,** *v.t.* incubate.
**Becher,** *m.* beaker; cup; bucket; goblet, bowl; (*Bot.*) calyx. **-bürste,** *f.* beaker brush. **-chen,** *n.* little cup.
**becherförmig,** *a.* cup-shaped, cyathiform.
**Becher-glas,** *n.* beaker. **-glaskolben, -kolben,** *m.* Erlenmeyer flask. **-hülle,** *f.* (*Bot.*) cupule. **-mensur,** *f.* measuring cup. **-werk,** *n.* bucket conveyor.
**Becken,** *n.* basin; tank; vessel; (*Anat.*) pelvis; cymbal.
**Becken-.** (*Anat.*) pelvic.
**Beckmann'sche Umlagerung.** Beckmann rearrangement.
**Becquerelstrahlen,** *m.pl.* Becquerel rays.
**Bed.,** *abbrev.* of Bedeutung.
**Bedacht,** *m.* consideration; care.
**Bedachung,** *f.* roofing.
**bedämpfen,** *v.t.* damp; treat with vapor; suffocate.
**bedanken,** *v.r.* thank; decline.
**Bedarf,** *m.* need, demand, requirement.
**Bedarfs-artikel, -gegenstand,** *m.* requirement, requisite, necessary article.
**bedauerlich,** *a.* regrettable.
**bedauern,** *v.t.* regret; pity.
**bedecken,** *v.t.* cover; (*Sugar*) bottom, clay.
**Bedeckung,** *f.* covering; coverage; cover.
**bedenken,** *v.t.* consider, heed, care for. — *v.r.* bethink oneself; hesitate.
**Bedenken,** *n.* consideration; hesitation; doubt; scruple.
**bedenklich,** *a.* doubtful; questionable; hazardous; serious.
**bedeuten,** *v.t.* mean, signify; point out, state. — **bedeutend,** *p.a.* considerable, important.
**bedeutsam,** *a.* significant; imposing.
**Bedeutung,** *f.* meaning, signification; importance, significance.
**bedeutungslos,** *a.* insignificant; meaningless.
**bedienbar,** *a.* operable, manipulable.
**bedienen,** *v.t.* serve, attend; operate, manipulate. — *v.r.* help oneself, make use.
**Bedienung,** *f.* service, attendance; operation, manipulation; attention; servants.
**Bedienungsvorschrift,** *f.* instructions for use.
**bedingen,** *v.t.* stipulate; contract for; limit, restrict. — **bedingt,** *p.a.* conditioned, limited, qualified, conditional; hypothetical.
**Bedingung,** *f.* condition, stipulation, term; limitation, restriction.
**Bedingungsgleichung,** *f.* equation of condition.
**bedingungs-los,** *a.* unconditional; unlimited. **-weise,** *adv.* conditionally.
**bedrahten,** *v.t.* wire.
**bedrucken,** *v.t.* print, print upon.
**Bedruckung,** *f.* printing, impression.
**Bedrückung,** *f.* oppression.
**bedürfen,** *v.i.* be in need; (*with gen.*) need, require, want.
**Bedürfnis,** *n.* want, requirement, necessity.
**beehren,** *v.t.* honor, favor. — *v.r.* have the honor.
**beeifern,** *v.r.* strive, endeavor.
**beeilen,** *v.r.* hasten, hurry.
**beeinflussbar,** *a.* capable of being influenced or affected, susceptible.
**beeinflussen,** *v.t.* influence, affect.
**Beeinflussung,** *f.* influence.
**beeinträchtigen,** *v.t.* injure, impair; encroach upon. — **beeinträchtigend,** *p.a.* injurious, detrimental.

**beeisen,** *v.t.* cover with ice; cover with iron; alum (silk).
**beenden, beendigen,** *v.t.* finish, end.
**beengen,** *v.t.* narrow, cramp.
**beerben,** *v.t.* be heir to, inherit.
**beerdigen,** *v.t.* bury, inter.
**Beere,** *f.* berry.
**beeren-ähnlich, -artig, -förmig,** *a.* berry-like, berry-shaped, bacciform.
**Beeren-farbstoff,** *m.* berry pigment. **-grün,** *n.* sap green.
**Beer-esche,** *f.* service tree (*Sorbus domestica*). **-gelb,** *n.* buckthorn yellow. **-schwamm,** *m.* frambesia, yaws.
**Beet,** *n.* (garden) bed.
**Beete,** *f.* beet, beetroot.
**befähigen,** *v.t.* enable, qualify.
**befahl,** *pret.* (of befehlen) commanded, etc.
**befallen,** *v.t.* befall; attack.
**befangen,** *p.a.* embarrassed; prejudiced.
**befassen,** *v.t.* handle; deal with. — *v.r.* engage, be engaged, deal (with).
**Befehl,** *m.* command, order, precept.
**befehlen,** *v.t.* command, order; commend, entrust. — **befehlend,** *p.a.* imperative.
**Befehls-.** control, master, pilot, command.
**befestigen,** *v.t.* fasten, fix, attach; establish; fortify.
**Befestigungs-mittel,** *n.* fixing agent. **-schraube,** *f.* setscrew.
**befeuchten,** *v.t.* moisten, dampen; wet, water.
**Befeuchtung,** *f.* moistening, dampening.
**Befeuchtungs-kammer,** *f.* moistening chamber. **-mittel,** *n.* moistening agent.
**Befeuerung,** *f.* firing, heating.
**befiehlt,** *pr. 3 sing.* (of befehlen) commands, etc.
**befinden,** *v.t.* find, think. — *v.r.* be, feel.
**Befinden,** *n.* condition, state; opinion.
**befindlich,** *a.* existing, present, situated.
**beflecken,** *v.t.* spot, stain, soil, blot, blur.
**befleissen, befleissigen,** *v.r.* apply oneself (to). — **beflissen,** *p.a.* studious, intent.
**befliss,** *pret.* of befleissen.
**beflissen,** *p.a.* see befleissen.
**beföhle,** *pret. subj.* of befehlen.
**befohlen,** *p.p.* (of befehlen) commanded, etc.
**befolgen,** *v.t.* follow (advice); obey (a command).
**befördern,** *v.t.* forward; convey, ship; further, promote, aid.
**Beförderung,** *f.* forwarding; conveyance, shipment; promotion, advancement; encouragement, stimulation.
**Beförderungsmittel,** *n.* aid, promoter, means of forwarding; (*Med.*) adjuvant.
**befrachten,** *v.t.* load.
**befreien,** *v.t.* set free, liberate, free; rescue, relieve, clear.
**befremden,** *v.t.* surprise.
**befremdlich,** *a.* strange, surprising.
**befriedigen,** *v.t.* satisfy, please. — **befriedigend,** *p.a.* satisfactory.
**befruchten,** *v.t.* fertilize, fecundate.
**Befruchtungsstaub,** *m.* pollen.
**befugen,** *v.t.* authorize; entitle; license.
**Befugnis,** *f.* right, authority, warrant.
**befühlen,** *v.t.* feel, handle, touch.
**Befund,** *m.* state, condition, circumstances; finding, award; result.
**befürchten,** *v.t.* fear, apprehend; suspect.
**befürworten,** *v.t.* recommend, support.
**begaben,** *v.t.* endow. — **begabt,** *p.a.* gifted.
**begann,** *pret.* (of beginnen) began.
**begasen,** *v.t.* gas; fumigate.
**Begattung,** *f.* copulation, coition.
**begeben,** *v.r.* go; happen; give up.
**Begebenheit,** *f.* occurrence, event; adventure.
**begegnen,** *v.i.* meet; happen; behave.
**begehen,** *v.t.* celebrate; commit; walk through.
**Begeher,** *n.* desire, demand.
**begehren,** *v.t.* desire, crave, want, demand.
**begeistern,** *v.t.* inspire, animate. — *v.r.* enthuse.
**begichten,** *v. t.* charge (a furnace).
**Begier, Begierde,** *f.* desire; avidity, affinity.
**begierig,** *a.* desirous, eager.
**begiessen,** *v.t.* wet, moisten; water, irrigate.
**Beginn,** *m.* beginning.
**beginnen,** *v.t. & i.* begin.
**begipsen,** *v.t.* plaster.
**beglasen,** *v.t.* glaze.
**Beglasung,** *f.* glaze, glazing.
**beglaubigen,** *v.t.* certify, attest, confirm.
**begleiten,** *v.t.* accompany, attend.
**Begleiter,** *m.* attendant, companion, associate, satellite; guide.
**Begleit-erscheinung,** *f.* attendant phenomenon. **-farbe,** *f.* (*Calico*) fitting color, illuminating color. **-gewebe,** *n.* connective tissue. **-körper,** *m.* accompanying substance (or body), impurity. **-linie,** *f.* (*Spect.*) satellite line. **-metall,** *n.* accompanying metal, foreign metal. **-stoff,** *m.* = Begleitkörper.
**beglücken,** *v.t.* bless, favor.
**begnadigen,** *v.t.* pardon, favor.
**begnügen,** *v.r.* be content.
**begönne,** *pret. subj.* of beginnen.
**begonnen,** *p.p.* (of beginnen) begun.
**begraben,** *v.t.* bury; conceal.
**Begräbnis,** *n.* burial; tomb.
**begreifen,** *v.t.* conceive, understand; include, comprise; imply.
**begreiflich,** *a.* conceivable, intelligible.
**begrenzen,** *v.t.* bound, limit, terminate; define.
**Begrenzung,** *f.* limit, boundary; limitation.
**Begrenzungs-fläche,** *f.* boundary surface, surface of contact, interface. **-linie,** *f.* boundary line.
**Begriff,** *m.* conception, idea, notion.

**begrifflich,** *a.* conceivable; conceptual, abstract.
**Begriffsbestimmung,** *f.* definition.
**begründen,** *v.t.* establish; base; prove; confirm, substantiate.
**Begründung,** *f.* establishment; foundation.
**begrüssen,** *v.t.* salute, greet.
**begünstigen,** *v.t.* favor; promote.
**Beguss,** *m.*, **-masse,** *f.* (*Ceram.*) slip, engobe.
**begutachten,** *v.t.* pass judgment on.
**Begutachtung,** *f.* opinion, judgment, appraisal.
**begütert,** *a.* wealthy.
**begütigen,** *v.t.* appease, pacify, quiet.
**behaart,** *a.* hairy.
**behaftet,** *a.* affected; contaminated; afflicted.
**behagen,** *v.t.* please.
**Behagen,** *n.* pleasure, comfort.
**behaglich,** *a.* agreeable, comfortable.
**behalten,** *v.t.* keep, retain; (*Math.*) carry.
**Behälter,** *m.* container, receiver, receptacle, tank, reservoir, vessel, etc.; conservatory. **-wagen,** *m.* tank car.
**Behältnis,** *n.* container, case, box, bin, etc.
**behandelbar,** *a.* susceptible of treatment, treatable, processable, workable.
**behandeln,** *v.t.* treat; handle, manipulate, operate, process, work.
**Behandlung,** *f.* treatment, etc. (see behandeln).
**Behandlungs-art,** *f.* kind of treatment. **-mittel,** *m.* agent, reagent. **-verfahren,** *n.*, **-weise,** *f.* method of treatment, procedure.
**Beharr-.** stationary.
**beharren,** *v.i.* continue, persist, persevere.
**beharrlich,** *a.* persistent, constant; persevering; stubborn.
**Beharrung,** *f.* continuance, permanence, persistence; inertia; obstinacy.
**Beharrungs-kraft,** *f.*, **-vermögen,** *n.* (*Physics*) inertia. **-zustand, Beharrzustand,** *m.* permanence; settled state; persistence; resistance (of a machine).
**behaupten,** *v.t.* maintain, assert, affirm.
**Behauptung,** *f.* assertion, proposition; maintaining.
**Behausung,** *f.* lodging, abode.
**beheben,** *v.t.* remove, eliminate, overcome.
**beheizen,** *v.t.* heat.
**Beheizung,** *f.* heating.
**Behelf,** *m.* shift, device, expedient.
**behelfsmässig,** *a.* makeshift, temporary.
**Behen-nuss,** *f.* ben nut. **-öl,** *n.* oil of ben. **-säure,** *f.* behenic acid.
**beherbergen,** *v.t.* harbor, shelter.
**beherrschen,** *v.t.* rule, control, command.
**beherzigen,** *v.t.* take to heart, consider.
**beherzigenswert,** *a.* worthy of consideration.
**beherzt,** *p.a.* courageous.
**behilflich,** *a.* helpful, useful.
**behindern,** *v.t.* hinder.
**Behinderung,** *f.* hindrance, hindering.
**Behörde,** *f.* authority, magistrate.
**behördlich,** *a.* official.
**Behuf,** *m.* purpose, object; behalf.
**behufs,** *prep.* in behalf of, in order to.
**behüten,** *v.t.* guard.
**behutsam,** *a.* cautious, careful.
**bei,** *prep.* at, near, by; on, in, about; with.
**beibehalten,** *v.t.* retain, keep, continue.
**Beibl.,** *abbrev.* (Beiblatt, -blätter) supplement(s).
**Beiblatt,** *n.* supplement, supplementary sheet.
**beibringen,** *v.t.* administer; produce; impart; teach.
**Beidringungsmittel,** *n.* vehicle (as for drugs).
**beidäugig,** *a.* binocular.
**beide,** *a.* both; either. **-mal,** *adv.* both times.
**beiderlei,** *a.* of both kinds, both.
**beiderseitig,** *a.* on both sides, mutual.
**beiderseits,** *adv.* on both sides, mutually.
**beidlebig,** *a.* amphibious.
**beidrecht,** *a.* (of fabrics) reversible.
**beidseitig,** *a.* on both sides, bilateral.
**beieinander,** *adv.* together.
**Beifall,** *m.* approval, applause.
**beifällig,** *a.* approving, favorable.
**beifolgend,** *p.a.* inclosed, annexed.
**beifügen,** *v.t.* add, annex, attach, subjoin.
**Beifuss,** *m.* artemisia, mugwort, wormwood.
**Beigabe,** *f.* addition, supplement.
**beigeben,** *v.t.* add.
**beigemischt,** *p.a.* admixed.
**Beigeschmack,** *m.* aftertaste, tang, flavor.
**Beih.,** *abbrev.* (Beiheft, -hefte) supplement(s).
**Beiheft,** *n.* supplemental part or number, supplement. (The word is sometimes used in titles of periodicals; as, *Kolloidchemische Beihefte.*)
**Beihilfe,** *f.* help, assistance; subsidy.
**beikommen,** *v.i.* approach, get at, reach.
**Beil,** *n.* hatchet; (**grosses**) ax.
**Beilage,** *f.* addition, supplement, appendix; enclosure.
**beiläufig,** *a.* incidental; approximate.
**beilegen,** *v.t.* add, enclose; settle; attribute.
**Beilstein,** *m.* axstone, nephrite.
**Beiluft,** *f.* admixed air; secondary air.
**beim,** *abbrev.* bei dem.
**beimengen,** *v.t.* admix, add.
**Beimengung,** *f.* admixture; impurity.
**beimessen,** *v.t.* attribute. — *v.r.* assume.
**beimischen,** *v.t.* admix, mix with.
**Beimischung,** *f.* admixture, mixture; infusion.
**beimischungsfrei,** *a.* free from admixture.
**beimpfen,** *v.t.* inoculate.
**Bein,** *n.* bone; leg.
**beinah, beinahe,** *adv.* almost, nearly.
**Beiname,** *m.* surname; nickname.
**Bein-asche,** *f.* bone ash. **-brech,** *m. & n.* (*Bot.*)

bog asphodel; (*Min.*) osteocolla. **-fäule, -fäulnis,** *f.* bone decay, caries. **-haut,** *f.* periosteum. **-kleider,** *pl.* trousers, breeches. **-mark,** *n.* bone marrow. **-mehl,** *n.* bone meal. **-schwarz,** *n.* bone black. **-türkis,** *m.* bone turquoise, odontolite. **-wurz,** *f.* comfrey (*Symphytum officinale*).

**beiordnen,** *v.t.* adjoin, coördinate.

**beipflichten,** *v.i.* assent, agree.

**Beirat,** *m.* advisory board; adviser.

**beisammen,** *adv.* together.

**Beisatz,** *m.* addition, admixture; alloy.

**Beischmack,** *m.* aftertaste, tang, flavor.

**Beisein,** *n.* presence.

**beiseite,** *adv.* aside, apart.

**beisetzen,** *v.t.* bury, inter.

**Beispiel,** *n.* example. **-zum —,** for example, e.g.

**beispiellos,** *a.* unexampled, unparalleled.

**beispielsweise,** *adv.* for example.

**beispringen,** *v.i.* assist.

**Beissbeere,** *f.* cayenne pepper.

**beissen,** *v.t.* bite. — *v.i.* bite, smart, burn. — **beissend,** *p.a.* biting, sharp, pungent, acrid, burning.

**Beiss-probe,** *f.* (*Brewing*) biting test. **-zange,** *f.* nippers, pincers.

**Beistand,** *m.* assistance; supporter.

**beistehen,** *v.t.* stand by, assist.

**beisteuern,** *v.t.* contribute.

**beistimmen,** *v.i.* agree, concur.

**Beitel,** *m.* chisel.

**Beitr.,** *abbrev.* (Beitrag. -träge) contribution(s).

**Beitrag,** *m.* contribution; share, quota; dues.

**beitragen,** *v.t.& i.* contribute.

**beitreiben,** *v.t.* collect; drive in.

**beitreten,** *v.t.* accede, join.

**beiwohnen,** *v.i.* be present; cohabit.

**Beiwerk,** *n.* accessory(-ies); attachment(s).

**Beiwert,** *m.* coefficient, factor.

**Beiwort,** *n.* adjective; epithet.

**Beizahl,** *f.* coefficient, factor.

**Beiz-artikel,** *m.* (*Calico*) mordant style. **-bad,** *n.* mordant bath, pickling bath, etc. (see Beize). **-behandlung,** *f.* mordanting, pickling, etc. (see beizen). **-brüchigkeit,** *f.* (*Metal.*) acid brittleness. **-brühe,** *f.* (*Leather*) bate, drench. **-bütte,** *f.* (*Leather*) drench pit, bate tub. **-charakter,** *m.* (*Dyeing*) mordant character.

**Beize,** *f.* corrosive; corrosion; (*Dyeing*) mordant; disinfectant; disinfection; (*Med.*) caustic, cauterization; (*Leather*) bate, drench; (*Metal.*) pickle; etching; staining; stain.

**beizempfindlich,** *a.* sensitive to corrosion, mordanting, etc. (see beizen).

**beizen,** *v.t.* corrode; mordant; cauterize; steep; bate, drench (hides); etch; pickle; blanch (metals); disinfect; stain; sauce (tobacco); carrot (fur). — **beizend,** *p.a.* corroding, etc.; corrosive, caustic; disinfectant.

**Beizen-dampffarbe,** *f.* mordant steam color. **-druck,** *m.* mordant printing. **-druckartikel,** *m.* mordant-printed style.

**beizenfärben,** *v.t.* dye on a mordant.

**Beizen-farbstoff,** *m.* mordant dye. **-gelb,** *n.* mordant yellow. **-klotzartikel,** *m.* mordant-padded style.

**Beizer,** *m.* pickler, etcher, etc. (see beizen).

**Beizerei,** *f.* (*Metal.*) pickling plant; pickling.

**Beiz-farbe,** *f.* mordant color. **-farbstoff,** *m.* mordant dye. **-flotte,** *f.* mordanting liquor or bath. **-flüssigkeit,** *f.* corrosive liquid, caustic liquor; mordant liquor; steeping liquor; stain; (*Metal.*) pickle; (*Leather*) bate, drench; disinfecting liquid. **-gelb,** *n.* mordant yellow. **-gerät,** *n.* apparatus for mordanting, steeping, etc. (see beizen). **-grund,** *m.* (*Dyeing*) mordanted bottom. **-kraft,** *f.* corrosive or caustic power; causticity; mordant strength; disinfecting power. **-lösung,** *f.* corroding solution, mordanting solution, etc. (see beizen and cf. Beizflüssigkeit). **-material,** *n.* (*Dyeing*) mordanting substance. **-mittel,** *n.* corrosive; caustic; mordant; disinfectant. **-ofen,** *m.* (*Tin Plate*) scaling furnace. **-sprödigkeit,** *f.* (*Metal.*) acid brittleness. **-stoff,** *m.* (*Dyeing*) mordant.

**Beizung,** *f.* corroding, etc. (see beizen).

**Beizwasser,** *n.* =Beizflüssigkeit; pickling plant sewage.

**bejahen,** *v.t.* affirm.

**bejahrt,** *a.* aged.

**bekalken,** *v.t.* lime.

**bekämpfen,** *v.t.* combat, oppose.

**Bekämpfung,** *f.* fighting (against), combating.

**Bekämpfungs-massnahme,** *f.* control measure (as for disease). **-mittel,** *n.* means of attack or control.

**bekannt,** *p.a.* see bekennen.

**bekanntlich, bekanntermassen,** *adv.* as is known; notoriously.

**Bekannt-machung,** *f.* publication, announcement, notice, bulletin. **-schaft,** *f.* acquaintance; knowledge.

**bekennen,** *v.t.* confess, acknowledge. — **bekannt,** *p.a.* known; noted, famous; acquainted (with).

**Bekenntnis,** *n.* confession; acknowledgment.

**beklagen,** *v.t.* deplore; pity. — *v.r.* complain.

**bekleben,** *v.t.* paste; placard; label; cover.

**Beklebezettel,** *m.* label.

**beklecken, bekleckern, beklecksen,** *v.t.* blur, blotch, blot, daub, stain.

**bekleiden,** *v.t.* cover, coat, line, face, box; clothe; invest; occupy.

**Bekleidung,** *f.* casing, lining, jacket, coating, clothing, etc. (see bekleiden).

**Bekohlung,** *f.* supplying with coal, coaling.
**bekommen,** *v.t.* get, receive. — *v.i.* agree (with).
**bekömmlich,** *a.* obtainable; good, beneficial.
**bekräftigen,** *v.t.* confirm, assert, emphasize; aggravate.
**bekränzen,** *v.t.* wreathe, festoon.
**bekritteln,** *v.t.* censure.
**bekrusten,** *v.t.* incrust, crust.
**Bekrustung,** *f.* incrustation.
**bekümmern,** *v.t.* afflict, trouble.
**bekupfern,** *v.t.* copper.
**-bel.** -ble.
**Bela,** *f.* (*Bot.*) bel (*Aegle marmelos*).
**beladen,** *v.t.* load, charge, burden.
**Beladen,** *n.*, **Beladung,** *f.* loading, charging; load, cargo, freight.
**Belag,** *m.* covering, coating, lining, plating.
**belagern,** *v.t.* besiege.
**Belang,** *m.* importance; amount.
**belangen,** *v.t.* concern; bring action against.
**belanglos,** *a.* unimportant.
**Belanussbaum,** *m.* bel, bael (*Aegle marmelos*).
**belassen,** *v.t.* leave.
**belasten,** *v.t.* load, weight, burden; charge.
**belästigen,** *v.t.* trouble, bother.
**Belästigung,** *f.* annoyance, trouble.
**Belastung,** *f.* load, burden; charge; burdening; debit; (*Med.*) taint.
**Belastungs-fähigkeit, -möglichkeit,** *f.* carrying capacity, load capacity.
**belaufen,** *v.r.* amount. — *v.t.* run over; cover; survey.
**beleben,** *v.t.* vivify, quicken, enliven; activate; revive, resuscitate; brighten, freshen (colors). — **belebt,** *p.a.* alive; lively; vivified, activated, etc.
**Belebtschlamm,** *m.* activated sludge.
**Belebungsmittel,** *n.* activator; restorative; freshener.
**belecken,** *v.t.* lick; play upon.
**beledern,** *v.t.* cover with leather, leather.
**Beleg,** *m.* covering, coating, lining; plating; incrustation; floor; proof; document. **-analyse,** *f.* analysis giving experimental proof; check analysis.
**belegen,** *v.t.* cover, line, face, overlay, coat; prove, check; illustrate.
**Beleg-körper,** *m.* covering body or substance. **-schaft,** *f.* (set of) workers, gang, crew. **-schicht,** *f.* covering layer.
**Belegung,** *f.* covering, coating, coat; charge.
**belehren,** *v.t.* instruct, advise.
**Belehrung,** *f.* instruction, advice.
**beleibt,** *a.* stout, corpulent.
**beleidigen,** *v.t.* offend, wrong, insult.
**beleimen,** *v.t.* glue, cover with glue.
**beleuchten,** *v.t.* light, illuminate; examine.
**Beleuchtung,** *f.* lighting, illumination; elucidation; examination.
**Beleuchtungs-dauer,** *f.* time of exposure (to light). **-einrichtung,** *f.* illuminating contrivance or installation. **-gerät,** *n.* illuminating apparatus, illuminator. **-kegel,** *m.* cone of illumination. **-linse,** *f.* illuminating lens. **-mittel,** *n.* illuminant. **-schirm,** *m.* reflector. **-spiegel,** *m.* reflecting mirror.
**Belgien,** *n.* Belgium.
**belgisch,** *a.* Belgian.
**belichten,** *v.t.* expose (to light); irradiate.
**Belichtung,** *f.* exposure (to light); irradiation.
**Belichtungs-karte,** *f.* (*Dyeing*) exposure card. **-messer,** *m.* exposure meter. **-stärke,** *f.* intensity of irradiation. **-zeit,** *f.* time of exposure (to light).
**belieben,** *v.t.* like, choose. — *v.i.* be pleasing. — **beliebt,** *p.a.* popular, favorite.
**Belieben,** *n.* inclination, pleasure.
**beliebig,** *a.* optional, arbitrary, random, any, whatever. — *adv.* optionally, at pleasure, as desired.
**beliebt,** *p.a.* see belieben.
**beliefern,** *v.t.* supply, furnish (with).
**Belit,** *n.*, **Belith,** *m.* (*Cement*) belite.
**bellen,** *v.i.* bark; clamor.
**belohnen,** *v.t.* reward, remunerate.
**belüften,** *v.t.* (*Aero.*) ventilate, pressurize.
**Belüftung,** *f.* airing, ventilation.
**belustigen,** *v.t.* amuse, divert.
**Bem.,** *abbrev.* of Bemerkung.
**bemächtigen,** *v.r.* take possession.
**bemalen,** *v.t.* paint, color, stain.
**bemänteln,** *v.t.* cover; color, varnish; palliate.
**bemerkbar,** *a.* perceptible; noticeable; remarkable.
**bemerken,** *v.t.* note, remark. notice.
**bemerkenswert,** *a.* worthy of note, remarkable.
**bemerklich,** *a.* = bemerkbar.
**Bemerkung,** *f.* observation, remark, note.
**bemessen,** *v.t.* proportion, regulate, measure. — *p.a.* measured, exact; symmetrical.
**bemodert,** *p.a.* moldy.
**bemoost,** *p.a.* mossy.
**bemühen,** *v.t.* trouble. — *v.r.* trouble; endeavor, strive.
**bemustern,** *v.t.* sample; match, (*Dyeing*) dye to pattern, imitate; ornament, figure.
**benachbart,** *p.a.* neighboring, adjacent, vicinal.
**benachrichtigen,** *v.t.* inform, notify.
**benachteiligen,** *v.t.* prejudice, harm, injure.
**benebelt,** *a.* fogged, dimmed; foggy, misty.
**Benediktinerlikör,** *m.* benedictine.
**benehmen,** *v.t.* take away, remove; affect, make dizzy. — *v.r.* behave.
**Benehmen,** *n.* behavior. conduct.
**benennen,** *v.t.* name, call.
**Benennung,** *f.* nomenclature; name, naming, title, denomination, term.
**Beneöl,** *n.* oil of ben.

**benetzbar,** *a.* wettable.
**benetzen,** *v.t.* wet; moisten; sprinkle.
**benetzungsfähig,** *a.* wettable, moistenable.
**Benetzungswärme,** *f.* heat of wetting.
**bengalisch,** *a.* Bengal.
**Bengel,** *m.* club; clapper; boor, chap.
**Benincopal-insäure,** *f.* benincopalinic acid. **-säure,** *f.* benincopalic acid.
**Benit, Benitzucker,** *m.* barley sugar.
**Ben-öl,** *n.* oil of ben. **-säure,** *f.* benic acid (behenic acid).
**benötigt,** *a.* needed, necessary; in need (of). — **benötigten Falls,** in case of need.
**benummern,** *v.t.* number.
**benutzbar,** *a.* utilizable, applicable, available.
**benutzen,** *v.t.* use, utilize, employ.
**Benutzer,** *m.* user.
**Benz-.** benz-, benzo- (preferably the latter before consonants; as, *Benztriazin,* benzotriazine). **-arsinigsäure,** *f.* benzarsinous acid. **-arsinsäure,** *f.* benzarsinic (benzarsonic) acid.
**Benzin,** *n.* gasoline, petrol; benzine. — **normales —,** benzine. **-dampf,** *m.* gasoline (or benzine) vapor. **-ersatz, -ersatzstoff,** *m.* gasoline substitute. **-kohlenwasserstoff,** *m.* aliphatic hydrocarbon; petroleum hydrocarbon. **-seife,** *f.* benzine soap. **-wagen,** *m.* gasoline automobile, petrol car.
**Benzochin-.** benzoquin-. **-hydron,** *n.* benzoquinhydrone.
**Benzochinon,** *n.* benzoquinone.
**Benzochlorid,** *n.* $\alpha, \alpha, \alpha$-trichlorotoluene.
**Benzoe,** *n. & f.* benzoin (gum). **-äther,** *m.* benzoic ether (ethyl benzoate). **-baum,** *m.* benzoin tree (*Styrax benzoin*). **-blumen,** *f. pl.* flowers of benzoin (benzoic acid).
**Benzoechtblau,** *n.* benzo fast blue.
**Benzoe-gummi,** *n.* gum benzoin, benzoin. **-harz,** *n.* benzoin (the resin). **-lorbeer,** *m.* spicebush (*Benzoin aestivale*). **-salz,** *n.* benzoate.
**benzoesauer,** *a.* of benzoic acid, benzoate of.
**Benzoesäure,** *f.* benzoic acid. **-äther,** *m.* benzoic ester, specif. ethyl benzoate.
**benzoesäurehaltig,** *a.* containing benzoic acid.
**Benzoeschmalz,** *n.* benzoinated lard, benzoated lard.
**benzoiniert,** *p.a.* benzoinated, benzoated.
**Benzol,** *n.* benzene ($C_6H_6$); benzol (commercial mixture). — **90er —,** 90 per cent benzol. **-bindung,** *f.* benzene linkage. **-derivat,** *n.* benzene derivative.
**Benzoleinsäure,** *f.* benzoleic acid.
**Benzolichtrot,** *n.* benzo light red.
**benzolisch,** *a.* benzene.
**Benzol-kern,** *m.* benzene nucleus. **-kohlenwasserstoffe,** *m.pl.* benzene hydrocarbons. **-lack,** *m.* benzol varnish. **-reihe,** *f.* benzene series. **-rest,** *m.* benzene residue. **-sulfosäure, -sulfonsäure,** *f.* benzenesulfonic acid, phenylsulfonic acid. **-vorerzeugnis,** *n.* crude benzol. **-wäsche,** *f.* benzol recovery (by washing); benzol recovery plant. **-wäscher,** *m.* benzol washer, benzol scrubber. **-waschöl,** *n.* benzol wash oil. **-wasserstoff,** *m.* hydrogenated benzene.
**Benzo-persäure,** *f.* peroxybenzoic acid, perbenzoic acid. **-phenol,** *n.* phenol ($C_6H_5OH$). **-schwarzblau,** *n.* benzo black-blue.
**benzoylieren,** *v.t.* benzoylate, introduce benzoyl into.
**Benzoylwasserstoff,** *m.* benzoyl hydride (benzaldehyde).
**beobachtbar,** *a.* observable.
**beobachten,** *v.t.* observe.
**Beobachter,** *m.* observer.
**Beobachtung,** *f.* observation; observance.
**Beobachtungs-fehler,** *m.* error of observation. **-fenster,** *n.* observation window, peephole. **-gabe,** *f.* faculty for observation. **-material,** *n.* observational material. **-rohr,** *n.*, **-röhre,** *f.* observation tube (as for a polariscope or spectroscope).
**beölen,** *v.t.* oil.
**bepacken,** *v.t.* load, pack.
**bepflastern,** *v.t.* plaster; pave.
**bepichen,** *v.t.* pitch.
**beplatten,** *v.t.* plate; pave, floor.
**bepudern,** *v.t.* powder.
**bequem,** *a.* convenient; easy; comfortable.
**bequemen,** *v.r.* conform, comply.
**Bequemlichkeit,** *f.* convenience, comfort; indolence.
**ber.,** *abbrev.* (berechnet) calculated.
**Ber.,** *abbrev.* (Bericht, Berichte) report(s); specif., *Berichte der deutschen chemischen Gesellschaft.*
**Berapp,** *m.* rough plaster, brown coat; roughcast.
**berappen,** *v.t.* rough-plaster; roughcast.
**beraten,** *v.t.* advise; consult.
**Berat. Ing.,** *abbrev.* (Beratender Ingenieur) consulting engineer.
**beratschlagen,** *v.r.* consult, deliberate.
**Beratung,** *f.* consultation, deliberation; conference, council; counsel, advice.
**berauben,** *v.t.* rob, deprive.
**beräuchern,** *v.t.* fumigate.
**berauschen,** *v.t.* intoxicate. — **berauschende Getränke,** intoxicating liquors.
**Berauschungsmittel,** *n.* intoxicant.
**Berberin,** *n.* berberine; barberry. **-saft,** *m.* barberry juice.
**Berberisrinde,** *f.* barberry bark.
**Berberitze,** *f.* barberry, berberis.
**berechenbar,** *a.* calculable; appreciable.
**berechnen,** *v.t.* calculate, compute; charge.

**Berechnung,** *f.* calculation; account.
**Berechnungsweise,** *f.* mode or method of calculation.
**berechtigen,** *v.t.* entitle, authorize, qualify.
**Berechtigung,** *f.* authorization, right.
**bereden,** *v.t.* persuade; talk over. — *v.r.* confer.
**Beredsamkeit,** *f.* eloquence.
**Bereich,** *m.* reach, range; domain; region.
**bereichern,** *v.t.* enrich.
**bereifen,** *v.t.* cover with frost, frost; hoop.
**Bereifung,** *f.* tire equipment, tires; hoar frost.
**bereinigen,** *v.t.* purify, cleanse, clear.
**bereit,** *a.* ready, prepared.
**bereiten,** *v.t.* prepare, make ready, make.
**bereits,** *adv.* already.
**Bereitschaft,** *f.* readiness, preparedness.
**bereitstellen,** *v.t.* prepare; make, manufacture.
**Bereitung,** *f.* preparation; manufacture.
**bereitwillig,** *a.* ready, willing, eager, prompt.
**bereuen,** *v.t.* repent, regret.
**Berg,** *m.* mountain; (*Mining*) gang, waste; hill. hump; (*Paper*) breasting (of a rag engine).
**Berg-.** mountain; rock; mineral; native; mining, mines. (See the following entries.)
**bergab,** *adv.* downhill.
**Berg-ader,** *f.* lode, vein. **-akademie,** *f.* school of mines. **-alaun,** *m.* rock alum, roche alum (Roman alum); alum stone, alunite.
**bergan,** *adv.* uphill.
**Berg-arbeit,** *f.* mining. **-art,** *f.* gang, matrix, vein stuff. **-asche,** *f.* an inferior kind of mineral blue. **-balsam,** *m.* petroleum. **-bau,** *m.* mining. **-baukunde,** *f.* science of mining. **-blau,** *n.* mineral blue, azurite. **-braun,** *n.* umber. **-butter,** *f.* (*Min.*) impure iron alum, iron sulfate or zinc sulfate.
**bergen,** *v.t.* save, shelter, conceal, hide. — **geborgen,** *p.a.* safe; well off.
**Berg-erz,** *n.* raw ore. **-farbe,** *f.* ocher.
**bergfein,** *a.* (*Min.*) native.
**Berg-fett,** *n.* mountain tallow, ozocerite. **-feuchtigkeit,** *f.* rock moisture, quarry water. **-flachs,** *m.* mountain flax, amianthus. **-fleisch,** *n.* mountain flesh (a variety of asbestos). **-fluss,** *m.* colored quartz; fluorite. **-gang,** *m.* vein, lode. **-gelb,** *n.* mountain yellow, yellow ocher. **-glas,** *n.* rock crystal (transparent quartz). **-glimmer,** *m.* margarite. **-gold,** *n.* gold found in primitive rocks. **-grün,** *n.* mineral green, green verditer (green basic copper carbonate). **-guhr,** *m.* mountain milk, agaric mineral (earthy calcium carbonate). **-gut,** *n.* minerals. **-haar,** *n.* amianthus. **-halde,** *f.* (*Mining*) dump, refuse heap. **-harz,** *n.* mineral pitch, asphalt.
**bergharzig,** *a.* asphaltic, bituminous.
**Bergholz,** *m.* rock wood (ligniform asbestos).
**bergig,** *a.* mountainous; hilly.
**berginisieren,** *v.t.* (*Fuels*) berginize, subject to the Bergius process.
**Berg-kalk,** *m.* rock lime; (*Geol.*) mountain limestone. **-kiesel,** *m.* rock flint, chert; felsite. **-kohle,** *f.* (mineral) coal. **-kork,** *m.* mountain cork (a light form of asbestos). **-kreide,** *f.* rock lime. **-kristall, -krystall,** *m.* rock crystal (transparent quartz). **-kupfer,** *n.* native copper. **-lasur,** *f.* azurite. **-leder,** *n.* mountain leather (a form of asbestos). **-mann,** *m.* miner.
**bergmännisch,** *a.* mining, pertaining to miners.
**Berg-mehl,** *n.* mountain flour (or meal), kieselguhr. **-melisse,** *f.* calamint. **-milch,** *m.* mountain milk, agaric mineral (earthy calcium carbonate). **-minze, -münze,** *f. lit.,* mountain mint (applied to several menthaceous plants, as catnip or catmint, calamint, field basil, etc.). **-naphta,** *f.* mineral naphtha, petroleum. **-öl,** *n.* petroleum. **-papier,** *n.* mountain paper (a form of asbestos). **-pech,** *n.* mineral pitch, asphalt. **-petersilie,** *f.* mountain parsley. **-rot,** *n.* realgar; Indian red; cinnabar. **-salz,** *n.* rock salt. **-schule,** *f.* school of mines. **-schwaden,** *m.* fire damp; choke damp. **-schwefel,** *m.* native sulfur. **-seife,** *f.* mountain soap (a kind of clay); rock butter (impure iron or zinc sulfate). **-talg,** *m.* mountain tallow, ozocerite; rock butter (impure iron or zinc sulfate). **-tee,** *m.* mountain tea, wintergreen. **-teegeist,** *m.* spirit of wintergreen, spirit of gaultheria. **-teeöl,** *n.* oil of wintergreen. **-teer,** *m.* mineral tar, maltha. **-torf,** *m.* mountain peat.
**Bergung,** *f.* saving, sheltering; salvage.
**Berg-unschlitt,** *m.* = Bergbutter. **-wachs,** *n.* mineral wax, ozocerite. **-werk,** *n.* mine. **-wesen,** *n.* mining. **-wetter,** *n.* (*Mining*) damp. **-wolle,** *f.* mineral wool (asbestos). **-zinn,** *n.* native tin; tinstone, cassiterite. **-zinnerz,** *n.* tinstone, cassiterite. **-zinnober,** *m.* native cinnabar. **-zunder,** *m.* mountain tinder (asbestos).
**Bericht,** *m.* report; notice, information.
**berichten,** *v.t.* inform, advise, notify. — *v.i.* report (on).
**Berichterstatter,** *m.* reporter, correspondent.
**berichtigen,** *v.t.* adjust, correct; settle (an account).
**Berichtigung,** *f.* correction; rectification; settlement.
**Berichtigungstafel,** *f.* correction table.
**berieseln,** *v.t.* cause to flow or trickle over; spray; scrub (gases or vapors); water, irrigate.
**Berieselungs-bütte,** *f.* (*Cellulose*) wash box. **-kühler,** *m.* trickle cooler, spray cooler. **-turm,** *m.* wash tower scrubbing tower, scrub-

ber; water-cooling tower. **-verflüssiger,** *m.* spray condenser.

**Berl. Ber.,** *abbrev.* (Berliner Berichte) *Berichte der deutschen chemischen Gesellschaft.*

**Berliner-blau,** *n.* Berlin blue, Prussian blue. **-blausäure,** *f.* hydrocyanic acid. **-braun,** *n.* Prussian brown. **-grün,** *n.* Prussian green. **-rot,** *n.* Berlin red (a red lake color). **-säure,** *f.* prussic acid. **-weiss,** *n.* a kind of white lead.

**Bernstein,** *m.* amber. — **schwarzer —,** jet.

**Bernstein-.** amber; succinic, succinyl, succino-. **-alaun,** *m.* aluminous amber. **-aldehyd,** *n.* succinaldehyde.

**bernsteinartig,** *a.* amber-like.

**Bernsteinerde,** *f.* mineral amber.

**bernsteinfarbig,** *a.* amber-colored.

**Bernstein-fett,** *n.* ambrain. **-firnis,** *m.* amber varnish. **-geist,** *m.* spirit of amber. **-lack,** *m.* amber varnish. **-öl,** *n.* oil of amber, oleum succini. **-salz,** *n.* succinate.

**bernsteinsauer,** *a.* of succinic acid, succinate of.

**Bernsteinsäure,** *f.* succinic acid.

**berosten,** *v.i.* rust, become rusty.

**Berstdruck,** *m.* bursting pressure.

**bersten,** *v.t.* burst, explode, rupture, crack.

**Berstprobe,** *f.* (*Paper*) burst(ing) test.

**Bertram,** *m.* pellitory (*Anacyclus pyrethrum* and similar plants). **-(s)wurzel, -wurz,** *f.* pellitory, pyrethrum (root of *Anacyclus pyrethrum*).

**berüchtigt,** *p.a.* notorious.

**berücksichtigen,** *v.t.* bear in mind, regard, consider, allow for.

**Berücksichtigung,** *f.* regard, consideration.

**Beruf,** *m.* calling, occupation, profession.

**berufen,** *v.t.* call, appoint. — *v.r.* appeal.

**Berufkraut,** *n.* any of various plants, specif. (*Pharm.*) fleabane (*Erigeron*).

**Berufs-.** professional, occupational, vocational. **-genossenschaft,** *f.* professional association; coöperative association. **-kleider,** *n.pl.* working clothes.

**berufsmässig,** *a.* professional.

**Berufung,** *f.* convening, convocation; nomination, appointment; (*Law*) appeal.

**beruhen,** *v.i.* rest, depend.

**beruhigen,** *v.t.* quiet; kill (molten metal); stabilize; reassure. — *v.r.* become quiet, moderate, abate. — **beruhigend,** *p.a.* quieting, sedative.

**Beruhigungsmittel,** *n.* sedative; anodyne.

**berühmt,** *p.a.* famous, celebrated.

**berühren,** *v.t.* touch; touch on. — **berührend,** *p.a.* touching, tangent.

**Berührende,** *f.* tangent.

**Berührung,** *f.* contact; touching; tangency.

**Berührungs-ebene,** *f.* tangential plane. **-elektrizität,** *f.* contact electricity. **-fläche,** *f.* surface of contact. **-linie,** *f.* tangent. **-punkt,** *m.* point of contact or tangency. **-spannung,** *f.* (*Elec.*) contact potential. **-stelle,** *f.* place of contact; mark (made by touching something).

**berussen,** *v.t.* soot, smoke, smut.

**Beryll,** *m.* beryl.

**beryllartig,** *a.* like beryl, berylline.

**Beryllerde,** *f.* beryllia (BeO).

**Beryllhydrat,** *n.* beryllium hydroxide.

**Beryllium-gehalt,** *m.* beryllium content. **-salz,** *n.* beryllium salt.

**bes.,** *abbrev.* (besonders) especially.

**besagen,** *v.t.* mean, signify, mention.

**besamen,** *v.t.* sow, seed, inseminate.

**besanden,** *v.t.* sand.

**besänftigen,** *v.t.* appease, soothe, calm.

**Besänftigungsmittel,** *n.* (*Med.*) sedative.

**Besatz,** *m.* border, edging, trimming; (*Metal.*) fettling; charge (of a crucible); stemming, tamping.

**Besatzung,** *f.* garrison, crew.

**beschädigen,** *v.t.* damage, injure.

**beschaffen,** *v.t.* procure; supply; make, execute. — *p.a.* constituted, conditioned.

**Beschaffenheit,** *f.* nature; state, condition; quality; disposition.

**beschaffenheitsmässig,** *a.* qualitative.

**Beschaffung,** *f.* procuring, etc. (see beschaffen); supply.

**beschäftigen,** *v.t.* occupy, busy, employ.

**Beschäftigung,** *f.* occupation, business.

**Beschallung,** *f.* acoustic irradiation.

**Beschaltung,** *f.* (*Elec.*) wiring.

**beschatten,** *v.t.* shade, shadow; hide.

**Beschau,** *f.* examination, inspection.

**beschauen,** *v.t.* examine, inspect; behold.

**beschaulich,** *a.* contemplative.

**beschäumt,** *p.a.* covered with foam, foamy.

**Bescheid,** *m.* decision, answer; information.

**bescheiden,** *v.t.* assign; inform; order; summon. — *v.r.* be content.

**bescheiden,** *a.* modest, unassuming.

**bescheinigen,** *v.t.* certify.

**bescheren,** *v.t.* give, bestow; shear; shave.

**beschichten,** *v.t.* cover with a layer, coat, plate, overlay.

**beschicken,** *v.t* load, charge, feed; prepare; mix; manage, attend to; exhibit.

**Beschickung,** *f.* loading, charging; load, charge; management; (*Minting*) alloy.

**Beschickungstrichter,** *m.* feed hopper.

**beschiessen,** *v.t.* bombard.

**Beschiessung,** *f.* bombardment.

**beschimmeln,** *v.i.* become moldy, mold.

**beschirmen,** *v.t.* shelter, cover; protect.

**Beschlag,** *m.* coating of some kind, as efflorescence, moisture on glass, tarnish on metals, clay to protect from heat, etc.; incrusta-

tion; deposit; fitting, mounting, hooping, etc.; seizure.
**beschlagen,** *v.i.* become coated, as with moisture, oxide, or mold; effloresce; tarnish; give an incrustation (before the blowpipe). — *v.t.* cover, mount or fit (with iron, metal, leather, etc.); lute. — *p.a.* versed, skilled.
**beschlagnehmen,** *v.t.* seize, attach; arrest.
**beschleunigen,** *v.t.* accelerate; hasten.
**Beschleuniger,** *m.* accelerator.
**Beschleunigung,** *f.* acceleration; despatch
**Beschleunigungsmittel,** *n.* accelerator.
**beschliessen,** *v.t.* finish, close; determine, resolve, decide.
**Beschluss,** *m.* conclusion; determination, decision; locking up, bond. — **einen — fassen,** pass a resolution, resolve, vote, decide. **-fassung,** *f.* conclusion, decision.
**beschmieren,** *v.t.* smear; (with fat) grease.
**beschmutzen,** *v.t.* soil, stain, foul, pollute.
**beschneiden,** *v.t.* cut, clip, trim, pare, dress; cut off, curtail.
**beschneit,** *p.a.* snow-covered.
**Beschönigung,** *f.* gloss, varnish; palliation.
**beschränken,** *v.t.* limit, confine. — **beschränkt,** *p.a.* limited; narrow.
**Beschränktheit,** *f.* limitedness.
**Beschränkung,** *f.* limiting, limitation, confinement.
**beschreiben,** *v.t.* describe; write on.
**Beschreibung,** *f.* description; writing.
**Beschriftung,** *f.* inscription; recording.
**beschuldigen,** *v.t.* accuse.
**Beschuss,** *m.* shooting, shelling, fire. **-probe,** *f.* shooting test; bombardment test.
**beschütten,** *v.t.* cover (with), spread (with).
**beschützen,** *v.t.* protect.
**beschwefeln,** *v.t.* sulfur.
**Beschwerde,** *f.* trouble, annoyance; complaint; malady.
**beschweren,** *v.t.* load; weight; charge; burden, annoy. — *v.r.* complain.
**beschwerlich,** *a.* burdensome, troublesome.
**Beschwerung,** *f.* loading, etc. (see beschweren); (*Elec.*) impedance.
**Beschwerungsmittel,** *n.* loading material, weighting agent.
**beschwichtigen,** *v.t.* allay, appease, soothe.
**beseelen,** *v.t.* animate, inspirit.
**besehen,** *v.t.* look at; inspect, examine.
**beseitigen,** *v.t.* remove, do away with.
**Beseitigung,** *f.* removal, elimination.
**Besen,** *m.* broom. **-ginster,** *m.*, **-kraut,** *n.* broom (*Cytisus scoparius*); (*Pharm.*) scoparius. **-stiel,** *m.* broomstick.
**besessen,** *p.p.* (of besitzen) possessed, etc.
**besetzbar,** *a.* capable of being occupied, etc. (see besetzen).
**besetzen,** *v.t.* occupy; set, trim, border, stock, fit; charge (a furnace or the like); fill (a position); engage.
**Besetzungszahl,** *f.* number of electrons in a shell.
**besichtigen,** *v.t.* inspect, view, examine.
**besiegeln,** *v.t.* seal.
**besiegen,** *v.t.* defeat, conquer.
**besinnen,** *v.r.* consider; recollect. — **besonnen,** *p.a.* considerate; discreet; prudent.
**Besinnung,** *f.* consideration; recollection; consciousness.
**besinnungslos,** *a.* unconscious.
**Besitz,** *m.* possession; property.
**besitzen,** *v.t.* possess, own, occupy, hold.
**Besitzer,** *m.* possessor, owner; occupant.
**Besitztum,** *n.* possession, property.
**Besitzung,** *f.* possession, property.
**Besk.** jelutong rubber.
**besonder,** *a.* particular, special, specific; separate; singular, odd.
**Besonderheit,** *f.* peculiarity, individuality; particular.
**besonders,** *adv.* especially; separately; singularly.
**besonnen,** *p.a.* see besinnen.
**Besonnung,** *f.* sunning, insolation.
**besorgen,** *v.t.* care for, attend to; do, effect; fear. — **besorgt,** *p.a.* anxious; careful.
**Besorgnis,** *f.* apprehension, fear; concern.
**Bespannung,** *f.* covering (as of cloth).
**bespinnen,** *v.t.* spin over, cover. — **besponnen,** *p.a.* spun-over, covered.
**besprechen,** *v.t.* discuss; arrange; conjure.
**Besprechung,** *f.* discussion; conference.
**besprengen,** *v.t.* sprinkle, spray.
**bespritzen,** *v.t.* sprinkle, spray, spatter.
**bespülen,** *v.t.* wash, bathe.
**Bessemer-birne,** *f.* Bessemer converter. **-ei,** *f.* Bessemer (steel) plant; Bessemerizing. **-eisen,** *n.* Bessemer iron.
**bessemern,** *v.t.* bessemerize.
**Bessemer-schlacke,** *f.* Bessemer slag. **-schmelze,** *f.* Bessemer heat. **-stahl,** *m.* Bessemer steel. **-verfahren,** *n.* Bessemer process.
**besser,** *a.* & *adv.* better.
**bessern,** *v.t.* better; correct. — *v.r.* grow better.
**Besserung,** *f.* betterment, improvement.
**Best.,** *abbrev.* (Bestimmung) determination; (Bestellung) order; (Bestand) amount.
**Bestand,** *m.* duration, stability; existence; amount, stock; crop, stand.
**beständig,** *a.* stable; constant, durable, resistant, permanent; proof; fast (colors); steady, steadfast. — **— machen,** render stable, etc.; stabilize.
**Beständig-keit,** *f.* stability, etc. (see beständig). **-machen,** *n.* stabilization.
**Bestandteil,** *m.* constituent; ingredient.
**bestärken,** *v.t.* confirm; strengthen.

**bestätigen,** *v.t.* confirm, ratify. — *v.r.* hold true.
**Bestätigung,** *f.* confirmation, verification; sanction; legalization.
**bestatten,** *v.t.* bury, inter.
**bestäuben,** *v.t.* dust, powder, cover with dust; pollinate. — **bestäubt,** *p.a.* dusty; pulverulent; dusted, etc.
**beste,** *a.* best. — **am besten,** best.
**bestechen,** *v.t.* stitch; bribe; charm.
**Besteck,** *n.* case, set (of instruments); cover (at table), tableware.
**bestecken,** *v.t.* stick (with); plant (with).
**Besteg,** *m.* (*Mining*) gouge, flucan.
**bestehen,** *v.i.* consist; exist; persist, insist. — *v.r.* resist; encounter; pass. — **— aus,** consist of.
**Bestehen,** *n.* composition; existence; persistence.
**bestellen,** *v.t.* order, appoint, engage; deliver; charge, prepare; arrange; till, plant.
**Besteller,** *m.* (*Com.*) orderer.
**Bestellschein,** *m.* order blank, requisition blank.
**Bestellung,** *f.* ordering, etc. (see bestellen); (*Com.*) order, commission.
**bestenfalls, bestens,** *adv.* at best.
**besterforscht,** *a.* best-investigated, best-known.
**besteuern,** *v.t.* tax, assess.
**Bestie,** *f.* beast, brute.
**bestimmbar,** *a.* determinable.
**bestimmen,** *v.t.* determine; fix, design, allot, define. — **bestimmt,** *p.a.* determined, determinate, definite, fixed, appointed, certain, specific.
**Bestimmtheit,** *f.* definiteness; determination; certainty.
**Bestimmung,** *f.* determination; appointment; definition; provision; destiny.
**Bestimmungsmethode,** *f.* method of determination.
**bestmeliert,** *a.* best-mixed.
**bestossen,** *v.t.* trim, plane, shape; hit.
**bestrafen,** *v.t.* punish.
**bestrahlen,** *v.t.* irradiate, expose (to rays); illuminate; sandblast.
**Bestrahlung,** *f.* irradiation, exposure (to rays); sandblasting.
**Bestrahlungs-gefäss,** *n.* irradiation vessel. **-zeit,** *f.* time of irradiation or exposure.
**bestreben,** *v.r.* strive, endeavor.
**Bestrebung,** *f.* striving, effort, endeavor; tendency.
**bestreichen,** *v.t.* coat, smear, spread; brush, stroke; sweep (over).
**bestreiten,** *v.t.* dispute; defray.
**bestreuen,** *v.t.* strew, sprinkle, powder.
**bestürzen,** *v.t.* charge, feed; cover; perplex, dismay, amaze.
**Bestwert,** *m.* best value, optimum value.
**Besuch,** *m.* visit; company.
**besuchen,** *v.t.* visit, resort to, attend.
**besudeln,** *v.t.* soil, contaminate, foul.
**betagt,** *p.a.* aged; due.
**betalgen,** *v.t.* tallow.
**Beta-naphtol,** *n.* beta naphthol, $\beta$-naphthol (2-naphthol). **-strahlen,** *m.pl.* beta rays.
**betätigen,** *v.t.* operate; put into operation, start; prove, manifest. — *v.r.* prove; participate (in).
**Betätigung,** *f.* operation; starting; activity; proving; participation.
**betäuben,** *v.t.* deafen, stun, stupefy, deaden.
**Betäubung,** *f.* stunning, stupefying; stupor; narcosis.
**Betäubungsmittel,** *n.* narcotic.
**betauen,** *v.t.* cover with dew, bedew.
**Bete,** *f.* beet, beetroot.
**beteeren,** *v.t.* tar.
**beteiligen,** *v.t.* give a share to; concern. — *v.r.* participate. — **beteiligt,** *p.a.* concerned, interested.
**Beteiligungszahl,** *f.* share, quota.
**Betel-nuss,** *f.* betel nut. **-pfeffer,** *m.* betel pepper, betel.
**beteuern,** *v.t.* protest, swear to.
**betiteln,** *v.t.* entitle, name.
**Beton,** *m.* concrete (made with cement), béton. **-bau,** *m.* concrete construction. **-bruch,** *m.* broken concrete; concrete fracture. **-eisen,** *n.* reinforcing iron.
**betonen,** *v.t.* accent, emphasize.
**Betonie,** *f.*, **Betonienkraut,** *n.* betony; water betony, water figwort.
**betonieren,** *v.t.* concrete, cover or lay with, or form of, concrete. — **betoniert,** *p.a.* concrete.
**Beton-mischer,** *m.*, **-mischmaschine,** *f.*, **-mischwerk,** *n.* concrete mixer. **-schicht,** *f.* layer of concrete.
**betr.,** *abbrev.* (betreffend) concerning, concerned, with reference to.
**Betracht,** *m.* consideration, regard, account.
**betrachten,** *v.t.* consider; regard; view, examine.
**beträchtlich,** *a.* considerable, important.
**Betrachtung,** *f.* consideration, reflection; inspection; analysis.
**Betrachtungszeichen,** *n.* reference symbol.
**Betrag,** *m.* amount, sum.
**betragen,** *v.t.* amount to. — *v.r.* behave.
**Betragen,** *n.* behavior, conduct.
**betrauen,** *v.t.* entrust.
**Betreff,** *m.* reference, regard (to). — **in — dessen,** as regards that.
**betreffen,** *v.t.* concern; befall; catch. — **betreffend,** *p.a.* concerning, concerned. — **betroffen,** *p.a.* disconcerted, dazed.
**betreffs,** *adv. with gen.* as regards.
**betreiben,** *v.t.* carry on, operate, run, conduct, pursue.

**betreten,** *v.t.* tread upon, enter upon. — *p.a.* beaten; confused.
**Betrieb,** *m.* work, working, operation, service; management; trade; works, factory, plant; impulse, impulsion. — **im —,** in operation; in practice. — **in — setzen,** set in operation, set going.
**betrieblich,** *a.* operative, working, functional.
**Betriebs-.** working, operating; industrial.
**betriebsam,** *a.* active, industrious.
**Betriebs-anlage,** *f.* plant, works. **-chemiker,** *m.* industrial chemist, works chemist. **-druck,** *m.* working pressure.
**betriebsfähig,** *a.* in working order, operable.
**betriebsfertig,** *a.* ready for operation.
**Betriebs-führung,** *f.* management, operation. **-gas,** *n.* fuel gas, motor gas. **-ingenieur,** *m.* works engineer. **-kontrolle,** *f.* control of (technical) operations. **-kosten,** *f.pl.* operating expenses. **-kraft,** *f.* motive power. **-laboratorium,** *n.* works laboratory, industrial laboratory. **-leiter,** *m.* manager. **-leitung,** *f.* management. **-prüfung,** *f.* works test.
**betriebssicher,** *a.* dependable (in operation).
**Betriebs-spannung,** *f.* (*Elec.*) operating voltage. **-stoff,** *m.* fuel; working material. **-stoffwechsel,** *m.* functional metabolism, basal metabolism. **-störung,** *f.* interruption of work, breakdown, shutdown. **-substanz,** *f.* working substance. **-technik,** *f.* operating technique, operating practice. **-verhältnisse,** *n.pl.* working conditions. **-versuch,** *m.* working test, bulk trial. **-wasser,** *n.* water for industrial use. **-wirtschaft,** *f.* economy of operation, industrial management.
**betriebswissenschaftlich,** *a.* relating to scientific management, efficiency.
**Betriebs-zeit,** *f.* working hours; shift; working season, campaign; operating time (required for any process). **-zustand,** *m.* working or operating condition.
**betrifft,** *pr. 3 sing.* (of betreffen) concerns, etc.
**betroffen,** *p.a.* see betreffen.
**Betrug,** *m.* fraud, deception.
**betrügen,** *v.t.* cheat, defraud, dupe.
**Bett,** *n.* bed.
**betteln,** *v.i.* beg.
**betten,** *v.t.* imbed, embed, bed; put to bed.
**Bett-stelle,** *f.* bedstead. **-tuch,** *n.* sheet.
**Bettung,** *f.* bedding, bed.
**Bettwanze,** *f.* bedbug.
**betüpfeln, betupfen, betüpfen,** *v.t.* dab, dip, tip; spot.
**Beuche,** *f.* bucking, bowking; bucking lye.
**beuchecht,** *a.* fast to bucking.
**beuchen,** *v.t.* buck (steep or boil in lye or suds).
**Beuch-fass,** *n.* bucking tub. **-flotte,** *f.* bucking liquor or lye. **-kessel,** *m.* bucking kier. **-lauge,** *f.* bucking lye. **-wasser,** *n.* buck.
**Beuge,** *f.* bend, bow; bending, flexure.
**beugen,** *v.t.* bend, flex; deflect; diffract (light); inflect (words); bow, humble.
**beugsam,** *a.* = biegsam.
**Beugung,** *f.* bending, etc. (see beugen); diffraction; flexure, flexion.
**Beugungs-bild,** *n.* (*Physics*) diffraction pattern. **-farbe,** *f.* (*Optics*) diffraction color. **-fleck,** *m.* (*Optics*) diffraction spot. **-gitter,** *n.* diffraction grating. **-strahl,** *m.* (*Optics*) diffraction ray.
**Beule,** *f.* bump, swelling, bulge; boil; blister.
**Beulenpest,** *f.* bubonic plague.
**beunruhigen,** *v.t.* disquiet, trouble.
**beurkunden,** *v.t.* authenticate, verify.
**beurteilen,** *v.t.* judge, estimate, criticize.
**Beurteilung,** *f.* judging, judgment; valuation, estimation; estimate; criticism.
**Beute,** *f.* booty, loot, spoil, prize; trough.
**Beutel,** *m.* bag; pouch; purse; sac, cyst, bursa. **-filter,** *n.* bag filter. **-gaze,** *f.* bolting gauze.
**beuteln,** *v.t.* bolt, sift. — *v.r.* bag.
**Beutel-sieb,** *n.* bolting sieve, bolter. **-tuch,** *n.* bolting cloth. **-zeug,** *n.* bolting apparatus; bolting cloth.
**Bevölkerung,** *f.* population.
**bevollmächtigen,** *v.t.* empower, authorize.
**bevor,** *conj.* before.
**bevorstehen,** *v.i.* approach, impend.
**bevorzugen,** *v.t.* prefer, favor.
**bewaffnen,** *v.t.* arm; equip; aid.
**Bewaffnung,** *f.* armament; equipment; armature (of a magnet).
**bewahren,** *v.t.* keep, preserve, protect.
**bewähren,** *v.t.* verify, approve, confirm. — *v.r.* prove true, prove good. — **bewährt,** *p.a.* tried, tested, approved.
**Bewahrungsmittel,** *n.* preservative; prophylactic.
**bewältigen,** *v.t.* overcome, master.
**bewandert,** *a.* versed, skilled, experienced.
**Bewandtnis,** *f.* case, state, situation.
**bewässern,** *v.t.* water, moisten, sprinkle, irrigate.
**Bewässerung,** *f.* watering, etc. (see bewässern).
**bewegbar,** *a.* movable, mobile.
**bewegen,** *v.t.& i.* move; agitate, stir, etc.; induce. — **bewegende Kraft,** motive power.
**Beweger,** *m.* motor; mover; agitator.
**Bewegkraft,** *f.* motive power.
**beweglich,** *a.* movable, mobile, portable, moving; versatile.
**Beweglichkeit,** *f.* mobility.
**Beweglichkeitsart,** *f.* kind of mobility, degree of freedom.
**Bewegung,** *f.* motion; movement, moving; stir, commotion.
**Bewegungs-.** motive, motor, motion. **-energie,** *f.* kinetic energy. **-grösse,** *f.* quantity of mo-

tion, momentum. **-kraft,** *f.* motive force, motive power. **-lehre,** *f.* mechanics; kinematics; kinetics.
**bewegungslos,** *a.* motionless.
**Bewegungs-maschine,** *f.* motor. **-richtung,** *f.* direction of motion. **-trieb,** *m.* momentum. **-zustand,** *m.* state of motion.
**bewehren,** *v.t.* arm; reinforce (as concrete).
**Bewehrung,** *f.* arming; reinforcement, stiffening, sheathing, wrapping.
**Beweis,** *m.* proof, evidence; argument. **-analyse,** *f.* documentary analysis.
**beweisbar,** *a.* provable, demonstrable.
**beweisen,** *v.t.* prove, demonstrate; show. — *v.r.* prove.
**Beweis-führung,** *f.* demonstration; reasoning. **-kraft,** *f.* conclusiveness, demonstrative power. **-last,** *f.* burden of proof.
**bewenden,** *v.i.* rest, drop.
**Bewerber,** *m.* candidate, applicant, aspirant.
**bewerfen,** *v.t.* plaster; pelt.
**bewerkstelligen,** *v.t.* accomplish, perform, effect.
**bewerten,** *v.t.* estimate, value, rate, grade.
**Bewertung,** *f.* estimation, valuation, rating.
**Bewetterung,** *f.* ventilation; air conditioning; weathering.
**bewickeln,** *v.t.* wrap round, envelop.
**bewilligen,** *v.t.* grant, permit.
**Bewilligung,** *f.* permission, consent; license.
**bewirken,** *v.t.* effect, cause, exert.
**bewirten,** *v.t.* entertain, treat.
**bewirtschaften,** *v.t.* manage, run; work.
**Bewitterung,** *f.* weathering.
**Bewitterungswiderstand,** *m.* resistance to weathering.
**bewog,** *pret.* (of bewegen) moved, etc.
**bewogen,** *p.p.* (of bewegen) moved, etc.
**bewohnen,** *v.t.* inhabit, occupy.
**Bewohner,** *m.* inhabitant, occupant, tenant.
**bewundern,** *v.t.* admire.
**bewunderns-wert, -würdig,** *a.* admirable, wonderful.
**Bewurf,** *m.* plastering, plaster, roughcast.
**bewusst,** *a.* conscious, aware; known.
**bewusstlos,** *a.* unconscious; senseless.
**Bewusstsein,** *n.* consciousness; knowledge.
**bez.,** *abbrev.* (beziehungsweise) respectively, or; (bezüglich) respecting; (bezogen) related; (bezahlt) paid.
**bezahlen,** *v.t.* pay.
**Bezahlung,** *f.* payment, settlement.
**bezähmen,** *v.t.* tame, restrain.
**bez. auf,** *abbrev.* (bezogen auf) referred to, relative to.
**bezeichnen,** *v.t.* mark, label; indicate; designate; signify, denote. — **bezeichnend,** *p.a.* significant; characteristic.
**Bezeichnung,** *f.* marking, notation; mark, sign, symbol; designation; note.
**Bezeichnungsweise,** *f.* manner (or method) of notation.
**bezeigen,** *v.t.* show, manifest.
**bezetteln,** *v.t.* label.
**bezeugen,** *v.t.* testify, certify.
**beziehen,** *v.t.* relate, refer; draw (money); order, buy (goods); enter; cover. — *v.r.* relate, refer; be overcast.
**Beziehung,** *f.* relation; reference, respect.
**beziehungs-los,** *a.* unrelated, irrelative. **-weise,** *adv.* respectively, or, and/or, as the case may be.
**beziffern,** *v.t.* mark with figures or ciphers, number; calculate, count. — *v.r.* amount.
**Bezirk,** *m.* region; circuit, district.
**Bezirks-.** district. **-verein,** *m.* district union.
**Bezoar-säure,** *f.* bezoardic acid (ellagic acid). **-stein,** *m.* bezoar stone, bezoar. **-wurzel,** *f.* (*Pharm.*) contrayerva.
**bezogen,** *p.a.* drawn, etc. (see beziehen); in reference (to), in regard (to). — **bezogenes Gewicht,** specific weight, specific gravity.
**Bezug,** *m.* relation, reference; cover, covering, coating.
**bezüglich,** *a.* & *prep.* relative, with reference (to), respecting, regarding.
**Bezugnahme,** *f.* reference.
**Bezugs-.** reference, standard. **-bedingungen,** *n.pl.* (*Com.*) terms. **-einheit,** *f.* reference unit. **-elektrode,** *f.* reference electrode. **-linie,** *f.* reference line. **-punkt,** *m.* reference point. **-quelle,** *f.* source of supply. **-seifenlösung,** *f.* standard soap solution. **-spektrum,** *n.* reference spectrum. **-substanz,** *f.* reference substance, standard substance. **-wert,** *m.* reference value; relative value.
**bezw.,** *abbrev.* beziehungsweise.
**bezwecken,** *v.t.* aim at, intend; peg.
**bezweifeln,** *v.t.* doubt, (call in) question.
**bezwingen,** *v.t.* subdue, overcome; restrain.
**bibasisch,** *a.* dibasic, bibasic.
**Bibel,** *f.* Bible.
**Biber,** *m.* beaver. **-geil,** *n.* castor, castoreum. **-geilkampher,** *m.* castorin. **-nell, -nelle,** *f.* burnet saxifrage (*Pimpinella saxifraga*). **-schwanz,** *m.* flat roofing tile.
**Bibirin,** *n.* bebeerine. **-säure,** *f.* bebeeric acid.
**Bibliothek,** *f.* library.
**Bibliothekar,** *m.* librarian.
**Bichromatlösung,** *f.* dichromate solution.
**bichromsauer,** *a.* of or combined with dichromic acid, dichromate of.
**bicyclish,** *a.* bicyclic.
**Biderivat,** *n.* di(substituted) derivative.
**biegbar,** *a.* capable of being bent, flexible.
**Biege,** *f.* bend, bow. **-festigkeit,** *f.* bending strength, flexural strength, transverse strength.
**biegen,** *v.t.* bend; curve; deflect; diffract,

refract (light); inflect (words). — *v.r.* bend, (of wood) warp. — *v.i.* bend.

**Biege-probe,** *f.* bending test or sample. **-rohr,** *n.*, **-röhre,** *f.* (glass) tube for bending. **-schlagfestigkeit,** *f.* bending strength under impacts. **-spannung,** *f.* bending stress, transverse stress. **-zahl,** *f.* bending number, bend-test number.

**biegfestig,** *a.* resistant to bending.

**biegsam,** *a.* flexible, pliable, pliant; ductile.

**Biegsamkeit,** *f.* flexibility; pliability; ductility.

**Biegung,** *f.* bending, etc. (see biegen); bend; flexure.

**biegungsfähig,** *a.* flexible, pliable; ductile.

**Biegungs-festigkeit,** *f.* = Biegefestigkeit. **-mikrowage,** *f.* a microbalance weighing by flection, as of a quartz filament.

**Biene,** *f.* bee.

**Bienen-harz,** *n.*, **-kitt,** *m.* bee glue, propolis. **-korb,** *m.* beehive. **-korb(koks)ofen,** *m.* beehive (coke) oven. **-wachs,** *n.* beeswax.

**Bier,** *n.* beer; (**englisches**) ale. **-blume,** *f.* head (froth) of beer. **-brauen,** *n.* beer brewing. **-brauerei,** *f.* beer brewing; brewery. **-essig,** *m.* malt vinegar, beer vinegar. **-fass,** *n.* beer barrel, beer keg. **-grand,** *n.* (*Brewing*) underback. **-hefe,** *f.* beer yeast, brewer's yeast. **-kessel,** *m.* (*Brewing*) boiling copper, boiler. **-pech,** *n.* brewer's pitch. **-prober,** *m.* beer tester, specif. beer hydrometer. **-schöne,** *f.* fining for beer. **-sieder,** *m.* (*Brewing*) kettleman. **-stein,** *m.* hard deposit from wort, beer scale. **-untersuchung,** *f.* examination of beer, beer analysis. **-wa(a)ge,** *f.* beer gage, beer hydrometer. **-würze,** *f.* beer wort, wort. **-zeug,** *n.* & *m.* beer yeast.

**Biestmilch,** *f.* colostrum.

**bieten,** *v.t.* offer; bid; show.

**Bijouterie,** *f.*, **-waren,** *f.pl.* jewelry.

**Bilanz,** *f.* balance; balance sheet.

**Bild,** *n.* image; figure; form; picture; diagram; illustration; photograph; idea, description.

**Bild.,** *abbrev.* (Bildung) formation.

**bilden,** *v.t.* form; shape, fashion; educate, cultivate, civilize. — *v.r.* form. — **bildend,** *p.a.* forming, etc.; component, constituent; formative; plastic (art).

**Bilderachat,** *m.* figured agate.

**Bildg.,** *abbrev.* (Bildung) formation.

**Bildhauer,** *m.* sculptor. **-gips,** *m.* sculptor's plaster. **-kitt, -leim,** *m.* badigeon. **-marmor,** *m.* statuary marble.

**bildlich,** *a.* figurative; typical; graphic.

**bildlos,** *a.* amorphous.

**Bildmarmor,** *m.* figured marble.

**Bildner,** *m.* component, constituent; former.

**Bildnis,** *n.* image, portrait, picture, likeness.

**bildsam,** *a.* plastic; flexible, ductile.

**Bild-samkeit,** *f.* plasticity; flexibility. **-schärfe,** *f.* (*Opt.*) sharpness of the image. **-schirm,** *m.* projection screen.

**bildschön,** *a.* most beautiful.

**Bild-stecher,** *m.* engraver. **-stein,** *m.* figure stone, agalmatolite. **-stock,** *m.* (*Printing*) cut, electro.

**Bildung,** *f.* formation; shape; structure; organization; development; education, culture.

**Bildungs-.** formation; formative; educational. **-energie,** *f.* energy of formation.

**bildungsfähig,** *a.* capable of formation or development; educable.

**Bildungs-geschwindigkeit,** *f.* speed of formation or development. **-gleichung,** *f.* equation of formation; structural equation. **-schicht,** *f.* formative layer; specif., (*Bot.*) cambium. **-wärme,** *f.* heat of formation. **-weise,** *f.* mode of formation.

**bildwerfen,** *v.t.* project (pictures).

**Bild-werfer,** *m.* projector (of pictures). **-werk,** *n.* sculpture, carving. **-wurf,** *m.* projection (of pictures). **-zeichen,** *n.* symbol.

**Billard,** *n.* billiards; billiard-table.

**Billet,** *n.* ticket; note.

**billig,** *a.* fair, just, reasonable; cheap.

**billigen,** *v.t.* approve of.

**Billigkeit,** *f.* equity, reasonableness; cheapness.

**Billion,** *f.* billion (in Germany $10^{12}$).

**Bilse,** *f.*, **Bilsenkraut,** *n.* henbane, hyoscyamus.

**Bimetall-.** bimetallic.

**Bims,** *m.* pumice, pumice stone. **-beton,** *m.* pumice (stone) concrete.

**bimsen,** *v.t.* rub with pumice stone, pumice.

**Bimsstaub,** *m.* pumice powder.

**Bimsstein, Bimstein,** *m.* pumice stone, pumice.

**bimsstein-ähnlich, -artig,** *a.* pumiceous.

**Bimssteinseife,** *f.* pumice soap.

**bin,** *pr. 1 sing.* (of sein) am.

**binär,** *a.* binary.

**Binarkies,** *m.* marcasite.

**Binde,** *f.* band; bandage; ligature; tie. **-elektron,** *n.* binding electron, valence electron. **-fähigkeit,** *f.* binding ability or strength. **-festigkeit,** *f.* adhesiveness. **-gewebe,** *f.* connective tissue. **-gewebesubstanz,** *f.* collagen. **-glied,** *n.* connecting member or link. **-haut,** *f.* conjunctiva. **-kraft,** *f.* combining power; binding power (of cements); cohesion. **-material,** *n.* binding material. **-mittel,** *n.* binding agent or material, binder, cementing material; bonding agent; cement, adhesive, agglutinant, medium.

**binden,** *v.t.* bind; fix, combine, unite; bond; tie, tie up; constrain. — *v.i.* bind; combine; set (of cement, etc.); harden. — **gebunden,** *p.a.* bound, combined, etc. — **gebundene Wärme,** latent heat.

**Binde-strich,** *m.* hyphen. **-substanz,** *f.* cement; (*Physiol.*) connective substance. **-ton,** *m.* ball clay; bonding clay. **-vermögen,** *n.* binding power; combining power; (of clays) plasticity. **-zeit,** *f.* (*Cement*) setting time.

**Bindfaden,** *m.* string, packthread.

**bindig,** *a.* binding, cohesive.

**Bindung,** *f.* binding, etc. (see binden, *v.t.* & *v.i.*); combination, union; bond; linkage; texture, weave.

**Bindungs-art,** *f.* kind of union, of combination, etc. (see binden). **-elektron,** *n.* bonding electron, linkage electron. **-energie,** *f.* bond energy, linkage energy.

**bindungsfähig,** *a.* capable of binding, of combining, etc. (see binden).

**Bindungsfähigkeit,** *f.* combining capacity, combining power; binding power.

**bindungsisomer,** *a.* showing isomerism due to different modes of union of the atoms (sometimes merely to different positions of a double bond).

**Bindungs-kraft,** *f.* combining force, linkage force. **-mittel,** *n.* = Bindemittel. **-refraktion,** *f.* bond refraction. **-system,** *n.* bond system, linkage system. **-vermögen,** *n.* = Bindevermögen. **-wärme,** *f.* heat of combination. **-weise,** *f.* mode of union.

**Bingel,** *f.*, **-kraut,** *n. Bot.* mercury (*Mercurialis*).

**Binitro-.** dinitro-. **-benzol,** *n.* dinitrobenzene.

**binnen,** *prep.* within.

**Binnen-.** internal, inner, inside, inland. **-druck,** *m.* internal pressure. **-handel,** *m.* domestic trade. **-raum,** *m.* inner or interior space. **-steuer,** *f.* internal revenue.

**Binom,** *n.* binomial.

**binomisch,** *a.* binomial.

**Binse,** *f.* rush; rattan.

**Biochemie,** *f.* biochemistry.

**biochemisch,** *a.* biochemical.

**biogen,** *a.* related to the life process, biogenic.

**Biolog, Biologe,** *m.* biologist.

**biologisch,** *a.* biological.

**Biophysik,** *f.* biophysics.

**Bioxyd,** *n.* bioxide, dioxide.

**Biquadrat,** *n.* (*Math.*) fourth power.

**Birektifikator,** *m.* double fractionating column.

**birgt,** *pr. 3 sing.* (of bergen) saves, shelters, etc.

**Birke,** *f.* birch.

**birken,** *a.* birch, birchen.

**Birken-holz,** *n.* birchwood. **-holzteer,** *m.* birch-(wood) tar. **-holzteerseife,** *f.* birch tar soap. **-kampher,** *m.* birch camphor, betulin. **-kohle,** *f.* birch charcoal. **-rinde,** *f.* birch bark. **-rindenöl, -öl,** *n.* oil of betula, oil of sweet birch. **-teer,** *m.* birch tar. **-teeröl,** *n.* birch tar oil.

**Birnäther,** *m.* = Birnenäther.

**Birne,** *f.* pear; pear-shaped object, as a bulb or ampoule; (*Metal.*) converter; (*Elec.*) bulb.

**Birnen-äther,** *m.*, **-essenz,** *f.* pear ether, pear essence. **-dephlegmator,** *m.* pear dephlegmator (fractionating column with pear-shaped bulbs).

**birnenförmig,** *a.* = birnförmig.

**Birnen-öl,** *n.* pear oil (amyl acetate). **-prozess,** *m.* (*Metal.*) converter process, Bessemer process. **-wein,** *m.* perry.

**Birnessig,** *m.* pear vinegar.

**birnförmig,** *a.* pear-shaped, pyriform.

**Birn-most,** *m.* pear juice, (new) perry. **-öl,** *n.* pear oil (amyl acetate). **-wein,** *m.* perry.

**birst,** *pr. 3 sing.* (of bersten) bursts, explodes, etc.

**bis,** *prep.* till, until, up to. — *conj.* till, until. — **— auf,** until; even to; except.

**Bisam,** *m.* musk; muskrat.

**bisamartig,** *a.* musky.

**Bisamkorn,** *n.* musk seed, abelmosk seed.

**bisher,** *adv.* hitherto, as yet.

**bisherig,** *a.* hitherto, till now.

**bislang,** *adv.* as yet, thus far.

**biss,** *pret.* (of beissen) bit.

**Biss,** *m.* bite; sting.

**Bisschen,** *n.* bit, little bit.

**Bissen,** *m.* morsel, bit; (*Med.*) bolus.

**Bisterbraun,** *n.* bister.

**bisterfarbig,** *a.* bister-colored, soot-brown.

**bisubstituiert,** *a.* disubstituted.

**bisw.,** *abbrev.* of bisweilen.

**bisweilen,** *adv.* sometimes, occasionally.

**Bitte,** *f.* request, prayer.

**bitten,** *v.t.* ask, beg, invite.

**Bitter-erde,** *f.* magnesia. **-harz,** *n.* bitter resin. **-holz,** *n.* bitterwood; quassia. **-kalk, -kalkspat,** *m.* dolomite. **-keit,** *f.* bitterness. **-klee,** *m.* buck bean (*Menyanthes*). **-kleesalz,** *n.* oxalic acid. **-kochsalz,** *n.* magnesium chloride.

**bitterlich,** *a.* bitterish. — *adv.* bitterly.

**Bitterling,** *m.* bitter mineral water.

**bitterlos,** *a.* free from bitterness.

**Bittermandel,** *f.* bitter almond. **-geist,** *m.* spirit (or essence) of bitter almond. **-öl,** *n.* oil of bitter almond, benzaldehyde; (**künstliches**) nitrobenzene. **-wasser,** *n.* bitter-almond water.

**Bittermittel,** *n.* bitter, bitters.

**bittern,** *v.t.* make bitter. — *v.i.* be bitter.

**Bitter-rinde,** *f.* bitter bark, specif. amargoso. **-salz,** *n.* Epsom salt (magnesium sulfate). **-salzerde,** *f.* magnesia. **-säure,** *f.* picric acid.

**bitterschmeckend,** *a.* bitter-tasting.

**Bitter-see,** *f.* bitter lake. **-spat,** *m.* magnesite; (sometimes) dolomite, bitter spar. **-stein,** *m.* nephrite; saussurite; picrolite. **-stoff,** *m.* bitter principle.

**bittersüss,** *a.* bittersweet.

**Bitter-süss,** *n.* bittersweet. **-süssigkeit,** *f.* bittersweetness. **-tropfen,** *m.pl.* bitters. **-wasser,** *n.* bitter water (containing Epsom salt); (*Pharm.*) bitter-almond water. **-wurzel,** *f.* gentian root.

**bitumenhaltig,** *a.* bituminiferous.

**bitumig,** *a.* bituminous.

**bituminieren, bituminisieren,** *v.t.* bituminize.

**Bituminisierung,** *f.* bituminization.

**bituminös,** *a.* bituminous.

**bizyklisch,** *a.* bicyclic.

**Blachmal,** *n.* dross (on melted silver); niello.

**blähen,** *v.t.* inflate, swell; cause flatulence.

**Blähsucht,** *f.* flatulence.

**Blähung,** *f.* inflation, swelling; flatulence.

**Blähungsmittel,** *n.* carminative.

**blähungstreibend,** *p.a.* carminative.

**Blähvermögen,** *n.* inflating or swelling power.

**blaken,** *v.i.* smoke.

**blamieren,** *v.t.* expose to ridicule.

**Blanc fixe.** blanc fixe, permanent white.

**blanchieren,** *v.t.* blanch, whiten.

**Blanchiersieb,** *n.* blanching sieve.

**Blanchissure,** *f.* light spot (due to imperfect dyeing).

**blank,** *a.* bright, clear, clean, polished; smooth; uncovered, bare; white, blank. **-beizen,** *v.t.* pickle, dip (metals).

**Blank-draht,** *m.* bright wire; galvanized wire. **-film,** *m.* (*Photog.*) film base. **-fix.** blanc fixe, permanent white. **-holz,** *n.* logwood.

**blankkochen,** *v.t.* (*Sugar*) boil down without graining.

**Blank-lack,** *m.* clear varnish. **-leder,** *n.* sleek leather, harness leather.

**blanko,** *a.* blank.

**blankputzen,** *v.t.* polish, scour.

**Blank-reiben,** *n.* polishing. **-stahl,** *m.* bright steel.

**blankstossen,** *v.t.* (*Leather*) glaze.

**Blanktran,** *m.* clear, light-yellow cod oil.

**Blas-.** blast. **-apparat,** *m.* blast apparatus. **-balg,** *m.* bellows.

**Bläschen,** *n.* small bubble, bleb; vesicle; pustule.

**Bläschen-.** vesicular.

**Blasdüse,** *f.* blast nozzle; blowgun.

**Blase,** *f.* bubble, bleb; blister, vesicle; cavity; (*Metal.*) blowhole; bladder; bladder-shaped vessel, as the body of a retort or still; still.

**Blase-.** blowing, blast. **-apparat,** *m.* still; blast apparatus. **-balg,** *m.* bellows. **-lampe,** *f.* blast lamp.

**blasen,** *v.t.* blow; (*Metal.*) smelt in a blast furnace; inject (steam).

**Blasen,** *n.* blowing, blow, blast.

**Blasen-.** bubble; bladder, vesical, vesico-; vesicular; blister.

**blasen-ähnlich, -artig,** *a.* bubble-like, bladder-like, vesicular.

**Blasen-bildung,** *f.* bubble formation; blister formation. **-galle,** *f.* bile from the gall bladder, cystic bile. **-gärung,** *f.* bubbling (or bubble) fermentation. **-gries(s),** *m.* urinary gravel. **-grün,** *n.* sap green. **-helm,** *m.* still head, helm. **-hohlraum,** *m.* (*Metal.*) blowhole. **-hut,** *m.* still head. **-käfer,** *m.* blister beetle; (*Pharm.*) Spanish fly, cantharis. **-kirsche,** *f.* bladder cherry, alkekengi. **-kopf,** *m.* still head. **-kupfer,** *n.* blister copper. **-pflaster,** *n.* (*Pharm.*) blister plaster, specif. cantharides cerate. **-raum,** *m.* (*Metal.*) blowhole. **-säure,** *f.* uric acid. **-stahl,** *m.* blister steel. **-stein,** *m.* urinary calculus. **-steinsäure,** *f.* uric acid. **-tang,** *m.* bladder wrack (*Fucus vesiculosus*).

**blasenweise,** *adv.* in bubbles, bubble by bubble.

**Blasenzählmethode,** *f.* bubble-counting method.

**blasenziehend,** *p.a.* blistering, vesicatory.

**Blase-ofen,** *m.* blowing furnace; blast furnace. **-probe,** *f.* bubble test.

**Blaser, Bläser,** *m.* blower; ventilator.

**Bläserei,** *f.* (glass) blowing, glassblowing shop.

**Blase-rohr,** *n.* blowpipe, blast pipe; nozzle (of bellows). **-tisch,** *m.* blast-lamp table; blowpipe table.

**blasig,** *a.* blistery, blistered, vesicular, bubbly, spongy. — **blasiger Kupferstein,** pimple metal.

**Blasig-keit,** *f.* blistered state. **-werden,** *n.* blistering.

**Blaslampe,** *f.* blast lamp.

**Bläslein,** *n.* small bubble or blister; pimple.

**Blas-rohr,** *n.*, **-röhre,** *f.* blast pipe, blast tube.

**blass,** *a.* pale. **-gelb,** *a.* pale yellow. **-rot,** *a.* pale red, pink. **-rötlich,** *a.* pale reddish, pinkish.

**bläst,** *pr. 3 sing.* of blasen.

**Blas-tisch,** *m.* = Blasetisch. **-vorrichtung,** *f.* blast apparatus, blower.

**Blatt,** *n.* leaf; lamina, lamella, plate, flake; sheet (as of paper); blade; membrane; journal, newspaper.

**blattartig,** *a.* leaf-like.

**Blatt-blau,** *n.* phyllocyanin. **-blei,** *n.* sheet lead.

**Blättchen,** *n.* lamina, lamella; small leaf, leaflet; flake; foil; slip (of paper).

**blättchenartig,** *a.* lamelliform, laminiform.

**Blättchenpulver,** *n.* leaf powder; flake powder.

**Blatt-eisen,** *n.* sheet iron. **-elektrometer,** *n.* leaf electrometer.

**Blatter,** *f.* blister, pimple, pustule; *pl.* smallpox.

**Blätter,** *pl.* (of Blatt) leaves, etc.

**Blätter-.** foliated, lamellar, laminated. **-aldehyd,** *n.* aldehyde of leaves (2-hexenal). **-blende,** *f.* foliated zinc blend. **-bruch,** *m.* lamellar cleavage.

**Blatterde,** *f.* leaf mold.
**Blätter-erde,** *f.* potassium acetate. *Obs.* **-erz,** *n.* foliated tellurium (nagyagite).
**blätterförmig,** *a.* in the form of leaflets or flakes; laminated; leaf-shaped.
**Blättergelb,** *n.* xanthophyll.
**Blattergift,** *n.* smallpox toxin, smallpox virus.
**Blättergips,** *m.* selenite.
**blätterig,** *a.* leafy, foliated, laminated.
**Blätter-kies,** *m.* lamellar pyrites. **-kohle,** *f.* foliated coal, slate coal.
**blättern,** *v.r.* flake, exfoliate.
**Blätter-spat,** *m.* foliaceous spar. **-stein,** *m.* variolite. **-tellur,** *n.* foliated tellurium (nagyagite). **-ton,** *m.* foliated clay. **-zeolith,** *m.* foliated zeolite (heulandite).
**Blatt-farbstoff,** *m.* leaf pigment. **-feder,** *f.* leaf spring. **-federchen,** *n.* = Blattkeim.
**blattförmig,** *a.* = blätterförmig.
**Blatt-gelb,** *n.* xanthophyll. **-gewebe,** *n.* leaf tissue, mesophyll. **-gold,** *n.* leaf gold, gold leaf, gold foil. **-grün,** *n.* leaf green, chlorophyll. **-keim,** *m.* plumule, (of malt, etc.) acrospire. **-kohle,** *f.* = Blätterkohle. **-kupfer,** *n.* sheet copper; copper foil. **-lack,** *m.* shellac. **-mark,** *n.* (*Bot.*) mesophyll. **-metall,** *n.* sheet metal; leaf metal, foil.
**blättrig,** *a.* = blätterig.
**Blatt-schichtung,** *f.* lamination. **-silber,** *n.* silver leaf. **-stahl,** *m.* sheet steel. **-zinn,** *n.* tin foil.
**blau,** *a.* blue. — **blaue Erde,** blue earth, specif. earthy vivianite. — **— schillern,** give a blue iridescence.
**Blau,** *n.* blue. **-asche,** *f.* saunders blue.
**Bläubad,** *n.* bluing bath.
**Blaubeere,** *f.* bilberry, whortleberry.
**blaublank,** *a.* (*Metal.*) polished blue.
**Blaubruch,** *m.* (*Iron*) blue-shortness.
**blaubrüchig,** *a.* brittle at blue heat, blue-short.
**Blau-brüchigkeit,** *f.* (*Iron*) blue-shortness. **-carmin,** *n.* indigo carmine. **-dämpfen,** *n.* (*Ceram.*) blue-smoking. **-druck,** *m.* blue-printing; blueprint; (*Calico*) blue print, specif. indigo print.
**Bläue,** *f.* blue; blueness.
**Blaueisen-erde,** *f.* earthy vivianite. **-erz,** *n.* vivianite. **-spat,** *n.*, **-stein,** *m.* vivianite; **(faseriger)** crocidolite.
**Blauel, Bläuel,** *m.* blued starch; beater, beetle.
**bläueln,** *v.t.* blue; beetle.
**blauempfindlich,** *a.* sensitive to blue.
**blauen, bläuen,** *v.t.* blue; dye blue; whiten (with bluing). — *v.i.* turn blue.
**Blau-erei,** *f.* indigo dyehouse. **-erz,** *n.* vivianite. **-farbe,** *f.* blue color; smalt. **-farbenglas,** *n.* smalt. **-färber,** *m.* dyer in blue. **-färbung,** *f.* blue coloration, blue color. **-fäule,** *f.* blue rot, sap rot, sap stain (of wood). **-gas,** *n.* Blau gas (named from its inventor).
**blau-gesäuert,** *a.* (*Old Chem.*) of or combined with hydrocyanic acid, cyanide of. **-glühend,** *a.* blue-hot.
**Blauglut,** *f.* blue-white incandescence.
**blau-grau,** *a.* blue-gray. **-grün,** *a.* blue-green.
**Blauholz,** *n.* logwood. **-schwarz,** *n.* logwood black. **-späne,** *m.pl.* logwood chips.
**Blau-kohl,** *m.* red cabbage. **-kreuzgeschoss,** *n.* "blue cross" projectile or shell. **-kreuzkampfstoff,** *m.* (*Mil.*) "blue cross" shell filling (diphenylchloroarsine or some other sternutative). **-küpe,** *f.* blue vat, specif. indigo vat. **-lack,** *m.* blue lake.
**bläulich,** *a.* bluish. **-grau,** *a.* bluish-gray. **-grün,** bluish-green. **-weiss,** bluish-white.
**Blau-mühle,** *f.* smalt mill. **-ofen,** *m.* flowing furnace, shaft furnace. **-öl,** *n.* blue oil; (*Org. Chem.*) cerulignol. **-papier,** *n.* blueprint paper. **-pause,** *f.* blueprint tracing, blue print. **-probe,** *f.* blue test.
**blaurot,** *a.* blue-red, violet.
**Blau-salz,** *n.* potassium ferrocyanide. **-sand,** *m.* coarsest smalt.
**blausauer,** *a.* of or combined with hydrocyanic acid, cyanide of. — **blausaures Salz,** cyanide. — **gelbes blausaures Kali,** potassium ferrocyanide. — **rotes blausaures Kali,** potassium ferricyanide.
**Blausäure,** *f.* hydrocyanic acid. **-gas,** *n.* hydrogen cyanide.
**blausäurehaltig,** *a.* containing hydrocyanic acid.
**Blau-säureverbindung,** *f.* compound with hydrogen cyanide; cyanide. **-säurevergiftung,** *f.* hydrocyanic acid poisoning. **-schlamm,** *m.* (*Geol.*) blue mud. **-schörl,** *m.* cyanite.
**blauschwarz,** *a.* blue-black.
**Blau-spat,** *m.* lazulite. **-stein,** *m.* bluestone, blue vitriol; lazulite; (*Metal.*) blue metal, blue mat(te). **-stich,** *m.* bluish tinge or tint. **-stift,** *m.* blue pencil. **-stoff,** *m.* cyanogen. **-sucht,** *f.* cyanosis.
**Bläuung,** *f.* bluing.
**Bläuungsfarbstoff,** *m.* bluing color.
**blau-verschoben,** *p.a.* displaced toward the blue. **-violett,** *a.* blue-violet.
**Blauvitriol,** *n.* blue vitriol.
**blauwarm,** *a.* blue-hot.
**Blau-wärme,** *f.* (*Metal.*) blue heat. **-wasser,** *n.* eau céleste (cupric ammonium sulfate solution). **-wassergas,** *n.* blue water gas, blue gas.
**Blech,** *n.* plate, sheet, sheet metal, specif. sheet iron; foil; **(weisses)** tin plate; **(schwarzes)** black iron plate. **-ausschnitt, -ausstoss,** *m* (*Metal.*) blank. **-büchse,** *f.* tin can, tin. **-dose,** *f.* tin box; tin can, tin. **-eisen,** *n.* sheet iron.

**blechen, blechern,** *a.* tin (plate); tinny.
**Blech-flasche,** *f.* narrow-necked tin vessel. **-gefäss,** *n.* tin (plate) vessel. **-glühofen,** *m.* plate-heating furnace. **-hafen,** *m.* tin can.
**blechig,** *a.* tinny.
**Blech-kanne,** *f.* tin can. **-kasten,** *m.* tin box; sheet-iron box. **-lack,** *m.* tinplate varnish; sheet-metal varnish. **-messing,** *n.* sheet brass. **-rohr,** *n.* sheet-iron tube; tin tube. **-schmied,** *m.* tinner. **-stärke,** *f.* plate (or sheet) thickness. **-tafel,** *f.* sheet iron, iron plate. **-trichter,** *m.* tin (plate) funnel. **-trommel,** *f.* tin (plate) drum. **-ware,** *f.* sheet-metal ware, (usually) tinware.
**Blei,** *n.* lead. **-abgang,** *m.* lead dross, lead scoria. **-ablagerung,** *f.* lead deposit. **-acetat,** *n.* lead acetate. **-ader,** *f.* lead vein. **-antimonerz,** *n.*, **-antimonglanz,** *m.* zinkenite. **-arbeit,** *f.* lead smelting; plumbing. **-arsenat,** *n.* lead arsenate. **-arsenglanz,** *m.* sartorite. **-arsenik,** *m.* lead arsenate; lead arsenide. **-art,** *f.* kind or variety of lead.
**bleiartig,** *a.* lead-like, leady, plumbeous.
**Blei-asche,** *f.* lead dross; lead ash; the gray film of oxide on lead exposed to air. **-auskleidung,** *f.* lead lining. **-azetat,** *n.* lead acetate. **-bad,** *n.* lead bath. **-baum,** *m.* lead tree, arbor saturni.
**bleiben,** *v.i.* remain, stay, last. — **bleibend,** *p.a.* permanent, lasting, durable, stable, (of colors) fast; persistent. — **bleibende Härte,** permanent hardness. — **— stehen,** remain standing; stop.
**Blei-bergwerk,** *n.* lead mine. **-blech,** *n.* sheet lead. **-block,** *m.* (*Expl.*) lead block, Trauzl block; (*Metal.*) lead pig. **-blüte,** *f.* mimetite. **-braun,** *n.* lead dioxide. **-buchse, -büchse,** *f.* lead box, case, or can.
**bleich,** *a.* pale, white.
**Bleich-anlage,** *f.* bleaching establishment, bleaching plant, bleachery. **-anstalt,** *f.* bleachery. **-artikel,** *m.* (*Calico*) bleach style. **-bad,** *n.* bleaching liquor or bath.
**bleichbar,** *a.* capable of being bleached.
**Bleich-beize,** *f.* bleaching mordant. **-chlor,** *n.* chlorine for bleaching; active chlorine.
**Bleiche,** *f.* bleaching; bleachery; paleness, whiteness.
**bleichecht,** *a.* fast to bleaching.
**bleichen,** *v.t.* bleach; whiten; blanch. — *v.i.* lose color, fade; turn white or pale.
**Bleicher,** *m.* bleacher.
**Bleich-erde,** *f.* bleaching earth, fuller's earth, adsorbing clay. **-erei,** *f.* bleaching; bleachery. **-essenz,** *f.* soda bleach liquor (sodium hypochlorite solution). **-fähigkeit,** *f.* capability of being bleached, bleachability. **-fass,** *n.* bleaching vat. **-fleck,** *m.* bleaching stain, bleach spot. **-flotte,** *f.* bleaching liquor. **-flüssigkeit,** *f.* bleaching liquor. **-gefäss,** *n.* bleaching vessel. **-grad,** *m.* degree of bleaching; degree of bleachability. **-gut,** *n.* batch of cloth for bleaching. **-holländer,** *m.* (*Paper*) poaching engine, poacher. **-hülfsmittel,** *n.* something used to assist bleaching, bleaching assistant. **-kalk,** *m.* chloride of lime (bleaching powder). **-kasten,** *m.* bleaching vat. **-kessel,** *m.* bleaching boiler or kier. **-lauge,** *f.* bleaching lye (or liquor).
**Bleichlorid,** *n.* lead chloride.
**Bleich-mittel,** *n.* bleaching agent, decolorant. **-öl,** *n.* bleaching oil. **-prozess,** *m.* bleaching process. **-pulver,** *n.* bleaching powder.
**Bleichromat,** *n.* lead chromate.
**Bleich-salz,** *n.* bleaching salt (chloride of lime, sodium hypochlorite, etc.). **-sand,** *m.* bleached sand. **-säure,** *f.* chloric acid. **-seife,** *f.* bleaching soap. **-soda,** *n.* bleaching soda. **-sucht,** *f.* chlorosis. **-ton,** *m.* bleaching clay. **-vermögen,** *n.* bleaching power. **-vorbereitungsmittel,** *n.* preliminary bleaching assistant. **-wasser,** *n.* bleaching liquor; Javelle water; chlorine water. **-wirkung,** *f.* bleaching action or effect. **-zweck,** *m.* bleaching purpose(s).
**Blei-dampf,** *m.* lead vapor, lead fume. **-draht,** *m.* lead wire. **-eisenstein,** *m.* (*Metal.*) iron-lead mat(te).
**bleien,** *v.t.* lead (specif., treat with tetraethyllead).
**Bleierde,** *f.* earthy cerussite.
**bleiern,** *a.* lead, leaden; dull, heavy.
**Blei-erz,** *n.* lead ore. **-essig,** *m.* vinegar of lead (aqueous solution of basic lead acetate). **-extrakt,** *m.* = Bleiessig. **-fahlerz,** *n.* bournonite. **-farbe,** *f.* lead color.
**blei-farben, -farbig,** *a.* lead-colored.
**Blei-feder,** *f.* lead pencil. **-flasche,** *f.* lead bottle. **-folie,** *f.* lead foil.
**blei-frei,** *a.* free from lead. **-führend,** *a.* lead-bearing, plumbiferous.
**Bleigang,** *m.* (*Mining*) lead vein.
**bleigefüttert,** *a.* lead-lined.
**Blei-gehalt,** *m.* lead content. **-gelb,** *n.* massicot; lead chromate. **-gerät,** *n.* lead apparatus or implement. **-gewinnung,** *f.* lead extraction, lead production. **-giesser,** *m.* plumber; lead founder. **-glanz,** *m.* lead glance, galena. **-glas,** *n.* lead glass; (*Min.*) anglesite. **-glasur,** *f.* lead glaze. **-glätte,** *f.* litharge. **-glimmer,** *m.* cerussite in micaceous form.
**bleigrau,** *a.* lead-gray.
**Blei-grube,** *f.* lead mine. **-gummi,** *m.* lead-pencil eraser; (*Min.*) plumboresinite.
**bleihaltig,** *a.* containing lead, plumbiferous.
**Blei-hornerz,** *n.* **-hornspat,** *m.* phosgenite. **-hütte,** *f.* lead works.
**Bleiion,** *n.* lead ion.

**bleiisch,** *a.* leady.

**Blei-jodat,** *n.* lead iodate. **-jodid,** *n.* lead iodide. **-kalk,** *m.* lead calx, lead oxide. **-kammer,** *f.* lead chamber. **-kammerkristalle,** *m.pl.* lead chamber crystals (nitrosylsulfuric acid). **-kammerverfahren,** *n.* lead chamber process. **-könig,** *m.* lead regulus. **-krankheit,** *f.* lead poisoning, plumbism. **-krätze,** *f.* lead waste, specif. lead dross. **-kugel,** *f.* lead ball; lead bullet. **-lasur,** *f.* linarite. **-leder,** *n.* (*Metal.*) silver containing much lead. **-legierung,** *f.* lead alloy. **-lot,** *n.* lead solder; plummet; plumb line. **-löter,** *m.* lead burner. **-lötung,** *f.* lead soldering. **-mangan,** *n.* lead-manganese. **-mehl,** *n.* lead dust. **-mennige,** *f.* minium, red lead. **-mine,** *f.* lead mine; lead (for pencils). **-mulde,** *f.* lead pig. **-mulm,** *m.* earthy galena. **-niere,** *f.* (*Min.*) bindheimite. **-ocker,** *m.* lead ocher. **-ofen,** *m.* lead furnace. **-öl,** *n.* (*Pharm.*) lead acetate in oil of turpentine. **-oxyd,** *n.* lead oxide, specif. PbO; **(rotes)** minium. **-oxydhydrat,** *n.* lead hydroxide. **-oxydsalz,** *n.* lead salt, specif. a salt of bivalent lead. **-oxydul,** *n.* lead suboxide, $Pb_2O$; (sometimes) lead monoxide, PbO. **-oxyduloxyd,** *n.* minium, $Pb_3O_4$. **-papier,** *n.* lead paper (for hydrogen sulfide tests); lead foil. **-peroxyd,** *n.* lead dioxide, $PbO_2$. **-pflaster,** *n.* lead plaster. **-pflastersalbe,** *f.* (*Pharm.*) diachylon ointment. **-plattenprobe,** *f.* (*Expl.*) lead plate test. **-raffination,** *f.* lead refining. **-rauch,** *m.* lead fume, lead smoke.

**bleireich,** *a.* rich in lead.

**Blei-rhodanid,** *n.* lead thiocyanate. **-rohr,** *n.*, **-röhre,** *f.* lead tube or pipe. **-röstprozess,** *m.* lead roasting. **-rot,** *n.* red lead, minium. **-safran,** *m.* orange lead. **-salbe,** *f.* (*Pharm.*) lead ointment, cerate of lead subacetate. **-salpeter,** *m.* lead nitrate. **-salz,** *n.* lead salt, specif. lead acetate. **-sammler,** *m.* lead accumulator; lead storage battery.

**bleisauer,** *a.* of or combined with plumbic acid, plumbate of.

**Blei-säure,** *f.* plumbic acid. **-schale,** *f.* lead dish, lead basin. **-schaum,** *m.* lead dross, lead ash(litharge). **-schlacke,** *f.* lead slag. **-schlange,** *f.* lead coil. **-schlich,** *m.* (*Mining*) lead slime. **-schnee,** *m.* lead snow ($PbSO_4 \cdot Pb(OH)_2$). **-schrot,** *n.* lead shot. **-schwamm,** *m.* lead sponge, spongy lead. **-sicherung,** *f.* lead fuse. **-spat,** *n.* cerussite; **(gelber)** wulfenite; **(roter)** crocoisite. **-speise,** *f.* lead speiss. **-spiegel,** *m.* specular galena. **-staub,** *m.* lead dust. **-stein,** *m.* lead mat(te). **-stift,** *m.* lead pencil, pencil. **-sulfat,** *n.* lead sulfate. **-superoxyd,** *n.* lead dioxide, $PbO_2$. **-tetraäthyl,** *n.* tetraethyllead. **-verbindung,** *f.* lead compound. **-vergiftung,** *f.* lead poisoning. **-verhüttung,** *f.* lead smelting. **-vitriol,** *m.* lead vitriol, lead sulfate, (*Min.*) anglesite. **-vitriolspat,** *m.* anglesite. **-wasser,** *n.* lead water, Goulard water. **-wasserstoff,** *m.* lead hydride. **-weiss,** *n.* white lead. **-weissalbe,** *f.* lead carbonate ointment. **-wismut,** *n.* lead-bismuth. **-zinnlot,** *n.* lead-tin solder. **-zinnober,** *m.* red lead, minium. **-zucker,** *m.* sugar of lead, lead acetate. **-zuckersalbe,** *f.* lead acetate ointment. **-zyanat,** *n.* lead cyanate.

**Blendart,** *f.* hybrid.

**Blende,** *f.* blend, glance (specif., zinc blend, ZnS); blind, screen, shutter, shield, diaphragm, stop, baffle; border.

**blenden,** *v.t.* blind, dazzle; screen (from light); dull.

**Blendenöffnung,** *f.* (*Photog.*) diaphragm aperture.

**Blendfarbstoff,** *m.* color for sighting.

**Bleuel,** *m.* beater, beetle; blued starch.

**bleueln,** *v.t.* beat, beetle; blue.

**blf.,** *abbrev.* (blätterförmig) in leaflets or flakes.

**blg.P.,** *abbrev.* (belgisches Patent) Belgian patent.

**Blick,** *m.* look, view, glance; flash; (*Metal.*) flashing (as of molten silver), fulguration, "blick."

**blicken,** *v.i.* glance, look; shine; (*Metal.*) flash, lighten, give the "blick."

**Blick-feld,** *n.* field of vision. **-gold,** *n.* refined gold still containing silver. **-silber,** *n.* (*Metal.*) refined silver still containing impurities.

**blieb,** *pret.* (of bleiben) remained.

**blies,** *pret.* (of blasen) blew.

**blind,** *a.* blind; dull, tarnished; false; (of tests, etc.) blank.

**Blind-darm,** *m.* caecum. **-feuer,** *n.* blank fire. **-gänger,** *m.* (*Expl.*) dud; misfire. **-heit,** *f.* blindness. **-kohle,** *f.* underburned charcoal. **-leitwert,** *m.* (*Elec.*) susceptance. **-licht,** *n.* flashlight.

**blindmachen,** *v.t.* blunt (glass).

**Blind-probe,** *f.* blank test. **-schlauch,** *m.* flexible tube closed at one end. **-strom,** *m.* (*Elec.*) wattless current. **-versuch,** *m.* blank test. **-wert,** *m.* blank value, reagent value. **-widerstand,** *m.* (*Elec.*) reactance.

**blinken, blinkern,** *v.i.* gleam, sparkle; blink.

**Blitz,** *m.* lightning; flash. **-ableiter,** *m.* lightning conductor.

**blitzen,** *v.i.* flash; glisten; lighten.

**Blitz-lampe,** *f.* flash lamp, flashlight. **-licht,** *n.* flashlight; flare. **-photographie,** *f.* flashlight photography. **-pulver,** *n.* lycopodium. **-röhre,** *f.* fulgurite. **-schlag,** *m.* lightning stroke. **-strahl,** *m.* lightning flash.

**Bllg.**, *abbrev.* (biologische Lösung) biological solution.
**Block**, *m.* block; pig; ingot; cake; (tree) trunk; log. **-blei**, *n.* pig lead.
**Blöckchen**, *n.* (small) ingot, (small) pig.
**Blockeisen**, *n.* ingot iron; ingot steel.
**blocken**, *v.t.* block; (*Metal.*) bloom, cog.
**Block-färbung**, *f.* (*Micros.*) staining *in toto.* **-hahn**, *m.* stopcock. **-holz**, *n.* wood in logs.
**blockieren**, *v.t.* block.
**Block-kondensator**, *m.* (*Elec.*) blocking condenser, stopping condenser. **-kupfer**, *n.* ingot copper. **-mühle**, *f.* block mill. **-schnitt**, *m.* die, matrix. **-seigerung**, *f.* (*Metal.*) segregation (in an ingot). **-zinn**, *n.* block tin.
**Blödsinn**, *m.* imbecility, insanity; nonsense.
**bloss**, *a.* bare, naked, nude; mere, sole. — *adv.* merely, only; barely; nakedly.
**Blösse**, *f.* bareness; unhaired hide, pelt.
**blosslegen, blosstellen**, *v.t.* lay bare, strip, expose.
**Blt.**, *abbrev.* (Blättchen) leaflets, lamellas.
**blühen**, *v.i.* bloom, blossom; flourish.
**Blume**, *f.* flower; bloom; (*Dyeing*) scum, flurry; aroma, bouquet.
**blümen**, *v.t.* flower, figure.
**Blumen-blatt**, *n.* petal. **-erde**, *f.* garden mold. **-gelb**, *n.* any yellow flower pigment. **-kohl**, *m.* cauliflower. **-seite**, *f.* (*Leather*) hair side. **-staub**, *m.* pollen. **-tee**, *m.* imperial tea. **-topf**, *m.* flower pot.
**blumig**, *a.* bloomy, flowery.
**Blunze, Blunzen**, *f.* a kind of German sausage or its casing.
**Blut**, *n.* blood. **-achat**, *m.* blood agate. **-ader**, *f.* vein.
**blutarm**, *a.* bloodless, anemic; very poor.
**Blutarmut**, *f.* blood deficiency, anemia.
**Blutbahn**, *f.* blood vessel.
**blutbildend**, *a.* blood-forming.
**Blut-blume**, *f.* arnica; bloodflower (*Haemanthus*). **-druck**, *m.* blood pressure.
**Blüte**, *f.* blossom, flower, bloom.
**blutecht**, *a.* (*Dyeing*) fast to bleeding.
**Blut-egel**, *m.* leech. **-eisenstein**, *m.* hematite. **-eiweiss**, *n.* blood albumin, serum albumin.
**bluten**, *v.i.* bleed; suffer; (of colors) bleed, run.
**Blüten-blatt**, *n.* petal. **-farbstoff**, *m.* flower pigment. **-hüllenblatt**, *n.* sepal. **-öl**, *n.* flower oil, attar. **-staub**, *m.* pollen.
**Blutentziehungsmittel**, *n.* hemagog.
**Blüten-wachs**, *m.* flower wax. **-weiss**, *n.* a form of calcium sulfate used in loading paper.
**Blut-erz**, *n.* hematite. **-farbe**, *f.* blood color; blood pigment. **-farbstoff**, *m.* coloring matter of the blood, blood pigment. **-faserstoff**, *m.* fibrin. **-fleck, -flecken**, *m.* blood stain. **-fluss**, *m.* hemorrhage.
**blutflüssig**, *a.* hemorrhagic.
**Blut-flüssigkeit**, *f.* blood plasma. **-gefäss**, *n.* blood vessel. **-gerinnung**, *f.* blood coagulation.
**blutgierig**, *a.* bloodthirsty.
**Blut-gift**, *n.* blood toxin. **-haargefäss**, *n.* capillary blood vessel. **-holz**, *n.* logwood.
**blutig**, *a.* bloody.
**Blut-klumpen**, *m.* blood clot. **-kohle**, *f.* blood charcoal. **-körperchen**, *n.* blood corpuscle. **-kraut**, *n.* any of various blood-red or blood-stanching plants. **-kreislauf**, *m.* blood stream; circulation of the blood. **-kuchen**, *m.* blood clot; placenta. **-lauf**, *m.* circulation of the blood.
**Blutlaugensalz**, *n.* potassium ferrocyanide (often with *adj.* **gelbes**). — **rotes —**, potassium ferricyanide.
**blut-leer**, *a.* anemic, bloodless. **-los**, *a.* bloodless.
**Blut-mehl**, *n.* blood meal. **-mittel**, *n.* (*Med.*) blood tonic. **-plättchen**, *n.* blood plate, blood platelet. **-reinigung**, *f.* blood purification.
**blutrot**, *a.* blood-red.
**Blut-rot**, *n.* hemoglobin; hematin. **-ruhr**, *f.* dysentery. **-säure**, *f.* thiocyanic acid. *Obs.* **-scheibe**, *f.* blood corpuscle. **-schlag**, *m.* apoplexy. **-seuche**, *f.* anthrax. **-stein**, *m.* bloodstone, hematite.
**blutstillend**, *p.a.* blood-stanching, hemostatic, styptic.
**Blut-stillstift**, *m.* styptic pencil. **-strom**, *m.* blood stream. **-sucht**, *f.* hemophilia. **-umlauf**, *m.* circulation of the blood.
**Blutung**, *f.* bleeding.
**Blut-untersuchung**, *f.* examination of blood. **-vergiftung**, *f.* blood poisoning. **-wärme**, *f.* blood heat. **-wasser**, *n.* blood serum. **-wassergefäss**, *n.* lymphatic vessel, lymphatic. **-wolle**, *f.* blood wool, plucked wool. **-wurz, -wurzel**, *f.* any of various plants of red sap or supposed blood-stanching properties, specif. bloodroot (either *Sanguinaria canadensis* or *Potentilla tormentilla*).
**Bock**, *m.* buck; (*Brewing*) bock beer; (*Tech.*) trestle, jack, horse, stand, stool; blunder. **-asche**, *f.* coal ashes. **-holz**, *n.* guaiacum wood, lignum vitae.
**bockig, böckig**, *a.* stubborn, refractory, resistant.
**Bock-leder**, *n.* goat leather, kid; buckskin. **-nuss**, *f.* souari nut (fruit of *Caryocar*). **-säure**, *f.* hircic acid (a mixture). **-seife**, *f.* mountain soap (kind of clay).
**Bocks-horn**, *n.* fenugreek. **-hörnlein**, *n.* carob bean.
**Boden**, *m.* soil; earth, ground, land; bottom; base; floor; plate, tray (in a distilling column); (*Dyeing*) blotch; loft, garret. **-analyse**, *f.* soil analysis. **-anspruch**, *m.* soil

requirement. **-art,** *f.* (kind or variety of) soil. **-beize,** *f.* (*Paints*) floor stain. **-bestandteil,** *m.* soil constituent. **-blatt,** *n.* flat bottom. **-elektrode,** *f.* hearth electrode. **-erschöpfung,** *f.* soil exhaustion. **-fläche,** *f.* floor space; bottom surface; ground; soil surface. **-güte,** *f.* soil quality, soil value. **-hals,** *m.* neck or tubulation at the bottom. **-hefe,** *f.* grounds, dregs, lees (of yeast). **-impfstoff,** *m.* soil inoculum. **-impfung,** *f.* soil inoculation. **-kappe,** *f.* bubble cap, tray cap (in a distilling column). **-kolloid,** *n.* soil colloid. **-kolonne,** *f.* plate-type column. **-körper,** *m.* a substance at the bottom of a liquid, a solid phase; soil substance. **-kraft,** *f.* soil fertility. **-kunde,** *f.* soil science, pedology. **-kupfer,** *n.* (*Copper*) bottoms. **-lack,** *m.* floor varnish. **-leder,** *n.* sole leather.

**bodenlos,** *a.* bottomless, abysmal.

**Boden-mehl,** *n.* fecula, starch. **-nähe,** *f.* (*Aero.*) ground (or sea) level. **-nährstoff,** *m.* soil nutrient. **-öl,** *n.* floor oil. **-pappe,** *f.* (*Agric.*) mulch paper. **-probe,** *f.* soil test; soil sample. **-satz,** *m.* deposit, sediment, dregs, bottoms, grounds, foot; (*Salt*) bitterings. **-säure,** *f.* soil acid. **-schicht,** *f.* bottom layer; soil layer; (*Geol.*) bed, stratum. **-schlamm,** *m.* sediment, sludge, settlings. **-see,** *m.* Lake of Constance. **-stein,** *m.* bottom stone, sole (of a furnace); (*Salt*) bittern; bed stone (of a mill). **-teig,** *m.* underdough. **-untersuchung,** *f.* soil investigation, examination of soil. **-ventil,** *n.* bottom valve. **-vergiftung,** *f.* soil poisoning. **-wasser,** *n.* ground water. **-zahl,** *f.* base number, base; number of plates (in a column). **-ziegel,** *m.* paving tile. **-zustand,** *m.* soil condition.

**bog,** *pret.* (of biegen) bent, curved, etc.

**Bogen,** *m.* bow, arc, bend, curve, curvature, arch; (*Elec.*) arc; sheet (of paper). **-flamme,** *f.* arc flame.

**bogenförmig,** *a.* bowed, curved, arched.

**Bogen-lampe,** *f.* arc lamp. **-lampenkohle,** *f.* arc carbon. **-licht,** *n.* arc light. **-linie,** *f.* curved line. **-mass,** *n.* circular measure. **-rohr,** *n.*, **-röhre,** *f.* bent or curved pipe or tube. **-schweissung,** *f.* arc welding. **-skala,** *f.* curved scale. **-spektrum,** *n.* arc spectrum. **-stück,** *n.* curved piece; (*Brewing*) return bend.

**Bohle,** *f.* plank.

**Böhmen,** *n.* Bohemia.

**böhmisch,** *a.* Bohemian.

**Bohne,** *f.* bean.

**bohnen,** *v.t.* wax.

**Bohnen-erz,** *n.* = Bohnerz. **-kraut,** *n.* summer savory (*Satureia hortensis*). **-kuchen,** *m.* bean cake. **-mehl,** *m.* bean meal, bean flour **-öl,** *n.* bean oil, esp. soybean oil.

**Bohner-masse,** *f.*, **-wachs,** *n.* floor wax, polishing wax.

**Bohn-erz,** *n.* pea ore (oölitic limonite). **-wachs,** *n.* polishing wax.

**bohren,** *v.t.* bore, drill.

**Bohrer,** *m.* borer, perforator, gimlet, auger, drill, bit; drill (the machine).

**Bohr-fett,** *n.* boring or drilling oil or paste. **-guss,** *m.* an easily drilled malleable cast iron. **-gut,** *n.* material obtained by boring. **-loch,** *n.* borehole, drill hole; (drilled) well. **-mehl,** *n.* borings, bore dust. **-öl,** *n.* (*Mach.*) cutting oil. **-probe,** *f.* core sample; boring test, drill test. **-rohr,** *n.* casing pipe, casing. **-rohrbenzin,** *n.* casinghead gasoline. **-schlamm,** **-schmand,** *m.* drilling mud, drilling slime. **-span,** *m.* boring, drilling. **-stahl,** *m.* boring steel, boring tool. **-stock,** *m.* boring stock, borer. **-turm,** *m.* (*Petroleum*) derrick.

**Bohrung,** *f.* boring, bore, bore hole; drilling; (drilled) well; caliber.

**Bohr-versuch,** *m.* boring experiment, drill test. **-vorrichtung,** *f.* boring or drilling device; specif., drilling jig.

**Boje,** *f.* buoy.

**Bol,** *m.* = Bolus.

**Bolivien,** *n.* Bolivia.

**Bolle,** *f.* bulb; onion.

**Bollengewächs,** *n.* bulb plant.

**Bollwerk,** *n.* bulwark.

**Bologneser,** *m.* Bolognese, Bologna. — — **Flasche,** Bologna flask. — — **Spat,** Bologna stone.

**Bolus,** *m.*, **-erde,** *f.* bole. — **roter Bolus,** reddle. — **weisser Bolus,** kaolin.

**Bolzen,** *m.* bolt; peg, pin; prop. **-mutter,** *f.* nut (to a bolt). **-scheibe,** *f.* washer (for a bolt).

**Bombage,** *f.* wrapping; (*Canning*) swell.

**Bombe,** *f.* bomb, shell; tank, cylinder (for gases).

**Bomben-ofen,** *m.* bomb furnace. **-rohr,** *n.* bomb tube. **-sauerstoff,** *m.* tank oxygen.

**Bomse,** *f.* (*Ceram.*) support.

**Bonducnuss,** *f.* bonduc nut, nicker nut.

**bonifizieren,** *v.t.* compensate, indemnify.

**Bonität,** *f.* good quality.

**Bonitierung,** *f.* valuation, appraisement.

**Boot,** *n.* boat.

**Bor,** *n.* boron.

**Bor-.** boric, boron, boro-, etc. **-ameisensäure,** *f.* boroformic acid.

**Borat,** *n.* borate.

**Bor-äthan,** *n.* bor(o)ethane (diborane, $B_2H_6$). **-äthyl,** *n.* borethyl (triethylborine).

**Borax-blei,** *n.* lead borate. **-eisen,** *n.* iron borate. **-honig,** *m.* borax honey. **-kalk,** *m.* calcium borate. **-perle,** *f.* borax bead.

**boraxsauer,** *a.* = borsauer.

**Borax-säure,** *f.* boric acid. **-see,** *m.* borax lake. **-seife,** *f.* borax soap. **-spat,** *m.* boracite. **-weinstein,** *m.* potassium borotartrate, (*Pharm.*) tartarus boratus.
**Borazit,** *n.* boracite.
**Bor-butan,** *n.* borobutane (tetraborane, $B_4H_{10}$). **-chlorid,** *n.* boron chloride.
**Bord,** *m.* border, edge, rim; (ship)board.
**bordeauxrot,** *a.* Bordeaux red, claret.
**Bordelaiser Brühe.** Bordeaux mixture.
**bördeln,** *v.t.* border, edge, flange, bead.
**Boretsch,** *m.* borage.
**Bor-fluorid,** *n.* boron fluoride; borofluoride. **-fluorwasserstoffsäure,** *f.*, **-fluorwasserstoff,** *m.* fluoboric acid, hydrofluoboric acid, $HBF_4$. **-flusssäure,** *f.* fluoboric acid.
**Borg,** *m.* borrowing, credit.
**Borgehalt,** *m.* boron content.
**borgen,** *v.t.* borrow; (less often) lend.
**Borium,** *n.* boron.
**Borjodid,** *n.* boron iodide.
**Bor-kalk,** *m.* calcium borate. **-karbid,** *n.* boron carbide.
**Borke,** *f.* bark; rind; crust, scab.
**Bormethyl,** *n.* trimethylborine, boron methyl, $B(CH_3)_3$.
**Born,** *m.* spring, well; (*Salt*) salt pit; brine.
**Borokalzit,** *n.* borocalcite.
**Borretsch, Borratz,** *m.* borage.
**Borsalbe,** *f.* (*Pharm.*) boric acid ointment.
**borsauer,** *a.* of or combined with boric acid, borate of.
**Borsäure,** *f.* boric acid. **-anhydrid,** *n.* boric anhydride ($B_2O_3$). **-seife,** f. boric-acid soap. **-weinstein,** *m.* = Boraxweinstein.
**Börse,** *f.* purse; Exchange.
**börsenfähig, börsengängig,** *a.* negotiable.
**Borst,** *m.* burst, crack, fissure.
**Borstahl,** *m.* boron steel.
**Borste,** *f.* bristle; fissure, crack; quill.
**börste,** *pret. subj.* of bersten.
**Borstickstoff,** *m.* boron nitride.
**borstig,** *a.* cracked; bristly; surly.
**Borte,** *f.* border, edging; lace.
**Bor-verbindung,** *f.* boron compound. **-wasser,** *n.* boric acid solution. **-wasserstoff,** *m.* boron hydride. **-wolframsäure,** *f.* borotungstic acid, (better) tungstoboric acid.
**bösartig,** *a.* malignant, virulent, malicious.
**Böschung,** *f.* slope, sloping.
**Böschungswinkel,** *m.* angle of slope.
**böse,** *a.* bad, evil; harmful, noxious; sore, aching. — **böses Wesen,** epilepsy. — **böses Wetter,** choke damp.
**bossieren,** *v.t.* emboss; chase; dress.
**Bossierwachs,** *n.* molding wax.
**bot,** *pret.* (of bieten) offered.
**Botanik,** *f.* botany.
**Botaniker,** *m.* botanist.
**botanisch,** *a.* botanical.
**Bote,** *m.* messenger.
**Botschaft,** *f.* message; embassy; *pl.* tidings.
**Böttcher,** *m.* cooper.
**Bottich,** *m.* vat, tub, tun, tank, back, vessel. **-gärung,** *f.* vat fermentation. **-kühler,** *m.* (*Brewing*) attemperator.
**Bougie,** *f.* candle; (*Med.*) bougie.
**Bouteille,** *f.* bottle.
**Bouteillenglas,** *n.* bottle glass.
**brach,** *pret.* (of brechen) broke, etc.
**brach,** *a.* fallow.
**brachte,** *pret.* (of bringen) brought, etc.
**Brachyachse,** *f.* (*Cryst.*) brachyaxis.
**Brack,** *m.* refuse.
**Brackgut,** *n.* refuse; damaged goods.
**brackig,** *a.* brackish.
**Brackwasser,** *n.* brackish water.
**Brambeere,** *f.* blackberry.
**Bramme,** *f.* slab (of iron), bloom.
**Brammen,** *n.*, **Brammen-.** (*Metal.*) slabbing.
**Brand,** *m.* burning (combustion, calcination, etc.); fire; charge (of a kiln or oven); blight, smut; gangrene, slough; brand.
**Brand-.** burn(ing), fire, incendiary. **-balsam,** *m.* ointment for burns. **-bombe,** *f.* incendiary bomb. **-eisen,** *n.* burnt iron. **-erz,** *n.* inflammable ore (as bituminous shale, or as idrialite).
**brandfest,** *a.* fireproof.
**Brand-fläche,** *f.* burned surface, burn. **-fleck, -flecken,** *m.* burn. **-gelb,** *n.* reddish yellow. **-geschoss,** *n.* incendiary shell. **-gold,** *n.* refined gold. **-granate,** *f.* incendiary shell. **-harz,** *n.* empyreumatic resin.
**brandig,** *a.* burnt; blasted; gangrenous.
**Brand-kitt,** *m.* fireproof cement or lute. **-loch,** *n.* fuse hole; vent hole, vent (as of a blasting cap). **-lunte,** *f.* slow match.
**brandmarken,** *v.t.* brand.
**Brand-messer,** *m.* pyrometer. **-mittel,** *n.* escharotic; remedy for burns; remedy for gangrene. **-öl,** *n.* empyreumatic oil (obtained by destructive distillation). **-pilz,** *m.* smut fungus. **-probe,** *f.* fire test, fire assay. **-riss,** *m.* fire crack. **-salbe,** *f.* salve for burns. **-satz,** *m.* (*Mil.*) an incendiary composition. **-schaden,** *m.* damage from fire. **-schiefer,** *m.* bituminous shale. **-silber,** *n.* refined silver. **-stein,** *m.* brick.
**brandstiftend,** *a.* incendiary.
**Brandstiftung,** *f.* incendiarism, arson.
**Brandung,** *f.* surf, breaker; seething.
**Brand-versicherung,** *f.* fire insurance. **-wunde,** *f.* burn. **-zeug,** *n.* = Brandsatz. **-ziegel,** *m.* firebrick.
**Bränke,** *f.* (*Brewing*) yeast tub.
**brannte,** *pret.* (of brennen) burned, etc.

**Brannt-hefe,** *f.* spent yeast. **-kalk,** *m.* caustic lime, quicklime.

**Branntwein,** *m.* spirits (brandy, whisky, etc.). **-blase,** *f.* still (for spirits). **-brenner,** *m.* distiller. **-brennerei,** *f.* distillation (of spirits); distillery. **-essig,** *m.* brandy vinegar. **-geist,** *m.* rectified spirit, alcohol. **-hefe,** *f.* alcohol ferment (*Saccharomyces cerevisii*). **-mixtur,** *f.* (*Pharm.*) mixture of brandy, brandy mixture. **-prober,** *m.* alcoholometer. **-vergiftung,** *f.* alcoholic poisoning. **-wa(a)ge,** *f.* alcoholometer.

**branstig,** *a.* of a burnt smell or taste.

**Brasil, Brasilien,** *n.* Brazil. **-holz,** *n.* Brazil wood.

**brasilianisch,** *a.* Brazilian, Brazil.

**Brasil-insäure,** *f.* brazilinic acid. **-kopalinsäure,** *f.* brazilcopalinic acid. **-kopalsäure,** *f.* brazilcopalic acid. **-säure,** *f.* brazilic acid.

**Brassidinsäure,** *f.* brassidic acid.

**Brassinsäure,** *f.* brassic acid (brassidic acid).

**brät,** *pr. 3 sing.* (of braten) roasts, etc.

**braten,** *v.t.* roast; calcine; grill, broil, bake, fry; burn, scorch.

**Braten,** *m.* roast (meat). **-fett,** *n.* drippings.

**Bratfrischarbeit,** *f.* roasting and refining.

**Brau, Bräu,** *m.* brew, quantity brewed at one time; malt liquor.

**Braubottich,** *m.* brewing vat or tun.

**Brauch,** *m.* custom, usage, practice.

**brauchbar,** *a.* useful, usable, serviceable, suitable.

**Brauchbarkeit,** *f.* usefulness, utility.

**brauchen,** *v.t.* use; want, need.

**Brauchwasser,** *n.* water fit for industrial use.

**Braue,** *f.* (eye)brow.

**brauen,** *v.t. & i.* brew.

**Brauer,** *m.* brewer.

**Brauerei,** *f.* brewing; brewery.

**Brauer-hefe,** *f.* brewer's yeast. **-lack,** *m.* brewer's varnish. **-pech,** *n.* brewer's pitch.

**Brau-gerste,** *f.* brewing barley. **-haus, Bräuhaus,** *n.*, **Brauhof,** *m.* brewery. **-industrie,** *f.* brewing industry, brewing. **-kessel,** *m.* (*Brewing*) kettle, copper. **-malz,** *n.* brewing malt. **-meister,** *m.* master brewer.

**braun,** *a.* brown; bay (horse); dark (person). — **brauner Glaskopf,** limonite.

**Braun,** *n.* brown. **-bleierz,** *n.* pyromorphite.

**Bräune,** *f.* quinsy; angina; brownness; (*Min.*) = Braunerz.

**Brauneisen, -erz,** *n.*, **-mulm,** *m.* = Brauneisenstein. **-ocker,** *m.* brown iron ocher. **-stein,** *m.* brown iron ore, limonite.

**Braunelle,** *f.* self-heal (*Prunella vulgaris*).

**bräunen,** *v.t.* brown; dye brown; bronze; burnish.

**Braun-erz,** *n.* limonite; vivianite; sphalerite. **-färbung,** *f.* brown color(ation).

**braun-gefärbt,** *a.* brown-colored. **-gelb,** *a.* brownish-yellow, yellowish-brown.

**Braunglühhitze,** *f.* dark red heat.

**braungrün,** *a.* brown-green.

**Braun-heil,** *n.* = Brunelle. **-holz,** *n.* logwood. **-holzpapier,** *n.* paper made from steamed mechanical wood pulp. **-holzpappe,** *f.* board made from steamed mechanical wood pulp. **-kalk,** *m.* dolomite. **-kohl,** *m.* broccoli; kale. **-kohle,** *f.* brown coal, lignite.

**braunkohlenhaltig,** *a.* lignitiferous, lignitic.

**Braunkohlen-klein,** *n.* lignite breeze, lignite slack. **-koks,** *m.* lignite coke. **-pech,** *n.* lignite pitch. **-schiefer,** *m.* lignite shale. **-schwelerei,** *f.* lignite coking; lignite-coking plant. **-schwelgas,** *n.* gas from lignite distillation. **-teer,** *m.* lignite tar. **-teeröl,** *n.* lignite tar oil. **-teerpech,** *n.* lignite pitch.

**Braun-kräusen,** *f.pl.* (*Brewing*) fuzzy heads. **-lauge,** *f.* brown liquor.

**bräunlich,** *a.* brownish. **-gelb,** *a.* brownish-yellow.

**Braunmanganerz,** *n.* (*Min.*) manganite.

**braunrot,** *a.* brown-red.

**Braunrot,** *n.* brown red; colcothar; Indian red.

**braunrotgrau,** *a.* drab.

**braunrötlich,** *a.* reddish-brown.

**Braun-salz,** *n.* any of certain brown dyes. **-schliff,** *m.* (*Paper*) steamed mechanical wood pulp, brown wood pulp.

**braunschwarz,** *a.* brown-black, very dark brown.

**Braunschweig,** *n.* Brunswick.

**Braunschweiger,** *a.* Brunswick. **-grün,** *n.* Brunswick green.

**Braun-späne,** *m.pl.* logwood shavings. **-spat,** *m.* dolomite.

**Braunstein,** *m.* pyrolusite, manganese dioxide; (**roter**) rhodochrosite; (**schwarzer**) hausmannite. **-blende,** *f.* alabandite. **-kies,** *m.* alabandite. **-kiesel,** *m.* rhodonite. **-rahm, -schaum,** *m.* bog manganese, wad.

**braunstichig,** *a.* brownish.

**Brauntran,** *m.* (*Leather*) blubber, thick cod oil.

**Bräunung,** *f.* browning; brown coloring; dyeing brown; bronzing.

**Braupfanne,** *f.* (*Brewing*) kettle, copper.

**Brause,** *f.* effervescence; sprinkler, rose, sprinkling can; spray.

**Brause-.** effervescing, effervescent. **-bad,** *n.* shower bath. **-lithiumcitrat,** *n.* (*Pharm.*) effervescent lithium citrate. **-magnesia,** *f.* (*Pharm.*) (effervescing) solution of magnesium citrate. **-mischung,** *f.* effervescing mixture.

**brausen,** *v.i.* effervesce, froth; roar; buzz. — **brausend,** *p.a.* effervescent.

**Brause-pulver,** *n.* effervescing powder; (**englisches**) Seidlitz powder. **-salz,** *n.* effervescent salt. **-ton,** *m.* bituminous clay. **-vorrichtung,** *f.* sprinkling or spraying device. **-wasser,** *n.* soda water. **-wein,** *m.* sparkling wine.

**Braut,** *f.* bride, betrothed.

**Brau-wasser,** *n.* water for brewing; mash liquor, liquor. **-wesen,** *n.* brewing business.

**brav,** *a.* brave, gallant, good.

**Breccie,** *f.* breccia.

**Breccientextur,** *f.* brecciated structure.

**Brech-.** breaking; broken; emetic. **-arznei,** *f.* emetic. **-backen,** *f.pl.* crusher jaws.

**brechbar,** *a.* refrangible; breakable, brittle.

**Brech-barkeit,** *f.* refrangibility, etc. (see brechbar). **-bohne,** *f.* kidney bean (*Phaseolus vulgaris*). **-eisen,** *n.* crowbar.

**brechen,** *v.t.* break; refract; mine, quarry; crush, pulverize, disintegrate; interrupt; vomit; pluck; fold; blend (colors); boil off (silk); sprout. — *v.i.* break; crack; crease, crinkle; (of dye baths) change, decompose. — **brechend,** *p.a.* breaking, etc.; refractive. — **gebrochen,** *p.a.* broken, etc.; fractional; crooked, bent; worn out; ruined.

**brechenerregend,** *a.* emetic.

**Brecher,** *m.* breaker, crusher, etc. (see brechen).

**Brech-haufen,** *m.* (*Brewing*) broken piece. **-körner,** *n.pl.* castor beans. **-koks,** *m.* crushed coke. **-kraft,** *f.* (*Opt.*) refractive power. **-mittel,** *n.* emetic. **-neigung,** *f.* (*Med.*) nausea. **-nuss,** *f.* nux vomica. **-pulver,** *n.* emetic powder. **-punkt,** *m.* point of refraction. **-stange,** *f.* crowbar, pinch bar. **-stoff,** *m.* emetic, specif. emetine.

**Brechung,** *f.* breaking, etc. (see brechen); (*Physics*) refraction.

**Brechungs-ebene,** *f.* (*Optics*) plane of refraction. **-exponent,** *m.* refractive index. **-gesetz,** *n.* law of refraction. **-index,** *m.* refractive index. **-koeffizient,** *m.* coefficient of refraction. **-kraft,** *f.* refractive power. **-messer,** *m.* refractometer. **-verhältnis,** *n.* refractive index. **-vermögen,** *n.* refractive power. **-winkel,** *m.* angle of refraction.

**Brech-walzwerk,** *n.* crushing rolls (or rollers), crushing mill. **-wein,** *m.* (*Pharm.*) wine of antimony, antimonial wine. **-weinstein,** *m.* tartar emetic. **-werk,** *n.* crusher. **-wurzel, -wurz,** *f.* ipecacuanha, ipecac.

**Brei,** *m.* (something of porridge-like consistency) pulp, mash, paste, slurry; magma; porridge, pap; (*Ceram.*) slip.

**breiartig, breiig, breiicht,** *a.* pulpy, pappy, pasty, semifluid, semiliquid.

**breit,** *a.* broad, wide; flat.

**breitblättrig,** *a.* broad-leaved.

**Breite,** *f.* breadth, width; latitude.

**breiten,** *v.t.* spread, extend, broaden, flatten.

**Breitengrad,** *m.* (degree of) latitude.

**breitflanschig,** *a.* wide-flanged.

**Breitleder,** *n.* sole leather.

**Breiumschlag,** *m.* poultice, cataplasm.

**breiweich,** *a.* pulpy, pappy.

**Brekzie,** *f.* breccia.

**Bremer,** *a.* Bremen. **-blau,** *n.* Bremen blue. **-grün,** *n.* Bremen green.

**Bremse,** *f.* brake; gadfly.

**bremsen,** *v.t.* brake, check, retard, slow, damp. — **gebremste Pferdestärke,** brake horsepower.

**Brems-futter,** *n.* brake lining. **-leistung,** *f.* brake horsepower. **-strahlen,** *f.pl.* rays due to retarding of particles. **-strahlung,** *f.* radiation due to retarding of particles (usually continuous radiation).

**Bremsung,** *f.* checking, retarding.

**Brems-vermögen,** *n.* braking power, retarding power. **-wirkung,** *f.* braking or retarding effect.

**Brenkas,** *n.* fine East-Indian tin

**Brenke,** *f.* (*Brewing*) yeast tub.

**Brenn-.** burning, of combustion, calorific; distilling; (*Optics*, etc.) focal. **-achse,** *f.* (*Opt.*) focal axis. **-apparat,** *m.* distilling apparatus, still; branding machine. **-arbeit,** *f.* fire assaying. **-ätzverfahren,** *n.* pyrography.

**brennbar,** *a.* combustible, burnable. — **brennbare Luft,** inflammable air (hydrogen).

**Brenn-barkeit,** *f.* combustibility. **-blase,** *f.* alembic, still. **-cylinder,** *m.* (*Pharm.*) moxa. **-dauer,** *f.* burning time or period; (of lamps, etc.) life.

**Brenne,** *f.* (*Metal.*) pickle, dip.

**Brennebene,** *f.* focal plane.

**brennen,** *v.t.* burn; calcine, roast; distill; fire, bake; anneal; refine, char; sinter; pickle (metal); scald; singe; cauterize; brand; curl (hair). — *v.i.* burn; smart, sting. — **brennend,** *p.a.* burning; caustic; pungent; smarting; ardent. — **gebrannt,** *p.a.* burnt, calcined, etc. — **gebrannte Erde,** terra cotta. — **gebrannte Magnesia,** magnesia usta (MgO). — **gebranntes Wasser,** distilled liquor; distilled water.

**Brennen,** *n.* burning, etc. (see brennen); combustion.

**Brenner,** *m.* burner; torch; distiller; brickmaker; lime burner.

**Brennerei,** *f.* distillery; distillation, distilling; plant (for burning lime, etc.); kiln; burning (of lime, brick, etc.). **-betrieb,** *m.* distillery management or operation. **-hefe,** *f.* distillery yeast. **-maische,** *f.* distillery mash.

**Brenner-kopf,** *m.* burner tip. **-mündung,** *f.* orifice of a burner.

**Brenn-fleck,** *m.* focus; burned spot. **-gas,** *n.* combustible gas, fuel gas. **-gerste,** *f.* distilling barley. **-geschwindigkeit,** *f.* velocity of combustion or of burning or of distillation.

-glas, *n.* burning glass. **-gut,** *n.* material to be burned or distilled. **-helm,** *m.* still head. **-herd,** *m.* hearth; refining furnace. **-holz,** *n.* firewood. **-kammer,** *f.* combustion chamber; firebox. **-kapsel,** *f.* sagger. **-kegel,** *m.* (*Ceram.*) pyrometric cone. **-kessel,** *m.* retort. **-kolben,** *m.* distilling flask, alembic. **-linie,** *f.* focal line. **-linse,** *f.* burning glass, convex lens. **-luft,** *f.* air for combustion; (*Old Chem.*) inflammable air (hydrogen). **-material,** *n.* combustible material, fuel. **-materialverbrauch,** *m.* fuel consumption. **-mittel,** *n.* caustic, corrosive. **-nessel,** *f.* (stinging) nettle (*Urticaceae*). **-ofen,** *m.* burning oven, baking oven, kiln, furnace, roasting furnace, calcining furnace, etc. **-öl,** *n.* burning oil; fuel oil. **-palme,** *f.* jaggery palm (*Caryota urens*). **-punkt,** *m.* focal point, focus; burning point, fire point. **-säure,** *f.* (*Metal.*) pickling acid. **-schnitt,** *m.* (*Distillation*) cut, fraction. **-schwindung,** *f.* (*Ceram.*) shrinkage in firing. **-silber,** *n.* amalgam for silvering. **-spiegel,** *m.* concave mirror. **-spiritus,** *m.* alcohol for burning. **-stahl,** *m.* blister steel. **-staub,** *m.* powdered fuel, fuel dust.

**Brennstoff,** *m.* fuel, combustible; (*Old Chem.*) phlogiston. **-aufwand,** *m.* fuel consumption. **-ausnutzung,** *f.* utilization of fuel. **-chemie,** *f.* fuel chemistry. **-verbrauch,** *m.* fuel consumption. **-wert,** *m.* fuel value. **-wirtschaft,** *f.* fuel economy. **-ziegel,** *m.* fuel briquet.

**Brennstunde,** *f.* burning hour, lamp hour.

**Brennung,** *f.* burning, etc. (see brennen); combustion.

**Brenn-versuch,** *m.* burning test. **-wärme,** *f.* heat of combustion; calcining heat, etc. (see brennen). **-weite,** *f.* focal distance, focal length. **-wert,** *m.* fuel value, calorific value. **-zeit,** *f.* time of burning, etc. (see brennen); (*Molding*) cure time. **-ziegel,** *m.* firebrick; fuel briquet. **-zone,** *f.* zone of combustion. **-zünder,** *m.* fuse; fuse train. **-zylinder,** *m.* (*Pharm.*) moxa.

**Brenz,** *n.* empyreuma, combustible.

**Brenz-.** pyro-. **-apfelsäure,** *f.* maleic acid. **-cain,** *n.* (*Pharm.*) pyrocain. **-catechin,** *n.* pyrocatechol, pyrocatechin.

**brenzeln,** *v.i.* have an empyreumatic odor or taste.

**Brenz-essigäther, -essiggeist,** *m.* acetone. **-gallussäure,** *f.* pyrogallic acid, pyrogallol. **-harz,** *n.* empyreumatic resin.

**brenzholzsauer,** *a.* of or combined with pyroligneous acid.

**Brenz-holzsäure,** *f.* pyroligneous acid. **-katechin,** *n.* pyrocatechol, pyrocatechin. **-katechingerbstoff,** *m.* pyrocatechol tannin.

**brenzlich, brenzlig,** *a.* empyreumatic, tarry; burnt. — **brenzlige Säuren,** pyro acids.

**Brenz-öl,** *n.* empyreumatic oil. **-säure,** *f.* pyro acid. **-schleimsäure,** *f.* pyromucic acid, furoic acid. **-terebinsäure,** *f.* pyroterebic acid. **-traubenalkohol,** *m.* pyroracemic alcohol (hydroxyacetone). **-traubensäure,** *f.* pyroracemic acid, pyruvic acid. **-weinsäure,** *f.* pyrotartaric acid.

**Bresche,** *f.* breccia.

**Brett,** *n.* board, plank; shelf; office.

**brettern,** *a.* of boards, boarded.

**Brett-mühle,** *f.* sawmill. **-stückchen,** *n.* piece of board.

**Brezel,** *f.* pretzel.

**Brezzie,** *f.* breccia.

**bricht,** *pr. 3 sing.* (of brechen) breaks, etc.

**Brief,** *m.* letter; paper, packet. **-chen,** *n.* note. **-geld,** *n.* postage.

**brieflich,** *a.* written. — *adv.* by letter, in writing.

**Brief-marke,** *f.* postage stamp. **-papier,** *n.* writing paper. **-schaften,** *f.pl.* writings, papers. **-stempel,** *m.* postmark. **-tisch,** *m.* desk. **-umschlag,** *m.* envelope, cover, wrapper. **-wage,** *f.* letter scales. **-wechsel,** *m.* correspondence.

**Bries,** *n.* thymus. **-eldrüse,** *f.* thymus gland.

**briet,** *pret.* (of braten) roasted, etc.

**Brikett,** *n.* briquet, briquette. **-bindemittel,** *n.* binder for briquets, briquet cement.

**brikettieren,** *v.t.* briquet.

**Brikettierfähigkeit,** *f.* briquetting property.

**Brikett-kohle,** *f.* briquet(ting) coal. **-pech,** *n.* briquetting pitch.

**brillant,** *a.* brilliant.

**Brillant-gelb,** *n.* brilliant yellow. **-grün,** *n.* brilliant green. **-weiss,** *n.* brilliant white.

**Brille,** *f.* spectacles, eyeglasses; gland (of a stuffing box).

**Brillenofen,** *m.* spectacle furnace.

**Brinellhärte,** *f.* Brinell hardness.

**brinellieren,** *v.t.* test with the Brinell machine.

**Brinell-probe,** *f.* Brinell test or sample. **-zahl,** *f.* Brinell number.

**bringen,** *v.t.* bring; carry, take, put; yield.

**brisant,** *a.* shattering, disruptive, brisant. — **brisanter Sprengstoff,** brisant (i.e., shattering) explosive.

**Brisanz,** *f.* brisance, shattering power. **-geschoss,** *n.* high-explosive shell, H.E. shell. **-sprengstoff,** *m.* high explosive, disruptive.

**Brise,** *f.* breeze.

**Bristolpappe,** *f.* Bristol board.

**Britischgummi,** *n.* British gum, dextrin.

**Bröckchen,** *n.* small bit, small piece, crumb.

**bröckelig,** *a.* brittle, friable, crumbly, fragile.

**Bröckeligkeit,** *f.* brittleness, friability.

**bröckeln,** *v.t.* crumble.

**Bröckelstärke,** *f.* lump starch.

**brocken,** *v.t.* crumble, break up.
**Brocken,** *m.* lump, fragment; crumb. **-gestein,** *n.* (*Petrog.*) breccia. **-glas,** *n.* broken glass, cullet. **-stärke,** *f.* lump starch. **-stein,** *m.* (*Petrog.*) breccia. **-torf,** *m.* lump peat.
**bröcklig,** *a.* = bröckelig.
**Bröckligkeit,** *f.* brittleness, friability.
**Brod,** *n.* = Brot.
**Brodel,** *m.* = Brodem.
**brodeln,** *v.i.* bubble; effervesce; boil.
**Brodem, Broden,** *m.* vapor, steam, exhalation; (*Mining*) foul air, damp.
**Brokat,** *m.* brocade. **-farbe,** *f.* brocade color (powdered bronze); brocade dye.
**Brom,** *n.* bromine.
**Brom-.** of or combined with bromine; bromo- (as *Brombenzoesäure*, bromobenzoic acid); bromide of (as *Brombaryum*, barium bromide). **-ammon,** *m.*, **-ammonium,** *n.* ammonium bromide. **-antimon,** *n.* antimony bromide. **-arsen,** *n.*, **-arsenik,** *m.* arsenic bromide. **-äther,** *m.* ethyl bromide. **-äthyl,** *n.* ethyl bromide. **-äthylen,** *n.* ethylene bromide. **-äthylformin,** *n.* (*Pharm.*) bromalin. **-atom,** *n.* bromine atom. **-baryum,** *n.* barium bromide. **-beere,** *f.* blackberry.
**brombeerrot,** *a.* blackberry-red.
**Brom-benzol,** *n.* bromobenzene. **-calcium,** *n.* calcium bromide. **-cyan,** *n.* cyanogen bromide, bromocyanogen. **-dampf,** *m.* bromine vapor. **-eisen,** *n.* iron bromide. **-flasche,** *f.* bromine bottle. **-fluor,** *n.* bromine fluoride. **-gehalt,** *m.* bromine content. **-gold,** *n.* gold bromide. **-goldkalium,** *n.* potassium auribromide, potassium bromoaurate.
**bromhaltig,** *a.* containing bromine.
**Brom-hydrat,** *n.* hydrobromide; bromine hydrate. **-hydrin,** *n.* bromohydrin.
**Bromid,** *n.* bromide (esp., an -ic bromide, as contrasted with Bromür).
**bromierbar,** *a.* capable of being brominated.
**bromieren,** *v.t.* brominate.
**Bromierung,** *f.* bromination.
**bromig,** *a.* bromous.
**Bromion,** *n.* bromide ion, bromine ion.
**Bromismus,** *m.* (*Med.*) bromism.
**Brom-jod,** *n.* iodine bromide. **-kalium,** *n.* potassium bromide. **-kalzium,** *n.*, **-kalk,** *m.* calcium bromide. **-kampher,** *m.* bromocamphor, (*Pharm.*) monobromated camphor. **-kohlenstoff,** *m.* carbon (tetra)bromide. **-körper,** *m.* (*Colloids*) "bromide body" (bromide ion). **-kupfer,** *n.* copper bromide. **-lauge,** *f.* bromine lye (solution of sodium hypobromite and bromide made by passing bromine into sodium hydroxide solution). **-lithium,** *n.* lithium bromide. **-lösung,** *f.* bromine solution. **-magnesium,** *n.* magnesium bromide. **-metall,** *n.* metallic bromide. **-methyl,** *n.* methyl bromide, bromomethane. **-methylat,** *n.* methobromide. **-natrium,** *n.* sodium bromide. **-natron,** *n.* sodium hypobromite. **-öldruck,** *m.* (*Photog.*) bromoil printing. **-olyse,** *f.* bromolysis. **-phosphor,** *m.* phosphorus bromide. **-radium,** *n.* radium bromide. **-salz,** *n.* bromide; bromate.
**bromsauer,** *a.* of or combined with bromic acid, bromate of.
**Brom-säure,** *f.* bromic acid. **-schwefel,** *m.* sulfur bromide. **-silber,** *n.* silver bromide. **-silizium,** *n.* silicon bromide. **-spat,** *n.* bromyrite (AgBr). **-stickstoff,** *m.* nitrogen bromide. **-toluol,** *n.* bromotoluene. **-überträger,** *m.* bromine carrier.
**Bromür,** *n.* (-ous) bromide. (Used for a metal in its lower valence, as *Eisenbromür*, ferrous bromide.)
**Brom-verbindung,** *f.* bromine compound. **-vergiftung,** *f.* bromine (or bromide) poisoning. **-wasser,** *n.* bromine water. **-wasserstoff,** *m.* hydrogen bromide; hydrobromic acid.
**bromwasserstoffsauer,** *a.* of or combined with hydrobromic acid, (usually) hydrobromide of.
**Brom-wasserstoffsäure,** *f.* hydrobromic acid. **-wismut,** *m.* & *n.* bismuth bromide. **-zahl,** *f.* bromine number. **-zink,** *n.* zinc bromide. **-zinn,** *n.* tin bromide.
**Bronce,** *f.* bronze.
**bronzeartig,** *a.* bronze-like, bronzy.
**Bronze-blau,** *n.* bronze blue, reflex blue. **-draht,** *m.* bronze wire. **-farbe,** *f.* bronze color. **-färben,** *n.* bronzing.
**bronzefarbig,** *a.* bronze-colored.
**Bronze-giesserei,** *f.* bronze foundry; bronze founding. **-glanz,** *m.* bronze luster. **-guss,** *m.* bronze casting, cast bronze. **-lack,** *m.* bronze varnish, bronzing lacquer. **-pulver,** *n.* bronze powder. **-tinktur,** *f.* bronzing liquid.
**bronzieren,** *v.t.* bronze. — **bronzierend,** *p.a.* bronzing; bronzy.
**Bronzier-pulver,** *n.* bronzing powder. **-salz,** *n.* bronzing salt, specif. antimony trichloride.
**Bronzierung,** *f.* bronzing.
**bronzig,** *a.* bronzy.
**Brosam, Brosame,** *f.* crumb, scrap.
**Bröschen,** *n.* sweetbread.
**broschieren,** *v.t.* stitch, sew, work; brocade; bind in paper cover.
**Broschüre,** *f.* stitched (but unbound) book; pamphlet, brochure.
**Brot,** *n.* bread; loaf. **-backen,** *n.* bread baking. **-brei,** *m.* bread paste.
**Brötchen,** *n.* roll.
**Brot-gärung,** *f.* panary fermentation, leavening

of bread. **-geschmack,** *n.* (*Brewing*) steam taste. **-herr,** *m.* employer. **-korn,** *n.* breadstuff.

**brotlaibartig,** *a.* loaf-like.

**brotlos,** *a.* unemployed, unprofitable.

**Brot-masse,** *f.* breadstuff. **-raffinade,** *f.* loaf sugar. **-rinde,** *f.* bread crust. **-teig,** *m.* bread dough. **-wurzel,** *f.* cassava; yam. **-zucker,** *m.* loaf sugar.

**Brown'sche Bewegung.** Brownian movement.

**Bruch,** *m.* fracture; fraction; break, breaking, breach, crack, cleft; fold, crease, wrinkle, crimp; quarry; fragments, scrap; rupture, (*Med.*) hernia. **-beanspruchung,** *f.* breaking stress. **-belastung,** *f.* breaking load. **-blei,** *n.* scrap lead. **-dehnung,** *f.* breaking elongation; stretch (of paper). **-ebene,** *f.* plane of fracture. **-eisen,** *n.* scrap iron.

**bruchfest,** *a.* resisting breakage, tenacious.

**Bruch-festigkeit,** *f.* resistance to fracture, breaking strength. **-fläche,** *f.* surface of fracture. **-gefüge,** *n.* fracture. **-gewicht,** *n.* fractional weight. **-glas,** *n.* broken glass, cullet. **-gramm,** *n.* fraction of a gram. **-grammgewicht,** *n.* fractional gram weight.

**brüchig,** *a.* brittle, short; friable; fragile; (of fabrics) tender; full of cracks; (*Geol.*) clastic, fragmental. — **— machen,** make brittle, embrittle. — **— werden,** become brittle, (of fabrics) tender.

**Brüchigkeit,** *f.* brittleness, etc. (see brüchig).

**Bruch-kupfer,** *n.* scrap copper. **-last,** *f.* breaking load. **-metall,** *n.* broken metal, scrap metal. **-modul,** *m.* modulus of rupture. **-probe,** *f.* breaking test, breakdown test. **-punkt,** *m.* breaking point. **-riss,** *m.* (*Metal.*) failure crack. **-silber,** *n.* broken silver, scrap silver. **-spannung,** *f.* breaking stress; tensile strength. **-stein,** *m.* quarry stone; broken stone. **-stelle,** *f.* broken place, place of fracture. **-strich,** *m.* (*Math.*) fraction stroke (between numerator and denominator). **-stück,** *n.* fragment; shred. **-stücke,** *pl.* debris; scrap. **-teil,** *m.* fraction. **-zahl,** *f.* fractional number.

**Brücke,** *f.* bridge; platform; (*Anat.*) pons.

**Brücken-atom,** *n.* bridge atom, bridging atom. **-bindung,** *f.* bridge bond, bridging bond. **-glühzünder,** *m.* (*Expl.*) bridge-wire cap. **-ring,** *m.* bridged ring. **-sauerstoff,** *m.* bridging oxygen, connecting oxygen. **-schaltung,** *f.* (*Elec.*) bridge connection, bridge. **-wa(a)ge,** *f.* platform balance. **-widerstand,** *m.* (*Elec.*) bridge resistance.

**Brüden,** *m.* liquid being evaporated, also the steam or vapor from it. **-dampf,** *m.* steam or vapor from an evaporating liquid.

**Bruder,** *m.* brother; friar.

**Brühe,** *f.* soupy liquid, liquor; broth, soup; gravy, sauce; (*Dyeing*) liquor, bath; (*Leather*) juice, liquor, drench, ooze; (*Tobacco*) sauce.

**brühen,** *v.t.* scald, treat with hot water; scour.

**brüh-gar,** *a.* (*Leather*) liquor-tanned. **-heiss,** *a.* scalding hot.

**Brüh-messer,** *m.* (*Leather*) barkometer. **-wasser,** *n.* water for scalding.

**brüllen,** *v.i.* roar, bellow, howl.

**brummen,** *v.i.* hum, buzz, low, growl, grumble.

**Brunelle,** *f.* self-heal (*Prunella vulgaris*).

**Brunft,** *f.* oestrus, estrus, heat. **-hormon,** *n.* (o)estrual hormone.

**Brunierbeize,** *f.* (*Metal.*) bronzing pickle.

**brunieren, brünieren,** *v.t.* burnish, polish; brown; bronze. — *v.i.* turn brown.

**Brünierstein,** *m.* burnishing stone; bloodstone.

**Brunnen,** *m.* well, spring; fountain; (mineral) waters. **-flasche,** *f.* mineral-water bottle; siphon bottle. **-kresse,** *f.* watercress. **-salz,** *n.* well salt, brine salt. **-wasser,** *n.* well water, spring water.

**Brunst,** *f.* ardor, fervor; oestrus, estrus.

**brünstig,** *a.* ardent; fervent; in heat.

**Brust,** *f.* breast; chest, thorax; front (of a blast furnace); brisket.

**Brust-.** of the breast or chest; thoracic; pectoral. **-angst,** *f.* angina pectoris. **-arznei,** *f.* chest medicine, pectoral. **-beere,** *f.* jujube, zizyphus. **-beindrüse,** *f.* thymus gland. **-bohrer,** *m.* breast drill. **-drüse,** *f.* mammary gland. **-fell,** *n.* pleura. **-fellentzündung,** *f.* pleurisy. **-fieber,** *n.* bronchitis. **-ganz,** *m.* thoracic duct. **-kasten, -korb,** *m.* thorax. **-krampf,** *m.* asthma. **-milch,** *f.* breast milk, human milk; pectoral emulsion. **-pulver,** *n.* pectoral powder, specif. compound licorice powder.

**brustreinigend,** *p.a.* expectorant.

**Brut,** *f.* brood, hatch; brooding, hatching. **-ei,** *n.* egg for hatching.

**brüten,** *v.i.* brood, hatch, incubate.

**Brut-kasten, -ofen, -schrank,** *m.* incubator.

**Brüt-ofen, -schrank,** *m.* incubator.

**brutto,** *a.* & *adv.* gross; over-all.

**Brutto-formel,** *f.* a formula indicating merely the number of atoms of each kind, and not their mode of union, an empirical molecular formula (*e.g.*, $C_3H_8$). **-gewicht,** *n.* gross weight. **-wert,** *m.* gross value.

**Brutwärme,** *f.* blood heat.

**Bruzin,** *n.* brucine.

**Bube,** *m.* boy; knave.

**Bubonenpest,** *f.* bubonic plague.

**Bucco-.** buchu. **-blätter,** *n.pl.* (*Pharm.*) buchu.

**Buch,** *n.* book; quire.

**Buchbinder-gold,** *n.* bookbinder's gold, leaf gold. **-kleister,** *m.* bookbinder's paste. **-leim,** *m.* bookbinder's glue. **-pappe,** *f.* binder's board.

**Buchdrucker,** *m.* printer. **-ei,** *f.* printing establishment, press; printing. **-farbe,** *f.* printing ink. **-schwärze,** *f.* printer's ink.

**Buchdruck-farbe,** *f.* printing ink. **-firnis,** *m.* printer's varnish.

**Buche,** *f.* beech.

**Buch-ecker,** *f.* beechnut. **-eckernöl, -ekernöl,** *n.* beechnut oil.

**Buchel,** *f.* beechnut.

**buchen, büchen,** *a.* beechen, of beech.

**buchen,** *v.t.* enter, book, register.

**Buchen-asche,** *f.* beech ashes. **-holz,** *n.* beechwood. **-holztteer,** *n.* beech tar. **-rinde,** *f.* beech bark. **-späne,** *m.pl.* beech shavings (or chips).

**Bücher-ei,** *f.* library; books. **-verzeichnis,** *n.* book list, book catalog.

**Buch-führen,** *n.* bookkeeping. **-gold,** *n.* leaf gold. **-halter,** *m.* bookkeeper, accountant. **-handel,** *m.* book trade, bookselling. **-händler,** *m.* bookseller; publisher.

**Büchnertrichter,** *m.* Büchner funnel.

**Buch-nuss,** *f.* beechnut. **-nussöl,** *n.* beechnut oil. **-öl,** *n.* beech(nut) oil.

**Buchsbaum,** *m.* box tree. **-holz,** *n.* boxwood.

**Büchse, Buchse,** *f.* box, chest, case, can, pot; rifle; (*Mach.*) bush, bushing, sleeve, box, socket.

**Büchsenfleisch,** *n.* canned meat, tinned meat.

**büchsenförmig,** *a.* box-shaped.

**Buchsenfrucht,** *f.* canned fruit, tinned fruit.

**Büchsen-gemüse,** *n.* canned vegetables. **-macher,** *n.* gunsmith.

**Buchsenmetal, Büchsenmetall,** *n.* bush metal, bearing metal.

**Büchsen-milch,** *f.* condensed (or evaporated) milk. **-mühle,** *f.* barrel mill. **-pulver,** *n.* rifle powder. **-schuss,** *m.* gunshot. **-stein,** *m.* iron pyrites.

**Buchstabe,** *m.* letter; character; type.

**Buchstabenrechnung,** *f.* algebra.

**buchstabieren,** *v.t.* spell.

**buchstäblich,** *a.* literal.

**Bucht,** *f.* bay, inlet; sinus.

**Buchublätter,** *n.pl.* (*Pharm.*) buchu.

**Buchung,** *f.* entry.

**Buchweizen,** *m.* buckwheat.

**Buckel,** *m.* hump; knob; knot.

**bücken,** *v.r.* stoop.

**Bückling,** *m.* red herring, bloater.

**Bucko-, Bucku-.** buchu. **-blätter,** *n.pl.* (*Pharm.*) buchu.

**Bude,** *f.* booth, stall, shop; hut; shed.

**Büffel,** *m.* buffalo; buff (leather). **-leim,** *m.* leather glue.

**Bug,** *m.* bend, bow; bow (of a boat).

**Bügel,** *m.* bow (any curved piece of metal, wood, or the like); hoop; guard, frame; clamp, clip, strap; loop; handle (of a pail, etc.); shackle; stirrup. — **durchlöcherter —,** beehive shelf (in a pneumatic trough).

**bügelecht,** *a.* fast to ironing.

**Bügeleisen,** *n.* flatiron.

**bügeln,** *v.t.* iron; press.

**Bügelschälchen,** *n.* little dish or cup (of bent metal).

**Bühne,** *f.* platform, scaffold; stage, theater.

**buk,** *pret.* (of backen) baked, etc.

**büken,** *v.t.* = beuchen.

**Bukett,** *n.* bouquet.

**Bukko-, Bukku-.** buchu.

**Bulbe,** *f.* bulb.

**Bulgarien,** *n.* Bulgaria.

**Bund,** *m.* band, tie; hoop, collar, flange; alliance. — *n.* bundle, bunch.

**Bündel,** *n.* bundle, bunch; parcel, packet; (of rays) pencil, beam; (of waves) packet.

**bündeln,** *v.t.* focus, concentrate; bundle, bunch.

**Bundes-rat,** *m.* federal council. **-tag,** *m.* federal diet.

**bündig,** *a.* flush; valid; concise; conclusive.

**Bündnis,** *n.* alliance.

**Bundstahl,** *m.* fagot steel.

**Bunsen-brenner,** *m.* Bunsen burner. **-flamme,** *f.* Bunsen (burner) flame. **-kohle,** *f.* carbon for the Bunsen cell.

**bunt,** *a.* variegated, many-colored, motley; mottled, speckled; colored; gay, fancy, gaudy.

**Bunt-ätzdruck,** *m.* colored discharge printing. **-ätze,** *f.* (*Dyeing*) color discharge. **-ätzfarbe,** *f.* color discharge paste. **-bleiche,** *f.* bleaching of colored goods. **-bleierz,** *n.* pyromorphite. **-druck,** *m.* color printing; color print. **-farbe,** *f.* variegated color; (any) iron oxide pigment.

**buntfärben,** *v.t.* stain; color, dye; mottle, marble.

**Buntfärberei,** *f.* dyeing in different colors.

**buntfarbig,** *a.* variegated; bright-colored.

**buntfleckig,** *a.* speckled, variegated.

**Bunt-gewebe,** *n.* colored fabric. **-glas,** *n.* stained glass. **-kupfererz,** *n.*, **-kupferkies,** *m.* bornite. **-öllack,** *m.* colored oil varnish. **-papier,** *n.* colored paper, stained paper; fancy paper; marbled paper. **-papierfarbe,** *f.* surface paper color. **-pappe,** *f.* colored (paper)board. **-reserve,** *f.* (*Calico*) color resist. **-sandstein,** *m.* mottled sandstone.

**bunt-scheckig,** *a.* variegated, mottled. **-schillernd,** *a.* iridescent, chatoyant.

**Bunt-schlichte,** *f.* sizing of (or size for) colored goods. **-stift,** *m.* colored pencil.

**Bürde,** *f.* burden, load, charge.

**Bureau,** *n.* office; bureau.

**Bürette,** *f.* buret, burette.

**Büretten-bürste,** *f.* buret brush. **-deckel,** *m.* buret cap. **-flasche,** *f.* volumetric flask. **-gestell,** *n.* buret stand. **-hahn,** *m.* buret cock.

**-halter,** *m.* buret holder. **-klemme,** *f.* buret clamp. **-schwimmer,** *m.* buret float. **-spitze,** *f.* buret tip. **-stativ,** *n.* buret stand, buret support. **-trichter,** *m.* funnel for filling burets.
**Burg,** *f.* castle, stronghold.
**bürge,** *pret. subj.* of bergen.
**bürgen,** *v.i.* give bail; vouch (for).
**Bürger,** *m.* citizen; townsman; civilian. **-krieg,** *m.* civil war.
**bürgerlich,** *a.* civil; common; civilian.
**Bürger-meister,** *m.* mayor, burgomaster. **-schaft,** *f.* community; the citizens. **-stand,** *m.* citizenry; middle class. **-steig,** *m.* sidewalk.
**Bürgschaft,** *f.* security; guarantee; bail.
**Burgunder,** *m.* Burgundy (wine). **-harz, -pech,** *n.* Burgundy pitch.
**burnet(t)isieren,** *v.t.* burnettize (impregnate with zinc chloride).
**Büro,** *n.* office. **-zeit,** *f.* office hours.
**Bursche,** *m.* fellow; lad; servant; student.
**Bürste,** *f.* brush.
**bürsten,** *v.t.* brush.
**Bürsten-entladung,** *f.* (*Elec.*) brush discharge. **-feuer,** *n.* (*Elec.*) brush sparking.
**Busch,** *m.* bush; copse; tuft.
**Büschel,** *m.* tuft, bunch, cluster; (*Elec.*) brush; bundle, pencil, beam (of rays). **-entladung,** *f.* (*Elec.*) brush discharge.
**büschelförmig,** *a.* tuft-like, tufted, clustered.
**Buschholz,** *n.* undergrowth, underwood.
**Busen,** *m.* bosom, breast; bay.
**Busse,** *f.* penance, fine, penalty.
**büssen,** *v.t.* atone for, make good.
**Bussole,** *f.* compass; galvanometer.
**Butan,** *n.* butane.
**Bütte, Butte,** *f.* tub, vat, back, tank, chest.
**butteln,** *v.i.* bubble.
**Büttenfärbung,** *f.* (*Paper*) vat coloring, pulp coloring.
**büttengefärbt,** *a.* (*Paper*) vat-colored, also unbleached.
**Bütten-leimung,** *f.* (*Paper*) vat sizing, pulp sizing. **-papier,** *n.* vat paper, handmade paper.
**Butter-.** butter; butyric, butyryl, butyro-.
**butter-ähnlich, -artig,** *a.* buttery, butyraceous.
**Butter-amylester,** *m.* amyl butyrate. **-äther,** *m.* butyric ether (ethyl butyrate). **-baum,** *m.* shea tree. **-blume,** *f.* buttercup. **-farbe,** *f.* butter color. **-fass,** *n.* churn. **-fett,** *n.* butter fat; butyrin. **-gärung,** *f.* butyric fermentation. **-gelb,** *n.* butter yellow.
**butterhaltig,** *a.* containing butter, butyraceous.
**butterig,** *a.* buttery.
**Butter-messer,** *m.* butyrometer. **-milch,** *f.* buttermilk.
**buttern,** *v.t.* churn; butter. — *v.i.* yield butter.
**Butter-nuss,** *f.* butternut. **-persäure,** *f.* peroxybutyric acid, perbutyric acid. **-prüfer,** *m.* butter tester.
**buttersauer,** *a.* of or combined with butyric acid, butyrate of.
**Buttersäure,** *f.* butyric acid. **-äther,** *m.* ethyl butyrate; *pl.* butyric esters. **-gärung,** *f.* butyric fermentation. **-pilz,** *m.* butyric acid bacteria.
**Butterstoff,** *m.* butyrin. *Obs.*
**Butyljodid,** *n.* butyl iodide.
**Butyropersäure,** *f.* peroxybutyric acid, perbutyric acid.
**b.w.,** *abbrev.* (bitte wenden) please turn over, p.t.o.
**Bz.,** *abbrev.* (Benzol) benzene; (*Com.*) benzol.
**bzgl.,** *abbrev.* (bezüglich) respecting.
**Bzl.,** *abbrev.* (Benzol) benzene; (*Com.*) benzol.
**Bzn.,** *abbrev.* (Benzin) benzine, gasoline.
**bzw.,** *abbrev.* (beziehungsweise) respectively, or.

# C

(See also under Z)

**C.**, *abbrev.* Celsius (centigrade); Chemisches Zentralblatt.
**ca.**, *abbrev.* (circa, zirka) about.
**Ca-, ca-.** see also Ka-, ka-.
**Cabanholz,** *n.* camwood.
**Cabesaseide,** *f.* cabeca, cabesse (silk).
**Cachou,** *n.* catechu.
**cachoutieren,** *v.t.* dye with catechu or cutch.
**Cadeöl,** *n.* oil of cade.
**Cadinöl, Cadiöl,** *n.* oil of cade.
**cadmieren,** *v.t.* treat or plate with cadmium.
**Cadmium-.** see Kadmium-.
**Caffee,** *m.* coffee (for compounds see Kaffee-).
**Cainca-säure,** *f.* cahincic acid. **-wurzel,** *f.* cahinca (root).
**Caincin,** *n.* cahincin.
**Cajeput-geist,** *m.* spirit of cajuput. **-öl,** *n.* cajuput oil.
**cal.,** *abbrev.* (gram) calorie.
**Cal.,** *abbrev.*, large calorie, kilogram calorie.
**calcifizieren,** *v.t.* calcify.
**calcinierbar,** *a.* calcinable.
**calcinieren,** *v.t.* calcine.
**Calcinier-herd,** *m.* calcining hearth. **-ofen,** *m.* calcining furnace or oven. **-topf,** *m.* calcining pot or crucible.
**Calcinierung,** *f.* calcination.
**Calciumgehalt,** *m.* calcium content.
**calciumhaltig,** *a.* containing calcium.
**Calcium-hydrat,** *n.* calcium hydroxide. **-hydrür,** *n.* calcium hydride ($CaH_2$). **-jodid,** *n.* calcium iodide. **-legierung,** *f.* calcium alloy. **-metall,** *n.* calcium metal, metallic calcium. **-rhodanid,** *n.* calcium thiocyanate. **-salz,** *n.* calcium salt. **-spiegel,** *m.* (*Biol.*) calcium level. **-sulfozyanid,** *n.* calcium thiocyanate. **-sulfuret,** *n.* calcium sulfide. **-verbindung,** *f.* calcium compound. **-wolframat,** *n.* calcium tungstate.
**Caledonischbraun,** *n.* Caledonian brown.
**calibrieren,** *v.t.* calibrate.
**Calisayarinde,** *f.* calisaya bark.
**Calit.** a ceramic for insulators. *T.N.*
**Calorienwert,** *m.* caloric value.
**calorimetrieren,** *v.t.* measure with the calorimeter.
**Calorimetrierung,** *f.* calorimetric measurement.
**calorimetrisch,** *a.* calorimetric.
**calorisch,** *a.* caloric, thermal.
**Calorstat,** *m.* thermostat.
**Calypsol.** a cold-resistant grease. *T.N.*
**Cambaholz, Cambalholz,** *n.* camwood.
**Cambogiasäure,** *f.* gambogic acid.
**cämentieren.** = zementieren.
**camouflieren,** *v.t.* camouflage.
**Campagne,** *f.* campaign, (working) season.
**Campane,** *f.* bell jar.
**Campecheholz,** *n.* logwood.
**Camphansäure,** *f.* camphanic acid.
**Campher,** *m.* camphor (for compounds see Kampher-).
**camphotetisch,** *a.* (*Org. Chem.*) camphothetic (isocampholytic).
**canadisch,** *a.* Canadian, Canada.
**Canarienfarbe,** *f.* canary color; canarin.
**cancerogen,** *a.* cancerogenic.
**Candarawachs,** *n.* carnauba wax.
**Candelillawachs,** *n.* candelilla wax.
**canneliert,** *a.* channeled.
**Cannelkohle,** *f.* cannel coal.
**Cantharinsäure,** *f.* cantharidic acid.
**Cantharsäure,** *f.* cantharic acid.
**Caoutschuk,** *m.* caoutchouc (for compounds see Kautschuk-).
**Capelle,** etc. = Kapelle, etc.
**capillar,** etc. = kapillar, etc.
**Capomesser,** *m.* a kind of meter for gases.
**Capriblau,** *n.* Capri blue.
**Caprinsäure,** *f.* capric acid.
**Capron-fett,** *n.* caproin. **-säure,** *f.* caproic acid.
**Caprylsäure,** *f.* caprylic acid.
**Capsel,** etc. = Kapsel, etc.
**Caragheenmoos,** *n.* carrageen moss, Irish moss.
**Caramelgeruch,** *m.* caramel odor.
**Caranna-gummi, -harz,** *n.* caranna (resin).
**Carapa-öl, -fett,** *n.* carap(a) oil.
**Carbamidsäure,** *f.* carbamic acid.
**carbaminsauer,** *a.* of or combined with carbamic acid, carbamate of.
**Carbaminsäure,** *f.* carbamic acid.
**Carbanilsäure,** *f.* carbanilic acid.
**Carbäthoxy-.** carbethoxy-.
**Carbäthoxyl,** *n.* carbethoxyl.
**Carbazotsilicium,** *n.* silicon carbonitride.
**carbidisch,** *a.* carbide.
**Carbid-kohle,** *f.* carbide carbon. **-ofen,** *m.* carbide furnace. **-schlacke,** *f.* carbide slag. **-schlamm,** *m.* carbide sludge. **-trommel,** *f.* carbide drum. **-verfahren,** *n.* carbide process.
**Carbochindolin,** *n.* carboquindoline.
**carbocyclisch,** *a.* carbocyclic.

**Carbol,** *n.* phenol, carbolic acid.
**Carbol-.** carbolic, carbolized, carbolated. **-kalk,** *n.* carbolated lime. **-öl,** *n.* carbolated oil. **-salbe,** *f.* (*Pharm.*) ointment of phenol.
**carbolsauer,** *a.* phenolate (or phenoxide) of.
**Carbolsäure,** *f.* carbolic acid, phenol. **-lösung,** *f.* carbolic acid solution. **-seife,** *f.* carbolic acid soap.
**carbolschwefelsauer,** *a.* (*Pharm.*) of or combined with sulfocarbolic acid, sulfocarbolate of.
**Carbol-schwefelsäure,** *f.* (*Pharm.*) sulfocarbolic acid, sulfophenic acid (*p*-phenolsulfonic acid.). **-seife,** *f.* carbolic soap. **-sulfosäure,** *f.* = Carbolschwefelsäure. **-vergiftung,** *f.* carbolic acid poisoning. **-wasser,** *n.* aqueous solution of phenol. **-watte,** *f.* carbolized cotton wool.
**Carbon,** *m.* carbon; (*Geol.*) Carboniferous.
**Carbonat,** *n.* carbonate. **-härte,** *f.* hardness due to carbonates. **-ion,** *n.* carbonate ion.
**Carbonatisierung,** *f.* (*Geol.*) calcification.
**Carbonatpuffer,** *m.* carbonate buffer.
**carbonieren,** *v.t.* carbonate; carbonize.
**Carbonisation,** *f.* carbonization; carbonation.
**carbonisch,** *a.* carbonaceous; (*Geol.*) Carboniferous.
**Carbonisier-anlage, -anstalt,** *f.* carbonizing plant. **-bad,** *n.* carbonizing bath.
**carbonisierecht,** *a.* fast to carbonizing.
**carbonisieren,** *v.t.* carbonize; carburize; carbonate.
**Carbonisier-flüssigkeit, -lauge,** *f.* carbonizing liquor. **-ofen,** *m.* carbonizing oven or stove.
**Carbonisierung,** *f.* carbonization; carbonation.
**Carbonitrieren,** *n.* (*Metal.*) carbonitriding (enriching the surface layer with both carbon and nitrogen by heating in a suitable medium).
**Carbonsäure,** *f.* carboxylic acid (a general term); (rarely) carbonic acid.
**-carbonsäure,** *f.* -carboxylic acid.
**Carbonspat,** *m.* (*Min.*) spathic carbonate.
**Carbonyl-gruppe,** *f.* carbonyl group. **-sauerstoff,** *m.* carbonyl oxygen. **-verbindung,** *f.* carbonyl compound.
**Carborund,** *n.* carborundum.
**Carboxylgruppe,** *f.* carboxyl group.
**carbozyklisch,** *a.* carbocyclic.
**Carbunkel,** *m.* carbuncle; anthrax.
**Carbür,** *n.* (ous) carbide (*cf.* Chlorür).
**Carburateur, Carburator,** *m.* carburetor.
**Carburationsapparat,** *m.* carburetor.
**carburieren,** *v.t.* carburet; carburize.
**Carburieröl,** *n.* carbureting (or carburizing) oil.
**Carburierung,** *f.* carbureting, carburation; carburization.
**cardieren,** *v.t.* (*Textiles*) card.
**Carenz,** *f.* omission.
**Carmin, etc.** = Karmin, etc.
**Carnauba-säure,** *f.* carnaubic acid. **-wachs,** *n.* carnauba wax.
**Carneol,** *m.* carnelian.
**Caro'sche Säure.** Caro's acid.
**Carotin,** *n.* carotene, (formerly) carotin.
**Carotte,** *f.* carrot.
**Carraghenmoos,** *n.* carrageen moss, Irish moss.
**Carreau,** *n.* check, square
**carrieren,** *v.t.* checker.
**cartesisch,** *a.* Cartesian.
**Carthaminsäure,** *f.* carthamic acid.
**Carub,** *m.*, **Carube,** *f.* carob.
**Cärul-, cärul-.** cerul-.
**caseinartig,** *a.* like casein, caseous.
**Casein-farbstoff,** *m.* casein paint. **-kitt,** *m.* casein cement. **-leim,** *m.* casein glue. **-lösung,** *f.* casein solution. **-natrium,** *n.* sodium caseinate.
**Cäsium,** *n.* cesium. **-alaun,** *m.* cesium alum.
**cäsiumbedeckt,** *a.* cesium-coated, cesiated.
**Cäsiumverbindung,** *f.* cesium compound.
**Cassawastärke,** *f.* tapioca.
**Cassia-öl,** *n.* cassia oil. **-rinde,** *f.* cassia bark.
**Cassie,** *f.* cassia.
**Cassien-.** cassia (see Kassien-).
**Cassiuspurpur,** *m.* purple of Cassius.
**Castillianer Seife.** castile soap.
**Castor-nuss,** *f.* castor bean. **-öl,** *n.* castor oil.
**Catech-.** see Katech-.
**Cathartinsäure,** *f.* cathartic acid.
**Cautel,** *f.* precaution.
**Cautschuk,** *m.* = Kautschuk.
**cbcm.,** *abbrev.* cubic centimeter, cc.
**cbm.,** *abbrev.* cubic meter, cu. m.
**cca.,** *abbrev.* (circa) about.
**ccm.,** *abbrev.* cubic centimeter(s), cc., c.c.
**Ce-, ce-.** see also Ze-, ze-.
**Ceara-kautschuk,** *m.* & *n.* Ceara rubber. **-wachs,** *n.* carnauba wax.
**Ceder,** *f.* cedar.
**Cedern-harz,** *n.* cedar resin. **-holz,** *n.* cedarwood, cedar. **-öl,** *n.* cedar oil.
**cedieren,** *v.t.* cede, assign, transfer.
**Cedratöl,** *n.* citron oil.
**Cedronsamen,** *m.* cedron seed.
**Cedroöl,** *n.* citron oil.
**Celasteröl,** *n.* celastrus oil, staff-tree oil.
**Celit,** *n.*, **Celith,** *m.* (*Cement*) celite.
**Cellit,** *n.* cellite (a cellulose acetate).
**cellonieren,** *v.t.* treat with Cellon-Lack.
**Cellon-Lack,** *m.* a cellulose acetate lacquer. *T.N.*
**celluloseartig,** *a.* cellulosic.
**Cellulosegärung,** *f.* cellulose fermentation.
**cellulosehaltig,** *a.* containing cellulose, cellulosic.
**Cellulose-lack,** *m.* cellulose lacquer. **-lackfarbe,** *f.* pigmented cellulose lacquer. **-lösung,**

*f* cellulose solution. **-schleim,** *m.* cellulose slime, pulp slime. **-schwefelsäure,** *f.* cellulosesulfuric acid. **-verdauung,** *f.* cellulose digestion. **-zahl,** *f.* cellulose number.

**Celsiusgrad,** *m.* Celsius (centigrade) degree.

**Cement, cementieren,** etc. = Zement, zementieren, etc.

**censieren,** *v.t.* criticize.

**Censur,** *f.* censorship; report.

**Cent-.** see Zent-.

**Cer,** *m.* cerium.

**Cerat,** *n.* cerate.

**Cerealien,** *pl.* cereals.

**Cer-erde,** *f.* cerium earth (class name). **-erz,** *n* cerium ore, esp. cerite. **-feuerzeug,** *n.* & *m.* cerium lighter.

**Ceri-.** ceric, cerium(IV). **-chlorid,** *n.* ceric chloride, cerium(IV) chloride.

**Cerinstein,** *m.* (*Min.*) cerite.

**Ceri-oxyd,** *n.* ceric oxide, cerium(IV) oxide. **-salz,** *n.* ceric salt, cerium(IV) salt. **-sulfat,** *n.* ceric sulfate, cerium(IV) sulfate.

**Ceriterde,** *f.* cerite earth.

**Ceriverbindung,** *f.* ceric compound, cerium(IV) compound.

**Cermischmetall,** *n.* mixed metal, misch metal (a mixture of rare-earth metals).

**Cero-.** cerous, cerium(III). **-ion,** *n.* cerous ion, cerium(III) ion. **-salz,** *n.* cerous salt, cerium(III) salt. **-sulfat,** *n.* cerous sulfate, cerium(III) sulfate.

**Cerotinsäure,** *f.* cerotic acid.

**Ceroverbindung,** *f.* cerous compound, cerium(III) compound.

**Ceroxyd,** *n.* cerium oxide.

**Cetanzahl,** *f.* cetane number.

**cet. par.,** *abbrev.* (*ceteris paribus*) other things being equal.

**Cetylsäure,** *f.* cetylic acid (palmitic acid).

**Ceylonzimt,** *m.* Ceylon cinnamon.

**Chagrin,** *m.* shagreen.

**chalkophil,** *a.* chalcophilic (having high affinity for sulfur).

**Chamäleon,** *n.* chameleon; chameleon mineral (potassium manganate). **-lösung,** *f.* potassium permanganate solution.

**Chamoisleder,** *n.* chamois leather, chamois.

**Chamotte,** etc. = Schamotte, etc.

**Champagner,** *m.* champagne. **-weisse,** *f.* a strongly foaming pale beer.

**Champignon,** *m.* mushroom (esp., *Agaricus* species).

**changeant, changierend,** *a.* changeable, shot (fabrics). — **— färben,** shot-dye.

**Changeantstoff,** *m.* shot fabric.

**Chappeseide,** *f.* spun silk.

**charakterisieren,** *v.t.* characterize.

**charakteristisch,** *a.* characteristic.

**chargieren,** *v.t.* charge, load.

**Charpie,** *f.* lint.

**Chaulmoogra-öl, Chaulmugra-öl,** *n.* chaulmoogra oil. **-säure,** *f.* chaulmoogric acid.

**Chaussee,** *f.* highway.

**Chef,** *m.* chief, head, principal. **-chemiker,** *m.* chief chemist.

**Cheiranthussäure,** *f.* cheiranthic acid.

**chelieren,** *v.t.* chelate.

**chem.,** *abbrev.* (chemisch) chemical.

**Chemiatrie,** *f.* chemiatry, iatrochemistry.

**Chemie,** *f.* chemistry. **-Aktien,** *f.pl.* chemical stocks or shares, "chemicals." **-Werte,** *m.pl.* (*Com.*) chemical issues.

**Chemigraphenlack,** *m.* chemigraphic varnish.

**Chemikalien,** *n.pl.* chemicals. **-handel,** *m.* trade in chemicals.

**chemikalisch,** *a.* chemical. — *adv.* chemically.

**Chemiker,** *m.* chemist. **-stelle,** *f.* position of chemist.

**chemisch,** *a.* chemical. — *adv.* chemically. — **chemische Wäsche,** drycleaning.

**Chemisch-blau,** *n.* chemic blue (indigo extract). **-gelb,** *n.* patent yellow, Cassel yellow (lead oxychloride). **-grün,** *n.* sap green.

**chemischrein,** *a.* chemically pure.

**Chemischrot,** *n.* Venetian red.

**chemisch-technisch,** *a.* chemicotechnical, technochemical. **-technologisch,** *a.* pertaining to chemical technology, chemico-technological.

**Chemismus,** *m.* chemism.

**chemotaktisch,** *a.* chemotactic.

**chemotechnisch,** *a.* = chemisch-technisch.

**Chem-Ztg.,** *abbrev.* of *Chemiker-Zeitung.*

**-chen.** little, small, -kin, -let.

**Chesterkäse,** *m.* Cheshire cheese.

**chevillieren,** *v.t.* gloss, polish, luster.

**Chibouharz,** *n.* cachibou.

**Chiffer, Chiffre,** *f.* cipher.

**chiffrieren,** *v.t.* cipher, code.

**chilenisch,** *a.* Chilean.

**Chilesalpeter,** *m.* Chile saltpeter (sodium nitrate).

**Chin-.** quin- (as in Chinin, Chinidin, etc.).

**China,** *f.* cinchona, Peruvian bark. **-alkaloid,** *n.* cinchona alkaloid. **-basen,** *f.pl.* cinchona bases, quinine bases. **-baum,** *m.* cinchona tree.

**chinabaumartig,** *a.* cinchonaceous.

**Chin-acetophenon,** *n.* quinacetophenone. **-acridin,** *n.* quinacridine. **-acridon,** *n.* quinacridone.

**China-eisenwein,** *m.* (*Pharm.*) bitter wine of iron. **-gerbsäure,** *f.* quinotannic acid. **-gras,** *n.* China grass (ramie). **-holz,** *n.* cinchona wood.

**Chinaldin,** *n.* quinaldine. **-säure,** *f.* quinaldic acid.

**Chin-alizarin,** *n.* quinalizarin. **-amin,** *n.* quinamine.

**China-öl,** *n.* balsam of Peru. **-rinde,** *f.* cinchona bark, Peruvian bark. **-rindensäure,** *f.* quinic acid. **-rot,** *n.* cinchona red.

**chinasauer,** *a.* of or combined with quinic acid, quinate of.

**China-säure,** *f.* quinic acid. **-seide,** *f.* China silk; Chinese silk. **-silber,** *n.* China silver (a plated alloy).

**Chinäthylin,** *n.* quinethyline.

**China-tinktur,** *f.* tincture of cinchona. **-toxin,** *n.* cinchona toxin. **-wein,** *m.* quinine wine. **-wurzel,** *f.* chinaroot.

**Chin-azolin,** *n.* quinazoline. **-azolon,** *n.* quinazolone. **-dolin,** *n.* quindoline.

**Chinen,** *n.* quinene.

**chinesisch,** *a.* Chinese. — **chinesisches Papier,** India paper.

**Chinesisch-grün,** *n.* Chinese green, lokao. **-rot,** *n.* Chinese red.

**Chinetum,** *n.* quinetum.

**Chin-hydrin,** *n.* quinhydrine. **-hydron,** *n.* quinhydrone. **-icin,** *n.* quinicine.

**Chinid,** *n.* quinide.

**Chinidin,** *n.* quinidine.

**chinieren,** *v.t.* weave or print chiné, cloud.

**Chinin,** *n.* quinine.

**Chinindolin,** *n.* quinindoline.

**Chinin-eisen, -eisencitrat,** *n.* citrate of iron and quinine. **-säure,** *f.* quininic acid. **-wein,** *m.* quinine wine.

**Chinisatin,** *n.* quinisatin.

**Chinit,** *n.* quinitol, quinite.

**Chinizarin,** *n.* quinizarin.

**Chino-.** quino-.

**chinoid,** *a.* quinoid, quinoidal.

**Chinoidin,** *n.* quinoidine.

**Chinol,** *n.* quinol.

**Chinolin,** *n.* quinoline. **-blau,** *n.* quinoline blue. **-gelb,** *n.* quinoline yellow. **-ium,** *n.* quinolinium. **-rot,** *n.* quinoline red. **-säure,** *f.* quinolinic acid.

**Chin-olizin,** *n.* quinolizine. **-olon,** *n.* quinolone. **-omethan,** *n.* quinomethan, quinomethane.

**Chinon,** *n.* quinone.

**Chino-pyran,** *n.* quinopyran. **-pyridin,** *n.* quinopyridine. **-sol,** *n.* (*Pharm.*) quinosol, chinosol. **-tin,** *n.* quinotine. **-toxin,** *n.* quinotoxin. **-tropin,** *n.* quinotropin.

**Chinova-bitter,** *n.* quinova bitter (quinovin). **-säure,** *f.* quinovic acid.

**Chin-ovin,** *n.* quinovin. **-ovose,** *f.* quinovose. **-oxalin,** *n.* quinoxaline.

**Chinoyl,** *n.* quinoyl.

**Chinuclidin,** *n.* quinuclidine.

**Chiretta,** *f.* chirata.

**Chirurg,** *m.* surgeon.

**Chirurgie,** *f.* surgery.

**chirurgisch,** *a.* surgical.

**Chlf.,** *abbrev.* chloroform.

**Chlor,** *n.* chlorine.

**Chlor-.** of or combined with chlorine, chloro- (as *Chlorbenzoesäure,* chlorobenzoic acid), chloride of (as *Chlorzink,* zinc chloride).

**chlorähnlich,** *a.* like chlorine, chlorinous.

**Chlor-alaun,** *m.* chloralum. **-alkalien,** *n.pl.* alkali-metal chlorides. **-allyl,** *n.* allyl chloride. **-aluminium,** *n.* aluminum chloride. **-ammon,** *m.*, **-ammonium,** *n.* ammonium chloride. **-amyl,** *n.* amyl chloride. **-antimon,** *n.* antimony chloride. **-arsenik,** *n.* chloride of arsenic. **-arseniklösung,** *f.* (*Pharm.*) solution of arsenious acid, hydrochloric solution of arsenic. **-arsinkampfstoff,** *m.* chlorodiphenylarsine, adamsite.

**chlorartig,** *a.* like chlorine, chlorinous.

**Chlorat,** *n.* chlorate. **-ätze,** *f.* (*Dyeing*) chlorate discharge. **-chlor,** *n.* chlorine in the form of chlorate.

**Chlor-äther,** *m.* chloric ether (old name for ethylene chloride). **-äthyl,** *n.* ethyl chloride, chloroethane. **-äthylen,** *n.* ethylene chloride. **-äthyliden,** *n.* ethylidene chloride.

**Chloration,** *f.* chlorination. — *n.* chlorate ion.

**Chloratspreng-mittel,** *n.*, **-stoff,** *m.* chlorate explosive.

**Chlor-azetyl,** *n.* acetyl chloride. **-azetylchlorid,** *n.* chloroacetyl chloride. **-barium, -baryum,** *n.* barium chloride. **-baryumlösung,** *f.* barium chloride solution. **-benzol,** *n.* chlorobenzene. **-benzyl,** *n.* benzyl chloride. **-bestimmung,** *f.* chlorine determination. **-blei,** *n.* lead chloride. **-bleiche,** *f.* chlorine bleaching. **-bleichlauge,** *f.* chlorine bleach liquor (esp., NaOCl solution). **-bleispat,** *m.* phosgenite. **-bor,** *n.* boron chloride. **-brom,** *n.* bromine chloride. **-bromsilber,** *n.* silver chlorobromide, (*Min.*) embolite. **-calcium,** *n.* calcium chloride. **-calciumrohr,** *n.*, **-calciumröhre,** *f.* calcium chloride tube. **-chrom,** *n.* chromium chloride, specif. chromic chloride. **-chrombeize,** *f.* chromium chloride mordant. **-chromsäure,** *f.* chlorochromic acid. **-cyan,** *n.* cyanogen chloride.

**chlorecht,** *a.* fast to chlorine.

**Chlorechtheit,** *f.* fastness to chlorine.

**Chloreisen,** *n.* iron chloride, specif. ferric chloride. **-oxyd,** *n.* ferric chloride, iron(III) chloride. **-oxydul,** *n.* ferrous chloride, iron(II) chloride.

**chloren,** *v.t.* chlore, chlorinate; (*Bleaching*) gas.

**Chlor-entwickler,** *m.* chlorine generator. **-entwicklung,** *f.* evolution or generation of chlorine. **-entwicklungsapparat,** *m.* chlorine generator. **-essigsäure,** *f.* chloroacetic acid.

**chlorfrei,** *a.* free from chlorine, chlorine-free.

**Chlor-gas,** *n.* chlorine gas. **-gehalt,** *m.* chlorine content. **-geruch,** *m.* chlorine odor. **-gold,**

*n.* gold chloride, specif. auric chloride. **-goldnatrium,** *n.* sodium chloroaurate.

**chlorhaltig,** *a.* containing chlorine.

**Chlor-hydrat,** *n.* hydrochloride; chlorine hydrate. **-hydrin,** *n.* chlorohydrin.

**Chlorid,** *n.* chloride (esp., an -ic chloride, as contrasted with Chlorür). **-chlor,** *n.* chlorine in the form of chloride.

**chloridhaltig,** *a.* containing chloride(s).

**Chloridlauge,** *f.* chloride solution.

**chlorierbar,** *a.* capable of chlorination.

**chlorieren,** *v.t.* chlorinate; (*Bleaching*) chemick; (*Metal.*) chloridize.

**Chlorierer,** *m.* chlorinator.

**Chlorierung,** *f.* chlorination; chloridizing.

**chlorierungsfähig,** *a.* chlorinatable; chloridizable.

**Chlorierungsmittel,** *n.* chlorinating agent; chloridizing agent.

**chlorig,** *a.* chlorous. — **chlorige Säure,** chlorous acid.

**chlorigsauer,** *a.* of or combined with chlorous acid, chlorite of.

**Chlorigsäure,** *f.* chlorous acid.

**Chlorion,** *n.* chlorine ion.

**Chlorit,** *n.* chlorite.

**chloritisch,** *a.* chloritic.

**chloritisieren,** *v.t.* chloritize.

**Chlorit-schiefer,** *m.* chlorite schist, chloritic schist. **-spat,** *m.* spathic chlorite, foliated chlorite.

**Chlor-jod,** *n.* iodine chloride, specif. iodine monochloride. **-kali,** *n.* chloride of potash (potassium hypochlorite); potassium chloride. **-kalilösung,** *f.* (*Pharm.*) solution of chlorinated potassa, Javelle water. **-kalium,** *n.* potassium chloride.

**Chlorkalk,** *m.* chloride of lime, bleaching powder. **-bad,** *n.* (*Bleaching*) chemic vat. **-bleiche,** *f.* bleaching with bleaching powder, chemicking. **-flüssigkeit,** *f.* (*Pharm.*) solution of chlorinated lime (bleaching powder solution). **-kufe,** *f.* chemic vat. **-lauge,** *f.* bleaching-powder liquor. **-lösung,** *f.* = Chlorkalkflüssigkeit.

**Chlorkalzium,** *n.* calcium chloride. **-rohr,** *n.*, **-röhre,** *f.* calcium chloride tube. **-röhrchen,** *n.* (small) calcium chloride tube.

**Chlor-kautschuk,** *m.* & *n.* chlorinated rubber. **-knallgas,** *n.* chlorine detonating gas (an explosive mixture of chlorine and hydrogen).

**Chlorkohlen-oxyd,** *n.* carbonyl chloride. **-oxydäther,** *m.* ethyl chloroformate. **-säure,** *f.* chlorocarbonic acid (chloroformic acid, ClCOOH). **-säureamid,** *n.* chlorocarbonyl amide (carbamyl chloride, $H_2NCOCl$). **-stoff,** *m.* carbon chloride, carbon tetrachloride (sometimes with the adj. **vierfach**). **-stoffsäure,** *f.* = Chlorkohlensäure. **-wasserstoff,** *m.* chlorinated hydrocarbon, chlorohydrocarbon.

**Chlor-kupfer,** *n.* copper chloride. **-lauge,** *f.* = Chlornatron. **-magnesium,** *n.* magnesium chloride. **-mangan,** *n.* manganese chloride. **-messer,** *m.* chlorometer. **-messung,** *f.* chlorometry. **-metall,** *n.* metallic chloride. **-metalloid,** *n.* chloride of a metalloid. **-methyl,** *n.* methyl chloride, chloromethane. **-methylat,** *n.* methochloride. **-methylen,** *n.* methylene chloride. **-natrium,** *n.* sodium chloride. **-natron,** *n.* chloride of soda (sodium hypochlorite). **-natronlösung,** *f.* (*Pharm.*) solution of chlorinated soda, Labarraque's solution. **-nickel,** *n.* nickel chloride.

**Chloro-benzal,** *n.* benzal chloride, benzylidene chloride. **-benzil,** *n.* dichlorobenzil, $C_6H_5COCCl_2C_6H_5$.

**chloroformieren,** *v.t.* chloroform.

**Chlorojodid,** *n.* chloro-iodide, iodochloride.

**chlorometrisch,** *a.* chlorometric.

**Chlorose,** *f.* (*Med.*) chlorosis.

**Chlor-oxyd,** *n.* chlorine oxide. **-phosphor,** *m.* phosphorus chloride. **-pikrin,** *n.* chloropicrin. **-platin,** *n.* platinic chloride. **-platinsäure,** *f.* chloroplatinic acid. **-quecksilber,** *n.* mercury chloride (either one). **-räucherung,** *f.* chlorine fumigation.

**chlorsauer,** *a.* of or combined with chloric acid, chlorate of.

**Chlor-säure,** *f.* chloric acid. **-säureanhydrid,** *n.* chloric anhydride, chlorine(V) oxide. **-schwefel,** *n.* sulfur chloride (esp. the monochloride). **-silber,** *n.* silver chloride. **-silicium,** *n.* silicon tetrachloride. **-soda,** *f.* = Chlornatron. **-stickstoff,** *m.* nitrogen chloride. **-strom,** *m.* stream of chlorine. **-strontium,** *n.* strontium chloride. **-sulfonsäure,** *f.* chlorosulfonic acid, chlorosulfuric acid. **-toluol,** *n.* chlorotoluene. **-übertrager,** *m.* chlorine carrier.

**Chlorung,** *f.* chlorination.

**Chlorür,** *n.* (-ous) chloride, (formerly) protochloride. (Used of a metal in its lower valence, as *Eisenchlorür*, ferrous chloride, iron(II) chloride.)

**Chlor-verbindung,** *f.* chlorine compound. **-verflüssigung,** *f.* chlorine liquefaction. **-wasser,** *n.* chlorine water.

**Chlorwasserstoff,** *m.* hydrogen chloride; hydrochloric acid. **-äther,** *m.* ethyl chloride.

**chlorwasserstoffsauer,** *a.* of or combined with hydrochloric acid, chloride (or hydrochloride) of.

**Chlor-wasserstoffsäure,** *f.* hydrochloric acid. **-wismut,** *n.* bismuth (tri)chloride. **-zink,** *n.* zinc chloride. **-zinn,** *n.* tin chloride.

**-zinnbad,** *n.* tin-chloride bath. **-zyan,** *n.* cyanogen chloride.
**Chm.,** *abbrev.* (Chemie) chemistry.
**Chokolade,** *f.* chocolate.
**Cholalsäure,** *f.* cholalic acid (cholic acid).
**Cholämie,** *f.* (*Med.*) cholemia.
**Cholecamphersäure,** *f.* cholecamphoric acid (choloidanic acid).
**Choleinsäure,** *f.* choleic acid, choleinic acid.
**Cholesterin,** *n.* cholesterol, cholesterin. **-säure,** *f.* cholesteric acid (cholesterol).
**Cholin,** *n.* choline.
**Cholsäure,** *f.* cholic acid.
**Chondron-insäure,** *f.* chondroninic acid. **-säure,** *f.* chondronic acid.
**Chor,** *m.* chorus; choir.
**Chorde,** *f.* chord.
**Christdorn,** *m.* holly.
**Christofle,** *n.* a kind of nickel silver. *T.N.*
**Christophs-kraut,** *n.*, **-wurz,** *f.* baneberry (*Actaea*).
**Christ-palmöl,** *n.* castor oil. **-wurz,** *f.* black hellebore; spring pheasant's-eye (*Adonis vernalis*).
**Chrom,** *n.* chromium; chrome. **-alaun,** *m.* chrome alum.
**Chromat,** *n.* chromate. — **saures —,** dichromate. **-ätze,** *f.* (*Dyeing*) chromate discharge. **-farbstoff,** *m.* chromate dye.
**chromatisch,** *a.* chromatic.
**chromatographieren,** *v.t.* subject to chromatographic adsorption, chromatograph.
**Chromatverfahren,** *n.* chromate process.
**Chromazetat,** *n.* chromium acetate.
**Chrom-bad,** *n.* chrome bath. **-beize,** *f.* chrome mordant.
**chrombeizen,** *v.t.* chrome-mordant.
**chrombeständig,** *a.* chrome-resistant.
**Chrom-blei,** *n.* lead chromate. **-bleispat,** *m.* (*Min.*) crocoite. **-braun,** *n.* chrome brown. **-chlorid,** *n.* chromic chloride, chromium(III) chloride. **-chlorür,** *n.* chromous chloride, chromium(II) chloride. **-druck,** *m.* (*Calico*) chrome printing.
**chromecht,** *a.* (*Dyeing*) fast to chrome (potassium or sodium dichromate).
**Chrom-echtschwarz,** *n.* fast chrome black. **-eisen, -eisenerz,** *n.*, **-eisenstein,** *m.* chrome iron ore, chromite.
**chromenthaltend,** *a.* = chromhaltig.
**Chrom-entwicklungsfarbstoff,** *m.* chrome-developed dye. **-erz,** *n.* chromium ore. **-farbe,** *f.* chrome color. **-fluorid,** *n.* chromic fluoride, chromium(III) fluoride.
**chromgar,** *a.* chrome-tanned.
**Chrom-gehalt,** *m.* chromium content. **-gelatine,** *f.* chromatized gelatin, bichromated gelatin. **-gelb,** *n.* chrome yellow (lead chromate); Cologne yellow (lead chromate and sulfate). **-gerberei, -gerbung,** *f.* chrome tanning. **-glimmer,** *m.* chrome mica. **-grün,** *n.* chrome green.
**chromhaltig,** *a.* containing chromium, chromiferous.
**Chrom-hydrat, -hydroxyd,** *n.* chromic hydroxide, chromium(III) hydroxide. **-hydroxydul,** *n.* chromous hydroxide, chromium(II) hydroxide.
**Chromi-.** chromic, chromium(III). **-chlorid,** *n.* chromic chloride, chromium(III) chloride. **-cyanwasserstoffsäure,** *f.* chromicyanic acid cyanochromic(III) acid.
**Chromierartikel,** *m.* (*Calico*) chrome style.
**chromierbar,** *a.* chromable.
**chromieren,** *v.t.* chrome.
**Chromierfarbstoff,** *m.* chrome dye.
**Chromierungsfarbe,** *f.* chrome dye.
**Chromi-hydroxyd,** *n.* chromic hydroxide, chromium(III) hydroxide. **-oxyd,** *n.* chromic oxide, chromium(III) oxide. **-rhodanwasserstoffsäure,** *f.* chromithiocyanic acid, thiocyanatochromic(III) acid. **-salz,** *n.* chromic salt, chromium(III) salt. **-sulfat,** *n.* chromic sulfate, chromium(III) sulfate. **-sulfocyansäure,** *f.* chromithiocyanic acid, thiocyanatochromic(III) acid. **-verbindung,** *f.* chromic compound, chromium(III) compound.
**Chrom-kali,** *n.* (**rotes**) potassium dichromate; (**gelbes**) potassium chromate. **-karbid,** *n.* chromium carbide. **-lack,** *m.* chrome lake. **-leder,** *n.* chrome leather. **-leim,** *m.* chrome gelatin; chrome glue. **-metall,** *n.* chromium metal. **-natron,** *n.* (**rotes**) sodium dichromate; (**gelbes**) sodium chromate. **-nickelstahl,** *m.* chrome-nickel steel.
**Chromo-.** chromous, chromium(II). **-chlorid,** *n.* chromous chloride, chromium(II) chloride.
**Chromocker,** *m.* chrome ocher.
**Chromo-hydroxyd,** *n.* chromous hydroxide, chromium(II) hydroxide. **-ion,** *n.* chromous ion, chromium(II) ion.
**Chromolyse,** *f.* (*Biol.*) chromatolysis, chromolysis.
**Chromooxyd,** *n.* chromous oxide, chromium(II) oxide.
**chromophor,** *a.* chromophoric, chromophore, chromophorous.
**Chromoverbindung,** *f.* chromous compound, chromium(II) compound.
**Chromoxychlorid,** *n.* chromium oxychloride (chromyl chloride).
**Chromoxyd,** *n.* chromium oxide, specif. chromic oxide, chromium(III) oxide. **-farbe,** *f.* chrome oxide color. **-hydrat,** *n.* chromium hydroxide, specif. chromic hydroxide, chromium(III) hydroxide. **-natron,** *n.* sodium chromite. **-salz,** *n.* chromic salt, chromium(III) oxide.

**Chromoxydul,** *n.* chromous oxide, chromium (II) oxide.

**Chromoxydul-.** chromous, chromium(II). **-hydrat,** *n.* chromous hydroxide, chromium(II) hydroxide. **-salz,** *n.* chromous salt, chromium(II) salt. **-verbindung,** *f.* chromous compound, chromium(II) compound.

**Chrom-rindleder,** *n.* chromed neat's leather. **-rot,** *n.* chrome red. **-salpetersäure,** *f.* chromonitric acid. **-salz,** *n.* chromium salt; chromate.

**chromsauer,** *a.* of or combined with chromic acid, chromate of. — **chromsaures Kali,** potassium chromate. — **doppelt (rotes, saures) chromsaures Kali,** potassium dichromate.

**Chromsäure,** *f.* chromic acid. **-anhydrid,** *n.* chromic anhydride, chromium(VI) oxide. **-gemisch,** *n.* chromic acid mixture. **-lösung,** *f.* chromic acid solution. **-salz,** *n.* salt of chromic acid, chromate.

**Chrom-schwarz,** *n.* (*Dyeing*) chrome black. **-schwefelsäure,** *f.* chromosulfuric acid. **-silber,** *n.* silver chromate. **-stahl,** *m.* chrome steel, chromium steel. **-sud,** *m.* chrome mordant. **-sulfat,** *n.* chromium sulfate. **-sulfozyanid,** *n.* chromium thiocyanate. **-sulfür,** *n.* chromous sulfide, chromium(II) sulfide. **-trioxyd,** *n.* chromium trioxide, chromium(VI) oxide. **-überzug,** *m.* chromium coating or plating. **-verbindung,** *f.* chromium compound. **-wolframstahl,** *m.* chrome-tungsten steel. **-zyanid,** *n.* chromium cyanide.

**chronisch,** *a.* chronic.

**Chrysatropasäure,** *f.* chrysatropic acid.

**Chrysenchinon, Chrysochinon,** *n.* chrysenequinone, chrysoquinone.

**Chrysokoll,** *n.* chrysocolla.

**Chrysolith,** *m.* (*Min.*) chrysolite.

**Chylus,** *m.* chyle.

**Ci-, ci-.** see also Zi-, zi-.

**Ciba-blau,** *n.* ciba blue. **-rot,** *n.* ciba red.

**Cibebe,** *f.* = Zibebe.

**Cichorie,** *f.* chicory.

**Cider-branntwein,** *m.* cider brandy, apple brandy. **-essig,** *m.* cider vinegar. **-trester,** *m.pl.* cider marc. **-wein,** *m.* (fermented) cider.

**Cie.,** *abbrev.* (Compagnie, Gesellschaft) Company, Co.

**cimolisch,** *a.* Cimolian. — **cimolische Erde,** Cimolian earth, cimolite.

**Cinchoninsäure,** *f.* cinchoninic acid.

**Cinchonsäure,** *f.* cinchonic acid.

**circa, cirka,** *adv.* about.

**cirkulieren,** *v.i.* circulate.

**Cis-körper,** *m.* cis substance. **-stellung,** *f.* cis position.

**Citat,** *n.* citation, quotation.

**citieren,** *v.t.* quote, cite; summon.

**Citrat, Citrone,** etc. = Zitrat, Zitrone, etc.

**civil,** *a.* civil; moderate.

**claircieren,** *v.t.* (*Sugar*), clear, purge.

**Cloake,** *f.* cloaca, sewer; sink; cesspool.

**Cloison,** *f.* partition, septum.

**Cnidiumsäure,** *f.* cnidic acid.

**coag-.** see koag-.

**Coaks,** *m.* & *m.pl.* coke.

**Cobalt-.** see Kobalt-.

**Coca-blätter,** *n.pl.* coca leaves. **-säure,** *f.* cocaic acid. **-wein,** *m.* (*Pharm.*) wine of coca.

**Coccinsäure,** *f.* coccinic acid.

**Cochenille,** *f.* cochineal.

**Cochenillen-farbstoff,** *m.* cochineal dye. **-rot,** *n.* cochineal red. **-scharlach,** *m.* cochineal scarlet. **-schildlaus,** *f.* cochineal insect.

**Cochenillesäure,** *f.* cochenillic acid.

**Cocon,** *m.* cocoon.

**Cocos,** etc. see Kokos, etc.

**Codöl,** *n.* cod-liver oil.

**Coffearin,** *n.* caffearine.

**Coffein,** *n.* caffeine.

**Cognak,** *m.* cognac.

**cohobieren,** *v.t.* cohobate.

**Colanuss,** *f.* cola nut.

**Colatur,** *f.* filtrate.

**Cölestin,** *m.* celestite, celestine.

**colieren,** etc. = kolieren, etc.

**Collodium,** etc. see Kollodium, etc.

**Colloid-.** see Kolloid-.

**Colloresin,** *n.* methyl cellulose. *T.N.*

**Colombin,** *n.* columbin.

**Colombowürzel,** *f.* calumba root, calumba.

**Colonne,** *f.* column.

**colorimetrisch,** *a.* colorimetric.

**Columbasäure,** *f.* columbic acid (from calumba).

**Columbeisen,** *n.* (*Min.*) columbite.

**Columbiakopalinsäure,** *f.* columbiacopalinic acid.

**Columbiakopalsäure,** *f.* columbiacopalic acid.

**Columbien,** *n.* Colombia.

**Columbowurzel,** *f.* calumba root, calumba.

**Colzaöl,** *n.* colza oil.

**com-.** see also kom-.

**combinieren,** *v.t.* combine.

**Commis,** *m.* clerk.

**comprimieren,** *v.t.* compress.

**Comptoir,** *n.* office, counting house.

**conc-.** see konz-.

**Condens-.** see Kondens-.

**conditionieren,** *v.t.* condition.

**conglobieren,** *v.t.* heap up.

**Congo-farbe,** *f.* Congo color, Congo dye. **-farbstoff,** *m.* Congo dye. **-gelb,** *n.* Congo yellow. **-gummi,** *n.* Congo rubber. **-papier,** *n.* Congo paper. **-rot,** *n.* Congo red.

**Conidien-.** (*Bot.*) conidial.

**Coniin,** *n.* conine, coniine.

**Conimaharz,** *n.* conima resin, conima.

**conphas,** *a.* in phase.
**Conserv-.** see Konserv-.
**Conspersasäure,** *f.* conspersic acid.
**constatieren,** *v.t.* ascertain, verify.
**continuierlich,** *a.* continuous.
**Continüküpe,** *f.* (*Dyeing*) continuous vat.
**Conto,** *n.* account.
**contrahieren,** *v.i.* & *t.* contract.
**Conus,** *m.* cone.
**conzentrisch,** *a.* concentric.
**Copaiva-balsam,** *m.* copaiba (balsam). **-öl,** *n.* oil of copaiba. **-säure,** *f.* copaivic acid.
**Copal-.** see Kopal-.
**Cops-färberie, -färbung,** *f.* cop dyeing.
**Cör-.** = cer-.
**Corozonuss,** *f.* ivory nut.
**corr.,** *abbrev.* (corrigiert) corrected.
**corrigieren,** *v.t.* correct.
**corrodieren,** *v.t.* & *i.* corrode.
**Cörulein,** *n.* cerulein.
**Cöruleum,** *n.* ceruleum.
**Cörulignol,** *n.* cerulignol.
**Cörulignon,** *n.* cerulignone.
**Cosinus,** *m.* (*Math.*) cosine.
**Costussäure,** *f.* costic acid, costusic acid.
**Cotorinde,** *f.* coto bark.
**Cotta,** *f.* = Deul.
**cottonisieren,** *v.t.* cottonize.
**Cottonöl,** *n.* cottonseed oil.
**Couleur,** *f.* color; caramel, burnt sugar; dark, coarse smalt; (*pl.*) fancy goods, colored goods.
**coupieren,** *v.t.* cut, cut short; dilute, weaken.
**Coupüre,** *f.* (*Calico*) reduced print.
**Courant,** *n.* currency; price list.
**Couvert,** *n.* envelope; cover.
**crabbecht,** *a.* (*Textiles*) fast to crabbing.
**Crackbenzin,** *n.* benzine or gasoline produced by cracking.
**cracken,** *v.t.* crack (as petroleum).
**Cracken,** *n.* crackene; cracking (of oils). **-chinon,** *n.* crackenequinone.
**Crack-kessel,** *m.* cracking retort. **-prozess,** *m.* cracking process.
**Crackung,** *f.* cracking (of oils).
**Crackverfahren,** *n.* cracking process.
**Creme,** *f.* cream.
**creme, cremefarben,** *a.* cream-colored.
**Cremor tartari.** cream of tartar.
**Crêpekautschuk,** *m.* & *n.* crepe rubber.
**Cresylsäure,** *f.* cresylic acid (cresol).
**Cristall,** etc. = Kristall, etc.
**Croceïnscharlach,** *m.* crocein scarlet.
**Croton-harz,** *n.* croton resin. **-öl,** *n.* croton oil. **-säure,** *f.* crotonic acid.
**crouponieren,** *v.t.* butt, crop or round (hides).
**Crystall-.** = Kristall-.
**C-Stoff,** *m.* a kind of rocket fuel.
**Cubeben,** *n.* cubebene. — *f.pl.* cubebs. **-öl,** *n.* cubeb oil. **-pfeffer,** *m.* cubebs. **-säure,** *f.* cubebic acid.
**Cuiteseide,** *f.* boiled-off silk.
**Cultur, Cultur-.** see Kultur, Kultur-.
**Cumalin,** *n.* coumalin (1,2-pyrone). **-säure,** *f.* coumalic (or cumalic) acid.
**Cumar-.** coumar- (or cumar-).
**Cumarinsäure,** *f.* coumarinic (or cumarinic) acid.
**Cumaronharz,** *n.* coumarone resin.
**Cumarsäure,** *f.* coumaric (or cumaric) acid.
**Cumin-öl,** *n.* cumin oil. **-samen,** *m.* cumin seed. **-säure,** *f.* cumic acid, cuminic acid.
**Cumo-chinol,** *n.* cumoquinol. **-chinon,** *n.* cumoquinone.
**Cumol,** *n.* cumene.
**Cuoxam,** *n.* cuprammonium.
**Cupri-.** cupric, copper(II). **-azetat,** *n.* cupric acetate, copper(II) acetate. **-carbonat,** *n.* cupric carbonate, copper(II) carbonate. **-chlorid,** *n.* cupric chloride, copper(II) chloride. **-hydroxyd,** *n.* cupric hydroxide, copper(II) hydroxide. **-ion,** *n.* cupric ion, copper(II) ion. **-oxalat,** *n.* cupric oxalate, copper(II) oxalate. **-oxyd,** *n.* cupric oxide, copper(II) oxide. **-salz,** *n.* cupric salt, copper(II) salt. **-sulfat,** *n.* cupric sulfate, copper(II) sulfate. **-sulfid,** *n.* cupric sulfide, copper(II) sulfide. **-verbindung,** *f.* cupric compound, copper(II) compound. **-weinsäure,** *f.* cupritartaric acid.
**Cupro-.** cuprous, copper(I), cupro-. **-chlorid,** *n.* cuprous chloride, copper(I) chloride. **-cyanür,** *n.* cuprous cyanide, copper(I) cyanide; cuprocyanide, cyanocuprate(I). **-jodid,** *n.* cuprous iodide, copper(I) iodide. **-mangan,** *n.* cupromanganese. **-oxyd,** *n.* cuprous oxide, copper(I) oxide. **-salz,** *n.* cuprous salt, copper(I) salt. **-sulfocyanür,** *n.* cuprous thiocyanate, copper(I) thiocyanate. **-verbindung,** *f.* cuprous compound, copper(I) compound.
**Cuproxam,** *n.* cuprammonium.
**Curcuma,** etc. see Kurkuma, etc.
**curs-.** see kurs-.
**Cuskhygrin,** *n.* cuscohygrine.
**Cuskorinde,** *f.* cusco bark.
**Cutin-insäure,** *f.* cutinic acid. **-säure,** *f.* cutic acid.
**Cuvette, Cüvette,** *f.* bulb; cell, vessel; trough.
**Cyan,** *n.* cyanogen.
**Cyan-.** of or combined with cyanogen, cyano- (as *Cyanpropionsäure*, cyanopropionic acid), cyanide of (as *Cyanammonium*, ammonium cyanide). **-alkali,** *n.* alkali cyanide. **-alkyl,** *n.* alkyl cyanide.
**Cyanamid-calcium,** *n.* calcium cyanamide. **-natrium,** *n.* sodium cyanamide.
**Cyanamido-dikohlensäure,** *f.* cyanamidodi-

carboxylic acid. **-kohlensäure,** *f.* cyanamidocarboxylic acid (cyanocarbamic acid).
**Cyanammonium,** *n.* ammonium cyanide.
**Cyanat,** *n.* cyanate.
**Cyan-äther,** *m.* cyanic ester. **-äthyl,** *n.* ethyl cyanide. **-bad,** *n.* cyanide bath. **-baryum,** *n.* barium cyanide. **-benzol,** *n.* cyanobenzene. **-bromid,** *n.* cyanogen bromide. **-calcium,** *n.* calcium cyanide. **-chlorid,** *n.* cyanogen chloride. **-doppelsalz,** *n.* double cyanide.
**Cyaneisen,** *n.* iron cyanide. **-kalium,** *n.* potassium ferrocyanide. **-verbindung,** *f.* iron cyanogen compound, specif. a ferrocyanide.
**Cyan-essigsäure,** *f.* cyanoacetic acid. **-gas,** *n.* cyanogen gas. **-gold,** *n.* gold cyanide. **-goldkalium,** *n.* potassium auri- or aurocyanide, potassium cyanoaurate.
**cyanhaltig,** *a.* containing cyanogen.
**Cyan-härtung,** *f.* (*Metal.*) cyanide hardening, cyaniding. **-hydrin,** *n.* cyanohydrin.
**Cyanid,** *n.* cyanide (esp. an -ic cyanide as contrasted with Cyanür).
**cyanidfrei,** *a.* cyanide-free.
**cyanig,** *a.* cyanous. *Obs.*
**cyanisieren,** *v.t.* cyanize.
**Cyan-jodid,** *n.* cyanogen iodide. **-kali,** *n.* potassium cyanide.
**cyankalisch,** *a.* potassium cyanide.
**Cyan-kalium,** *n.* potassium cyanide. **-kaliumlösung,** *f.* potassium cyanide solution. **-kobalt,** *m.* cobalt cyanide. **-kohlensäure,** *f.* cyanocarbonic acid. **-kupfer,** *n.* copper cyanide. **-laugerei, -laugung,** *f.* cyaniding, cyanidation. **-lösung,** *f.* cyanide solution. **-metall,** *n.* metallic cyanide. **-methyl,** *n.* methyl cyanide. **-natrium,** *n.* sodium cyanide. **-platin,** *n.* platinum cyanide.
**Cyanquecksilber,** *n.* mercury cyanide. **-kalium,** *n.* mercury potassium cyanide. **-oxyd,** *n.* mercuric cyanide, mercury(II) cyanide.
**Cyansalz,** *n.* cyanogen salt, cyanide. **-badhärtung,** *f.* (*Metal.*) cyanide hardening, cyaniding.
**cyansauer,** *a.* of or combined with cyanic acid, cyanate of.
**Cyan-säure,** *f.* cyanic acid; cyano acid. **-schlamm,** *m.* cyanide sludge. **-senföl,** *n.* cyanomustard oil. **-silber,** *n.* silver cyanide. **-stickstoff,** *m.* cyanonitride. **-toluol,** *n.* cyanotoluene.
**Cyanür,** *n.* (-ous) cyanide. Cf. Cyanid.
**Cyanur-.** cyanuric; cyanuryl. **-säure,** *f.* cyanuric acid.
**Cyan-verbindung,** *f.* cyanogen compound. **-vergiftung,** *f.* cyanogen poisoning. **-wasserstoff,** *m.* hydrogen cyanide; hydrocyanic acid.
**cyanwasserstoffsauer,** *a.* of or combined with hydrocyanic acid, cyanide of.
**Cyan-wasserstoffsäure,** *f.* hydrocyanic acid. **-zink,** *n.* zinc cyanide.
**cyclisch,** *a.* cyclic.
**Cyclisieren,** *n.* cyclization.
**Cyclogeraniumsäure,** *f.* cyclogeranic acid.
**cyklisch,** *a.* cyclic.
**cylindern,** etc. see zylindern, etc.
**Cymol,** *n.* cymene.
**Cyper-.** cypress; Cyprus, Cyprian; copper.
**Cypern,** *n.* Cyprus. **-holz,** *n.* wood of the Spanish elm (*Cordia gerascanthus*).
**Cypervitriol,** *m.* (*Old Chem.*) blue vitriol.
**Cypressen-holz,** *n.* cypress wood. **-nuss,** *f.* cypress cone. **-öl,** *n.* cypress oil.
**cyprisch,** *a.* Cyprian. — **cyprischer Vitriol,** blue vitriol, copper sulfate.
**cystenartig,** *a.* cyst-like.
**Cystenflüssigkeit,** *f.* cystic fluid.
**cystenförmig,** *a.* cystiform.
**Cystinuriker,** *m.* one who has cystinuria.
**C.Z.,** *abbrev.* (Cellulosezahl) cellulose number; *Chemisches Zentralblatt.*

# D

**d.,** *abbrev.* (der, die, das) the, of the, etc.; (dieser, dieses, etc.) this, of this, etc.

**D.,** *abbrev.* (Dichte) density, specific gravity; (Deutsch) German; (Durchmesser) diameter.

**da,** *adv.* there; present; then. — *conj.* when, as, while, since.

**D.A.,** *abbrev.* (Deutsches Arzneibuch) German Pharmacopeia.

**D.A.-B.,** *abbrev.* (Deutsches Apothekerbuch) German Dispensatory.

**dabei,** *adv.* thereby, there, near, besides; therein.

**Dach,** *n.* roof; dome (of a boiler); house. **-bau,** *m.*, **-bedeckung,** *f.*, **-belag,** *m.* roofing. **-blech,** *n.* sheet metal for roofing. **-boden,** *m.* loft. **-deckerei, -deckung,** *f.* roofing.

**Dachel, Dächel,** *m.* (*Metal.*) lump, bloom.

**Dach-filz,** *m.* roofing felt. **-gesellschaft,** *f.* holding company. **-gestein,** *n.* (*Mining*) overlying rock. **-kammer,** *f.* attic, garret. **-kohle,** *f.* upper coal. **-pappe,** *f.* composition roofing, roofing paper. **-pfanne,** *f.* pantile.

**Dachs,** *m.* badger; dachshund.

**Dachschiefer,** *m.* roofing slate.

**Dächsel,** *m.* adze.

**Dachsfett,** *n.* badger fat.

**Dachstein,** *m.* tile, slate; bituminous shale; (*Mining*) roof rock.

**dachte,** *pret.* (of denken) thought.

**Dachung,** *f.* roofing.

**Dach-wurz,** *f.* common houseleek. **-ziegel,** *m.* (roofing) tile. **-ziegelei,** *f.* tilery, tile kiln.

**dad. gek.,** *abbrev.* (dadurch gekennzeichnet) thereby characterized.

**dadurch,** *adv.* thereby, thus; thru this, by this, by that, in this way.

**dafür,** *adv.* therefore, for it; instead of it.

**dagegen,** *adv.* against it; in comparison; in return. — *conj.* on the other hand; whereas.

**daheim,** *adv.* at home.

**daher,** *adv.* hence, thence, therefore.

**dahin,** *adv.* thither, there, thereto; away, over, gone; along.

**dahingestellt,** *a.* undecided, uncertain.

**dahinstehen,** *v.i.* remain uncertain.

**dahinter,** *adv.* behind it; after that.

**damalig,** *a.* at or of that time, then being.

**damals,** *adv.* at that time, then.

**damasc-.** see damasz-.

**damassé,** *a.* damasked, damask.

**Damast,** *m.* damask. **-stahl,** *m.* damask steel, Damascus steel. **-stoff,** *m.* damask (the fabric).

**damaszener,** *a.* Damascene, Damascus, damask.

**damaszieren,** *v.t.* damascene, damask.

**Damaszierung,** *f.* damascening.

**Dame,** *f.* lady; queen (at cards); king (checkers).

**Damen-binde,** *f.* sanitary napkin. **-brett,** *n.* checkerboard. **-spiel,** *n.* checkers, draughts

**Damhirschfell,** *n.* buckskin.

**damit,** *adv.* therewith, with, by it. — *conj.* in order that.

**Damm,** *m.* dam, dike, bank; (*Med.*) perineum

**Dammar-firnis,** *m.* dammar varnish. **-harz,** *n.* dammar resin, dammar.

**dämmen,** *v.t.* dam, dam up, stop up; curb.

**Dammerde,** *f.* mold, humus: (*Founding*) pit sand.

**Dämmerung,** *f.* twilight, dusk; dawn.

**Dammgrube,** *f.* foundry pit.

**Dämmung,** *f.* damming, stopping up; insulation.

**Dampf,** *m.* vapor; steam; fume, smoke. — **direkter —,** live steam. — **indirekter —,** exhaust steam. — **stickender —,** choke damp.

**Dämpfapparat,** *m.* steaming apparatus.

**dampfartig,** *a.* vaporous, vapory.

**Dampf-artikel,** *m.* (*Calico*) steam style. **-auflösung,** *f.* volatilization. **-bad,** *n.* steam bath; vapor bath. **-behälter,** *m.* steam vessel. **-betrieb,** *m.* steam working, steam drive. **-bildung,** *f.* formation of vapor; formation of steam. **-blase,** *f.* bubble of vapor or steam; still heated by steam. **-blasen,** *n.* injection of steam, distilling with steam. **-blasenbildung,** *f.* bubble formation, (*Mach.*) vapor lock. **-bleiche,** *f.* steam bleaching. **-bleicherei,** *f.* steam bleaching; steam bleachery. **-chlor, -chloren,** *n.* steam chemicking. **-darre,** *f.* steam kiln.

**dampfdicht,** *a.* steam-tight, vapor-tight.

**Dampf-dichte, -dichtigkeit,** *f.* vapor density; density of steam. **-dichtebestimmung,** *f.* vapor-density determination. **-dichtung,** *f.* steam packing. **-druck,** *m.* vapor pressure; steam pressure; steam printing. **-druckerei,** *f.* steam printing. **-druckerniedrigung,** *f.* vapor-pressure lowering. **-druckmesser,** *m.* manometer; steam gage. **-druckregler,** *m.* steam-pressure regulator. **-druckzünder,** *m.* vapor-pressure igniter. **-düse,** *f.* steam nozzle.

**dampfecht,** *a.* fast to steaming.

**dampfempfindlich,** *a.* susceptible to steaming.
**dampfen,** *v.i.* give off vapor or steam, steam; evaporate; fume, smoke. — *v.t.* steam.
**dämpfen,** *v.t.* damp, smother; put out (fire); subdue (color or sound); treat with steam, steam; stew; evaporate (fruit).
**Dampf-entwässerer,** *m.* steam desiccator, steam drier. **-entwickelung,** *f.* evolution of vapor; steam generation. **-entwickler,** *m.* steam generator.
**Dampfer,** *m.* steamer, steamboat.
**Dämpfer,** *m.* damper; steamer, steam cooker.
**Dampf-erzeuger,** *m.* steam generator, boiler. **-erzeugung,** *f.* steam generation; production of vapor. **-farbe,** *f.* (*Dyeing*) steam color. **-färberei,** *f.* steam printing. **-fass,** *n.* steam drum.
**dampfförmig,** *a.* in the form of vapor or steam, vaporous.
**Dampf-gas,** *n.* dry steam, superheated steam. **-gebläse,** *n.* steam blast; steam blower. **-gummi,** *n.* dextrin. **-hahn,** *m.* steam cock.
**dampfhaltig,** *a.* containing vapor or steam; humid, moist.
**Dampf-heizrohr,** *n.* steam (heating) pipe. **-heizung,** *f.* steam heating. **-holzschliff,** *m.* steamed mechanical wood pulp. **-hülle,** *f.* steam jacket; vaporous envelope.
**dampfig,** *a.* vapory, steamy.
**Dampf-kanal,** *m.* steam pipe; steam port. **-kasten,** *m.* steam box, steam chest; steaming chamber.
**Dampfkessel,** *m.* steam boiler. **-anlage,** *f.* steam boiler plant, steam plant. **-bekleidung,** *f.* boiler covering or casing. **-blech,** *n.* boiler plate. **-kohle,** *f.* steam coal. **-speisung,** *f.* steam boiler feed.
**Dampfkoch-.** steam boiling. **-apparat, -kessel, -topf,** *m.* steam cooker.
**Dampf-kochung,** *f.* steam cooking. **-kolben,** *m.* steam piston. **-kraft,** *f.* steam power. **-kühlung,** *f.* vapor cooling. **-leitung,** *f.* steam piping, steam line; conduction of vapor or steam. **-leitungsrohr,** *n.* steampipe. **-mantel,** *m.* steam jacket. **-maschine,** *f.* steam engine. **-messer,** *m.* manometer; steam gage.
**Dämpfmittel,** *n.* neutralizer (for acids).
**Dampf-mühle,** *f.* steam mill. **-ofen,** *m.* steam oven; steam furnace. **-phase,** *f.* vapor phase. **-probe,** *f.* steam test. **-rohr,** *n.*, **-röhre,** *f.* steam pipe. **-rohrleitung,** *f.* steam piping. **-schale,** *f.* evaporating dish or basin. **-scheider,** *m.* vapor separator (to catch liquid carried up in evaporation). **-schiff,** *n.* steamboat. **-schlange,** *f.* steam coil. **-schmierung,** *f.* steam lubrication. **-schwarz,** *n.* (*Dyeing*) steam black. **-schwelung,** *f.* destructive distillation with steam. **-spannung,** *f.* vapor tension; steam tension. **-strahl,** *m.* steam jet; steam blast. **-strom,** *m.* current of steam or vapor. **-topf,** *m.* (steam) digester. autoclave; steam sterilizer. **-trichter,** *m.* steam funnel. **-trockenapparat,** *m.* steam drier. **-trockenofen, -trockenschrank,** *m.* steam drying oven. **-trockner,** steam drier. **-turbine,** *f.* steam turbine. **-überdruck,** *m.* excess vapor pressure; excess steam pressure. **-überhitzer,** *m.* steam superheater.
**Dämpfung,** *f.* damping, etc. (see dämpfen).
**Dämpfungsvorrichtung,** *f.* damping device, damper.
**Dampf-ventil,** *n.* steam valve. **-verbrauch,** *m.* steam consumption. **-vulkanisation,** *f.* *Rubber*) steam cure. **-wagen,** *m.* steam car; locomotive. **-wärme,** *f.* heat of vaporization; vaporizing temperature. **-wäscherei,** *f.* steam laundry. **-wassertopf,** *m.* steam trap. **-weg,** *m.* = Dampfkanal. **-zucker,** *m.* sugar refined with steam. **-zuführung, -zuleitung,** *f.* steam supply. **-zylinderöl,** *n.* steam cylinder oil.
**danach,** *adv.* after that, thereupon, for it, accordingly.
**daneben,** *adv.* near it, beside it, besides.
**Dänemark,** *n.* Denmark.
**Dank,** *m.* thanks; reward.
**dankbar,** *a.* thankful; acceptable.
**danken,** *v.t.* thank.
**dann,** *adv.* then.
**Dän.P.,** *abbrev.* (dänisches Patent) Danish patent.
**D'Anversblau,** *n.* Antwerp blue.
**D.Ap.,** *abbrev.* (Deutsches Apothekerbuch) German Dispensatory.
**daran,** *adv.* thereon, thereat, about it, of it, in it. **-geben,** *v.t.* give up. **-liegend,** *a.* adjacent.
**darauf,** *adv.* thereupon, thereon, afterward.
**daraufolgend,** *a.* following, subsequent.
**Darauflassen,** *n.* (*Brewing*) doubling.
**daraus,** *adv.* therefrom, thence, out of that, of it.
**darben,** *v.i.* starve.
**darbieten,** *v.t.* present, offer.
**darein,** *adv.* therein, thereinto, in there.
**darf,** *pr. 1 & 3 sing.* (of dürfen) may.
**darin,** *adv.* therein, in it.
**darlegen,** *v.t.* explain; present, state; show, display, exhibit; lay down.
**Darlegung,** *f.* explanation, etc. (see darlegen); program.
**Darlehen,** *n.* (*Com.*) loan.
**Darm,** *m.* gut, intestine. — **blinder —,** caecum. — **dicker —,** colon. — **dünner —,** small intestine. — **gerader —,** rectum. — **langer —,** ileum. — **leerer —,** jejunum.
**Darm-bein,** *n.* ilium. **-drüse,** *f.* intestinal gland. **-entzündung,** *f.* enteritis. **-fäule,** *f.* dysentery. **-fell,** *n.* peritoneum. **-gang,** *m.*

intestinal tract. **-gas,** *n.* intestinal gas. **-gicht,** *f.* ileus. **-gift,** *n.* enterotoxin. **-haut,** *f.* intestinal coat. **-inhalt,** *m.* intestinal contents. **-kanal,** *n.* intestinal canal. **-kot,** *m.* feces. **-netz,** *n.* omentum. **-rohr,** *n.* intestinal canal. **-ruhr,** *f.* dysentery. **-saft,** *m.* intestinal juice. **-saite,** *f.* catgut, gut string. **-schlauch,** *m.* gut. **-schleimhaut,** *f.* intestinal mucosa. **-stein,** *m.* enterolith. **-stiel,** *m.* vitelline duct. **-system,** *n.* digestive tract. **-tiere,** *n.pl.* metazoa. **-verdauung,** *f.* intestinal digestion. **-wand,** *f.* intestinal wall.

**darnach,** *adv.* = danach.

**Darr-arbeit,** *f.* (*Metal.*) liquation. **-boden,** *m.* drying floor, kiln floor. **-brett,** *n.* drying board.

**Darre,** *f.* drying, kiln-drying; drying room or kiln; (*Brewing*) malt kiln; (*Metal.*) liquation hearth; withering.

**darreichen,** *v.t.* offer; administer (drugs).

**darren,** *v.t.* dry, kiln-dry; kiln; (*Metal.*) liquate; (*Metal.*) torrefy.

**Darr-fax,** *m.* (*Brewing*) kilnman. **-fläche,** *f.* drying surface, kiln surface. **-gekrätz,** *n.* liquation dross or slag. **-gewicht,** *n.* kiln-dry weight. **-haus,** *n.* drying house. **-holz,** *n.* kiln-dried wood. **-kammer,** *f.* drying room. **-kupfer,** *n.* liquated copper. **-malz,** *n.* kiln-dried malt, cured malt. **-ofen,** *m.* drying kiln, drying oven; (*Metal.*) liquation hearth. **-raum,** *m.* kiln chamber. **-reife,** *f.* (*Brewing*) kiln fitness. **-schrank,** *m.* drying cabinet, drying oven. **-staub,** *m.* malt dust.

**Darrung,** *f.* drying, etc. (see darren).

**Darst.,** *abbrev.* (Darstellung) preparation.

**darstellbar,** *a.* capable of being prepared, etc. (see darstellen).

**darstellen,** *v.t.* prepare; produce, make, manufacture; exhibit, display; present; represent; describe; (*Math.*) construct.

**Darstellung,** *f.* preparation; production, manufacture; exhibition, display; description; representation; (*Math.*) construction.

**Darstellungs-verfahren,** *n.* process of preparation or production. **-weise,** *f.* method of preparation; manner of representation, style.

**dartun,** *v.t.* prove; verify.

**darüber,** *adv.* over it, over there, about it, more, meantime. **-gelagert,** *p.a.* super(im)posed.

**darum,** *adv.* around it, about it, therefore.

**darunter,** *adv.* thereunder, under it, among them, by it. **-liegend,** *a.* underlying, subjacent.

**das,** *article.* the. — *pron.* this, that, it, which.

**Dasein,** *n.* presence; being, existence.

**daselbst,** *adv.* there, in that place, *ibidem.*

**dasjenige,** *pron.* that one, the one, that, it.

**dass,** *conj.* that.

**dastehen,** *v.i.* stand there; stand out.

**Daten,** *n.pl.* data; dates.

**datieren,** *v.t.* date.

**Dattel,** *f.* date. **-baum,** *m.*, **-palme,** *f.* date tree, date palm. **-pflaume,** *f.* persimmon, date plum. **-wein,** *m.* date wine. **-zucker,** *m.* date sugar.

**Datum,** *n.* date; datum.

**Daube,** *f.* stave.

**Dauer,** *f.* duration; life (of patents, etc.); period, time; durability, permanence.

**Dauer-.** permanent, continuous, lasting, perennial, chronic. **-ausscheider,** *m.* (*Biol.*) chronic carrier. **-beanspruchung,** *f.* continuous stress, fatigue stress. **-belastung,** *f.* steady load, permanent load. **-beobachtung,** *f.* continuous observation. **-betrieb,** *m.* continuous operation. **-biegefestigkeit,** *f.* bending endurance. **-bier,** *n.* lager beer. **-bleiche,** *f.* continuous bleaching. **-bruch,** *m.* (*Mech.*) fatigue fracture. **-entladung,** *f.* continuous discharge. **-farbe,** *f.* permanent or lasting color. **-festigkeit,** *f.* durability; (*Mech.*) fatigue strength, endurance. **-flamme,** *f.* pilot flame. **-fleisch,** *n.* preserved meat. **-form,** *f.* permanent form; permanent mold. **-gewächs,** *n.* perennial plant, perennial. **-gewebe,** *n.* permanent tissue.

**dauerhaft,** *a.* durable, lasting, permanent; fast (colors); tough (leather).

**Dauer-haftigkeit,** *f.* durability, permanence. **-haltbarkeit,** *f.* (*Mech.*) fatigue endurance. **-hefe,** *f.* permanent yeast, zymin. **-leistung,** *f.* continuous output. **-magnet,** *m.* permanent magnet. **-milch,** *f.* sterilized milk; condensed milk; dried milk.

**dauern,** *v.i.* last, continue, endure, keep. — **dauernd,** *p.a.* lasting, permanent; perennial.

**Dauer-pflanze,** *f.* perennial (plant). **-prüfmaschine,** *f.* endurance testing machine. **-prüfung,** *f.* test of long duration. **-riss,** *m.* fatigue crack. **-schlagfestigkeit,** *f.* (*Mech.*) resistance to repeated impact, impact endurance. **-spore,** *f.* resting spore. **-standfestigkeit,** *f.* (*Mech.*) resistance to creep stress. **-strom,** *m.* continuous current. **-träger,** *m.* (*Biol.*) chronic carrier. **-veränderung,** *f.* permanent change. **-verhalten,** *n.* durability, permanence. **-versuch,** *m.* endurance test. **-waren,** *f.pl.* preserved foods. **-weide, -wiese,** *f.* permanent meadow or pasture. **-zustand,** *m.* steady state.

**Daum, Daumen,** *m.* thumb; inch; (*Mech.*) part resembling a thumb, as a cam or finger.

**Daumen-mutter,** *f.* (*Mach.*) thumb nut. **-rad,** *n.* cam wheel. **-schraube,** *f.* thumb screw. **-welle,** *f.* camshaft.

**Däumling,** *m.* little thumb; (*Mech.*) cam, knob, or the like.

**Daune,** *f.* down.
**davon,** *adv.* thereof, therefrom, thereby, away.
**davontragen,** *v.t.* carry away, obtain.
**davor,** *adv.* before it, for it, from it.
**dawider,** *adv.* against it, against.
**dazu,** *adv.* thereto, therefor, besides, in addition. — **noch dazu,** moreover.
**dazu-geben,** *v.t.* add (to it), contribute (to it). **-gehörig,** *a.* belonging to it, pertaining to it.
**dazumal,** *adv.* then.
**dazwischen,** *adv.* between, between them, inter-. **-liegend,** *a.* lying between, intermediate. **-schalten, -schieben, -stellen,** *v.t.* put between, interpose, interpolate. **-treten,** *v.i.* come between, intervene.
**d.Bl.,** *abbrev.* (dieses Blattes) of this journal.
**dch.,** *abbrev.* (durch) thru, by.
**DD.,** *abbrev.* (Dampfdichte) vapor density.
**D.D.,** *abbrev.* (Dichten) densities.
**DE.,** *abbrev.* (Dielektrizitätskonstante) dielectric constant.
**-de.** A suffix attached to verbal roots to form nouns which denote the result of the action or the thing done; as, *Zierde*, ornament, from *zieren*, adorn.
**Debet,** *n.* debit.
**Decaeder,** *n.* decahedron.
**decantieren,** *v.t.* decant.
**decarbonisieren,** *v.t.* decarbonize, decarburize.
**Dechema,** *abbrev.* of *De*utsche Gesellschaft für *chem*isches *A*pparatewesen.
**dechiffrieren,** *v.t.* decipher.
**Dechsel,** *f.* adze.
**Deck-.** covering, cover, protecting. **-anstrich,** *m.* (*Painting*) finishing coat, top coat. **-appretur,** *f.* top finish.
**deckbar,** *a.* coverable; superposable.
**Deckblatt,** *n.* veneer; wrapper (of a cigar); (*Bot.*) bract.
**Decke,** *f.* cover, covering (of various kinds); integument, coat; roof; ceiling; blanket; (*Sugar*) cleansing, purging (also, fine liquor); (*Brewing*) head.
**Deckel,** *m.* cover, lid, cap. **-abfall,** *m.* carding waste.
**deckeln,** *v.t.* provide with a cover or lid. — **gedeckelt,** *p.a.* with cover(s), covered.
**decken,** *v.t.* cover; top (paper); cleanse, wash, purge; clay (sugar); superpose. — *v.i.* (of colors) cover. — *v.r.* coincide (with). — **deckend,** *p.a.* covering, etc.; (of paints) = deckfähig.
**Decken,** *n.* covering; cleansing, washing; (*Paints*) covering power, opacity; (*Sugar*) claying; superposition.
**Decken-.** overhead, ceiling, roof; covering. **-gewebe,** *n.* epithelial tissue. **-lampe,** *f.* ceiling lamp, dome lamp. **-licht,** *n.* skylight. **-strich,** *m.* (*Leather*) daub.
**Decker,** *m.* coverer; (*Tobacco*) wrapper. **-druck,** *m.* (*Calico*) blotch print.
**deckfähig,** *a.* of good covering power, opaque.
**Deck-fähigkeit,** *f.* covering power, opacity. **-farbe,** *f.* body color, opaque color, coating color.
**deckfarbig,** *a.* of good body, opaque.
**Deck-firnis,** *m.* covering varnish, protecting varnish. **-frucht,** *f.* (*Agric.*) cover crop. **-glas,** *n.* cover glass, glass cover. **-gläschen,** *n.* (*Micros.*) cover glass. **-hülle,** *f.* covering, etc. (see Hülle). **-hütchen,** *n.* cover cap; (*Expl.*) capsule.
**deckig,** *a.* (*Biol.*) imbricate.
**Deck-kläre,** *f.*, **-klärsel,** *n.* (*Sugar*) fine liquor (claircé) for cleansing the crystals. **-kraft,** *f.* covering power, body (of pigments and dyes). **-lack,** *m.* coating varnish or lacquer. **-mittel,** *n.* covering material or medium. **-name,** *m.* trade name; code name; pseudonym; alias. **-papp,** *m.*, **-pappe,** *f.* (*Calico*) resist, resist paste. **-pappdruck,** *m.* resist printing. **-plättchen,** *n.* cover plate, cover slide. **-schicht,** *f.* covering layer, protective layer; (*Geol.*) overlying stratum; (of varnish) top coat.
**Decksel,** *n.* = Deckkläre.
**Deck-sirup,** *m.* (*Sugar*) liquored sirup (obtained by cleansing the crystals with fine liquor). **-span,** *m.* veneer. **-stopfen,** *n.* stopper with projecting rim, flanged stopper.
**Deckung,** *f.* covering, cover; concealment, mask; remittance; security; superposition; (*Photog.*) density; (*Geom.*) congruence. — **zur — bringen,** cause to coincide.
**Deck-weiss,** *n.* zinc white. **-weissfarbe,** *f.* (*Varnish*) white enamel. **-wort,** *n.* code word. Cf. Deckname. **-ziegel,** *m.* cover tile; coping brick.
**decolorieren,** *v.t.* decolorize.
**decrepitieren,** *v.i.* decrepitate.
**Decreusage,** *f.* (*Silk*) determination of gum.
**Decylsäure,** *f.* decylic acid (decoic acid).
**deduzieren,** *v.t.* deduce.
**defekt,** *a.* defective.
**Defibreur,** *m.* (*Paper*) pulp grinder.
**defibriniert,** *a.* defibrinated.
**definieren,** *v.t.* define. — **definiert,** *p.a.* definite.
**deflagrieren,** *v.t.* deflagrate.
**deformierbar,** *a.* deformable.
**Deformierbarkeit,** *f.* deformability.
**deformieren,** *v.t.* deform.
**degallieren,** *v.t.* degall.
**Degea,** *abbrev.* of *De*utsche *G*asglühlicht-*A*uer Gesellschaft.
**Degen,** *m.* sword.
**deglutieren,** *v.t.* swallow.
**degommieren,** *v.t.* degum.
**degorgieren,** *v.t.* = ausschlämmen.

**degradieren,** *v.t.* degrade.
**degraissieren, degrassieren,** *v.t.* = entfetten.
**Degras,** *n.* (*Leather*) dégras, stuff.
**degummierecht,** *a.* fast to degumming.
**degummieren,** *v.t.* degum, ungum, strip (silk), boil off (silk); malt.
**Degussa,** *abbrev.* *De*utsche *G*old- *u.* *S*ilber-*S*cheide*a*nstalt.
**dehnbar,** *a.* capable of being stretched, extensible, (of metals) malleable, ductile; expansible, (of gases) elastic; dilatable.
**Dehnbarkeit,** *f.* extensibility, etc. (see dehnbar).
**Dehnbarkeitsmesser,** *m.* ductilimeter; dilatometer.
**dehnen,** *v.t.* & *r.* extend, stretch; expand, dilate, distend.
**Dehnkraft,** *f.* force or power of extension or expansion.
**Dehnung,** *f.* extension; stretching; elongation; tension; expansion; dilation.
**dehnungsfähig,** *a.* extensible; expansible.
**Dehnungs-kraft,** *f.* = Dehnkraft. **-messer,** *m.* extensometer; dilatometer. **-wärme,** *f.* heat of extension. **-zahl,** *f.* coefficient of extension or expansion.
**Dehydratation,** *f.* dehydration.
**Dehydratisierung,** *f.* dehydration.
**dehydrieren,** *v.t.* dehydrogenize, dehydrogenate; dehydrate.
**Dehydrierung,** *f.* dehydrogenation; dehydration.
**Dehydro-camphersäure,** *f.* dehydrocamphoric acid. **-chinacridon,** *n.* dehydroquinacridone. **-chinin,** *n.* dehydroquinine. **-schleimsäure,** *f.* dehydromucic acid.
**Deich,** *m.* dike.
**Deil,** *m.* bloom, lump, cake (of metal).
**dein,** *pron.* thy, thine, your, yours.
**deinige,** *pron.* thine, yours.
**dekadisch,** *a.* decadic. — **dekadische Logarithmen,** common logarithms.
**Dekaeder,** *m.* decahedron.
**dekantieren,** *v.t.* decant.
**Dekantier-apparat,** *m.* decanting apparatus. **-gefäss,** *n.* decanting vessel. **-glas,** *n.* decanting glass, glass decanting jar. **-topf,** *m.* (earthenware) decanting jar.
**Dekantierung,** *f.* decanting, decantation.
**Dekantierzylinder,** *m.* decanting cylinder.
**dekapieren,** *v.t.* scour, descale, pickle (metals).
**dekarbonisieren,** *v.t.* decarbonize, decarburize.
**dekatieren,** *v.t.* hot-press, decatize (cloth).
**Dekatur,** *f.* (*Textiles*) decatizing, hot pressing or steaming.
**dekaturecht,** *a.* fast to decatizing.
**dekaustizieren,** *v.t.* decausticize.
**deklinieren,** *v.t.* & *i.* decline, deviate.
**Dekokt,** *n.* decoction.
**dekonzentriert,** *a.* (*Optics*) defocused.
**Dekorations-farbe,** *f.* decorative color. **-lack,** *m.* decorative varnish.
**dekorieren,** *v.t.* decorate.
**dekrepitieren,** *v.i.* decrepitate.
**Dekyl,** *n.* decyl.
**deliquescieren,** *v.i.* deliquesce.
**Delle,** *f.* dent.
**Delphin,** *m.* dolphin. **-öl,** *n.*, **-tran,** *m.* dolphin oil.
**dem,** *article.* to the, the. — *pron.* (to) this, (to) that, (to) him, (to) it, (to) whom, (to) which.
**Demant,** *m.* diamond; adamant. **-blende,** *f.* eulytite. **-spat,** *m.* adamantine spar (corundum).
**dementsprechend,** *adv.* correspondingly, accordingly.
**demethylieren,** *v.t.* demethylate.
**demgegenüber,** *adv.* as opposed to that or it, on the other hand.
**demgemäss, demnach,** *adv.* accordingly, therefore.
**demnächst,** *adv.* soon after, shortly.
**demolieren,** *v.t.* demolish.
**Demontage,** *f.* demounting, dismantling, disassembly.
**demontierbar,** *a.* dismountable, demountable.
**demontieren,** *v.t.* dismount, demount, take apart or down, disassemble, dismantle.
**demulzieren,** *v.i.* soften, become demulcent.
**demungeachtet,** *adv.* notwithstanding, nevertheless.
**Demut,** *f.* humility.
**demzufolge,** *adv.* accordingly.
**den,** *article.* the; (with *pl.*) to the. — *pron.* this, that, him, it, whom, which, to these, to those.
**denaturieren,** *v.t.* denature, denaturize.
**Denaturiermittel,** *n.* denaturant.
**Denaturierung,** *f.* denaturing, denaturation.
**Denaturierungsmittel,** *n.* denaturant.
**denaturisieren,** *v.t.* = denaturieren.
**Dendrachat, Dendritenachat** *m.* dendritic agate.
**dendrisch, dendritisch,** *a.* dendritic.
**denen,** *pron.pl.* (to) these, (to) those, (to) them, (to) which, (to) whom.
**Denitrierbad,** *n.* denitrating bath.
**denitrieren,** *v.t.* denitrate.
**Denitriermittel,** *n.* denitrating agent.
**Denitrierung,** *f.* denitration.
**denitrifizieren,** *v.t.* denitrify.
**Denkart,** *f.* way of thinking, disposition.
**denkbar,** *a.* thinkable, conceivable.
**denken,** *v.t.* & *i.* think; imagine.
**Denk-mal,** *n.* monument; memorial. **-münze** *f.* commemorative medal. **-schrift,** *f.* memoir; memorandum; memorial.
**denkwürdig,** *a.* memorable, notable.
**denn,** *conj.* for, because, then.
**dennoch,** *conj.* yet, however.

**Densität,** *f.* density.
**Depesche,** *f.* dispatch.
**Dephlegmator,** *m.* dephlegmator (specif., a fractionating column).
**dephlegmieren,** *v.t.* dephlegmate.
**Deplacement,** *n.* displacement.
**deplacieren,** *v.t.* displace.
**Depolarisator,** *m.* depolarizer.
**depolarisieren,** *v.t.* depolarize.
**depolymerisieren,** *v.t.* depolymerize.
**deprimieren,** *v.t.* depress.
**depur.,** *abbrev.* (*depuratus, -a, -um*) purified.
**der (die, das),** *article.* the; to the; (with *pl.*) of the. — *pron.* this, that, he (she, it), who, which, to whom, to which.
**Der.,** *abbrev.* (Derivat) derivative.
**derart,** *adv.* in such a way, so much.
**derartig,** *a.* such, of that kind.
**derb,** *a.* solid, compact, dense, firm, strong; hardy, stout; rough, rude; (*Min.*) massive.
**Derb-erz,** *n.* massive ore. **-gehalt,** *m.* solid contents, cubical contents, actual volume.
**Derbheit,** *f.* solidity, etc. (see derb).
**derb-stückig,** *a.* lumpy, large-sized (as ore). **-wandig,** *a.* stout-walled, thick-walled.
**dereinst,** *adv.* some day; once, one day.
**deren,** *pron.* of this, of that, of her, of it, her, its, of whom, of which, whose, of these, of those, of them, their.
**derer,** *pron.pl.* of these, of those, of them, their.
**dergestalt,** *adv.* such, so.
**dergl.,** *abbrev.* (dergleichen) the like.
**dergleichen,** *a.* such, the like.
**Derivat,** *n.* derivative.
**derivieren,** *v.t.* derive.
**derjenige,** *pron.* that one, the one, that, he, it.
**dermassen,** *adv.* so much, so.
**dermatisch,** *a.* cutaneous.
**derselbe,** *a.* the same, this, the latter.
**derzeit,** *adv.* at this time; at that time.
**derzeitig,** *a.* of the time being; present.
**des,** *article.* of the. — *pron.* of this, of that, of him, of it, his, its.
**des-.** dis-, de-; as, *Des*tillat, distillate, *des*oxydieren, deoxidize.
**des.,** *abbrev.* (desmotrop) desmotropic.
**Desagregation,** *f.* disaggregation, disintegration.
**desamidieren,** *v.t.* deaminate; deamidate.
**Desamidierung,** *f.* deamination; deamidation.
**desarsenizieren,** *v.t.* dearsenicate.
**Desensibilisator,** *m.* desensitizer.
**desensibil(is)ieren,** *v.t.* desensitize.
**desfalls,** *adv.* in that case.
**desgl.,** *abbrev.* of desgleichen.
**desgleichen,** *adv.* likewise; ditto.
**deshalb,** *adv.* therefore.
**deshydrieren,** *v.t.* dehydrogenate.
**Deshydrierung,** *f.* dehydrogenation.
**Desinfektion,** *f.* disinfection.
**Desinfektions-mittel,** *n.* disinfectant. **-wasser,** *n.* disinfecting liquid.
**Desinfektor,** *m.* disinfector; disinfectant.
**desinfektorisch,** *a.* disinfectant.
**desinfizieren,** *v.t.* disinfect. — **desinfizierend,** *p.a.* disinfectant.
**Desinfizierung,** *f.* disinfection.
**Desintegrator,** *m.* disintegrator.
**desintegrieren,** *v.t.* disintegrate.
**desmotrop,** *a.* desmotropic.
**Desmotropie,** *f.* desmotropism, desmotropy.
**Desodorationsmittel,** *n.* deodorizer.
**desodorisieren, desodorieren,** *v.t.* deodorize.
**Desodorisierung,** *f.* deodorization.
**Desodorisierungsmittel,** *n.* deodorant.
**Desoxy-.** deoxy-, desoxy-.
**Desoxydation,** *f.* deoxidation.
**Desoxydations-mittel,** *n.* deoxidizing agent. **-wirkung,** *f.* deoxidizing action or effect.
**desoxydieren,** *v.t.* deoxidize.
**Desoxydierung,** *f.* deoxidation.
**dessen,** *pron.* of this, of that, of him, of it, his, its, of whom, of which, whose.
**dessenungeachtet,** *adv.* nevertheless; irrespective.
**Dessin,** *m. & n.* design, pattern.
**dessinieren,** *v.t.* design.
**dest.,** *abbrev.* (destilliert) distilled.
**Dest.,** *abbrev.* (Destillation) distillation.
**Destillat,** *n.* distillate.
**Destillateur,** *m.* distiller; stillman.
**Destillation,** *f.* distillation.
**Destillations-apparat,** *m.* distilling apparatus. **-aufsatz,** *m.* fractionating column. **-benzin,** *n.* straight-run gasoline. **-gas,** *n.* gas from distillation, specif. coke-oven gas. **-gefäss,** *n.* distilling vessel. **-gerät,** *n.* distilling apparatus. **-hut,** *m.* receiver. **-kokerie,** *f.* by-product coking; by-product coke plant. **-kolben,** *m.* distilling flask. **-ofen,** *m.* = Destillierofen. **-rohr,** *n.*, **-röhre,** *f.* distillation tube, distilling tube. **-rückstand,** *m.* residue from distillation. **-tiegel,** *m.* distilling crucible. **-verfahren,** *n.* distillation process. **-vorlage,** *f.* distillation receiver.
**Destillatsammelgefäss,** *n.* receiver; (*Petroleum*) run-down tank or drum.
**Destillier-apparat,** *m.* distilling apparatus, still. **-aufsatz,** *m.* fractionating column.
**destillierbar,** *a.* distillable.
**Destillierbarkeit,** *f.* distillability.
**Destillier-betrieb,** *m.* distilling plant or operation. **-blase,** *f.* distilling vessel, retort, body of a still. **-brücke,** *f.* distillation bridge.
**destillieren,** *v.t.* distill.
**Destillier-gefäss,** *n.* distilling vessel. **-glas,** *n.* distilling vessel (of glass). **-haus,** *n.* still-house. **-helm,** *n.* still head. **-kolben,** *m.*

distilling flask; retort. **-kolonne,** *f.* distilling column. **-ofen,** *m.* distilling furnace; by-product coke oven. **-rohr,** *n.* distilling tube. **-säule,** *f.* distilling column. **-topf,** *m.* distilling pot.

**Destillierung,** *f.* distillation.

**desto,** *adv.*, **desto-.** so much, so much the. — je . . . — . . ., the . . . the . . .

**destomehr,** *a.* & *adv.* so much the more, the more.

**Destrictasäure,** *f.* destrictic acid.

**Destrictinsäure,** *f.* destrictinic acid.

**deswegen,** *adv.* for that reason, therefore.

**deszendent,** *a.* descending, descendent.

**Detacheur,** *m.* (*Dyeing*) spot cleaner.

**detachieren,** *v.t.* free from stains; detach.

**Detachiermittel,** *n.* detergent, cleaner.

**Detachur,** *f.* removal of spots or stains.

**detonieren,** *v.i.* detonate. — **detonierender Sprengstoff,** (*Expl.*) detonator. — **detonierende Strecke,** (*Expl.*) detonating column.

**Detoniersprengstoff,** *m.* (*Expl.*) detonator.

**deuchte,** *pret.* (of dünken) thought.

**Deul,** *m.* bloom, lump, cake (of metal).

**deutbar,** *a.* explainable, explicable.

**deuten,** *v.i.* point. — *v.t.* indicate; explain.

**deutlich,** *a.* clear, distinct, plain, evident.

**Deuto-chlorür,** *n.* deutochloride. *Obs.* **-jodür,** *n.* deutoiodide, deutiodide. *Obs.*

**deutsch,** *a.* German. — **deutsche Folie,** German foil (made from an alloy of tin). — **deutsches Geschirr,** (*Paper*) stampers. — **Deutsches Reich,** (the) German State, German Government (formerly also, German Empire).

**Deutschland,** *n.* Germany.

**Deutung,** *f.* interpretation, explanation.

**Devise,** *f.* motto, device; trade-mark; (*pl.* **Devisen**) foreign exchange.

**devonisch,** *a.* Devonian.

**Dewargefäss,** *n.*, **Dewarsches Gefäss.** Dewar vessel.

**Dextronsäure,** *f.* dextronic (D-gluconic) acid.

**dezentrieren,** *v.t.* decenter.

**Dezi-.** deci-. **-gramm,** *n.* decigram.

**dezimal,** *a.* decimal.

**Dezimal,** *n.*, **Dezimale,** *f.* decimal.

**Dezimal-bruch,** *m.* decimal fraction. **-bruchstelle, -stelle,** *f.* decimal place. **-wa(a)ge,** *f.* decimal balance.

**dgl.,** *abbrev.* (dergleichen) the like; (desgleichen) likewise, ditto.

**d.h.,** *abbrev.* (das heisst) that is, i.e.

**d.i.,** *abbrev.* (das ist) that is, i.e.

**Diachylonsalbe,** *f.* diachylon ointment.

**Dialysator,** *m.* dialyzer.

**Dialyse,** *f.* dialysis.

**dialysierbar,** *a.* dialyzable.

**dialysieren,** *v.t.* dialyze.

**Dialysierpapier,** *n.* dialyzing paper.

**dialytisch, dialysisch,** *a.* dialytic.

**diamagnetisch,** *a.* diamagnetic.

**Diamant,** *m.* diamond.

**diamantartig,** *a.* diamond-like, adamantine.

**diamanten,** *a.* adamantine; diamond.

**diamantförmig,** *a.* diamond-shaped; diamond-like.

**Diamant-glanz,** *m.* adamantine luster. **-kitt,** *m.* diamond cement. **-mörser,** *m.* diamond mortar (small steel mortar). **-pulver,** *n.* diamond dust. **-schwarz,** *n.* diamond black. **-spat,** *m.* adamantine spar (corundum). **-stahl,** *m.* very hard steel, tool steel.

**Diamido-.** diamino-, diamido- (see Amido-). **-benzol,** *n.* diaminobenzene. **-toluol,** *n.* diaminotoluene.

**Diamin-blau,** *n.* diamine blue. **-farbstoff,** *m.* diamine dye.

**Diaminosäure,** *f.* diamino acid.

**Diaminschwarz,** *n.* diamine black.

**Dianenbaum,** *m.* arbor Dianae (silver tree).

**Dianilgelb,** *n.* dianil yellow.

**diaphan,** *a.* diaphanous.

**Diaphoresie,** *f.* diaphoresis.

**diaphoretisch,** *a.* diaphoretic.

**Diaphragma,** *n.* diaphragm.

**Diastasewirkung,** *f.* diastatic action.

**diastatisch,** *a.* diastatic.

**Diät,** *f.* diet.

**Diätetik,** *f.* dietetics.

**diätetisch,** *a.* dietetic.

**Diäth-.** dieth-.

**diatherm, diatherman,** *a.* diathermic, diathermanous.

**diatomisch,** *a.* diatomic.

**Diazetyl-.** diacetyl-.

**Diazo-benzol,** *n.* diazobenzene. **-essigsäure,** *f.* diazoacetic acid. **-körper,** *m.* diazo compound. **-lösung,** *f.* diazo solution. **-salz,** *n.* diazo salt (usually a diazonium salt). **-schwarz,** *n.* diazo black.

**diazotierbar,** *a.* diazotizable.

**diazotieren,** *v.t.* diazotize.

**Diazotierung,** *f.* diazotizing, diazotization.

**Diazotierungs-bad,** *n.* diazotizing bath. **-farbstoff,** *m.* diazotizing dye; diazotizable dye. **-verfahren,** *n.* diazotizing process.

**Diazoverbindung,** *f.* diazo compound.

**dibenzoyliert,** *p.a.* having two benzoyl groups introduced, dibenzoyl-.

**Dibrombenzol,** *n.* dibromobenzene.

**Dicarbonsäure,** *f.* dicarboxylic acid.

**Dichinol,** *n.* diquinol.

**Dichinolin,** *n.* diquinoline.

**Dichinoyl,** *n.* diquinoyl.

**Dichloräthylen,** *n.* dichloroethylene.

**Dichlormethan,** *n.* dichloromethane.

**Dichroismus,** *m.* dichroism.

**dichroitisch,** *a.* dichroic.

**dichromsauer,** *a.* of or combined with dichromic acid, dichromate of.
**Dichromsäure,** *f.* dichromic acid.
**Dichrosalz,** *n.* dichroic salt.
**dicht,** *a.* tight; dense; close; close-textured; firm, compact, thick, impervious; (*Min.*) massive. — *adv.* close, near, near by; tightly, densely, etc. **-brennen,** *v.t.* (*Ceram.*) vitrify.
**Dichte,** *f.* density; tightness, thickness, firmness; (of paper) bulking quality; (of paint, etc.) body. **-bestimmung,** *f.* density determination. **-flasche,** *f.* specific-gravity bottle. **-messer,** *m.* instrument for measuring density, densimeter; specif., hydrometer. **-messung,** *f.* density measurement, densimetry, densitometry.
**dichten,** *v.t.* make tight, lute, pack, calk; condense, compact; compose (poetry).
**Dichter,** *m.* poet.
**dicht-gedrängt,** *p.a.* tight-pressed, compact. **-gepackt,** *a.* close-packed.
**Dichtheit,** *f.* tightness, imperviousness; density, firmness, compactness.
**Dichtigkeit,** *f.* = Dichte.
**Dichtigkeits-grad,** *m.* degree of denseness, tightness, etc.; consistency. **-messer,** *m.* = Dichtemesser.
**dichtschliessend,** *p.a.* closing tightly, tight.
**Dichtschweissung,** *f.* close weld(ing).
**Dichtung,** *f.* making tight; luting; packing, stuffing; seal; joint; poetry.
**Dichtungs-fett,** *n.* joint grease, packing grease. **-material, -mittel,** *n.*, **-stoff,** *m.* luting, calking or packing material.
**dick,** *a.* thick; dense; big, bulky, fat, swollen.
**Dick-auszug,** *m.* inspissated extract. **-darm,** *m.* large intestine; colon.
**Dicke,** *f.* thickness, etc. (see dick); (of sheet metal, etc.) gage; consistency (of a liquid); mother, dregs.
**Dickenmesser,** *m.* thickness gage, caliper.
**Dickfarbe,** *f.* thick color, body color.
**dickflüssig,** *a.* thickly liquid, viscous, viscid.
**Dickflüssigkeit,** *f.* viscosity; thick liquid.
**dickgrell,** *a.* (of pig iron) dead-white.
**Dickheit,** *f.* thickness, denseness, compactness.
**dickig,** *a.* (proposed term for) consistent, firm, stiff.
**Dickigkeit,** *f.* (proposed term for) consistency, firmness, stiffness.
**dicklich,** *a.* thickish, somewhat thick.
**Dick-maische,** *f.* (*Brewing*) thick mash, decoction. **-milch,** *f.* curdled milk, curds. **-mittel,** *n.* thickening agent, thickener. **-öl,** *n.* thick oil, heavy oil; specif., a viscous product formed by the exposure of oil of turpentine to the air; stand oil. **-ölfirnis,** *m.* thick oil varnish.
**dickölig,** *a.* of the nature of a thick oil.
**Dick-pfanne,** *f.* concentration pan. **-saft,** *m.* inspissated juice; (*Sugar*) thick juice, sirup.
**dick-schalig,** *a.* thick-shelled; (of grain) husky. **-sirupartig,** *a.* of the nature of a thick sirup. **-tafelig,** *a.* in thick plates. **-teer,** *m.* thick tar, heavy tar. **-wandig,** *a.* thick-walled.
**Dicyan,** *n.* dicyanogen, cyanogen gas.
**Didym,** *n.* didymium.
**die,** *article.* the. — *pron.* this, that, these, those, she, who, which.
**Dieb,** *m.* thief. **-stahl,** *m.* theft, larceny.
**diejenige,** *pron.* that one, the one, that, she, it.
**Diele,** *f.* board, plank, deal.
**Dielektrikum,** *n.* dielectric.
**dielektrisch,** *a.* dielectric.
**Dielektrizitätskonstante,** *f.* dielectric constant.
**dienen,** *v.i.* serve.
**Diener,** *m.* servant.
**dienlich,** *a.* serviceable, useful, fit.
**Dienst,** *m.* service; duty, employment.
**Dienstag,** *m.* Tuesday.
**dienstbereit,** *a.* ready for service.
**Dienst-herr,** *m.* employer, master. **-leistung,** *f.* service, functioning. **-lohn,** *m.* wages.
**dienstlos,** *a.* out of employment.
**Dienststelle,** *f.* office, agency, department.
**dies,** *pron.* see dieser.
**diesbez.,** *abbrev.* of diesbezüglich.
**diesbezüglich,** *a.* concerning this.
**diese,** *pron.* see dieser.
**dieselbe,** *pron.* the same.
**Diesel-kraftstoff, -treibstoff,** *m.* Diesel fuel, Diesel oil. **-öl,** *n.* Diesel oil. **-zahl,** *f.* Diesel (index) number.
**dieser, diese, dieses, dies,** *pron.* this, this one, the latter. — **diese,** *pl.* these.
**diesig,** *a.* hazy, misty.
**diesmal,** *adv.* this time, now.
**Dietrich,** *m.* skeleton key, picklock.
**differentiieren,** *v.t.* differentiate.
**Differenzbildung,** *f.* (*Math.*) subtraction.
**Differenzial-gleichung,** *f.* differential equation. **-rechnung,** *f.* differential calculus. **-strom,** *m.* differential current.
**differenzierbar,** *a.* differentiable.
**differenzieren,** *v.t.* differentiate.
**Differenzierung,** *f.* differentiation.
**Differenzstrom,** *m.* differential current.
**differieren,** *v.i.* differ.
**diffundieren,** *v.t.* diffuse.
**Diffuseur,** *m.* diffuser.
**diffusionsfähig,** *a.* diffusible.
**Diffusions-fähigkeit,** *f.* diffusibility. **-geschwindigkeit,** *f.* velocity of diffusion. **-gleichung,** *f.* diffusion equation. **-glühen,** *n.* (*Metal.*) diffusion annealing, homogenizing. **-hülse,** *f.* diffusion shell. **-produkt,** *n.* diffusate. **-verfahren,** *n.* diffusion process. **-vermögen,**

*n.* diffusibility. **-vorgang,** *m.* diffusion process. **-wärme,** *f.* heat of diffusion.
**Digallussäure,** *f.* digallic acid.
**digerieren,** *v.t.* digest.
**Digerier-flasche,** *f.* digestion bottle. **-ofen,** *m.* digestion oven, digester.
**Digerierung,** *f.* digestion.
**Digestionsalz, Digestivsalz,** *n.* digestive salt (potassium chloride).
**Digestionskolben,** *m.* digestion flask.
**Digestivmittel,** *n.* digestive.
**Digestor,** *m.* digester.
**Digestorium,** *n.* hood, fume cupboard.
**digonal,** *a.* twofold; two-sided.
**Diharnstoff,** *m.* diurea(urazine).
**diheteroatomig,** *a.* diheteratomic.
**dihexaedrisch,** *a.* (*Cryst.*) dihexahedral.
**dihydratisch,** *a.* dihydric.
**Dijod-.** diiodo-.
**Dika-brot,** *n.* dika bread. **-fett,** *n.* dika fat, dika oil.
**Dikarb-.** see Dicarb-.
**diktieren,** *v.t.* dictate.
**Dilemöl,** *n.* dilem oil, Java oil (a kind of patchouli oil).
**Dilettant,** *m.* amateur.
**Dille,** *f.* socket, nozzle.
**Dill-kraut,** *n.* dill. **-öl,** *n.* oil of dill, dill oil. **-samen,** *m.* dill seed.
**dimensionieren,** *v.t.* dimension.
**dimer,** *a.* dimeric.
**Dimethyläther,** *m.* dimethyl ether.
**dimethyliert,** *p.a.* dimethylated, dimethyl-.
**dimetrisch,** *a.* (*Cryst.*) dimetric (tetragonal).
**Dimilchsäure,** *f.* dilactic acid (dilactylic acid).
**dimorph, dimorphisch,** *a.* dimorphous.
**Dimorphie,** *f.*, **Dimorphismus,** *m.* dimorphism.
**DIN,** *abbrev.* (*D*eutsche *I*ndustrie*n*ormalien) German industrial standards.
**Dina-.** Dinas.
**Dinapht-, Dinaphto-.** dinaphtho-.
**Dinaphtyl,** *n.* dinaphthyl.
**Dinaphtylen-.** dinaphthylene-.
**Dinaphtylin,** *n.* dinaphthyline.
**Dinas-stein,** *m.* Dinas brick, silica brick. **-ton,** *m.* Dinas clay. **-ziegel,** *m.* = Dinaziegel.
**Dinaton,** *m.* Dinas clay.
**Dinatrium-.** disodium.
**Dinaziegel,** *m.* Dinas brick, silica brick.
**Ding,** *n.* thing; object; being.
**dingen,** *v.t.* hire. — *v.i.* bargain.
**Dingglas,** *n.* (*Optics*) objective.
**Dinicotinsäure,** *f.* dinicotinic acid.
**dinitriert,** *p.a.* having two nitro groups introduced, dinitro-.
**Dinkel,** *m.* spelt, German wheat.
**Dinte,** *f.* (more commonly, Tinte) ink.
**diorithaltig,** *a.* containing diorite, dioritic.
**Diorsellinsäure,** *f.* diorsellinic acid.

**Dioxy-.** dioxy-; dihydroxy-. (See note under Oxy-.) **-benzol,** *n.* dihydroxybenzene. **-chinolin,** *n.* dihydroxyquinoline. **-chinon,** *n.* dihydroxyquinone.
**Dioxyd,** *n.* dioxide.
**Dioxy-naphtalin,** *n.* dihydroxynaphthalene. **-toluol,** *n.* dihydroxytoluene.
**diözisch,** *a.* (*Biol.*) dioecious.
**diphasisch,** *a.* diphase, diphasic.
**Diphensäure,** *f.* diphenic acid.
**Diphenyl-arsenchlorür,** *n.* diphenylarsenious chloride (chlorodiphenylarsine). **-borchlorid,** *n.* diphenylboron chloride. **-schwarz,** *n.* diphenyl black.
**Diphosphorsäure,** *f.* diphosphoric (pyrophosphoric) acid.
**Diphtal-.** diphthal-.
**Dipl.-Ing.,** *abbrev.* (*Dipl*om-*Ing*enieur) graduate in engineering from a school of university rank.
**Diploeder,** *n.* (*Cryst.*) diplohedron, diploid.
**dipol,** *a.* dipolar.
**Dipol-kraft,** *f.* dipole force. **-messung,** *f.* dipole measurement. **-strahlung,** *f.* dipole radiation.
**Dippelsöl,** *n.* Dippel's oil.
**Diptam,** *m.* (*Bot.*) dittany.
**direktfärbend,** *a.* direct-coloring, direct.
**Direktfarbstoff,** *m.* direct dye, substantive dye.
**Direktive,** *f.* instructions.
**direktziehend,** *a.* (*Dyeing*) direct.
**Dirhodan-.** dithiocyano-.
**Dirigent,** *m.* director, manager, head.
**dirigieren,** *v.t.* direct, manage, rule.
**Disäure,** *f.* diacid (often, pyro acid).
**Disazo-farbstoff,** *m.* disazo dye. **-verbindung,** *f.* disazo compound.
**Dischwefelsäure,** *f.* disulfuric acid, pyrosulfuric acid.
**dischweflig,** *a.* disulfurous, pyrosulfurous.
**diskontieren,** *v.t.* discount.
**diskontinuierlich,** *a.* discontinuous.
**Diskontinuität,** *f.* discontinuity.
**diskret,** *a.* discrete, distinct, discontinuous.
**diskutieren,** *v.t.* discuss.
**dispensieren,** *v.t.* dispense; exempt, excuse.
**Dispergens,** *m.* dispersion agent.
**dispergierbar,** *a.* dispersible.
**Dispergierbarkeit,** *f.* dispersibility.
**dispergieren,** *v.t.* disperse. — **dispergierend,** *p.a.* dispersing, dispersive.
**dispergierfähig,** *a.* dispersible.
**Dispergiermittel,** *n.* dispersing agent.
**Dispergierung,** *f.* dispersing, dispersion.
**Dispergierungs-mittel,** *n.* dispersing agent. **-zahl,** *f.* dispersion number.
**Dispergiervermögen,** *n.* dispersing power.
**dispers,** *a.* dispersed, disperse.
**Dispersions-grad,** *m.* degree of dispersion.

**-mittel,** *n.* dispersion medium, dispersion agent. **-vermögen,** *n.* dispersive power.
**Dispersität,** *f.* dispersity.
**Dispersitätsgrad,** *m.* degree of dispersion.
**Disponent,** *m.* manager, agent, accountant.
**disponibel,** *a.* disposable, available.
**disponieren,** *v.t.* dispose.
**Disproportionierung,** *f.* disproportionation.
**Diss.,** *abbrev.* dissertation; dissociation.
**Dissertation,** *f.* dissertation, thesis.
**dissezieren,** *v.t.* dissect.
**dissimilieren,** *v.t.* decompose.
**dissociierbar,** *a.* dissociable.
**dissociieren,** *v.t. & i.* dissociate.
**Dissousgas,** *n.* dissolved (acetylene) gas.
**Dissoz.,** *abbrev.* (Dissoziation) dissociation.
**Dissoziations-grad,** *m.* degree of dissociation. **-spannung,** *f.* dissociation tension. **-vermögen,** *n.* dissociating power. **-wärme,** *f.* heat of dissociation. **-zustand,** *m.* dissociated condition.
**dissoziierbar,** *a.* dissociable.
**dissoziieren,** *v.t. & i.* dissociate.
**Distel,** *f.* thistle.
**distillieren,** *v.t.* distill. See Destill-.
**Disulfaminsäure,** *f.* disulfamic acid.
**Disulfosäure,** *f.* disulfonic acid.
**Ditarinde,** *f.* dita bark.
**Dithiokohlensäure,** *f.* (either) dithiocarbonic acid; specif., dithiolcarbonic acid (HSCOSH).
**dithionig,** *a.* dithioncus, (less desirably) hyposulfurous.
**dithionigsauer,** *a.* of or combined with dithionous acid, dithionite of.
**Dithionsäure,** *f.* dithionic acid.
**Dithiophosphorsäure,** *f.* dithiophosphoric acid.
**Diüberjodsäure,** *f.* diperiodic acid.
**diuretisch,** *a.* diuretic.
**Divaricatinsäure,** *f.* divaricatinic acid.
**Divaricatsäure,** *f.* divaricatic acid.
**divergierend,** *p.a.* diverging, divergent.
**dividieren,** *v.t.* divide.
**Diweinsäure,** *f.* ditartaric acid.
**Diwolframsäure,** *f.* ditungstic acid.
**Dizimmtsäure,** *f.* dicinnamic acid.
**Dizyan,** *n.* = Dicyan.
**d.J.,** *abbrev.* (dieses Jahres) of this year.
**DK,** *abbrev.* (Dielektrizitätskonstante) dielectric constant.
**d.M.,** *abbrev.* (dieses Monats) of this month, inst.
**d.O.,** *abbrev.* (der Obige, die Obige, das Obige) the above.
**Döbel, Dobel,** *m.* pin, peg, dowel.
**Docent,** *m.* teacher, lecturer.
**doch,** *conj.* yet, however, surely, indeed.
**Docht,** *m.* wick. **-kohle,** *f.* (*Elec.*) cored carbon.
**Docke,** *f.* bundle, skein; plug; baluster; mandrel; doll; dock.
**docken,** *v.t.* wind (into skeins).
**Dodekaeder,** *n.* dodecahedron.
**dodekaedrisch,** *a.* dodecahedral.
**Doggererz,** *n.* (*Mining*) dogger ore.
**Döglingstran,** *m.* doegling oil.
**Dohle,** *f.* jackdaw; sewer.
**Dokimasie,** *f.* docimasy.
**Dokosan,** *n.* docosane.
**Dokumentiertinte,** *f.* record ink.
**Dolde,** *f.* umbel, (of hops) cone, strobile.
**dolden-blumig, -blütig,** *a.* umbelliferous.
**dolieren,** *v.t.* (*Leather*) pare, shave.
**Dolmetsch, Dolmetscher,** *m.* interpreter.
**dolomithaltig,** *a.* dolomitic.
**dolomitisch,** *a.* dolomitic.
**dolomitisieren,** *v.t.* (*Min.*) dolomitize.
**Dom,** *m.* dome, cupola; cover; cathedral.
**Doma,** *n.* (*Cryst.*) dome.
**Donau,** *f.* Danube.
**Donner,** *m.* thunder. **-keil,** *m.* thunderbolt; belemnite.
**donnern,** *v.i.* thunder; strike, peal.
**Donner-stein,** *m.* thunderstone, belemnite. **-strahl,** *m.* lightning flash.
**Doppel,** *n.* duplicate.
**Doppel-.** double; doubly; bi-, di-.
**doppelatomig,** *a.* diatomic.
**Doppel-ausschlag,** *m.* double throw or deflection (as of a balance needle). **-bier,** *n.* double beer. **-bild,** *n.* double image. **-bindung,** *f.* double bond, double linkage. **-boden,** *m.* double bottom, false bottom; jacket. **-bogen,** *m.* double bend; U-tube, U-pipe.
**doppel-borsauer,** *a.* biborate (tetraborate) of. **-brechend,** *a.* doubly refracting.
**Doppelbrechung,** *f.* double refraction.
**doppelbreit,** *a.* double-width.
**Doppel-brillantscharlach,** *m.* double brilliant scarlet. **-centner,** *m.* = Doppelzentner. **-chlorid,** *n.* double chloride; bichloride, dichloride. **-chlorzinn,** *n.* = Doppeltchlorzinn.
**doppel-chromsauer,** *a.* bichromate (dichromate) of. **-fädig,** *a.* two-threaded, bifilar. **-farbig,** *a.* dichroic, dichromatic.
**Doppel-farbigkeit,** *f.* dichroism. **-färbung,** *f.* (*Micros.*) double staining, also counterstaining. **-fernrohrlupe,** *f.* binocular magnifier. **-gänger,** *m.* double. **-gas,** *n.* a mixture of coal gas and water gas. **-gestaltung,** *f.* dimorphism. **-gitter,** *m.* (*Elec.*) double grid. **-glocke,** *f.* double bell jar. **-härten,** *n.* (*Metal.*) double quench. **-jodquecksilber,** *n.* biniodide of mercury (mercuric iodide). **-kessel,** *m.* double (or jacketed) boiler or kettle.
**doppel-kohlensauer,** *a.* bicarbonate of. **-lebig,** *a.* amphibious.
**Doppel-linie,** *f.* double line, doublet. **-lötung,** *f.*

double seal (in glass). **-mantel,** *m.* (double-wall) jacket. **-mantelgafäss,** *n.* double-walled vessel. **-metall-.** bimetallic. **-molekül, -molekel,** *n.* double molecule. **-muffelofen,** *m.* double muffle furnace.

**doppeln,** *v.t.* double; duplicate.

**Doppelofen,** *m.* double furnace or oven.

**doppeloxalsauer,** *a.* binoxalate of.

**Doppel-oxyd,** *n.* binoxide (dioxide); double oxide. **-punkt,** *m.* (*Printing*) colon.

**doppelpolig,** *a.* bipolar.

**Doppel-salz,** *n.* double salt. **-schale,** *f.* double dish, dish with cover (as a Petri dish). **-schicht,** *f.* double layer.

**doppel-schichtig,** *a.* two-layered. **-schlicht,** *a.* dead smooth, (of files) superfine.

**Doppelschwefel-eisen,** *n.* iron disulfide. **-zinn,** *n.* tin disulfide, stannic sulfide.

**doppelschwefelsauer,** *a.* bisulfate of.

**Doppelschwefelsäure,** *f.* disulfuric acid.

**doppel-schwefligsauer,** *a.* bisulfite of. **-seitig,** *a.* bilateral; double-faced.

**Doppelschweisstahl,** *m.* double-shear steel.

**Doppelsilikat,** *n.* double silicate; bisilicate.

**doppelsinnig,** *a.* ambiguous.

**Doppelspat,** *m.* Iceland spar.

**doppelstark,** *a.* double-strength.

**Doppel-stück,** *n.* duplicate. **-sulfat,** *n.* double sulfate; bisulfate. **-sulfit,** *n.* double sulfite; bisulfite.

**doppelt,** *a.* double, duplex, dual, twofold; (in old names of compounds) bi-, bin-. — *adv.* doubly, twice. **-basisch,** *a.* bibasic (dibasic). **-borsauer,** *a.* biborate (tetraborate) of. **-brechend,** *a.* birefringent.

**Doppeltchlorzinn,** *n.* tin (IV) chloride, stannic chloride, $SnCl_4$.

**doppelt-chromsauer,** *a.* bichromate (dichromate) of. **-hochrund,** *a.* convexo-concave; biconvex. **-hohl,** *a.* concavo-concave. **-kieselsauer,** *a.* bisilicate of. **-kleesauer,** *a.* binoxalate of. **-kohlensauer,** *a.* bicarbonate of. **-kohlensaures Salz,** bicarbonate. **-normal,** *a.* double normal, twice normal.

**Doppeltonfarbe,** *f.* double-tone color.

**Doppeltschwefeleisen,** *n.* iron disulfide.

**doppelt-schwefelsauer,** *a.* bisulfate (acid sulfate) of. **-schwefligsauer,** *a.* bisulfite (acid sulfite) of. **-selenigsauer,** *a.* biselenite of. **-selensauer,** *a.* biselenate of. **-titansauer,** *a.* bititanate of. **-ungesättigt,** *a.* doubly unsaturated. **-vanadinsauer,** *a.* bivanadate of. **-weinsauer,** *a.* bitartrate (acid tartrate) of. **-wirkend,** *a.* double-acting. **-wolframsauer,** *a.* bitungstate of.

**Doppelumsetzung,** *f.* double decomposition.

**Doppelung,** *f.* doubling.

**Doppel-verbindung,** *f.* double compound. **-wägung,** *f.* double weighing.

**doppelwandig,** *a.* double-walled.

**Doppelweghahn,** *m.* two-way cock.

**doppelwirkend,** *p.a.* double-acting; amphichroic, amphoteric.

**Doppel-wirkung,** *f.* double action. **-wurzel,** *f.* (*Math.*) double root. **-zentner,** *m.* double centner, 100 kilograms. **-zersetzung,** *f.* double decomposition. **-zünder,** *m.* combination fuse.

**doppelzüngig,** *a.* double-dealing.

**Döpper,** *m.* (*Mach.*) riveting die, riveting set.

**Dorf,** *n.* village.

**Dorn,** *m.* thorn; spine; (*Mach.*) pin, spike, plug, tongue, bolt, mandrel, etc.; (*Metal.*) slag (of copper).

**dornartig,** *a.* thorn-like, spiked.

**dornen, dörnen,** *v.t.* (*Mach.*) punch, drift; indent.

**Dornenstein,** *m.* = Dornstein.

**Dörnerschlacke,** *f.* (*Metal.*) bulldog.

**dornig,** *a.* thorny, spiny.

**Dornstein,** *m.* (*Salt Manuf.*) thornstone (scale of calcium carbonate and sulfate on thorn walls).

**dorren,** *v.i.* dry; wither.

**dörren,** *v.t.* dry, desiccate; cure (by drying); scorch.

**Dörrgemüse,** *n.* dried vegetables.

**Dorr-klassierer, -klassifikator,** *m.* Dorr classifier.

**Dörrobst,** *n.* dried fruit.

**Dorschleber-tran,** *m.*, **-öl,** *n.* cod-liver oil.

**dort,** *adv.* there; yonder.

**dorthin,** *adv.* thither, there, that way.

**dortig,** *a.* of that place, in that place.

**Dose,** *f.* box; can, tin; capsule.

**Dosen-barometer,** *n.* aneroid barometer. **-konserven,** *f.pl.* canned goods, tinned goods. **-milch,** *f.* condensed (or evaporated) milk.

**Dosieranlage,** *f.* dosing plant.

**dosieren,** *v.t.* determine; (*Pharm., etc.*) dose; measure out.

**Dosierung,** *f.* determination; dosing, dosage; dose.

**Dosis,** *f.* dose; dosage.

**Dossierung,** *f.* slope.

**Dost, Dosten,** *m.* origanum, origan.

**Dostenöl,** *n.* origanum oil.

**Dostkraut,** *n.* origanum, origan.

**Dotter,** *m.* egg yolk, vitellus. — *f.* any of several plants, as wild flax.

**Dotter-.** yolk, vitelline. **-gelb,** *n.* egg yolk, egg yellow. **-öl,** *n.* gold-of-pleasure oil, camelina (seed) oil.

**doubeln,** *v.t.* double, duplicate.

**doublieren,** *v.t.* double, concentrate.

**Dozent,** *m.* teacher, lecturer.

**D. P.,** *abbrev.* (deutsches Patent) German patent.

**D.P.a.,** *abbrev.* (*d*eutsche *P*atent*a*nmeldung) application for a German patent.
**D. Prior.,** *abbrev.* (deutsche Priorität) German priority.
**Drache, Drachen,** *m.* dragon; kite.
**Drachenblut, -gummi,** *n.* dragon's blood.
**dragieren,** *v.t.* coat (pills or the like).
**Dragun,** *m.*, **-trat, -wermutkraut,** *n.* tarragon.
**Draht,** *m.* wire; (*Spinning*) twist, thread; grain (of wood). **-asbestgewebe,** *n.* asbestos wire gauze. **-band,** *n.* wire tape, metal tape. **-bund,** *m.* coil of wire. **-bürste,** *f.* wire brush. **-dreieck,** *n.* wire triangle.
**drahten, drähtern,** *a.* of wire; wiry. — **drahten,** *v.t.* wire.
**Draht-faser,** *f.* (*Paper*) wire mold. **-gaze,** *f.* wire gauze. **-geflecht,** *n.* wire netting. **-gewebe,** *n.* wire cloth, wire gauze. **-gewicht,** *n.* wire weight, (often) rider. **-glas,** *n.* armored glass, wire glass. **-klemme,** *f.* wire clamp; (*Elec.*) binding post. **-korb,** *m.* wire basket. **-lehre,** *f.* wire gage.
**drahtlos,** *a.* wireless; radio.
**Draht-maske,** *f.* wire mask. **-netz,** *n.* wire gauze, wire net. **-prüfung,** *f.* wire testing. **-rolle,** *f.* coil of wire. **-seil,** *n.* wire cable, wire rope, wire cord. **-sieb,** *n.* wire sieve, wire screen, wire cloth. **-stärke,** *f.* wire thickness, wire diameter. **-stift,** *m.* wire nail, wire tack, wire pin. **-zange,** *f.* pliers, nippers. **-ziehen,** *n.* wire drawing. **-zug,** *m.* wire drawing; wire mill.
**drainieren,** *v.t.* drain.
**drall,** *a.* tight; buxom.
**Drall,** *m.* twist; torque; spin (of electrons); spiral thread; rifling.
**Drän,** *m.* drain.
**dränen,** *v.t. & i.* drain.
**drang,** *pret.* (of dringen) pressed, penetrated.
**Drang,** *m.* throng, pressure, impulse, craving.
**drängen,** *v.t. & i.* press, crowd, urge; drive (gases.) — **gedrängt,** *p.a.* crowded; compact; succinct.
**dränieren,** *v.t. & i.* drain.
**Dränrohr,** *n.*, **-röhre,** *f.* drain pipe.
**Dränung,** *f.* drainage, draining.
**drasch,** *pret.* (of dreschen) thrashed.
**Drass,** *m.* dregs (of oil).
**drauf,** *adv.* thereupon, thereon, afterward.
**Draufsicht,** *f.* top view, plan view, plan.
**draussen,** *adv.* without, out, abroad.
**drechseln,** *v.t.* turn (on a lathe); elaborate.
**Dreck,** *m.* dirt, dung, filth; (*Metal.*) dross.
**Dreckseisen,** *n.* pig iron.
**Dreh-.** rotatory, rotary, rotating, rotational, revolving, turning, torsional. **-achse,** *f.* axis of rotation (or of revolution); knife edge (of a balance); pin. **-bank,** *f.* lathe.
**drehbar,** *a.* capable of being turned or twisted, turning, rotary, rotatory, revolving. — **— eingesetzt,** pivoted.
**Drehbarkeit,** *f.* turnability, rotatability; versatility.
**Dreh-bewegung,** *f.* rotatory motion, rotary motion. **-bottich,** *m.* rotating tub. **-ebene,** *f.* plane of rotation or revolution.
**drehen,** *v.t.* turn, rotate; twist; roll; spin; wind. — *v.r.* turn, rotate, revolve. — **drehend,** *p.a.* turning, etc.; rotatory.
**Dreher,** *m.* turner; rotator; (*Mech.*) crank, handle (for turning), etc.
**Dreh-federwage,** *f.* torsion balance. **-feld,** *n.* (*Elec.*) rotating field. **-gelenk,** *n.* swivel joint. **-geschwindigkeit,** *f.* speed (or velocity) of rotation or of revolution. **-impuls,** *m.* angular momentum, moment of momentum. **-kalzinierofen,** *m.* revolving roaster. **-kocher,** *m.* rotary boiler. **-kondensator,** *m.* (*Elec.*) adjustable condenser. **-kraft,** *f.* torsional force. **-krankheit,** *f.* staggers. **-kreuz,** *n.* turnstile; (*Brewing*) sparger; rotating shutter. **-moment,** *n.* moment of rotation; twisting or torsional moment. **-ofen,** *n.* revolving furnace, rotary furnace, rotary kiln. **-punkt,** *m.* center of motion, turning point, pivot, fulcrum. **-richtung,** *f.* direction of rotation. **-schalter,** *m.* (*Elec.*) rotary switch. **-scheibe,** *f.* potter's wheel; lapidary's wheel; turntable. **-sinn,** *m.* direction of rotation or revolution. **-späne,** *m.pl.* turnings. **-spannung,** *f.* torsional strain. **-spiegelung,** *f.* (*Cryst.*) rotatory reflection, combined rotation and reflection. **-spindel,** *f.* revolving spindle, live spindle. **-spulgalvanometer,** *n.* moving-coil galvanometer. **-stahl,** *m.* turning tool, lathe tool. **-strom,** *m.* (*Elec.*) rotary current, multiphase current; alternating current. **-trommel,** *m.* rotary drum.
**Drehung,** *f.* rotation, turn, turning, torsion, revolution, twisting.
**Drehungs-achse,** *f.* axis of rotation (or of revolution), turning axis. **-festigkeit,** *f.* resistance to torsion.
**drehungsfrei,** *a.* not rotatory, irrotational.
**Drehungs-grad,** *m.* degree of rotation. **-kraft,** *f.* rotatory power. **-schwingung,** *f.* torsional vibration. **-streuung,** *f.* rotatory dispersion. **-vermögen,** *n.* rotatory power. **-winkel,** *m.* angle of rotation.
**Dreh-vektor,** *m.* rotation vector. **-vermögen,** *n.* rotatory power. **-wage,** *f.* torsion balance. **-zahl,** *f.* number of revolutions. **-zähler,** *m.* revolution counter. **-zahlgeber,** *m.* tachometer, speedometer. **-zahlmesser,** *m.* revolution counter. **-zylinder,** *m.* revolving cylinder.
**drei,** *a.* three.
**drei-, Drei-.** three-, tri-, triple.

**drei-achsig,** *a.* triaxial. **-atomig,** *a.* triatomic. **-basisch,** *a.* tribasic.
**Drei-bein,** *n.* tripod. **-blatt,** *n.* trefoil.
**dreiblätterig,** *a.* three-leaved.
**Drei-brenner,** *m.* triple burner. **-bund,** *m.* triple alliance.
**dreidimensional,** *a.* tridimensional.
**Dreieck,** *n.* triangle.
**dreieckig,** *a.* triangular, three-cornered.
**Dreiecks-koordinaten,** *f.pl.* triangular coördinates. **-lehre,** *f.* trigonometry.
**Dreier-gemisch,** *n.* triple mixture. **-gruppe,** *f.* group of three, 3-group.
**dreierlei,** *a.* of three kinds, of three sorts.
**Dreierstoss,** *m.* three-body collision, threefold collision.
**dreifach,** *a.* triple, threefold, treble, tri. — **— Chlorantimon,** antimony trichloride. — **— Chlorjod,** iodine trichloride. — **— Schwefelarsen,** arsenic trisulfide. — **dreifache Bindung,** triple bond.
**dreifachfrei,** *a.* trivariant.
**Dreifachverbindung,** *f.* ternary compound.
**Dreifarben-.** three-color, trichrome. **-druck,** *m.* three-color print(ing).
**dreifarbig,** *a.* tricolor(ed), trichromatic.
**Dreifarbigkeit,** *f.* trichroism.
**dreiflächig,** *a.* three-faced, trihedral.
**Dreiflächner,** *m.* (*Geom.*) trihedron.
**dreiflammig,** *a.* three-flame, triple (burner).
**Dreifuss,** *m.* tripod.
**drei-füssig,** *a.* three-footed, tripedal. **-gliedrig,** *a.* three-membered; (*Math.*) trinomial. **-gruppig,** *a.* of three groups, three-group. **-halsig,** *a.* three-necked.
**Drei-halskolben,** *m.* three-necked flask. **-heit,** *f.* triad. **-kantfeile,** *f.* three-cornered file, triangular file.
**drei-kantig,** *a.* three-cornered, triangular. **-kernig,** *a.* trinuclear.
**Dreikörper, -apparat,** *m.* triple-effect apparatus.
**Dreileiter-.** (*Elec.*) three-wire.
**dreimal,** *adv.* three times, thrice.
**dreimalig,** *a.* done three times, triple.
**Dreiphasenstrom,** *m.* (*Elec.*) triphase current.
**dreiphasig,** *a.* three-phase, triphase.
**dreipolig,** *a.* three-pole.
**Dreipunkt-.** three-point.
**dreiquantig,** *a.* of three quanta, three-quantum.
**Drei-ring,** *m.* three-membered ring. **-salz,** *n.* trisalt (neutral salt of a triacid); triple salt.
**drei-säurig,** *a.* triacid. **-schenkelig,** *a.* three-legged.
**Dreischenkelrohr,** *n.* three-way tube, T-tube.
**drei-schichtig,** *a.* three-layered. **-seitig,** *a.* three-sided, trilateral, triangular.
**dreissig,** *a.* thirty.
**dreissigste,** *a.* thirtieth.
**dreist,** *a.* bold, confident, daring.
**Dreisteinwurzel,** *f.* feverroot (*Triosteum*).
**dreistellig,** *a.* three-place.
**Dreistoff-.** three-component, ternary. **-legierung,** *f.* three-component alloy, ternary alloy.
**drei-stufig,** *a.* three-stage. **-stündig,** *a.* three-hour, for three hours. **-teilig,** *a.* three-part, tripartite. **-undeinachsig,** *a.* (*Cryst.*) monotrimetric (hexagonal). **-wandig,** *a.* three-walled, triple-walled.
**Dreiweg-, Dreiwege-.** three-way. **-hahn,** *m.* three-way cock. **-schalter,** *m.* three-way switch. **-stück,** *n.* three-way piece, three-way tube. **-verbindung,** *f.* three-way connection.
**dreiwertig,** *a.* trivalent.
**Dreiwertigkeit,** *f.* trivalence.
**dreiwinkelig,** *a.* triangular.
**Dreizack,** *m.* trident.
**dreizählig,** *a.* threefold, triple, ternary; (*Cryst.*) trigonal.
**dreizehn,** *a.* thirteen.
**Drell,** *m.* ticking, drill, canvas.
**Dresbacherblau,** *n.* Dresbach blue (Prussian blue).
**dreschen,** *v.t.* thrash, thresh.
**dressieren,** *v.t.* dress, finish.
**drgl.,** *abbrev.* (dergleichen) the like.
**D. R. G. M.,** *abbrev.* (Deutsches Reichs-Gebrauchsmuster) German registered design. Cf. Gebrauchsmuster.
**Drill-achse,** *f.* (in quantum theory) rotator. **-bohrer,** *m.* drill.
**drillen,** *v.t.* drill; turn, twist.
**Drillich,** *m.* ticking, tick, drill, denim.
**Drilling,** *m.* triplet; (*Mach.*) lantern. **-salz,** *n.* triple salt.
**Drillung,** *f.* drilling; turning, twisting; twist, torsion.
**Drillungskristall,** *m.* "twister" crystal.
**drin,** *adv.* therein.
**Dr.-Ing.,** *abbrev.* (Doktor-Ingenieur) doctor-engineer (doctor of technical science and graduate in engineering).
**dringen,** *v.i.* press, rush, penetrate. — **dringend,** *p.a.* pressing, urgent. — **gedrungen,** *p.a.* compact; compelled; thickset.
**dringlich,** *a.* pressing, urgent.
**Dringlichkeit,** *f.* urgency.
**drinnen,** *adv.* within, in, indoors.
**drischt,** *pr. 3 sing.* (of dreschen) thrashes.
**dritt,** *a.* third. — **Drittes Reich,** Third Reich (1933–45).
**Drittel,** *n.* third. **-alkohol,** *m.* (*Bact.*) a mixture of alcohol with double the amount of water, Ranvier's alcohol.
**drittelsauer,** *a.* tribasic.
**Drittelsilber,** *n.* tiers-argent (silver 1, aluminum or nickel silver 2).
**drittens,** *adv.* thirdly, in the third place.

**dritthalb,** *a.* two and a half.
**drittrangig,** *a.* third-rate.
**droben,** *adv.* up there, above.
**Droge,** *f.* drug.
**Drogen-händler,** *m.* druggist. **-handlung,** *f.* drug business; drugstore. **-kunde, -lehre,** *f.* pharmacology. **-waren,** *f.pl.* drugs.
**Drogerie,** *f.* = Drogenhandlung. **-geschäft,** *n.* drug business, drug trade.
**Drogett, Droget,** *m.* drugget.
**Drogist,** *m.* druggist.
**Drogue, Droguett,** etc. see Droge, Drogett, etc.
**drohen,** *v.i.* threaten, menace.
**dröhnen,** *v.i.* rumble, boom, roar.
**drollig,** *a.* droll, comical.
**drosch,** *pret.* (of dreschen) thrashed.
**Drossel,** *f.* thrush (bird); throttle; (*Elec.*) choking coil. **-ader,** *f.* jugular vein. **-bein,** *n.* collar bone, clavicle. **-klappe,** *f.* (*Mach.*) throttle valve; damper.
**drosseln,** *v.t.* throttle; choke; baffle.
**Drossel-spule,** *f.* (*Elec.*) choke coil, choking coil, reactor. **-ventil,** *n.* throttle valve.
**D.R.P.,** *abbrev.* (deutsches Reichs-Patent) German patent; (Deutsche Reichspost) German Post.
**D.R.P. angem.,** *abbrev.* (deutsches Reichs-Patent angemeldet) German patent applied for.
**Dr.phil.,** *abbrev.* doctor of philosophy, Ph.D.
**drüben,** *adv.* over there, yonder.
**drüber,** *adv.* = darüber.
**Druck,** *m.* pressure; compression; oppression; impression, print, printing. **-abfall,** *m.*, **-abnahme,** *f.* fall in pressure. **-änderung,** *f.* change in pressure. **-ansatz,** *m.* (*Calico*) printing color, printing paste. **-anstieg,** *m.* rise in pressure. **-apparat,** *m.* pressure apparatus. **-behälter,** *m.* pressure reservoir. **-beuche,** *f.* bucking under pressure. **-birne,** *f.* a globular cistern for raising liquids by gas pressure, monte-jus, acid egg. **-blau,** *n.* (*Dyes*) printing blue. **-bombe,** *f.* pressure bomb. **-buchstabe,** *m.* type. **-destillation,** *f.* pressure distillation.
**druckdicht,** *a.* tight.
**Druck-einfluss,** *m.* influence of pressure. **-einheit,** *f.* unit of pressure. **-elektrizität,** *f.* piezoelectricity.
**drucken,** *v.t.* print; stamp.
**drücken,** *v.t.* press; squeeze; push; oppress.
**Druckentwickelung,** *f.* development of pressure.
**Drucker,** *m.* printer.
**Drücker,** *m.* trigger; handle; pusher.
**Druckerei,** *f.* printing; printing establishment; (*Calico*) print works.
**Druckerfarbe,** *f.* printer's ink.
**Druck-erhitzung,** *f.* heating under pressure. **-erhöhung,** *f.* increase of pressure. **-erniedrigung,** *f.* lowering of pressure.
**Druckerschwärze,** *f.* printer's ink.
**Druck-farbe,** *f.* printing color, printing ink. **-fehler,** *m.* misprint, typographical error.
**druckfest,** *a.* resistant to pressure.
**Druck-festigkeit,** *f.* resistance to pressure or compression, compression strength, crushing strength. **-filter,** *n.* pressure filter. **-firnis,** *m.* printer's varnish. **-flasche,** *f.* pressure bottle; aspirator. **-gärung,** *f.* pressure fermentation. **-gefälle,** *n.* pressure gradient; pressure drop. **-gefäss,** *n.* pressure vessel. **-heft,** *n.* pamphlet, booklet, brochure. **-höhe,** *f.* (*Mech.*) head. **-kattun,** *m.* printed calico. **-kessel,** *m.* (*Mach.*) pressure chamber. **-kleister,** *m.* printing starch. **-knopf,** *m.* push button. **-kocher,** *m.* pressure boiler. **-kolben,** *m.* pressure flask; (*Mach.*) piston, plunger. **-kraft,** *f.* compressive force, crushing stress. **-lack,** *m.* printers' lake. **-legung,** *f.* publishing; impression. **-leitung,** *f.* high-pressure piping. **-luft,** *f.* compressed air. **-luftkessel,** *m.* pressure tank. **-luftpumpe,** *f.* pump for compressing air, air compressor. **-maschine,** *f.* printing machine. **-messer,** *m.* pressure gage, manometer. **-messung,** *f.* pressure measurement. **-minderer,** *m.* pressure reducer. **-minderventil,** *m.* (pressure-reducing) valve. **-papier,** *n.* printing paper. **-platte,** *f.* printing plate, engraving. **-probe,** *f.* compression test; compression test specimen; pressure test; (of barley) squeezing test; (printer's) proof. **-prüfung,** *f.* pressure test(ing). **-pumpe,** *f.* pressure pump, force pump. **-regler,** *m.* pressure regulator. **-rohr,** *n.*, **-röhre,** *f.* pressure tube; force pipe. **-rückgang,** *m.* pressure drop. **-sache,** *f.* printed matter. **-schlauch,** *m.* pressure tubing; pressure hose. **-schmierung,** *f.* pressure lubrication, forced(-feed) lubrication. **-schraube,** *f.* pressure screw, setscrew; (*Aero.*) pusher propeller. **-schreiber,** *m.* pressure recorder, manograph. **-schrift,** *f.* publication; pamphlet; leaflet; print; type. **-schwarz,** *n.* (*Dyes*) printing black. **-seite,** *f.* (printed) page; compression face. **-spannung,** *f.* compressive stress. **-steigerung,** *f.* rise of pressure. **-stempel,** *m.* piston; pressure stamp. **-stock,** *m.* (*Printing*) cut, electro. **-stutzen,** *m.* pressure connection, pressure joint. **-ventil,** *n.* pressure valve, discharge valve. **-veränderung,** *f.* change in pressure. **-verfahren,** *n.* printing process. **-verminderung,** *f.* diminution or decrease of pressure. **-wage,** *f.* pressure balance. **-walze,** *f.* pressing (or pressure) roller (or roll, cylinder); printing roller. **-wasser,** *n.* pressure water, water under pressure.

**Druckwasser-.** hydraulic.
**Druck-welle,** *f.* pressure wave. **-zeug,** *n.* printing cloth. **-zunahme,** *f.* increase of pressure. **-zwiebel,** *f.* pressure bulb.
**Drudenfuss,** *m.* lycopodium, club moss.
**drum, drunter.** = darum, darunter.
**Drüschen,** *n.* small gland, glandule.
**Druse,** *f.* druse. — *pl.* **Drusen,** dregs, lees; husks; (*Med.*) strangles.
**Drüse,** *f.* gland.
**drusen,** *v.i.* become dreggy.
**Drüsen-.** glandular.
**drüsenartig,** *a.* glandular.
**Drusen-asche,** *f.* calcined (wine) lees. **-branntwein,** *m.* spirits distilled from fermented lees.
**drusenförmig,** *a.* drusy, drused.
**Drüsen-gewebe,** *n.* glandular tissue. **-krankheit,** *f.* gland disease; scrofula. **-kropf,** *m.* goiter.
**Drusenöl,** *m.* oil from dregs of wine, grapeseed oil.
**Drüsensaft,** *m.* glandular secretion.
**Drusenschwarz,** *n.* Frankfort black (from wine lees).
**Drüsensekret,** *n.* glandular secretion.
**drusig, drusicht,** *a.* drusy, drused.
**drüsig, drüsicht,** *a.* gland-like; glandular.
**d.s.,** *abbrev.* (dass sind) that is, i.e.
**Dschunke,** *f.* junk.
**dsgl.,** *abbrev.* (desgleichen) likewise, ditto.
**ds.J.,** *abbrev.* (dieses Jahres) of this year.
**Dtz., Dtzd.,** *abbrev.* (Dutzend) dozen.
**du,** *pron.* thou, you.
**d.U.,** *abbrev.* (der Unterzeichnete) the undersigned.
**dualistisch,** *a.* dualistic.
**dubbeln, dubben,** *v.t.* double; duplicate.
**Dübel,** *m.* pin, peg, plug, dowel, key.
**Dublett,** *n.* doublet.
**dublieren,** *v.t.* double; (*Metal.*) concentrate.
**Dublierstein,** *m.* concentrated metal, regulus.
**ducken,** *v.t.* humble. — *v.r.* duck; give in. — *v.i.* submit.
**Ducker,** *m.* siphon; one that ducks.
**Duckstein,** *m.* calcareous tufa.
**duff,** *a.* dull, dead.
**Duft,** *m.* odor; fragrance, perfume, aroma; vapor, exhalation.
**düfteln,** *v.i.* have a slight odor or fragrance.
**duften,** *v.i.* be fragrant; smell; sweat. — *v.t.* perfume.
**Duftessig,** *m.* aromatic vinegar.
**duftig,** *a.* fragrant, odorous; vaporous, misty.
**Duftigkeit,** *f.* = Duft; mistiness.
**duftlos,** *a.* odorless, inodorous.
**Duft-losigkeit,** *f.* lack of odor. **-öl,** *n.* fragrant oil, perfume oil.
**duftreich,** *a.* fragrant; odorous.
**Duftstoff,** *m.* odorous substance, aromatic principle, perfume.
**Dugongöl,** *n.* dugong oil.
**Düker,** *m.* siphon.
**Duktilität,** *f.* ductility.
**Dulcit,** *n.* dulcitol, dulcite.
**dulden,** *v.t.* bear, endure, suffer.
**Dulzin,** *n.* dulcin.
**Dulzit,** *n.* dulcitol, dulcite.
**dumm,** *a.* stupid, dull, silly.
**dumpf,** *a.* damp, musty; hollow; dull; close
**dumpfig,** *a.* musty, moldy, sultry.
**Dung,** *m.* manure, fertilizer; dung.
**dungartig,** *a.* dung-like, stercoraceous.
**Dünge-gips,** *m.* gypsum for manuring. **-jauche,** *f.* dung water, liquid manure. **-kalk,** *m.* manuring lime. **-mittel,** *n.* manure, fertilizer.
**düngen,** *v.t.* manure, fertilize.
**Düngepulver,** *n.* powdered manure.
**Dünger,** *m.* manure, fertilizer; dung. **-bedarf,** *m.* fertilizer requirement.
**Dungerde,** *f.* mold, humus, compost.
**Düngerfabrik,** *f.* fertilizer factory.
**düngerfordernd,** *a.* requiring fertilizer.
**Dünger-salz,** *n.* = Düngesalz. **-versuch,** *m.* fertilizer experiment. **-wert,** *m.* manurial value.
**Düngesalz,** *n.* saline manure, fertilizer salt.
**Dung-fabrik,** *f.* fertilizer factory. **-jauche,** *f.* dung water, liquid manure. **-mittel,** *n.* manure, fertilizer. **-pulver,** *n.* powdered manure, poudrette. **-salz,** *n.* saline manure, fertilizer salt.
**Düngung,** *f.* manuring, fertilizing.
**dunkel,** *a.* dark; dim, obscure.
**Dunkel,** *n.* dark, darkness, obscurity.
**dunkelblau,** *a.* dark blue.
**Dunkelbraun,** *n.* dark brown.
**dunkelfarbig,** *a.* dark-colored.
**Dunkel-färbung,** *f.* darkening. **-feld,** *n.* dark field, dark ground. **-feldbeleuchtung,** *f* dark-field illumination.
**dunkelgelb,** *a.* dark yellow.
**Dunkel-glühhitze,** *f.* = Dunkelrotglut. **-grau,** *n.* dark gray.
**dunkelgrün,** *a.* dark green.
**Dunkel-heit,** *f.* darkness; obscurity. **-kammer,** *f.* dark room; camera obscura.
**dunkeln,** *v.t.* & *i.* darken; deepen, sadden (colors).
**Dunkel-öl,** *n.* (*Petroleum*) black oil. **-raum,** *m.* dark space.
**dunkelrot,** *a.* dark red.
**Dunkelrot-glut,** *f.* dull red heat (above 700°). **-gültigerz, -giltigerz,** *n.* dark red silver ore (pyrargyrite).
**Dunkel-stellung,** *f.* (*Optics*) dark position. **-strahlung,** *f.* invisible radiation. **-strom,** *m.*

dark current. **-tran,** *m.* dark train oil, specif. dark brown cod oil.

**Dunkelungsbad,** *n.* (*Dyeing*) saddening liquor.

**dünken,** *v.i.* seem, appear.

**dünn,** *a.* thin; dilute, rare, slender, feeble.

**Dünnbier,** *n.* small beer.

**dünnblättrig,** *a.* thin-leaved, laminated.

**Dünndarm,** *m.* small intestine.

**Dünne,** *f.* thinness.

**dünnen,** *v.t.* thin.

**dünnflüssig,** *a.* thinly liquid, highly fluid; watery.

**Dünnflüssigkeit,** *f.* thinly liquid state.

**dünn-geschichtet,** *a.* in thin layers or strata. **-häutig,** *a.* thin-skinned; filmy.

**Dünn-heit,** *f.* thinness, diluteness, rarity, slenderness. **-maische,** *f.* (*Brewing*) thin mash. **-saft,** *m.* (*Sugar*) thin juice.

**dünn-schalig,** *a.* thin-skinned; thin-shelled. **-schlagen,** *v.t.* beat out, beat thin. **-schleifen,** *v.t.* grind thin.

**Dünnschliff,** *m.* thin section; veneer.

**dünnschuppig,** *a.* in thin scales.

**Dünnstein,** *m.* (*Metal.*) thin mat(te); (*Jewelry*) table stone.

**dünntafelig,** *a.* in thin plates.

**Dünnteer,** *m.* thin tar, fluid tar.

**dünn-walzen,** *v.t.* roll out, roll thin. **-wandig,** *a.* thin-walled.

**Dunst,** *m.* vapor; steam, fume, damp; smoke; haze; fine shot; flue dust. **-abzug,** *m.* hood (for fumes). **-abzugsrohr,** *n.* vent pipe.

**dunstartig,** *a.* vaporous.

**Dunst-bad,** *n.* vapor bath. **-bläschen,** *n.* bubble of vapor.

**dunsten,** *v.i.* evaporate, vaporize; smoke, fume, steam.

**dünsten,** *v.i.* steam, vapor, smoke. — *v.t.* stew.

**Dunst-essig,** *m.* aromatic vinegar. **-fang,** *m.* hood.

**dunstförmig,** *a.* vaporous.

**Dunsthülle,** *f.* vaporous envelope, atmosphere.

**dunstig, dünstig,** *a.* vaporous, vapory; steamy; foggy; misty, hazy; damp, moist.

**Dunstigkeit,** *f.* vaporousness; fogginess; dampness.

**Dunst-kreis,** *m.* atmosphere. **-loch,** *n.* vent; air hole.

**dunstlos,** *a.* vaporless, fumeless.

**Dunst-messer,** *m.* atmometer. **-mittel,** *n.* (*Leather*) mulling agent. **-rohr,** *n.* ventilating pipe.

**duplizieren,** *v.t.* duplicate, double.

**dupliziert,** *a.* duplicate, double.

**Duralblech,** *n.* duralumin sheet.

**durch,** *prep.* thru; by, owing to. — *adv.* thru.

**durch-.** thru, thru and thru, thoroly.

**durcharbeiten,** *v.t.* work, work thru, finish; knead (dough); elaborate; (*Dyeing*) pole.

**durchätzen,** *v.t.* eat thru, corrode.

**durchaus,** *adv.* thruout, completely, absolutely, by all means.

**durchbacken,** *v.t.* bake thoroly.

**durchbeissen,** *v.t.* bite thru, eat thru.

**durchbeizen,** *v.t.* corrode (thoroly or thru); steep thoroly.

**durchbelichten,** *v.t.* irradiate thoroly.

**durchbeuteln,** *v.t.* bolt (flour).

**durchbiegen,** *v.r.* sag, bend. — *v.t.* break by bending.

**Durchbiegung,** *f.* sagging; flexure; deflection.

**Durchbiegungsmesser,** *m.* deflectometer.

**durchbilden,** *v.t.* perfect, develop fully; design; construct.

**durchbittern,** *v.t.* make thoroly bitter.

**durchblasen,** *v.t.* blow thru; bubble.

**durchblättern,** *v.t.* turn the pages of, glance thru; split into lamellas.

**durchbläuen,** *v.t.* blue thoroly.

**durchblicken,** *v.t.* look thru; detect. — *v.i.* appear, become visible.

**durchbohren,** *v.t.* perforate; bore thru, punch; pierce; penetrate.

**Durchbohrung,** *f.* perforation; boring thru.

**durchbrechen,** *v.t.* break, break thru, cut, pierce, punch, perforate. — *v.i.* break thru, break out; appear; break. — **durchbrochen,** *p.a.* pierced, perforated, openwork.

**durchbrennen,** *v.t.* burn thru; burn thoroly; melt thru. — *v.i.* burn thru, burn out; (of machinery) race.

**durchbringen,** *v.t.* bring thru, put thru. — *v.r.* get along, manage.

**Durchbruch,** *m.* breaking out or thru; escape (of gas); irruption, eruption; opening, aperture, breach, crevasse; (*Brewing*) collapse (of the head).

**durchdampfen,** *v.t.* fill with vapor or fumes.

**durchdämpfen,** *v.t.* steam.

**durchdiffundieren,** *v.t. & i.* diffuse thru.

**durchdringbar,** *a.* permeable, penetrable.

**Durchdringbarkeit,** *f.* permeability, penetrability.

**durchdringen,** *v.t. & i.* penetrate; permeate, pervade; percolate. — **durchdringend,** *p.a.* penetrating, penetrative.

**durchdringlich,** *a.* permeable, pervious.

**Durchdringlichkeit,** *f.* penetrability, permeability.

**Durchdringung,** *f.* penetration; permeation.

**Durchdringungsvermögen,** *n.* penetrating power.

**durchdrücken,** *v.t.* = durchpressen.

**Durchdrungenheit,** *f.* (state of) permeation.

**durch-duften, -düften,** *v.t.* scent, perfume.

**durch-dunsten, -dünsten,** *v.t.* permeate with vapor. — *v.i.* pass thru as vapor.

**durcheinander,** *adv.* confusedly. **-schütteln,** *v.t.* shake (thoroly).

**Durchfahrt,** *f.* thorofare, passage, gateway.

**Durchfall,** *m.* screenings; diarrhea; failure.

**durchfallen,** *v.i.* fall thru; (of light) be transmitted; (of beer) clear; (of beer head) fall back; fail.

**durchfärbbar,** *a.* penetrable with color.

**Durchfärbemittel,** *n.* penetrating agent.

**durchfärben,** *v.t.* dye thoroly; color thruout; penetrate.

**Durchfärbevermögen,** *n.* penetrating power.

**durchfaulen,** *v.i.* rot thru, rot completely.

**durchfeuchten,** *v.t.* soak; saturate with moisture.

**durchfeuern,** *v.t.* fire or heat thoroly.

**durchfiltrieren, -filtern,** *v.t.* filter thru, filter.

**durchfliessen,** *v.i.* flow thru; diffuse.

**Durchfliessung,** *f.*, **Durchfluss,** *m.* flowing thru, flow; diffusion. **-geschwindigkeit,** *f.* rate of flow or diffusion. **-zeit,** *f.* time of flow (thru).

**durchforschen,** *v.t.* investigate thoroly.

**Durchforschung,** *f.* examination, investigation.

**durchfressen,** *v.t.* eat thru, corrode.

**durchfrieren,** *v.t.* freeze thru, chill.

**Durchfuhr,** *f.* transport, conveyance.

**durchführbar,** *a.* practicable, feasible.

**Durchführbarkeit,** *f.* practicability, feasibility.

**durchführen,** *v.t.* lead thru, convey thru; carry thru, execute, perform, accomplish, conduct; (*Tinplate*) dip, wash.

**Durchführung,** *f.* leading thru, etc. (see durchführen).

**Durchgabe,** *f.* filtration; transmission.

**Durchgang,** *m.* passage; duct; transit.

**durchgängig,** *a.* penetrable, permeable; thoro; general, usual.

**Durchgangs-hahn,** *m.* straightway cock. **-ventil,** *n.* straight-through valve, straightway valve.

**durchgären,** *v.i.* ferment thoroly.

**durchgeben,** *v.t.* filter, strain; transmit.

**durchgehen,** *v.i.* go thru; run away; (of light) be transmitted. — *v.t.* go thru, examine. — **— lassen,** let thru, pass thru. — **durchgehend,** *p.a.* piercing, pervading; passing thru; transmitted (light); thoro; continuous.

**durchgehends,** *adv.* thruout; generally.

**durchgerben,** *v.t.* tan thoroly.

**Durchgerbungszahl,** *f.* degree of tanning, tanning number.

**Durchgeseihtes,** *n.* filtrate.

**durchgiessen,** *v.t.* pour thru, filter, strain.

**durchglühen,** *v.t.* heat redhot; anneal thoroly.

**durchgreifen,** *v.i.* penetrate; act vigorously. — **durchgreifend,** *p.a.* penetrative; thoro; vigorous.

**Durchgriff,** *m.* penetration; thoro grasp.

**Durchguss,** *m.* filter, strainer; pouring thru, filtration; gutter; sink.

**Durchhang,** *m.* sag, dip, slack.

**durchhärten,** *v.t.* (*Metal.*) depth-harden.

**durchheizen, durchhitzen,** *v.t.* heat thoroly.

**durchkälten,** *v.t.* chill thoroly.

**durchklären,** *v.t.* clear or clarify thoroly.

**durchkneten,** *v.t.* knead thoroly.

**durchkochen,** *v.t.* boil thoroly.

**Durchkohlung,** *f.* (thoro) charring or carbonization.

**durchkommen,** *v.i.* come thru, get along, recover.

**durchkreuzen,** *v.t.* cross, traverse, intersect.

**durchkriechen,** *v.i.* & *t.* creep thru; penetrate.

**durchkühlen,** *v.t.* cool or chill thoroly.

**Durchlass,** *m.* filter, sieve; passage, opening; outlet; letting thru; transmission (as of light).

**durchlassen,** *v.t.* filter, strain; transmit (light, etc.); let thru; let pass.

**durchlässig,** *a.* permeable, pervious, penetrable.

**Durchlässigkeit,** *f.* permeability, perviousness; transmittancy.

**Durchlassung,** *f.* filtering, etc. (see lassen); (of light, etc.) transmission.

**Durchlauf,** *m.* sieve, colander; running thru, flow, passage; (*Med.*) diarrhea.

**durchlaufen,** *v.i.* filter; run thru, flow thru. — — *v.t.* run thru, pass thru, traverse. — **durchlaufend,** *p.a.* continuous.

**Durchläufermineral,** *n.* mineral occurring in all zones.

**Durchlauf-messer,** *m.* meter (for water, gas, etc.). **-öl,** *n.* flux oil (for asphalt).

**durchlaugen,** *v.t.* lye or lixiviate thoroly.

**durchläutern,** *v.t.* purify or refine thoroly.

**durchleiten,** *v.t.* pass thru, conduct.

**durchleuchten,** *v.t.* illuminate; irradiate. — *v.i.* shine thru; transmit light. — **durchleuchtend,** *p.a.* transparent; translucent.

**Durchleuchtung,** *f.* illumination; irradiation; light transmission; fluoroscopy.

**durchlochen,** *v.t.* perforate, punch; core (fruit).

**durchlöchern,** *v.t.* perforate; pierce, punch.

**durchlüften,** *v.t.* ventilate, air, aerate.

**durchlüftungsfähig,** *a.* capable of ventilation or aëration.

**durchmachen,** *v.t.* go thru; experience.

**durchmengen,** *v.t.* mix thoroly; intermix.

**durchmessen,** *v.t.* pass thru, traverse, measure.

**Durchmesser,** *m.* diameter.

**durchmischen,** *v.t.* mix thoroly; intermix; blend.

**durchmustern,** *v.t.* examine closely, scrutinize; inspect, review, scan, explore.

**durchnässen,** *v.t.* wet thoroly, soak, steep.

**durchnehmen,** *v.t.* go over, criticize.

**durchnetzen,** *v.t.* = durchnässen.

**durchölen,** *v.t.* oil (thoroly).
**durchpatentieren,** *v.t.* (*Wire*) patent by passing through a furnace and then cooling.
**durchperlen,** *v.i.* bubble thru.
**durchpressen,** *v.t.* & *i.* press thru, force thru, squeeze thru; strain, filter.
**Durchprüfung,** *f.* thoro testing or examining.
**durchqueren,** *v.t.* traverse, cross.
**durchquetschen,** *v.t.* = durchpressen.
**durchräuchern,** *v.t.* fumigate; smoke thoroly.
**durchrechnen,** *v.t.* calculate; recalculate, check.
**durchreiben,** *v.t.* rub thru, strain; chafe, gall.
**durchreissen,** *v.t.* & *i.* tear asunder, break.
**durchrosten,** *v.i.* rust thru, rust completely.
**durchrösten,** *v.t.* roast thoroly.
**durchrühren,** *v.t.* stir thoroly, agitate.
**durchsättigen,** *v.t.* saturate.
**Durchsatz,** *m.* throughput (of a furnace, etc.); infiltration; diffusion.
**durchsäuern,** *v.t.* acidify; make sour; leaven thoroly.
**durchsaugen,** *v.t.* suck thru, force thru by suction.
**durchscheinen,** *v.i.* shine thru. — **durchscheinend,** *p.a.* translucent; transparent.
**durchschiessen,** *v.t.* shoot thru; insert; interleave; interline. — *v.i.* shoot (thru).
**Durchschlag,** *m.* filter, strainer; screen, sieve; punch, drift, piercer; opening; puncture; rupture; carbon copy. **-boden,** *m.* perforated bottom.
**durchschlagen,** *v.t.* filter, strain; sieve; punch, puncture, perforate; rupture; beat thru; traverse. — *v.i.* get thru, penetrate; (of paper) blot; (*Elec.*) spark; act.
**Durchschlag-festigkeit,** *f.* (*Elec.*) dielectric strength, disruptive strength. **-papier,** *n.* copying paper, carbon paper.
**Durchschlagskraft,** *f.* piercing, perforating or penetrating effect; (*Paper*) puncture resistance.
**Durchschlagspannung,** *f.* breakdown voltage, disruptive voltage.
**durchschmelzen,** *v.t.* & *i.* melt thru; melt or fuse thoroly.
**Durchschmelzung,** *f.* melting thru or thoroly; internal seal.
**durchschmieren,** *v.t.* grease or lubricate thoroly.
**durchschmolzen,** *p.p.* of durchschmelzen.
**durchschneiden,** *v.t.* intersect, cross; cut thru; pierce; cut across; traverse, cross.
**Durchschnitt,** *m.* cut, section; intersection; average, mean.
**durchschnittlich,** *a.* average. — *adv.* on an average.
**Durchschnitts-bestimmung,** *f.* average determination. **-ertrag,** *m.* average yield; average profit. **-muster,** *n.* average sample. **-probe,** *f.* average sample. **-punkt,** *m.* point of intersection. **-temperatur,** *f.* mean temperature. **-wert,** *m.* average value. **-zahl,** *f.* mean.
**Durchschreibpapier,** *n.* copying paper, carbon paper.
**Durchschrift,** *f.* carbon copy.
**Durchschuss,** *m.* woof, weft; interleaf; (*Printing*) white space, blank.
**durchschütteln,** *v.t.* shake thoroly, agitate.
**durchschwängern,** *v.t.* impregnate thoroly.
**durchschwefeln,** *v.t.* sulfur(ize) thoroly.
**durchschwelen,** *v.i.* smolder. — *v.t.* cause to smolder.
**durchschwitzen,** *v.i.* sweat, ooze thru.
**durch-seigen, -seigern, -seihen,** *v.t.* strain, filter, percolate.
**Durchseiher,** *m.* strainer, filter, percolator.
**Durchseihung,** *f.* straining, filtration, percolation.
**durchsetzen,** *v.t.* permeate, infiltrate; disseminate; (*Min.*) intermingle; (*Mining*) sieve, sift; intersect; carry thru, put thru.
**Durchsicht,** *f.* looking thru, view, inspection, revision; undertone (of a color); transparency. — **in der —,** by transmitted light.
**durchsichtbar,** *a.* transparent.
**durchsichtig,** *a.* transparent; clear.
**Durchsichtigkeit,** *f.* transparency; clearness.
**Durchsichts-bild,** *n.* (*Photog.*) diapositive. **-farbe,** *f.* transmitted color; transparent color.
**durchsickern,** *v.i.* & *r.* trickle thru, ooze thru, filter thru, percolate. — *v.t.* strain, filter.
**durchsieben,** *v.t.* sift, sieve, screen, bolt.
**durchsieden,** *v.t.* boil thoroly.
**durchsintern,** *v.i.* trickle thru, percolate.
**durchspülen,** *v.t.* rinse well, wash well.
**durchstechen,** *v.t.* pierce, stab, cut; (*Metal.*) smelt.
**Durchstich,** *m.* piercing, cutting, cut; excavation.
**durchstossen,** *v.t.* push thru, punch, pierce.
**durchstrahlen,** *v.i.* radiate thru, shine thru. — *v.t.* penetrate with rays, irradiate.
**Durchstrahlung,** *f.* penetration with rays, irradiation.
**durchstreichen,** *v.t.* run thru, go thru; sift, screen; cross out. — **durchstreichende Linie,** trajectory.
**durchströmen,** *v.t.* stream thru, flow thru.
**Durchströmung,** *f.* streaming thru; perfusion.
**durchsuchen,** *v.t.* search thru, examine closely.
**durchsüssen,** *v.t.* sweeten thoroly; edulcorate.
**durchtränken,** *v.t.* saturate, impregnate, infiltrate.
**Durchtränkung,** *f.* saturation, impregnation.
**durchtreiben,** *v.t.* drive or force thru; specif., distil. — **durchtrieben,** *p.a.* cunning, sly.
**durchtrocknen,** *v.t.* & *i.* dry thoroly.
**Durchvulkanisation,** *f.* thoro vulcanization.

**durchwachsen,** *v.t. & i.* grow thru. — *v.r.* interpenetrate, intermingle.
**durchwandern,** *v.i.* pass thru; diffuse.
**Durchwanderung,** *f.* passing thru; diffusion.
**durchwärmen,** *v.t.* warm or heat thoroly, heat moderately till the temperature is equalized.
**durchwärmig,** *a.* diathermic.
**Durchwärmigkeit,** *f.* diathermancy.
**Durchwärmzeit,** *f.* time required for equalization of temperature on heating.
**durchwaschen,** *v.t.* wash thru; wash thoroly.
**durchwässern,** *v.t.* soak, drench.
**durchweg,** *adv.* thruout.
**durchweichen,** *v.t. & i.* soften; soak, steep.
**Durchweichungsgrube,** *f.* (*Metal.*) soaking pit.
**durchwerfen,** *v.t.* sift, screen, bolt; traject.
**Durchwurf,** *m.* sieve, screen, riddle; screenings.
**Durchzeichenpapier,** *n.* tracing paper.
**durchzeichnen,** *v.t.* trace.
**durchziehen,** *v.t.* draw thru; intermix; traverse; penetrate. — *v.r.* pass thru.
**Durchzieh-glas,** *n.* (*Micros.*) slide. **-lassen,** *n.* allowing penetration (as of heat).
**Durchzug,** *m.* passage; circulation; draft; girder.
**dürfen,** *v.i.* be permitted; need; dare; be likely; may.
**durfte,** *pret.* of dürfen.
**dürftig,** *a.* scanty, poor; needy.
**Duro-chinon,** *n.* duroquinone. **-hydrochinon,** *n.* durohydroquinone.
**Durol,** *n.* durene.
**dürr,** *a.* dry, arid; dried, withered, dead; barren, sterile, lean; plain.
**Dürre,** *f.* dryness, etc. (see dürr); drought.
**Durst,** *m.* thirst.
**dursten, dürsten,** *v.i.* be thirsty.
**durstig,** *a.* thirsty; eager.
**Düse,** *f.* nozzle, twyer (or tuyère), blast pipe; jet; tip, head (of a burner); die (for wire-drawing or the like).
**Düsen-regler,** *m.* nozzle regulator. **-rohr,** *n.* blast pipe.
**düster,** *a.* dark, dusky; gloomy, sad.
**Düte, Dute,** *f.* = Tüte.
**Dütenpapier,** *n.* bag paper.
**Dutzend,** *n.* dozen.
**Dynamik,** *f.* dynamics.
**dynamisch,** *a.* dynamic.
**dystektisch,** *a.* dystectic.
**Dz., dz.,** *abbrev.* (Doppelzentner) double centner, 100 kilograms.

# E

**E.,** *abbrev.* (Erstarrungspunkt) freezing point.
**Ebbe,** *f.* ebb, ebb tide.
**ebd.,** *abbrev.* (ebenda) in the same place.
**eben,** *a.* even; plane; level; flat, smooth. — *adv.* evenly; exactly; even, just.
**Eben,** *n.* ebony. **-baum,** *m.* ebony tree.
**Ebenbild,** *n.* image, likeness.
**ebenbürtig,** *a.* equal, equally good; equal in birth or rank.
**ebenda,** *adv.* in the same place, *ibidem.*
**ebendort,** *adv.* at that place, there, *ibidem.*
**Ebene,** *f.* plane; level; plain.
**ebenen,** *v.t.* level, flatten, smooth, plane.
**Ebenenormale,** *f.* normal to (a, the) plane.
**ebenerwähnt,** *a.* just-mentioned.
**ebenfalls,** *adv.* likewise, also, equally.
**ebenflächig,** *a.* flat-surfaced, plane.
**Ebenheit,** *f.* evenness, etc. (see eben).
**Ebenholz,** *n.* ebony.
**ebenieren,** *v.t.* ebonize.
**Ebenmass,** *n.* symmetry; harmony. **-fläche,** *f.* plane of symmetry.
**ebenmässig,** *a.* symmetrical, proportionate.
**ebenso,** *adv.* just so, just as, likewise.
**ebensogut,** *adv.* just as well.
**ebensolch,** *a.* similar, like, of the same kind.
**ebensoviel,** *a.* just as much, as much, as many.
**ebensowenig,** *adv.* just as little.
**Eber,** *m.* boar; hog. **-esche,** *f.* mountain ash, service tree. **-raute,** *f.* southernwood, abrotanum (*Artemisia abrotanum*). **-wurz, -wurzel,** *f.* carline thistle (*Carlina*); carline root.
**Ebne,** *n.* plane; plain.
**ebnen,** *v.t.* level, flatten, smooth, plane.
**ebullieren,** *v.i.* boil up; break out.
**ebullioskopisch,** *a.* ebullioscopic.
**Ecballiumsäure,** *f.* ecballic acid.
**Echappé-Öl,** *n.* recovered oil.
**echt,** *a.* genuine, true, real; pure, unadulterated; (of colors) fast; ingrain.
**Echt-base,** *f.* (*Dyeing*) fast color base. **-baumwollblau,** *n.* fast cotton blue. **-blau,** *n.* fast blue. **-braun,** *n.* fast brown. **-färben,** *n.* fast dyeing.
**echtfarbig,** *a.* fast-dyed.
**Echt-gelb,** *n.* fast yellow. **-grün,** *n.* fast green.
**Echtheit,** *f.* genuineness, etc. (see echt).
**Echtheits-grad,** *m.* (*Dyeing*) degree of fastness. **-prüfung,** *f.* (*Dyeing*) fastness test.
**Echt-rot,** *n.* fast red. **-säurefuchsin,** *n.* fast acid fuchsine. **-schwarz,** *n.* fast black.
**Eck,** *n.* angle; summit (of a crystal).
**Ecke,** *f.* corner, angle; edge (plane angle); summit (of a crystal); quoin.
**Eckeisen,** *n.* angle iron; (*Metal.*) angular iron.
**Ecker,** *f.* acorn; beechnut. **-doppe,** *f.* acorn cup.
**Eckholz,** *n.* squared timber.
**eckig,** *a.* angular, cornered, angled; awkward.
**Ecrasement,** *m.* crushing.
**Ecrüseide,** *f.* raw silk.
**edel,** *a.* noble (as applied to metals, resisting oxidation, as gold and the platinum metals and, to a lesser extent, silver and some others; as applied to gases, inert, as argon); rare (as earths); precious (stones, etc.); (*Mining*) rich; vital (organs, parts).
**Edel-erde,** *f.* rare earth. **-erz,** *n.* rich ore, ore containing precious metals. **-faser,** *f.* staple fiber, staple rayon. **-galmei,** *m.* smithsonite. **-gamander,** *m.* wall germander (*Teucrium chamaedrys*). **-gas,** *n.* noble gas, inert gas, rare gas (any gas of the argon group). **-gasschale,** *f.* shell of an inert gas, completed shell (of electrons). **-glanz,** *m.* a special lustrous finish on metal, paper, or the like. **-holz,** *n.* fine wood. **-kastanie,** *f.* Spanish chestnut (*Castanea sativa*). **-kunstharz,** *n.* fine plastic, cast resin. **-metall,** *n.* noble or precious metal (see edel).
**edelmütig,** *a.* noble, generous.
**Edel-pelz,** *m.* genuine fur, valuable fur. **-porzellan,** *n.* hard porcelain. **-rost,** *m.* patina, aerugo nobilis. **-salze,** *n.pl.* = Abraumsalze. **-schrott,** *m.* pure scrap (metal). **-spat,** *m.* adularia. **-stahl,** *m.* refined steel; specif., any of certain superior alloy steels. **-stein,** *m.* precious stone, gem, jewel. **-tanne,** *f.* any of certain firs, esp. silver fir (*Abies alba* and *A. pectinata*). **-tannenöl,** *n.* silver fir oil.
**edieren,** *v.t.* edit; publish.
**edulkorieren,** *v.t.* edulcorate, wash.
**Efeu,** *m.* ivy.
**Effekt,** *m.* effect; power; security (stock, bond, etc.).
**effektiv,** *a.* effective; efficient. — *adv.* actually.
**Effektivwert,** *m.* effective value.
**Effektkohle,** *f.* carbon for flame arc.
**efferveszieren,** *v.i.* effervesce.
**effloreszieren,** *v.i.* effloresce.
**Effluvien,** *n.pl.* effluvia.
**Eg.,** *abbrev.* (Eisessig) glacial acetic acid.
**egal,** *a.* equal; even (colors).
**egalisieren,** *v.t.* equalize; level, flatten;

straighten. — *v.i.* (*Dyeing*) dye evenly, dye level.

**Egalisierer,** *m.* equalizer; (*Dyeing*) leveling agent.

**Egalisier-farbstoff,** *m.* leveling dye. **-lack,** *m.* (*Leather*) top coat.

**Egalisierung,** *f.* equalization, etc. (see egalisieren).

**Egalität,** *f.* equality, evenness, uniformity.

**Egel,** *m.* leech.

**Egge,** *f.* harrow; selvage.

**eggen,** *v.t.* harrow.

**Egoutteur,** *m.* (*Paper*) dandy roll.

**egrainieren, egrenieren,** *v.t* gin (cotton).

**Egreniermaschine,** *f.* (cotton) gin.

**ehe,** *conj.* before, ere.

**Ehe,** *f.* matrimony, marriage.

**ehedem,** *adv.* formerly.

**ehemalig,** *a.* former, past, late.

**ehemals,** *adv.* formerly.

**eher,** *adv.* sooner, earlier, rather.

**ehern,** *a.* brazen of brass, of bronze.

**eheste,** *a.* soonest, next. — **am ehesten,** most nearly; soonest, first.

**ehm.,** *abbrev.* (ehemals) formerly.

**ehmalig,** etc. see ehemalig, etc.

**ehrbar,** *a.* honorable; reputable; modest.

**Ehrbegierde,** *f.* ambition.

**Ehre,** *f.* honor; character; reputation.

**ehren,** *v.t.* honor; esteem.

**Ehren-.** honorary, honorable, honor.

**ehrenhaft,** *a.* honorable.

**Ehren-mitglied,** *n.* honorary member. **-preis,** *m.* speedwell, veronica; prize. **-rettung,** *f.* vindication; apology. **-stelle,** *f.* honor, preferment.

**ehren-voll,** *a.* honorable, creditable. **-wert,** *a.* honorable, respectable.

**Ehrgeiz,** *m.* ambition.

**ehrlich,** *a.* honest, fair, honorable, decent.

**Ei,** *n.* egg; ovum. **-albumin,** *n.* egg albumin, ovalbumin.

**Eibe,** *f.* yew.

**Eibisch,** *m.* marsh mallow (the plant). **-wurzel,** *f.* marsh mallow root. **-zucker,** *m.* marshmallow (the confection).

**Eich-amt,** *n* gaging office, office of weights and measures. **-apfel,** *m.* oak gall, gall nut. **-baum,** *m.* oak tree.

**Eiche,** *f.* oak; gage, standard.

**Eichel,** *f.* acorn; glans penis. **-doppe,** *f.* acorn cup.

**eichelförmig,** *a.* acorn-shaped, glandiform.

**Eichel-kernöl,** *n.* acorn oil. **-stärke,** *f.* acorn starch. **-zucker,** *m.* acorn sugar, quercitol.

**eichen,** *a.* oak, oaken.

**eichen,** *v.t.* gage, measure, standardize, calibrate; test or adjust (weights or measures).

**Eichen,** *n.* little egg; ovule; gaging, calibration. **-gallapfel,** *m.*, **-galle,** *f.* oak gall. **-gerbsäure,** *f.*, **-gerbstoff,** *m.* quercitannic acid, oak tannin. **-holz,** *n.* oak wood, oak. **-kern,** *m.* acorn. **-lohe,** *f.* tanbark (from oak). **-mehl,** *n.* powdered oak bark. **-rinde,** *f.* oak bark. **-rindengerbsäure,** *f.* quercitannic acid. **-rot,** *n.* oak red. **-samen,** *m.* acorn.

**Eicher,** *m.* gager.

**eichfähig,** *a.* capable of adjustment.

**Eich-gas,** *n.* standard gas. **-gerät,** *n.* calibrating apparatus. **-holz,** *n.* oak wood, oak. **-kurve,** *f.* calibration curve. **-mass,** *n.* gage, standard (measure). **-meister,** *m.* gager, adjuster. **-nagel,** *m.* gage mark. **-punkt,** *m.* reference point. **-schein,** *m.* certificate (that an instrument has been standardized).

**Eichung,** *f.* gaging, etc. (see eichen, *v.t.*).

**Eichwert,** *m.* reference value, standard value.

**Eid,** *m.* oath.

**Eidechse,** *f.* lizard.

**Eidgenoss,** *m.* confederate, ally.

**Eidotter,** *m.* egg yolk. **-fett,** *n.* lecithin.

**Eier,** *n.pl.* eggs. **-albumin,** *n.* egg albumin, ovalbumin. **-dotter,** *m.* yolk of eggs. **-drüse,** *f.* corpus luteum. **-frucht,** *f.* eggplant. **-gang,** *m.* oviduct. **-öl,** *n.* egg-yolk oil, egg oil. **-pulver,** *n.* egg powder, custard powder. **-schale,** *f.* egg shell. **-schalenglanz,** *m.* egg-shell luster. **-stein,** *m.* oölite, egg stone.

**eiersteinartig,** *a.* oölitic.

**Eier-stock,** *m.* ovary. **-weiss,** *n.* white of eggs.

**Eifer,** *m.* zeal, eagerness, passion. **-sucht,** *f.* jealousy; rivalry; envy.

**eiförmig,** *a.* egg-shaped, oval, ovoid.

**eifrig,** *a.* zealous, earnest, ardent, eager.

**eig.,** *abbrev.* (eigentlich) proper; properly; (eigen, eigene, etc.) see eigen.

**Eig.,** *abbrev.* (Eigenschaft) property.

**Eigelb,** *n.* egg yolk.

**eigen,** *a.* own, individual, proper, characteristic, intrinsic, inherent, specific, special, true, self-, idio-, auto-; odd; exact.

**Eigenart,** *f.* peculiarity, individuality.

**eigenartig,** *a.* peculiar; singular; individual; original, unique.

**Eigen-artigkeit,** *f.* peculiarity. **-atmung,** *f.* autorespiration (of yeast). **-belastung,** *f.* dead load, dead weight. **-bewegung,** *f.* proper motion, individual motion. **-dämpfung,** *f.* self-damping. **-drehimpuls,** *m.* proper (or characteristic) angular momentum. **-drehung,** *f.* proper rotation. **-farbe,** *f.* proper color, intrinsic color, natural color.

**eigenfarbig,** *a.* self-colored, colored.

**Eigen-farbstoff,** *m.* self-dye, self-color. **-form,** *f.* characteristic form, true form. **-frequenz,** *f.* proper, characteristic, or natural frequency. **-funktion,** *f.* proper function, characteristic function, "eigenfunktion." **-gewicht,** *n.*

specific gravity; its own weight; dead weight; proper weight.
**eigenhändig,** *a.* with one's own hand.
**Eigenlast,** *f.* dead load, dead weight.
**eigenmächtig,** *a.* arbitrary; despotic.
**Eigen-mittel,** *n.* (*Med.*) specific remedy; private means. **-name,** *m.* proper name.
**eigennützig,** *a.* selfish.
**eigens,** *adv.* expressly.
**Eigenschaft,** *f.* property; quality; characteristic.
**Eigenschaftswort,** *n.* adjective; epithet.
**Eigenschwingung,** *f.* proper, natural or characteristic vibration.
**eigenschwingungsfrei,** *a.* aperiodic, deadbeat.
**Eigen-sinn,** *m.* wilfulness, stubbornness. **-spannung,** *f.* internal stress; (*Elec.*) natural voltage. **-strahlung,** *f.* proper or characteristic radiation; fluorescent radiation.
**eigentlich,** *a.* proper, true, real, intrinsic; actual, itself, themselves. — *adv.* properly, really.
**Eigentum,** *n.* property.
**eigentümlich,** *a.* characteristic; peculiar; inherent; specific.
**Eigentümlichkeit,** *f.* characteristic; peculiarity.
**Eigen-vergiftung,** *f.* autointoxication. **-vergrösserung,** *f.* natural size, actual size. **-viskosität,** *f.* specific viscosity. **-volumen,** *n.* its own volume, individual volume. **-wärme,** *f.* specific heat; body heat. **-wert,** *m.* proper, characteristic or inherent value, "eigenwert." **-zündung,** *f.* self-ignition, compression ignition. **-zustand,** *m.* proper or characteristic state.
**Eigg.,** *abbrev.* (Eigenschaften) properties.
**eignen,** *v.t.* suit, qualify; appropriate. — *v.r.* be qualified, be suited, be adapted. — **geeignet,** *p.a.* suited, adapted, suitable, fit, proper.
**Eignung,** *f.* qualification, adaptation; suitability; aptitude.
**eigtl.,** *abbrev.* of eigentlich.
**Eiklar,** *n.* egg white, glair.
**Eikosan,** *n.* eicosane, icosane, eikosane.
**Eil-.** quick, fast, express.
**Eiland,** *n.* island.
**Eile,** *f.* haste; speed.
**eilen,** *v.i.* hasten, hurry.
**eilfertig,** *a.* hasty.
**Eilgut,** *n.* rapid-transit goods; fast freight; express goods.
**eilig,** *a.* hasty, speedy.
**Eilzug,** *m.* express train, fast train.
**Eimer,** *m.* bucket, pail.
**Eimerchen,** *n.* little pail, small liquid container.
**ein,** *a.* a, an; one.
**ein,** *adv.* in, within, into; (of an electric switch) on.
**ein-, Ein-.** one-, single, mono-, uni-.
**einachsig,** *a.* uniaxial.
**einander,** *adv.* one another, each other.
**einarmig,** *a.* one-armed.
**einäschern,** *v.t.* incinerate, calcine; burn to ashes.
**Einäscherung,** *f.* incineration, calcination.
**einatembar,** *a.* respirable.
**einatmen,** *v.t.* inhale.
**Einatmung,** *f.* inhalation.
**einatomar, einatomig,** *a.* monatomic.
**Einatomigkeit,** *f.* monatomicity.
**einätzen,** *v.t.* etch.
**Einätzung,** *f.* etching.
**einäugig,** *a.* monocular; one-eyed.
**Einbad-.** one-bath, single-bath, one-dip.
**einbadig,** *a.* single-bath.
**Einbad-schwarz,** *n.* (*Dyeing*) one-dip black. **-verfahren,** *n.* single-bath process.
**einbalgen,** *v.t.* encyst.
**einbalsamieren,** *v.t.* embalm.
**Einbalsamierung,** *f.* embalmment.
**Einband,** *m.* binding; cover.
**einbasisch, einbasig,** *a.* monobasic.
**Einbau,** *m.* building in; installation.
**einbauen,** *v.t.* build in; fit in; install.
**einbegreifen,** *v.t.* include; imply.
**einbehalten,** *v.t.* keep back, retain.
**einbeizen,** *v.t.* etch in.
**einbetonieren,** *v.t.* embed, or set, in concrete.
**einbetten,** *v.t.* embed, bed, set, mount.
**Einbettung,** *f.* embedding, bedding, mounting.
**einbeziehen,** *v.t.* = hineinziehen.
**einbiegen,** *v.t.* bend in, turn down, deflect. — *v.r.* sag.
**Einbiegung,** *f.* curvature, inflection.
**einbilden,** *v.r.* imagine, think; pride oneself. — **eingebildet,** *p.a.* imaginary; conceited.
**Einbildung,** *f.* imagination, fancy.
**einbinden,** *v.t.* bind, bind in, fasten, tie up.
**einblasen,** *v.t.* blow in, blow into, insufflate, bubble thru, inject (gas).
**einblauen, einbläuen,** *v.t.* blue.
**einblenden,** *v.t.* focus, concentrate (rays).
**Einblick,** *m.* insight; eyepiece.
**Einbrand,** *m.* burning in, burn, brand; penetration. **-tiefe,** *f.* depth of burn or fusion.
**einbrechen,** *v.i.* break (into); break (in); begin. — *v.t.* break in.
**Einbrennemaille,** *f.* baking (or stoving) enamel.
**einbrennen,** *v.t.* burn in; heat up; bake, stove (enamels); anneal (colors); cauterize; brand; sulfur, match (casks).
**Einbrenn-farbe,** *f.* ceramic color. **-firnis,** *m.* stoving varnish; baking lacquer or enamel. **-kunst,** *f.* encaustic art. **-lack,** *m.* stoving lacquer or enamel.
**einbringen,** *v.t.* bring in, get in, yield; insert, introduce.

**Einbruch,** *m.* breaking in; break; penetration; breaking down; burglary.
**einbrühen,** *v.t.* steep in boiling water, scald.
**einbürgern,** *v.t.* adopt; naturalize. — *v.r.* gain vogue, come into use; become naturalized.
**Einbusse,** *f.* loss, damage.
**einbüssen,** *v.t.* lose.
**Eindampfapparat,** *m.* evaporating apparatus.
**eindampfen,** *v.i.* become thickened by evaporation, boil down.
**eindampfen, eindämpfen,** *v.t.* evaporate, concentrate by evaporation, boil down, inspissate; steam; smoke.
**Eindampfen,** *n.* = Eindampfung.
**Eindampfer,** *m.* evaporator, concentrator.
**Eindampf-gerät,** *n.* evaporator. **-schale,** *f.* evaporating dish or pan, evaporator.
**Eindampfung, Eindämpfung,** *f.* evaporation, etc. (see eindampfen).
**eindecken,** *v.t.* cover.
**Eindecker,** *m.* (*Aero.*) monoplane.
**Eindeckung,** *f.* covering; roofing.
**eindellen,** *v.t.* dent.
**eindeutig,** *a.* plain, clear, unequivocal, unambiguous, well-defined.
**eindichten,** *v.t.* condense.
**Eindickanlage,** *f.* concentrating plant.
**eindickbar,** *a.* capable of being thickened or concentrated.
**Eindicke,** *f.* thickening, concentration, inspissation.
**eindicken,** *v.t.* thicken, concentrate, inspissate.
**Eindicker,** *m.* thickener.
**Eindickung,** *f.* thickening; concentration; inspissation; livering (of paints); bodying (of oils).
**Eindickungsmittel,** *n.* thickening agent.
**eindimensional,** *a.* unidimensional.
**eindorren,** *v.i.* shrink in drying; dry up.
**eindrängen,** *v.t.* force in, intrude.
**Eindrehschnecke,** *f.* (*Mach.*) feed screw.
**eindringen,** *v.t.* press in, penetrate, infiltrate.
**eindringlich,** *a.* impressive; forcible.
**Eindringtiefe,** *f.* (depth of) penetration.
**Eindringungs-fähigkeit,** *f.* penetrativity. **-tiefe,** *f.* (depth of) penetration.
**Eindruck,** *m.* impression; imprint; indentation.
**eindrucken,** *v.t.* (*Calico*) block in, ground in.
**eindrücken,** *v.t.* imprint, impress, stamp; crush in; flatten; press, compress.
**Eindruck-farbe,** *f.* (*Calico*) grounding in. **-messer,** *m.* penetrometer.
**eindunsten, eindünsten,** *v.t.* evaporate down, concentrate by evaporation; impregnate with vapor. — *v.i.* evaporate down.
**Eindunstung,** *f.* evaporation; impregnation with vapor.
**einebnen,** *v.t.* level, even up, grade, flatten.
**ein-einwertig,** *a.* uni-univalent.
**einen,** *v.t.* & *r.* unite.
**einengen,** *v.t.* concentrate; compress, confine, narrow, contract.
**einer,** *pron.* one.
**Einer,** *m.* unit, digit.
**einerlei,** *a.* of one kind, all the same. — **— ob,** regardless of whether.
**einerseits,** *adv.* on the one hand; on one side.
**einfach,** *a.* simple; single; elementary; primary (colors); plain. — **einfacher Körper,** simple or elementary substance, element.
**einfach-.** (in old names of compounds) proto- (mono-; -ous). — **— -Bromjod,** iodine monobromide. — **— -Chlorjod,** iodine monochloride. — **— -Chlorschwefel,** protochloride of sulfur (sulfur monochloride). — **— -Chlorzinn,** protochloride of tin (stannous chloride). — **— -Schwefeleisen,** protosulfide of iron (ferrous sulfide). — **— -Schwefelmetall,** protosulfide (monosulfide; -ous sulfide). — **— -Schwefelzinn,** protosulfide of tin (stannous sulfide).
**einfach-brechend,** *a.* singly refracting. **-frei,** *a.* having one degree of freedom, univariant.
**Einfachheit,** *f.* simplicity; singleness.
**einfach-kohlensauer,** *a.* neutral carbonate of. **-schwefligsauer,** *a.* neutral sulfite of. **-weinsauer,** *a.* neutral tartrate of. **-wirkend,** *p.a.* single-acting.
**einfädeln,** *v.t.* thread; contrive.
**einfädig,** *a.* unifilar.
**einfahren,** *v.t.* carry in, get in, break in, break.
**Einfahrt,** *f.* entrance.
**Einfall,** *m.* falling in, fall, decay, inroad, idea; (*Physics*) incidence.
**einfallen,** *v.i.* fall upon, fall in, interrupt, occur; (*Mining*) dip; (*Optics*) be incident. — **einfallend,** *p.a.* (*Optics*) incident.
**Einfalls-lot,** *n.* perpendicular, ordinate. **-strahl,** *m.* incident ray. **-winkel,** *m.* angle of incidence.
**Einfalt,** *f.* simplicity, simpleness.
**Einfang,** *m.* capture; enclosure.
**einfangen,** *v.t.* capture, catch, seize.
**Einfangung,** *f.* capture (as of an electron).
**einfärben,** *v.t.* color or dye or stain well; dye in the grain; ink.
**einfarbig,** *a.* of one color, monochromatic.
**Einfärbung,** *f.* coloring, etc. (see einfärben).
**einfassen,** *v.t.* enclose, fill, case, barrel; bind, trim, set; border; surround.
**einfetten,** *v.t.* grease, oil; lubricate.
**Einfettung,** *f.* greasing, oiling; lubrication.
**einfeuchten,** *v.t.* moisten, dampen, wet.
**einfinden,** *v.r.* appear.
**Einfl.,** *abbrev.* of Einfluss.
**einflammig,** *a.* single-flame.
**einflechten,** *v.t.* weave in, interweave.

**einfliessen,** *v.i.* flow in; come in.
**einflössen,** *v.t.* instill, infuse.
**Einfluss,** *m.* influence; effect; influx; influent.
**einflussreich,** *a.* influential.
**Einfluss-rohr,** *n.*, **-röhre,** *f.* inlet pipe, influx pipe (or tube).
**einformen,** *v.t.* (*Ceram.*) mold on a jigger.
**einförmig,** *a.* uniform; monotonous.
**einfressen,** *v.t.* corrode, attack; devour.
**einfrieren,** *v.i.* freeze, congeal, freeze up.
**einfritten,** *v.t.* frit.
**einfügen,** *v.t.* insert; fit in; rabbet.
**Einfuhr,** *f.* importation, import; bringing in; supply.
**einführen,** *v.t.* introduce; import; inaugurate.
**Einführung,** *f.* introduction; importation; installation.
**Einfuhrwaren,** *f.pl.* imports.
**einfüllen,** *v.t.* fill, fill in, fill up, pour in.
**Einfüll-hahn,** *m.* feed cock. **-stoff,** *m.* filling, packing. **-trichter,** *m.* funnel tube; charging hopper. **-wägepipette,** *f.* weighing pipet(te).
**Eingabe,** *f.* presentation; petition; (*Patents*) amendment.
**Eingang,** *m.* entrance; importation; introduction; shrinking; mouth; receipt.
**eingängig,** *a.* (*Mach.*) single-thread.
**eingangs,** *adv.* at the outset.
**eingeben,** *v.t.* give, administer.
**eingebildet,** *p.a.* see einbilden.
**eingeboren,** *p.a.* inborn, innate; native.
**eingebrannt,** *p.p.* of einbrennen.
**eingedenk,** *a.* mindful.
**eingegossen,** *p.a.* poured in; infused.
**eingehen,** *v.i.* go in, come in, enter, arrive; cease; agree; (of fabrics) shrink. — **eingehend,** *p.a.* going in, etc.; thoro, exhaustive; (*Geom.*) re-entrant. — *adv.* thoroly, exhaustively.
**eingemacht,** *p.p.* of einmachen.
**Eingemachtes,** *n.* preserves, conserves.
**eingenommen,** *p.a.* see einnehmen.
**eingesalzen,** *p.a.* see einsalzen.
**eingeschichtet,** *p.p.* of einschichten.
**eingeschliffen,** *p.p.* ground in; engraved.
**eingeschlossen,** *p.p.* of einschliessen.
**eingeschmolzen,** *p.p.* of einschmelzen.
**eingesprengt,** *p.p.* of einsprengen.
**eingestehen,** *v.i.* confess; admit, grant.
**Eingeweide,** *n.* viscera, entrails; intestines.
**Eingeweide-.** visceral; intestinal.
**eingiessen,** *v.t.* pour in; infuse.
**Eingiessung,** *f.* pouring in; infusion; transfusion.
**eingipsen,** *v.t.* set in plaster of Paris.
**eingraben,** *v.t.* engrave; dig in; bury.
**eingreifen,** *v.i.* catch, lock, interlock; act (chemically); infringe. — **eingreifend,** *p.a.* radical.
**Eingreifen,** *n.* intervention, interference; (chemical) action; (*Mach.*) gearing, gear, connection, engagement.
**eingrenzen,** *v.t.* inclose; limit; localize.
**Eingriff,** *m.* = Eingreifen. — **im —,** in gear.
**Einguss,** *m.* pouring in; infusion; mold; ingot; (*Founding*) gate, runner, sprue.
**Einhalt,** *m.* check, restraint, interruption.
**einhalten,** *v.t.* keep in, take in, stop, keep; keep to, observe. — *v.i.* cease.
**einhändigen,** *v.t.* hand over, deliver.
**einhängen,** *v.t.* hang up or in, suspend.
**einhauen,** *v.t.* cut in, cut open, break in.
**einhäusig,** *a.* (*Biol.*) monoecious.
**einheimisch,** *a.* domestic; native; indigenous; home-made; endemic.
**Einheit,** *f.* unit; unity.
**einheitlich,** *a.* unitary; uniform, homogeneous; centralized. — *adv.* uniformly, consistently; simply.
**Einheitlichkeit,** *f.* uniformity, homogeneity.
**Einheits-.** unit; standard, normal, uniform. **-gewicht,** *n.* unit weight; specific gravity. **-gitter,** *n.* (*Cryst.*) unit lattice. **-masse,** *f.* unit mass. **-volumen,** *n.* unit volume. **-zelle,** *f.* unit cell.
**einhellig,** *a.* unanimous, united.
**einher,** *adv.* along.
**einholen,** *v.t.* overtake; obtain; haul in.
**einhüllen,** *v.t.* imbed; enwrap, envelop, cover.
**einig,** *a.* united, in accord; one, one only.
**einigen,** *v.t.* unite; unify. — *pron.* to (or for) some.
**einiger,** *pron.* some; several.
**einigermassen,** *adv.* in some degree, somewhat.
**Einigkeit,** *f.* unity, union, harmony.
**Einigung,** *f.* unification, union; agreement.
**Einigungskitt,** *m.* cement; putty.
**einimpfen,** *v.t.* inoculate.
**einjährig,** *a.* of one year, annual.
**einkalken, einkälken,** *v.t.* treat in lime, soak in lime water.
**einkapseln,** *v.t.* encapsulate, encyst, enclose.
**Einkauf,** *m.* buying, purchase.
**einkellern,** *v.t.* store (in a cellar), cellar, lay in.
**einkerben,** *v.t.* notch, indent.
**Einkerbung,** *f.* notching, notch, indentation.
**einkernig,** *a.* uninuclear, mononuclear.
**einkitten,** *v.t.* cement in, cement.
**einklammern,** *v.t.* enclose in brackets or parentheses; cramp.
**Einklang,** *m.* harmony, unison, accord.
**einkleiden,** *v.t.* clothe, dress; coat.
**einklemmen,** *v.t.* clamp; pinch, nip; jam.
**einkochen,** *v.t.* boil down, evaporate. — *v.i.* thicken by boiling.
**Einkochung,** *f.* boiling down, evaporation.
**Einkommen,** *n.* income; revenue; profit.
**Einkristall,** *m.* single crystal, monocrystal.

**einkrücken,** *v.t.* crutch (soap).
**Einkrüstung,** *f.* incrusting, incrustation.
**Einkünfte,** *f.pl.* income, revenue.
**einlaben,** *v.t.* curdle, coagulate.
**einladen,** *v.t.* load in; invite.
**Einlage,** *f.* something laid or put in; inclosure; charge; filler; lining; deposit; investment.
**einlagern,** *v.t.* intercalate; infiltrate; embed, imbed; store.
**Einlagerung,** *f.* intercalation, etc. (see einlagern).
**Einlagerungsverbindung,** *f.* intercalation compound.
**Einlass,** *m.* inlet, intake; letting in, admission. **-druck,** *m.* intake pressure.
**einlassen,** *v.t.* let in, admit; insert, introduce.
**Einlass-farbe,** *f.* (*Leather*) graining color. **-grund,** *m.* (*Paints*) sealer. **-öffnung,** *f.* inlet, intake. **-rohr,** *n.*, **-röhre,** *f.* inlet tube or pipe. **-stück,** *n.* inserted piece, insert. **-ventil,** *n.* inlet valve.
**Einlauf,** *m.* running in, influx; inlet. **-druck,** *m.* intake pressure. **einlaufecht,** *a.* unshrinkable.
**einlaufen,** *v.i.* enter; arrive; shrink, contract.
**Einlauftrichter,** *m.* inflow funnel; feed hopper.
**einlaugen,** *v.t.* soak in lye, buck.
**einlegen,** *v.t.* put, place, lay (in); soak, steep; pickle; preserve, put up (fruits, etc.); imbed; insert; inlay.
**einleiten,** *v.t.* introduce; (of gases) conduct, pass or convey in, inject; preface; initiate, start.
**Einleitung,** *f.* introduction, etc. (see einleiten); preface; preparation.
**Einleitungsrohr,** *n.* inlet tube, tube by which gases are introduced, feed pipe.
**einlenken,** *v.t.* guide (a missile, a ship).
**einleuchten,** *v.i.* be clear.
**Einlinienspektrum,** *n.* spectrum of single lines.
**einlöten,** *v.t.* solder in.
**einmachen,** *v.t.* preserve, conserve, pickle; temper (lime); knead (dough); wrap up.
**Einmachesalz,** *n.* preserving salt.
**Einmachessig,** *m.* pickling vinegar.
**einmaischen,** *v.t.* (*Brewing*) dough in.
**Einmaischtemperatur,** *f.* (*Brewing*) doughing-in temperature, initial temperature (of the mash).
**einmal,** *adv.* once; ever. — **auf —,** all at once, suddenly. — **nicht —,** not even.
**einmalig,** *a.* single; unique; solitary.
**Einmalschmelzerei,** *f.* (*Iron*) single refining.
**einmarinieren,** *v.t.* pickle.
**einmauern,** *v.t.* wall in, build in, embed.
**einmengen,** *v.t.* mix in, mix, intermix.
**einmischen,** *v.t.* mix in, intermix, blend. — *v.r.* interfere.
**einmitten,** *v.t.* center.
**einmünden,** *v.i.* empty, discharge, disembogue; (*Anat.*) inosculate; enter, fit (in).
**einmütig,** *a.* of one mind, united.
**Einnahme,** *f.* taking in, receipt, receipts, income.
**einnehmen,** *v. t.* take in, take, receive; occupy; captivate; overcome. — **eingenommen,** *p.a.* prejudiced; infatuated; dizzy.
**einnormal,** *a.* (of solutions) normal.
**Einöde,** *f.* desert, wild.
**einölen,** *v.t.* oil; lubricate.
**einordnen,** *v.t.* arrange; classify.
**Einordnung,** *f.* arrangement; classification.
**einpacken,** *v.t.* pack, pack up; embed.
**einpassen,** *v.t.* fit in; adjust.
**Einphasen-.** (*Elec.*) single-phase.
**einphasig,** *a.* one-phase, single-phase, monophase, uniphase.
**einpilieren,** *v.t.* mill (soap).
**einpökeln,** *v.t.* pickle, corn.
**einpolig,** *a.* unipolar.
**einprägen,** *v.t.* impress, imprint.
**einpressen,** *v.t.* press, compress; force in.
**einprozentig,** *a.* one per cent.
**einpudern,** *v.t.* powder; dust.
**einpumpen,** *v.t.* pump in.
**einquantig,** *a.* of one quantum, one-quantum.
**Einquell-bottich,** *m.*, **-kufe,** *f.* soaking tub, steeping vessel.
**einquellen,** *v.t.* steep, soak.
**Einquellwasser,** *n.* steeping water.
**einrahmen,** *v.t.* frame.
**Einrahmung,** *f.* framing, frame.
**einräuchern,** *v.t.* fumigate; smoke.
**Einräucherung,** *f.* fumigation.
**einräumen,** *v.t.* stow away; furnish; yield, concede.
**einrechnen,** *v.t.* count in, include.
**Einrede,** *f.* objection, protest.
**einreden,** *v.t.* talk into. — *v.i.* interrupt; object.
**einregeln, einregulieren,** *v.t.* regulate, adjust.
**einreiben,** *v.t.* rub in, smear.
**Einreibesalbe,** *f.* rubbing ointment.
**Einreibung,** *f.* rubbing in, smearing; liniment, embrocation.
**Einreibungsmittel,** *n.* rubbing agent, specif. liniment.
**einreichen,** *v.t.* hand in, present, deliver.
**einreihen,** *v.t.* arrange, range, set in order; insert; enroll.
**einreihig,** *a.* single-series, single-row.
**einreissen,** *v.t.* rend; demolish. — *v.i.* tear; spread.
**Einreissfestigkeit,** *f.* tearing strength.
**einrennen,** *v.t.* melt down; run down.
**Einrennen,** *n.* melting down, first smelting.
**einrichten,** *v.t.* arrange, set right, adjust, orient; organize; establish, install, set up.
**Einrichtung,** *f.* arrangement; contrivance; ap-

paratus; device; establishment; installation; equipment, outfit, fittings, furniture; setting (of bones).

**Einriss,** *m.* rent, fissure, crack.

**einrollen,** *v.t. & r.* roll, roll up, curl.

**einrosten,** *v.i.* rust in, be covered with rust.

**einrücken,** *v.t.* (*Mach.*) engage, cause to engage, throw in.

**einrühren,** *v.t.* mix by stirring, stir up; dilute; stir in; temper (mortar); beat (eggs).

**einrussen,** *v.t.* cover with soot.

**eins,** *a.* one.

**einsacken,** *v.t.* pack in bags or sacks, bag, sack; encyst.

**Einsackstelle,** *f.* sunk spot (in a casting).

**einsäen,** *v.t.* sow in (as crystals into a solution).

**einsalben,** *v.t.* grease, anoint; embalm.

**einsalzen,** *v.t.* salt, salt down, corn, brine. — **eingesalzen,** *p.a.* salted, corned, salt.

**Einsalzung,** *f.* salting, etc. (see einsalzen).

**einsam,** *a.* alone, solitary, retired.

**Einsattelung,** *f.* dip, valley (of a curve).

**Einsatz,** *m.* putting in, insertion; inauguration; casehardening; something put in, insert, as a tray, a nest (of boxes or the like), or a charge (in a furnace), or a liner (in a centrifugal drum); filler, filling; duty, mission; onset, start. **-fähigkeit,** *f.* (*Metal.*) casehardenability. **-gewichte,** *n.pl.* weights in nests, nest of weights. **-gut,** *n.* (*Metal.*) charging material. **-härten,** *n.*, **-härtung,** *f.* casehardening. **-kessel,** *m.pl.* set of kettles. **-korb,** *m.* test-tube basket or cage. **-mittel,** *n.* (*Metal.*) casehardening compound, carburizer. **-pulver,** *n.* cementing powder. **-stahl,** *m.* casehardened steel. **-stück,** *n.* inserted piece, insert. **-tür,** *f.* charging door.

**einsäuern,** *v.t.* acidify, sour; vinegar, pickle; leaven.

**Einsäuerung,** *f.* acidification, souring; pickling; leavening.

**Einsäuerungsbad,** *n.* acid bath.

**Einsauge-.** absorbent; lymphatic. **-mittel,** *n.* absorbent.

**einsaugen,** *v.t.* absorb; suck up, suck in. — *v.r.* be absorbed, soak in. — **einsaugend,** *p.a.* absorbent, absorptive.

**Einsaug-mittel,** *n.* absorbent. **-rohr,** *n.* suction pipe or tube.

**Einsaugung,** *f.* absorption; suction; imbibition.

**Einsaugungsfähigkeit,** *f.* absorptivity.

**einsäurig,** *a.* monoacid, monacid.

**einschalten,** *v.t.* put in, insert, introduce; interpolate; switch in, switch on.

**Einschalter,** *m.* (*Elec.*) circuit closer, switch.

**einschärfen,** *v.t.* enjoin, impress.

**Einschätzung,** *f.* assessment.

**einschenken,** *v.t.* pour in, pour out (into something).

**einschichten,** *v.t.* embed; stratify, arrange in layers; interstratify; pack.

**einschichtig,** *a.* of one layer, single.

**einschiebbar,** *a.* capable of being shoved in.

**einschieben,** *v.t.* shove in, put in, insert.

**einschl.,** *abbrev.* (einschliesslich) inclusive(ly).

**einschläfern,** *v.t.* make drowsy, narcotize; lull. — **einschläfernd,** *p.a.* soporific, narcotic, hypnotic.

**Einschläferungsmittel,** *n.* soporific, narcotic, hypnotic.

**einschlaffen,** *v.i.* fall asleep.

**Einschlag,** *m.* striking (in), impact; wrapper, envelope; plait, fold; woof; admixture; sulfur match (for casks); handshake.

**einschlagen,** *v.t.* strike in, drive in; break; punch; wrap up, cover; follow, adopt; dip (sheet metal); sulfur (wine). — *v.i.* sink in; strike; succeed; shake hands.

**einschlägig,** *a.* belonging, related, pertinent, appropriate.

**Einschlag-lupe,** *f.* folding magnifier. **-papier,** *n.* wrapping paper. **-punkt,** *m.* point of impact.

**einschleifen,** *v.t.* grind in; engrave.

**einschliessen,** *v.t.* include, inclose, surround, seal in, lock in, confine; occlude; embed.

**einschliesslich,** *adv.* inclusive, inclusively.

**Einschliessung,** *f.* inclusion, etc. (see einschliessen).

**einschlucken,** *v.t.* absorb; gulp down.

**einschlüpfen,** *v.i.* soak in; slip in.

**Einschluss,** *m.* inclusion, etc. (see einschliessen). **-lack,** *m.* (*Micros.*) varnish for cell making, ringing varnish. **-mittel,** *n.* (*Micros.*) embedding medium, mounting medium. **-rohr,** *n.*, **-röhre,** *f.* sealed tube. **-thermometer,** *n. & m.* thermometer with enclosed scale.

**einschmalzen, einschmälzen,** *v.t.* grease, oil.

**einschmauchen,** *v.t.* smoke; fumigate.

**einschmelzen,** *v.t. & i.* melt down; melt in, fuse in, seal in; remelt.

**Einschmelz-flasche,** *f.* bottle closed by fusion. **-glas,** *n.* fusible glass (for sealing in platinum points, etc.). **-probe,** *f.* (*Metal.*) melt-down test, first test. **-rohr,** *n.*, **-röhre,** *f.* sealing tube (in which substances are inclosed by sealing). **-schlacke,** *f.* (*Metal.*) first slag.

**Einschmelzungsglas,** *n.* = Einschmelzglas.

**einschmieren,** *v.t.* smear, grease, lubricate.

**Einschmierung,** *f.* greasing, lubrication.

**einschneiden,** *v.t.* cut in, cut, cut up, cut out; notch; indent. — **einschneidend,** *p.a.* incisive.

**Einschnitt,** *m.* incision, cut, notch, groove, slot, excavation.

**einschnüren,** *v.t.* constrict; contract; bind up.

**Einschnürung,** *f* constriction; contraction; (*Metal.*) necking; binding up.

**einschränken,** *v.t.* confine, limit, restrain.

**einschrauben,** *v.t.* screw in, screw on, screw down.
**einschreiben,** *v.t.* inscribe, note, register, enter.
**einschrumpfen,** *v.i.* shrink, shrivel, contract.
**Einschuss,** *m.* impurity; inclusion; woof, weft.
**einschütten,** *v.t.* pour in, put in; feed, charge.
**einschwärzen,** *v.t.* blacken; ink.
**einschwefeln,** *v.t.* sulfur, sulfurize.
**einschwöden,** *v.t.* lime (hides).
**einsehen,** *v.t.* look into, understand, perceive.
**Einsehen,** *n.* insight, judgment.
**einseifen,** *v.t.* soap.
**ein-seigen, -seihen,** *v.t. & i.* infiltrate.
**einseitig,** *a.* one-sided, unilateral; partial; unbalanced (diet).
**einsenken,** *v.t.* sink, plunge, dip; plant.
**einsetzen,** *v.t.* set in, put in, insert; plant; (*Metal.*) caseharden; preserve (fruits); establish; install; charge.
**Einsetzen,** *n.* setting in, etc. (see einsetzen); (*Metal.*) casehardening; (*Ceram.*, etc.) charging.
**Einsetzer,** *m.* combustion boat.
**Einsetz-gewichte,** *n.pl.* nest of weights. **-tür,** *f.* charging door.
**Einsicht,** *f.* examination; insight, intelligence.
**einsichtig,** *a.* intelligent, judicious.
**einsickern,** *v.i.* trickle in, soak in, infiltrate.
**einsieden,** *v.t. & i.* boil down.
**Einsonderungsdrüse,** *f.* endocrine gland.
**einspannen,** *v.t.* fasten in, insert, clamp, grip, fix, attach, frame.
**Einspannung,** *f.* fastening in, etc. (see einspannen); grip.
**einspeicheln,** *v.t.* salivate. — *v.i.* be salivated.
**einsperren,** *v.t.* shut in, shut up, confine.
**einspielen,** *v.t.* put into play, engage; balance (scales). — *v.i.* balance; level.
**Einsprache,** *f.* objection, exception.
**einsprengen,** *v.t.* sprinkle; intersperse, disseminate; interstratify; burst open.
**Einsprengling,** *m.* interspersed body or substance.
**einspringen,** *v.i.* spring in; (of fabrics) shrink; (of an angle) re-enter.
**einspritzen,** *v.t.* squirt in, inject, syringe.
**Einspritzer,** *m.* injector; syringe.
**Einspritz-hahn,** *m.* injection cock. **-rohr,** *n.* injection pipe or tube.
**Einspritzung,** *f.* injection.
**Einspruch,** *m.* objection, exception; claim.
**Einsprung,** *m.* shrinkage; springing in.
**einst,** *adv.* once; some time.
**einstampfen,** *v.t.* ram down, compress; stamp, reduce, pulverize.
**Einstandspreis,** *m.* cost price.
**einstäuben,** *v.t.* dust, powder.
**einstechen,** *v.t.* stick in, pierce, perforate.
**einstecken,** *v.t.* put in, stick in; put up with.
**einstehen,** *v.i.* answer, guarantee.
**einsteigen,** *v.i.* enter, step in.
**Einstell-.** adjusting; focusing; reference.
**einstellbar,** *a.* adjustable.
**einstellen,** *v.t.* put in, set in; standardize (a solution); stop, suspend; adjust, set, regulate; put up, lay up; make up; engage (help); (*Optics*) focus. — *v.r.* appear; (of a magnet) set. — **— auf,** standardize against; make up to (a standard volume).
**Einsteller,** *m.* regulator, thermostat. (See also einstellen).
**Einstell-lupe,** *f.* focusing lens. **-marke,** *f.* reference mark. **-schraube,** *f.* adjusting screw.
**Einstellung,** *f.* putting in, standardization, etc. (see einstellen); reference; standard (of a solution).
**Einstich,** *m.* puncture; injection; incision. **-farbe,** *f.* (*Dyeing*) fancy color.
**Einstieg,** *m.* entrance.
**einstimmen,** *v.i.* chime in, agree, accord.
**einstimmig,** *adv.* unanimously.
**einstossen,** *v.t.* thrust in, ram in; break in.
**einstrahlen,** *v.t.* radiate upon, irradiate.
**Einstrahlung,** *f.* radiation taken in, (loosely) absorption; irradiation.
**einstreichen,** *v.t.* nick, slit (e.g. with a file); rub; take in; coat.
**einstreuen,** *v.t.* strew, sprinkle; intersperse.
**Einstrichmittel,** *n.* coating agent.
**einströmen,** *v.i.* stream in, flow in.
**Einströmungs-rohr,** *n.*, **-röhre,** *f.* inlet tube or pipe, admission tube or pipe.
**Einströmventil,** *n.* inlet valve.
**einstufen,** *v.t.* grade.
**einstufig,** *a.* single-stage.
**einstündig,** *a.* of an hour's duration, one hour's.
**einstürzen,** *v.i.* fall in, collapse. — *v.t.* throw in; demolish.
**einstweilen,** *adv.* meanwhile, for a time.
**einstweilig,** *a.* temporary, provisional.
**einsumpfen,** *v.t.* wet, soak.
**einsüssen,** *v.t.* sweeten, edulcorate.
**eintägig,** *a.* of a day's duration, one day's.
**eintauchen,** *v.t.* dip, plunge, immerse; steep. — *v.i.* dip in, sink in.
**Eintauch-refraktometer,** *n.* immersion refractometer. **-tiefe,** *f.* depth of immersion.
**Eintausch,** *m.* exchange, bartering.
**einteeren,** *v.t.* tar.
**einteigen,** *v.t.* impaste, make into paste or dough; (*Brewing*) dough in.
**einteilbar,** *a.* divisible; distinguishable.
**einteilen,** *v.t.* divide; distribute; separate; classify. — **in Grade —,** graduate.
**einteilig,** *a.* one-part, unipartite, single.
**Einteilung,** *f.* division; graduation; separation; classification; distribution.
**eintönig,** *a.* monotonous.

**Eintracht,** *f.* harmony; unity.
**Eintrag,** *m.* entry; charge; woof; (*Paper*) furnish; damage, prejudice.
**eintragen,** *v.t.* carry in; introduce; add; enter, record; register; yield.
**einträglich,** *a.* profitable.
**Eintragung,** *f.* carrying in, etc. (see eintragen).
**eintränken,** *v.t.* soak, steep, impregnate; dip.
**einträufeln,** *v.t.* drop in, add by drops; instill.
**eintreffen,** *v.i.* arrive; happen.
**eintreiben,** *v.t.* drive in; rub in; collect.
**eintreten,** *v.i.* enter; set in, commence; occur.
**eintrichtern,** *v.t.* pour in with a funnel.
**Eintritt,** *m.* entrance, entry; inlet; admission; appearance; commencement; (*Optics*) incidence.
**Eintritts-druck,** *m.*, **-spannung,** *f.* pressure on admission. **-temperatur,** *f.* temperature of admission.
**eintrocknen,** *v.i.* dry, dry up; shrink in drying.
**eintropfen, eintröpfeln,** *v.t.* drop in; instill.
**ein-und-einachsig,** *a.* (*Cryst.*) orthorhombic.
**einverleiben,** *v.t.* incorporate, embody.
**einverleihen,** *v.t.* introduce.
**Einvernehmung,** *f.* understanding.
**einverstanden,** *p.a.* agreed.
**Einverständnis,** *n.* agreement, understanding; concord, accord.
**Einw.,** *abbrev.* (Einwirkung) action, influence.
**Einwa(a)ge,** *f.* weighed portion.
**Einwägelöffel,** *m.* weighing-in spoon.
**einwägen,** *v.t.* weigh in, weigh and put in; level.
**Einwägung,** *f.* weighing (in); leveling; amount weighed out.
**einwalken,** *v.t.* full closely; force (oil, etc.) by fulling. — *v.i.* & *r.* shrink by fulling.
**Einwand,** *m.* objection, exception.
**einwandern,** *v.i.* diffuse in; immigrate.
**Einwanderung,** *f.* diffusion; immigration.
**einwandfrei,** *a.* unobjectionable, unexceptionable.
**einwärts,** *adv.* inward.
**einwaschen,** *v.t.* wash.
**einwässerig,** *a.* (*Dyeing*) one-bath.
**einwässern,** *v.t.* lay in water, steep, soak.
**Einwässerung,** *f.* steeping, soaking.
**einweben,** *v.t.* inweave. — *v.r.* shrink.
**Einweg-.** one-way.
**einweibig,** *a.* monogynous.
**einweichbar,** *a.* capable of being steeped, etc. (see einweichen).
**Einweichbottich,** *m.* steeping vat; soaking tub.
**einweichen,** *v.t.* steep, soak, macerate, digest, infuse; ret (flax).
**Einweich-flüssigkeit,** *f.* soaking liquor. **-mittel,** *n.* steeping agent.
**Einweichung,** *f.* steeping, etc. (see einweichen).
**Einweisung,** *f.* instruction, direction.
**einwenden,** *v.t.* object, oppose.
**einwerfen,** *v.t.* throw in.
**einwertig,** *a.* univalent, monovalent.
**Einwertigkeit,** *f.* univalence, monovalence.
**einwickeln,** *v.t.* wrap up, wrap in, inclose.
**Einwickelpapier,** *n.* wrapping paper.
**Einwieg-.** see Einwäg-.
**einwilligen,** *v.i.* consent, approve, agree.
**einwirken,** *v.i.* act; exert influence. — *v.t.* work in, weave in.
**Einwirkung,** *f.* action; influence, effect.
**Einwirkungs-dauer,** *f.* duration of action. **-produkt,** *n.* resultant product.
**Einwohner,** *m.* inhabitant.
**Einwurf,** *m.* objection; reply; insertion; charging, feeding; slot; hopper. **-trichter,** *m.* feed hopper.
**Einzahlung,** *f.* payment, installment; share.
**einzehren,** *v.i.* & *r.* suffer loss by evaporation.
**Einzehrung,** *f.* loss by evaporation.
**einzeichnen,** *v.t.* draw in, draw; note, mark.
**Einzel-.** single, individual, particular, separate. **-beobachtung,** *f.* single observation. **-bestimmung,** *f.* single determination. **-blech,** *n.* single tinplate. **-darstellung,** *f.* single presentation, separate treatment or treatise, (sometimes) monograph. **-erscheinung,** *f.* single or isolated phenomenon. **-fall,** *m.* particular case, individual case. **-heit,** *f.* detail, particular; singleness.
**Einzeller,** *m.* unicellular organism, protozoan.
**einzellig,** *a.* single-celled, unicellular.
**Einzel-lupe,** *f.* single lens, simple magnifier. **-messung,** *f.* single measurement. **-molekül,** *n.* single molecule.
**einzeln,** *a.* single, separate, individual. — **im einzelnen,** in detail; retail.
**Einzel-potential,** single potential. **-schrift,** *f.* monograph. **-teil,** *m.* single part; component part; detail. **-teilchen,** *n.* single particle. **-verkauf,** *m.* retail, retailing. **-vorgang,** *m.* single or separate process or reaction. **-wert,** *m.* single or individual value.
**einziehen,** *v.t.* draw in, pull in; retract; absorb; reduce, lessen; collect; confiscate. — *v.i.* soak in, infiltrate; enter. — *v.r.* shrink, contract; retire.
**Einziehungsmittel,** *n.* absorbent.
**einzig,** *a.* only, single, sole, unique.
**einzuckern,** *v.t.* sugar; preserve (with sugar).
**Einzug,** *m.* entry, entrance.
**eirund,** *a.* oval.
**Eis,** *n.* ice.
**Eis-.** ice, glacial, freezing. **-abkühlung,** *f.* cooling or refrigeration with ice.
**eisähnlich,** *a.* ice-like, resembling ice, glacial.
**Eis-alaun,** *m.* rock alum. **-ansatz,** *m.* deposit or layer of ice.
**eisartig,** *a.* ice-like, icy, glacial.
**Eis-belag, -beleg,** *m.* coating of ice. **-bereitung,**

*f.* ice making. **-bildung,** *f.* formation of ice. **-blumen,** *f.pl.* frostwork. **-blumenbildung,** *f.* (of varnish) reticulation. **-blumenlack,** *m.* crystal lacquer.

**Eischale,** *f.* eggshell.

**Eiseln,** *n.*, **Eiselung,** *f.* (*Varnish*) crystallization.

**Eisen,** *n.* iron; (in certain cases) steel; iron (or steel) instrument or utensil; horseshoe.

**Eisen-.** iron, ferro-, ferruginous. **-abbrand,** *m.* iron waste. **-abfälle,** *m.pl.* scrap iron. **-abscheidung,** *f.* separation of iron.

**eisenähnlich,** *a.* = eisenartig.

**Eisen-alaun,** *m.* iron alum (ferric potassium sulfate). **-amiant,** *m.* (*Iron*) fibrous silica. **-ammonalaun,** *m.* ammonium ferric alum. **-ammonalaunlösung,** *f.* solution of ammonium iron salt, esp. ammonium ferric alum. **-antimonerz,** *n.*, **-antimonglanz,** *m.* berthierite.

**eisenarm,** *a.* poor in iron, low-iron.

**Eisenarsenik,** *n.* iron arsenide, specif. (*Min.*) löllingite or leucopyrite.

**eisenartig,** *a.* iron-like, ferruginous, chalybeate.

**Eisen-arznei,** *f.* ferruginous remedy. **-asbest,** *m.* fibrous silica formed in iron manufacture. **-aufnahme,** *f.* absorption of iron. **-bad,** *m.* iron bath. **-bahn,** *f.* railroad, railway. **-bedarf,** *m.* iron requirement. **-beize,** *f.* iron mordant, iron liquor. **-beizung,** *f.* iron pickling; iron mordanting. **-beschwerung,** *f.* weighting with iron. **-bestimmung,** *f.* iron determination. **-beton,** *m.* ferro-concrete, reinforced concrete, armored concrete. **-betonbau,** *m.* ferro-concrete construction. **-bitterkalk,** *m.* ferruginous dolomite, ferromagnesian limestone. **-blau,** *n.* = Blaueisenspat. **-blauerde,** *f.* earthy vivianite. **-blaupapier,** *n.* blueprint paper.

**eisenblausauer,** *a.* of or combined with ferrocyanic acid, ferrocyanide of.

**Eisen-blausäure,** *f.* ferrocyanic acid. **-blauspat,** *m.* = Blaueisenspat. **-blech,** *n.* sheet iron, iron plate. **-blende,** *f.* pitchblende. **-block,** *f.* ingot, bloom, or block of iron. **-blumen,** *f.pl.* iron flowers (ferric chloride). **-blüte,** *f.* flos ferri (coralloid form of aragonite). **-bor,** *n.* iron boride. **-braun,** *n.* iron brown, mineral brown. **-bromid,** *n.* iron bromide, specif. ferric bromide, iron(III) bromide. **-bromür,** *n.* ferrous bromide, iron(II) bromide. **-bromürbromid,** *n.* ferrosoferric bromide, iron(II, III) bromide. **-bronze,** *f.* iron bronze, ferrobronze. **-brühe,** *f.* iron mordant, iron liquor. **-cement,** *m.* & *n.* ferro-concrete.

**eisenchamois,** *a.* iron-buff.

**Eisen-chinawein,** *m.* iron and quinine wine. **-chlorid,** *n.* iron chloride, specif. ferric chloride, iron(III) chloride. **-chlorür,** *n.* ferrous chloride, iron(II) chloride. **-chlorürchlorid,** *n.* ferrosoferric chloride, iron(II, III) chloride. **-chlorwasserstoff,** *m.* ferrichloric acid. **-chrom,** *n.* ferrochrome, ferrochromium; (*Min.*) chromic iron, chromite. **-chromschwarz,** *n.* iron-chrome black. **-chrysolith,** *m.* hyalosiderite; fayalite. **-cyanfarbe,** *f.* iron cyanogen pigment. **-cyanid,** *n.* iron cyanide, specif. ferric cyanide, iron(III) cyanide; ferrocyanide. **-cyankalium,** *n.* potassium ferrocyanide. **-cyanür,** *n.* ferrous cyanide, iron(II) cyanide. **-cyanürcyanol,** *n.* Prussian blue. **-cyanürzinkoxyd,** *n.* zinc ferrocyanide. **-cyanverbindung,** *f.* iron cyanogen compound, ferro- or ferricyanogen compound. **-draht,** *m.* iron wire. **-drahtnetz,** *n.* iron gauze.

**eisenempfindlich,** *a.* sensitive to iron.

**Eisenerde,** *f.* ferruginous earth, iron earth; (*Ceram.*) a kind of hard stoneware. — **blaue —,** earthy vivianite.

**Eisen-erz,** *n.* iron ore. **-fällung,** *f.* iron precipitation. **-fänger,** *m.* iron trap. **-farbe,** *f.* iron color.

**eisenfarbig,** *a.* iron-colored.

**Eisen-feilicht,** *n.*, **-feile,** *f.* **-feilspäne,** *m.pl.* iron filings. **-feilstaub,** *m.* fine iron filings. **-feinschlacke,** *f.* iron refinery slag. **-firnis,** *m.* varnish for iron. **-flasche,** *f.* iron cylinder (for gases). **-fleck,** *m.* iron spot, iron stain.

**eisenfleckig,** *a.* iron-stained.

**Eisenflüssigkeit,** *f.* iron liquid or liquor.

**eisenfrei,** *a.* free from iron.

**Eisen-frischerie,** *f.* iron refinery; iron refining, puddling. **-frischflammofen,** *m.* puddling furnace. **-frischschlacke,** *f.* finery cinders.

**eisenführend,** *a.* iron-bearing, ferriferous.

**Eisen-gallustinte,** *f.* iron gallate ink. **-gang,** *m.* iron lode, iron-ore vein. **-gans,** *f.* iron pig. **-gaze,** *f.* iron gauze. **-gefäss,** *n.* iron vessel. **-gehalt,** *m.* iron content. **-gelb,** *n.* iron yellow. **-gerbung,** *f.* iron tannage. **-gestell,** *n.* iron stand, iron frame. **-gewinnung,** *f.* iron production. **-giesserei,** *f.* iron foundry; iron founding. **-gilbe,** *f.* yellow ocher. **-glanz,** *m.* iron glance, specular iron (form of hematite). **-glas,** *n.* (*Min.*) fayalite. **-glimmer,** *m.* micaceous iron ore (form of hematite). **-glimmerschiefer,** *m.* itabirite. **-granat,** *m.* iron garnet (almandite).

**eisengrau,** *a.* iron-gray.

**Eisen-graupen,** *f.pl.* granular bog iron ore. **-grund,** *m.* iron liquor, iron mordant. **-guss,** *m.* iron casting; cast iron.

**eisenhaltig,** *a.* containing iron, ferriferous, ferruginous, chalybeate.

**Eisenhammerschlag,** *m.* iron (hammer) scale.

**eisenhart,** *a.* as hard as iron.

**Eisen-hart, -hardt,** *m.* ferriferous gold sand; vervain. **-hochofen,** *m.* iron blast furnace. **-holz,** *n.* ironwood. **-hut,** *m.* aconite, monkshood; (*Mining*) gossan. **-hütchen, -hutkraut,** *n.* aconite, monkshood. **-hütte,** *f.* ironworks, iron mill; forge.

**Eisenhütten-chemie,** *f.* ironworks chemistry, ferro-metallurgical chemistry. **-kunde,** *f.* metallurgy of iron. **-leute,** *pl.* iron metallurgists. **-mann,** *m.* iron metallurgist.

**eisenhüttenmännisch,** *a.* ferro-metallurgical.

**Eisenhütten-werk,** *n.* ironworks, iron mill, steel mill. **-wesen,** *n.* metallurgy of iron.

**Eisen-hydroxyd,** *n.* ferric hydroxide, iron(III) hydroxide. **-hydroxydul,** *n.* ferrous hydroxide, iron(II) hydroxide. **-jodid,** *n.* iron iodide, specif. ferric iodide, iron(III) iodide. **-jodür,** *n.* ferrous iodide, iron(II) iodide. **-jodürjodid,** *n.* ferrosoferric iodide, iron(II,III) iodide. **-kalium,** *n.* potassium ferrate. **-kaliumalaun,** *m.* iron potassium alum, ferric potassium sulfate. **-karbid, -karburet,** *n.* iron carbide. **-kern,** *m.* iron core.

**Eisenkies,** *m.* iron pyrites, pyrite. — **hexagonaler —,** pyrrhotite. — **rhombischer —,** marcasite.

**Eisenkiesel,** *m.* ferruginous flint or chert.

**eisenkiesführend,** *a.* pyritic.

**Eisen-kitt,** *m.* iron-rust cement. **-kobalterz,** *n.*, **-kobaltkies,** *m.* cobaltite or smaltite rich in iron. **-kohlenoxyd,** *n.* iron carbonyl. **-kohlenstoff,** *m.* iron carbide. **-kohlenstofflegierung,** *f.* iron-carbon alloy. **-korn,** *n.* (*Metal.*) ferrite grain. **-kraut,** *n.* vervain, verbena. **-lack,** *m.* iron varnish; iron lake. **-lebererz,** *n.* hepatic iron ore. **-legierung,** *f.* iron alloy, ferroalloy. **-lila,** *n.* alizarin lake. **-löffel,** *m.* iron spoon. **-lösung,** *f.* iron solution.

**eisenmagnetisch,** *a.* ferromagnetic.

**Eisen-mangan,** *n.* ferromanganese. **-manganerz,** *n.* manganiferous iron ore, ferriferous manganese ore. **-mangel,** *m.* lack of iron. **-mann,** *m.* (*Mining*) a scaly form of hematite. **-menge,** *f.* amount of iron. **-mennige,** *f.* red ocher. **-mittel,** *n.* (*Med.*) ferruginous remedy. **-mohr,** *m.* aethiops martialis ($Fe_3O_4$ as a black powder); earthy magnetite. **-molybdän,** *n.* ferromolybdenum. **-mulm,** *m.* earthy iron ore. **-natronsalz,** *n.* iron sodium salt. **-nickel,** *n.* ferronickel. **-nickelkies,** *m.* pentlandite. **-niederschlag,** *m.* precipitate of iron. **-niere,** *f.* eaglestone. **-ocker, ocher,** *m.* iron ocher, ocher.

**Eisenoxyd,** *n.* iron oxide, specif. ferric oxide, iron(III) oxide. — **salpetersaures —,** ferric nitrate, iron(III) nitrate (and so for other salts).

**Eisenoxyd-gelb,** *n.* iron yellow. **-hydrat,** *n.* ferric hydroxide, iron(III) hydroxide. **-oxydul,** *n.* ferrosoferric oxide, iron(II,III) oxide.

**eisenoxydreich,** *a.* rich in iron oxide.

**Eisenoxyd-salz,** *n.* ferric salt, iron(III) salt. **-sulfat,** *n.* ferric sulfate, iron(III) sulfate.

**Eisenoxydul,** *n.* ferrous oxide, iron(II) oxide. — **salpetersaures —,** ferrous nitrate, iron(II) nitrate (and so for other salts).

**Eisenoxydul-hydrat,** *n.* ferrous hydroxide, iron(II) hydroxide. **-oxyd,** *n.* ferrosoferric oxide, iron(II,III) oxide, magnetic iron oxide ($Fe_3O_4$). **-salz,** *n.* ferrous salt, iron(II) salt. **-sulfat,** *n.* ferrous sulfate, iron(II) sulfate. **-verbindung,** *f.* ferrous compound, iron(II) compound.

**Eisen-oxydverbindung,** *f.* ferric compound, iron(III) compound. **-pastille,** *f.* (*Pharm.*) reduced iron lozenge. **-pecherz,** *n.* limonite; pitticite; triplite. **-phosphor,** *n.* iron phosphide. **-probe,** *f.* iron test; iron sample. **-pulver,** *n.* iron powder. **-quarz,** *m.* ferriferous quartz. **-rahm,** *m.* a porous form of hematite.

**eisenreich,** *a.* rich in iron.

**Eisen-reihe,** *f.* iron series. **-resin, -resinit,** *m.* (*Min.*) humboldtine. **-rhodanid,** *n.* ferric thiocyanate, iron(III) thiocyanate. **-rhodanür,** *n.* ferrous thiocyanate, iron(II) thiocyanate. **-rogenstein,** *m.* oölitic iron ore. **-rohr,** *n.*, **-röhre,** *f.* iron pipe or tube. **-rost,** *m.* iron rust. **-rostwasser,** *n.* iron liquor, iron mordant. **-rot,** *n.* colcothar. **-safran,** *m.* saffron (or crocus) of Mars. **-salmiak,** *m.* (*Pharm.*) ammoniated iron, iron and ammonium chloride. **-salz,** *n.* iron salt. **-sand,** *m.* ferruginous sand. **-sau,** *f.* iron sow.

**eisensauer,** *a.* of or combined with ferric acid, ferrate of.

**Eisen-säuerling,** *m.* chalybeate water (mineral water containing iron salts). **-säure,** *f.* ferric acid. **-schaum,** *m.* (*Metal.*) kish; (*Min.*) = Eisenrahm. **-schlacke,** *f.* iron slag; finery cinders. **-schmelze,** *f.* iron smelting; iron smeltery; iron founding. **-schmelzhütte,** *f.* iron foundry. **-schörl,** *m.* bog iron ore. **-schrott,** *m.* iron scrap.

**eisenschüssig,** *a.* ferriferous, ferruginous.

**Eisen-schutz,** *m.* protection of iron (esp. against rusting), rust-proofing. **-schutzanstrich,** *m.* antirust paint. **-schutzfarbe,** *f.* protective paint for iron. **-schutzmittel,** *n.* antirusting composition, rust-proofing agent. **-schwamm,** *m.* iron sponge, spongy iron. **-schwarz,** *n.* iron black (precipitated antimony); graphite; lampblack; (*Dyeing*) iron black, copperas black. **-schwärze,** *f.* graphite; earthy magnetite; (*Dyeing*) iron liquor; (*Leather*) currier's ink. **-selenür,** *n.* ferrous selenide, iron(II) selenide. **-silberglanz,** *m.* sternbergite. **-silicium,** *n.* iron silicide. **-sinter,** *m.* dross of iron, iron scale; pitticite. **-späne,** *m.pl.* iron turnings or borings. **-spat,** *m.* siderite. **-spiegel,** *m.* specular iron (hematite). **-staub,** *m.* iron dust.

**Eisenstein,** *m.* ironstone, iron ore. — **spatiger —,** spathic iron ore, siderite.

**Eisen-steinmark,** *n.* lithomarge containing iron. **-sublimat,** *n.* iron sublimate (ferric chloride). **-sulfat,** *n.* iron sulfate, specif. ferrous sulfate. iron(II) sulfate. **-sulfid,** *n.* iron sulfide, specif. ferric sulfide, iron(III) sulfide. **-sulfür,** *n.* ferrous sulfide, iron(II) sulfide. **-sumpferz,** *n.* bog iron ore. **-teil,** *m.* iron part. **-tiegel,** *m.* iron crucible. **-tinte,** *f.* iron ink. **-titan,** *n.* ferrotitanium; (*Min.*) ilmenite. **-ton,** *m.* clay ironstone; iron clay. **-tongranat,** *m.* almandite. **-trümmerlagerstätte,** *f.* clastic iron-ore deposit. **-untersuchung,** *f.* examination of iron, iron analysis. **-vanadin,** *n.* ferrovanadium. **-verbindung,** *f.* iron compound. **-verhüttung,** *f.* iron smelting. **-verlust,** *m.* loss of iron. **-violettholz,** *n.* granadilla wood, red ebony.

**Eisenvitriol,** *m.* iron vitriol (hydrous ferrous sulfate, copperas). — **roter —,** red vitriol, botryogen.

**Eisen-wasser,** *n.* chalybeate water. **-wein,** *m.* (*Pharm.*) iron wine. **-weinstein,** *m.* (*Pharm.*) iron and potassium tartrate, tartrated iron. **-werk,** *n.* ironworks, iron mill. **-wolfram,** *n.* ferrotungsten. **-zeit,** *f.* iron age. **-zement,** *m.* & *n.* ferroconcrete. **-zinkblende,** *f.* marmatite. **-zinkspat,** *m.* ferruginous calamine. **-zinnerz,** *n.* ferriferous cassiterite. **-zucker,** *m.* (*Pharm.*) saccharated ferric oxide. **-zukkersirup,** *m.* (*Pharm.*) sirup of ferric oxide.

**Eisenzyan-** = Eisencyan-.

**eisern,** *a.* of iron, iron, ferrous.

**Eis-erzeugung,** *f.* ice production. **-essig,** *m.* glacial acetic acid. **-farbe,** *f.* (*Dyeing*) ice color.

**eisgekühlt,** *a.* cooled with ice, ice-cooled.

**Eisglas,** *n.* frosted glass.

**eisig,** *a.* icy, ice-like.

**Eisigkeit,** *f.* iciness.

**eiskalt,** *a.* ice-cold.

**Eis-kasten,** *m.* ice chest, ice box. **-kraut,** *n.* ice plant (*Mesembryanthemum crystallinum*).

**eiskühlen,** *v.t.* cool with ice.

**Eis-mühle,** *f.* ice mill. **-phosphorsäure,** *f.* glacial phosphoric acid. **-punkt,** *m.* freezing point. **-schale,** *f.* ice basin, ice bowl. **-schrank,** *m.* ice box or chest, refrigerator. **-spat,** *m.* glassy feldspar, sanidine (or rhyacolite). **-stein,** *m.* cryolite. **-trichter,** *m.* ice funnel. **-wasser,** *n.* ice water. **-zacken, -zapfen,** *m.* icicle. **-zeit,** *f.* glacial period, ice age.

**eitel,** *a.* pure; idle; vain.

**Eiter,** *m.* pus.

**eiter-ähnlich, -artig,** *a.* purulent.

**Eiterbakterien,** *n.pl.* pyogenic bacteria.

**eiter-befördernd,** *a.* suppurative. **-bildend,** *a* pyogenic.

**Eiterbildung,** *f.* suppuration, pyogenesis.

**eitererzeugend,** *p.a.* suppurative, pyogenic.

**Eitergang,** *m.* fistula.

**eiterig, eitericht,** *a.* purulent.

**eitern,** *v.i.* suppurate.

**Eiter-pilz,** *m.* pyogenic organism. **-stoff,** *m.* purulent matter.

**Eiterung,** *f.* suppuration.

**Eiterungserreger,** *m.* suppurative agent.

**Eitervergiftung,** *f.* pyemia.

**eiterziehend,** *p.a.* suppurative, pyogenic.

**Eiweiss,** *n.* albumin; albumen, white of egg; protein.

**Eiweiss-.** albuminous, albuminoid; protein. **-abbau,** *m.* proteolysis. **-abbauprodukt,** *n.* protein decomposition product.

**eiweiss-ähnlich,** *a.* albuminoid. **-arm,** *a.* poor in albumin or in protein.

**Eiweissart,** *f.* variety of albumin; variety of protein.

**eiweissartig,** *a.* albuminous; albuminoid; glairy.

**Eiweiss-bedarf,** *m.* albumin requirement; protein requirement. **-drüse,** *f.* salivary gland.

**eiweiss-förmig,** *a.* albuminous. **-haltig,** *a.* containing albumin (or albumen), albuminous; containing protein.

**Eiweiss-harnen,** *n.* albuminuria. **-körper,** *m.* albuminous substance, protein. **-leim,** *m.* albumin glue; gluten protein. **-lösung,** *f.* albumin solution. **-nahrung,** *f.* albuminous food. **-papier,** *n.* albuminized paper.

**eiweiss-reich,** *a.* rich in albumin (or in protein). **-spaltend,** *p.a.* proteolytic.

**Eiweiss-spaltung,** *f.* cleavage of albumin; protein cleavage, proteolysis. **-sparmittel,** *n.* albumin sparer; protein sparer. **-stoff,** *m.* albuminous substance, protein; albumen; albumin. **-verbindung,** *f.* albuminous compound, protein; albuminate.

**Eizelle,** *f.* ovum.

**EK, E.K.,** *abbrev.* (elektromotorische Kraft) electromotive force, E.M.F.

**Eka-bor,** *n.* ekaboron. **-silizium,** *n.* ekasilicon.

**Ekel,** *m.* nausea; disgust.

**ekel-erregend,** *a.* nauseating, disgusting. **-haft,** *a.* disgusting, offensive.

**eklatant,** *a.* brilliant, bright.

**Ekrüseide,** *f.* ecru silk.

**Ekzem,** *n.* eczema.

**-el.** A suffix attached to verb roots to denote the instrument of an action, -er; as, *Hebel,* lever, from *heben,* lift.

**Elaidinsäure,** *f.* elaidic acid.
**Elainsäure,** *f.* oleic acid.
**Elaio-, Eläo-.** eleo-, elaeo-, elaio-.
**Elasticität,** *f.* elasticity.
**elastisch,** *a.* elastic.
**Elastizität,** *f.* elasticity.
**Elastizitäts-grenze,** *f.* elastic limit. **-modul,** *m.* modulus of elasticity. **-verstärker,** *m.* (*Rubber*) elasticator. **-zahl,** *f.* modulus of elasticity.
**Elatinsäure,** *f.* elatinic acid.
**Elatsäure,** *f.* elatic acid.
**Elefanten-laus,** *f.* cashew nut. **-nuss,** *f.* ivory nut.
**elekt.,** *abbrev.* (elektrisch) electric.
**Elekt.,** *abbrev.* (Elektrizität) electricity.
**Elektawolle,** *f.* first-class wool.
**elektiv,** *a.* selective.
**Elektivnährboden,** *m.* (*Bact.*) selective medium.
**Elektric-.** see Elektriz-.
**elektrifizieren,** *v.t.* electrify.
**Elektrifizierung,** *f.* electrification.
**Elektrik,** *f.* (science of) electricity.
**Elektriker,** *m.* electrician.
**elektrisch,** *a.* electric.
**elektrisierbar,** *a.* electrifiable.
**elektrisieren,** *v.t.* electrify.
**Elektrisierung,** *f.* electrification.
**Elektrizität,** *f.* electricity.
**Elektrizitäts-entladung,** *f.* electric discharge. **-ladung,** *f.* electric charge. **-lehre,** *f.* (science of) electricity. **-leiter,** *m.* electric conductor. **-menge,** *f.* quantity of electricity. **-messer,** *m.* electrometer. **-messung,** *f.* electrometry. **-wage,** *f.* electrometer. **-zeiger,** *m.* electroscope.
**Elektroanalyse,** *f.* electroanalysis.
**elektroanalytisch,** *a.* electroanalytical.
**Elektro-chemie,** *f.* electrochemistry. **-chemiker,** *m.* electrochemist.
**elektrochemisch,** *a.* electrochemical.
**Elektroden-abstand,** *m.* distance between electrodes. **-kohle,** *f.* electrode carbon.
**elektrodenlos,** *a.* electrodeless, without electrodes.
**Elektrodenspannung,** *f.* electrode potential.
**elektrodynamisch,** *a.* electrodynamic.
**Elektro-eisen,** *n.* electric iron, electric steel. **-fluss-stahl,** *m.* electric steel.
**elektrogalvanisch,** *a.* electrogalvanic.
**Elektro-herdofen,** *m.* electric hearth furnace. **-hochofen,** *m.* electric shaft furnace. **-ingenieur,** *m.* electrical engineer. **-karren,** *m.* electric truck. **-korund,** *m.* electrocorundum. fused alumina.
**Elektrolyse,** *f.* electrolysis. **-bad,** *n.* electrolytic bath.
**Elektrolysen-endlauge,** *f.* spent electrolyte. **-schlamm,** *m.* electrolytic slime.
**elektrolysieren,** *v.t.* electrolyze.
**Elektrolyt,** *m.* electrolyte. **-eisen,** *n.* electrolytic iron.
**elektrolytisch,** *a.* electrolytic.
**Elektrolyt-kupfer,** *n.* electrolytic copper. **-nickel,** *n.* electrolytic nickel. **-silber,** *n.* electrolytic silver. **-zinn,** *n.* electrolytic tin.
**elektromagnetisch,** *a.* electromagnetic.
**Elektromagnetismus,** *m.* electromagnetism.
**elektro-mechanisch,** *a.* electromechanical. **-metrisch,** *a.* electrometric.
**Elektromotor,** *m.* electric motor.
**elektromotorisch,** *a.* electromotive.
**Elektron,** *n.* electron; electrum; amber.
**Elektronen-abgabe,** *f.* electron emission. **-bahn,** *f.* electronic path or orbit. **-beugung,** *f.* electron diffraction. **-bremsung,** *f.* deflection or retardation of electrons. **-drall,** *m.* electron spin. **-einfang,** *m.* electron capture.
**elektronenerzeugend,** *a.* generating electrons, electronogenic.
**Elektronen-gas,** *n.* electron gas. **-hülle,** *f.* electronic envelope or sheath; electron shell. **-lehre,** *f.* electronics. **-ort,** *n.* electron position or locus. **-physik,** *f.* electronic physics, electronics. **-quelle,** *f.* source of electrons. **-röhre,** *f.* electron tube, vacuum tube. **-rumpf,** *m.* electronic core or kernel. **-schale,** *f.* electron(ic) shell. **-schleuder,** *m.*, **-spritze,** *f.* electron gun. **-sprung,** *m.* electron jump. **-stauung,** *f.* electron accumulation. **-stoss,** *m.* electronic collision or impact. **-strahl,** *m.* electron beam or ray. **-strahlen,** *m.pl.* electron radiation. **-technik,** electronic technology. **-theorie,** *f.* theory of electrons. **-übergang,** *m.* electron transition or migration. **-übermikroskop,** *n.* electronic microscope, supermicroscope. **-unterhülle,** *f.* electron subshell. **-welle,** *f.* electron wave. **-wolke,** *f.* cloud of electrons. **-wucht,** *f.* electronic collision force. **-zahl,** *f.* number of electrons.
**Elektronik,** *f.* electronics.
**Elektroniker,** *m.* electronic technician, electronician.
**elektronisch,** *a.* electronic.
**Elektroofen,** *m.* electric furnace.
**elektrooptisch,** *a.* electro-optic.
**Elektro-phor,** *m.* electrophorus. **-phorese,** *f.* electrophoresis.
**elektroplattieren,** *v.t.* electroplate.
**Elektro-plattierung,** *f.* electroplating. **-porzellan,** *n.* electrical porcelain. **-positivität,** *f.* electropositive state or quality. **-raffination,** *f.* electrorefining. **-roheisen,** *n.* (*Iron*) electric pig. **-schmelzen,** *n.* electric smelting. **-schweissung,** *f.* electric welding.
**elektroskopisch,** *a.* electroscopic.
**Elektro-stahl,** *m.* electric steel. **-statik,** *f.* electrostatics.

**elektrostatisch,** *a.* electrostatic.
**Elektro-synthese,** *f.* electrosynthesis. **-technik,** *f.* electrotechnics, electrical engineering. **-techniker,** *m.* electrotechnician, electrical engineer, electrician.
**elektrothermisch,** *a.* electrothermal.
**Elektrowerk,** *n.* electric works.
**Element,** *n.* element; (*Elec.*) cell.
**elementar,** *a.* elementary.
**Elementar-analyse,** *f.* elementary analysis. **-bestandteil,** *m.* elementary constituent. **-ladung,** *f.* elementary charge, unit charge. **-stoff,** *m.* elementary substance, element.
**Elementart,** *f.* (*Elec.*) kind of element, type of cell.
**Elementar-teilchen,** *n.* elementary particle, subatomic particle. **-zelle,** *f.* unit cell.
**Elementen-glas,** *n.* (glass) battery jar. **-messung,** *f.* stoichiometry. **-verwandlung,** *f.* transformation of elements, transmutation.
**Element-gefäss, -glas,** *n.* (*Elec.*) battery jar. **-grösse,** *f.* (*Elec.*) size of cell. **-kohle,** *f.* (*Elec.*) cell carbon. **-schlamm,** *m.* (*Elec.*) battery mud.
**Elemi-harz,** *n.* elemi, gum elemi. **-öl,** *n.* elemi oil. **-säure,** *f.* elemic acid.
**Elen,** *m. & n.* elk.
**Elend,** *n.* misery, distress, penury.
**elend,** *a.* miserable, pitiful, needy, ill.
**Elenfett,** *n.* elk fat.
**Elephanten-.** see Elefanten-.
**elf,** *a.* eleven.
**Elfenbein,** *n.* ivory. — **gebranntes —,** burnt ivory, ivory black. — **künstliches —,** artificial ivory, specif. celluloid.
**elfenbein-ähnlich, -artig,** *a.* ivory-like, eburnean. **-farbig,** *a.* ivory-colored.
**Elfenbein-gelb,** *n.* ivory yellow. **-karton,** *m.* (*Paper*) ivory board. **-küste,** *f.* Ivory Coast. **-nuss,** *f.* ivory nut. **-papier,** *n.* ivory paper. **-schwarz,** *n.* ivory black. **-substanz,** *f.* dentine. **-surrogat,** *n.* ivory substitute, artificial ivory.
**elfenbeinweiss,** *a.* ivory-white.
**elft,** *a.* eleventh.
**eliminieren,** *v.t.* eliminate.
**Eliminierung,** *f.* elimination.
**Ellagengerbsäure,** *f.* ellagic acid.
**Ellagsäure, Ellagensäure,** *f.* ellagic acid.
**Ellbogen,** *m.* elbow.
**Elle,** *f.* ell, yard; ulna.
**Ellenbogen,** *m.* elbow.
**Ellenwaren,** *f.pl.* dry goods, draper's goods.
**Eller,** *f.* alder.
**Ellipsenbahn,** *f.* elliptic orbit.
**ellipsoidförmig,** *a.* ellipsoidal.
**elliptisch,** *a.* elliptic, elliptical.
**Elmsfeuer,** *n.* (*Physics*) (St.) Elmo's fire.
**eloxieren,** *v.t.* eloxate, treat by the eloxal process.
**Else,** *f.* (*Bot.*) alder; shad. **-beere,** *f.* service berry.
**Elsholtziasäure,** *f.* elsholtzic acid.
**elterlich,** *a.* parental.
**Eltern,** *pl.* parents.
**Eluat,** *n.* extracted material, extract.
**eluieren,** *v.t.* elute, wash out, extract.
**elutrieren,** *v.t.* elutriate, wash.
**Eluvialboden,** *m.* eluvial soil.
**Email,** *n.* enamel.
**emailartig,** *a.* enamel-like.
**Email-beiag,** *m.* coating of enamel. **-draht,** *n.* enameled wire. **-farbe,** *f.* enamel color. **-gefäss,** *n.* enameled vessel. **-glas,** *n.* enamel glass, fusible glass. **-lack,** *m.* enamel varnish, enamel.
**Emaille,** *f.* = Email.
**emaillieren,** *v.t.* enamel.
**Emaillier-ofen,** *m.* enameling oven. **-überzug,** *m.* coat of enamel.
**Emaillierung,** *f.* enameling.
**Email-ofenlack,** *m.* stoving enamel. **-schicht,** *f.* coat of enamel.
**Emballage,** *f.* packing; package.
**Embeliasäure,** *f.* embelic acid.
**Embryonal-.** embryonic.
**Emetäthylin,** *n.* emetethyline.
**emetisch,** *a.* emetic.
**Emissions-lehre,** *f.* emission theory. **-verhältnis,** *n.* emissivity. **-vermögen,** *n.* emissive power.
**emittieren,** *v.t.* emit.
**EMK., E.M.K.,** *abbrev.* (elektromotorische Kraft) electromotive force, E.M.F.
**emollieren,** *v.t.* soften.
**empfahl,** *pret.* (of empfehlen) recommended, etc.
**Empfang,** *m.* receipt; reception.
**empfangen,** *v.t.* receive; accept. — *v.i.* conceive.
**Empfänger,** *m.* receiver; addressee, consignee.
**empfänglich,** *a.* receptive, susceptible.
**Empfänglichkeit,** *f.* receptivity, susceptibility.
**Empfängnis,** *n.* conception.
**Empfangs-.** receiving.
**empfehlen,** *v.t.* recommend. — *v.r.* take leave, say goodby; pay one's respects; (impersonally) be proper, be well.
**empfehlenswert,** *a.* to be recommended, advisable; eligible.
**empfiehlt,** *pr. 3 sing.* of empfehlen.
**empfindbar,** *a.* sensible, perceptible; sensitive.
**Empfindbarkeit,** *f.* perceptibility; sensitiveness.
**empfinden,** *v.t.* experience, feel, sense; perceive.
**empfindlich,** *a.* sensitive; susceptible; (of fabrics, etc.) delicate; sensible; irritable; severe. — **— machen,** render sensitive, etc.; sensitize.

**empfindlichen,** *v.t.* render sensitive, sensitize.

**Empfindlich-keit,** *f.* sensitiveness, sensitivity, etc. (see empfindlich). **-machung,** *f.* sensitization.

**Empfindlichung,** *f.* sensitization.

**Empfindung,** *f.* sensation, feeling; sentiment.

**Empfindungszelle,** *f.* sensory cell.

**empföhle,** *pret. subj.* of empfehlen.

**empfohlen,** *p.p.* of empfehlen.

**empirisch,** *a.* empiric(al).

**empor,** *adv.* up, upward, on high.

**emporblühen,** *v.i.* grow, rise, prosper.

**empören,** *v.t.* stir up, excite; shock.

**empor-kommen,** *v.i.* rise, emerge, mount, ascend; prosper. **-steigen,** *v.i.* rise, mount, ascend.

**empyreumatisch,** *a.* empyreumatic.

**emsig,** *a.* diligent, industrious.

**Emulgator,** *m.* emulsifier.

**emulgierbar,** *a.* emulsifiable.

**Emulgierbarkeit,** *f.* emulsifiability.

**emulgieren,** *v.t.* emulsify.

**Emulgier-fähigkeit,** *f.* emulsifying capacity. **-mittel,** *n.* emulsifying agent.

**Emulgierung,** *f.* emulsification.

**Emulgierungs-körper,** *m.* emulsifying agent. **-öl,** *n.* emulsifying oil.

**emulsieren,** *v.t.* emulsify, emulsionize.

**Emulsierung,** *f.* emulsification.

**Emulsierungsmittel,** *n.* emulsifying agent.

**emulsionbildend,** *a.* emulsion-forming, emulsive.

**emulsionieren,** *v.t.* emulsify, emulsionize.

**Emulsionierung,** *f.* emulsification.

**Emulsions-bildner,** *m.* emulsifying agent, emulsifier. **-bildung,** *f.* formation of an emulsion.

**emulsionsfähig,** *a.* emulsifiable.

**Emulsionsfarbe,** *f.* distemper color.

**Emulsionsverfahren,** *n.* emulsion process.

**emulzieren,** *v.t.* emulsify, emulsionize.

**-en.** (1) Case ending of certain nouns. (2) A suffix used like the English -en to form adjectives of material; as, *silbern,* of silver. *eichen,* oaken. (3) In *Org. Chem.,* the equivalent of the English -ene; as, *Propen,* propene.

**Enantiotropie,** *f.* enantiotropy, -tropism.

**End-.** final, terminal, end. **-anzeiger,** *m.* indicator. **-ausbeute,** *f.* final yield. **-bahn,** *f.* final path or orbit. **-destillat,** *n.* final distillate. **-druck,** *m.* final pressure.

**Ende,** *f.* end; limit, termination; point; purpose.

**End-ecke,** *f.*, **-eck,** *n.* terminal angle, summit.

**endemisch,** *a.* endemic.

**enden,** *v.t. & r.* end, terminate, cease.

**End-ergebnis,** *n.* final result; final product. **-ertrag,** *m.* final yield. **-erzeugnis,** *n.* final product, end product. **-fläche,** *f.* terminal face, end face. **-geschwindigkeit,** *f.* terminal velocity. **-glied,** *n.* terminal member, end member.

**endgültig,** *a.* final, conclusive, definitive.

**endigen,** *v.t. & r.* end, terminate, cease.

**Endivie,** *f.* endive.

**End-kohlenstoff,** *m.* terminal carbon (atom). **-lage,** *f.* end position; final position. **-lauge,** *f.* final liquor; spent liquor or solution; (*pl.*) foots. **-laugenkalk,** *m.* (*Agric.*) a product made by treating the mother liquor from potassium chloride manufacture with lime.

**endlich,** *a.* finite; final; late. — *adv.* finally; after all.

**endlos,** *a.* endless; infinite.

**End-lösung,** *f.* final solution. **-niveau,** *n.* final level. **-nüance,** *f.* final shade. **-nutzung,** *f.* final yield.

**Endosmose,** *f.* endosmosis.

**endosmotisch,** *a.* endosmotic.

**Endothel,** *n.* endothelium.

**endotherm, endothermisch,** *a.* endothermic.

**End-produkt,** *n.* final product, end product. **-punkt,** *m.* end point, final point; terminus. **-quantenzahl,** *f.* final quantum number. **-reaktion,** *f.* end reaction, final reaction. **-resultat,** *n.* final result. **-silbe,** *f.* final syllable, termination. **-spannung,** *f.* (*Elec.*) final voltage. **-stadium,** *n.* final stage.

**endständig,** *a.* standing at the end, end, terminal.

**End-stellung,** *f.* end position, final position. **-stück,** *n.* endpiece, terminal piece. **-term,** *m.* final term. **-ung,** *f.* ending, termination. **-urteil,** *n.* final judgment or decision. **-wert,** *m.* final value **-zustand,** *m.* final state or condition. **-zweck,** *m.* end, aim, purpose.

**Energetik,** *f.* energetics.

**energetisch,** *a.* energetic, energy.

**Energie-abgabe,** *f.* release of energy. **-abnahme,** *f.* decrease in energy. **-änderung,** *f.* energy change. **-art.** *f.* form of energy. **-aufspeicherung,** *f.* energy storage. **-aufwand,** *m.* expenditure of energy. **-bedarf,** *m.* energy demand, energy requirement. **-bilanz,** *f.* energy balance. **-gleichung,** *f.* energy equation. **-inhalt,** *m.* energy content. **-leistung,** *f.* energy output.

**energieliefernd,** *a.* energy-producing.

**Energie-niveau,** *n.* energy level. **-prinzip,** *n.* energy principle. **-quant, -quantum,** *n.* energy quantum. **-quantelung,** *f.* energy quantization. **-quelle,** *f.* source of energy.

**energiereich,** *a.* rich in energy.

**Energie-schwelle,** *f.* energy threshold. **-stufe,** *f.* energy step or stage, energy level. **-umwandlung,** *f.* transformation of energy. **-verbrauch,** *m.* consumption of energy. **-verlust,** *m.* loss of energy. **-wirtschaft,** *f* power industry. **-zufuhr,** *f.* addition of energy; supply of energy.

**energisch,** *a.* energetic.

**eng, enge,** *a.* narrow; close, tight.

**engbenachbart,** *a.* closely adjacent.

**Enge,** *f.* narrowness; closeness, tightness.

**Engel,** *m.* angel. **-rot,** *n.* colcothar. **-süss,** *n.* (*Pharm.*) polypody root. **-wurz, -wurzel,** *f.* (*Pharm.*) angelica.

**Enghalsflasche,** *f.* narrow-necked bottle.

**enghalsig,** *a.* narrow-necked.

**Engländer,** *m.* Englishman; monkey wrench.

**Englergrad,** *m.* Engler degree, Engler number.

**englisch,** *a.* English. — **englische Erde,** rotten stone. — **englisches Gewürz, englischer Piment,** pimento, allspice. — **englisches Kollodium,** flexible collodion. — **englische Küpe,** (*Dyeing*) bisulfite zinc-lime vat. — **englisches Leder,** moleskin. — **englisches Pflaster,** court-plaster. — **englisches Pulver,** powder of Algaroth (SbOCl). — **englisches Rot,** English red, colcothar. — **englisches Salz,** Epsom salt. — **englische Schwefelsäure, englisches Vitriolöl,** English sulfuric acid, English oil of vitriol (ordinary concentrated sulfuric acid made by the lead chamber process).

**Englisch-gelb,** *n.* patent yellow (lead oxychloride). **-leder,** *n.* moleskin. **-pflaster,** *n.* court plaster. **-rot,** *n.* colcothar. **-salz,** *n.* Epsom salt.

**eng-lochig,** *a.* with small holes, fine-pored. **-maschig,** *a.* close-meshed, fine-meshed.

**Engobe,** *m.* engobe, slip.

**engobieren,** *v.t.* (*Ceram.*) coat with engobe, slip.

**Engpass,** *m.* narrow pass; "bottleneck."

**engporig,** *a.* fine-pored, finely porous.

**en gros.** wholesale.

**Engrospreis,** *m.* wholesale price.

**enkaustisch,** *a.* encaustic.

**Enkel,** *m.* ankle; grandchild, grandson.

**Enlevage,** *f.* (*Dyeing*) discharge. **-druck,** *m.* discharge printing.

**Enolisierung,** *f.* enolization.

**enorm,** *a.* enormous.

**-ensäure.** -enoic acid (Geneva system).

**ent-.** A verbal prefix having the following principal meanings: (1) With nouns, deprive of, de-, dis-, di-, un-; as *entschwefeln,* desulfurize. (2) With verbs, away, out, dis-, de-, un-, in-, ex-, e-; as *entdecken,* discover; *entwickeln,* evolve. (3) With verbs, begin to, start; as *entflammen,* inflame; *entschlafen,* fall asleep.

**entaktivieren,** *v.t.* render inactive, deactivate.

**Entaktivierung,** *f.* deactivation.

**entalkoholisieren,** *v.t.* dealcoholize.

**entalkylieren,** *v.t.* dealkylate.

**entamidieren,** *v.t.* deprive of amidogen, deaminate, deaminize, deamidize.

**entarretieren,** *v.t.* release; unlock.

**entarsenizieren,** *v.t.* dearsenicate, deprive of arsenic.

**entarten,** *v.i.* degenerate, deteriorate. — *v.t.* render degenerate. — **entartet,** *p.a.* degenerate, debased; abnormal.

**Entartung,** *f.* degeneration, deterioration; degeneracy.

**Entartungsreaktion,** *f.* degeneration reaction.

**Entaschung,** *f.* ash removal.

**entasphaltieren,** *v.t.* remove asphalt from, deasphaltize, deasphalt.

**entbasten,** *v.t.* degum (silk); decorticate.

**Entbastung,** *f.* degumming; decortication.

**Entbastungsmittel,** *n.* degumming or decorticating agent.

**entbehren,** *v.t.* be without, lack; do without, dispense with.

**entbehrlich,** *a.* dispensable, unnecessary.

**entbinden,** *v.t.* disengage, set free, liberate, release; evolve (gases); (*Med.*) deliver.

**Entbindung,** *f.* disengagement, setting free, liberation, release; evolution (of gases); (*Med.*) delivery.

**Entbindungs-flasche,** *f.* generating flask (or bottle). **-rohr,** *n.* delivery tube.

**entbittern,** *v.t.* deprive of bitterness.

**entblättern,** *v.t.* defoliate.

**entbleien,** *v.t.* deprive of lead.

**entblössen,** *v.t.* uncover, strip; deprive.

**entbrausen,** *v.i.* escape with effervescence.

**entbrennen,** *v.i.* light, kindle, be inflamed.

**entbromen,** *v.t.* debrominate.

**entbunden,** *p.p.* (of entbinden) disengaged, etc.

**entbutanisieren,** *v.t.* debutanize.

**entchloren,** *v.t.* dechlorinate.

**Entchlorung,** *f.* dechlorination.

**entdampfen,** *v.t.* free from vapor. — *v.i.* escape as vapor.

**entdecken,** *v.t.* discover; disclose.

**Entdecker,** *m.* discoverer; detector.

**Entdeckung,** *f.* discovery; disclosure.

**entdenaturieren,** *v.t.* free from denaturants.

**entdolomitisieren,** *v.t.* dedolomitize.

**entdunsten,** *v.t.* & *i.* = entdampfen.

**Ente,** *f.* duck; duck-shaped vessel (as one for catalytic hydrogenation); canard.

**entehren,** *v.t.* dishonor.

**enteisen,** *v.t.* de-ice.

**enteisenen,** *v.t.* deprive of iron, deferrize.

**Enteisenung,** *f.* removal of iron, deferrization.

**Enteiser,** *m.* de-icer.

**Enteisungs-flüssigkeit,** *f.* anti-icing fluid. **-mittel,** *n.* de-icing agent, anti-icing fluid.

**entemulsionieren, entemulgieren,** *v.t.* de-emulsify.

**Entenfuss,** *m.* podophyllum, duck's-foot.

**Entfall,** *m.* loss, waste, scrap.

**entfallen,** *v.i.* drop, slip, fall; escape; become waste.
**entfalten,** *v.t.* unfold, unroll, open, display; evolve, develop.
**Entfaltung,** *f.* unfolding, etc. (see entfalten).
**entfärbbar,** *a.* capable of being decolorized or bleached.
**entfärben,** *v.t.* decolorize, bleach; make pale. — *v.r.* fade; grow pale.
**Entfärbung,** *f.* decolorization, decoloration, bleaching; growing pale; paleness.
**Entfärbungs-kohle,** *f.* decolorizing carbon. **-messer,** *m.* decolorimeter. **-mittel,** *n.* decolorizing agent, decolorant.
**entfasern,** *v.t.* free of fibers, string (beans).
**entfernen,** *v.t.* remove. — *v.r.* withdraw, depart. — **entfernt,** *p.a.* far, distant; removed.
**Entfernung,** *f.* removal; distance; retirement; absence.
**Entfernungskraft,** *f.* centrifugal force.
**entfetten,** *v.t.* remove fat or oil or grease from, defat, degrease, ungrease, unoil, scour.
**Entfettung,** *f.* removal of fat, etc. (see entfetten).
**Entfettungsmittel,** *n.* scouring agent, degreasing agent; (*Med.*) remedy for obesity.
**Entfeuchter,** *m.* desiccator.
**entfilzen,** *v.t.* unfelt.
**entflammbar,** *a.* flammable, inflammable.
**Entflammbarkeit,** *f.* (in)flammability.
**entflammen,** *v.t.* inflame, kindle. — *v.r.* (of kerosene, etc.) flash.
**Entflammprüfung,** *f.* ignition test; flash test.
**Entflammung,** *f.* inflammation; flash.
**Entflammungs-probe,** *f.* flash test. **-punkt,** *m.* flashing point, flash point. **-temperatur,** *f.* kindling temperature (of kerosene, etc.), flash point.
**entfleischen,** *v.t.* strip of flesh, flesh.
**entfliessen,** *v.i.* flow; emanate.
**entflocken,** *v.t. & i.* deflocculate.
**Entflockung,** *f.* deflocculation.
**entfremden,** *v.t.* estrange; abandon; conceal.
**entführen,** *v.t.* carry off.
**entfuseln,** *v.t.* remove fusel oil from, rectify.
**entgasen,** *v.t.* extract gas from, degas, outgas.
**Entgasung,** *f.* degassing, outgassing; dry distillation.
**Entgasungs-gas,** *n.* coke-oven gas. **-mittel,** *n.* degassing agent. **-wärme,** *f.* (*Coke*) heat of carbonization.
**entgegen,** *prep.* against; opposite; toward. — *adv.* counter, oppositely. **-arbeiten,** *v.i.* work against, counteract. **-gehen,** *v.i.* go to meet, encounter, face. **-gesetzt,** *p.a.* opposite; opposed, contrary, inverse, reverse. **-halten,** *v.t.* contrast; oppose; offer. **-kommen,** *v.i.* come to meet, approach; coöperate. **-stehen,** *v.i.* be opposite or opposed (to). **-wirken,** *v.i.* work in opposition, counteract.
**entgegnen,** *v.i.* reply, answer.
**entgehen,** *v.i.* escape, avoid.
**entgeisten,** *v.t.* deprive of spirit or alcohol, dealcoholize.
**entgelten,** *v.t.* pay for.
**entgerben,** *v.t.* detan.
**entgerbern,** *v.t.* wash, scour (wool).
**entgiften,** *v.t.* deprive of poison, detoxicate.
**Entgiftung,** *f.* detoxication; (*Mil.*) decontamination.
**Entgiftungs-mittel,** *n.*, **-stoff,** *m.* detoxicating agent; (*Mil.*) decontaminating agent.
**entglasbar,** *a.* devitrifiable.
**entglasen,** *v.t.* devitrify.
**Entglasung,** *f.* devitrification.
**entgolden,** *v.t.* extract the gold from; ungild.
**entgrannen,** *v.t.* awn, hummel (barley).
**entgummieren,** *v.t.* degum.
**enth.,** *abbrev.* (enthaltend) containing.
**enthaaren,** *v.t.* unhair, depilate. — **enthaarend,** *p.a.* depilatory.
**Enthaarung,** *f.* unhairing, depilation.
**Enthaarungsmittel,** *n.* depilatory.
**enthalogenisieren,** *v.t.* dehalogenate, dehalinate.
**enthalten,** *v.t.* contain; include. — *v.r.* abstain.
**enthaltsam,** *a.* abstemious, temperate.
**enthärten,** *v.t.* soften; (*Metal.*) anneal.
**Enthärtung,** *f.* softening; (*Metal.*) annealing.
**Enthärtungsmittel,** *n.* (*Water*) softening agent.
**entharzen,** *v.t.* deprive of resin, deresinify.
**Entharzung,** *f.* freeing from resin, extraction of resin.
**enthäuten,** *v.t.* skin, flay.
**entheben,** *v.t.* exonerate, exempt; dismiss.
**Entholzung,** *f.* delignification.
**enthüllen,** *v.t.* unfold, unveil, disclose.
**enthülsen,** *v.t.* husk, hull, shell, peel, etc.
**enthydratisieren,** *v.t.* dehydrate.
**entionisieren,** *v.t.* de-ionize.
**Entionisierung,** *f.* de-ionization.
**entkalken, entkälken,** *v.t.* decalcify, delime, unlime, free from lime.
**Entkalkung,** *f.* decalcification, deliming.
**Entkalkungs-flüssigkeit,** *f.* decalcifying solution, deliming solution. **-mittel,** *n.* deliming agent.
**entkampfern,** *v.t.* decamphorate, deprive of camphor.
**entkarboxylieren,** *v.t.* deprive of carboxyl, decarboxylate.
**entkeimen,** *v.t.* degerminate; sterilize; disinfect. — *v.i.* germinate, sprout.
**Entkeimung,** *f.* removal of germs, degermination; sterilization; disinfection; germination.
**entkieseln,** *v.t.* desilicify.
**Entkieselung,** *f.* desilicification.

**entkleiden,** *v.t.* undress, strip.
**entkletten,** *v.t.* free from burs, debur, bur.
**entkohlen,** *v.t.* decarbonize, decarburize.
**Entkohlung,** *f.* decarbonization, decarburization.
**entkörnen,** *v.t.* = auskörnen.
**entkräften, entkräftigen,** *v.t.* exhaust; debilitate, weaken.
**entkrusten,** *v.t.* descale.
**entkupfern,** *v.t.* free from copper, decopper.
**entkuppeln,** *v.t.* uncouple, disconnect.
**entladen,** *v.t.* discharge; unload. — *v.r.* explode, go off.
**Entlade-spannung,** *f.* (*Elec.*) discharge voltage. **-strom,** *m.* (*Elec.*) discharge current.
**Entladung,** *f.* discharge; unloading.
**Entladungsröhre,** *f.* (*Elec.*) discharge tube, Geissler tube.
**entlang,** *adv.* along.
**entlangstreichen,** *v.i.* move along, pass along.
**entlassen,** *v.t.* let go, dismiss, discharge.
**entlasten,** *v.t.* unload, discharge; release, disengage, relieve.
**entlauben,** *v.t.* defoliate, strip of leaves.
**entlausen,** *v.t.* delouse.
**entleeren,** *v.t.* empty, discharge; deflate; drain.
**Entleerung,** *f.* emptying, discharging, discharge, drainage, deflation.
**Entleerungskammer,** *f.* discharging chamber.
**entlegen,** *a.* distant, remote.
**entlehnen,** *v.t.* borrow, take, derive.
**entleimen,** *v.t.* degum; desize; unglue.
**entleuchten,** *v.t.* deprive of light, render nonluminous. — *v.i.* shine, radiate.
**entlüften,** *v.t.* deprive of air, deaerate, exhaust; ventilate.
**Entlüfter,** *m.* exhauster; deaerator; ventilator.
**Entlüftungs-rohr,** *n.* vacuum pipe or tube; ventilating pipe. **-ventil,** *n.* deaerating valve, vent valve.
**entmagnetisieren,** *v.t.* demagnetize.
**entmanganieren, entmanganisieren,** *v.t.* demanganize.
**Entmanganung,** *f.* demanganization.
**Entmessingung,** *f.* debrassing.
**entmethylieren,** *v.t.* demethylate.
**Entmilzung,** *f.* splenectomy.
**entmischen,** *v.t.* & *i.* separate into component parts, disintegrate, decompose, dissociate, segregate, unmix; demulsify.
**Entmischung,** *f.* disintegration, etc. (see entmischen); (*Metal.*) coring; demulsification.
**entmutigen,** *v.t.* discourage.
**Entnahme,** *f.* taking, etc. (see entnehmen).
**entnässen,** *v.t.* deprive of moisture, dry.
**entnebeln,** *v.t.* free from mist, fog, or fume.
**Entnebelung,** *f.* mist or fume dispersion.
**entnehmen,** *v.t.* take; take out, withdraw, abstract; draw, borrow; infer.
**entnimmt,** *pr. 3 sing.* (of entnehmen) takes, etc.
**entnommen,** *p.p.* taken, etc. (see entnehmen).
**entölen,** *v.t* remove oil from, unoil, de-oil.
**Entomologe,** *m.* entomologist.
**Entoplasma,** *n.* endoplasm.
**entorientieren,** *v.t.* deorient.
**entparaffinieren,** *v.t.* free from paraffin, dewax.
**entpechen,** *v.t.* free from pitch.
**entpesten,** *v.t.* disinfect.
**entphenolen,** *v.t.* dephenolize, dephenolate.
**entphosphern, entphosphoren,** *v.t.* dephosphorize.
**Entphospherung, Entphosphorung,** *f.* dephosphorization.
**Entpolymerisation, Entpolymerisierung,** *f.* depolymerization.
**entpressen,** *v.t.* press out, squeeze out; extort.
**entpropanisieren,** *v.t.* depropanize.
**Entquellung,** *f.* shrinkage (of gels), syneresis.
**entrahmen,** *v.t.* remove the cream from, skim.
**entraten,** *v.t.* & *i.* dispense (with).
**enträtseln,** *v.t.* unriddle, decipher, explain.
**entregen,** *v.t.* de-energize; deactivate.
**entreissen,** *v.t.* snatch or tear away; rescue.
**entrichten,** *v.t.* pay (debts).
**entriechen,** *v.t.* deodorize.
**Entriechung,** *f.* deodorization.
**entriegeln,** *v.t.* unbar, unblock, release.
**entrieseln,** *v.i.* trickle away.
**entrinden,** *v.t.* decorticate, bark, peel.
**Entropie,** *f.* entropy.
**entrosten,** *v.t.* free from rust, clean the rust from.
**Entrostungsmittel,** *n.* rust remover.
**entröten,** *v.t.* free from red color.
**entrücheln,** *v.t.* deodorize.
**Entrüchelung,** *f.* deodorization.
**entsagen,** *v.t.* renounce, give up.
**entsalzen,** *v.t.* free from salt.
**entsanden,** *v.t.* remove sand from, desand.
**Entsatz,** *m.* relief, rescue.
**entsäuern,** *v.t.* free from acid, deacidify; deoxidize.
**Entsäu(e)rung,** *f.* deacidification; deoxidation.
**entschädigen,** *v.t.* indemnify, compensate for.
**entschälen,** *v.t.* shell, peel; (*Silk*), scour, degum.
**entschäumen,** *v.t.* skim, scum, despumate. — *v.i.* foam off, despumate.
**Entschäumer,** *m.* skimmer, scummer, foam remover; antifoam agent.
**entscheiden,** *v.t.* decide. — **entscheidend,** *p.a.* decisive; final.
**Entscheidung,** *f.* decision; crisis.
**entscheinen,** *v.t.* debloom.
**Entscheinung,** *f.* deblooming.
**Entscheinungsmittel,** *n.* deblooming agent.
**entschieden,** *p.a.* decided, determined.
**entschlacken,** *v.t.* free from slag or dross.

**Entschlackung,** *f.* removal of slag or dross.
**entschlagen,** *v.r.* divest oneself, forget.
**entschlammen,** *v.t.* free from mud or slime.
**entschleimen,** *v.t.* free from slime.
**Entschleimung,** *f.* removal of slime.
**entschlichten,** *v.t.* free from size, desize, undress (linen).
**Entschlichtungs-bad,** *n.* desizing bath. **-mittel,** *n.* desizing agent.
**entschlickern,** *v.t.* (*Metal.*) free from dross.
**entschliessen,** *v.r.* resolve, decide.
**Entschlossenheit,** *f.* resolution, decision.
**Entschluss,** *m.* resolution; decision.
**entschmelzen,** *v.i.* melt away.
**entschuldigen,** *v.t.* excuse.
**entschwefeln,** *v.t.* desulfurize.
**Entschwefelung,** *f.* desulfurization.
**Entschwefelungsmittel,** *n.* desulfurizing agent.
**entschweissen,** *v.t.* degrease, scour (wool).
**entschwinden,** *v.i.* disappear, vanish.
**entseifen,** *v.t.* free from soap, rinse.
**entsetzen,** *v.t.* displace, remove; relieve. — *v.r.* be horrified.
**entsetzlich,** *a.* terrible, atrocious. — *adv.* enormously, awfully.
**entseuchen,** *v.t.* disinfect.
**Entseuchung,** *f.* disinfection.
**entsilbern,** *v.t.* desilver, desilverize.
**Entsilberung,** *f.* desilvering, desilverizing.
**entsilizieren,** *v.t.* desiliconize.
**entsinnen,** *v.r.* remember.
**entsintern,** *v.t.* desinter.
**entspannen,** *v.t.* = abspannen.
**Entspannung,** *f.* = Abspannung; (*Petroleum*) flash evaporation.
**Entspannungs-trommel,** *f.* (*Petroleum*) flash drum. **-turm,** *m.* (*Petroleum*) flash tower. **-ventil,** *n.* relief valve.
**entspr.,** *abbrev.* of entsprechend.
**entsprechen,** *v.i.* correspond; answer. — **entsprechend,** *p.a.* corresponding; concordant; suitable; according (to).
**entspringen,** *v.i.* spring, arise; escape.
**entstählen,** *v.t.* (*Metal.*) soften.
**entstand,** *pret.* (of entstehen) arose, etc.
**entstänkern,** *v.t.* deodorize.
**Entstänkerung,** *f.* deodorization.
**Entstänkerungspatrone,** *f.* deodorizing cartridge.
**entstauben,** *v.t.* free from dust; dust (off).
**Entstaubung,** *f.* dust removal.
**entstehen,** *v.i.* arise, originate; be formed; result. — **eben entstehend,** nascent; incipient.
**Entstehung,** *f.* origin, genesis, formation, nascence.
**Entstehungs-art, -weise,** *f.* mode of origin. **-moment,** *n.* moment of formation. **-zentrum,** *n.* center of origin. **-zustand,** *m.* nascent state; embryonic state.
**entsteinen,** *v.t.* remove the stones from, stone, seed.
**Entsteinmaschine,** *f.* stoner, seeder.
**entstellen,** *v.t.* disfigure, distort.
**entströmen,** *v.i.* flow, stream, issue, escape (from).
**enttäuschen,** *v.t.* undeceive, disappoint.
**entteeren,** *v.t.* deprive of tar, detar.
**Entteerung,** *f.* tar removal, tar separation.
**enttrüben,** *v.t.* uncloud, clear (up).
**Entvulkanisation,** *f.* devulcanization.
**entvulkanisieren,** *v.t.* devulcanize.
**entw.,** *abbrev.* (entweder) either.
**Entw.,** *abbrev.* (Entwickelung) evolution, development.
**entwachsen,** *v.t.* dewax. — *v.i.* outgrow.
**Entwaldung,** *f.* deforestation.
**entwärmen,** *v.t.* deprive of heat.
**entwässerbar,** *a.* capable of being dehydrated, etc. (see entwässern).
**entwässern,** *v.t.* free from water, dehydrate; hydro-extract; concentrate, rectify, (*Old Chem.*) dephlegmate; drain. — **entwässert,** *p.a.* freed from water, dehydrated, anhydrous; concentrated, rectified; drained.
**Entwässerung,** *f.* water removal, dehydration; hydro-extraction; desiccation; concentration; drainage; sewerage.
**Entwässerungs-mittel,** *n.* dehydrating agent. **-rohr,** *n.*, **-röhre,** *f.* drain pipe.
**entweder,** *conj.* either.
**entweichen,** *v.i.* escape; leak.
**Entweichung,** *f.* escaping, escape.
**Entweichungsventil,** *n.* escape valve, delivery valve.
**entwerfen,** *v.t.* trace out, design, plan.
**entwerten,** *v.t.* depreciate; cancel (stamps).
**entwesen,** *v.t.* disinfect; free from vermin.
**Entwesung,** *f.* disinfection; freeing from vermin.
**entwickelbar,** *a.* developable.
**entwickeln,** *v.t.* develop; evolve; disengage, generate (gases); unfold, display. — *v.r.* develop; be evolved. — **entwickelnd,** *p.a.* developing, etc.; nascent.
**Entwickelung,** *f.* developing, development; evolution; disengagement, generating (of gases); unfolding, explanation.
**Entwickelungsbad,** *n.* developing bath.
**entwickelungsfähig,** *a.* capable of being developed or evolved; viable.
**Entwickelungs-farbstoff,** *m.* developing dye. **-flüssigkeit,** *f.* (*Photog.*) developing liquid, developer. **-gefäss,** *n.* generating vessel, generator (for gases). **-geschichte,** *f.* history of (the) development. **-geschwindigkeit,** *f.* speed of development. **-kolben,** *m.* generating flask. **-mittel,** *n.* developer. **-rohr,** *n.*, **-röhre,** *f.* delivery tube or pipe.

**entwickelungsträge,** *a.* slow in developing.
**Entwickelungsverfahren,** *n.* process of development or evolution.
**Entwickler,** *m.* generator (for gases); (*Photog. & Dyeing*) developer; evolver, etc. (see entwickeln). **-bottich,** *m.* developing tank. **-schale,** *f.* developing dish or tray.
**Entwicklung,** *f.* = Entwickelung.
**entwirren,** *v.t.* unravel, disentangle.
**entwöhnen,** *v.t.* disaccustom, wean.
**Entwurf,** *m.* sketch, outline, plan, draft.
**entzerren,** *v.t.* correct, rectify, equalize.
**entziehen,** *v.t.* abstract, extract; take away, remove, withdraw, deprive.
**Entziehung,** *f.* abstraction, extraction; removal, withdrawal; deprivation.
**entziffern,** *v.t.* decipher.
**entzinken,** *v.t.* dezinc, free from zinc.
**Entzinkung,** *f.* dezincking, removal of zinc.
**entzinnen,** *v.t.* detin, untin.
**entzischen,** *v.i.* escape with hissing.
**entzücken,** *v.t.* ravish, charm.
**entzuckern,** *v.t.* extract sugar from, deprive of sugar.
**Entzuckerung,** *f.* extraction of sugar.
**Entzug,** *m.* = Entziehung.
**entzündbar,** *a.* flammable, inflammable.
**Entzündbarkeit,** *f.* (in)flammability.
**entzünden,** *v.t.* ignite, kindle, inflame. — *v.r.* take fire, ignite.
**entzundern,** *v.t.* free from scale, descale, scale.
**entzündlich,** *a.* (in)flammable; inflammatory.
**Entzündlichkeit,** *f.* (in)flammability.
**Entzündung,** *f.* ignition, inflammation; (*Med.*) (in combination) -itis.
**Entzündungs-gemisch,** *n.* ignition mixture. **-probe,** *f.* ignition test. **-punkt,** *m.* kindling point, ignition point; (of kerosene, etc.) burning point. **-rohr,** *n.*, **-röhre,** *f.* ignition tube.
**entzwei,** *adv.* in two, asunder.
**entzweit,** *p.a.* at variance.
**Enzian,** *m.* gentian. **-branntwein,** *m.* gentian spirit. **-wurzel,** *f.* gentian root.
**Enzyklopädie,** *f.* encyclopedia.
**Enzymart,** *f.* (kind or sort of) enzyme.
**enzymatisch,** *a.* enzymatic, enzymic.
**Enzymentschlichtung,** *f.* enzyme desizing.
**enzymisch,** *a.* enzymic.
**Enzym-präparat,** *n.* enzyme preparation. **-wirkung,** *f.* enzyme action.
**Eocän, Eozän,** *n.* (*Geol.*) Eocene.
**E.P.,** *abbrev.* (englisches Patent) English patent, British patent; (Erstarrungspunkt) freezing point, solidification point, etc.
**Epheu,** *m.* ivy.
**Epidemie,** *f.* epidemic.
**epidemisch,** *a.* epidemic.
**Epidotisierung,** *f.* epidotization.
**Epihydrinsäure,** *f.* epihydrinic acid.
**Epithel,** *n.* epithelium. **-zelle,** *f.* epithelial cell.
**Epizuckersäure,** *f.* episaccharic acid.
**Eppich,** *m.* celery.
**Eprouvette,** *f.* cylinder (narrow cylindrical vessel), tube, specif. test tube.
**EPS,** *abbrev.* (effektive Pferdestärke) actual horsepower.
**Equisetsäure,** *f.* equisetic (aconitic) acid.
**er,** *pron.* he, it.
**er-.** A verbal prefix which, prefixed to verbs, signifies "out, forth," denoting either the perfecting of an action, as *erfinden*, find out, invent, or the commencement of an action or state, as *erscheinen*, shine forth, appear. With adjectives it signifies "make" or "become"; as, *ergänzen*, make whole, complete; *erkalten*, become cold, cool.
**-er.** (1) A plural ending of some nouns; as, *Männer*, men. (2) A suffix denoting agent, instrument, or some one in close relation, -er, -or, -ist; as, *Erfinder*, inventor; *Heber*, siphon (lifter); *Physiker*, physicist. (3) A suffix forming adjectives from names of cities, etc.; as, *Pariser*, Parisian, Paris.
**Er.,** *abbrev.* (Erstarrungspunkt) freezing point, solidification point.
**erachten,** *v.t.* consider, regard, deem.
**Erachten,** *n.* opinion, judgment. — **meines Erachtens,** in my opinion.
**Erb-.** inheritance, hereditary, genetic.
**erbarmen,** *v.r.* pity, have mercy.
**erbauen,** *v.t.* build, construct; edify.
**Erbauung,** *f.* building, foundation; edification.
**Erbe,** *m.* heir. — *n.* inheritance.
**erbeben,** *v.i.* shake, tremble.
**Erbeinheit,** *f.* (*Biol.*) genetic unit or factor, gene.
**erben,** *v.t.* inherit.
**erbieten,** *v.r.* offer.
**Erbinerde,** *f.* erbia, erbium oxide.
**erbitten,** *v.t.* request; persuade.
**erbittern,** *v.t.* exasperate.
**Erbkrankheit,** *f.* hereditary disease.
**erblasen,** *v.t.* (*Metal.*) subject to or obtain by the blast, blast, blow.
**erblassen,** *v.i.* fade; pale; die.
**erblich,** *a.* hereditary.
**erblicken,** *v.t.* behold, see.
**erbohren,** *v.t.* get by boring, bore.
**erbötig,** *a.* willing, ready.
**erbrechen,** *v.t.* break open; vomit. — *v.r.* vomit.
**erbreiten,** *v.i.* broaden.
**erbringen,** *v.t.* produce, adduce.
**Erbschaft,** *f.* inheritance.
**Erbse,** *f.* pea.
**Erbsen-baum,** *m.* Siberian acacia. **-erz,** *n.* pea ore (form of limonite).

**erbsen-förmig,** *a.* pea-like, pisiform. **-gross,** *a.* of the size of a pea.
**Erbsengrösse,** *f.* pea size.
**erbsengrün,** *a.* pea-green.
**Erbsen-mehl,** *n.* pea flour, pea meal. **-stein,** *m.* peastone, pisolite (a granular limestone).
**Erbskohle,** *f.* pea coal.
**Erbsubstanz,** *f.* (*Biol.*) germ plasm.
**Erd-.** earth, earthy, terrestrial, mineral, ground, soil, geo-. **-ableitung,** *f.* (*Elec.*) earth connection, ground. **-achse,** *f.* axis of the earth.
**erdacht,** *p.a.* devised, invented.
**Erdalkali,** *n.* alkaline earth. **-halogen,** *n.* alkaline-earth halide. **-metall,** *n.* alkaline-earth metal. **-salze,** *n.pl.* salts of the alkaline-earth metals.
**erdalkalisch,** *a.* alkaline-earth.
**Erdapfel,** *m.* potato; cyclamen; mandrake; truffle.
**Erd-arbeit,** *f.* excavating; earthwork. **-art,** *f.* kind or type of earth or soil.
**erdartig,** *a.* earthy.
**Erd-asphalt,** *m.* earthy asphalt; native asphalt. **-ball,** *m.* terrestrial globe. **-balsam,** *m.* petroleum (old name). **-beben,** *n.* earthquake. **-bebenkunde,** *f.* seismology. **-beere,** *f.* strawberry.
**erdbeer-farben, -farbig,** *a.* strawberry-colored.
**Erd-beschleunigung,** *f.* acceleration of gravity. **-beschreibung,** *f.* geography. **-birne,** *f.* Jerusalem artichoke. **-boden,** *m.* ground, soil. **-bohrer,** *m.* soil borer.
**erdbraun,** *a.* khaki.
**Erd-brot,** *n.* sow bread (*Cyclamen europaeum*). **-chlorid,** *n.* chloride of an earth metal.
**Erde,** *f.* earth; soil; ground.
**erdehaltig,** *a.* containing earth, earthy.
**Erdeichel,** *f.* earthnut (peanut, *Arachis hypogaea*, or heath pea, *Lathyrus tuberosus*).
**erden,** *v.t.* (*Elec.*) ground, earth; treat with fuller's earth.
**Erdenge,** *f.* isthmus.
**erdenken,** *v.t.* devise, invent.
**erdenklich,** *a.* conceivable.
**Erdfarbe,** *f.* earthy color, mineral color.
**erd-farbig, -farben,** *a.* earth-colored. **-feucht,** *a.* moist (like damp earth).
**Erd-flachs,** *m.* amianthus. **-forscher,** *m.* geologist. **-gang,** *m.* vein; tunnel, gallery. **-gas,** *n.* natural gas. **-gasbenzin,** *n.* natural gasoline (or petrol), casinghead gasoline. **-gasruss,** *m.* (natural) gas black. **-gelb,** *n.* yellow ocher.
**erdgelb,** *a.* ocherous, ochery.
**Erd-gemisch,** *n.* mixture of earths. **-geruch,** *m.* earthy odor. **-geschmack,** *m.* earthy taste, flavor of the soil. **-geschoss,** *n.* ground floor. **-glas,** *n.* selenite. **-grün,** *n.* = Berggrün; = Grünerde. **-gürtel,** *m.* zone.
**erdhaltig,** *a.* containing earth, earthy.
**Erdharz,** *n.* asphalt, bitumen; fossil resin. — **gelbes —,** amber.
**erdharz-ig, -artig, -haltig,** *a.* asphaltic, bituminous.
**erdichten,** *v.t.* invent, fabricate.
**erdig,** *a.* earthy; terrestrial. — **erdiges Wasser,** natural water containing calcium salts.
**Erd-innere,** *n.* interior of the earth. **-kalk,** *m.* marly limestone.
**Erdkobalt,** *m.* earthy cobalt, asbolite. — **grüner —,** nickel ocher (annabergite); **roter —,** cobalt crust (earthy erythrite); **roter strahliger —,** cobalt bloom (erythrite).
**Erd-kohle,** *f.* earthy coal, lignitic earth. **-körper,** *m.* terrestrial body. **-krume,** *f.* black earth, vegetable mold. **-kruste,** *f.* earth's crust. **-kugel,** *f.* terrestrial globe. **-kunde,** *f.* geography; geology; geognosy.
**erdmagnetisch,** *a.* geomagnetic.
**Erd-mandel,** *f.* chufa (*Cyperus esculentus*), chufa tuber. **-mehl,** *n.* = Kieselgur. **-messkunst,** *f.* geodesy.
**Erdmetall,** *n.* earth metal. — **alkalisches —,** alkaline-earth metal.
**Erdmineral,** *n.* earthy mineral.
**Erdnuss,** *f.* earthnut, ground nut (most commonly the peanut, *Arachis hypogaea*). **-öl,** *n.* peanut oil, arachis oil. **-säure,** *f.* arachidic acid (old name).
**Erdoberfläche,** *f.* earth's surface.
**Erdöl,** *n.* petroleum. **-bearbeitung,** *f.* petroleum refining. **-erzeugnis,** *f.* petroleum product.
**erdölhaltig,** *a.* containing petroleum, petroliferous.
**Erdöl-industrie,** *f.* petroleum (or oil) industry. **-lager,** *n.* petroleum deposit. **-rückstand,** *m.* petroleum residue.
**Erd-oxyd,** *n.* oxide of an earth metal. **-pech,** *n.* mineral pitch, asphalt, bitumen.
**erdpech-artig,** *a.* asphaltic. **-haltig,** *a.* containing asphalt, asphaltic.
**Erd-probe,** *f.* soil sample; soil test. **-rauch,** *m.* fumitory (*Fumaria*). **-reich,** *n.* ground, earth, land. **-rinde,** *f.* earth's crust. **-rohr,** *n.* underground pipe.
**erdrücken,** *v.t.* stifle, smother; repress; crush.
**Erd-salz,** *n.* rock salt; saline efflorescence on soil. **-scheibe,** *f.* = Erdbrot. **-schellack,** *m.* acaroid resin. **-schicht,** *f.* layer of earth, stratum. **-schierling,** *m.* hemlock (*Conium maculatum*). **-schlacke,** *f.* earthy slag. **-schluss,** *m.* (*Elec.*) earth connection, ground. **-scholle,** *f.* clod. **-schwamm,** *m.* mushroom. **-schwefel,** *n.* **-schwefelsamen,** *m.* lycopodium. **-seife,** *f.* mountain soap (species of clay). **-stein,** *m.* eaglestone, aetites. **-strom,** *m.* earth current. **-talg,** *m.* mineral tallow,

hatchettite (or ozocerite). **-talk,** *m.* earthy talc. **-teer,** *m.* mineral tar, maltha, pissasphalt. **-teil,** *m.* part of the world, continent.
**erdulden,** *v.t.* suffer, endure.
**Erdung,** *f.* (*Elec.*) ground(ing), earth(ing).
**Erdverbindung,** *f.* (*Elec.*) ground connection.
**erdverlegt,** *a.* laid in the ground, underground.
**Erd-wachs,** *n.* mineral wax, earth wax (ozocerite). **-wärme,** *f.* heat of the earth.
**-erei.** A suffix forming nouns of action, place, condition, etc., -ing, -ery; as, *Bäckerei*, bakery, baker's trade; *Stickerei*, embroidery.
**ereignen,** *v.r.* happen, occur.
**Ereignis,** *n.* event, occurrence.
**ereilen,** *v.t.* overtake.
**Eremakausie,** *f.* eremacausis (slow combustion).
**erfahren,** *v.t.* learn; hear; experience; undergo. — *p.a.* experienced; expert.
**Erfahrung,** *f.* experience; knowledge, practice.
**erfahrungs-mässig, -gemäss,** *a.* according to experience, empirical; usual.
**Erfahrungswert,** *m.* experimental value, empirical value.
**erfassbar,** *a.* attainable; comprehensible.
**erfassen,** *v.t.* seize, grasp; comprehend; detect.
**Erfassung,** *f.* seizing, etc. (see erfassen).
**erfinden,** *v.t.* invent; find out.
**Erfinder,** *m.* inventor; designer; author.
**Erfindergeist,** *m.* inventive spirit.
**erfinderisch, erfindsam,** *a.* inventive, ingenious.
**Erfindung,** *f.* invention; discovery; device.
**Erfolg,** *m.* result; success.
**erfolgen,** *v.i.* follow, result; take place, occur.
**erfolg-los,** *a.* unsuccessful, ineffective. **-reich,** *a.* successful, effective.
**erforderlich,** *a.* requisite, necessary.
**erfordern,** *v.t.* require, demand.
**Erfordernis,** *n.* exigency, necessity; requisite, requirement.
**erforschen,** *v.t.* investigate; explore; discover.
**Erforscher,** *m.* investigator; explorer; discoverer.
**Erforschung,** *f.* investigation, research; exploration; discovery.
**erfragen,** *v.t.* ascertain, inquire.
**erfreuen,** *v.t.* delight, rejoice. — *v.r.* be glad; be possessed.
**erfreulich,** *a.* delightful, gratifying.
**erfreulicherweise,** *adv.* happily, fortunately.
**erfrieren,** *v.i.* freeze; (*Metal.*) chill.
**erfrischen,** *v.t.* refrigerate; freshen, refresh. — **erfrischendes Mittel,** refrigerant.
**Erfrischung,** *f.* refrigeration; refreshing; refreshment.
**Erfrischungsmittel,** *n.* refrigerant; refreshment.
**erfroren,** *p.p.* (of erfrieren) frozen.
**erfüllen,** *v.t.* impregnate; fill, fill up; fulfill.
**ergänzen,** *v.t.* supply, complete, make up, restore, replenish, supplement. — **ergänzend,** *p.a.* complementary, supplementary.
**Ergänzung,** *f.* completion, restoration; supplement; complement; supply, supplying; replenishment.
**Ergänzungs-band,** *m.* supplementary volume, supplement. **-buch,** *n.* supplemental volume, supplement. **-farbe,** *f.* complementary color. **-nährstoff, -stoff,** *m.* accessory food factor, vitamin. **-werk,** *n.* supplement. **-winkel,** *m.* complementary angle.
**Erg.-Bd.,** *abbrev.* (Ergänzungsband) supplementary volume.
**ergeben,** *v.t.* yield; show. — *v.r.* result, appear; submit; devote oneself. — *p.a.* devoted; obedient; resigned.
**ergebenst,** *a.* most humble. — *adv.* yours truly.
**Ergebnis,** *n.* result; product; yield.
**ergebnislos,** *a.* without result, futile.
**ergehen,** *v.i.* be issued; happen; fare.
**ergiebig,** *a.* productive, plentiful, rich.
**Ergiebigkeit,** *f.* richness; productiveness; yield, return; plenty, abundance.
**ergiessen,** *v.t.* & *i.* pour forth, discharge.
**erglänzen,** *v.i.* shine, gleam, sparkle.
**erglühen,** *v.i.* begin to glow, glow. — *v.r.* kindle.
**ergodisch,** *a.* ergodic.
**Ergosterin,** *n.* ergosterol, ergosterin.
**ergreifen,** *v.t.* seize, grasp; resort to; take up; affect, strike.
**ergründen,** *v.t.* investigate; discover; fathom.
**ergrünen,** *v.i.* turn green, green.
**Erguss,** *m.* effusion, discharge, overflow. **-gestein,** *n.* effusive rock.
**erh.,** *abbrev.* (erhitzt) heated.
**Erh.,** *abbrev.* (Erhitzung) heating.
**erhaben,** *a.* raised, elevated; relief; convex (lens); high; sublime, grand, illustrious. — **erhabene Arbeit,** relief, rilievo.
**Erhabenheit,** *f.* elevation; convexity; prominence; relief; grandeur, eminence.
**erhaltbar,** *a.* preservable; obtainable.
**erhalten,** *v.t.* keep, preserve, maintain, support; receive, obtain, get, acquire. — *v.r.* keep; remain steady.
**erhältlich,** *a.* obtainable, available.
**Erhaltung,** *f.* conservation; preservation; maintenance; support; obtaining.
**Erhaltungs-mittel,** *n.* preservative; antiseptic; support. **-umsatz,** *m.* basal metabolism.
**erharten,** *v.i.* harden, set (esp., harden, as distinguished from abbinden).
**erhärten,** *v.t.* harden; confirm, verify; aver. — *v.i.* = erharten.
**Erhärtung,** *f.* hardening; confirmation; declaration.
**erheben,** *v t.* raise. — *v.r.* rise.

**erheblich,** *a.* important, considerable.
**Erhebung,** *f.* raising; elevation; rising; inquiry; collection.
**erheischen,** *v.t.* demand, require.
**erheitern,** *v.t.* brighten; cheer. — *v.r.* clear up; cheer up.
**erhellen,** *v.t.* light up, illuminate; brighten, lighten (colors); (*Photog.*) expose; clarify. — *v.i.* become clear, appear.
**Erhellung,** *f.* illumination; (*Photog.*) exposure.
**erhielt,** *pret.* kept, etc. (see erhalten).
**erhitzen,** *v.t.* heat. — *v.r.* grow hot; become angry. — **erhitzend,** *p.a.* heating; stimulating.
**Erhitzer,** *m.* heater; still.
**Erhitzung,** *f.* heating; growing hot.
**Erhitzungsrückstand,** *m.* residue on heating.
**erhoben,** *p.p.* (of erheben) raised.
**erhöhen,** *v.t.* raise, erect, elevate; heighten, advance, increase; improve.
**Erhöhung,** *f.* raising, etc. (see erhöhen); prominence.
**Erholung,** *f.* recovery; recuperation; recreation, relaxation.
**erhören,** *v.t.* hear; grant.
**erinnern,** *v.t.* remind; state; admonish. — *v.r.* remember.
**Erinnerung,** *f.* memory, recollection; reminder, admonition.
**Eriochromschwarz,** *n.* eriochrome black.
**Erk.,** *abbrev.* (Erkennung) detection, recognition.
**erkalten,** *v.i.* cool, grow cold.
**erkälten,** *v.t.* cool, chill. — *v.r.* catch cold.
**Erkaltung,** *f.* cooling.
**Erkältung,** *f.* cold, catarrh; cooling.
**erkannt,** *p.a.* detected, etc. (see erkennen).
**erkaufen,** *v.t.* purchase, buy; bribe, corrupt.
**erkennbar,** *a.* knowable, discernible, perceptible, recognizable.
**erkennen,** *v.t.* detect, recognize, distinguish, know; acknowledge; (*Med.*) diagnose. — *v.i.* decide, pass sentence.
**erkenntlich,** *a.* grateful.
**Erkenntnis,** *f.* perception; knowledge; decision.
**Erkennung,** *f.* detection, recognition; (*Med.*) diagnosis; trade name.
**Erkennungs-marke,** *f.* identification mark. **-zeichen,** *n.* characteristic, distinctive mark; diagnostic symptom.
**erklärbar,** *a.* explainable, explicable.
**erklären,** *v.t.* explain, illustrate; declare, announce. — *v.r.* explain; grow clear.
**erklärlich,** *a.* evident, obvious, apparent.
**Erklärung,** *f.* explanation, illustration; declaration.
**Erklärungsversuch,** *m.* explanatory experiment; attempted explanation.
**erkranken,** *v.i.* fall ill, sicken.
**erkrankt,** *p.a.* ill, sick, diseased.
**Erkrankung,** *f.* illness, falling sick.
**erkundigen,** *v.r.* inquire.
**Erkundigung,** *f.* inquiry.
**erlangen,** *v.t.* reach, obtain, attain, acquire.
**Erlanger-blau,** *n.* Erlanger blue (a kind of Prussian blue). **-leder,** *n.* glove kid.
**Erlass,** *m.* order, decree, edict; reduction, allowance, remission.
**erlassen,** *v.t.* issue, proclaim; remit, exempt, let off.
**erlauben,** *v.t.* allow, permit.
**Erlaubnis,** *f.* permission; grant; license.
**erlaucht,** *a.* illustrious, noble.
**erläutern,** *v.t.* explain, illustrate.
**Erle,** *f.* alder.
**erleben,** *v.t.* experience, pass thru.
**Erlebnis,** *n.* occurrence, event; experience.
**erledigen,** *v.t.* dispose of, settle, arrange; accomplish, perform; vacate.
**erlegen,** *v.t.* lay down, pay; kill. — *p.p.* of erliegen.
**-erlei.** An adjective ending denoting "kinds"; as, *zweierlei*, of two kinds.
**erleichtern,** *v.t.* make lighter or easier, facilitate, alleviate.
**erleiden,** *v.t.* suffer; undergo.
**Erlen-baum,** *m.* alder (tree). **-holz,** *n.* alder wood. **-kohle,** *f.* alder charcoal.
**Erlenmeyerkolben,** *m.* Erlenmeyer flask, conical flask.
**erlesen,** *v.t.* choose, select.
**erleuchten,** *v.t.* illuminate, light.
**erliegen,** *v.i.* sink, succumb.
**erlitten,** *p.p.* (of erleiden) suffered, undergone.
**erlogen,** *p.a.* fabricated, false.
**Erlös,** *m.* proceeds.
**erlöschen,** *v.i.* go out, be extinguished; grow dull or dim; (of lime) slake; expire, become extinct; be effaced. — **erloschen,** *p.a.* gone out, etc. (see erlöschen); dull, dim, dead.
**erlösen,** *v.t.* redeem, save; realize (money).
**ermächtigen,** *v.t.* empower, authorize.
**ermahnen,** *v.t.* exhort, remind.
**Ermangelung, Ermanglung,** *f.* default, want.
**ermässigen,** *v.t.* moderate, reduce.
**ermatten,** *v.t. & i.* tire.
**ermessen,** *v.t.* judge; conceive.
**Ermessen,** *n.* judgment; discretion. — **meines Ermessens,** in my judgment.
**ermitteln,** *v.t.* ascertain, find out.
**Ermittelung,** *f.* ascertaining, ascertainment, finding out, discovery; (*Analysis*) determination.
**ermöglichen,** *v.t.* make possible.
**ermüden,** *v.t.* tire, fatigue, exhaust.
**Ermüdung,** *f.* fatigue; tiring.
**Ermüdungs-festigkeit,** *f.* resistance to fatigue, fatigue strength. **-gift,** *n.* fatigue toxin.

-**grenze,** *f.* endurance limit. -**kampfstoff,** *m.* (*Mil.*) harassing agent. -**prüfung,** *f.* fatigue test. -**riss,** *m.* fatigue crack. -**schutzmittel,** *n.* fatigue inhibitor. -**stoff,** *m.* product of fatigue. -**versuch,** *m.* endurance test, fatigue test.

**ermuntern,** *v.t.* rouse, encourage, urge.

**ermutigen,** *v.t.* encourage.

**-ern.** A suffix forming adjectives of material; as, *eisern,* of iron.

**ernähren,** *v.t.* nourish, feed; support. — **ernährend,** *p.a.* nourishing, nutritive.

**Ernährung,** *f.* nutrition; alimentation; feeding; subsistence; support.

**Ernährungs-bedürfnis,** *n.* food requirement. -**boden,** *m.* nutritive medium. -**flüssigkeit,** *f.* nutritive liquid. -**geschäft,** *n.* nutrition. -**kanal,** *m.* alimentary canal. -**kunde,** *f.* dietetics. -**stoff,** *n.*, -**substanz,** *f.* alimentary substance, food substance, nutrient. -**vergiftung,** *f.* alimentary intoxication. -**versuch,** *m.* experiment on nutrition. -**wert,** *m.* nutritive value.

**ernennen,** *v.t.* nominate, appoint.

**erneuen, erneuern,** *v.t.* renew; refresh (colors); regenerate (steam); repair; restore; renovate.

**erneuert, erneut,** *p.a.* renewed, fresh.

**erniedrigen,** *v.t.* lower; decrease; humble.

**Erniedrigung,** *f.* lowering, depression; humiliation.

**ernst,** *a.* serious, earnest; severe.

**Ernst,** *m.* earnest, earnestness, seriousness; severity.

**Ernstfall,** *m.* emergency.

**ernsthaft,** *a.* earnest, serious; severe.

**Ernte,** *f.* harvest; crop; yield; gathering. -**ertrag,** *m.* crop yield, crop. -**maschine,** *f.* harvester.

**ernten,** *v.t.* harvest, reap, gather.

**erobern,** *v.t.* conquer, win.

**erodieren,** *v.t.* erode.

**eröffnen,** *v.t.* open; discover, disclose; start. — **eröffnend,** *p.a.* opening, disclosing; (*Med.*) aperient.

**Eröffnung,** *f.* opening; beginning; communication; declaration.

**erörterbar,** *a.* discussable, debatable.

**erörtern,** *v.t.* discuss; debate.

**Erörterung,** *f.* discussion; debate.

**erproben,** *v.t.* test, try.

**erquicken,** *v.t.* refresh, revive.

**erraten,** *v.t.* guess, solve.

**erratisch,** *a.* erratic.

**errechnen,** *v.t.* calculate, compute.

**erregbar,** *a.* excitable, irritable, sensitive.

**Erregbarkeit,** *f.* excitability; sensitivity.

**erregen,** *v.t.* excite; stimulate; energize; agitate, irritate. — **erregend,** *p.a.* exciting, stimulating, stimulant. — **erregendes Mittel,** stimulant. — **erregt,** *p.a.* excited; energized; active.

**Erreger,** *m.* exciter, etc. (see erregen). -**feld,** *n.* exciting field. -**flüssigkeit,** *f.* exciting fluid. -**linie,** *f.* exciting line. -**salz,** *n.* exciting salt (as ammonium chloride in the Leclanché cell). -**spannung,** *f.* exciting voltage. -**strom,** *m.* (*Elec.*) exciting current.

**Erregung,** *f.* excitation, etc. (see erregen).

**Erregungsflüssigkeit,** *f.* exciting fluid.

**erreichbar,** *a.* attainable, available.

**erreichen,** *v.t.* reach, attain, obtain, get.

**erretten,** *v.t.* save, rescue.

**errichten,** *v.t.* erect; establish.

**erringen,** *v.t.* obtain, achieve, win.

**Errungenschaft,** *f.* acquisition, achievement, improvement.

**Ersatz,** *m.* substitution, replacement; substitute; equivalent; reserve, spare; compensation.

**Ersatz-.** equivalent; substitute; duplicate, extra, spare. -**brennstoff,** *m.* substitute fuel. -**deckel,** *m.* extra cover, spare cover. -**elektron,** *n.* equivalent or replacing electron. -**fähigkeit,** *f.* capability of replacement; equivalency. -**gewicht,** *n.* equivalent weight, equivalent. -**leim,** *m.* size substitute; glue substitute. -**menge,** *f.* equivalent amount, equivalent. -**mittel,** *n.* substitute, surrogate. -**stoff,** *m.* substitute. -**stück,** *n.*, -**teil,** *m.* extra part, spare part. -**waren,** *f.pl.* substitutes.

**ersaufen,** *v.i.* drown; flood; (of lime) overslake.

**ersäufen,** *v.t.* drown; flood.

**erschaffen,** *v.t.* create.

**erschallen,** *v.i.* sound, resound.

**erscheinen,** *v.i.* appear; be clear.

**Erscheinung,** *f.* phenomenon; appearance; vision.

**Erscheinungsform,** *f.* phase; state; manifestation; form.

**erschlaffen,** *v.t.* & *i.* relax, slacken.

**erschliessen,** *v.t.* open; disclose; infer, conclude.

**erschmelzen,** *v.t.* smelt; melt.

**erschöpfen,** *v.t.* exhaust. — **erschöpfend,** *p.a.* exhausting; exhaustive, thoro.

**Erschöpfung,** *f.* exhaustion.

**erschrecken,** *v.t.* frighten, startle. — *v.i.* & *r.* be frightened. — **erschrocken,** *p.p.* frightened.

**erschüttern,** *v.t.* shake; jar; thrill. — *v.i.* shake; vibrate; (*Mach.*) chatter; tremble.

**erschütternd,** *p.a.* concussive; thrilling.

**Erschütterung,** *f.* concussion; percussion; shaking; vibration; shock; commotion.

**erschütterungs-fest,** *a.* shockproof; vibrationproof. -**frei,** *a.* free from vibration, vibrationless.

**Erschütterungsladung,** *f.* (*Expl.*) cracking charge.
**erschweren,** *v.t.* weight, load (silk, etc.); reduce (dyes); make heavy (or difficult); aggravate.
**Erschwerung,** *f.* weighting, etc. (see erschweren); impediment.
**erschwingen,** *v.t.* afford.
**ersehen,** *v.t.* see, learn, find.
**ersetzbar,** *a.* replaceable, etc. (see ersetzen).
**ersetzen,** *v.t.* replace, substitute, displace; replenish; compensate; recover.
**Ersetzung,** *f.* replacement, substitution, etc. (see ersetzen).
**ersichtlich,** *a.* visible, evident, manifest.
**ersinnen,** *v.t.* devise, conceive.
**ersoffen,** *p.p.* (of ersaufen). drowned; flooded; overslaked.
**ersparen,** *v.t.* spare, save.
**Ersparnis,** *f.* saving(s), economy.
**ersparnishalber,** *adv.* for sake of economy.
**erspriesslich,** *a.* useful, advantageous.
**erst,** *adv.* first; only; yet. — **— recht,** all the more.
**Erst-.** first, initial, original, primary.
**erstarren,** *v.i.* solidify, congeal, freeze; (of cement, etc.) set; harden; coagulate; become stiff or torpid.
**Erstarrung,** *f.* solidification, congelation, etc. (see erstarren).
**Erstarrungs-kurve,** *f.* freezing-point curve. **-punkt,** *m.* freezing point; setting point, solidification point; coagulation point. **-wärme,** *f.* heat evolved on solidification, heat of fusion.
**erstatten,** *v.t.* render, return, restore, repay.
**erstaunen,** *v.i.* be surprised or astonished (at).
**Erstaunen,** *n.* astonishment, surprise.
**Erstausscheidung,** *f.* first separation, first substance to separate.
**erste,** *a.* first, prime, head. — **der (die, das) erstere,** the former. — **in erster Linie,** first of all, primarily.
**erstellen,** *v.t.* prepare, set up, make; plot (a curve).
**erstens,** *adv.* in the first place.
**ersterwähnt,** *a.* first-mentioned.
**erstgenannt,** *a.* first-named, first, former.
**ersticken,** *v.t.* suffocate, choke, stifle.
**erstickend,** *p.a.* suffocating, stifling, asphyxiating. — **erstickender Kampfstoff,** (*Mil.*) lung irritant.
**Erstickung,** *f.* suffocation; choking; asphyxia.
**erstklassig,** *a.* first-class, first-rate.
**erstlich,** *a.* & *adv.* first.
**Erstlings-.** first.
**Erstmilch,** *f.* colostrum.
**Erstp.,** *abbrev.* (Erstarrungspunkt) freezing point.
**erstrahlen,** *v.i.* radiate, gleam, shine.
**erstrangig,** *a.* of first importance.
**erstreben,** *v.t.* strive for; attain.
**erstrebenswert,** *a.* worthy of effort.
**erstrecken,** *v.r.* extend, amount, reach.
**Erststrom,** *m.* (*Elec.*) primary current.
**ersuchen,** *v.t.* request, beseech, apply to.
**ertappen,** *v.t.* catch; surprise.
**erteilen,** *v.t.* give, impart, bestow, allot; grant (patents).
**Erteilungsakten,** *f.pl.* patent record(s).
**ertönen,** *v.i.* sound, resound.
**Ertrag,** *m.* yield; produce; proceeds, profit.
**ertragen,** *v.t.* bear, endure, tolerate.
**erträglich,** *a.* tolerable; middling, passable.
**ertraglos,** *a.* profitless; unproductive.
**Ertragsermittelung,** *f.* ascertainment of yield.
**ertragsfähig,** *a.* productive.
**Ertrags-fähigkeit,** *f.* productivity. **-feststellung,** *f.* determination of yield. **-vermögen,** *n.* producing power, productivity.
**ertränken,** *v.t.* drown.
**ertrinken,** *v.i.* drown.
**ertrüben,** *v.i.* become turbid.
**erübrigen,** *v.i.* remain (to say). — *v.t.* save, spare.
**Erucasäure,** *f.* erucic acid.
**eruieren,** *v.t.* ascertain, find out.
**Eruptiv-gang,** *m.* eruptive vein or lode; dike. **-gestein,** *n.* eruptive rock.
**erw.,** *abbrev.* (erwärmt) warmed; (erwähnt) mentioned.
**erwachen,** *v.i.* wake, awake.
**erwachsen,** *p.a.* grown, adult; arisen.
**erwägen,** *v.t.* consider, weigh.
**erwählen,** *v.t.* choose; elect.
**erwähnen,** *v.t.* mention.
**erwärmen,** *v.t.* warm, heat (moderately).
**Erwärmung,** *f.* warming, (moderate) heating.
**Erwärmungs-kraft,** *f.* heating power, calorific power. **-verlust,** *m.* thermal loss, heat loss.
**erwarten,** *v.t.* expect, await.
**Erwartung,** *f.* expectation, expectance, expectancy.
**Erwartungswert,** *m.* expectancy value, expectancy; expected value.
**erwecken,** *v.t.* waken; rouse, animate.
**erwehren,** *v.r.* keep off, restrain.
**erweichen,** *v.t.* & *i.* soften; soak; plasticize; mellow. — **erweichend,** *p.a.* softening; emollient, demulcent.
**Erweichung,** *f.* softening; mollification.
**Erweichungs-mittel,** *n.* softening agent, softener; (*Pharm.*) emollient, demulcent. **-punkt,** *m.* softening point.
**Erweis,** *m.* proof, demonstration.
**erweisen,** *v.t.* prove; show, demonstrate. — *v.r.* prove, be found.
**erweitern,** *v.t.* widen, expand, extend, enlarge,

distend, dilate. — *v.r.* expand, grow large, dilate.

**Erweiterung,** *f.* widening, etc. (see erweitern).

**Erwerb,** *m.* acquisition; gain, profit; industry.

**erwerben,** *v.t.* acquire; earn, gain.

**erwidern,** *v.t.* return; reply.

**erwies,** *pret.* (of erweisen) proved, showed.

**erwünscht,** *p.a.* wished for, desired; agreeable.

**Erz,** *n.* ore; metal, esp. bronze.

**erz-.** (with adjectives) extremely.

**Erz-.** ore, metalliferous; bronze; arch-, chief, foremost, high. **-abfälle,** *m.pl.* tailings. **-ader,** *f.* ore vein, metalliferous vein.

**erzählen,** *v.t.* tell, relate, report.

**Erz-arbeit,** *f.* (*Tin*) concentrate smelting. **-arbeiter,** *m.* worker in bronze, metal worker.

**erzarm,** *a.* poor in metal, lean.

**Erz-aufbereitung,** *f.* ore dressing. **-brecher,** *m.*, **-brechmaschine,** *f.* ore crusher, ore breaker. **-brocken,** *m.* lump of ore.

**erzdumm,** *a.* extremely stupid.

**Erzeisen,** *n.* mine iron (obtained from ore without addition of fluxes).

**erzeugen,** *v.t.* produce; make, manufacture; generate (as gases); beget.

**Erzeuger,** *m.* producer; generator; maker.

**Erzeugnis,** *n.* production, product; produce.

**Erzeugung,** *f.* production, etc. (see erzeugen).

**Erzeugungsort,** *m.* place of production.

**Erz-fall,** *m.* (*Mining*) ore shoot. **-farbe,** *f.* bronze color.

**erz-farben, -farbig,** *a.* bronze-colored.

**Erzfrischverfahren,** *n.* (*Metal.*) ore process, direct process.

**erzführend,** *p.a.* ore-bearing.

**Erz-gang,** *m.* ore vein, lode. **-gestein,** *n.* ore in mass, rock composed of ore. **-gicht,** *f.* charge of ore. **-giesser,** *m.* bronze founder, brass founder. **-giesserei,** *f.* bronze foundry, brass foundry. **-glühfrischen,** *n.* (*Iron*) refining with ore. **-graupe,** *f.* coarse grain of ore. **-grube,** *f.* mine, pit.

**erzhaltig,** *a.* containing ore, ore-bearing.

**Erzhütte,** *f.* smelting house.

**erziehen,** *v.t.* educate; bring up, rear; raise.

**Erzieher,** *m.* educator; tutor; trainer.

**erziehlich,** *a.* educational.

**erzielen,** *v.t.* obtain, attain; produce, raise.

**erzittern,** *v.i.* tremble, shake, vibrate.

**Erz-kies,** *m.* metalliferous pyrites. **-klein,** *n.* ore fines. **-körper,** *m.* ore body. **-kunde,** *f.* metallurgy. **-lager,** *n.* bed of ore, ore deposit. **-lagerstätte,** *f.* ore deposit. **-laugerei,** *f.* ore leaching; ore leaching plant. **-laugung,** *f.* ore leaching. **-metalle,** *n.pl.* ore metals, heavy metals. **-mittel,** *n.* ore (as opposed to gang). **-mühle,** *f.* ore mill. **-muster,** *n.* ore sample. **-mutter,** *f.* matrix. **-niere,** *f.* kidney-shaped ore. **-ofen,** *m.* ore furnace, smelting furnace. **-probe,** *f.* ore assay, ore assaying; ore sample.

**erzreich,** *a.* rich in ore.

**Erz-röster,** *m.* ore burner, calciner. **-scheider,** *m.* ore separator. **-schlamm,** *m.* ore slime; ore slurry. **-schlauch,** *m.* ore pipe, ore chimney. **-stahl,** *m.* ore steel, mine steel. Cf. Erzeisen. **-staub,** *m.* ore dust. **-stück,** *n.* lump of ore. **-tasche,** *f.* ore pocket; ore bin.

**erzürnen,** *v.t.* anger, provoke. — *v.r.* grow angry; quarrel.

**Erzverhüttung,** *f.* ore reduction.

**erzwingen,** *v.t.* force, enforce; extort.

**Erzzerkleinerung,** *f.* ore crushing.

**es,** *pron.* it. — **— gibt,** there is, there are.

**Eschappéöl,** *n.* regained oil.

**Esche,** *f.* ash, ash tree.

**Eschel,** *m.* zaffer; (*Founding*) black spot.

**Eschen-holz,** *n.* ash wood, ash. **-wurz,** *f.* (*Bot.*) fraxinella.

**Esdragol,** *n.* estragole.

**Esdragon,** *m.* tarragon.

**E.S.E.,** *abbrev.* (elektrostatische Einheit) electrostatic unit.

**Esel,** *m.* ass, donkey; (wooden) horse; (*Mach.*) ram, monkey; (*Brewing*) scooper.

**Eseresamen,** *m.* Calabar bean.

**Esparsette,** *f.* sainfoin.

**Espe,** *f.* aspen.

**Espen-holzschliff,** *m.* aspen wood pulp. **-stoff,** *m.* (*Paper*) aspen pulp.

**essbar,** *a.* edible.

**Esse,** *f.* forge; hearth; chimney, stack.

**Esseisen,** *n.* (*Metal.*) tuyère, twyer.

**essen,** *v.t.* eat.

**Essen,** *n.* eating; meal; food; dish. **-gas,** *n.* chimney gas, stack gas. **-klappe,** *f.* damper.

**essentiell,** *a.* essential.

**Essenz,** *f.* essence.

**Essig,** *m.* vinegar.

**Essig-.** vinegar; acetic, aceto-. **-aal,** *m.*, **-älchen,** *n.* vinegar eel. **-aldehyd,** *n.* acetaldehyde.

**essigartig,** *a.* acetous, acetic; vinegar-like.

**Essig-äther,** *m.* acetic ether (ethyl acetate). **-bereitung,** *f.* vinegar making. **-bildung,** *f.* acetification. **-essenz,** *f.* vinegar essence (concentrated solution of acetic acid). **-ester,** *m.* acetic ester (ethyl acetate). **-fabrik,** *f.* vinegar factory. **-gärung,** *f.* acetic fermentation. **-geist,** *m.* acetone. **-gut,** *n.* alcoholic liquid for quick vinegar process.

**essighaltig,** *a.* containing vinegar.

**Essig-honig,** *m.* oxymel. **-messer,** *m.* acetometer. **-mutter,** *f.* mother (of vinegar). **-naphta,** *f.* ethyl acetate. **-pilz,** *m.* vinegar plant, mother. **-prüfer, -prober,** *m.* vinegar tester, acetometer. **-rose,** *f.* French rose, red rose.

**essigsalpetersauer,** *a.* acetate-nitrate of.
**Essigsalz,** *n.* acetate.
**essigsalzsauer,** *a.* acetate-chloride of, (formerly) acetomuriate of.
**essigsauer,** *a.* of or combined with acetic acid, acetate of; acetic, acetous; sour, like vinegar. — **essigsaure Eisenflüssigkeit,** (*Pharm.*) solution of ferric acetate, liquor ferri acetici. — **essigsaures Salz,** salt of acetic acid, acetate. — **essigsaure Tonerde,** aluminum acetate.
**Essigsäure,** *f.* acetic acid. **-anhydrid,** *n.* acetic anhydride. **-äther,** *m.* acetic ether (ethyl acetate). **-äthylester, -äthyläther,** *m.* ethyl acetate. **-gärung,** *f.* acetic fermentation.
**essigsäurehaltig,** *a.* containing acetic acid.
**Essigsäure-messer,** *m.* acetometer. **-messung,** *f.* acetometry. **-rest,** *m.* acetic acid residue (acetyl). **-salz,** *n.* salt of acetic acid, acetate.
**Essigschaum,** *m.* flower of vinegar.
**essigschwefelsauer,** *a.* acetate-sulfate of.
**Essig-sirup,** *m.* oxymel. **-sprit,** *m.* triple vinegar (10–12 per cent acetic acid). **-ständer,** *m.* vinegar tun, graduator (in the quick vinegar process). **-stube,** *f.* vinegar room (warm room for the quick vinegar process). **-zucker,** *m.* (*Pharm.*) oxysaccharum.
**Ess-kohle,** *f.* forge coal. **-lust,** *f.* appetite. **-waren,** *f.pl.* provisions, eatables.
**Ester,** *m.* ester; specif., ethyl ester.
**ester-ähnlich,** *a.* resembling an ester. **-artig,** *a.* ester-like; in the form of ester.
**Ester-bildung,** *f.* ester formation, esterification. **-gummi,** *n.* ester gum. **-harz,** *n.* resin ester; rosin ester.
**esterifizieren,** *v.t.* esterify.
**Ester-lack,** *m.* ester varnish. **-säure,** *f.* ester acid. **-verseifung,** *f.* ester saponification. **-zahl,** *f.* ester number.
**Estragon,** *m.* tarragon. **-essig,** *m.* tarragon vinegar. **-öl,** *n.* tarragon oil.
**Estrich,** *m.* plaster floor; layer of mortar. **-gips,** *m.* estrich gypsum, flooring plaster (a form of anhydrous calcium sulfate similar to Keene's cement). **-stein,** *m.* a kind of paving brick.
**Estrifikation,** *f.* esterification.
**estrifizieren,** *v.t.* esterify.
**etablieren,** *v.t.* establish.
**Etablissement,** *n.* establishment.
**Etage,** *f.* floor, story; stage; deck.
**Etagenofen,** *m.* shelved oven or kiln.
**Etagere,** *f.* shelf, stand, support, rack.
**Etalonapparat,** *m.* standard(ized) apparatus.
**Etappe,** *f.* stage.
**Etat,** *m.* (financial) statement. **-jahr, Etatsjahr,** *n.* fiscal year.
**Etikette,** *f.*, **Etikett,** *n.* label; tag; etiquet(te).
**etikettieren,** *v.t.* label; tag.
**etliche,** *a.* some, several, a few.
**Etui,** *n.* case, box.
**etw.,** *abbrev.* (etwas) something.
**etwa,** *adv.* perhaps; about; perchance.
**etwaig,** *a.* likely to be, contingent, possible.
**etwas,** *pron.* some, something, somewhat.
**E.T.Z.,** *abbrev.* of *Elektrotechnische Zeitschrift.*
**Eucalyptusöl,** *n.* eucalyptus oil.
**euch,** *pron.* you, to you, yourselves.
**Euchinin,** *n.* (*Pharm.*) euquinine.
**Euchlor, Euchlorin,** *n.* euchlorine.
**eudiometrisch,** *a.* eudiometric.
**euer,** *pron.* of you, your, yours.
**Eugensäure,** *f.* eugenic acid (eugenol).
**Euklas,** *m.* (*Min.*) euclase.
**euklidisch,** *a.* Euclidean.
**Eule,** *f.* owl.
**eurig,** *pron.* yours.
**europäisch,** *a.* European.
**eustasisch,** *a.* Eustachian.
**Eutektikum,** *n.* (*pl.* **Eutektika**) eutectic.
**eutektisch,** *a.* eutectic.
**eutektoidisch,** *a.* eutectoid.
**Euter,** *n.* udder.
**ev.,** *abbrev.* of eventuell.
**evakuieren,** *v.t.* evacuate, empty, exhaust.
**Evakuierungskessel,** *m.* vacuum boiler, vacuum pan.
**evaporieren,** *v.t. & i.* evaporate.
**event.,** *abbrev.* of eventuell.
**eventuell,** *a.* eventual; conditional; contingent. — *adv.* eventually; if necessary, perhaps, or, or in certain cases.
**Everninsäure,** *f.* everninic acid.
**Evernsäure,** *f.* evernic acid.
**evolvieren,** *v.t.* evolve.
**evomieren,** *v.t.* vomit.
**evtl.,** *abbrev.* of eventuell.
**ewig,** *a.* eternal, perpetual. — *adv.* ever, unceasingly.
**Ewigkeit,** *f.* eternity; perpetuity.
**Exaktheit,** *f.* exactness.
**Examen,** *n.* examination.
**Excenter,** *m.* eccentric.
**Excentricität,** *f.* eccentricity.
**excentrisch,** *a.* eccentric.
**Exempel,** *n.* example, instance; problem.
**Exemplar,** *n.* specimen; sample; copy.
**Exhaustor,** *m.* exhauster.
**existenzfähig,** *a.* capable of existence.
**existieren,** *v.i.* exist.
**exkl.,** *abbrev.* of exklusiv.
**exklusiv,** *a.* exclusive. — *adv.* exclusively.
**exolieren,** *v.t.* anodize.
**exosmotisch,** *a.* exosmotic.
**exotherm, exothermisch,** *a.* exothermic.
**expandieren,** *v.t. & r.* expand.
**expedieren,** *v.t.* dispatch, forward.
**Expedition,** *f.* expedition; office.

**Experimentalchemie,** *f.* experimental chemistry.
**Experimentator,** *m.* experimenter; experimentalist.
**experimentell,** *a.* experimental.
**Experimentieranlage,** *f.* experimental equipment or establishment.
**experimentieren,** *v.i.* experiment.
**Experimentierung,** *f.* experimentation.
**Expertist,** *f.* expert investigation or report.
**explizieren,** *v.t.* explain.
**explizit,** *a.* explicit, clear, plain.
**explodierbar,** *a.* explosive, explodable.
**Explodierbarkeit,** *f.* explodability.
**explodieren,** *v.i.* explode. — **explodierend,** *p.a.* exploding, explosive.
**explosibel,** *a.* explosive, explodable.
**Explosibilität,** *f.* explodability.
**explosionsartig,** *a.* explosive.
**Explosionsdruck,** *m.* explosion pressure.
**explosionsfähig,** *a.* explosive.
**Explosions-fähigkeit,** *f.* explosiveness, explosibility. **-gefahr,** *f.* danger of explosion. **-gemisch,** *n.* explosive mixture. **-grenze,** *f.* explosion limit, explosive limit. **-kette,** *f.* explosion chain or train. **-kraft,** *f.* explosive force or power. **-motor,** *m.* explosion engine. **-raum,** *m.* explosion chamber.
**explosionssicher,** *a.* explosion-proof.
**Explosions-stoss,** *m.* explosive impact, explosion impulse. **-ursache,** *f.* cause of explosion. **-vorgang,** *m.* explosive process. **-wärme,** *f.* heat of explosion. **-welle,** *f.* explosion wave.
**Explosiv-geschoss,** *n.* explosive projectile. **-kraft,** *f.* explosive force or power. **-maschine,** *f.* internal-combustion engine. **-stoff,** *m.* explosive substance, explosive. **-stoffchemie,** *f.* chemistry of explosives. **-verbrennung,** *f.* explosive combustion.
**exponieren,** *v.t.* expose; expound.
**Exposition,** *f.* exposure; exposition.
**Expositions-dauer,** *f.* time or duration of exposure. **-zeit,** *f.* time of exposure.
**Exsiccator, Exsikkator,** *m.* exsiccator, desiccator.
**Exsudat,** *n.* exudate, exudation.
**Extr.,** *abbrev.* (Extrakt) extract.
**Extrabenzin,** *n.* supergasoline, high-octane gasoline.
**extrahierbar,** *a.* extractable, extractible.
**extrahieren,** *v.t.* extract.
**Extrahierung,** *f.* extraction, extracting.
**Extraktbrühe,** *f.* extract liquor.
**Extrakteur,** *m.* extractor.
**Extraktgehalt,** *m.* extract content.
**Extraktions-anlage,** *f.* extraction plant. **-apparat,** *m.* extraction apparatus. **-dauer,** *f.* time of extraction. **-flüssigkeit,** *f.* extraction liquid, liquid extract. **-gefäss,** *n.* extraction vessel. **-hülse,** *f.* extraction shell or thimble. **-kolben,** *m.* extraction flask. **-mittel,** *n.* extracting agent, extraction solvent. **-mühle,** *f.* extraction mill. **-rückstand,** *m.* extraction residue.
**Extraktivstoff, Extraktstoff,** *m.* extractive substance or matter, extractive.
**Extraktwolle,** *f.* extract wool, extracted wool.
**extrapolatorisch,** *a.* pertaining to extrapolation. — *adv.* by extrapolation.
**extrapolieren,** *v.t.* extrapolate.
**extremkurz,** *a.* (of waves) ultrashort.
**Extremwert,** *m.* extreme value.
**Exzent-.** see Excent-.
**EZ.,** *abbrev.* (Esterzahl) ester number.

# F

**f.,** *abbrev.* (fest) solid; (fein) fine; (für) for; (folgende) following.
**F.,** *abbrev.* (Fusionspunkt) melting point, m.p., m.; Fahrenheit; (feinste Sorte) finest grade.
**f.a.B.,** *abbrev.* (frei an Bord) free on board, f.o.b.
**Fabel,** *f.* fable; fiction.
**fabelhaft,** *a.* fabulous.
**Fabellehre,** *f.* mythology.
**Fabrik,** *f.* factory, works, mill, plant, establishment. **-anlage,** *f.* manufacturing plant, factory; establishment of a factory.
**Fabrikant,** *m.* manufacturer, maker.
**Fabrik-arbeit,** *f.* factory labor; manufactured article; machine work. **-arbeiter,** *m.* factory worker.
**Fabrikat,** *n.* manufacture, make; product; (textile) fabric.
**Fabrikation,** *f.* manufacturing, manufacture, production, fabrication, processing.
**fabrikationsecht,** *a.* fast to processing.
**Fabrikations-gang,** *m.* manufacturing process, processing. **-prozess,** *m.* manufacturing process. **-wasser,** *n.* water for manufacturing use.
**fabrikatorisch,** *a* manufacturing, factory, industrial.
**Fabrikatur,** *f.* manufacture, make.
**Fabrik-betrieb,** *m.* factory management or practice. **-direktor,** *m.* works manager. **-gold,** *n.* (strong) gold leaf. **-laboratorium,** *n.* factory laboratory, works laboratory. **-leiter,** *m.* works manager. **-marke,** *f.* trademark.
**fabrikmässig,** *a.* & *adv.* by factory methods, on a factory scale, industrial(ly); by machinery.
**Fabrik-öl,** *n.* oil for manufacturing purposes, specif. an inferior grade of olive oil. **-preis,** *m.* factory price. **-ware,** *f.* manufactured article; factory quality. **-wäsche,** *f.* factory scouring (of wool). **-wesen,** *n.* manufacturing industry; factory system. **-zeichen,** *n.* manufacturer's mark, trademark.
**fabrizieren,** *v.t.* make, manufacture.
**fäcal,** *a.* fecal.
**Fäcalien, Fäces,** *pl.* feces.
**facettiert,** *p.a.* faceted.
**-fach.** -fold; as, *hundertfach,* hundredfold.
**Fach,** *n.* branch, department, line, profession, subject; division, compartment, cell; shelf.
**Fach-.** professional, technical, expert. **-arbeiter,** *m.* specialist, skilled worker, expert.
**fachartig,** *a.* cellular.
**Fach-ausdruck,** *m.* technical term or expression. **-bildung,** *f.* professional education, technical education. **-blatt,** *n.* = Fachzeitschrift.
**fächeln,** *v.t.* fan.
**Fächer,** *m.* fan; flapper. **-brenner,** *m.* fantail burner.
**fächerförmig,** *a.* fan-shaped.
**Fächergerste,** *f.* bearded barley.
**fächerig,** *a.* divided into compartments; locular.
**Fachgebiet,** *n.* field of work, specialty.
**fachgemäss,** *a.* workman-like.
**Fach-genosse,** *m.* professional colleague. **-kenntnis,** *f.* technical knowledge. **-kollege,** *m.* professional colleague.
**fach-kundig, -kundlich,** *a.* skilled, expert. **-lich,** *a.* professional, technical.
**Fach-literatur,** *f.* technical (or trade) literature. **-mann,** *m.* professional man, specialist, expert.
**fach-männisch,** *a.* professional, expert. **-mässig,** *a.* professional.
**Fach-ordnung,** *f.* classification. **-schule,** *f.* technical school, special school. **-schrift(en)-tum,** *n.* technical literature. **-sprache,** *f.* technical language, professional terminology.
**fach-sprachlich,** *adv.* in technical language. **-technisch,** *a.* technical.
**Fach-werk,** *n.* framework, bay-work; latticework; checkerwork. **-wissenschaft,** *f.* special branch of science, specialty. **-wort,** *n.* technical word or term. **-wörterbuch,** *n.* technical dictionary. **-zeitschrift,** *f.* special periodical, technical journal, trade journal.
**Facit,** *n.* sum, result, answer.
**Fackel,** *f.* torch. **-baum,** *m.* marsh elder. **-föhre,** *f.* Scotch pine (*Pinus sylvestris*). **-glanz,** *m.* (of wine) perfect clearness. **-kohle,** *f.* cannel coal. **-palme,** *f.* sago palm.
**Façon,** *f.* fashion; cut, style.
**façonnieren,** *v.t.* figure; fashion.
**Factis,** *n.* factice.
**Fädchen,** *n.* small thread, filament.
**fade,** *a.* insipid, flat, stale.
**Faden,** *m.* thread; filament, fiber; (of wood) grain; twine; fathom; (*Sugar*) string.
**faden-ähnlich, -artig, -förmig,** *a.* thread-like, filamentous, filiform.
**Faden-glas,** *n.* spun glass, fiber glass; filigree glass. **-holz,** *n.* cordwood. **-kreuz,** *n.* (*Optics*) cross hairs, reticle. **-länge,** *f.* (*Dyeing*) length of fiber. **-molekül,** *n.* filamentary

molecule. **-netz,** *n.* = Fadenkreuz. **-nudeln,** *f.pl.* vermicelli. **-pilze,** *m.pl.* (*Bot.*) filamentous fungi, Hyphomycetes. **-spannung,** *f.* (*Elec.*) filament voltage. **-strich,** *m.* (*Optics*) spider line, cross hair. **-strom,** *m.* (*Elec.*) filament current. **-zähler,** *m.* thread counter.
**fadenziehend,** *p.a.* ropy, stringy.
**fädig,** *a.* filar, threaded, thready, filaceous.
**Fahamblätter,** *n.pl.* faham leaves (*Angraecum fragrans*).
**fähig,** *a.* capable, able; apt.
**-fähig.** capable of, -able, -ible.
**Fähigkeit,** *f.* capability, ability, capacity.
**fahl,** *a.* fallow (pale, pale yellow); fawn (light yellowish-brown); dun (grayish-brown); earth-colored; ashy; sallow; faded.
**Fahlband,** *n.* (*Mining*) fahlband.
**fahlblau,** *a.* pale blue, grayish-blue.
**Fahlerz,** *n.* fahlerz, fahlore (tetrahedrite-tennantite); (**dunkles**) tetrahedrite; (**lichtes**) tennantite.
**fahl-gelb,** *a.* fallow, yellowish. **-grau,** *a.* grayish, ashy-gray.
**Fahlleder,** *n.* russet leather (for uppers).
**fahlrot,** *a.* fawn, pale yellowish-brown.
**Fahlstein,** *m.* pale gray slate.
**fahnden,** *v.t. & i.* search for, search.
**Fahne,** *f.* flag, "policeman" (for precipitates); flag, standard; vane; (of a dish) marli; (printer's) proof.
**Fahnenschraube,** *f.* wing nut, wing screw.
**Fahrbahn,** *f.* track, runway.
**fahrbar,** *a.* passable; transportable, movable, portable.
**Fahrbenzin,** *n.* (standard) gasoline.
**fahren,** *v.i.* go, travel, ride, drive.
**Fahr-geld,** *n.* fare; freight. **-karte,** *f.* ticket.
**fahrlässig,** *a.* negligent, careless.
**Fahr-rad,** *n.* bicycle. **-stuhl,** *m.* elevator, hoist; wheel chair.
**Fahrt,** *f.* passage, journey, trip, drive.
**Fährte,** *f.* trail, track.
**Fahr-weg,** *m.* wagon road, driveway. **-zeug,** *n.* vehicle; vessel; craft.
**fäkal,** *a.* fecal.
**Fäkalien,** *n.pl.* feces.
**Fäkalstoff,** *m.* fecal substance.
**Faktis,** *n.* factice (rubber substitute).
**faktisch,** *a.* real, actual, *de facto.*
**Faktor,** *m.* factor; manager, agent.
**Faktorentabelle,** *f.* table of factors.
**Faktur, Faktura,** *f.* invoice.
**Fäkulenz,** *f.* feculence, sediment, dregs.
**Fakultät,** *f.* faculty; (*Math.*) factorial. — ***n*** **Fakultät,** factorial *n*, *n*!
**fakultativ,** *a.* optional, facultative.
**falb,** *a.* pale yellow, pale, fallow.
**Fall,** *m.* fall, descent, drop; case; event; yield.
**Fäll-apparat,** *m.* precipitation apparatus. **-bad,** *n.* precipitating bath.
**fällbar,** *a.* precipitable; fit to fell.
**Fäll-barkeit,** *f.* precipitability. **-bottich,** *m.* precipitating vat.
**Falle,** *f.* trap; valve; bolt. — *dative* of Fall.
**fallen,** *v.i.* separate, be deposited; fall, drop; (*Mining*) dip. — **— in (etwas),** verge on; strike.
**Fallen,** *n.* separating, etc. (see fallen); yield, produce.
**fällen,** *v.t.* precipitate; drop; fell; pass (judgment).
**Fäller,** *m.* precipitator.
**Fällflüssigkeit,** *f.* precipitating liquid.
**Fall-gesetz,** *n.* law of gravity. **-hammer,** *m.* drop hammer; (*Expl.*) falling weight. **-hammerprobe,** *f.* (*Expl.*) falling-weight test. **-höhe,** *f.* height of fall; depth of sedimentation.
**fallieren,** *v.i.* fail.
**fällig,** *a.* due, payable.
**Fällkessel,** *m.* precipitating vessel; (*Cellulose*) hydrolyzer.
**Fallkraut,** *n.* (*Bot.*) arnica.
**Fäll-methode,** *f.* precipitation method. **-mittel,** *n.* precipitating agent, precipitant.
**Fall-pendel,** *n.* (*Expl.*) friction pendulum. **-probe,** *f.* drop test.
**Fällprodukt,** *n.* precipitate.
**Fallrohr,** *n.* down pipe, waste pipe.
**falls,** *conj.* in case.
**Fall-schirm,** *m.* parachute. **-schirmleuchte,** *f.* parachute flare. **-silber,** *n.* deposited silver. **-sucht,** *f.* epilepsy. **-tür,** *f.* trapdoor.
**Fällung,** *f.* precipitation, precipitating, etc. (see fällen).
**Fällungs-becherglas,** *n.* precipitation beaker. **-kraft,** *f.* precipitating power. **-mittel,** *n.* precipitant. **-reagens,** *n.* precipitation reagent. **-reaktion,** *f.* precipitation reaction. **-vermögen,** *n.* precipitating power. **-wärme,** *f.* heat of precipitation. **-wert,** *m.* precipitation value.
**Fall-werk,** *n.* drop machine; stamp; pile driver. **-winkel,** *m.* angle of inclination; angle of fall. **-zünder,** *m.* percussion fuse.
**falsch,** *a.* false, counterfeit, pseudo-; artificial; adulterated; wrong; deceitful. **-blau,** *a.* navy blue.
**fälschen,** *v.t.* falsify, adulterate, sophisticate, counterfeit; forge; vitiate.
**Fälscher,** *m.* adulterator; adulterant; falsifier, forger.
**fälschlich,** *a.* false; erroneous. **-erweise,** *adv.* falsely; erroneously.
**Fälschung,** *f.* falsification, etc. (see fälschen); fraud.
**Fälschungs-mittel,** *n.*, **-stoff,** *m.* adulterant.

**-falt.** = -faltig.

**Falt,** *m.* hinge, joint.

**Falte,** *f.* fold, plait, crease; flexure, bend, turn; wrinkle.

**falten,** *v.t.* fold, plait; wrinkle.

**Faltenfilter,** *n.* plaited filter, folded filter, fluted filter.

**falten-frei, -los,** *a.* without folds (or wrinkles), creaseless, smooth.

**Falten-punkt,** *m.* (in a curve) point of sharp change of direction. **-rohr,** *n.* flexible tube or pipe. **-werfen,** *n.* creasing, puckering, crimping.

**Falter,** *m.* folder, creaser; lepidopter (butterfly, moth); third stomach of ruminants.

**faltig,** *a.* having folds, plaits or creases; wrinkled; puckered.

**-faltig, -fältig.** -fold, -ple, -ply; as, *vierfaltig,* fourfold, quadruple, four-ply.

**Faltprobe,** *f.* folding test.

**Faltung,** *f.* folding, plaiting, plication, wrinkling.

**Faltungspunkt,** *m.* plait point, point of plication or folding.

**Falz,** *m.* fold; groove, flute, notch.

**falzen,** *v.t.* fold; groove, flute, rabbet; (*Leather*) pare, shave.

**Falz-festigkeit,** *f.* folding endurance. **-ziegel,** *m.* interlocking tile.

**Fam.,** *abbrev.* (Familie) family.

**Familie,** *f.* family.

**fand,** *pret.* (of finden) found, discovered.

**Fang,** *m.* catch, capture; trap; collector; stab; fang; talon.

**fangen,** *v.t.* catch; capture, secure; soften (hides).

**Fänger,** *m.* catcher, trap.

**Fang-mittel,** *n.* (*Elec.*) gettering agent, getter. **-stoff,** *m.* (*Paper*) stuff from the save-all.

**Fantasie-.** fancy.

**Faradaykäfig,** *m.* Faraday cage.

**faradisch,** *a.* faradic.

**Farb-abänderung,** *f.* change in color. **-abstreichrakel,** *m.* & *f.* color doctor. **-abstufung,** *f.* color gradation. **-anstrich,** *m.* coat of color, coat of paint. **-bad,** *n.* dye bath. **-band,** *n.* typewriter ribbon.

**färbbar,** *a.* colorable, stainable.

**Färbbarkeit,** *f.* colorability, stainability.

**Farb-base,** *f.* color base. **-becher,** *m.* dye beaker (for dyeing tests). **-bestimmung,** *f.* color determination. **-bier,** *n.* dark beer for coloring. **-brühe,** *f.* dye liquor. **-deckschicht,** *f.* color coat. **-druck,** *m.* color printing; color print.

**Farbe,** *f.* color; dye; pigment; stain; paint; hue, tint; (*Leather*) weak ooze, also a container for it; (*Lead*) skimmings.

**Färbe,** *f.* dyeing; staining; coloring. **-artikel,** *m.* (*Calico*) dyed style. **-bad,** *n.* dye bath. **-becher,** *m.* dye beaker, dye pot. **-bier,** *n.* dark beer for coloring. **-bottich,** *m.* dye vat, dye beck. **-brühe,** *f.* dyeing liquor. **-buch,** *n.* dye book.

**farbecht,** *a.* of fast color.

**Farbechtheit,** *f.* color fastness.

**Färbeeigenschaft,** *f.* coloring (or dyeing) property.

**färbefähig,** *a.* capable of being colored, dyed or stained.

**Färbe-fass,** *n.* dye beck, dye tub. **-flechte,** *f.* archil, dyer's moss. **-flotte,** *f.* dye liquor, dye bath. **-flüssigkeit,** *f.* dyeing liquid, dye liquor; staining fluid. **-ginster,** *m.* = Färberginster. **-grad,** *m.* degree of coloring.

**farbehaltend,** *a.* holding color, fast.

**Färbe-holz,** *n.* dyewood. **-kessel,** *m.* dyeing kettle. **-kraft,** *f.* dyeing power; coloring power.

**Färbekraut,** *n.* dyer's weed. — **gelbes —,** yellowweed.

**Färbe-kufe, -küpe,** *f.* dyeing vat, dye vat, dye beck. **-lack,** *m.* lac dye.

**farbelos,** *a.* colorless; achromatic.

**Färbe-malz,** *n.* = Farbmalz. **-mittel,** *n.* coloring agent, pigment, dye.

**färben,** *v.t.* color, dye, stain. — **in der Wolle —,** dye in grain.

**Farben-abbeizmittel,** *n.* paint remover. **-abstreichmesser,** *n.* (*Dyeing*) knife for removing excess dye, color doctor. **-abstufung,** *f.* color gradation. **-abweichung,** *f.* chromatic aberration. **-änderung,** *f.* alteration of color. **-auftrag,** *m.* coat of color. **-bild,** *n.* colored image; colored spectrum. **-bildung,** *f.* color formation, coloration.

**farbenblind,** *a.* color-blind.

**Farben-bogen,** *m.* iris. **-brechung,** *f.* refraction of colors; color blending. **-brühe,** *f.* dyeing liquor, dye liquor. **-buchdruck,** *m.* color printing. **-chemie,** *f.* color chemistry. **-chemiker,** *m.* color chemist, paint chemist.

**farbenchemisch,** *a.* relating to color chemistry or dye chemistry.

**färbend,** *p.a.* coloring, dyeing, staining.

**Farben-distel,** *f.* safflower (*Carthamus tinctorius*). **-druck,** *m.* color printing; color print.

**farbenempfindlich,** *a.* color-sensitive.

**Farben-empfindlichkeit,** *f.* color sensitivity. **-empfindung,** *f.* sensation of color. **-erde,** *f.* colored earth. **-erscheinung,** *f.* color phenomenon; appearance of color.

**farbenerzeugend,** *p.a.* color-producing, chromogenic.

**Farben-erzeuger,** *m.* chromogen. **-erzeugung,** *f.* production of colors. **-fabrik,** *f.* color factory, dye factory. **-fabrikant,** *m.* color maker, dye maker. **-fehler,** *m.* color defect;

chromatic aberration. **-filter,** *n.* color filter, color screen. **-gebung,** *f.* coloring, coloration. **-glanz,** *m.* brilliancy of color. **-glas,** *n.* colored glass, stained glass. **-gleichheit,** *f.* equality or sameness of color. **-grund,** *m.* ground color. **-holz,** *n.* dyewood. **-industrie,** *f.* color industry, paint industry, dye industry. **-karte,** *f.* color chart. **-körper,** *m.* coloring body; coloring matter. **-körperchen,** *n.* pigment granule. **-lack,** *m.* lake. **-lehre,** *f.* science of color, chromatics. **-leiter,** *m.* color scale.

**farbenlos,** *a.* colorless; achromatic.

**Farben-lösungsmittel,** *n.* color solvent, dye solvent. **-malz,** *n.* = Farbmalz. **-mass,** *n.*, **-massstab,** *m.* colorimeter. **-messapparat,** *m.* colorimeter. **-messer,** *m.* chromatometer; colorimeter; *n.* color knife. **-messkunst,** *f.* colorimetry. **-messung,** *f.* measurement of colors, chromatometry, colorimetry. **-mischung,** *f.* color mixing, color blending. **-mühle,** *f.* color mill. **-ofen,** *m.* enameling furnace. **-probe,** *f.* color test; dye test, dye trial. **-rand,** *m.* iris. **-reaktion,** *f.* color reaction. **-reiben,** *n.* color grinding. **-reiber,** *m.* color grinder.

**farben-reich,** *a.* richly colored. **-rein,** *a.* colorless. **-richtig,** *a.* orthochromatic.

**Farben-saum,** *m.* color(ed) fringe. **-schiller,** *m.* play of colors, iridescence, schiller.

**farbenschillernd,** *a.* iridescent, chatoyant.

**Farben-schimmer,** *m.* = Farbenschiller. **-schmelzofen,** *m.* enameling furnace. **-sehen,** *n.* color vision. **-skala,** *f.* color scale, color chart. **-spektrum,** *n.* colored spectrum, color spectrum, chromatic spectrum. **-spiel,** *n.*, **-spielung,** *f.* play of colors. **-steindruck,** *m.* chromolithography. **-stift,** *m.* colored pencil or crayon. **-stoff,** *m.* = Farbstoff. **-strahl,** *m.* colored ray. **-stufe,** *f.* color gradation, shade, tint. **-stufenmesser,** *m.* tintometer. **-tafel,** *f.* color table, color chart. **-ton,** *m.* color tone, hue. **-umschlag,** *m.* color change.

**farbenverändernd,** *a.* altering color or colors.

**Farben-veränderung,** *f.* discoloration; change in color. **-verdünner,** *m.* (color) thinner. **-verdünnung,** *f.* color thinning or dilution. **-vergleich,** *m.* color comparison, color matching. **-waren,** *f.pl.* = Farbwaren. **-wechsel,** *m.* play of colors, change of color. **-wert,** *m.* color value. **-wirkung,** *f.* color effect. **-wurzel,** *f.* madder. **-zerstreuung,** *f.* (*Optics*) chromatic aberration, also dispersion.

**Färbeprozess,** *m.* dyeing process, dyeing; coloring process.

**Färber,** *m.* dyer. **-baum,** *m.* Venetian sumac (*Cotinus coggygria*). **-blume,** *f.* woodwaxen.

**Farberde,** *f.* (*Ceram.*) colored coating clay.

**Färberdistel,** *f.* safflower (*Carthamus tinctorius*); sawwort (*Serratula tinctoria*).

**Färberei,** *f.* dyeing; dye house, dye works.

**Färbereiche,** *f.* dyer's oak, quercitron.

**färbereichemisch,** *a.* pertaining to the chemistry of dyeing.

**Färber-erde,** *f.* Armenian bole. **-flechte,** *f.* archil, dyer's moss. **-flotte,** *f.* dye liquor, dye bath. **-ginster,** *m.* dyer's broom (*Genista tinctoria*). **-holz,** *n.* dyer's wood, dyewood.

**färberisch,** *a.* dyeing, tinctorial.

**Färber-kraut,** *n.* dyer's weed. **-kreuzdorn,** *m.* dyer's buckthorn, specif. *Rhamnus infectoria*. **-küpe,** *f.* dyer's vat, dye vat. **-lack,** *m.* lac dye. **-maulbeerbaum,** *m.* dyer's mulberry (*Morus tinctoria*). **-meister,** *m.* head dyer, foreman dyer. **-moos,** *n.* dyer's moss, archil. **-ochsenzunge,** *f.* dyer's alkanet (*Alkanna tinctoria*). **-öl,** *n.* dyer's oil. **-rinde,** *f.* quercitron bark. **-rot,** *n.* alizarin. **-röte,** *f.* madder. **-saflor,** *m.* safflower.

**Farberscheinung,** *f.* = Farbenerscheinung.

**Färber-waid,** *m.* dyer's woad. **-wau,** *m.* yellowweed. **-wurzel,** *f.* madder.

**Färbe-sieb,** *n.* color strainer, color sieve. **-stoff,** *m.* coloring matter, pigment, dyestuff, dye. **-trog,** *m.* staining trough or box. **-vermögen,** *n.* coloring power, tinctorial power, dyeing value.

**Farbewaren,** *f.pl.* = Farbwaren.

**Färbe-weise,** *f.* method of dyeing, dye process. **-wurzel,** *f.* madder. **-zwecke,** *m.pl.* dyeing purposes.

**Färbfass,** *n.* dyeing vat, dye vat.

**Farbfehler,** *m.* color defect; chromatic aberration.

**farbfertig,** *a.* ready for dyeing (or coloring).

**Farb-film,** *m.* color film. **-filter,** *n.* color filter, color screen. **-flotte,** *f.* dye liquor, dye bath. **-flüssigkeit,** *f.* (*Micros.*) staining solution. **-fülle,** *f.* (*Dyeing*) body. **-gehalt,** *m.* content of dye or color. **-glas,** *n.* color glass, colored glass, stained glass. **-gut,** *n.* goods to be dyed. **-holz,** *n.* dyewood.

**farbig, farbicht,** *a.* colored; stained; chromatic.

**Farbigkeit,** *f.* color (the quality).

**Farb-kissen,** *n.* ink pad, inking pad. **-kochapparat,** *m.* color boiler, color kettle. **-kopie,** *f.* colored copy, color print. **-körper,** *m.* coloring substance, coloring matter.

**farbkorrigiert,** *a.* color-corrected, achromatized.

**Farbkraft,** *f.* coloring power, tinctorial power.

**farbkräftig,** *a.* of strong tinctorial or coloring power, (*Dyeing*) productive.

**Farb-kreide,** *f.* colored crayon. **-küche,** *f.* color shop, color house. **-kuchen,** *m.* color cake, dye cake. **-kunde,** *f.* color (or dye) technology.

**farbl.**, *abbrev.* (farblos) colorless.
**Farblack,** *f.* color lake, lake; lacquer.
**farblos,** *a.* colorless; achromatic.
**Farb-losigkeit,** *f.* colorlessness; achromatism. **-lösung,** *f.* (*Micros.*) staining solution. **-malz,** *n.* coloring malt, amber malt (darkened by roasting). **-material,** *n.* coloring material; dyeing material, dye, dyestuff.
**farbmessend,** *p.a.* colorimetric.
**Farb-messer,** *m.* colorimeter. **-messung,** *f.* colorimetry. **-mine,** *f.* colored lead (for pencils). **-mischer,** *m.* color mixer. **-mittel,** *n.* coloring agent. **-mühle,** *f.* color mill. **-muster,** *n.* color pattern; color sample. **-nuance,** *f.* color shade, tint. **-pflanze,** *f.* dye plant. **-rakel,** *m.* & *f.* color doctor. **-raster,** *m.* color screen. **-reaktion,** *f.* color reaction.
**farbrichtig,** *a.* orthochromatic.
**Farb-säure,** *f.* color acid. **-stärke,** *f.* strength or depth of color, shade. **-stein,** *m.* dyestone. **-stift,** *m.* colored pencil.
**Farbstoff,** *m.* dyestuff, dye; coloring matter; pigment; stain. **-aufnahme,** *f.* dye absorption. **-base,** *f.* color base. **-bildung,** *f.* dye or color formation; (*Biol.*) chromogenesis. **-brühe,** *f.* dye liquor.
**farbstofferzeugend,** *p.a.* chromogenic.
**Farbstof(f)fabrik,** *f.* dye factory.
**farbstoffhaltig,** *a.* containing coloring matter, dye or pigment.
**Farbstofflösung,** *f.* dye solution, staining solution.
**Farb-stufe,** *f.* color gradation, tint, shade. **-substanz,** *f.* coloring substance, coloring matter. **-tiefe,** *f.* depth of color. **-ton,** *m.* color tone, tint. **-treue,** *f.* color fidelity. **-trog,** *m.* color vat, color trough, color box. **-überzug,** *m.* paint coat. **-umschlag,** *m.* color change.
**Färbung,** *f.* dyeing, coloring, coloration, staining, pigmentation; hue, tinge; dye.
**färbungsfähig,** *a.* capable of being dyed, colored, or stained.
**Färbungs-mittel,** *n.* coloring agent, colorant (dye, stain, pigment). **-vermögen,** *n.* tinctorial power, coloring power.
**Farb-veränderung,** *f.* alteration of color. **-wandel,** *m.* color change. **-waren,** *f.pl.* coloring or dyeing materials, dyes, pigments, paints. **-wechsel,** *m.* color change, play of colors. **-werk,** *n.* dye factory, dye works. **-wert,** *m.* color value. **-zelle,** *f.* (*Biol.*) pigment cell. **-zerstäuber,** *m.* color atomizer, paint sprayer. **-zusatz,** *m.* addition or admixture of color.
**Farin, -zucker,** *m.* brown sugar, muscovado.
**Farinade,** *f.* = Farin.
**Farn,** *m.*, **-kraut,** *n.* fern.
**farnkrautartig,** *a.* fern-like.
**Farn-krautöl,** *n.* fern oil. **-wurzel,** *f.* (*Pharm.*) aspidium.
**Farren,** *m.*, **-kraut,** *n.* fern.
**Faschine,** *f.* fagot, fascine.
**Fasel,** *f.* kidney bean.
**faseln,** *v.r.* unravel. — *v.i.* drivel.
**Faser,** *f.* fiber; filament; thread; string; grain (of wood); (*Brewing*) pulp.
**Faser-.** fibrous, fibro-.
**faserähnlich,** *a.* fibroid.
**Faseralaun,** *m.* halotrichite.
**faserartig,** *a.* fibery, fibrous, filamentary; grained.
**Faser-asbest,** *m.* fibrous asbestos. **-asche,** *f.* fiber ash. **-bildung,** *f.* fiber formation, fibration. **-blende,** *f.* fibrous sphalerite.
**Fäserchen,** *n.* little fiber, fibril, filament.
**Faserfärbung,** *f.* coloration of the fiber.
**faserförmig,** *a.* fibrous, filiform.
**Faser-gehalt,** *m.* fiber content; (*Paper*) fiber yield. **-gewebe,** *n.* fibrous tissue; fibrous texture. **-gips,** *m.* fibrous gypsum. **-haut,** *f.* (*Anat.*) fibrous membrane.
**faserig,** *a.* fibrous, fibery, fillamentous, stringy. **-kristallinisch,** *a.* fibrocrystalline.
**Faser-kalk,** *m.* fibrous calcite or aragonite. **-kiesel,** *m.* fibrolite. **-kohle,** *f.* fibrous coal. **-kunde,** *f.* fiber technology.
**faserlos,** *a.* fiberless.
**fasern,** *v.r.* & *i.* feaze, fuzz; (*Paper*) assume a mottled appearance due to different absorptiveness of the fibers.
**Faser-pflanze,** *f.* fiber plant, textile plant. **-platte,** *f.* fiber board. **-richtung,** *f.* direction of the fiber or grain. **-rohstoff,** *m.* fibrous raw material. **-salz,** *n.* fibrous salt. **-schutzmittel,** *n.* fiber-protecting agent.
**Faserstoff,** *m.* fibrin; fibrous material. — **vegetabilischer —,** vegetable fibrin (gluten; cellulose); vegetable fiber.
**faserstoff-artig, -haltig, -ig,** *a.* fibrinous.
**Fasertorf,** *m.* fibrous peat.
**Faserung,** *f.* fibrillation; texture; grain.
**faserzellartig,** *a.* fibrocellular.
**Faserzeolith,** *m.* natrolite.
**fasrig,** *a.* fibrous, fibery, filamentous, stringy.
**Fass,** *n.* cask, barrel, keg; vat, tank, tub, tun; drum.
**fassbar,** *a.* comprehensible; graspable, seizable.
**Fassbier,** *n.* draft beer.
**Fässchen,** *n.* small barrel, keg; drum.
**fassen,** *v.t.* seize, grasp, take; put, mount, set; hold, contain, include; cask, tun (wine, etc.). — *v.i.* take, hold well; (of cement, etc.) set. — *v.r.* compose oneself; express oneself. — **gefasst,** *p.a.* seized, etc.; composed, calm; prepared.
**Fassfärbung,** *f.* drum dyeing.
**fassgar,** *a.* (*Leather*) drum-tanned.

**Fass-gärung,** *f.* cask fermentation. **-gärungs-system,** *n.* (*Brewing*) cleansing system. **-geläger,** *n.* cask deposit, bottoms. **-geschmack,** *m.* taste of the cask. **-hahn,** *m.* spigot, faucet, cock. **-leimung,** *f.* (*Paper*) tub sizing.

**fasslich,** *a.* comprehensible; conceivable.

**Fassloch,** *n.* bunghole.

**Fasson,** *f.* form, shape, design, style.

**fassonieren,** *v.t.* form, shape, fashion.

**Fass-pech,** *n.* cooper's pitch; pitch in casks. **-talg,** *m.* tallow in casks.

**Fassung,** *f.* seizing, etc. (see fassen); casing; mounting, mount; frame; holder; socket; wording; composure.

**Fassungs-raum,** *m.*, **-vermögen,** *n.* capacity, content, volume; power of comprehension.

**Fass-waren,** *f.pl.* goods in casks or barrels. **-zwickel,** *m.* (*Brewing*) try cock.

**fast,** *adv.* almost, nearly.

**Fastage,** *f.* casks, cooperage, barrels and casks.

**fasten,** *v.i.* fast.

**Fastenzeit,** *f.* Lent.

**faul,** *a.* rotten, putrid, bad, decaying; lazy, slow; (*Metal.*) short, brittle. — **fauler Heinz,** (*Old Chem.*) athanor (kind of furnace).

**faulbar,** *a.* putrescible.

**Faul-baum,** *m.* alder buckthorn (*Rhamnus frangula*); bird cherry (*Prunus padus*). **-becken,** *n.* septic tank. **-bruch,** *m.* shortness, brittleness.

**faulbrüchig,** *a.* short, brittle.

**Faul-butte, -bütte,** *f.* fermenting trough, rotting vat.

**Fäule,** *f.* rottenness, putridity; dry rot; blight; (*Mining*) rotten lode.

**faulen,** *v.i.* rot, putrefy; (*Tech.*) ferment. — **faulend,** *p.a.* rotting, putrescent, septic.

**fäulen,** *v.t.* cause to putrefy, rot.

**Faulenzer,** *m.* idler; book of tables, reckoner; (*Brewing*) Y connection.

**Faul-gas,** *n.* sewer gas. **-grube,** *f.* fermenting pit.

**faulig, faulicht,** *a.* rotten, putrid, putrefactive, putrescent; fetid.

**Fäulnis,** *f.* putrefaction, putridness, rottenness, rot, sepsis. **-alkaloid,** *n.* ptomaine. **-bakterien,** *n.pl.* putrefactive bacteria. **-base,** *f.* ptomaine.

**fäulnis-befördernd, -bewirkend,** *a.* septic; putrefactive.

**Fäulnisbeständigkeit,** *f.* resistance to rotting, imputrescibility.

**fäulniserregend,** *a.* putrefactive, septic.

**Fäulniserreger,** *m.* putrefactive agent.

**fäulnisfähig,** *a.* putrefiable, putrescible.

**Fäulnis-gärung,** *f.* putrefactive fermentation, putrefaction. **-geruch,** *m.* putrid or rotten odor. **-gift,** *n.* septic poison.

**fäulnis-hemmend, -hindernd,** *p.a.* antiseptic.

**Fäulniskeim,** *m.* putrefaction germ.

**fäulnis-sicher,** *a.* antifouling. **-unfähig,** *a.* unputrefiable, imputrescible. **-verhindernd, -verhütend,** *a.* antiseptic; antifouling. **-widrig,** *a.* antiseptic. **-wirkend,** *a.* putrefactive, septic.

**Faul-raum,** *m.* (*Sewage*) digestion tank. **-schlamm,** *m.* sapropel (decomposing slime at the bottom of stagnant waters); (*Sewage*) activated sludge; (*Metal.*) debris.

**Faulung, Fäulung,** *f.* rotting, putrefaction, decay.

**Faul-weizen,** *m.* wheat smut. **-werden,** *n.* = Faulung.

**Faum,** *m.* foam, froth.

**Faust,** *f.* fist; grasp, grip. **-formel,** *f.* rule of thumb, rough formula.

**faustgross,** *a.* of the size of a fist.

**Faust-handschuh,** *m.* mitten. **-regel,** *f.* rule of thumb. **-skizze,** *f.* rough sketch.

**Fayence-blau,** *n.* china blue. **-druck,** *m.* (*Calico*) faience printing.

**Fäzes,** *f.pl.* feces.

**Fazett, Fazette,** *f.* facet.

**Fazies,** *f.* facies, face, aspect.

**fbls.,** *abbrev.* (farblos) colorless.

**fechten,** *v.i.* fight; fence.

**Feder,** *f.* feather; plume; pen; (*Mech.*) spring; tongue (of lumber).

**federähnlich,** *a.* feather-like, feathery.

**Federalaun,** *m.* feather alum (halotrichite, alunogen or epsomite); amianthus.

**federartig,** *a.* feather-like, feathery.

**Feder-barometer,** *m.* aneroid barometer. **-bart,** *m.* vane or web of a feather, vexillum. **-busch,** *m.* plume; tuft, crest. **-chen,** *n.* little feather, pen, or spring; (*Bot.*) plumule. **-druckmesser,** *m.* spring manometer. **-erz,** *n.* feather ore (form of jamesonite). **-fahne,** *f.* feather flag, trimmed feather for removing precipitates; = Federbart.

**federförmig,** *a.* feathered, feathery, plumiform.

**Feder-gips,** *m.* fibrous gypsum. **-haar,** *n.* filamentous hair.

**federhart,** *a.* springy, elastic; (*Metal.*) spring-hard.

**Feder-härte,** *f.* (*Metal.*) spring temper. **-harz,** *n.* rubber, caoutchouc; elaterite.

**federicht, federig,** *a.* feathery, plumose, feathered.

**Feder-kiel,** *m.* quill. **-kleid,** *n.* plumage. **-klemme,** *f.* spring clip. **-kraft,** *f.* elastic force; elasticity.

**federkräftig,** *a.* elastic, springy.

**Federmesser,** *n.* penknife.

**federn,** *v.i.* be elastic, spring; lose feathers, molt.

**federnd,** *p.a.* springy, elastic.

**Feder-ring,** *m.* spring washer, lock washer.

**-salz,** *n.* feather salt (any of various fibrous or plumose mineral varieties). **-stahl,** *m.* spring steel.

**Federung,** *f.* springing; springiness, elasticity; spring suspension.

**Feder-ventil,** *n.* spring valve. **-vieh,** *n.* poultry. **-wa(a)ge,** *f.* spring balance. **-wechsel,** *m.* molting. **-weiss,** *n.* amianthus; French chalk; fibrous gypsum. **-zange,** *f.* spring pincers.

**fedrig,** *a.* elastic.

**Fedrigkeit,** *f.* elasticity.

**Fege,** *f.* sieve, screen, riddle.

**fegen,** *v.t.* sweep; clean; winnow.

**Fege-salpeter,** *m.* saltpeter sweepings. **-sand,** *m.* scouring sand. **-schober,** *m.* (*Salt*) scum pan.

**Fegsel,** *n.* sweepings.

**Fehl-.** false, wrong, bad, vain, mis-, mal-. **-anweisung,** *f.* wrong indication, misreading.

**fehlbar,** *a.* fallible.

**Fehl-betrag,** *m.* deficit, deficiency. **-bohrung,** *f.* (*Oil, Gas*) dry hole. **-druck,** *m.* misprint.

**fehlen,** *v.i.* fail; err; be missing, lack.

**Fehler,** *m.* error; fault, defect, flaw; mistake. **-ausgleichung,** *f.* equalization or compensation of errors.

**fehlerbehaftet,** *a.* affected by error.

**Fehler-beseitigung,** *f.* elimination of errors. **-rechnung,** *f.* calculation of errors.

**fehlerfrei,** *a.* faultless, sound, clear, perfect.

**Fehlergrenze,** *f.* limit of error; tolerance.

**fehlerhaft,** *a.* faulty, defective; incorrect.

**Fehlerquelle,** *f.* source of error.

**Fehl-farbe,** *f.* off color. **-geburt,** *f.* miscarriage.

**fehlgehen,** *v.i.* go wrong.

**Fehl-gewächs,** *n.* crop failure. **-gewicht,** *n.* short weight. **-griff,** *m.* mistake, blunder. **-guss,** *m.* spoiled casting, waste.

**Fehlingsche Lösung.** Fehling('s) solution.

**Fehl-kochung,** *f.* defective boiling. **-schluss,** *m.* false inference. **-schuss,** *m.* misfire; miss. **-zündung,** *f.* misfire.

**feien,** *v.t.* make proof, charm (against).

**Feier,** *f.* holiday, festival, celebration; rest.

**feierlich,** *a.* festive; solemn; majestic.

**feiern,** *v.t.* celebrate, observe. — *v.i.* rest from work, strike, be idle.

**Feier-stunde,** *f.* leisure hour. **-tag,** *m.* holiday.

**feig,** *a.* rotten; cowardly.

**Feigbohne,** *f.* lupine.

**feige,** *a.* rotten; cowardly.

**Feige,** *f.* fig.

**Feigen-baum,** *m.* fig tree. **-wachs,** *n.* gondang wax. **-wein,** *m.* fig wine.

**feil,** *a.* for sale; mercenary.

**Feile,** *f.* file; filings; polish.

**feilen,** *v.t.* file; polish. **-hart,** *a.* (*Metal.*) file-hard.

**Feilenhärte,** *f.* (*Metal.*) file hardness.

**Feilhieb,** *m.* file cut, notch.

**Feilicht,** *n.* filings.

**feilschen,** *v.i.* bargain.

**Feil-sel,** *n.*, **-späne,** *m.pl.*, **-staub,** *m.* filings. **-strich,** *m.* file mark, file cut.

**fein,** *a.* fine; thin. — *adv.* finely.

**Fein-arbeit,** *f.* fine or delicate work; (*Metal.*) refining. **-aufspaltung,** *f.* fine separation. **-bau,** *m.* fine structure. **-bewegung,** *f.* (*Micros.*, etc.) slow motion, fine adjustment.

**feinblasig,** *a.* having minute bubbles or blisters.

**Fein-blech,** *n.* (*Metal.*) thin plate, sheet. **-brand,** *m.* highly rectified spirit.

**feinbrennen,** *v.t.* refine (metals); rectify (spirits) highly.

**Feinbrenner,** *m.* refiner.

**Feind,** *m.* enemy, foe.

**feindlich,** *a.* hostile, opposed.

**Feindruckmesser,** *m.* micromanometer.

**Feindschaft,** *f.* hostility, enmity.

**Feine,** *f.* fineness; fines.

**Fein-einstellung,** *f.* fine adjustment. **-eisen,** *n.* refined iron; light section steel.

**feinen, feinern,** *v.t.* refine.

**Fein-erz,** *n.* fine ore. **-farbe,** *f.* (*Dyeing*) pastel shade.

**feinfaserig,** *a.* fine-fibered, fine-grained.

**feinfein,** *a.* very fine, superfine.

**Fein-feuer,** *n.* refinery. **-gefüge,** *n.* fine structure, microstructure; fine texture. **-gehalt,** *m.* fineness (of metals). **-gehaltsstempel,** *m.* hall mark. **-gemisch,** *n.* fine mixture; lean mixture (of motor fuel and air).

**fein-gepulvert,** *p.a.* finely powdered. **-geschichtet,** *a.* thin-layered, thin-bedded. **-gespitzt,** *a.* fine-pointed, sharp-pointed. **-geteilt,** *p.a.* finely divided; finely graduated.

**Fein-gewicht,** *n.* refined weight, exact weight. **-gold,** *n.* fine gold.

**Feinheit,** *f.* fineness; fine detail; smartness.

**Feinheits-grad,** *m.* (degree of) fineness. **-grenze,** *f.* limit of fineness.

**Fein-kies,** *m.* fine ore, fines. **-kohle,** *f.* fine coal, slack. **-korn,** *n.* fine grain. **-korneisen,** *n.* fine-grained iron.

**fein-körnig,** *a.* fine-grained. **-kristallinisch,** *a.* finely crystalline.

**Feinkupfer,** *n.* fine copper.

**fein-lochig,** *a.* fine-holed, fine-pored. **-machen,** *v.t.* refine. **-mahlen,** *v.t.* grind fine, triturate.

**Feinmahlgut,** *n.* material to be pulverized.

**fein-maschig,** *a.* fine-meshed. **-mehlig,** *a.* finely powdered.

**Fein-messen,** *n.* precision measurement. **-messer,** *m.* micrometer; vernier. **-messgerät,** *n.* precision measuring instrument. **-messlehre,** *f.* micrometer caliper or gage. **-mess-**

schraube, *f.* micrometer screw. **-messung,** *f.* precision measurement. **-metall,** *n.* fine metal. **-mühle,** *f.* wood pulp refiner. **-ofen,** *m.* refining furnace. **-passung,** *f.* close fit, tight fit.

**feinporig,** *a.* finely porous.

**Fein-probe,** *f.* delicate test. **-prozess,** *m.* refining process. **-puddeln,** *n.* (*Metal.*) refining puddling.

**fein-pulvern,** *v.t.* powder fine, pulverize. **-pulvrig,** *a.* pulverulent.

**Fein-schlacke,** *f.* refinery slag. **-schlag,** *m.* fines.

**fein-schleifen,** *v.t.* grind smooth. **-schmeckend,** *a.* delicate (in taste); savory.

**Fein-schmecker,** *m.* epicure. **-schraube,** *f.* fine-adjustment screw. **-schrot,** *n.* & *m.* fine groats; (*Brewing*) finely crushed malt.

**feinschuppig,** *a.* fine-scaled, fine-scaly.

**Fein-schutt,** *m.* fine debris. **-sehrohr,** *n.* microscope. **-sicherung,** *f.* (*Elec.*) microfuse. **-silber,** *n.* fine silver, refined silver. **-skala,** *f.* fine scale; vernier. **-sprit,** *m.* (*Alcohol*) fine spirit. **-stein,** *m.* (*Metal.*) converter mat(te).

**feinstellen,** *v.t.* adjust, regulate.

**Feinstellschraube,** *f.* adjusting screw; micrometer screw.

**feinstgepulvert,** *a.* very finely powdered.

**Feinstruktur,** *f.* fine structure.

**feinstrukturell,** *a.* fine-structure.

**Feinstsehrohr,** *n.* ultramicroscope.

**Fein-talg,** *m.* refined tallow. **-treiben,** *n.* (*Metal.*) refining.

**Feinung,** *f.* refining.

**Feinungsschlacke,** *f.* refining slag, final slag.

**Feinverschiebung,** *f.* fine displacement.

**feinverteilt,** *p.a.* finely divided.

**Feinwa(a)ge,** *f.* precision balance.

**fein-zellig,** *a.* fine-celled, finely cellular. **-zerkleinert,** *a.* finely divided, finely ground. **-zerrieben,** *a.* finely ground. **-zerteilt,** *p.a.* finely divided.

**Feinzeug,** *n.* (*Paper*) pulp, stuff. **-holländer,** *m.* (*Paper*) beater, beating engine.

**Fein-zink,** *n.* high-grade zinc. **-zinn,** *n.* grain tin. **-zucker,** *m.* refined sugar.

**feist,** *a.* fat; plump.

**Felbel,** *m.* & *f.* shag (the cloth or its nap).

**Feld,** *n.* field; land, ground; pane, panel, compartment; sphere, scope. **-bau,** *m.* agriculture, farming. **-beleuchtung,** *f.* (*Micros.*) ground illumination. **-brand,** *m.* (*Ceram.*) clamp burning. **-chen,** *n.* small area, (*Bot.*) areole. **-dichte,** *f.* intensity of field. **-dienst,** *m.* active (military) service. **-elektron,** *n.* field electron.

**feldfrei,** *a.* field-free.

**Feld-frucht,** *f.* farm product. **-gerät,** *n.* agricultural implements; field equipage. **gleichung,** *f.* (*Math.*) field equation.

**feldgrau,** *a.* field-gray, military-gray.

**Feld-kamille,** *f.* camomile (*Matricaria chamomilla*). **-klee,** *m.* white clover; rabbit-foot clover. **-kümmel,** *m.* wild caraway; wild thyme. **-messen,** *n.* land surveying. **-ofen,** *m.* (*Ceram.*) clamp kiln. **-rauch,** *m.*, **-raute,** *f.* fumitory (*Fumaria*).

**Feldspat,** *m.* feldspar.

**feldspat-ähnlich, -artig,** *a.* feldspathic.

**Feldspatgestein,** *n.* feldspathic rock.

**feldspat-haltig, -isch,** *a.* feldspathic.

**Feld-stärke,** *f.* field intensity. **-stecher,** *m.* field glass. **-stein,** *m.* compact feldspar; boulder; landmark. **-strom,** *m.* (*Elec.*) field current. **-thymian,** *m.* wild thyme. **-wirtschaft,** *f.* agriculture. **-ziegel,** *m.* clamp brick (brick burnt in a clamp). **-zug,** *m.* campaign.

**Felge,** *f.* fallow (land); rim (of a wheel), felly.

**Fell,** *n.* skin, hide, pelt; (*Rubber*) sheet. **-abfälle,** *m.pl.* skin (or hide) parings or cuttings. **-eisen,** *n.* knapsack; valise; mail bag. **-leim,** *m.* hide glue. **-schmitzer,** *m.* dyer of skins. **-späne,** *m.pl.* hide parings.

**Felpel,** *m.& f.* = Felbel.

**Fels,** *m.* rock; cliff. **-alaun,** *m.* rock alum. **-art,** *f.* (kind or variety of) rock.

**Felsen,** *m.* rock; cliff. **-ader,** *f.* dike. **-alaun,** *m.* rock alum. **-boden,** *m.* rock soil. **-gebirge,** *n.* Rocky Mountains. **-glas,** *n.* ("rock glass") a resistant glass for bomb and combustion tubes. **-glimmer,** *m.* mica.

**felsenhart,** *a.* hard as rock, rocky.

**Felsen-öl,** *n.* rock oil (petroleum). **-salz,** *n.* saltpeter.

**Fels-gestein,** *n.* rock material; rock formation. **-glimmer,** *m.* mica.

**felsig,** *a.* rocky, rock-like.

**Felsöl,** *n.* petroleum.

**Fenchel,** *m.* fennel. **-geruch,** *m.* fennel odor. **-holz,** *n.* sassafras wood. **-öl,** *n.* fennel oil. **-wasser,** *n.* (*Pharm.*) fennel water.

**Fenchocamphersäure,** *f.* fenchocamphoric acid.

**Fenster,** *n.* window. **-glas,** *n.* window glass. **-glimmer,** *m.* muscovite. **-kitt,** *m.* glazier's putty.

**fensterlos,** *a.* windowless.

**Fensterscheibe,** *f.* window pane.

**Ferien,** *f.pl.* holidays, vacation.

**Ferment,** *n.* ferment; enzyme.

**fermentieren,** *v.i.* ferment.

**Fermentierung,** *f.* fermentation.

**Fermentierungsvorgang,** *m.* fermentation process.

**Fermentwirkung,** *f.* ferment action, fermentation.

**fern,** *a.* far, distant.

**Fern-.** far, distant, long-distance, remote, tele-, perspective.

**Fernambukholz, Fernambuk,** *n.* Brazil wood.

**Fern-aufnahme,** *f.* telephotography. **-bild,** *n.* telephotograph; television picture.

**Ferne,** *f.* distance, remoteness.

**ferner,** *a.* farther, further. — *adv.* further, besides.

**Fernewirkung,** *f.* action at a distance.

**Fernglas,** *n.* telescope; field glass.

**fernhalten,** *v.t. & i.* keep away, keep off.

**Fern-hörer,** *m.* telephone receiver. **-messer,** *m.* range finder.

**fernmündlich,** *a.* telephonic.

**Fern-photographie,** *f.* telephotography. **-rakete,** *f.* long-range rocket.

**Fernrohr,** *n.* telescope; field glass.

**fernrohrartig,** *a.* telescope-like, telescopic.

**Fernrohrlupe,** *f.* telescopic magnifier.

**fernsagen,** *v.i.* telephone.

**Fern-schreiber,** *m.* teletypewriter, teleprinter; telegraph.

**Fernseh-.** television.

**Fern-sehen,** *n.* television. **-sicht,** *f.* perspective; vista.

**Fernsprech-.** telephonic, telephone.

**fernsprechen,** *v.i.* telephone.

**Fern-sprecher,** *m.* telephone. **-steuerung,** *f.* remote control. **-wirkung,** *f.* distance effect, action at a distance; remote control. **-zeichnung,** *f.* perspective drawing.

**Ferri-.** ferric, ferri-, iron(III). **-acetat,** *n.* ferric acetate, iron(III) acetate. **-ammonsulfat,** *n.* ammonium ferric sulfate. **-bromid,** *n.* ferric bromide, iron(III) bromide. **-chlorid,** *n.* ferric chloride, iron(III) chloride. **-chlorwasserstoff, -chlorwasserstoffsäure,** *f.* ferrichloric acid. **-cyan,** *n.* ferricyanogen. **-cyaneisen,** *n.* ferrous ferricyanide (Turnbull's blue). **-cyanid,** *n.* ferric cyanide, iron(III) cyanide; ferricyanide.

**Ferricyan-kalium,** *n.* potassium ferricyanide. **-natrium,** *n.* sodium ferricyanide. **-silber,** *n.* silver ferricyanide. **-ür,** *n.* (-ous) ferricyanide. **-verbindung,** *f.* ferricyanide. **-wasserstoff,** *m.*, **-wasserstoffsäure,** *f.* ferricyanic acid.

**Ferridcyankalium,** *n.* potassium ferricyanide.

**Ferrieisencyanür,** *n.* = Ferriferrocyanid.

**Ferriferro-cyanid,** *n.* ferric ferrocyanide (Prussian blue). **-jodid,** *n.* ferrosoferric iodide. **-oxyd,** *n.* ferrosoferric oxide, iron(II,III) oxide.

**Ferri-hydroxyd,** *n.* ferric hydroxide, iron(III) hydroxide. **-ion,** *n.* ferric ion. **-jodat,** *n.* ferric iodate. **-jodid,** *n.* ferric iodide, iron(III) iodide. **-kaliumsulfat,** *n.* ferric potassium sulfate. **-nitrat,** *n.* ferric nitrate, iron(III) nitrate. **-oxyd,** *n.* ferric oxide, iron(III) oxide. **-phosphat,** *n.* ferric phosphate. **-rhodanid,** *n.* ferric thiocyanate (or sulfocyanate). **-salz,** *n.* ferric salt, iron(III) salt. **-sulfat,** *n.* ferric sulfate. **-sulfid,** *n.* ferric sulfide, iron(III) sulfide.

**ferritisch,** *a.* ferritic.

**Ferri-verbindung,** *f.* ferric compound, iron(III) compound. **-zyan,** *n.* ferricyanogen.

**Ferrizyan-.** see Ferricyan-.

**Ferro-.** ferrous, ferro-, ferroso-, iron(II). **-ammonsulfat,** *n.* ammonium ferrous sulfate. **-azetat,** *n.* ferrous acetate, iron(II) acetate. **-bor,** *n.* ferroboron. **-bromid,** *n.* ferrous bromide, iron(II) bromide. **-chlorid,** *n.* ferrous chloride, iron(II) chloride. **-chrom,** *n.* ferrochrome, ferrochromium.

**Ferrocyan,** *n.* ferrocyanogen. **-eisen,** *n.* ferric ferrocyanide (Prussian blue).

**Ferrocyanid,** *n.* ferrous cyanide, iron(II) cyanide; ferrocyanide.

**Ferrocyan-kalium,** *n.* potassium ferrocyanide. **-kupfer,** *n.* cupric ferrocyanide. **-natrium,** *n.* sodium ferrocyanide. **-silber,** *n.* silver ferrocyanide. **-verbindung,** *f.* ferrocyanide. **-wasserstoff,** *m.*, **-wasserstoffsäure,** *f.* ferrocyanic acid. **-zink,** *n.* zinc ferrocyanide. **-zinn,** *n.* tin ferrocyanide.

**Ferroferri-cyanid,** *n.* ferrous ferricyanide. **-oxyd,** *n.* ferrosoferric oxide, iron(II,III) oxide.

**Ferro-hydroxyd,** *n.* ferrous hydroxide, iron(II) hydroxide. **-ion,** *n.* ferrous ion. **-jodid,** *n.* ferrous iodide, iron(II) iodide. **-kaliumsulfat,** *n.* ferrous potassium sulfate. **-karbonat,** *n.* ferrous carbonate. **-legierung,** *f.* ferroalloy.

**ferromagnetisch,** *a.* ferromagnetic.

**Ferro-mangan,** *n.* ferromanganese. **-molybdän,** *n.* ferromolybdenum. **-nitrat,** *n.* ferrous nitrate, iron(II) nitrate. **-oxalat,** *n.* ferrous oxalate. **-oxyd,** *n.* ferrous oxide. **-phosphat,** *n.* ferrous phosphate. **-phosphor,** *n.* ferrophosphorus. **-salz,** *n.* ferrous salt, iron(II) salt. **-silizium,** *n.* ferrosilicon. **-sulfat,** *n.* ferrous sulfate. **-sulfid,** *n.* ferrous sulfide. **-titan,** *n.* ferrotitanium. **-vanadin,** *n.* ferrovanadium. **-verbindung,** *f.* ferrous compound, iron(II) compound. **-wolfram,** *n.* ferrotungsten. **-zirkon,** *n.* ferrozirconium. **-zyan,** *n.* ferrocyanogen.

**Ferrozyan-.** see Ferrocyan-.

**Ferse,** *f.* heel.

**fertig,** *a.* ready; done, finished; ready-made; skilful; insolvent.

**fertigen,** *v.t.* make ready; finish; prepare; make; manufacture; do.

**Fertig-erzeugnis,** *f.* finished product. **-frischofen,** *m.* finishing furnace. **-keit,** *f.* readiness;

skill, dexterity. **-machen,** *n.* finishing. **-macher,** *m.* finisher. **-raffination,** *f.* (*Lead*) refining. **-schlacke,** *f.* (*Metal.*) white slag. **-sinterung,** *f.* (*Metal.*) final sintering. **-stellen,** *n.*, **-stellung,** *f.* finishing.

**Fertigung,** *f.* making ready; making, manufacture, production; doing.

**Fertigware,** *f.* finished article, finished goods.

**Fertilität,** *f.* fertility.

**Ferulasäure,** *f.* ferulic acid.

**fesseln,** *v.t.* fetter, bind; fasten; anchor; captivate.

**fest,** *a.* solid; firm, compact, strong; fast, fixed, tight; stable; permanent; proof; steady. — *adv.* firmly, closely, strongly.

**Fest,** *n.* feast, festival, holiday.

**-fest,** proof, resistant.

**fest-backen,** *v.i.* cake together (on heating), clinker, frit. **-binden,** *v.t.* bind fast, fasten, tie, unite.

**Feste,** *f.* compact rock; fortress.

**fest-fressen,** *v.r.* & *i.* bind fast, seize, jam. **-frieren,** *v.i.* freeze solid, freeze hard. **-gebunden,** *a.* firmly bound or united. **-gewachsen,** *a.* grown fast, grown on. **-geworden,** *p.a.* solidified. **-haften,** *v.i.* cling tight, adhere strongly.

**festhalten,** *v.t.* hold fast, retain; fix; stop, arrest; record. — *v.i.* hold, adhere, cling, stick. — **festhaltend,** *p.a.* adhesive; tenacious, retentive.

**festigen,** *v.t.* make firm, consolidate, fix.

**Festigkeit,** *f.* solidity, etc. (see fest); (of metals) tenacity; (*Mech.*) strength, resistance.

**Festigkeits-grenze,** *f.* (*Mech.*) limit of resistance, breaking point. **-lehre,** *f.* strength of materials. **-probe, -prüfung,** *f.* strength (esp. tensile-strength) testing or test. **-zahl,** *f.* coefficient of resistance.

**fest-kitten,** *v.t.* cement (or lute) tight. **-kleben,** *v.t.* & *i.* stick fast, stick on.

**Festland,** *n.* continent, mainland.

**festlegen,** *v.t.* fix; place; define; stipulate; bed; moor; arrest.

**Festlegung,** *f.* fixation, etc. (see festlegen); convention, agreement.

**festlich,** *a.* festive; solemn, impressive.

**festliegend,** *a.* fixed.

**festmachen,** *v.t.* solidify; consolidate; make fast, fasten, fix; settle.

**Fest-mass,** *n.* solid measure. **-punkt,** *m.* fixed point; fixed target.

**Festschrift,** *f.* festival (or anniversary) publication.

**festsetzen,** *v.t.* establish, settle, fix.

**Fest-setzung,** *f.* establishment, settlement, arrangement; appointment; imprisonment. **-sitz,** *m.* tight fit, snug fit.

**feststehen,** *v.i.* stand fast, be fixed. — **feststehend,** *p.a.* stationary; stable; established, settled, fixed.

**feststellbar,** *a.* ascertainable, determinable; fastenable.

**feststellen,** *v.t.* establish, ascertain, determine; fix, fasten; stop.

**Fest-stellung,** *f.* establishing, etc. (see feststellen); statement. **-stern,** *m.* fixed star. **-stoffgehalt,** *m.* solid content(s).

**Festungsachat,** *m.* fortification agate.

**festweich,** *a.* semisolid.

**Fest-werden,** *n.* solidification; coagulation. **-wert,** *m.* fixed value, constant. **-zahl,** *f.* fixed number, constant.

**fett,** *a.* fatty, oily; aliphatic; fat; rich, fertile, profitable; (of varnish, etc.) high-grade, long-oil. — **fettes Puddeln,** (*Iron*) pig boiling.

**Fett,** *n.* fat; grease. **-abfall,** *m.*, **-abfälle,** *m.pl.* refuse fat. **-abscheider,** *m.* grease separator.

**fettähnlich,** *a.* fat-like, fatty, lipoid.

**Fettalkohol,** *m.* fat alcohol.

**fett-arm,** *a.* poor in fat. **-aromatisch,** *a.* aliphatic-aromatic. **-artig,** *a.* fat-like, fatty, lipoid.

**Fett-bedarf,** *m.* fat requirement. **-bestandteil,** *m.* fatty constituent. **-bestimmung,** *f.* fat determination. **-bildung,** *f.* fat formation. **-brühe,** *f.* (*Leather*) fat liquor. **-büchse,** *f.* grease cup; grease box.

**fettdicht,** *a.* fat-tight, grease-proof.

**Fettdruck,** *m.* bold-faced type, boldface.

**fettdrucken,** *v.t.* print in boldface.

**Fettdrüse,** *f.* sebaceous gland.

**Fette,** *f.* fatness, greasiness.

**fettecht,** *a.* insoluble in fat.

**fetten,** *v.t.* oil, grease, lubricate; stuff, dub (leather); fatten.

**Fett-entziehung,** *f.* fat extraction. **-farbe,** *f.* fat-soluble color, oil color. **-farbstoff,** *m.* color for fats; (*Micros.*) fat stain; (*Biochem.*) lipochrome, lutein. **-fleck, -flecken,** *m.* grease spot.

**fett-frei,** *a.* fat-free, free from fat. **-gar,** *a.* (*Leather*) oil-tanned.

**Fett-garleder,** *n.* oil-tanned leather, chamois. **-gas,** *n.* oil gas.

**fett-gebunden,** *p.a.* united to an aliphatic compound or radical. **-gedruckt,** *p.a.* printed in boldface.

**Fett-gehalt,** *m.* fat content. **-gerbung,** *f.* oil tannage, oil dressing. **-geruch,** *m.* odor of grease. **-geschmack,** *m.* fatty taste, greasy taste. **-gewebe,** *n.* adipose tissue. **-glanz,** *m.* greasy luster.

**fett-glänzend,** *a.* having a greasy luster. **-haltig,** *a.* containing fat, fatty, greasy.

**Fett-härtung,** *f.* hardening of fat(s). **-harz,** *n.* oleoresin. **-harzreserve,** *f.* (*Calico*) fat resin resist. **-haut,** *f.* (*Leather*) corium, derma. **-heit,** *f.* fatness, etc. (see fett).

**fettig,** *a.* fatty, fat, greasy, oily; adipose.

**Fettigkeit,** *f.* fattiness, fatness, greasiness, oiliness, lubricity.

**Fett-industrie,** *f.* fat industry. **-kalk,** *m.* fat lime. **-kohle,** *f.* fat coal, coal rich in volatile matter. **-körper,** *m.* fatty compound, fat; aliphatic compound; fatty or greasy matter. **-kügelchen,** *n.* fat globule.

**fett-lickern,** *v.t.* (*Leather*) fat-liquor. **-lösend,** *a.* fat-dissolving.

**Fett-löser,** *m.* fat dissolver, fat solvent. **-löserseife,** *f.* fat-dissolving soap.

**fettlöslich,** *a.* soluble in fat.

**Fett-lösungsmittel,** *n.* solvent for fats. **-magen,** *m.* abomasum, fourth stomach (of ruminants). **-noppe,** *f.* grease spot (in fabrics). **-öl,** *n.* fatty oil. **-ponceau,** *f.* fat ponceau. **-presse,** *f.* (*Mach.*) grease gun. **-puddeln,** *n.* (*Iron*) wet puddling, pig boiling. **-quarz,** *m.* greasy (lustered) quartz.

**fettreich,** *a.* rich in fat.

**Fett-reihe,** *f.* fatty series, aliphatic series. **-reservemittel,** *n.* fat resist, wax resist. **-rest,** *m.* fat residue; fatty residue. **-salbe,** *f.* fatty ointment.

**fettsauer,** *a.* of or combined with fatty acid; (formerly) sebacate of.

**Fett-säure,** *f.* fatty acid; fat acid; (old name for) sebacic acid. **-schicht,** *f.* layer of fat or grease. **-schliff,** *m.* greased ground joint. **-schmiere,** *f.* (*Leather*) fat liquor. **-schmierung,** *f.* grease lubrication. **-schwarz,** *n.* fat-soluble black. **-schweiss,** *m.* yolk (of wool); fatty sweat. **-seife,** *f.* soap from fats; (*Soap*) lard soap. **-sein,** *n.* fatness, fattiness, greasiness; ropiness (of wine).

**fettspaltend,** *p.a.* fat-cleaving, lipolytic.

**Fett-spaltung,** *f.* cleavage of fat, lipolysis. **-spaltungsmittel,** *n.* fat-splitting agent, lipolytic agent. **-spritze,** *f.* grease gun. **-stein,** *m.* eleolite. **-stift,** *m.* wax pencil, wax crayon. **-stoff,** *m.* fat; fatty matter; (formerly) adipocere. **-stoffwechsel,** *m.* fat metabolism. **-substanz,** *f.* fatty substance, fat. **-sucht,** *f.* fatty degeneration. **-teilchen,** *n.* fat particle. **-ton,** *m.* fuller's earth.

**Fettung,** *f.* oiling, etc. (see fetten).

**Fett-verbindung,** *f.* fatty compound, aliphatic compound. **-verseifung,** *f.* saponification of fat. **-wachs,** *n.* adipocere.

**fettwachsartig,** *a.* adipocerous.

**Fettwolle,** *f.* wool in the yolk, grease wool.

**Fetzen,** *m.* shred, tatter, scrap; trifle.

**feucht,** *a.* moist; humid, damp; (of malt) slack. — **auf feuchtem Wege,** in the wet way, by wet process.

**Feuchte,** *f.* moistness, dampness, humidity. **-kammer,** *f.* moist chamber. **-messer,** *m.* hygrometer; psychrometer.

**feuchten,** *v.t.* moisten, dampen, wet.

**Feuchter,** *m.* moistener, damper, wetter.

**Feucht-gewicht,** *n.* moist weight, drained weight. **-heit,** *f.* moistness, dampness.

**Feuchtigkeit,** *f.* moisture; moistness, dampness, humidity; humor; phlegm.

**Feuchtigkeitsanzeiger,** *m.* moisture indicator, hygroscope, hygrometer.

**feuchtigkeitsfest,** *a.* moisture-resistant, moistureproof.

**Feuchtigkeits-gehalt,** *m.* moisture content. **-grad,** *m.* degree of moisture or humidity. **-messer,** *m.* hygrometer; psychrometer. **-niederschlag,** *m.* deposit of moisture. **-prüfer,** *m.* moisture tester.

**feuchtigkeitssicher,** *a.* moistureproof, moisture-resistant.

**Feuchtigkeitszeiger,** *m.* hygroscope.

**Feuchtkammer,** *f.* moist chamber.

**feuchtlich,** *a.* slightly moist.

**Feucht-messer,** *m.* hygrometer; psychrometer. **-walze,** *f.* dampening roller, damping roll.

**feuchtwarm,** *a.* moist and warm.

**Feuer,** *n.* fire; furnace, hearth, forge; light (as for a signal), beacon.

**feuerbeständig,** *a.* resistant to fire or heat; fireproof; refractory.

**Feuer-beständigkeit,** *f.* fire-resistant quality, fireproofness; refractoriness. **-bestattung,** *f.* cremation. **-blende,** *f.* fireblende, pyrostilpnite. **-brücke,** *f.* fire bridge. **-buchse, -büchse,** *f.* fire box.

**feuer-fangend,** *a.* flammable, inflammable. **-farbig,** *a.* flame-colored.

**feuerfest,** *a.* fireproof; refractory. — **feuerfester Ton,** fireclay. — **feuerfester Ziegel,** firebrick.

**Feuer-festigkeit,** *f.* fireproofness; refractoriness. **-fläche,** *f.* heating surface.

**feuerflüssig,** *a.* molten, fused; liquid at a high temperature.

**Feuer-führung,** *f.* firing. **-gas,** *n.* flue gas, burnt gas. **-gefahr,** *f.* danger of fire, fire hazard.

**feuergefährlich,** *a.* liable to take fire, (in)flammable.

**Feuer-gefährlichkeit,** *f.* (in)flammability. **-gradmesser,** *m.* pyrometer. **-gradmessung,** *f.* pyrometry. **-grube,** *f.* ash pit. **-haken,** *m.* fire hook, poker. **-haut,** *f.* (fire-resistant) lining, liner. **-holz,** *n.* firewood.

**feuerig,** *a.* = feurig.

**Feuer-kammer,** *f.* fire chamber, fire box. **-kitt,** *m.* fireproof cement. **-krücke,** *f.* furnace rake, rabble. **-kunst,** *f.* pyrotechnics. **-leitung,** *f.* priming, train; (*Mil.*) fire control.

**feuerlos,** *a.* fireless, lusterless.

**Feuer-löschapparat,** *m.* extinguisher. **-lösch-mittel,** *n.* fire-extinguishing substance. **-losigkeit,** *f.* lack of brilliance. **-luft,** *f.* furnace gas; (Scheele's name for) oxygen. **-material,** *n.* fuel, combustible. **-melder,** *m.* fire alarm. **-messer,** *m.* pyrometer. **-messung,** *f.* pyrometry.

**feuern,** *v.t.* fire, heat, burn; (*Wine*) sulfur. — *v.i.* fire, spark, glow.

**Feuer-porzellan,** *n.* refractory porcelain. **-probe,** *f.* fire test. **-punkt,** *m.* fire point; (*Optics*) focus; (*Mining*) hearth. **-raum,** *m.* fireplace, fire box, furnace, hearth. **-regen,** *m.* rain of fire, fiery rain. **-rohr,** *n.* fire tube, flue; firearm. **-rohrkessel,** *m.* fire-tube boiler, tubular boiler.

**feuerrot,** *a.* fiery red.

**Feuer-saft,** *m.* (*Iron*) slag bath. **-schlauch,** *m.* fire hose. **-schutzmittel,** *n.* fireproofing agent. **-schwaden,** *m.* fire-damp. **-schwamm,** *m.* tinder, punk.

**Feuersgefahr,** *f.* danger of fire, fire hazard.

**feuersicher,** *a.* fireproof, fire-resistant.

**Feuerstein,** *m.* flint; firebrick.

**feuersteinartig,** *a.* flint-like, flinty.

**Feuer-steinknolle,** *f.* flint nodule. **-stoff,** *m.* (*Old Physics*) caloric. **-strahl,** *m.* jet or flash of fire. **-ton,** *m.* fire clay.

**Feuerung,** *f.* firing, fire, heating; fuel; furnace; fireplace, hearth.

**Feuerungs-anlage,** *f.* furnace, hearth, fireplace. **-bedarf,** *m.* fuel requirement. **-gewölbe,** *n.* furnace arch. **-material,** *n.* fuel. **-öl,** *n.* fuel oil. **-raum,** *m.* = Feuerraum.

**feuerungstechnisch,** *a.* pyrotechnic.

**feuer-verbleit,** *a.* hot-leaded. **-vergoldet,** *a.* fire-gilt.

**Feuer-vergoldung,** *f.* fire gilding. **-versicherung,** *f.* fire insurance. **-versilberung,** *f.* fire silvering. **-verzinken,** *n.*, **-verzinkung,** *f.* hot galvanizing. **-verzinnen,** *n.*, **-verzinnung,** *f.* hot tinning, hot tin-coating. **-waffe,** *f.* firearm. **-werk,** *n.* firework, fireworks. **-werker,** *m.* pyrotechnist. **-werkerei, -werkerkunst,** *f.* pyrotechnics. **-werkskörper,** *n.pl.* fireworks.

**feuerwiderstandsfähig,** *a.* resistant to fire.

**Feuer-zange,** *f.* fire tongs. **-zeug,** *n.* lighter. **-ziegel,** *m.* firebrick. **-zug,** *m.* flue, fire tube; train of explosives.

**feurig,** *a.* fiery; igneous; burning, hot, ardent, spirited; (of wine) generous; (of colors) bright, loud. — **feuriger Schwaden,** fire damp.

**feurig-flüssig,** *a.* igneous. **-rot,** *a.* fiery red; red-hot.

**ff.,** *abbrev.* (feinfein) very fine; (feuerfest) fireproof, refractory; (und folgende) and following, *et seq.*

**FF., Ff.,** *abbrev.* (Fusionspunkte) melting points.

**F.f.,** *abbrev.* (Fortsetzung folgt) to be continued.

**Fibel,** *f.* primer; manual.

**Fiber,** *f.* fiber; specif., henequen. **-dichtung,** *f.* fiber packing.

**Fibrille,** *f.* fibril.

**fibrin-haltig,** *a.* containing fibrin, fibrinous. **-ös,** *a.* fibrinous.

**fibrös,** *a.* fibrous.

**ficellieren,** *v.t.* wire (bottles).

**Fichte,** *f.* spruce (*Picea*); (loosely) pine, fir.

**Fichten-harz,** *n.* (strictly) spruce resin; (commonly) rosin. **-harzöl,** *n.* (commonly) rosin oil. **-holz,** *n.* (strictly) spruce wood. **-holzkohle,** *f.* (strictly) spruce charcoal; (loosely) pine charcoal. **-holzschliff,** *m.* mechanical wood pulp. **-holzteer,** *m.* (strictly) spruce tar; pine tar. **-nadelöl,** *n.* (commonly) oil from the needles of any of various conifers, "pine-needle oil." **-nadelteer,** *m.* (strictly) spruce-needle tar; (commonly) "pine-needle tar." **-pech,** *n.* = Fichtenharz. **-rinde,** *f.* spruce bark; (commonly, for tanning) fir bark. **-säure,** *f.* pinic acid. **-span,** *m.* spruce (or loosely, pine) shaving, chip, or splint. **-sprossen,** *f.pl.* (*Pharm.*) pine shoots. **-wolle,** *f.* pine wool. **-zucker,** *m.* pinitol, pinite.

**-ficiren, -ficirung.** = -fizieren, -fizierung.

**F.i.D.,** *abbrev.* (Faden in Dampf) thread in vapor.

**Fieber,** *n.* fever. — **aussetzendes —,** intermittent fever.

**fieberartig,** *a.* feverish, febrile.

**Fieberarznei,** *f.* febrifuge, antipyretic.

**fieber-fest,** *a.* immune to fever. **-haft,** *a.* feverish, fevered, febrile.

**Fieber-klee,** *m.* buck bean (*Menyanthes*). **-kraut,** *n.* feverfew. **-mittel,** *n.* febrifuge, antipyretic.

**fiebern,** *v.i.* have fever; rave.

**Fieber-pulver,** *n.* fever powder, ague powder (antimonial powder). **-rinde,** *f.* cinchona bark.

**fieber-vertreibend, -widrig,** *a.* febrifuge, antifebrile.

**Fieder,** *f.* leaflet; pinnule. **-streifung,** *f.* striation.

**fiel,** *pret.* (of fallen) separated, fell, etc.

**Fig.,** *abbrev.* (Figur) figure.

**Figurendruck,** *m.* (*Calico*) topical printing, figure printing. **-artikel,** *m.* (*Calico*) topical style.

**figurieren,** *v.t.* figure.

**figürlich,** *a.* figurative.

**fiktiv,** *a.* fictive, imaginary, fictitious.

**Filial-.** branch; as, *Filialanstalt*, branch establishment.

**Filiale,** *f.* branch (establishment).

**Filiasäure,** *f.* filicic acid.

**Filicinsäure,** *f.* filicinic acid.
**Filigran,** *n.* filigree.
**Filixsäure,** *f.* filicic acid.
**filmbildend,** *a.* film-forming.
**Film-bildschicht,** *f.* (*Photog.*) film emulsion, film layer, film coat. **-schicht,** *f.* film layer.
**Filteranlage,** *f.* filtration plant.
**filterbar,** *a.* filterable.
**Filter-blatt,** *n.* filter, filter paper, filter leaf. **-dauer,** *f.* time of filtering. **-element,** *n.* filter cell. **-fläche,** *f.* filter surface, filtering area. **-flasche,** *f.* filter flask. **-gaze,** *f.* filter gauze. **-gefäss,** *n.* filter(ing) vessel. **-gehäuse,** *n.* filter case, filter casing, filter housing. **-gerät,** *n.* filter apparatus, filter. **-gestell,** *n.* filter stand. **-gläschen,** *n.* small filter glass or tube. **-halter,** *m.* filter holder. **-kegel,** *m.* filter cone. **-kerze,** *f.* filter candle. **-kies,** *m.* filter(ing) gravel. **-kohle,** *f.* filter(ing) charcoal. **-kolonne,** *f.* filter(ing) column. **-konus,** *m.* filter cone. **-körper,** *m.* filtering material. **-kuchen,** *m.* filter cake; (*Petroleum*) slack wax. **-lage,** *f.* filter layer, filter bed. **-masse,** *f.* (*Brewing*) pulp, filter mass. **-mittel,** *n.* filter material, filtering medium.
**filtern,** *v.t.* filter; strain.
**Filter-papier,** *n.* filter paper. **-plättchen,** *n.* (small) filter plate. **-platte,** *f.* filter plate. **-presse,** *f.* filter press. **-pressentuch,** *m.* filterpress cloth. **-rand,** *m.* edge of a filter. **-rohr,** *n.*, **-röhre,** *f.* filter tube or pipe, screen pipe. **-rückstand, -rest,** *m.* residue on the filter, filtration residue. **-schablone,** *f.* form for cutting filters. **-schale,** *f.* filter(ing) dish. **-schicht,** *f.* filter bed; filter layer. **-schlauch,** *m.* filter hose. **-schoner,** *m.* filter cone. **-sieb,** *n.* filtering sieve, strainer. **-stativ,** *n.* filter stand. **-stein,** *m.* = Filtrierstein. **-stoff,** *m.* filter material; filter cloth. **-tiegel,** *m.* filtering crucible. **-träger,** *m.* filter holder, filter ring. **-trichter,** *m.* filter funnel. **-tuch,** *m.* filter cloth. **-turm,** *m.* filter tower, filtering tower.
**Filterung,** *f.* filtering, filtration.
**Filterungs-dauer,** *f.* time of filtering. **-hilfmittel,** *n.* filtering aid.
**Filter-vorsatz,** *m.* air filter (in a gas mask). **-wäger,** *m.* filter weigher. **-watte,** *f.* filter wadding. **-zelle,** *f.* filter cell, filter unit.
**Filtrat,** *n.* filtrate.
**filtrationsfähig,** *a.* capable of filtration.
**Filtrationskraft,** *f.* filtering power.
**Filtratleistung,** *f.* filtrate output.
**Filtricht,** *n.* filtrate.
**Filtrier-apparat,** *m.* filtering apparatus. **-aufsatz,** *m.* filtering attachment.
**filtrierbar,** *a.* filterable.
**Filtrier-barkeit,** *f.* filterability, filtering property. **-becher,** *m.* filtering beaker. **-beutel,** *m.* filtering bag, percolator. **-einlage,** *f.* (charge of) filtering material.
**filtrieren,** *v.t.* filter, strain.
**Filtrierer,** *m.* filterer, strainer.
**Filtrier-erde,** *f.* filtering earth. **-fläche,** *f.* filtering surface or area. **-flasche,** *f.* filtering flask. **-gestell,** *n.* filter stand. **-hut,** *m.* (paper) filtering funnel. **-kessel,** *m.* filtering boiler. **-konus,** *m.* filter cone. **-korb,** *m.* filtering basket. **-nutsche,** *f.* suction filter. **-papier,** *n.* filter paper. **-papierstreifen,** *m.* strip of filter paper. **-platte,** *f.* filter plate. **-presse,** *f.* filter press. **-pumpe,** *f.* filter pump. **-ring,** *m.* filter ring. **-rohr,** *n.*, **-röhre,** *f.* filter tube, filtering tube. **-sack,** *m.* filtering bag, bag filter. **-schale,** *f.* filtering dish (with perforated bottom). **-schicht,** *f.* filter bed. **-schwierigkeit,** *f.* difficulty in filtering. **-sieb,** *n.* filtering sieve, strainer. **-stativ,** *n.* filter stand. **-stein,** *m.* filter stone, filtering stone. **-stoff,** *m.* filtering material. **-stutzen,** *m.* filtering jar (a cylindrical jar with lip). **-tasse,** *f.* filtering cup (with perforated cover for holding a funnel). **-trichter,** *m.* filtering funnel. **-tuch,** *m.* filtering cloth; percolator.
**Filtrierung,** *f.* filtering, filtration.
**Filtrum,** *n.* filter.
**Filz,** *m.* felt; tomentum; blanket; felt hat· miser; (*Metal.*) slime ore.
**filzartig,** felt-like, felty.
**Filzbarkeit,** *f.* felting property.
**filzen,** *v.t.* felt.
**filzfähig,** *a.* capable of felting.
**Filz-fähigkeit,** *f.* felting property. **-falte,** *f.* (*Paper*) crease in the felt. **-gewebe,** *n.* felted tissue. **-haar,** *n.* felted hair.
**filzig,** *a.* of felt, felt-like, tomentous; stingy.
**Filz-malz,** *n.* felted malt. **-schlauch,** *m.* (tubular) felt jacket. **-tuch,** *n.* felted cloth, felt; blanket. **-wirkung,** *f.* felting effect.
**filzwollen,** *a.* of or like felted wool.
**Fimmel,** *m.* female hemp; (*Mining*) wedge.
**finden,** *v.t.* find; discover. — *v.r.* understand; be found, exist.
**Findigkeit,** *f.* ingenuity, ingeniousness.
**Findling,** *m.* foundling; (*Geol.*) erratic block.
**fing,** *pret.* (of fangen) caught, etc. — **fing an,** began.
**Finger-futter,** *n.* finger stall. **-hut,** *m.* thimble; foxglove, digitalis. **-hutkraut,** *m.* foxglove, digitalis. **-ling,** *m.* finger stall. **-nagel,** *m.* fingernail. **-probe,** *f.* rule of thumb. **-spitze,** *f.* finger tip. **-stein,** *m.* belemnite. **-zeig,** *m.* pointing with the finger; indication, hint, cue.
**fingieren,** *v.t.* simulate, invent. — **fingiert,** *p.a.* fictitious, imaginary.
**Finne,** *f.* pimple, pustule; stud, knot; fin.

**finster,** *a.* dark; obscure; gloomy.
**Finsternis,** *f.* darkness; obscurity; gloom; (*Astron.*) eclipse.
**Firma,** *f.* firm.
**firn,** *a.* of last year.
**Firn,** *m.* glacier snow, névé, firn. **-blau,** *n.* glacier blue.
**Firnis,** *m.* varnish.
**firnisartig,** *a.* varnish-like.
**Firnis-ersatz,** *m.* varnish substitute. **-fabrikant** *m.* varnish maker. **-farbe,** *f.* varnish color. **-glasur,** *f.* spirit enamel. **-industrie,** *f.* varnish industry. **-papier,** *n.* glazed paper.
**firnissen,** *v.t.* varnish.
**First,** *m.* top; ridge; (*Mining*) roof.
**Fisch,** *m.* fish. **-augenstein,** *m.* apophyllite. **-bein,** *n.* whalebone. **-blase,** *f.* fish bladder; sounds, isinglass. **-düngemittel,** *n.*, **-dünger,** *m.* fish manure, fish guano.
**fischen,** *v.t. & i.* fish.
**Fischerei,** *f.* fishing; fishery.
**fischig,** *a.* fishy.
**Fisch-körner,** *n.pl.* Indian berries (cocculus indicus). **-leim,** *m.* fish glue, isinglass. (*Pharm.*) ichthyocolla. **-leimgummi,** *n.* sarcocolla. **-mehl,** *n.* fish meal. **-öl,** *n.* fish oil; ichthyol. **-ölseife,** *f.* fish oil soap. **-schwanz,** *m.* fish tail. **-schwanzbrenner,** *m.* fishtail burner. **-speck,** *m.* fish blubber. **-tran,** *m.* fish oil, train oil. **-zucht,** *f.* fish culture, pisciculture.
**Fisetholz, Fisettholz,** *n.* young fustic (*Cotinus coggygria*).
**Fistel,** *f.* fistula; falsetto. **-holz,** *n.* = Fisetholz. **-kassie,** *f.* purging cassia, cassia fistula.
**fistulös,** *a.* fistular, fistulous.
**Fitze,** *f.* (*Textiles*) hank, skein.
**fix,** *a.* fixed; fast; smart. — **fixe Luft,** fixed air (old name for carbon dioxide).
**Fixage,** *f.* fixing, fixation.
**Fix-bleiche,** *f.* bleaching with bleaching powder. **-färberei,** *f.* tipping (of plush), dyeing by staining; fast dyeing.
**Fixierbad,** *n.* fixing bath.
**fixierbar,** *a.* fixable.
**Fixierbarkeit,** *f.* fixability.
**fixieren,** *v.t.* fix; harden; mordant (silk); set (wool); stare at.
**Fixier-flüssigkeit,** *f.* fixing liquid or liquor. **-mittel,** *n.* fixing agent, fixative; hardening agent. **-natron,** *n.* sodium thiosulfate. **-salz,** *n.* fixing salt (specif., sodium thiosulfate, "hypo"). **-ton,** *m.* fixing clay.
**Fixierung,** *f.* fixing, fixation; hardening.
**Fixierungsmittel,** *n.* = Fixiermittel.
**Fix-punkt,** *m.* fixed point. **-stern,** *m.* fixed star. **-wert,** *m.* fixed value.
**-fizieren.** -fy (as *esterifizieren*, esterify).
**-fizierung.** -fication.

**fl.,** *abbrev.* (flüssig) liquid; (flüchtig) volatile.
**Fl.,** *abbrev.* (Flüssigkeit) liquid.
**flach,** *a.* flat; level, even, smooth, plain; shallow. **-bodig,** *a.* flat-bottomed.
**Flach-brenner,** *m.* flat-flame burner. **-draht,** *m.* flat wire. **-druck,** *m.* flat printing; lithoprinting.
**Fläche,** *f.* surface, face; area; flatness; plain, plane; level; sheet.
**Flacheisen,** *n.* flat bar iron, flat steel.
**Flächen-anziehung,** *f.* surface attraction, adhesion. **-berührung,** *f.* surface contact. **-druck,** *m.* surface pressure; (*Calico*) blotch print, also blotch printing. **-einheit,** *f.* unit of surface or area. **-farbe,** *f.* surface color.
**flächenförmig,** *a.* flat, plane, sheet-like.
**Flächengrosse,** *f.* amount of surface, area.
**flächenhaft,** *a.* flat, plane, sheet-like.
**Flächen-helle, -helligkeit,** *f.* surface luminosity. **-inhalt,** *m.* area. **-kathode,** *f.* flat cathode, plate cathode. **-mass,** *n.* surface measure, square measure. **-messer,** *m.* planimeter. **-raum,** *m.* area.
**flächenreich,** *a.* having many faces, polyhedral.
**Flächen-satz,** *m.* theorem of conservation of areas. **-wert,** *m.* surface value. **-winkel,** *m.* plane angle. **-zahl,** *f.* number of faces; square number.
**flächenzentriert,** *a.* (*Cryst.*) face-centered.
**Flachfeile,** *f.* flat file.
**flachgewunden,** *p.a.* planispiral.
**Flach-glas,** *n.* flat glass, specif. plate glass. **-heit,** *f.* flatness, etc. (see flach).
**-flächig.** -faced, -hedral.
**Flach-kupfer,** *n.* flat copper. **-land,** *n.* flat land, level country.
**Flächner,** *m.* polyhedron.
**flachrund,** *a.* round and flat-bottomed.
**Flachs,** *m.* flax.
**Flachschnitt,** *m.* horizontal section.
**flächsen,** *a.* flaxen, of flax.
**flachs-farben, -farbig,** *a.* flax-colored, flaxen. **-gelb,** *a.* flaxen.
**Flachs-gewebe,** *n.* linen goods, linen. **-leinwand,** *f.* flax linen. **-samen,** *m.* flaxseed, linseed. **-samenöl,** *n.* flaxseed oil, linseed oil. **-stein,** *m.* amianthus.
**Flach-stab,** *m.* flat bar. **-stahl,** *m.* flat steel, flats.
**Flachswachs,** *n.* flax wax.
**Flachwasser,** *n.* shallow water.
**Flachzange,** *f.* tongs with flat jaws, flat pliers.
**flackerig,** *a.* flaring, flickering, flashing.
**flackern,** *v.i.* flare, flicker, flash.
**Flacon,** *n. & m.* small bottle, phial.
**Fladdermine,** *f.* (*Mil.*) land mine, contact mine.
**Fladenlava,** *f.* block lava.

**Flader,** *f.* curl, speckle, streak; flaw.
**fladerig,** *a.* curled, etc. (see Flader).
**Flagge,** *f.* flag, colors.
**Flak,** *abbrev.* (*Flugabwehrkanone*) antiaircraft gun or fire, flak. **-granate,** *f.* antiaircraft shell, AA shell.
**Flakon,** *n.* & *m.* small bottle, phial.
**Flakrakete,** *f.* antiaircraft rocket.
**flambieren,** *v.t.* flame, singe.
**flämig,** *a.* (of leather) streaky.
**flämisch,** *a.* Flemish.
**Flamm-.** see also Flammen-.
**flammbar,** *a.* flammable, inflammable.
**Flämmchen,** *n.* flamelet, small flame.
**Flammdruck,** *m.* chiné printing.
**Flamme,** *f.* flame; light.
**flammen,** *v.t.* flame, blaze; singe; sear; water, cloud (fabric, etc.). — *v.i.* flame; burn, glow.
**flammenbeständig,** *a.* flame-resistant, flame-proof.
**Flammenbogen,** *m.* flaming arc; electric arc.
**flammenfarbig,** *a.* flame-colored.
**Flammen-färbung,** *f.* flame coloration. **-feuer,** *n.* blazing fire. **-fläche,** *f.* flame surface. **-frischarbeit,** *f.* fining in a reverberatory furnace. **-härten,** *n.* flame hardening. **-höhe,** *f.* height of flame.
**flammenlos,** *a.* flameless.
**Flammen-ofen,** *m.* = Flammofen. **-öl,** *n.* flame-thrower oil. **-opal,** *m.* fire opal. **-rohr,** *n.*, **-röhre,** *f.* = Flammrohr. **-rückschlag,** *m.* backfiring, striking back.
**flammensicher,** *a.* flameproof.
**Flammen-spektrum,** *n.* flame spectrum. **-strahl,** *m.* jet of flame. **-werfer,** *m.* flame projector, flame thrower.
**flammfarbig,** *a.* flame-colored; rainbow-colored.
**Flamm-färbung,** *f.* flame coloration. **-gas,** *n.* flame gas.
**flammicht,** *a.* (of fabrics) watered; (of wood) veined, grained.
**flammieren,** *v.t.* = flammen, *v.t.*
**flammig,** *a.* flame-like, flaming; (of fabrics, etc.) watered; veined, grained. — **— meliert,** (*Textiles*) jaspé.
**Flamm-kohle,** *f.* coal that burns with flame, open-burning coal. **-ofen,** *m.* flame furnace, reverberatory furnace. **-ofenfrischen,** *n.* reverberatory refining. **-ölbombe,** *f.* (flaming) oil bomb. **-punkt,** *m.* flash point; point of ignition. **-punktprüfer,** *m.* flash-point tester. **-punkt(s)apparat,** *m.* flash-point apparatus. **-rohr,** *n.*, **-röhre,** *f.* fire tube, flue. **-rohrkessel,** *m.* fire-tube boiler. **-schutzmittel,** *n.* flameproofing agent.
**flammsicher,** *a.* flameproof.
**Flammsichermachen,** *n.* flameproofing.
**flandrisch,** *a.* Flanders, Flemish.
**Flanell,** *m.* flannel.
**Flanke,** *f.* flank, side.
**flankieren,** *v.t.* flank.
**Flansch, Flantsch,** *m.*, **Flansche, Flantsche,** *f.* flange.
**flanschen, flantschen,** *v.t.* flange.
**Flanschenverbindung,** *f.* flanged joint, flange union.
**Flarakete,** *f.* (*Flugabwehrrakete*) antiaircraft rocket.
**Fläschchen,** *n.* small bottle or flask.
**Flasche,** *f.* bottle; flask; jar; (for gas) cylinder; (*Founding*) casting box, flask; (*Mech.*) block.
**Flaschen-abteilung,** *f.* (*Brewing*) bottlery. **-bier,** *n.* bottled beer.
**flaschenförmig,** *a.* bottle-shaped, flask-shaped.
**Flaschen-gas,** *n.* cylinder gas, bottled gas. **-gestell,** *n.* bottle rack, flask rack. **-glas,** *n.* bottle glass.
**flaschengrün,** *a.* bottle-green.
**Flaschen-hals,** *m.* neck of a bottle or flask. **-inhalt,** *m.* contents of a bottle or flask or gas cylinder. **-kappe, -kapsel,** *f.* bottle cap. **-kürbis,** *m.* bottle gourd; calabash. **-schild,** *n.* bottle (flask, etc.) label. **-stöpsel, -verschluss,** *m.* bottle (or flask) stopper or fastener. **-zug,** *m.* set of pulleys, block and tackle.
**Flaser,** *f.* curl, speckle, streak; flaw.
**flaserig,** *a.* curled, speckled, streaked.
**Flattermine,** *f.* (*Mil.*) land mine, contact mine.
**flattern,** *v.i.* flutter, flicker; float, wave; dangle; be flighty.
**Flatterruss,** *m.* lampblack.
**Flattierfeuer,** *n.* choked fire.
**flau,** *a.* faint, feeble, weak; dull, slack, flat.
**flauen,** *v.t.* buddle. — *v.i.* be weak, be dull.
**Flaum,** *m.* down, nap, fluff; (of fabrics) pile.
**flaumartig, flaumig,** *a.* downy, fluffy, pubescent.
**Flaus, Flausch,** *m.* tuft; pad; plug; nappy cloth.
**Flaveanwasserstoff,** *m.* old name for cyanothioformamide, $CNCSNH_2$.
**Flechse,** *f.* tendon, sinew.
**Flechte,** *f.* lichen; plait, twist; skin eruption.
**flechten,** *v.t.* plait, twist, braid, interweave.
**Flechten-farbstoff,** *m.* lichen coloring matter. **-rot,** *n.* orcein. **-säure,** *f.* fumaric acid (old name). **-stärkemehl,** *n.* lichenin, moss starch. **-stoffe,** *m.pl.* lichen substances.
**Fleck,** *m.* spot; speck, stain, blot, flaw, patch; *pl.* measles. **-analyse,** *f.* spot analysis.
**flecken,** *v.t.* spot, stain, speckle, mottle; patch. — *v.i.* spot, stain, blot.
**Flecken,** *m.* spot, speck, stain, flaw, taint. — *m.pl.* measles. **-bildung,** *f.* spotting, staining.
**fleckenempfindlich,** *a.* liable to spot or stain.
**Flecken-entfernung,** *f.* spot (or stain) removal.

**-entfernungsmittel,** *n.* spot remover, stain remover.

**flecken-frei, -los,** *a.* stainless, spotless.

**Flecken-reiniger,** *m.* cleaner, scourer, spot (or stain) remover. **-reinigung,** *f.* stain (or spot) removal. **-seife,** *f.* scouring soap. **-wasser,** *n.* = Fleckwasser.

**Fleckfieber,** *n.* spotted fever, specif. typhus.

**fleckig,** *a.* spotted, speckled, stained, mottled, flawy; freckled. — **— werden,** spot, stain.

**Fleck-schierling,** *m.* poison hemlock (*Conium maculatum*). **-seife,** *f.* scouring soap. **-stein,** *m.* scouring stone (clay for stain removal). **-storchschnabelwurzel,** *f.* (*Pharm.*) geranium, cranesbill. **-wasser,** *n.* scouring water, cleaning liquid (for removing spots), specif. Javelle water.

**Fledermaus,** *f.* bat. **-brenner,** *m.* batswing burner.

**flehen,** *v.i.* make entreaty. — *v.t.* entreat.

**Fleisch,** *n.* flesh, meat; (of fruit) pulp.

**Fleisch-.** flesh, fleshy, meat, muscle, sarco-, sarcous. **-beschau,** *f.* meat inspection. **-brühe,** *f.* meat broth, bouillon.

**fleischen,** *v.t.* flesh.

**Fleischer,** *m.* butcher. **-talg,** *m.* unmelted tallow.

**Fleischfarbe,** *f.* flesh color.

**fleisch-farbig, -farben,** *a.* flesh-colored.

**Fleisch-faser,** *f.* muscle fiber. **-fäulnis,** *f.* spoiling or putrefaction of meat.

**fleischfressend,** *p.a.* meat-eating, carnivorous.

**Fleisch-gift,** *n.* meat toxin, ptomaine. **-gummi,** *n.* sarcocolla.

**fleischig,** *a.* fleshy, flesh-like, pulpy.

**Fleisch-kohle,** *f.* animal charcoal. **-konserve,** *f.* preserved meat, canned meat, tinned meat. **-kost,** *f.* meat diet; meat food. **-leim,** *m.*, **-leimgummi,** *n.* sarcocolla.

**fleischlos,** *a.* meatless; fleshless.

**Fleisch-mehl,** *n.* meat meal, tankage. **-milchsäure,** *f.* sarcolactic acid.

**fleischrot,** *a.* flesh-colored.

**Fleisch-saft,** *m.* meat juice, extract of meat. **-seite,** *f.* flesh side. **-tee,** *m.* beef tea. **-vergiftung,** *f.* meat poisoning. **-waren,** *f.pl.* meats, esp. dried meats. **-wasser,** *n.* meat broth. **-zucker,** *m.* inositol, inosite.

**Fleiss,** *m.* diligence, industry, purpose.

**fleissig,** *a.* diligent, industrious.

**flexibel,** *a.* flexible.

**flicht,** *pr. 3 sing.* (of flechten) plaits, etc.

**flicken,** *v.t.* patch, mend, repair.

**Flickgewebe,** *n.* scar tissue; mending tissue.

**Flieder,** *m.* elder; (**spanischer**) lilac. **-blüte,** *f.* elder blossom; lilac blossom.

**fliederfarbig,** *a.* lilac(colored).

**Fliederöl.** *n.* lilac oil; elder oil.

**Fliege,** *f.* fly; sight (of a gun).

**fliegen,** *v.i.* fly.

**Fliegen-gift,** *n.* fly poison. **-holz,** *n.* quassia wood. **-kobalt,** *m.* = Fliegenstein. **-leim,** *m.* fly glue. **-papier,** *n.* fly paper. **-pilz,** *m.* = Fliegenschwamm. **-pulver,** *n.* fly powder. **-schwamm,** *m.* fly agaric, fly amanita (*Amanita muscaria*). **-stein,** *m.* native arsenic.

**Flieger,** *m.* flier, specif. aviator. **-benzin,** *n.* aviation gasoline. **-bild,** *n.* air photograph. **-bombe,** *f.* aerial bomb.

**fliegerisch,** *a.* flying, aviation, aerial.

**Fliegerschutz,** *m.* air defense.

**Flieglack,** *m.* airplane varnish, airplane dope.

**fliehen,** *v.t.* & *i.* flee.

**Fliehkraft,** *f.* centrifugal force.

**Flies, Fliess,** *n.* fleece.

**Fliese,** *f.* flag, floor tile, wall tile, paving brick.

**Fliess-arbeit,** *f.* continuous operation or production. **-band,** *n.* assembly line.

**fliessbar,** *a.* capable of flowing, flowable.

**Fliess-barkeit,** *f.* flowing quality, fluidity; fusibility. **-bereich,** *m.* plastic range. **-betrieb,** *m.* = Fliessarbeit. **-druck,** *m.* flow pressure; hydraulic pressure. **-eigenschaft,** *f.* rheologic property.

**fliessen,** *v.i.* flow; run; melt; blot; (of colors) run; creep; bleed. — **fliessend,** *p.a.* flowing, running; melting; fluid, liquid; (*Math.*) mobile; continuous; fluent. — **fliessende Hitze,** melting heat. — **fliessende Bindung,** floating linkage.

**Fliessen,** *n.* flowing, flow, etc. (see fliessen).

**fliessfähig,** *a.* capable of flowing, etc. (see fliessen); fusible.

**Fliess-feder,** *f.* fountain pen. **-figur,** *f.* flow figure. **-geschwindigkeit,** *f.* velocity of flow. **-glätte,** *f.* wet litharge. **-grenze,** *f.* (*Metals*) flow limit, yield point. **-harz,** *n.* oleoresin, specif. turpentine. **-kohle,** *f.* liquid coal (colloidal suspension of coal in oil), colloidal fuel. **-körper,** *m.* flowing substance, nonsolid. **-kunde,** *f.* rheology. **-ofen,** *m.* pyrites kiln. **-papier,** *n.* blotting paper, absorbent paper. **-probe,** *f.* flow test or sample; pour(ing) test. **-punkt,** *m.* flowing point; yield point; melting point. **-sand,** *m.* quicksand. **-textur,** *f.* (*Petrog.*) fluidal (or flow) structure. **-verzug,** *m.* flow distortion. **-vorgang,** *m.* flow process. **-wasser,** *n.* running water; (*Physiol.*) lymph.

**Flimmer,** *m.* glitter; glimmer, flicker; tinsel, spangle; mica.

**Flimmer-.** ciliated, ciliary, vibrating. **-messer,** *m.* scintillometer.

**flimmern,** *v.i.* glitter, glisten, sparkle, scintillate, glimmer, flicker. — **flimmernd,** *p.a.* glittering, etc; micaceous.

**Flimmerschein,** *m.* sparkling luster.

**flink,** *a.* agile, quick, alert.
**flinken,** *v.i.* shine, sparkle, glisten.
**Flint,** *n.* flint glass; flint.
**Flinte,** *f.* (shot)gun; (formerly) musket.
**Flinten-lauf,** *m.* gun barrel. **-schrot,** *n.* gunshot, small shot.
**Flintstein,** *m.* flintstone, flint.
**Flinz,** *m.* siderite.
**Flitsch,** *m.*, **Flitsche,** *f.*, **Flitschenerz,** *n.* = Flittererz.
**Flitter,** *m.* spangle, shining platelet; flake; tinsel. **-draht,** *m.* tinsel wire. **-erz,** *n.* ore in glittering laminas. **-glas,** *n.* pounded glass for frosting. **-gold,** *n.* Dutch metal, tombac (a kind of brass used for tinsel).
**flittern,** *v.i.* glitter, glisten, sparkle.
**Flitter-sand,** *m.* micaceous sand. **-silber,** *n.* silver-colored tinsel.
**Flitzwagen,** *m.* jeep.
**Fll.,** *abbrev.* (Flüssigkeiten) liquids.
**flocht,** *pret.* (of flechten) plaited, etc.
**Flocke,** *f.* flake, flock.
**flocken,** *v.t. & i.* form flakes or flocks, flake, flocculate.
**flockenartig,** *a.* flake-like, flocculent.
**Flocken-bildner,** *m.* flocculating agent, flocculant. **-bildung,** *f.* flock formation, flocculation. **-bildungzerstörer,** *m.* deflocculant. **-erz,** *n.* mimetite. **-graphit,** *m.* flake graphite. **-papier,** *n.* flock paper. **-reaktion,** *f.* flocculation reaction.
**flockenrissig,** *a.* flaky.
**Flocken-salpeter,** *m.* efflorescent saltpeter. **-stoff,** *m.* (*Textiles*) nap cloth.
**flockig,** *a.* flocculent, flocky, flaky. **-käsig,** *a.* curdy.
**Flockseide,** *f.* floss silk, silk waste.
**Flockung,** *f.* flocculation.
**Flockwolle,** *f.* short wool, flock wool.
**Floconné,** *m.* nap cloth.
**flog,** *pret.* (of fliegen) flew.
**floh,** *pret.* (of fliehen) fled.
**Floh,** *m.* flea.
**flohbraun,** *a.* puce.
**Floh-farbe,** *f.* puce color. **-kraut,** *n.* fleabane. **-krautöl,** *n.* (usually) pennyroyal oil. **-samen,** *m.* fleawort seed, psyllium seed.
**Flor,** *m.* bloom, blooming; gauze; nap, pile.
**Florentiner Flasche.** Florentine receiver (for essential oils).
**Florettseide,** *f.* floss silk.
**Florida-bleicherde, -erde,** *f.* Florida (bleaching) earth.
**Florstoff,** *m.* gauze.
**floss,** *pret.* (of fliessen) flowed, etc.
**Floss,** *n.* (*Metal.*) pig; raft, float. — **blumiges —,** white pig with granular fracture.
**Flosse,** *f.* fin; blade; float; (*Metal.*) pig.
**Flosseisen,** *n.* white pig iron.
**flössen,** *v.t.* float; infuse; refine (tin).
**Flossenbett,** *n.* (*Metal.*) pig mold.
**Flossofen,** *m.* flowing furnace.
**Flotationschemie,** *f.* flotation chemistry.
**flotationsfähig,** *a.* floatable.
**Flotationsverfahren,** *n.* flotation process.
**Flotator,** *m.* flotation machine.
**flotierbar,** *a.* floatable.
**flotieren,** *v.t.* float.
**flott,** *a.* brisk (of a reaction), smooth; afloat; gay, flush.
**Flotte,** *f.* liquor; specif., dye liquor, dye bath; fleet, navy.
**Flotten-flüssigkeit,** *f.* dye liquor. **-gefäss,** *n.* (*Dyeing*) color reservoir. **-länge,** *f.* (*Dyeing*) volume of liquor. **-menge,** *f.* (*Dyeing*) amount (or ratio) of liquor. **-stand,** *m.* (*Dyeing*) height of the liquor. **-verhältnis,** *n.* liquor consistency; (*Dyeing*) ratio of goods to liquor.
**flottieren,** *v.t.* float. — *v.i.* float; fluctuate.
**Flott-seide,** *f.* untwisted silk. **-stahl,** *m.* ingot steel, run steel.
**Flötz,** *n.* layer, stratum, bed, seam. **-erz,** *n.* ore in beds. **-gestein,** *n.* stratified rock. **-kalk,** *m.* bedded limestone.
**Flöz,** *n.* = Flötz.
**Fluat,** *n.* fluosilicate.
**fluatieren,** *v.t.* treat (waterproof, weatherproof) with fluosilicate.
**Fluatlösung,** *f.* fluosilicate solution.
**Fluch,** *m.* curse.
**Flucht,** *f.* flight; line, row; alignment; play, swing; escape. **-ebene,** *f.* vanishing plane.
**fluchten,** *v.t.* align. — *v.i.* be in alignment.
**flüchten,** *v.t.* flee, escape.
**Fluchtholz,** *n.* rule, level.
**flüchtig,** *a.* volatile; fugitive; fleeting, fragile, fleet, fickle, hasty. — **flüchtiges Laugensalz,** ammonium carbonate. — **flüchtiges Öl,** volatile oil, essential oil. — **flüchtige Salbe,** ammonia liniment, volatile liniment.
**flüchtigen,** *v.t.* volatilize.
**Flüchtigkeit,** *f.* volatility; fleetness, etc. (see flüchtig).
**Flucht-linie,** *f.* vanishing line. **-linientafel,** *f.* nomographic chart, nomogram; alignment chart. **-punkt,** *m.* vanishing point.
**fluchtrecht,** *a.* flush, in alignment.
**Fludor.** A kind of solder. *T.N.*
**Flug,** *m.* flight, flying; flock; swarm. **-abwehr,** *f.* air defense, antiaircraft defense. **-asche,** *f.* light (or flying) ashes, flue dust. **-bahn,** *f.* line of flight, flight path, trajectory. **-benzin,** *n.* aviation gasoline. **-blatt,** *n.* fly sheet, handbill; pamphlet.
**Flügel,** *m.* wing; flap, lobe, vane, branch; casement (of a window); blade (as of a screw propeller); grand piano.

**flügelförmig,** *a.* wing-shaped.
**flügelig,** *a.* winged, bladed, vaned.
**Flügel-gebläse,** *n.* fan blower. **-kühler,** *m.* fan cooler. **-mine,** *f.* winged bomb, airplane bomb. **-mutter,** *f.* (*Mech.*) wing nut, thumb nut.
**flügeln,** *v.t.* wing. — **geflügelt,** *p.a.* winged.
**Flügel-pumpe,** *f.* vane pump, (semi)rotary pump. **-rad,** *n.* screw wheel, worm wheel; screw propeller; (*Brewing*) flighter. **-schraube,** *f.* wing screw, wing nut.
**flugfähig,** *a.* volatile; (of dust, etc.) flying easily, light.
**Flugfeld,** *n.* flying field, airfield.
**flügge,** *a.* fledged.
**Flug-hafen,** *m.* airport. **-koks,** *m.* flue coke, coke dust. **-kraft,** *f.* power of flight, flight power, **-linie,** *f.* = Flugbahn; airline. **-mehl,** *n.* mill dust. **-platz,** *m.* airfield, airport. **-post,** *f.* air mail, air post. **-rost,** *m.* rust in thin film.
**flugs,** *adv.* quickly, instantly.
**Flug-sand,** *m.* drifting (or drifted) sand, blown sand; quicksand. **-schrift,** *f.* handbill; pamphlet. **-staub,** *m.* flue dust; (*Metal.*) smoke, fume; chimney soot; flying dust. **-staubkammer,** *f.* condensing chamber. **-weg,** *m.* airway; flight path, course. **-wesen,** *n.* aviation, aeronautics. **-zeug,** *n.* airplane, aeroplane, aircraft. **-zeuglack,** *m.* airplane varnish, airplane dope.
**Fluh,** *f.* concrete; rock mass.
**fluhen,** *v.t.* concrete, cover with (lay with, form of) concrete.
**Fluidität,** *f.* fluidity.
**Fluidum,** *n.* fluid.
**fluktuieren,** *v.i.* fluctuate.
**fluktuös,** *a.* fluctuating.
**Flunder,** *m.* flounder.
**Fluor,** *n.* fluorine.
**Fluor-.** of or combined with fluorine, fluoro-, fluo-, fluoride of (see instances following). **-ammonium,** *n.* ammonium fluoride. **-anthenchinon,** *n.* fluoranthenequinone. **-antimon,** *n.* antimony fluoride. **-arsen,** *n.* arsenic fluoride. **-baryum,** *n.* barium fluoride. **-benzol,** *n.* fluorobenzene, fluobenzene. **-bor,** *n.* boron fluoride. **-borsäure,** *f.* fluoboric acid. **-brom,** *n.* bromine fluoride. **-chrom,** *n.* chromium fluoride. **-eisen,** *n.* iron fluoride.
**Fluorescenz, Fluoreszenz,** *f.* fluorescence.
**fluoreszenzerzeugend,** *a.* fluorogenic.
**Fluoreszenz-farbe,** *f.* fluorescence color; luminous paint. **-messer,** *m.* fluorometer.
**fluorescieren, fluoreszieren,** *v.i.* fluoresce. — **fluoreszierend,** *p.a.* fluorescent.
**Fluorgehalt,** *m.* fluorine content.
**fluorhaltig,** *a.* containing fluorine.
**Fluorid,** *n.* fluoride (esp. an -ic fluoride as contrasted with Fluorür).
**Fluor-jod,** *n.* iodine fluoride. **-kalium,** *n.* potassium fluoride. **-kalzium,** *n.* calcium fluoride. **-kiesel,** *m.* silicon fluoride. **-kieselsäure,** *f.* fluosilicic acid. **-kohlenstoff,** *m.* carbon fluoride. **-lithium,** *n.* lithium fluoride. **-metall,** *n.* metallic fluoride. **-natrium,** *n.* sodium fluoride. **-phosphat,** *n.* fluophosphate. **-phosphor,** *m.* phosphorus fluoride. **-salz,** *n.* fluoride. **-schwefel,** *m.* sulfur fluoride. **-selen,** *n.* selenium fluoride. **-silber,** *n.* silver fluoride. **-silikat,** *n.* fluosilicate. **-silizium,** *n.* silicon fluoride. **-siliziumverbindung,** *f.* fluosilicate. **-tantalsäure,** *f.* fluotantalic acid. **-tellur,** *n.* tellurium fluoride. **-titan,** *n.* titanium fluoride. **-toluol,** *n.* fluorotoluene, fluotoluene.
**Fluorür,** *n.* (-ous) fluoride. Cf. Chlorür.
**Fluor-verbindung,** *f.* fluorine compound. **-wasserstoff,** *m.* hydrogen fluoride; hydrofluoric acid.
**fluorwasserstoffsauer,** *a.* of or combined with hydrofluoric acid, fluoride or hydrofluoride of.
**Fluor-wasserstoffsäure,** *f.* hydrofluoric acid. **-zink,** *m.* & *n.* zinc fluoride. **-zinn,** *n.* tin fluoride.
**Fluo-sulfosäure,** *f.* fluosulfonic acid. **-verbindung,** *f.* fluorine compound.
**Flur,** *f.* & *m.* field; land; floor; vestibule; (of fabrics) pile.
**Fluss,** *m.* flux; fluor spar; enamel; (*Gems*) paste; fusion; flow, flowing; (*Soap*) figging; river, stream; discharge; catarrh.
**flüss.,** *abbrev.* (flüssig) liquid.
**Fluss-bett,** *n.* river bed. **-bild,** *n.* flow sheet. **-dichte,** *f.* flux density. **-eisen,** *n.* mild (soft, low-carbon) steel, ingot steel. **-erde,** *f.* earthy fluorite. **-gebiet,** *n.* river basin. **-gold,** *n.* river gold. **-harz,** *n.* animé, gum animé.
**flüssig,** *a.* liquid; fluid. — — **machen,** liquefy. — — **werdend,** liquescent. — **flüssiges Chlorzink,** (*Pharm.*) solution of zinc chloride (and so for similar names). — **flüssiger Extrakt,** fluidextract, fluid extract.
**Flüssiggas,** *n.* liquefied gas.
**Flüssigkeit,** *f.* liquid; liquidity; fluidity; fluid; liquor; (*Physiol.*) humor.
**Flüssigkeits-.** liquid, fluid, hydraulic, hydrostatic. **-bad,** *n.* liquid bath. **-dichtemesser,** *m.* hydrometer. **-druck,** *m.* pressure of a liquid, hydrostatic pressure. **-förderung,** *f.* conveyance of liquids. **-gemisch,** *n.* mixture of liquids, liquid mixture. **-grad,** *m.* degree of fluidity; viscosity. **-gradmesser,** *m.* viscosimeter. **-linse,** *f.* (*Micros.*) immersion objective. **-mass,** *n.* liquid measure. **-menge,**

*f.* amount of liquid. **-messer,** *m.* liquid meter; hydrometer. **-oberfläche,** *f.* liquid surface. **-pressung,** *f.* liquid pressure, hydraulic pressure. **-reibung,** *f.* fluid friction. **-säule,** *f.* column of liquid. **-spiegel,** *m.* surface of a liquid. **-spindel,** *f.* hydrometer; float. **-stand,** *m.* level of a liquid. **-strom,** *m.* liquid stream, current of liquid. **-verlust,** *m.* loss or waste of liquid. **-zerstäuber,** *m.* atomizer.

**flüssigmachen,** *v.t.* liquefy.

**Flüssig-machen,** *n.*, **-machung,** *f.* liquefaction.

**Flüssigwerden,** *n.* fusion, liquefaction, liquescence.

**flüssigwerdend,** *a.* liquescent.

**Fluss-kalkstein,** *m.* limestone used as a flux. **-kies,** *m.* river gravel; river shingle.

**flusskieselsauer,** *a.* of or combined with fluosilicic acid, fluosilicate of.

**Fluss-kieselsäure,** *f.* fluosilicic acid. **-metall,** *n.* liquid metal. **-mittel,** *n.* fluxing material, flux; antirheumatic. **-ofen,** *m.* flowing furnace. **-pferd,** *n.* hippopotamus. **-pulver,** *n.* flux powder, powdered flux. **-punkt,** *m.* melting point. **-sand,** *m.* river sand.

**flusssauer,** *a.* = fluorwasserstoffsauer.

**Fluss-säure,** *f.* hydrofluoric acid. **-schmiedeeisen,** *n.* ingot iron (as distinguished from ingot steel).

**Flussspat,** *m.* fluor spar, fluorite. **-erde,** *f.* earthy fluorite. **-pulver,** *n.* fluor spar powder. **-säure,** *f.* hydrofluoric acid.

**Fluss-stahl,** *m.* ingot steel; medium- or high-carbon steel. **-stahldraht,** *m.* ingot steel wire. **-stein,** *m.* compact fluorite. **-ton,** *m.* river clay. **-wasser,** *n.* river water. **-wasserstoffsäure,** *f.* hydrofluoric acid.

**flüstern,** *v.t. & i.* whisper.

**Flut, Fluth,** *f.* flood; (high) tide.

**fluten,** *v.i.* flood, swell, surge; fluctuate.

**Flutlicht,** *n.* floodlight.

**Fluxmittel,** *n.* flux.

**focht,** *pret.* (of fechten) fought.

**Föhre,** *f.* Scotch pine or fir (*Pinus sylvestris*); pine (*Pinus* species).

**fokussieren,** *v.t.* focus.

**Fokustiefe,** *f.* focal depth.

**folg.,** *abbrev.* (folgend) following.

**Folge,** *f.* sequence, series, set; future; consequence, result; conclusion; compliance.

**folgen,** *v.t.* follow.

**folgender-massen, -weise,** *adv.* as follows, in the following manner.

**folgen-los,** *a.* without result. **-reich,** *a.* having important results, momentous. **-schwer,** *a.* momentous, important.

**Folge-produkt,** *n.* member of a series of products, specif. metabolon; secondary product. **-punkte,** *m.pl.* (*Magnetism*) consequent points (or poles). **-reaktion,** *f.* consequent reaction, secondary reaction.

**folge-recht, -richtig,** *a.* consequent; conclusive; logical.

**Folgerichtigkeit,** *f.* logicalness, consistency.

**folgern,** *v.t.* conclude, infer.

**Folgerung,** *f.* conclusion, inference, induction.

**Folge-wirkung,** *f.* resultant, consequence. **-zeit,** *f.* period following.

**folglich,** *adv.* consequently.

**folgsam,** *a.* obedient.

**Folie,** *f.* foil; film (as of viscose).

**Folienlack,** *m.* foil-coating lacquer.

**foliieren,** *v.t.* cover with foil, silver; page (a book).

**Follikel,** *m.* follicle.

**Fond,** *m.* foundation, base, basis; capital, funds; (*Dyeing*) ground, bottom. **-farbe,** *f.* ground color or shade.

**Fonziermaschine,** *f.* (*Paper*) staining machine.

**forcieren,** *v.t.* force; overtax; overload.

**Forcierkrankheit,** *f.* strain disease (of metals).

**Fordbecher,** *m.* Ford viscosimeter.

**Förder-anlage,** *f.* conveying equipment. **-band,** *n.* conveyor belt.

**Förderer,** *m.* promoter; accelerator; conveyer.

**Förder-gut,** *n.* goods to be conveyed or forwarded; output. **-höhe,** *f.* delivery head, pressure head. **-kohle,** *f.* rough coal, coal directly from the mine, run-of-mine.

**förderlich,** *a.* serviceable; speedy.

**Förder-menge,** *f.* output. **-mittel,** *n.* transportation means; conveyer.

**fordern,** *v.t.* demand, ask, require; summon; challenge.

**fördern,** *v.t.* further, promote, help; hasten, accelerate; raise, draw out, get out; convey, transport, forward, transfer; feed.

**Förder-quantum,** *n.* (*Mining*) output. **-schnecke,** *f.* screw conveyer.

**Forderung,** *f.* demand, requirement, etc. (see fordern); claim.

**Förderung,** *f.* furthering, etc. (see fördern).

**Förderungsmittel,** *n.* (*Pharm.*) adjuvant.

**Förder-werk,** *n.* conveyer; elevator, lift. **-wirkung,** *f.* promoting effect.

**Forelle,** *f.* trout.

**Forelleneisen,** *n.* mottled white pig iron.

**forensisch,** *a.* forensic.

**Form,** *f.* form; shape, cut, size; mold; tuyère; design; profile; (*Soap*) frame. **-änderung,** *f.* change of form; deformation, strain.

**formänderungsfähig,** *a.* capable of deformation; plastic; ductile.

**Form-änderungsfähigkeit,** *f.* ductility; plasticity. **-änderungsmesser,** *m.* deformometer; strainometer. **-art,** *f.* form species. **-artikel,** *m.* molded article or goods.

**Format,** *n.* format. size.

**formbar,** *a.* capable of being shaped, plastic, workable, moldable, etc.
**Formbarkeit,** *f.* plasticity; workability.
**formbeständig,** *a.* retaining form or shape.
**Form-bildung,** *f.* (*Biol.*) morphogeny; structure. **-eisen,** *n.* sectional (or structural) iron or steel.
**Formel,** *f.* formula. **-bild,** *n.* (structural) formula.
**Formelement,** *n.* structural element.
**Formel-gewicht,** *n.* formula weight. **-register,** *n.* formula index.
**formen,** *v.t.* form, shape, fashion, mold, cast; (*Soap*) frame.
**Formensand,** *m.* molding sand.
**Formerde,** *f.* molding clay, modeling clay.
**Formerei, Förmerei,** *f.* molding, forming; molding house.
**Former-pech,** *n.* molder's pitch. **-stoff,** *m.* plastic material, plastic.
**Form-festigkeit,** *f.* stability of shape. **-gebung,** *f.* fashioning, shaping, molding.
**form-gerecht, -getreu,** *a.* true in form, undistorted.
**Formgips,** *m.* plaster of Paris (good grade).
**formhaltend,** *a.* retaining form or shape.
**Form-heizung,** *f.* (*Rubber*) mold cure. **-holz,** *n.* plastic wood.
**Formiat,** *n.* formate.
**formieren,** *v.t.* form.
**Formiersäure,** *f.* (*Elec.*) forming acid.
**-förmig.** -shaped, -formed, -form, -oid.
**Form-kasten,** *m.* (*Founding*) molding box, flask. **-körper,** *m.* molded body. **-lehre,** *f.* profile gage.
**förmlich,** *a.* formal; plain; downright.
**Formling,** *m.* molded article; briquet; casting.
**formlos,** *a.* formless, shapeless, amorphous.
**Formmasse,** *f.* molding material, molding batch.
**Formopersäure,** *f.* peroxyformic acid, performic acid.
**Form-sand,** *m.* molding sand. **-schwindung,** *f.* shrinking, shrinkage. **-stahl,** *m.* structural steel; profile steel. **-stein,** *m.* shaped brick; (*Lead*) pipe stone. **-stück,** *n.* shaped part. **-ton,** *m.* molding clay.
**Formular,** *n.* form, blank (to fill out).
**formulieren,** *v.t.* formulate.
**Formulierung,** *f.* formulation.
**Formung,** *f.* forming, formation, shaping, etc. (see formen).
**Form-veränderung,** *f.* change of form; modification. **-wechsel,** *m.* change of form.
**Formylsäure,** *f.* formic acid.
**forsch,** *a.* vigorous; dashing.
**forschen,** *v.i.* investigate, search.
**Forscher,** *m.* investigator; inquirer; spy.
**Forschung,** *f.* investigation, research; inquiry.
**Forschungs-anstalt,** *f.* research institution. **-arbeit,** *f.* research work, research. **-bericht,** *m.* research report, research paper. **-gebiet,** *n.* field of research. **-geist,** *m.* spirit of research or inquiry. **-laboratorium,** *n.* research laboratory.
**Forst,** *m.* forest.
**Förster,** *m.* forester; forest ranger.
**Forstkunde,** *f.* forestry.
**forstlich,** *a.* forest, forestal.
**Forst-mann,** *m.* forester. **-wesen,** *n.*, **-wirtschaft,** *f.* forestry.
**fort,** *adv.* on, along, forth, away, off. — **— und —,** on and on, forever.
**fortan,** *adv.* henceforth.
**fortbestehen,** *v.i.* continue.
**Fortbewegung,** *f.* locomotion, progression.
**fortbringen,** *v.t.* carry away, remove; convey; rear; support, maintain.
**Fortdauer,** *f.* permanence, duration.
**fortdauern,** *v.i.* continue, last.
**fortdiffundieren,** *v.t.* diffuse away.
**Fortdruck,** *m.* separate print, separate.
**fortentwickeln,** *v.t. & r.* continue developing.
**fortfahren,** *v.i.* set off, depart; go on, continue.
**fortfallen,** *v.i.* be wanting, be omitted; cease.
**fortfliessen,** *v.i.* flow or run off or away.
**fortführen,** *v.t.* carry away, convey; continue, prosecute.
**Fortgang,** *m.* going away, etc. (see fortgehen); process; progress, advance.
**fortgehen,** *v.i.* go away, go off, go, depart; go on, proceed, continue.
**fortgesetzt,** *a.* continued.
**fortglimmen,** *v.i.* smolder (on); glimmer (on).
**fortkochen,** *v.t. & i.* boil away, boil off.
**fortkommen,** *v.i.* get away; get on, progress.
**Fortkommen,** *n.* escape; getting on, success.
**fortlassen,** *v.t.* let go; leave out, omit.
**fortlaufend,** *p.a.* continuous, continual, successive, consecutive.
**fortleiten,** *v.t.* carry off; transmit, conduct.
**fortnehmen,** *v.t.* take away, remove.
**fortoxydieren,** *v.t. & i.* oxidize away or off.
**fortpflanzen,** *v.t.* propagate, transmit, communicate; reproduce.
**Fortpflanzung,** *f.* propagation, transmission, communication; reproduction.
**Fortpflanzungs-geschwindigkeit,** *f.* velocity of propagation (or of transmission). **-richtung,** *f.* direction of propagation (or of transmission).
**fortrücken,** *v.t.* move away. — *v.i.* move on, advance.
**Fortsatz,** *m.* continuation; (*Med.*) process; (*Mach.*) catch, stop.
**fortschaffen,** *v.t.* take away, remove, get rid of, dismiss.
**fortschreiten,** *v.i.* step forward; progress, ad-

vance. — **fortschreitend,** *p.a.* progressive; onward, advancing.
**Fortschritt,** *m.* advance, advancement, progress.
**fortsetzen,** *v.t.* continue, carry on; set away.
**Fortsetzung,** *f.* continuation; prosecution, pursuit.
**fortspülen,** *v.t.* wash away, rinse away.
**fortwährend,** *p.a.* continual, continuous, permanent, constant. — *adv.* continually.
**forzieren,** *v.t.* force; overtax.
**fossil,** *a.* fossil. — **fossiles Wachs,** fossil wax, ozocerite.
**fossilführend, fossilienhaltig,** *a.* fossiliferous.
**fötal,** *a.* fetal.
**foto-chemisch,** *a.* photochemical. **-graphisch,** *a.* photographic.
**Fotozelle,** *f.* photoelectric cell.
**Foulardfärbung,** *f.* pad dyeing.
**foulardisieren,** *v.t.* (*Dyeing*) pad, slop-pad.
**Fournier,** *n.* veneer.
**fournieren,** *v.t.* veneer, inlay.
**F.P.,** *abbrev.* (französisches Patent) French patent; (Fusionspunkt, Fliesspunkt) melting point, m.p.
**Fp.,** *abbrev.* (Fusionspunkt) melting point; (Füllpulver) shell explosive.
**Fp. 02,** *abbrev.* (Füllpulver 02) TNT.
**fr.,** *abbrev.* (frei) free.
**Fr.,** *abbrev.* (Franken) francs.
**Fracht,** *f.* freight; cargo, load, shipment. **-brief,** *m.* way bill, bill of lading.
**frachtfrei,** *a.* freight-free, carriage paid.
**Fracht-geld,** *n.* freight; cartage. **-gut,** *n.* freight. **-unkosten,** *f.pl.* freight charges.
**Frage,** *f.* question, problem; demand. — **in — kommen,** be in question, be concerned.
**Fragebogen,** *m.* questionnaire.
**fragen,** *v.t. & i.* ask, question. — **es fragt sich,** it is a question.
**Frage-stellung,** *f.* question, questioning. **-zeichen,** *n.* interrogation point.
**fraglich,** *a.* questionable, doubtful; in question, aforementioned.
**fragwürdig,** *a.* questionable, doubtful.
**frakt.,** *abbrev.* (fraktioniert) fractionated.
**fraktionär,** *a.* fractional.
**Fraktionier-apparat,** *m.* fractionating apparatus. **-aufsatz,** *m.* fractionating attachment, distilling tube. **-boden,** *m.* fractionating plate or tray. **-destillation,** *f.* fractional distillation.
**fraktionieren,** *v.t.* fractionate. — **fraktionierte Destillation,** fractional distillation. — **fraktionierte Fällung,** fractional precipitation.
**Fraktionier-kolben,** *m.* fractionating flask. **-rohr,** *n.,* **-röhre,** *f.* fractionating tube. **-röhrchen,** *n.* small fractionating tube. **-turm,** *m.* fractionating tower.
**Fraktionierung,** *f.* fractionation.
**Fraktions-aufsatz,** *m.* fractionating attachment, distilling tube, fractionating column. **-hut,** *m.* a kind of receiver (for fractionating). **-kolben,** *m.* fractionating flask. **-rohr,** *n.,* **-röhre,** *f.* fractionating tube. **-vorlage,** *f.* receiver (for fractionating).
**Fraktur,** *f.* fracture.
**Frambösie,** *f.* (*Med.*) frambesia, yaws.
**Frankfurterschwarz,** *n.* Frankfort black.
**franko,** *adv.* postpaid, prepaid.
**Frankreich,** *n.* France.
**Franse,** *f.* fringe.
**Franz-band,** *m.* calf binding; calf-bound book. **-branntwein,** *m.* brandy, cognac. **-gold,** *n.* French leaf gold (pale, due to silver alloy).
**Franzose,** *m.* Frenchman; monkey wrench.
**Franzosen-harz,** *n.* guaiacum. **-holz,** *n.* guaiacum, lignum vitae.
**französisch,** *a.* French. — **französische Beeren,** Avignon berries.
**Franztopas,** *m.* smoky topaz.
**Fräs-.** (*Mach.*) milling.
**Fräse,** *f.* milling machine; milling cutter.
**fräsen,** *v.t.* (*Mach.*) mill.
**frass,** *pret.* (of fressen) corroded, etc.
**Frass,** *m.* food, feed; corrosion. **-gift,** *n.* stomach poison.
**Frau,** *f.* woman; wife; lady; Mrs.
**Frauen-arzt,** *m.* gynecologist. **-distel,** *f.* Scotch thistle. **-eis,** *n.* (*Min.*) selenite.
**Frauenglas,** *n.* (*Min.*) selenite. — **russisches —,** muscovite.
**Frauenhaar,** *n.* (*Bot.*) maidenhair.
**frauenhaft,** *a.* woman-like, womanly.
**Frauen-heilkunde,** *f.* gynecology. **-milch,** *f.* human milk. **-spat,** *m.* (*Min.*) selenite. **-spiegel,** *m.* Venus's looking glass.
**Fräulein,** *n.* young lady, single lady, Miss.
**frbl.,** *abbrev.* (farblos) colorless.
**Frdl.,** *abbrev.* Friedländers Fortschritte der Teerfarbenfabrikation.
**frech,** *a.* bold, brazen.
**frei,** *a.* free; uncombined; liberal; bold; open; postpaid, prepaid. — **— werden,** be set free, be disengaged.
**-frei.** free (from), -less, an- (as *wasserfrei,* free from water, anhydrous).
**Frei-ballon,** *m.* free balloon. **-brief,** *m.* license, charter, patent, permit. **-couvert,** *n.* stamped envelope.
**freidrehen,** *v.t.* (*Ceram.*) throw.
**Frei-gabe, -gebung,** *f.* release.
**frei-geben,** *v.t.* release, set free. **-gebig,** *a.* generous; prodigal. **-geworden,** *a.* liberated, released. **-halten,** *v.t.* exonerate; pay for (someone).
**Freiharzgehalt,** *m.* content of free resin (or rosin).
**freiharzreich,** *a.* rich in free resin (or rosin).
**Freiheit,** *f.* freedom; degree of freedom; lib-

erty; franchise. **in — setzen,** set free, liberate.

**Frei-heitsgrad,** *m.* degree of freedom. **-heizung,** *f.* (*Rubber*) open cure. **-lager,** *n.* bonded warehouse. **-lagerprüfung,** *f.* (*Paints,* etc.) exposure test(ing).

**freilassen,** *v.t.* set free, liberate.

**Freileitung,** *f.* (*Elec.*) open wire, overhead line; open-air piping.

**frei-lich,** *adv.* to be sure, indeed; of course. **-liegend,** *a.* exposed.

**Freiluftbewitterung,** *f.* open-air weathering.

**freimachen,** *v.t.* set free, liberate, disengage; prepay.

**Frei-marke,** *f.* postage stamp. **-mut,** *m.* frankness, sincerity. **-sein,** *n.* free state, freedom.

**frei-sinnig,** *a.* large-minded; liberal. **-sprechen,** *v.t.* acquit; dispense.

**Frei-staat,** *m.* republic. **-werden,** *n.* becoming free, liberation.

**frei-werdend,** *p.a.* (being) set free; nascent. **-willig,** *a.* spontaneous; voluntary; free.

**Frei-williger, -willige,** *m.* volunteer.

**fremd,** *a.* foreign; independent; strange; exotic; belonging to others. **-artig,** *a.* extraneous, foreign; heterogeneous; odd.

**Fremd-befruchtung,** *f.* cross-fertilization. **-bestandteil,** *m.* foreign ingredient, foreign matter.

**Fremde,** *m.& f.* stranger; foreigner; visitor; *f.* foreign country.

**fremdfarbig,** *a.* artificially colored.

**Fremd-gas,** *n.* foreign gas. **-körper,** *m.* foreign substance; foreign body. **-metall,** *n.* foreign metal.

**fremd-sprachig, -sprachlich,** *a.* foreign-language.

**Fremdstoff,** *m.* foreign substance, impurity; by-product.

**fremdstoffig,** *a.* heterogeneous.

**Fremd-stoffigkeit,** *f.* heterogeneity. **-wort,** *n.* foreign word.

**Frequenz,** *f.* frequency; crowd; attendance; traffic. **-messer,** *m.* frequency meter, wavemeter, ondometer. **-wert,** *m.* frequency value, frequency.

**fressen,** *v.t.* corrode; eat. — *v.r. & i.* (*Mach.*) bind, seize, jam. — **fressend,** *p.a.* corrosive.

**Fressen,** *n.* food.

**fressgierig,** *a.* greedy, voracious.

**Fresszelle,** *f.* phagocyte.

**Freude,** *f.* joy, comfort, enjoyment.

**freudig,** *a.* joyful, glad, hearty.

**freuen,** *v.t.* make glad, rejoice. — *v.r.* be glad, rejoice.

**Freund,** *m.* friend; acquaintance.

**freundlich,** *a.* friendly; kind, cheerful, pleasant.

**Freundschaft,** *f.* friendship; acquaintance; favor; friends, kindred.

**Friede,** *f.* peace.

**friedfertig,** *a.* peaceable.

**Friedhof,** *m.* cemetery.

**friedlich,** *a.* peaceful, peaceable.

**frieren,** *v.i.* freeze, congeal; feel cold. — **gefroren,** *p.a.* frozen, congealed.

**Frieren,** *n.* freezing; chill; shivering; ague.

**Frierpunkt,** *m.* freezing point.

**Friesel,** *m.* miliary fever.

**Frikassee,** *n.* fricassee; mincemeat.

**friktionieren,** *v.t.* subject to friction; glaze by friction (as cellulose).

**Friktions-antrieb,** *m.* (*Mach.*) friction drive. **-messer,** *m.* tribometer. **-zünder,** *m.* friction igniter.

**frisch,** *a.* fresh; green (hide); new; lively, vigorous, gay. — *adv.* freshly; cheerily.

**Frischarbeit,** *f.* fining process, fining.

**frischbereitet,** *a.* freshly prepared.

**Frisch-blei,** *n.* refined lead. **-dampf,** *m.* live steam. **-eisen,** *n.* refined iron.

**frischen,** *v.t.* fine, refine; revive (litharge); reduce (lead); reclaim (as rubber or oil).

**Frischer,** *m.* finer, refiner.

**Frischerei,** *f.* finery, refinery; fining, refining **-roheisen,** *n.* forge pig.

**Frisch-erz,** *n.* raw ore. **-esse,** *f.* refining furnace, refinery. **-feuer,** *n.* refining fire, refinery. **-feuereisen,** *n.* refined iron, charcoal hearth iron. **-fleisch,** *n.* fresh meat.

**frisch-gebrannt,** *p.a.* freshly burned. **-gefällt,** *p.a.* freshly precipitated. **-gelöscht,** *a.* freshly quenched or slaked.

**Frisch-gewicht,** *n.* fresh (undried) weight. **-glätte,** *f.* a litharge containing silver. **-herd,** *m.* refining furnace; forge hearth. **-lauge,** *f.* fresh lye, fresh liquor; specif., (*Paper*) white liquor. **-lech,** *m.* crude mat(te). **-ling,** *m.* (*Metal.*) scoria; young boar. **-luft,** *f.* fresh air. **-ofen,** *m.* refining furnace, refinery. **-periode,** *f.* (*Metal.*) oxidizing period. **-prozess,** *m.* (*Metal.*) fining (or refining) process. **-roheisen,** *n.* pig iron for fining. **-schlacken,** *f.pl.* refinery cinders. **-schlamm,** *m.* raw sludge, fresh sludge. **-stahl,** *m.* steel made in a refinery, German steel, natural steel. **-stück,** *n.* (*Copper*) liquation cake.

**Frischung,** *f.* fining, etc. (see frischen).

**Frisch-verfahren,** *n.* (*Iron*) fining process. **-wasser,** *n.* fresh water. **-wirkung,** *f.* (*Metal.*) fining, refining.

**frisst,** *pr. 2 & 3 sing.* of fressen.

**Frist,** *f.* time, space of time, interval; respite.

**fristen,** *v.t.* prolong, delay.

**Fritte,** *f.* frit.

**fritten,** *v.t.* frit, sinter.

**Frittenporzellan,** *n.* soft porcelain, frit porcelain.

**Frittofen,** *m.* frit kiln; (*Glass*) calcar.
**Frittporzellan,** *n.* = Frittenporzellan.
**Frittung,** *f.* fritting, sintering.
**froh,** *a.* glad, joyful, cheerful, happy.
**fröhlich,** *a.* joyful, glad, merry.
**Frohsinn,** *m.* cheerfulness.
**fromm,** *a.* gentle; pious; brave.
**frommen,** *v.i.* avail.
**fror,** *pret.* (of frieren) froze, etc.
**Frosch,** *m.* frog; (*Mach.*) cam, arm, dog, etc. **-arten,** *f.pl.* batrachians. **-laich,** *m.* frog spawn. **-laichpflaster,** *n.* (*Pharm.*) lead plaster. **-laichpilz,** *m.* (*Bot.*) leuconostoc. **-löffel,** *m.* water plantain (*Alisma*).
**Frost,** *m.* frost, cold; chill.
**frostbeständig,** *a.* frostproof.
**Frost-beständigkeit,** *f.* resistance to frost. **-beule,** *f.* chilblain.
**frösteln,** *v.t.* chill. — *v.i.* feel chilly.
**frostempfindlich,** *a.* sensitive to frost.
**Frost-grad,** *m.* degree of frost, degree below 0° C. **-mischung,** *f.* freezing mixture. **-punkt,** *m.* freezing point. **-schaden,** *m.* damage by frost. **-schnitt,** *m.* frozen section. **-schutzmittel,** *n.* antifreezing agent, antifreeze; antifrost agent.
**frostsicher,** *a.* frost-resistant.
**frottieren,** *v.t* rub; brush.
**Frucht,** *f.* fruit; grain; crop; fetus, embryo; profit, produce, product. — **-abtreibungsmittel,** *n.* abortifacient.
**fruchtartig,** *a.* fruit-like, fruity.
**Fruchtäther,** *m.* fruit essence, specif. amyl acetate.
**fruchtbar,** *a.* fruitful, fertile, plenteous.
**Frucht-brand,** *m.* ergot. **-branntwein,** *m.* fruit brandy.
**fruchten,** *v.i.* bear fruit, have effect.
**Frucht-essenz,** *f.* fruit essence, fruit extract. **-essig,** *m.* fruit vinegar. **-fleisch,** *n.* fruit pulp. **-folge,** *f.* (*Agric.*) crop rotation. **-gelée,** *n.* jam. **-halter,** *m.* uterus. **-knoten,** *m.* (*Bot.*) ovary. **-konserve,** *f.* preserved fruit. **-saft,** *m.* fruit juice. **-säure,** *f.* fruit acid. **-wasser,** *n.* amniotic fluid. **-wasserhaut,** *f.* amnion. **-wechsel,** *m.* rotation of crops. **-zucker,** *m.* fruit sugar, levulose.
**frug,** *pret.* (of fragen) asked.
**früh,** *a.* early; premature. — *adv.* early, soon.
**Frühe,** *f.* earliness, early morning.
**früher,** *a.* earlier, former. — *adv.* formerly.
**Frühling,** *m.*, **Frühjahr,** *n.* spring.
**frühreif,** *a.* early-ripe; precocious.
**Frühstück,** *n.* breakfast.
**frühzeitig,** *a.* early; premature; precocious.
**Frühzündung,** *f.* premature ignition, preignition.
**Fuchs,** *m.* fox; trestle, jack; flue; sorrel horse; freshman; fluke; (*Metal.*) piece of iron that cannot be melted. **-brücke,** *f.* flue bridge. **fett,** *n.* fox fat. **-gas,** *n.* flue gas.
**fuchsig,** *a.* foxy (yellowish- or reddish-brown).
**fuchsinschweflige Säure.** Schiff's reagent.
**Fuchsintinktion,** *f.* staining with fuchsin.
**fuchsrot,** *a.* foxy, reddish-brown.
**Fuchtel,** *f.* blade, sword, rod.
**Fuder,** *n.* cartload; large wine measure.
**Fug,** *m.* right, authority.
**Fugazität,** *f.* fugacity.
**Fuge,** *f.* joint; slit; groove; suture.
**fugen, fügen,** *v.t.* join, unite; joint; add.
**fugenlos,** *a.* jointless, seamless.
**füglich,** *adv.* reasonably; well, easily.
**fügsam,** *a.* tractable, pliant.
**Fügung,** *f.* joining; jointing; resignation; degree.
**fühlbar,** *a.* sensible, palpable, perceptible.
**fühlen,** *v.t., i. & r.* feel.
**Fühlen,** *n.* feeling, sensation, perception.
**Fühler,** *m.* feeler, antenna, tentacle; probe.
**Fühlung,** *f.* feeling, sensation; touch, contact.
**fuhr,** *pret.* (of fahren) went, traveled, etc.
**Fuhre,** *f.* carrying, carriage, cart, load.
**führen,** *v.t.* lead, guide, conduct, carry, convey; bear, wear; construct; carry on; run (a machine); cause.
**Führer,** *m.* leader; guide, conductor; driver; pilot.
**Fuhrmann,** *m.* carter, driver, carrier.
**Führung,** *f.* leading, etc. (see führen); conduct; guide.
**Führungsstange,** *f.* guide rod.
**Fuhrwerk,** *n.* vehicle.
**Füll-.** filling, bottling, feed, stuffing. **-apparat,** *m.* filling apparatus, bottling apparatus. **-appretur,** *f.* (*Textiles*) filling, filling finish.
**Fülle,** *f.* filling; fullness, abundance; (of colors) body, depth.
**füllen,** *v.t.* fill, fill up; pour, put (in); charge; load (paper, etc.); plump (leather); stuff. — *v.r.* fill.
**Füllen,** *n.* filling, etc. (see füllen); foal; colt.
**Füller,** *m.* filler; loader; fountain pen.
**Fullererde,** *f.* fuller's earth.
**Füll-feder,** *f.* fountain pen. **-flüssigkeit,** *f.* filling liquid; (*Micros.*, etc.) immersion liquid. **-halter,** *m.* fountain pen. **-haus,** *n.* filling house, filling room; (*Soap*) frame room. **-horn,** *n.* cornucopia. **-kelle,** *f.* filling ladle; pot ladle. **-koks,** *m.* bed coke. **-körper,** *m.* filling body, filler, packing body or material. **-körpersäule,** *f.* packed column or tower. **-kraft,** *f.* filling power. **-löffel,** *m.* filling ladle. **-masse,** *f.* filling material; (*Sugar*) fillmass, massecuite. **-material, -mittel,** *n.* filling material, filling, stuffing, filler; loading material. **-pulver,** *n.* filling powder, filling (for explosive shells). **-pulver 02,** TNT.

**-rohr,** *n.*, **-röhre,** *f.* filling tube, feed pipe, spout. **-saure,** *f.* electrolyte (for storage batteries), accumulator acid. **-sel,** *n.* stuffing. **-stoff,** *m.* = Füllmaterial. **-strich,** *m.* filling mark, "full" mark. **-ton,** *m.* filling clay, filler clay. **-trichter,** *m.* filling funnel, funnel, hopper.

**Füllung,** *f.* filling, stuffing, packing; charge; seal; panel.

**Füllungsgrad,** *m.* degree of filling, degree to which something is filled.

**fulminant,** *a.* fulminating.

**fulminieren,** *v.i.* fulminate.

**fum.,** *abbrev.* fumaroid.

**Fumarsäure,** *f.* fumaric acid.

**Fund,** *m.* discovery; finding; find.

**Fundament,** *n.* foundation, base, basis; (*Metal.*, etc.) bottom plate, soleplate.

**fundieren,** *v.t.* found; fund.

**Fundierung,** *f.* foundation.

**fündig,** *a.* ore-bearing.

**Fund-ort,** *m.*, **-stätte,** *f.* locality (where something is discovered), habitat. **-zettel,** *m.* (*Min.*, etc.) locality label.

**fünf,** *a.* five.

**fünf-, Fünf-.** five-, penta-, quinque-, quintuple.

**fünf-atomig,** *a.* pentatomic. **-basisch,** *a.* pentabasic.

**Fünfeck,** *n.* pentagon.

**fünfeckig,** *a.* pentagonal.

**fünffach,** *a.* fivefold, quintuple, penta-. — **—-Chlorphosphor,** phosphorus pentachloride. — **—-Schwefelantimon,** antimony pentasulfide. — **fünffaches Chlorid,** pentachloride.

**fünf-gliedrig,** *a.* five-membered. **-mal,** *adv.* five times.

**Fünfring,** *m.* five-membered ring.

**fünfseitig,** *a.* five-sided, pentahedral.

**fünfte,** *a.* fifth.

**Fünftel,** *n.* fifth, fifth part.

**fünfwertig,** *a.* quinquevalent, pentavalent.

**Fünfwertigkeit,** *f.* quinquevalence, pentavalence.

**fünfzig, funfzig,** *a.* fifty.

**fungieren,** *v.i.* function, act; officiate.

**fungizid,** *a.* fungicidal.

**fungös,** *a.* fungous.

**Funk,** *m.* radio, wireless.

**Funke,** *f.* spark; sparkle.

**funkelig,** *a.* sparkling, glittering.

**funkeln,** *v.i.* sparkle, scintillate; glitter.

**funkelnagelneu,** *a.* brand-new.

**funken,** *v.i.* spark. — *v.t.* radio.

**Funken,** *m.* spark; sparkle.

**funkenähnlich,** *a.* spark-like.

**Funken-auswurf,** *m.* spark emission. **-bildung,** *f.* spark formation, sparking, sparkling. **-entladung,** *f.* spark discharge.

**funkenfrei,** *a.* free from sparks, sparkless; (*Elec.*) nonarcing.

**Funken-garbe,** *f.* shower of sparks. **-geber,** *m.* sparking device, spark coil. **-holz,** *n.* touchwood. **-induktor,** *m.* spark coil, induction coil.

**funkenlos,** *a.* sparkless.

**Funken-sammler,** *m.* spark condenser. **-schlagweite,** *f.* sparking distance. **-spannung,** *f.* spark voltage. **-spektrum,** *n.* spark spectrum. **-spiel,** *n.* play of sparks. **-sprühen,** *n.* emission of sparks, scintillation.

**funkensprühend,** *a.* emitting sparks; sparkling, scintillating.

**Funken-strecke,** *f.* spark gap. **-zünder,** *m.* spark igniter, (*Expl.*) jump-spark cap. **-zündung,** *f.* spark ignition.

**Funk-gerät,** *n.* radio set, wireless set; radar set; radio station. **-kerze,** *f.* spark plug, igniter plug.

**Funkmess-.** radar.

**Funk-messgerät,** *n.* radar set. **-netz,** *n.* radio network. **-technik,** *f.* radio technology.

**funktionell,** *a.* functional.

**Funktionentafel,** *f.* table of functions.

**funktionieren,** *v.i.* function.

**Funktions-erprobung, -prüfung,** *f.* operational testing or test.

**Funkwesen,** *n.* radio, wireless.

**für,** *prep.* for. — **— sich,** of itself, *per se;* **was — ein,** what kind of.

**Furche,** *f.* furrow; groove, channel; wrinkle.

**furchen,** *v.t.* furrow; crease; groove.

**Furchenspatel,** *f.* grooved spatula.

**Furcht,** *f.* fear; fright, horror, dread.

**furchtbar,** *a.* fearful, terrible, dreadful.

**fürchten,** *v.t.* & *r.* fear, be afraid.

**fürchterlich,** *a.* frightful, horrid; tremendous.

**furchtsam,** *a.* timid.

**Furchung,** *f.* furrowing; segmentation; cleavage.

**Furnier,** *n.* veneer.

**furnieren,** *v.t.* veneer, inlay; incrust.

**Furnierholz,** *n.* veneer wood; plywood.

**Furoylierung,** *f.* furoylation.

**Fürsorge,** *f.* care, solicitude.

**Fürst,** *m.* prince.

**fürstenmässig, fürstlich,** *a.* princely.

**fürwahr,** *adv.* in truth, indeed.

**Fürwort,** *n.* pronoun.

**Fusel,** *m.* fusel oil; bad spirits, bad liquor. **-branntwein,** *m.* spirits containing fusel oil.

**fuselfrei,** *a.* free from fusel oil.

**Fusel-geruch,** *m.* odor of fusel oil. **-geschmack,** *m.* taste of fusel oil.

**fuselhaltig,** *a.* containing fusel oil.

**fuselig,** *a.* containing fusel oil; intoxicated.

**Fuselöl,** *n.* fusel oil.

**fusionieren,** *v.t.* fuse; amalgamate.

**Fusionspunkt,** *m.* fusing point, melting point.

**Fuss,** *m.* foot (in various senses); base; establishment; standard; footing.

**Fuss-.** foot, pedal, ped-; low, bottom, base, inferior. **-blatt,** *n.* May apple (*Podophyllum peltatum*); sole (of the foot).

**Fussboden,** *m.* floor, flooring; ground. **-decklack,** *m.* floor varnish. **-farbe,** *f.* floor stain. **-öl,** *n.* floor oil. **-platte,** *f.* floor tile. **-wachs,** *n.* floor wax, floor polish. **-ziegel,** *m.* paving tile, paving brick.

**Fussbrett,** *n.* pedal.

**fussen,** *v.i.* stand; rely, depend. — *v.t.* found, base. — *v.r.* rely.

**fussfällig,** *a.* prostrate.

**Fuss-gänger,** *m.* pedestrian. **-gelenk,** *n.* ankle joint. **-gestell,** *n.* pedestal, base, foot. **-glätte,** *f.* black, impure litharge. **-mehl,** *n.* the lowest grade of flour. **-note,** *f.* footnote. **-pfund,** *n.* foot pound. **-puder,** *m.* foot powder. **-punkt,** *m.* (*Math.*) foot; (*Astron.*) nadir; base. **-teppich,** *m.* carpet, rug. **-wurzel,** *f.* tarsus. **-zehe,** *f.* toe. **-zylinder,** *m.* cylinder with a base.

**Fustage,** *f.* barrels, casks; package.

**Fustik, -holz,** *n.* fustic, specif. young fustic.

**Futter,** *n.* food, feed, fodder, forage; lining, casing, case, coating, covering; chuck (of a lathe).

**Futteral,** *n.* case, casing, box.

**Futter-bohne,** *f.* horse bean. **-erbse,** *f.* field pea (*Pisum arvense*). **-gerste,** *f.* winter barley. **-getreide,** *n.* grain for feeding. **-gewächse,** *n.pl.* forage plants, fodder plants. **-gras,** *n.* green fodder. **-kalk,** *m.* a calcium compound (esp. acid calcium phosphate) added to feed, "feed lime." **-klee,** *m.* red clover. **-korn,** *n.* grain for feeding. **-kräuter,** *n.pl.* = Futtergewächse. **-leder,** *n.* lining leather. **-masse,** *f.* (*Metal.*) lining material. **-mehl,** *n.* low-grade flour or meal. **-mittel,** *n.* foodstuff; feeding stuff; lining.

**füttern, futtern,** *v.t.* feed; line, case, coat.

**Futter-pflanze,** *f.* forage plant. **-reservestoff,** *m.* reserve food material. **-rohr,** *n.* (*Petroleum,* etc.) casing pipe, casing; lining tube, liner. **-rübe,** *f.* common turnip (*Brassica rapa*); fodder beet, mangel. **-salz,** *n.* a salt added to feed, esp. $CaHPO_4$. **-stein,** *m.* lining brick. **-stoff,** *m.* feeding stuff, feed; lining. **-stroh,** *n.* forage straw, feeding straw.

**Fütterung,** *f.* feeding; feed, food, fodder, forage; lining, casing, sheathing.

**Fütterungs-stoff,** *m.* lining material. **-versuch,** *m.* feeding experiment.

**Futter-verbrauch,** *m.* food (or feed) consumption. **-wert,** *m.* forage value, feed value. **-wicke,** *f.* common vetch (*Vicia sativa*). **-wurzel,** *f.* forage root.

**F.Z J,** *abbrev.* (Farbzahl gegen Jod) iodine number.

# G

**G.,** *abbrev.* (Gewicht) weight; (Gesellschaft) society, company, Co.
**gab,** *pret.* (of geben) gave, yielded, etc.
**Gabanholz,** *n.* camwood; (red) sandalwood.
**Gabe,** *f.* gift; giving; dose; alms.
**Gabel,** *f.* fork; crotch; (*Bot.*) tendril.
**gabel-artig, -förmig, -ig,** *a.* forked, furcate, bifurcated.
**Gabel-klammer,** *f.* forked clamp. **-mehl,** *n.* superfine flour.
**gabeln,** *v.r.* fork, bifurcate, branch.
**Gabel-rohr,** *n.*, **-röhre,** *f.* forked tube or pipe, Y tube. **-teilung,** *f.* forking, bifurcation.
**Gabelung,** *f.* forking, bifurcation, branching.
**Gadolinerde,** *f.* gadolinia, gadolinium oxide.
**gaffen,** *v.i.* gape; crack.
**Gagat,** *m.*, **-kohle,** *f.* jet.
**Gagel,** *m.*, **-kraut,** *n.* sweet gale (*Myrica gale*).
**Gähr-.** see Gär-.
**gähren,** *v.i.* ferment.
**gährfähig,** *a.* fermentable.
**Gais,** *f.* = Geiss.
**Galanga-öl,** *n.* galingale oil, galanga oil, **-wurzel,** *f.* galingale.
**Galanterie-arbeit,** *f.*, **-waren,** *f.pl.* fancy goods, notions.
**Galban, -harz,** *n.* galbanum.
**Galgant,** *m.* galingale. **-öl,** *n.* galingale oil. galanga oil. **-wurzel,** *f.* galingale (root).
**Galgen,** *m.* gallows; (upright) frame. **-holz,** *n.* rotten wood, touchwood.
**Galizenstein, Galitzenstein,** *m.* white vitriol (zinc sulfate); (blauer) blue vitriol.
**galizisch,** *a.* Galician.
**gallabtreibend,** *a.* cholagog.
**Gallaminblau,** *n.* gallamine blue.
**Gallapfel,** *m.* (nut) gall, gallnut.
**Galläpfel-abkochung,** *f.* nutgall decoction. **-aufguss,** *m.* infusion of nutgalls. **-beize,** *f.* (*Dyeing*) gall steep, galling. **-gerbsäure,** *f.* gallotannic acid.
**galläpfelsauer,** *a.* gallotannate of.
**Galläpfel-säure,** *f.* gallotannic (ordinary tannic) acid. **-tinktur,** *f.* tincture of gallnuts.
**Gallat,** *n.* gallate.
**Gallbeize,** *f.* (*Dyeing*) gall steep.
**Galle,** *f.* gall, bile; gall, protuberance; nutgall, gallnut; (*Min.*) nodule; flaw; (*Glass*) gall, sandiver; bubble, bleb, blister.
**Galleiche,** *f.* gall oak.
**gallen, gällen,** *v.t.* gall, treat with gallnuts; remove the gall from.
**gallenabführend,** *a.* cholagog.
**Gallenabsonderung,** *f.* secretion of bile.
**gallenartig,** *a.* biliary.
**Gallen-behälter,** *m.* gall bladder. **-bitter,** *n* picromel.
**gallenbitter,** *a.* bitter as gall.
**Gallen-blase,** *f.* gall bladder. **-blasenstein,** *m.* = Gallenstein. **-braun,** *n.* bilirubin. **-darm,** *m.* duodenum. **-farbstoff,** *m.* bile pigment, biliary pigment. **-fett,** *n.* cholesterol. **-fettsäure,** *f.* bile acid. **-fistel,** *f.* biliary fistula. **-gang,** *m.* bile duct. **-gelb,** *n.* bilirubin. **-gerbstoff,** *m.* (nut)gall tannin (gallotannic acid). **-grün,** *n.* biliverdin. **-salz,** *n.* bile salt. **-säure,** *f.* bile acid. **-seife,** *f.* gall soap, ox-gall soap. **-stein,** *m.* gallstone, biliary calculus. **-steinfett,** *n.* cholesterol. **-stoff,** *m.* bile substance (or constituent); (formerly) bilin. **-süss,** *n.* picromel. **-talg,** *m.* cholesterol.
**gallentreibend,** *a.* cholagog.
**Gallen-wachs,** *n.* cholesterol. **-zucker,** *m.* picromel.
**Gallert,** *n.* jelly; gelatin; glue.
**gallert-ähnlich, -artig,** *a.* jelly-like, gelatinous; colloidal.
**Gallerte,** *f.* = Gallert.
**Gallertgewebe,** *n.* gelatinous tissue.
**gallertig,** *a.* jelly-like, gelatinous.
**Gallert-kapsel,** *f.* gelatin capsule. **-masse,** *f.* gelatinous mass, jelly-like substance. **-moos,** *n.* Iceland moss; carrageen. **-säure,** *f.* pectic acid. **-schicht,** *f.* gelatin(ous) layer. **-substanz,** *f.* colloidal substance, colloid.
**Galletseide,** *f.* silk waste.
**Gallgerbsäure,** *f.* gallotannic acid.
**Galli-.** gallic (relating to trivalent gallium). **-chlorid,** *n.* gallic chloride, gallium(III) chloride.
**gallieren,** *v.t.* treat with gallnut decoction, gall; sumach.
**gallig,** *a.* biliary, bilious; bitter, like gall.
**Galli-hydroxyd,** *n.* gallic hydroxide, gallium-(III) hydroxide. **-oxyd,** *n.* gallic oxide, gallium(III) oxide.
**Gallipotharz,** *n.* galipot.
**Gallisalz,** *n.* gallic salt, gallium(III) salt.
**gallisieren,** *v.t.* (*Wine*) gallize.
**Gallitzenstein,** *m.* = Galizenstein.
**Gallium-chlorid,** *n.* gallium chloride, specif. gallic chloride, gallium(III) chloride. **-chlorür,** *n.* gallous chloride, gallium(II) chloride.

**-oxydul,** *n.* gallous oxide, gallium(II) oxide, GaO.

**Gallo-.** gallous (relating to bivalent gallium). **-chlorid,** *n.* gallous chloride, gallium(II) chloride, $GaCl_2$. **-oxyd,** *n.* gallous oxide, gallium(II) oxide, GaO. **-verbindung,** *f.* gallous compound, gallium(II) compound.

**Gall-seife,** *f.* = Gallenseife. **-stoff,** *m.* bile substance; bilin.

**Gallus,** *m.* nutgalls, gallnuts. **-aldehyd,** *n.* gallaldehyde. **-gerbsäure,** *f.* gallotannic acid, tannic acid (proper), tannin.

**gallussauer,** *a.* of or combined with gallic acid, gallate of.

**Gallus-säure,** *f.* gallic acid. **-säuregärung,** *f.* gallic fermentation. **-tinte,** *f.* nutgall ink.

**Galmei,** *m.* calamine (hydrous zinc silicate, also zinc carbonate).

**galt,** *pret.* (of gelten) was worth, etc.

**galvanisch,** *a.* galvanic.

**galvanisieren,** *v.t.* galvanize.

**Galvanis-ieren,** *n.*, **-ierung,** *f.* galvanization.

**Galvanismus,** *m.* galvanism.

**galvanometrisch,** *a.* galvanometric.

**Galvanoplastik,** *f.* galvanoplastics.

**galvanoplastisch,** *a.* galvanoplastic.

**Galvanostegie,** *f.* electroplating, electrodeposition.

**Gamander,** *m.* germander (*Teucrium*).

**Gambe,** *f.* (*Ceram.*) jamb.

**Gambir,** *n.* gambier, yellow catechu.

**Gambohanf,** *m.* gambo hemp, ambary hemp (*Hibiscus cannabinus*).

**Gammastrahlen,** *m.pl.* gamma rays.

**Gang,** *m.* motion, action, running, working state; course, path, passage; (*Mining*) seam, vein, gallery; (*Geol.*) hade; (*Mech.*) gear, thread; pitch (of a screw); (*Med.*) duct, canal; going, gait, pace, walk; speed; trend, drift; round, shift; progress; process; way. **-art,** *f.* gang, matrix; gait, pace.

**gangbar,** *a.* pervious; passable; current; in going condition; marketable; in regular demand; (*Pharm.*) officinal.

**Gang-erz,** *n.* vein ore. **-gestein,** *n.* (*Mining*) gang. **-höhe,** *f.* pitch (of a screw).

**gängig,** *a.* current; marketable, salable.

**Gangmasse,** *f.* (*Mining*) gang.

**Gangrän,** *f.* gangrene.

**Gang-stein,** *m.* (*Mining*) gang. **-unterschied,** *m.* (*Elec.*) phase difference.

**Gans,** *f.* goose; (*Metal.*) pig; (*Salt*) lump of salt; (*Mining*) hard rock.

**Gänse-blume,** *f.* daisy. **-fett,** *n.* goose fat. **-füsschen,** *n.pl.* quotation marks. **-hals,** *m.* gooseneck. **-haut,** *f.* gooseflesh, creeps. **-kiel,** *m.* goose quill; quill pen. **-leberpastete,** *f.* pâté de foie gras.

**Ganter,** *m.* support (for casks).

**ganz,** *a.* whole; all, full, perfect. — *adv.* wholly, entirely, all, quite, fully, very. — **ganz und gar,** absolutely. — **im ganzen,** on the whole.

**Ganz,** *f.* (*Metal.*) pig.

**Ganze, Ganzes,** *n.* whole; whole number.

**Ganz-fabrikat,** *n.* finished article. **-form,** *f.* pig mold, pig bed. **-heit,** *f.* entirety, totality, whole. **-holländer,** *m.* (*Paper*) beater, beating engine. **-holz,** *n.* unhewn timber, round timber. **-lederband,** *m.* (full) leather binding, (full) calf.

**gänzlich,** *a.* whole, full, complete. — *adv.* wholly, absolutely.

**Ganz-mahlen,** *n.* (*Paper*) beating.

**Ganzmetall-.** all-metal.

**Ganz-stoff,** *m.* = Ganzzeug. **-stoffholländer,** *m.* = Ganzholländer.

**ganzzahlig,** *a.* integral.

**Ganzzeug,** *n.* finished product; (*Paper*) whole stuff, stuff, pulp. **-holländer,** *m.* beating engine, beater, hollander. **-kasten,** *m.* (*Paper*) stuff chest.

**gar,** *a.* done; purified; (*Metal.*) refined; (*Leather*) tanned, also dressed; ready. — *adv.* fully, quite, very, at all, even. — **— machen,** finish; (*Metal.*) refine, bring to nature; (*Leather*) tan or dress. — **— nicht,** not at all.

**Gar-.** finishing; dressing; (*Metal.*) refining, refined.

**Gär-.** fermenting, fermentation.

**Garaffel,** *f.* (*Bot.*) avens (*Geum*).

**Gäransteig,** *m.* the period during which enzyme action mounts to a maximum.

**garantieren,** *v.t.* guarantee, warrant.

**Garanzin,** *n.* garancine.

**Gararbeit,** *f.* refining.

**Garaus,** *m.* finishing stroke, ruin.

**gärbar,** *a.* fermentable.

**Gärbarkeit,** *f.* fermentability.

**Garbe,** *f.* sheaf; (*Iron*) fagot, pile; caraway; yarrow (*Achillea*).

**gärben,** *v.t.* (*Iron*) pile and weld, refine.

**Gärbottich,** *m.* fermenting vat or tub, fermenter.

**Garbrand,** *m.* (*Ceram.*) finishing burn.

**garbrennen,** *v.t.* (*Ceram.*) fire to maturity.

**Garbrühe,** *f.* finishing liquor, dressing liquor.

**Garbstahl, Gärbstahl,** *m.* shear steel, refined iron.

**Gär-bütte,** *f.* = Gärbottich. **-chemie,** *f.* = Gärungschemie. **-dauer,** *f.* duration of fermentation.

**Gardine,** *f.* curtain.

**Gärdruck,** *m.* fermentation pressure.

**Gardschanbalsam,** *m.* gurjun balsam, gurjun.

**Gärdünger,** *m.* fermented manure.

**Gare,** *f.* refined state, finished state; (*Leather*) dressed state, dressing, hides dressed at one time, tawing paste; (of soil) friable state, mellowness; refining; refinery.

**Gäre,** *f.* fermentation; yeast; (*Wine*) bouquet.

**Gareisen,** *n.* refined iron; trial rod (for testing melted copper).

**garen,** *v.t.* dress, refine, finish (any technical product); coke (coal).

**gären,** *v.i.* ferment. — **gegoren,** *p.a.* fermented.

**Garerz,** *n.* roasted ore.

**gärfähig,** *a.* fermentable.

**Gärfähigkeit,** *f.* fermentability.

**Garfass,** *n.* dressing vat or tub.

**Gär-fass,** *n.* fermenting cask, union. **-flüssigkeit,** *f.* fermentable liquid.

**garfrischen,** *v.t.* refine thoroly.

**Gärführung,** *f.* method of fermentation.

**Gargang,** *m.* (*Metal.*) good working order, normal working; thoro refining; refining process.

**Gärgefäss,** *n.* fermenting vessel.

**Gargekrätz,** *n.* refinery slag.

**Gärgeschirr,** *n.* fermenting vessel.

**Gar-heit,** *f.* finished state; (*Metal.*) refined state. **-herd,** *m.* refining hearth.

**Gär-kammer,** *f.* fermenting room. **-kasten,** *m.* fermentation vat. **-keller,** *m.* fermenting cellar. **-kessel,** *m.* fermenting vat. **-kölbchen,** *n.* (*Urinalysis*) fermentation saccharimeter. **-kraft,** *f.* fermenting power.

**Gar-krätze,** *f.* refinery slag. **-kupfer,** *n.* refined copper. **-leder,** *n.* dressed leather.

**Gär-lehre,** *f.* zymology. **-luft,** *f.* foul air, mephitis.

**garmachen,** *v.t.* = gar machen, under gar.

**Gär-messer,** *m.* zymometer. **-mittel,** *n.* ferment.

**Garn,** *n.* yarn; thread, twine; net. **-druck,** *m.* (*Textiles*) yarn printing.

**Garnele, Garneele,** *f.* shrimp; prawn.

**Garnfärberei,** *f.* yarn dyeing.

**garnfarbig,** *a.* yarn-dyed.

**garnieren,** *v.t.* trim, garnish; line, bush.

**Garnitur,** *f.* trimming(s), fitting(s), mounting(s), furniture; set; outfit.

**Garnschlichtung,** *f.* yarn sizing.

**Gar-ofen,** *m.* refining furnace. **-probe,** *f.* refining assay.

**Gär-probe,** *f.* fermentation sample or test. **-produkt,** *n.* fermentation product. **-prozess,** *m.* fermentation (process). **-raum,** *m.* fermenting room.

**Gar-rösten,** *n.* (*Metal.*) finishing roast. **-schaum,** *m.* (*Iron*) kish. **-scheibe,** *f.* (*Copper*) disk of refined copper. **-schlacke,** *f.* refining slag, rich slag.

**garschmelziges Eisen.** low-silicon pig; open white pig.

**Garspan,** *m.* (*Copper*) coating of metal on the trial rod.

**Gärstoff,** *m.* ferment.

**Garstück,** *n.* lump of purified salt.

**Gärtätigkeit,** *f.* fermentative activity.

**Garten,** *m.* garden. **-bau,** *m.* **-baukunst,** *f.* horticulture. **-distel,** *f.* artichoke. **-kunst,** *f.* horticulture. **-raute,** *f.* garden rue, common rue.

**Gärtner,** *m.* gardener.

**Gärtnerei,** *f.* gardening, horticulture.

**gärtüchtig,** *a.* (of yeast) vital.

**Garung,** *f.* dressing, etc. (see garen).

**Gärung,** *f.* fermentation. — **— erregend, — erzeugend,** fermentative. — **— hemmend, — verhindernd,** antifermentative.

**Gärungs-alkohol,** *m.* ethyl alcohol. **-amylalkohol,** *m.* amyl alcohol of fermentation (a mixture of 2- and 3- methylbutanol). **-buttersäure,** *f.* (ordinary) butyric acid. **-chemie,** *f.* fermentation chemistry, zymurgy.

**gärungserregend,** *p.a.* fermentative, zymogenic.

**Gärungserreger,** *m.* ferment.

**gärungs-erzeugend,** *a.* = gärungserregend. **-fähig,** *a.* fermentable.

**Gärungs-fähigkeit,** *f.* fermentability. **-fuselöl,** *n.* fusel oil. **-gewerb(e),** *n.* fermentation industry.

**gärungshemmend,** *a.* arresting fermentation, antifermentative.

**Gärungs-kohlensäure,** *f.* carbon dioxide from fermentation. **-kölbchen,** *n.* fermentation tube. **-kraft,** *f.* fermentative power. **-küpe,** *f.* (*Dyeing*) fermentation vat, steeping vat. **-lehre,** *f.* zymology. **-messer,** *m.* zymometer. **-mikrobe,** *m.* fermentation organism. **-milchsäure,** *f.* fermentation lactic acid. **-mittel,** *n.* fermenting agent, ferment. **-pilz,** *m.* fermentation fungus. **-probe,** *f.* fermentation test. **-stoff,** *m.* ferment. **-technik,** *f.* zymotechnics, zymotechnology.

**gärungs-technisch,** *a.* zymotechnic(al). **-unfähig,** *a.* unfermentable.

**Gärungsverfahren,** *n.* fermentation method or process.

**gärungsverhindernd,** *a.* antifermentative.

**Gärungs-vermögen,** *n.* fermentative power. **-vorgang,** *m.* fermentation process.

**gärungswidrig,** *a.* antizymotic, antifermentative.

**Garungszeit,** *f.* (*Coke*) coking period.

**Gärungszeit,** *f.* time of fermentation.

**Gär-verfahren,** *n.* = Gärungsverfahren. **-vermögen,** *n.* fermenting capacity. **-vorgang,** *m.* fermentation process.

**Garwa(a)ge,** *f.* (*Salt*) brine gage.

**Gärwärme,** *f.* heat of fermentation.

**Garzeit,** *f.* (*Coke*) coking period.

**Gas-abführung,** *f.* = Gasableitung. **-abgabe,** *f.* evolution or escape of gas. **-ableitung,** *f.* drawing off or removal of gas; gas delivery tube, gas outlet. **-ableitungsrohr,** *n.* gas delivery tube. **-abwehr,** *f.* (*Mil.*) gas defense.

**-abwehrmittel,** *n.* gas defense equipment. **-abzug,** *m.* = Gasableitung; (of a blast furnace) downcomer. **-abzugrohr,** *n.* gas delivery tube; (of a blast furnace) downcomer.

**gasähnlich,** *a.* resembling gas, gaseous.

**Gasanalyse,** *f.* gas analysis.

**gasanalytisch,** *a.* gas-analysis, gas-analytical.

**Gas-anfall,** *m.* gas collected, gas yield. **-angriff,** *m.* gas attack. **-anlage,** *f.* gas plant, gas works, gashouse. **-ansammlung,** *f.* accumulation of gas. **-anstalt,** *f.* gas plant, gas works, gashouse. **-anstaltskoks,** *m.* gashouse coke, gas coke. **-anzeiger,** *m.* gas detector. **-anzug,** *m.* gas-protection clothing. **-anzünder,** *m.* gas lighter.

**gasarm,** *a.* poor in gas, (of coals) lean.

**Gasart,** *f.* kind of gas.

**gasartig,** *a.* gasiform, gaseous.

**Gas-artigkeit,** *f.* gaseousness. **-aufnahme,** *f.* gas absorption. **-aufsaugung, -aufzehrung,** *f.* gas absorption. **-ausbruch,** *m.* outburst of gas. **-austreibung,** *f.* gas expulsion, outgassing. **-austritt,** *m.* escape of gas.

**gasbehaftet,** *a.* affected or contaminated by gas.

**Gas-behälter,** *m.* gas container, gas holder, gasometer, gas tank. **-bekleidung,** *f.* gas-protection clothing. **-beleuchtung,** *f.* gas lighting, illumination with gas. **-benzin,** *n.* (*Petroleum*) light ends (propane, butane), bottled gas. **-bereitung,** *f.* gas making. **-beschädigter,** *m.* (*Mil.*) gas casualty. **-beschuss,** *m.* gas-shell fire.

**gasbildend,** *p.a.* gas-forming.

**Gas-bildner,** *m.* gas former, gas producer. **-bildung,** *f.* formation of gas, gasification, gas production. **-bindung,** *f.* gas fixation, specif. gettering. **-bläschen,** *n.* small gas bubble. **-blase,** *f.* gas bubble; (*Metal.*) blowhole. **-bleiche,** *f.* gas bleaching, (*Paper*) potching. **bohrloch,** *n.* gas well. **-bohrung,** *f.* drilling for gas; gas well. **-bombe,** *f.* gas cylinder; (*Mil.*) gas bomb. **-brand,** *m.* (*Med.*) gas gangrene. **-brenner,** *m.* gas burner.

**gäschen,** *v.i.* foam, froth.

**gasdicht,** *a.* gas-tight.

**Gas-dichte,** *f.* gas(eous) density. **-dichtigkeit,** *f.* impermeability to gas. **-druck,** *m.* gas pressure, gaseous pressure. **-druckmesser,** *m.* manometer, pressure gage; (*Mil.*) accelerometer. **-durchlässigkeit,** *f.* permeability for gas.

**Gase,** *f.* gauze; canvas.

**Gas-einsatz,** *m.* (*Mil.*) employment of gas. **-einschluss,** *m.* gas occlusion. **-einsteller,** *m.* gas regulator.

**gasen,** *v.t.* & *i.* gas.

**Gasentbindung,** *f.* generation of gas.

**Gasentbindungs-flasche,** *f.* gas-generating bottle or flask, gas generator. **-rohr,** *n.* gas delivery tube.

**Gas-entladung,** *f.* (*Elec.*) gas discharge. **-entweichung,** *f.* escape of gas. **-entwick(e)lung,** *f.* evolution of gas. **-entwick(e)lungsapparat,** *m.* gas generator. **-entwickler,** *m.* gas generator. **-erdmine,** *f.* (*Mil.*) chemical land mine. **-erkennung,** *f.* gas detection or recognition. **-erkennungsmittel,** *n.* gas detector.

**gaserzeugend,** *a.* gas-producing.

**Gas-erzeuger,** *m.* gas generator, gas producer. **-erzeugergas,** *n.* producer gas. **-erzeugung,** *f.* production of gas, gasification. **-erzeugungsanlage,** *f.* gas plant, gas works.

**gasf.,** *abbrev.* (gasförmig) gaseous.

**Gas-fabrik,** *f.* gas works. **-fach,** *n.* gas engineering. **-fang,** *m.* (*Metal.*) gas take, gas catcher.

**gasfest,** *a.* gasproof, gas-tight.

**Gas-feuerung,** *f.* gas heating, gas firing; gas furnace. **-flamme,** *f.* gas flame. **-flammkohle,** *f.* = Flammkohle. **-flammofen,** *m.* gas-fired reverberatory furnace. **-flasche,** *f.* gas cylinder, gas bottle.

**gasförmig,** *a.* gaseous, gasiform.

**Gas-förmigkeit,** *f.* gaseousness. **-frischen,** *n.* (*Metal.*) gas puddling.

**gasführend,** *a.* containing gas, gassy.

**Gasgebläse,** *n.* gas blast; gas blast apparatus.

**gas-gefeuert,** *a.* gas-fired, gas-heated. **-gefüllt,** *a.* gas-filled.

**Gas-gehalt,** *m.* gas content. **-gemenge, -gemisch,** *n.* gaseous mixture, gas mixture, mixture of gases. **-geruch,** *m.* odor of gas. **-geschoss,** *n.* gas projectile; specif., gas shell.

**gasgeschützt,** *a.* gasproofed.

**Gas-gesetz,** *n.* gas law. **-gestalt,** *f.* gaseous form. **-gewinnung,** *f.* gas production. **-gleichgewicht,** *n.* gas equilibrium. **-gleichung,** *f.* gas equation. **-glocke,** *f.* gas holder, gas bell. **-glühlicht,** *n.* incandescent gas light. **-glühlichtkörper, -glühlichtstrumpf,** *m.* gas mantle. **-granate,** *f.* gas shell; gas grenade. **-granatenangriff,** *m.* gas shell attack. **-hahn,** *m.* gas cock, gas tap. **-halter, -hälter,** *m.* = Gasbehälter.

**gashaltig,** *a.* containing gas.

**Gas-handwerfer,** *m.* (*Mil.*) chemical mortar. **-haut,** *f.* gas film. **-heizung,** *f.* gas heating. **-hohlraum,** *m.* gas pocket. **-hülle,** *f.* gaseous envelope.

**gasieren,** *v.t.* gas.

**gasig,** *a.* gaseous.

**Gas-kalk,** *m.* gas lime. **-kammer,** *f.* gas chamber. **-kampf,** *m.* gas warfare, chemical warfare. **-kampfflasche,** *f.* a small gas cylinder for cloud gas attacks. **-kampfstoff,** *m.* war gas. **-kette,** *f.* (*Elec.*) gas cell.

**gaskinetisch,** *a.* pertaining to the kinetics of gases.

**Gas-kocher,** *m.* gas burner (on which a vessel may be set), gas hot plate. **-kohle,** *f.* gas coal; gas-retort carbon. **-koks,** *m.* gas coke. **-kraftmaschine,** *f.* gas engine.

**gaskrank,** *a.* affected by gas, gassed.

**Gas-krieg,** *m.* gas warfare, chemical warfare. **-leitung,** *f.* gas conduction; gas pipe line, gas supply; flue. **-leitungsröhre,** *f.* gas-conducting tube, gas tube; gas pipe. **-licht,** *n.* gaslight. **-löslichkeit,** *f.* gas solubility. **-luftgemisch,** *n.* mixture of gas and air. **-maschine,** *f.* = Gasmotor. **-maske,** *f.* gas mask, respirator. **-menge,** *f.* amount of gas. **-messer,** *m.* gas meter; gasometer. **-messrohr,** *n.*, **-messröhre,** *f.* = Gasmessungsrohr. **-messung,** *f.* measurement of gases or of gas. **-messungsrohr,** *n.*, **-messungsröhre,** *f.* gas-measuring tube; eudiometer. **-mine,** *f.* gas mine, chemical mine; (gas) projector drum. **-mischung,** *f.* gas mixture; gas mixing. **-mörser,** *m.* (*Mil.*) chemical mortar. **-motor,** *m.* gas engine, gas motor, internal-combustion engine. **-nitrieren,** *n.* (*Metal.*) gas nitriding. **-ofen,** *m.* gas furnace; gas-fired kiln; gas stove; coke oven. **-öl,** *n.* gas oil. **-olin,** *n.* a light petroleum fraction boiling about 30–80°C.

**gasometrisch,** *a.* gasometric, gasometrical.

**gasös,** *a.* gaseous.

**Gas-pfeife,** *f.* gas pipe. **-pressung,** *f.* gas pressure. **-probe,** *f.* gas test; gas testing; gas sample. **-prüfer,** *m.* gas tester; eudiometer. **-quelle,** *f.* gas well. **-raum,** *m.* gas volume, volume of gas.

**gasreich,** *a.* rich in gas, (of coals) fat.

**Gas-reiniger,** *m.* gas purifier. **-reinigungsmasse,** *f.* gas-purifying material. **-rest,** *m.* gas residue. **-rohr,** *n.*, **-röhre,** *f.* gas tube; gas pipe. **-russ,** *m.* gas soot, gas black. **-sack,** *m.* gas bag. **-sammelrohr,** *n.* gas-collecting tube. **-sammler,** *m.* gas collector, gas tank. **-sauger,** *m.* gas exhauster. **-schlauch,** *m.* gas tubing, gas tube. **-schmelzschweissung,** *f.* gas welding, autogenous welding.

**Gasschutz,** *m.* protection against gas, gas defense. **-dienst,** *m.* gas defense service. **-gerät,** *n.* gas-defense equipment. **-lager,** *n.* gas defense depot. **-salbe,** *f.* (*Mil.*) protective ointment.

**Gas-schwaden,** *m.* gas fumes. **-schweissen,** *n.* gas welding.

**Gasse,** *f.* street, lane, alley; (*Founding*) channel.

**gassicher,** *a.* gasproof.

**Gas-spannung,** *f.* gas pressure. **-spüren,** *n.* gas detection. **-spürstoff,** *m.* gas-detection agent. **-stoffwechsel,** *m.* gaseous metabolism, gas exchange, respiration. **-strahl,** *m.* gas jet. **-strom,** *m.* current of gas, stream of gas. **-strömung,** *f.* gas flow, gas current. **-sumpf,** *m.* a dense, low-lying gas cloud.

**Gast,** *m.* guest; visitor, stranger, customer.

**Gäst,** *f.* yeast.

**Gastechnik,** *f.* gas engineering.

**gastechnisch,** *a.* relating to gas engineering.

**Gas-teer,** *m.* gas tar. **-teilung,** *f.* device (as a T tube) for dividing a gas supply.

**Gast-haus,** *n.*, **-hof,** *m.* inn, hotel. **-mahl,** *n.* banquet, feast.

**Gas-trenner,** *m.* gas separator. **-trennung,** *f.* separation of gas(es). **-trockner,** *m.* gas drier.

**Gastrolle,** *f.* star role, star part.

**Gasuhr,** *f.* gas meter.

**gasundurchlässig,** *a.* impermeable to gas.

**Gas-ventil,** *n.* gas valve. **-verbrauch,** *m.* gas consumption. **-verdichter,** *m.* gas compressor. **-verflüssigung,** *f.* liquefaction of gas(es). **-vergiftung,** *f.* gas poisoning. **-verschluss,** *m.* gas seal. **-volum, -volumen,** *n.* gas volume, volume of gas.

**gasvolumetrisch,** *a.* gasometric.

**Gas-vulkanisation,** *f.* (*Rubber*) gas cure. **-wa(a)ge,** *f.* gas balance. **-wanne,** *f.* gas trough, pneumatic trough. **-waschaufsatz,** *m.* gas-washing attachment, washing tube. **-wascher,** *m.* gas washer.

**Gaswasch-flasche,** *f.* gas-washing bottle. **-rohr,** *n.* gas-washing tube. **-turm,** *m.* gas-washing tower, gas scrubber.

**Gas-wasser,** *n.* gas liquor. **-wechsel,** *m.* gas exchange; specif., (*Physiol.*) gaseous metabolism. **-werfer,** *m.* gas projector, chemical projector. **-werferangriff,** *m.* (gas) projector attack. **-werk,** *n.* gas works. **-wolke,** *f.* gas wave, gas cloud. **-wolkenangriff,** *m.* gas wave attack, cloud gas attack. **-zähler,** *m.* gas meter. **-zementieren,** *n.* gas cementation. **-zufuhr,** *f.* gas supply. **-zuleiter,** *m.*, **-zuleitungsrohr,** *n.*, **-zuleitungsröhre,** *f.* gas inlet tube or pipe, gas conductor. **-zünder,** *m.* gas lighter. **-zustand,** *m.* gaseous condition.

**Gatsch,** *m.* (*Petroleum*) slack wax, crude scale wax.

**Gatte,** *m.* husband.

**Gatter,** *n.* grate, grating, lattice; railing; enclosure; saw frame; frame saw; reel.

**gattern,** *v.t.* refine (tin).

**gattieren,** *v.t.* mix; sort, classify. — *v.i.* (*Metal.*) make up the charge.

**Gattierung,** *f.* mixing; mixture of ores; sorting.

**Gattin,** *f.* wife.

**Gattung,** *f.* genus; kind, sort; family, race; gender.

**Gattungsname,** *m.* generic name.

**Gau,** *m. & n.* province, district, region.
**Gauchheil,** *n.* scarlet pimpernel (*Anagallis arvensis*); self-heal (*Prunella vulgaris*).
**gaufrieren, gauffrieren,** *v.t.* goffer, emboss.
**gaukelhaft,** *a.* juggling, deceptive.
**gaukeln,** *v.i.* juggle; flit about.
**Gaumen,** *m.* (hard) palate. **-segel,** *n.*, **-vorhang,** *m.* soft palate.
**gautschen,** *v.t.* (*Paper*) couch.
**Gayerde,** *f.*, **Gaysalpeter,** *m.* native saltpeter earth, saltpeter sweepings.
**Gaze,** *f.* gauze; canvas.
**gazeartig,** *a.* gauze-like, gauzy.
**Gazepapier,** *n.* tissue paper.
**gbr.,** *abbrev.* (gebräuchlich) usual, usually; (gebraucht) used; (gebrannt) burned.
**ge-.** A prefix used in forming the past participle of most verbs, in forming collective nouns (as *Gerät*, apparatus, tools) and in various other ways.
**G.E.,** *abbrev.* (Gewichtseinheit) unit of weight.
**Geäder,** *n.* veins, veined structure; system of blood vessels.
**geadert, geädert,** *a.* veined, veiny; marbled.
**geb.,** *abbrev.* (gebunden) bound; (gebildet) formed, also educated; (geboren) born.
**Gebäck,** *n.* baking, batch; baker's wares, pastry.
**Gebälk,** *n.*, **Gebälke,** *f.* timber work.
**gebar,** *pret.* (of gebären) bore.
**Gebärde,** *f.* gesture; demeanor; mien.
**Gebaren,** *n.* behavior; appearance.
**gebären,** *v.t.* bear, bring forth. — **geboren,** *p.a.* born, native, nee.
**Gebären,** *n.* childbirth, parturition.
**Gebärmutter,** *f.* uterus, womb.
**Gebärung,** *f.* behavior; appearance.
**Gebäude,** *n.* building, structure; mine; system.
**gebd.,** *abbrev.* (gebunden) bound.
**Gebein,** *n.* skeleton, bones; *pl.* remains.
**geben,** *v.t.* give; yield; emit, evolve; furnish; add; show; express; transmit, send (signals). — *v.r.* give; abate; relent; prove; (of cloth) stretch. — **es gibt,** there is, there are; **nichts —,** care nothing.
**Geber,** *m.* giver, donor; (*Teleg.*, etc.) transmitter, sender.
**Gebet,** *n.* prayer. — **ins — nehmen,** question closely.
**gebeten,** *p.p.* (of bitten) asked, begged.
**gebiert,** *pr. 3 sing.* (of gebären) bears.
**Gebiet,** *n.* territory, region, area, district, department; zone, field, range; domain, sphere.
**gebieten,** *v.t.* order, command. — *v.i.* rule.
**gebieterisch,** *a.* imperative, imperious.
**Gebilde, Gebild,** *n.* structure, organization, system; form; image; pattern; diaper; (*Geol.*) formation.
**Gebinde,** *n.* bundle; package; skein, hank; barrel, cask; range (of tiles); truss.
**Gebirge,** *n.* mountains, mountain system, highlands, rock; ground; country; (*Mining*) gang.
**Gebirgs-art,** *f.* kind of stone or rock. **-bildung, -formation,** *f.* mountainous formation; rock formation; orogenesis. **-kunde, -lehre,** *f.* orology; geognosy. **-zug,** *m.* mountain range.
**Gebiss,** *n.* set of teeth, denture, dentition.
**gebissen,** *p.p.* (of beissen) bitten.
**Gebläse,** *n.* blast; bellows, blower, blast apparatus; fan, ventilator. **-kies,** *m.* blasting sand, blasting grit. **-lampe,** *f.* blast lamp. **-luft,** *f.* blast air, air blast. **-maschine,** *f.* blast engine, blower. **-messer,** *m.* blast meter. **-ofen,** *m.* blast furnace. **-röhre,** *f.* blast pipe, tuyère. **-vorrichtung,** *f.* blast apparatus, blowing apparatus. **-wind,** *m.* blast.
**geblättert,** *a.* foliated; foliate; lamellar.
**gebleit,** *a.* leaded (as gasoline).
**geblichen, gebleicht,** *p.p.* (of bleichen) bleached.
**geblieben,** *p.p.* (of bleiben) remained.
**geblümt,** *a.* flowered, figured.
**Geblüt,** *n.* blood (entire blood in the body); blood, race.
**gebogen,** *p.p.* (of biegen) bent, curved, etc.
**geboren,** *p.p.* (of gebären) born, native.
**geborgen,** *p.p.* of bergen (which see).
**geborsten,** *p.p.* (of bersten) burst, etc.
**Gebot,** *n.* bidding, bid; command, commandment.
**geboten,** *p.p.* (of bieten and gebieten) offered; ordered.
**gebr.,** *abbrev.* = gbr.
**Gebr.,** *abbrev.* (Gebrüder) brothers.
**gebracht,** *p.p.* (of bringen) brought.
**gebrannt,** *p.p.* burned, etc. See **brennen.**
**Gebräu,** *n.* brewing, brew, gyle.
**Gebrauch,** *m.* use; usage; custom; fashion.
**gebrauchen,** *v.t.* use, employ, make use of. — **gebraucht,** *p.a.* used; second-hand; worn out, spent.
**gebräuchlich,** *a.* usual, customary, ordinary, common. — **am gebräuchlichsten,** most commonly, usually.
**Gebrauchs-anweisung,** *f.* directions for use. **-dosis,** *f.* usual dose.
**gebrauchs-fähig,** *a.* usable, serviceable, ready for use. **-fertig,** *a.* ready for use.
**Gebrauchs-gegenstand,** *m.*, **-gut,** *n.* commodity. **-last,** *f.* (*Mach.*) working load. **-muster,** *n.* sample for experiments or tests; commercial sample; registered design, petty patent (a kind of patent, good for a short term only). **-porzellan,** *n.* household porcelain. **-vorschrift,** *f.* directions (for use). **-wasser,** *n.* service water, tap water.

**gebraucht,** *p.p.* (of brauchen and gebrauchen). See gebrauchen.
**Gebräude,** *f.* = Gebräu.
**gebrech,** *a.* brittle, soft.
**gebrechen,** *v.i.* be lacking.
**Gebrechen,** *n.* want, defect, infirmity.
**gebrechlich,** *a.* fragile, frail, weak, unsound.
**gebremst,** *p.p.* of bremsen (which see).
**gebrochen,** *p.p.* of brechen (which see).
**Gebrüder,** *m.pl.* brothers.
**Gebrüll,** *n.* roaring.
**Gebrumm,** *n.* humming, murmuring.
**Gebühr,** *f.* due, duty, charge, fee, tax; decency.
**gebühren,** *v.i.* be due, belong. — *v.r.* be proper, be fitting. — **gebührend,** *p.a.* due, fit, proper. — *adv.* duly.
**Gebund, Gebünde,** *n.* bunch, bundle, skein.
**gebunden,** *p.p.* (of binden) bound, etc.
**Geburt,** *f.* birth; labor; offspring; descent, race; origin.
**gebürtig,** *a.* native, born.
**Geburtshilfe,** *f.* obstetrics, midwifery.
**geburtshilflich,** *a.* obstetric.
**Geburts-kunde, -lehre,** *f.* obstetrics. **-not,** *f.* labor. **-tag,** *m.* birthday.
**Gebüsch,** *n.* bushes, thicket.
**gedacht,** *p.p.* (of denken and gedenken) thought; imagined. — *p.a.* above-mentioned.
**Gedächtnis,** *n.* remembrance, memory, memorial. **-münze,** *f.* commemorative medal.
**Gedanke,** *m.* thought; idea; opinion.
**Gedanken-folge,** *f.*, **-gang,** *m.* train (or sequence) of thought.
**gedanklich,** *a.* intellectual.
**Gedärm,** *n.* intestines, entrails.
**Gedeck,** *n.* covering; cover (at table).
**gedeckelt,** *p.a.* see deckeln.
**gedeihen,** *v.i.* thrive, grow; proceed; (of slaking lime) swell.
**gedeihlich,** *a.* beneficial, favorable, profitable.
**gedenken,** *v.i.* think, be mindful. — *v.t.* intend.
**Gedenken,** *n.* memory.
**gedeucht,** *p.p.* (of dünken) seemed.
**Gedicht,** *n.* poem.
**gedichtet,** *p.p.* (of dichten) made tight, etc.
**gediegen,** *a.* (*Min.*) native; pure, unmixed; (of elements) free; genuine, superior.
**Gediegenheit,** *f.* native state; purity; intrinsic worth.
**gedieh,** *pret.* (of gedeihen) thrived, etc.
**gediehen,** *p.p.* (of gedeihen) thrived, etc.
**Gedränge,** *n.* thronging, crowd; dilemma.
**gedrängt,** *p.p.* & *p.a.* see drängen.
**gedroschen,** *p.p.* (of dreschen) threshed.
**gedrungen,** *p.p.* of dringen (which see).
**Geduld,** *f.* patience; endurance.
**gedurft,** *p.p.* (of dürfen) been permitted, etc.
**geeignet,** *p.a.* see eignen.
**gef.,** *abbrev.* (gefunden) found; (gefällig) kind; (gefälligst) please.
**Gefahr,** *f.* danger; risk, hazard.
**gefährden,** *v.t.* endanger, imperil.
**Gefahrenpunkt,** *m.* danger point.
**gefährlich,** *a.* dangerous.
**gefahrlos,** *a.* without danger, safe.
**Gefährte,** *m.* companion, associate.
**Gefäll, Gefälle,** *n.* fall; gradient, incline, slope; income; taxes; head (of water).
**gefallen,** *p.p.* (of fallen and gefallen) separated; fallen; pleased.
**gefallen,** *v.i.* please.
**Gefallen,** *n.* pleasure; favor.
**gefällig,** *a.* pleasing; obliging, kind.
**gefälligst,** *adv.* please, pray.
**gefällt,** *p.p.* (of fällen) precipitated.
**Gefangene,** *m.* & *f.* prisoner.
**Gefängnis,** *n.* prison; confinement.
**gefärbt,** *p.p.* colored; dyed; stained.
**Gefäss,** *n.* vessel, receptacle, container; blood vessel; (of a sword) hilt.
**Gefäss-.** (*Med.*) vascular. **-barometer,** *n.* cistern barometer. **-bau,** *m.* vascular structure. **-einmündung,** *f.* anastomosis. **-haut,** *f.* vascular membrane.
**gefässig,** *a.* vascular.
**Gefäss-kunde,** *f.* ceramic art. **-ofen,** *m.* (furnace containing receptacles), retort furnace, crucible furnace, pot furnace, etc.
**gefasst,** *p.p.* & *p.a.* see fassen.
**Gefäss-versuch,** *m.* (*Agric., Bot.*) pot experiment. **-wand,** *f.* wall of a (or the) vessel.
**Gefecht,** *n.* fighting, fight, battle, combat.
**Gefechtskopf,** *m.* war head (of a torpedo).
**gefedert,** *a.* elastic, springy.
**Gefieder,** *n.* feathering, plumage.
**gefiel,** *pret.* (of gefallen) pleased.
**gefl.,** *abbrev.* (gefällig) kind; (gefälligst) please.
**Geflecht,** *n.* plaited or woven work, network, netting; texture; plexus.
**gefleckt,** *p.p.* (of flecken) spotted, etc.
**geflissentlich,** *a.* willful, intentional.
**geflochten,** *p.p.* (of flechten) plaited, etc.
**geflogen,** *p.p.* (of fliegen) flown.
**geflohen,** *p.p.* (of fliehen) fled.
**geflossen,** *p.p.* (of fliessen) flowed, etc.; molten.
**Geflügel,** *n.* fowls, poultry.
**geflügelt,** *a.* winged; pinnate; alate.
**gefochten,** *p.p.* (of fechten) fought.
**Gefolge,** *n.*, **Gefolgschaft,** *f.* attendants, followers, train.
**Gef. P.,** *abbrev.* (Gefrierpunkt) freezing point.
**gefrässig,** *a.* voracious.
**Gefrierapparat,** *m.* freezing (or freezing-point) apparatus.
**gefrierbar,** *a.* congealable, freezable.
**Gefrier-barkeit,** *f.* congealability. **-durchschnitt,** *m.* (*Micros.*) frozen section.

**gefrieren,** *v.i.* freeze, congeal.

**Gefrierer,** *m.* freezer, congealer.

**Gefrier-fleisch,** *n.* frozen meat. **-punkt,** *m.* freezing point. **-punktsbestimmung,** *f.* freezing-point determination. **-punkt(s)erniedrigung,** *f.* freezing-point lowering. **-salz,** *n.* freezing salt, specif. ammonium nitrate. **-schnitt,** *m.* (*Micros.*) frozen section. **-schrank,** *m.* refrigerator; freezing chamber. **-schutz,** *m.* antifreeze. **-schutzmittel,** *n.* antifreeze agent. **-versuch,** *m.* freezing experiment or test. **-vorrichtung,** *f.* freezing apparatus.

**Gefrisch,** *n.* reclaimed rubber.

**gefroren,** *p.p.* (of frieren and gefrieren) frozen, congealed.

**Gefrorene,** *n.* something frozen, ice cream, ice.

**Gefüge,** *n.* structure; texture; bed, stratum; system, order. **-art,** *f.* kind or type of structure. **-bestandteil,** *m.* structural constituent. **-lehre,** *f.* science of structure, specif. metallography.

**gefügelos,** *a.* structureless, textureless.

**gefügig,** *a.* pliable, pliant, flexible.

**Gefühl,** *n.* feeling; touch, sensation, sensitiveness.

**Gefühlsnerv,** *m.* sensory nerve.

**gefunden,** *p.p.* (of finden) found.

**geg.,** *abbrev.* of gegen.

**gegangen,** *p.p.* (of gehen) gone.

**gegast,** *p.p.* (of gasen) gassed. — **gegaste Lauge,** (*Paper*) gassed liquor (tower liquor treated with gas from the cookers).

**gegebenenfalls,** *adv.* in an emergency, if necessary, in such a case.

**gegen,** *prep.* toward, against, about, compared with, opposite.

**Gegen-.** counter-, contra-, anti-.

**gegenarbeiten,** *v.i.* work against, oppose.

**Gegen-arznei,** *f.* antidote. **-bemerkung,** *f.* reply, rejoinder. **-bewegung,** *f.* countermovement. **-beweis,** *m.* counterevidence. **-beziehung,** *f.*, **-bezug,** *m.* correlation. **-bild,** *n.* counterpart, antitype; inverted image.

**Gegend,** *f.* region, quarter, vicinity.

**Gegendruck,** *m.* counterpressure, back pressure, resistance.

**gegen-einander,** *adv.* toward (or against) each other or one another; reciprocally, mutually. **-elektromotorisch,** *a.* counterelectromotive, back-electromotive.

**Gegen-email,** *n.* counterenamel. **-farbe,** *f.* complementary color; contrast color. **-färbung,** *f.* contrast coloring or staining. **-feuer,** *n.* backfire; (*Mil.*) counterfire. **-flüssigkeit,** *f.* counterliquid (as in titration). **-füssler,** *m.pl.* antipodes. **-gewicht,** *n.* counterweight, counterpoise. **-gift,** *n.* antidote; antivenin. **-grund,** *m.* contrary reason, objection. **-ion,** *m.* ion of opposite charge. **-klopfmittel,** *n.* antiknock agent. **-kraft,** *f.* opposing force, counterforce. **-lauf,** *m.* reverse motion; countercurrent.

**gegenläufig,** *a.* running oppositely, countercurrent.

**Gegen-läufigkeit,** *f.* oppositeness (in direction), opposition. **-massnahme,** *f.* countermeasure.

**gegenmischbar,** *a.* consolute.

**Gegen-mittel,** *n.* preventive, antidote, remedy. **-mutter,** *f.* lock nut, check nut.

**gegenphasig,** *a.* of opposite phase.

**Gegen-polung,** *f.* reversal of polarity; opposition of polarity. **-probe,** *f.* contrasting sample or test; check test. **-reaktion,** *f.* counterreaction, opposite reaction. **-reiz,** *m.* counterirritation; counterirritant. **-reizmittel,** *n.* counterirritant. **-reizung,** *f.* counterirritation. **-satz,** *m.* opposition, opposite, contrast, return. **-schein,** *n.* reflection; counterglow; (*Astron.*) opposition. **-schmelz,** *m.* counterenamel. **-seite,** *f.* opposite side; (of a coin) reverse.

**gegen-seitig,** *a.* mutual, reciprocal, common; opposite, adverse. **-sinnig,** *a.* of opposite sense or direction; irrational.

**Gegen-sonne,** *f.* mock sun, parhelion. **-spülung,** *f.* counterwashing, reverse circulation. **-stand,** *m.* object; matter, subject, article.

**gegenständlich,** *a.* opposite.

**Gegenstandsglas,** *n.* object glass.

**gegenstandslos,** *a.* objectless, meaningless; annulled.

**Gegen-stoff,** *m.* antisubstance, antibody; antidote. **-strahl,** *m.* reflected ray, reflection. **-strom,** *m.* countercurrent, inverse current, counterflow. **-stromkühler,** *m.* countercurrent condenser or cooler. **-stück,** *n.* counterpart, match.

**Gegentakt-.** (*Elec.*) push-pull.

**Gegen-teil,** *n.* contrary, opposite, converse.

**gegenteilig,** *a.* opposite, contrary.

**gegenüber,** *prep.* over against, opposite, in contrast with. — *adv.* opposite. **-liegend,** *p.a.* opposite. **-stellen,** *v.t.* oppose; contrast; compare.

**Gegen-überstellung,** *f.* opposition; contrast; comparison. **-versuch,** *m.* control experiment. **-wart,** *f.* presence; present.

**gegenwärtig,** *a.* present. — *adv.* at present.

**Gegen-welle,** *f.* countershaft. **-wert,** *m.* equivalent.

**gegenwirken,** *v.i.* counteract, react. — **gegenwirkend,** *p.a.* counteractive, reactive; antagonistic.

**Gegen-wirkung,** *f.* counteraction, reaction. **-zug,** *m.* countermove.

**gegessen,** *p.p.* (of essen) eaten.

**geglättet,** *p.p.* (of glätten) smoothed, etc.

**geglichen,** *p.p.* (of gleichen) equalized, etc.
**geglitten,** *p.p.* (of gleiten) glided, etc.
**geglommen,** *p.p.* of glimmen.
**geglüht,** *p.p.* (of glühen) glowed, etc.
**Gegner,** *m.* opponent, enemy.
**gegolten,** *p.p.* of gelten.
**gegoren,** *p.p.* (of gären) fermented.
**gegossen,** *p.p.* (of giessen) poured, etc.
**gegr.,** *abbrev.* (gegründet) founded.
**gegriffen,** *p.p.* (of greifen) grasped, etc.
**geh.,** *abbrev.* geheftet (see under heften).
**Geh.,** *abbrev.* of Gehalt.
**gehaben,** *v.r.* behave, fare.
**Gehalt,** *m.* contents, content; capacity, extent, yield, standard (of coins), strength; salary, pay; value.
**Gehaltsbestimmung,** *f.* determination of content, analysis, assay.
**Gehänge,** *n.* slope; hanging, pendant.
**gehärtet,** *p.p.* (of härten) hardened.
**Gehäuse,** *n.* case, casing, housing, box, shell.
**geheftet,** *p.a.* see heften.
**geheim,** *a.* secret; confidential, private, hidden. — **geheime Tinte,** sympathetic ink, invisible ink.
**Geheimmittel,** *n.* secret remedy, patent medicine, nostrum.
**Geheimnis,** *f.* secret, secrecy, mystery.
**geheimnisvoll,** *a.* mysterious, mystic, occult.
**Geheim-rat,** *m.* privy councilor. **-schrift,** *f.* secret writing, code, cipher. **-tinte,** *f.* invisible ink.
**Geheiss,** *n.* command, bidding.
**gehen,** *v.i.* go; walk, travel, pass; fare. — **es geht um,** it is a question of. — **vor sich —,** go on, take place.
**Geheul,** *n.* howling.
**Gehilfe,** *m.* helper, assistant.
**Gehirn,** *n.* brain. — **kleines —,** cerebellum.
**Gehirn-.** cerebral. **-anhang,** *m.* pituitary body, hypophysis. **-entzündung,** *f.* encephalitis. **-fett,** *n.* cerebrin.
**Gehirnhaut-.** meningeal.
**Gehirn-hautentzündung,** *f.* meningitis. **-kapsel,** *f.* cranium. **-rinde,** *f.* cerebral cortex. **-wasser,** *n.* cerebrospinal fluid.
**gehoben,** *p.p.* (of heben) lifted, raised, etc.
**geholfen,** *p.p.* (of helfen) helped, assisted.
**Gehölz,** *n.* wood, woodland, copse.
**Gehör,** *n.* hearing; ear.
**Gehör-.** auditory, acoustic, audio-, hearing.
**gehorchen,** *v.i.* obey; respond.
**gehören,** *v.i.* belong. — *v.r.* be becoming, be proper.
**gehörig,** *a.* belonging; appertaining, relating; requisite; due, proper, appropriate.
**Gehörlehre,** *f.* acoustics.
**gehorsam,** *a.* obedient.
**Gehorsam,** *m.*, **Gehorsamkeit,** *f.* obedience.
**Gehörwasser,** *n.* (*Anat.*) fluid of the inner ear, liquor Cotunii.
**Gehre, Gehrung,** *f.* bevel, miter.
**Gehülfe,** *m.* = Gehilfe.
**Geier,** *m.* vulture.
**Geige,** *f.* violin.
**Geigen-harz,** *n.* rosin, colophony. **-lack,** *m.* violin varnish.
**geil,** *a.* luxuriant; rich; proud (flesh); lustful; (of animals) in heat.
**Geiss,** *f.* (she) goat; doe. **-bart,** *m.*, **-bartskraut,** *n.* goatsbeard (*Spiraea aruncus*). **-blatt,** *n.* honeysuckle (*Lonicera*). **-bock,** *m.* he-goat.
**Geissel,** *f.* flagellum, cilium; whip, scourge. **-färbung,** *f.* (*Micros.*) flagellum staining. **-tierchen,** *n.* (*Biol.*) flagellate.
**Geissfuss,** *m.* (*Bot.*) goatsfoot; (*Tech.*) any of various tools.
**Geisslersches Rohr.** Geissler tube.
**Geissraute,** *f.* goat's-rue (*Galega officinalis*).
**Geist,** *m.* spirit; ghost; mind, intelligence.
**geistig,** *a.* spirituous, alcoholic; (of wine, etc.) strong, generous; volatile; spiritual; mental; intellectual.
**Geistigkeit,** *f.* spirituousness, etc. (see geistig).
**geist-lich,** *a.* spiritual; clerical. **-los,** *a.* spiritless, lifeless, dull. **-reich, -voll,** *a.* ingenious, clever; sprightly, smart, witty.
**Geiz,** *m.* avarice, stinginess; shoot, sucker.
**geizig,** *a.* avaricious; stingy; sparing (of).
**gek.,** *abbrev.* (gekennzeichnet) distinguished, characterized.
**gekannt,** *p.p.* (of kennen) known.
**gekernt,** *a.* having a nucleus, nucleated.
**geklommen,** *p.p.* of klimmen and klemmen.
**geklungen,** *p.p.* (of klingen) sounded, rung.
**gekniffen,** *p.p.* (of kneifen) nipped, etc.
**Geknister,** *n.* decrepitation; crunching.
**gekonnt,** *p.p.* (of können) been able.
**gekoren,** *p.p.* (of küren) chosen, elected.
**gekörnelt,** *p.p.* (of körneln) granulated.
**gekörnt,** *p.a.* (from körnen) granulated, granular.
**Gekrätz,** *n.* waste, refuse, dross, slag. **-ofen,** *m.* (*Metal.*) almond furnace.
**Gekriech,** *n.* (*Geol.*, etc.) creep.
**gekrischen,** *p.p.* (of kreischen) shrieked, etc.
**gekrochen,** *p.p.* (of kriechen) crept, crawled.
**Gekrös-.** mesenteric.
**Gekröse,** *n.* mesentery; giblets.
**Gekrösgang,** *m.* pancreatic duct.
**gekupfert,** *p.a.* (from kupfern) coppered.
**gel.,** *abbrev.* (gelöst) dissolved.
**geladen,** *p.p.* (of laden) loaded, etc.
**Geläger,** *n.* deposits, dregs, bottoms.
**gelagert,** *p.p.* (of lagern) stored, etc.
**Gelände,** *n.* land, ground, country, terrain.
**Geländer,** *n.* railing, balustrade.

**gelang,** *pret.* (of gelingen) succeeded.
**gelangen,** *v.i.* arrive (at), reach (to), come.
**gelartig,** *a.* gel-like, of the nature of a gel, gelatinous.
**Gelass,** *m.* room, space.
**Gelatine,** *f.* gelatin.
**gelatineartig,** *a.* gelatinous.
**Gelatin(e)-folie,** *f.* sheet gelatin; gelatin foil. **-kapsel,** *f.* gelatin capsule. **-leim,** *m.* gelatin glue. **-lösung,** *f.* gelatin solution. **-schicht,** *f.* gelatin layer or film. **-stichkultur,** *f.* gelatin stab culture.
**gelatinieren,** *v.t. & i.* gelatinize.
**Gelatiniermittel,** *n.* gelatinizing agent.
**Gelatinierung,** *f.* gelatinization.
**Gelatinierungsmittel,** *n.* gelatinizing agent.
**gelatinisieren,** *v.t. & i.* gelatinize.
**gelatinös,** *a.* gelatinous.
**geläufig,** *a,* fluent, ready; familiar.
**gelaunt,** *a.* disposed.
**Geläut, Geläute,** *n.* ringing; chimes.
**gelb,** *a.* yellow. — **gelbes Blutkraut,** goldenseal (*Hydrastis canadensis*). — **gelbes Blutlaugensalz,** potassium ferrocyanide. — **gelbe Erde,** yellow ocher. — **gelber Ingwer,** turmeric. — **gelbe Quecksilbersalbe,** *f.* (*Pharm.*) ointment of mercuric nitrate. — **gelbe Rübe,** carrot.
**Gelb,** *n.* yellow. **-antimonerz,** *n.* cervantite. **-beeren,** *f.pl.* yellow berries, buckthorn berries. **-beize,** *f.* (*Dyeing*) buff liquor. **-beizen,** *n.* (*Metal.*) yellowing.
**gelbblausauer,** *a.* of or pertaining to ferrocyanic acid, ferrocyanide of.
**Gelbblausäure,** *f.* ferrocyanic acid.
**Gelbbleierz,** *n.* yellow lead ore, wulfenite.
**gelb-braun, -bräunlich,** *a.* yellowish-brown.
**Gelbbrenne,** *f.* pickle (for brass).
**gelbbrennen,** *v.t.* (*Metal.*) dip, pickle.
**Gelbbrennsäure,** *f.* pickling acid, pickle.
**Gelbe,** *n.* yellow (of an egg), yolk.
**Gelbeisen-erz,** *n.,* **-stein,** *m.* yellow clay ironstone; (**okriges**) yellow ocher; copiapite. **-kies,** *m.* pyrite.
**gelbeln,** *v.i.* turn yellowish.
**Gelb-erde,** *f.* yellow ocher. **-erz,** *n.* yellow ore, specif. (1) chalcopyrite, (2) limonite.
**gelb-färben,** *v.t.* color yellow. **-farbig,** *a.* yellow.
**Gelb-färbung,** *f.* yellow coloration, yellow color; yellow dyeing. **-fieber,** *n.* yellow fever.
**gelb-gar,** *a.* (*Leather*) tanned. **-giessen,** *v.t.* cast in brass.
**Gelb-giesserei,** *f.* brass foundry. **-glut,** *f.* yellow heat (about 1100°C.).
**gelb-grau,** *a.* yellowish-gray. **-grün,** *a.* yellowish green.
**Gelb-guss,** *m.* yellow brass. **-harz,** *n.* yellow resin; yellow rosin. **-heit,** *f.* yellowness. **-holz,** *n.* fustic, specif. old fustic; yellowwood.
**Gelbildung,** *f.* gel formation.
**Gelb-ingwer,** *m.* turmeric. **-kali,** *n.* potassium ferrocyanide. **-kraut,** *n.* yellowweed, dyer's rocket (*Reseda luteola*).
**Gelbkreuz-geschoss,** *n.* (*Mil.*) "yellow cross" projectile or shell. **-kampfstoff, -stoff,** *m.* "yellow cross" shell filling (mustard gas or other vesicant).
**Gelbkupfer,** *n.* brass; crude copper. **-erz,** *n.* chalcopyrite.
**gelb-lich,** *a.* yellowish. **-lichgrau,** *a.* yellowish-gray. **-rot,** *a.* yellowish-red.
**Gelb-pech,** *n.* yellow pitch. **-scheibe,** *f.* (*Photog.*) yellow filter. **-schoten,** *f.pl.* wongshy (pods of *Gardenia grandiflora*). **-stich,** *m.* yellow cast, yellow tinge.
**gelbstichig,** *a.* yellow-tinged, yellowish.
**Gelbsucht,** *f.* jaundice.
**gelbweiss,** *a.* yellowish-white, cream-colored.
**Gelb-wurz, -wurzel,** *f.* turmeric; yellowroot (*Xanthorrhiza*).
**Geld,** *n.* money. **-anlage,** *f.* investment. **-hilfe,** *f.* financial aid, subsidy. **-mittel,** *n.pl.* (pecuniary) means. **-münze,** *f.* coin. **-schrank,** *m.* safe. **-strafe,** *f.* fine. **-stück,** *n.* piece of money, coin. **-verschreibung,** *f.* promissory note. **-wesen,** *n.* monetary matters, finances.
**Gele,** *pl.* gels.
**Gelée,** *n.* jelly.
**gelegen,** *p.p.* of liegen. — *a.* situated; convenient, suitable; important.
**Gelegenheit,** *f.* occasion, opportunity; convenience; locality.
**gelegentlich,** *a.* occasional, accidental, incidental. — *adv.* occasionally; incidentally; second-hand; with regard (to), regarding.
**gelehrig,** *a.* teachable, docile.
**Gelehrsamkeit,** *f.* learning, scholarship.
**Gelehrte, Gelehrter,** *m.* learned man, scholar, savant.
**geleimt,** *p.p.* (of leimen) glued; sized.
**Geleise,** *n.* track; rails.
**geleiten,** *v.t.* accompany, conduct, escort.
**Gelenk,** *n.* joint; link; hinge.
**Gelenk-.** articular. **-basalt,** *m.* flexible basalt. **-flüssigkeit,** *f.* synovial fluid.
**gelenkig,** *a.* jointed, articulate; hinged; flexible, pliable; supple; nimble.
**Gelenk-quarz,** *m.* flexible sandstone, itacolumite. **-saft,** *m.,* **-schmiere,** *f.* (*Anat.*) synovia. **-schwamm,** *m.* white swelling. **-steifheit,** *f.* ankylosis. **-wasser,** *n.* synovia, synovial fluid.
**gelernt,** *p.a.* skilled.
**Gelf,** *m.* silver-bearing pyrites. **-erz, -kupfer,** *n.* chalcopyrite.
**geliehen,** *p.p.* (of leihen) lent; borrowed.
**gelieren,** *v.t.* cause to gel, gelatinize.

**gelind, gelinde,** *a.* gentle; soft, mild. — **—kochen,** simmer.
**gelingen,** *v.i.* succeed. — **gelungen,** *p.a.* successful; excellent.
**gelitten,** *p.p.* (of leiden) suffered, undergone.
**geloben,** *v.t.* promise, pledge.
**gelogen,** *p.p.* (of lügen) lied, etc.
**geloschen, gelöscht,** *p.p.* (of löschen) extinguished, etc. — **gelöschter Kalk,** slaked lime, hydrated lime.
**gelöst,** *p.p.* (of lösen) dissolved; solved, etc.
**Gelöste,** *n.* dissolved substance, solute.
**Gelotong.** (*Rubber*) jelutong.
**Gelsemien,** *n.* gelsemium.
**Gelseminsäure, Gelsemiensäure,** *f.* gelsemic acid.
**Gelseminwurzel,** *f.* gelsemium root.
**gelt,** *a.* barren; (of cows) dry.
**Gelte,** *f.* pail, tub.
**gelten,** *v.i.* be worth; have weight; be current, be valid; be in force; pass, be considered; apply; concern.
**Geltung,** *f.* worth, value, validity, currency, importance.
**gelungen,** *p.p.* and *p.a.* see gelingen.
**Gelüst,** *n.* desire, longing.
**Gelzustand,** *m.* gel state, gel condition.
**gem.,** *abbrev.* (gemein, gemeinsam) common; (gemischt) mixed; (gemahlen) ground, milled.
**Gemach,** *n.* room, apartment; closet.
**gemächlich,** *a.* slow, gentle, easy.
**Gemahl,** *m.* consort, husband.
**gemahnen,** *v.t.* remind.
**Gemälde,** *n.* picture, painting, drawing. **-firnis,** *m.* painter's varnish, picture varnish.
**gemäss,** *prep.* (following its object) according to, conformably to. — *a.* conformable, agreeable.
**gemässigt,** *p.a.* temperate, moderate.
**Gemäuer,** *n.* masonry.
**gemein,** *a.* common; general, ordinary, vulgar.
**Gemeinde,** *f.* community; municipality; congregation.
**Gemeinheit,** *f.* commonness, meanness.
**gemeinsam,** *a.* common; mutual, joint.
**Gemeinschaft,** *f.* community; partnership; society; intercourse.
**gemein-schaftlich,** *a.* common, mutual. **-verständlich,** *a.* popular.
**Gemenganteil,** *m.* ingredient of a mixture.
**Gemenge,** *n.* mixture; (*Glass*) frit; (*Petrog.*) conglomerate. **-asche,** *f.* (*Assaying*) test ash. **-gestein,** *n.* conglomerate. **-stoff, -teil,** *m.* = Gemenganteil.
**Gemeng-stoff, -teil,** *m.* = Gemenganteil.
**gemieden,** *p.p.* (of meiden) avoided.
**gemindert,** *p.p.* (of mindern) diminished, etc.
**Gemisch,** *n.* mixture, mixing, mix; admixture; composition; alloy. **-bilder,** *m.* emulsifier.
**gemischt,** *p.p.* (of mischen) mixed, etc. **-basig,** *a.* (*Petroleum*) mixed-base, intermediate-base.
**Gemme,** *f.* gem, cameo.
**gemocht,** *p.p.* of mögen.
**gemolken,** *p.p.* (of melken) milked.
**Gemse, Gems,** *f.* chamois (goat).
**Gemsenfett,** *n.* chamois fat.
**Gemsleder,** *n.* chamois leather, chamois.
**Gemüll, Gemülm,** *n.* rubbish.
**Gemüse,** *n.* vegetables. **-pflanzen,** *f.pl.* culinary plants; vegetables.
**gemusst,** *p.p.* (of müssen) been obliged.
**gemustert,** *p.p.* & *p.a.* figured, etc. (see mustern); fancy.
**Gemüt,** *n.* mind; heart, feeling.
**gemütlich,** *a.* good-hearted, genial, pleasant.
**gen.,** *abbrev.* (genannt) named, mentioned.
**Gen,** *n.* (*Biol.*) gene.
**genannt,** *p.p.* (of nennen) named, mentioned.
**genas,** *pret.* (of genesen) recovered.
**genau,** *a.* accurate, exact, precise; true, close, tight; intimate.
**Genaueres,** *n.* more exact information.
**Genauigkeit,** *f.* accuracy, precision, etc. (see genau).
**Genauigkeits-arbeit,** *f.* precision work. **-grad,** *m.* degree of accuracy. **-grenze,** *f.* limit of accuracy.
**genehm,** *a.* agreeable; acceptable.
**genehmigen,** *v.t.* approve of, assent to; allow.
**geneigt,** *p.a.* see neigen.
**Geneigtheit,** *f.* inclination; disposition.
**generalisieren,** *v.t.* generalize.
**General-nenner,** *m.* common denominator. **-register,** *n.* collective index. **-versammlung,** *f.* general meeting, general assembly; stockholders' (shareholders') meeting.
**Generator-betrieb,** *m.* producer operation. **-gas,** *n.* generator gas, producer gas.
**generell,** *a.* general.
**generisch,** *a.* generic.
**Genese,** *f.* genesis.
**genesen,** *v.i.* recover, convalesce; be delivered.
**Genetik,** *f.* genetics.
**genetisch,** *a.* genetic.
**Genever,** *m.* geneva, Holland gin.
**Genf,** *n.* Geneva.
**genial,** *a.* gifted, of genius.
**Genick,** *n.* back of the neck, nape.
**Genie,** *n.* genius; engineer corps. **-corps,** *n.* engineer corps.
**genieren,** *v.t.* incommode, trouble.
**geniessbar,** *a.* palatable; edible, esculent.
**geniessen,** *v.t.* enjoy; take, taste (food or drink).
**genommen,** *p.p.* (of nehmen) taken; received.
**genoss,** *pret.* (of geniessen) enjoyed, etc.

**Genoss, Genosse,** *m.* companion, associate, partner, accomplice; (*pl.*) company.
**genossen,** *p.p.* (of geniessen) enjoyed, etc.
**Genossenschaft,** *f.* fellowship, partnership, company, association, coöperative.
**Genre,** *n.* kind, sort; (*Calico*) style.
**Gentiana-blau,** *n.* gentian blue. **-violett,** *n.* gentian violet.
**genuesisch,** *a.* Genoese, Genoa.
**genug,** *adv.* enough.
**Genüge,** *f.* sufficiency. — **zur —,** enough.
**genügen,** *v.i.* be enough, suffice; comply (with). — **genügend,** *p.a.* sufficient; satisfactory.
**genügsam,** *a.* easily pleased, content, temperate.
**Genugtuung,** *f.* satisfaction, amends.
**Genuss,** *m.* enjoyment, pleasure; taking (food or drink); utilization; benefit, use. **-mittel,** *n.* any substance used to heighten the enjoyment of food (including condiments, beverages, etc.), food supplement; luxury food.
**genusssüchtig,** *a.* pleasure-seeking.
**Genusszweck,** *m.* table purposes, food purposes.
**Genzian,** *m.* gentian.
**Geochemie,** *f.* geochemistry.
**geodätisch,** *a.* geodetic.
**Geolog, Geologe,** *m.* geologist.
**geologisch,** *a.* geological.
**geometrisch,** *a.* geometric(al).
**geometrisieren,** *v.t. & i.* geometrize.
**Georgine,** *f.* dahlia.
**gepaart,** *p.p.* of paaren (which see).
**Gepäck,** *n.* baggage, luggage.
**gepanzert,** *p.a.* armored; metal-clad.
**gepfiffen,** *p.p.* (of pfeifen) piped, whistled.
**gepflogen,** *p.p.* (of pflegen) attended to, etc.
**Gepflogenheit,** *f.* usage, custom, habit.
**Gepräge,** *n.* impression; stamp, coinage; character.
**geprägt,** *p.p.* (of prägen) stamped, etc.
**gepriesen,** *p.p.* (of preisen) praised.
**gepulvert,** *p.p.* powdered, pulverized.
**gequollen,** *p.p.* (of quellen) swelled, etc.
**gerad-, Gerad-.** See also Grad-, grad-.
**gerade,** *a.* straight; direct; even; upright. — *adv.* straightly, directly, exactly, just; plainly.
**Gerade,** *f.* straight line, right line.
**gerade-faserig,** *a.* straight-fibered, straight-grained. **-zu,** *adv.* straight on; immediately; absolutely.
**gerad-linig,** *a.* rectilinear, straight-line. **-sichtig,** *a.* direct-vision. **-wandig,** *a.* straight-walled, with straight sides. **-wertig,** *a.* of even valence. **-zahlig,** *a.* even-numbered.
**Geranium-öl,** *n.* geranium oil. **-säure,** *f.* geranic acid.
**gerannt,** *p.p.* (of rennen) run, etc.
**Gerät,** *n.* apparatus, instrument, implement, device, tool, utensil. — **Geräte,** *n.pl.* apparatus(es), instruments, etc.; equipment; plant; furniture, chattels.
**Geräte-brett,** *n.* instrument board or panel. **-glas,** *n.* apparatus glass.
**geraten,** *p.p.* of geraten and raten.
**geraten,** *v.i.* come, fall, light, get; turn out, prosper. — *p.a.* prosperous, successful; (from raten) advisable.
**Geratewohl, aufs.** at random, haphazard.
**Gerätschaft,** *f.* implement, tool, instrument, apparatus, outfit.
**geräuchert,** *p.p.* (of räuchern) fumigated, etc. — **geräucherter Kautschuk,** (*Rubber*) smoked sheet.
**geraum,** *a.* ample, long.
**geräumig,** *a.* roomy, ample, large, spacious.
**Geräusch,** *n.* noise; murmur, clatter.
**geräusch-los,** *a.* noiseless. **-sicher,** *a.* soundproof. **-voll,** *a.* noisy.
**Gerb-anlage,** *f.* tannery. **-auszug,** *m.* tanning extract.
**gerbbar,** *a.* tannable, etc. (see gerben).
**Gerbbeschleuniger,** *m.* tanning accelerator.
**Gerbbrühe, Gerbebrühe, Gerbeflüssigkeit,** *f.* tan liquor, tanner's liquor, ooze.
**Gerbe-methode,** *f.* tanning method. **-mittel,** *n.* tanning material, tan.
**gerben,** *v.t.* tan; hull (grain); polish (metal); refine, fine (steel). — **sämisch —,** chamois; **weiss —,** taw.
**Gerber,** *m.* tanner, tawer, currier. **-baum,** *m.* tanner's sumac.
**Gerberei,** *f.* tanning; tannery. **-abfälle,** *m.pl.* tanner's waste.
**Gerber-fett,** *n.* (*Leather*) dégras, stuff. **-hof,** *m.* tan yard. **-kalk,** *m.* slaked lime; gas lime. **-lohe,** *f.* tanbark; tan liquor. **-strauch,** *m.* tanner's sumac (*Rhus coriaria*); ink plant (*Coriaria*). **-wolle,** *f.* skin wool, pelt wool.
**Gerbe-theorie,** *f.* theory of tanning. **-vermögen,** *n.* tanning power. **-versuch,** *m.* tanning experiment or trial.
**Gerb-extrakt,** *m. & n.* tanning extract. **-leim,** *m.* tannic acid glue, size made from gelatin and sulfite liquor. **-lohe,** *f.* tanbark; tan liquor. **-lösung,** *f.* tanning (tannic acid) solution. **-material,** *n.* tanning material. **-öl,** *n.* tanning oil. **-pflanze,** *f.* tanniferous plant. **-prozess,** *m.* tanning process. **-rinde,** *f.* tanbark.
**gerbsauer,** *a.* of or combined with tannic acid, tannate of.
**Gerbsäure,** *f.* tannic acid. **-lösung,** *f.* tannic acid solution. **-messer,** *m.* tannometer, barkometer.
**Gerbstahl,** *m.* shear steel, refined iron; polishing steel, burnisher.
**Gerbstoff,** *m.* tanning principle, tanning matter, tan; specif., tannic acid, tannin.

**gerbstoffartig,** *a.* tannin-like, tannic.

**Gerbstoff-auszug,** *m.* tanning extract. **-bestimmung,** *f.* determination of tanning matter. **-extrakt,** *m.* tannin extract. **-gehalt,** *m.* tannin content.

**gerbstoffhaltig,** *a.* tanniferous.

**Gerbstoff-lösung,** *f.* tannin solution. **-rot,** *n.* phlobaphene. **-vorbeize,** *f.* tannin mordant.

**Gerbung,** *f.* tanning (or tannage), etc. (see gerben).

**Gerbwert,** *m.* tanning value.

**gerecht,** *a.* right, rightful, true, just, fair, proper, legitimate; fit, skilled. — **— werden,** do justice (to).

**Gerechtigkeit,** *f.* justice; rightness, fairness; law.

**Gerede,** *n.* talk, talking.

**Gereibe,** *n.* rubbing.

**gereichen,** *v.i.* turn out, prove, redound.

**gereinigt,** *p.p.* (of reinigen) purified, etc.

**gereuen,** *v.t.* repent, regret.

**Gericht,** *n.* court; judgment; jurisdiction; dish.

**gerichtet,** *p.p.* (of richten) directed, etc.

**gerichtlich,** *a.* judicial, forensic, legal.

**Gerichts-.** judicial, forensic, legal. **-amt,** *n.* court, tribunal. **-amtmann,** *m.* judge. **-barkeit,** *f.* jurisdiction. **-chemie,** *f.* forensic chemistry. **-chemiker,** *m.* forensic chemist, legal chemist. **-hof,** *m.* court, tribunal. **-rat,** *m.* judge; counselor.

**gerieben,** *p.p.* (of reiben) rubbed, ground, etc.

**gerieft,** *a.* grooved, channeled.

**geriet,** *imperfect* (of geraten) came, etc.

**gering,** *a.* small, slight, little, limited; deficient, inferior, low, base.

**geringer,** *a.* inferior, less.

**gering-fügig,** *a.* unimportant, trifling, trivial. **-haltig,** *a.* poor, low, low-grade, lean.

**Geringhaltigkeit,** *f.* poor or low quality.

**geringst,** *a.* least, slightest, lowest.

**geringwertig,** *a.* of small or low value, low-grade, poor, inferior.

**gerinnbar,** *a.* coagulable.

**Gerinnbarkeit,** *f.* coagulability.

**Gerinne,** *n.* running, flowing; channel, gutter.

**gerinnen,** *v.i.* coagulate, curd, curdle, congeal, jelly, gel; (*Cement*) set.

**Gerinnsel,** *n.* coagulum; curd, curds; clot.

**Gerinnstoff,** *m.* coagulant, coagulator.

**Gerinnung,** *f.* coagulation, etc. (see gerinnen); coagulum.

**gerinnungsfähig,** *a.* coagulable, etc. (see gerinnen).

**Gerinnungs-fähigkeit,** *f.* coagulability. **-masse,** *f.* coagulum; gel. **-mittel,** *n.* coagulant, coagulator. **-zeit,** *f.* coagulation time; (of cement) setting time.

**Gerippe,** *n.* skeleton; framework.

**gerippt,** *p.a.* see rippen.

**gerissen,** *p.p.* (of reissen) torn, pulled, etc.; (of a line) broken.

**geritten,** *p.p.* (of reiten) ridden.

**Germani-.** germanic, germanium(IV). **-chlorid,** *n.* germanic chloride, germanium(IV) chloride.

**Germanium-chlorid,** *n.* germanium chloride, specif. germanic chloride. **-chlorür,** *n.* germanous chloride, germanium(II) chloride. **-fluorwasserstoffsäure,** *f.* fluogermanic acid. **-oxyd,** *n.* germanium oxide; specif. germanic oxide. **-oxydul,** *n.* germanous oxide, germanium(II) oxide. **-säure,** *f.* germanic acid. **-sulfid,** *n.* germanium sulfide, specif. germanic sulfide. **-sulfür,** *n.* germanous sulfide, germanium(II) sulfide. **-wasserstoff,** *m.* germanium hydride.

**Germano-.** germanous, germanium(II). **-sulfid,** *n.* germanous sulfide, germanium(II) sulfide.

**Germer,** *m.* white hellebore (*Veratrum*). **-wurzel,** *f.* white hellebore root.

**gern, gerne,** *adv.* gladly, with pleasure. — **ich möchte —,** I should like.

**gerochen,** *p.p.* (of riechen) smelled.

**Geröll, Gerölle,** *n.* gravel, shingle, boulders; rubble, rubbish.

**geronnen,** *p.p.* (of gerinnen) coagulated, etc.

**Gerste,** *f.* barley.

**Gersten-graupen,** *f.pl.* peeled barley, pearl barley. **-korn,** *n.* barleycorn. **-malz,** *n.* barley malt. **-mehl,** *n.* barley flour. **-schleim,** *m.* barley water. **-schrotbeize,** *f.* barley dressing. **-stärke,** *f.* barley starch. **-stoff,** *m.* hordein. **-wasser,** *n.* barley water. **-zucker,** *m.* barley sugar.

**Geruch,** *m.* smell, odor, scent, savor, aroma.

**geruchfrei,** *a.* free from odor, odorless.

**Geruchgras,** *n.* fragrant grass, specif. vernal grass (*Anthoxanthum odoratum*).

**geruchlos,** *a.* odorless, inodorous; savorless; unable to smell. — **— machen,** deodorize.

**Geruchlos-igkeit,** *f.* inodorousness. **-machung,** *f.* deodorization.

**geruchreich,** *a.* rich in odor, odorous, fragrant.

**Geruchs-.** olfactory. **-probe,** *f.* olfactory test, test by smell. **-reiz,** *m.* olfactory irritant or stimulus.

**Geruchstoff,** *m.* odorous substance.

**Gerücht,** *n.* report, rumor.

**Gerümpel,** *n.* lumber, trash.

**gerungen,** *p.p.* (of ringen) wrung, etc.

**Gerüst,** *n.* frame, framework; scaffold; crate. **-eiweiss,** *n.* albuminoid, scleroprotein. **-werk,** *n.* framework; (*Anat.*) stroma.

**ges.,** *abbrev.* (gesättigt) saturated; (gesetzlich) by law; (gesamt) total.

**Ges.,** *abbrev.* (Gesellschaft) society, company.

**gesalzen,** *p.p.* (of salzen) salted.

**gesammelt,** *p.a.* collected, assembled, accumulated.

**Ges.-Amt,** *abbrev.* (Gesundheitsamt) health office, board of health.

**gesamt,** *a.* total, entire, whole, complete, general, all-round, over-all.

**Gesamt-alkali,** *n.* total alkali. **-analyse,** *f.* total analysis. **-ansicht,** *f.* general view. **-azidität,** *f.* total acidity. **-bedarf,** *m.* total requirement. **-brechung,** *f.* (*Physics*) total refraction. **-druck,** *m.* total pressure. **-echtheit,** *f.* all-round fastness. **-gebiet,** *n.* entire territory, whole field. **-gewicht,** *n.* total weight. **-härte,** *f.* total hardness. **-härtebestimmung,** *f.* determination of total hardness. **-heit,** *f.* totality; generality; the whole. **-ladung,** *f.* total charge, net charge. **-lösliches,** *n.* total soluble matter. **-mass,** *n.* over-all dimension. **-menge,** *f.* total quantity. **-rohfaser,** *f.* total crude fiber. **-rückstand,** *m.* total residue. **-säure,** *f.* total acid. **-schwefel,** *m.* total sulfur. **-spannung,** *f.* (*Elec.*) total voltage, over-all voltage. **-stickstoff,** *m.* total nitrogen. **-strom,** *m.* (*Elec.*) total current. **-summe,** *f.* sum total, total. **-verhalten,** *n.* general behavior **-volum,** *n.* total volume. **-wärme,** *f.* total heat. **-wassergehalt,** *m.* total water content. **-wert,** *m.* total value. **-widerstand,** *m.* total resistance. **-wirkungsgrad,** *m.* total (or over-all) efficiency. **-zahl,** *f.* total number.

**gesandt,** *p.p.* (of senden) sent.

**Gesandte,** *m.* messenger; ambassador.

**Gesang,** *m.* singing; song; canto.

**Gesäss,** *n.* seat; floor.

**Gesäss-.** (*Anat.*) gluteal.

**gesättigt,** *p.p.* (of sättigen) saturated, etc.

**Geschabsel,** *n.* scrapings.

**Geschäft,** *n.* business; affair; transaction; trade, commerce; house, firm; bargain.

**geschäftig,** *a.* busy; active; fussy.

**geschäftlich,** *a.* business; business-like; commercial; professional.

**Geschäftsbetrieb,** *m.* management (of a business).

**geschah,** *pret.* (of geschehen) happened, etc.

**geschehen,** *v.i.* happen, occur, be done.

**Geschehnis,** *n.* occurrence, event.

**gescheit,** *a.* sensible, clever, knowing.

**Geschenk,** *n.* present, gift.

**Geschichte,** *f.* history; tale; thing.

**geschichtet,** *p.p.* (of schichten) stratified.

**geschichtlich,** *a.* historical.

**Geschick,** *n.* skill; order; fate, destiny.

**Geschicklichkeit,** *f.* skill, cleverness, art.

**geschickt,** *a.* skillful, skilled, qualified.

**Geschiebe,** *n.* rubble, boulder, detritus; shoving.

**geschieden,** *p.p.* (of scheiden) separated, etc.

**geschieht,** *pr. 3* sing. (of geschehen) happens.

**geschienen,** *p.p.* (of scheinen) shone; seemed.

**Geschirr,** *n.* vessel; vessels, ware; utensils, tools, apparatus, gear; harness; plant, mill; (*Leather*) vat. **-leder,** *n.* harness leather.

**geschlämmt,** *p.p.* (of schlämmen) elutriated, etc.

**Geschlecht,** *n.* sex; genus; kind, species, race, family, stock, generation; gender.

**geschlecht-lich,** *a.* sexual; generic. **-los,** *a.* sexless, asexual.

**Geschlechts-.** sexual; generic. **-art,** *f.* generic character, genus. **-drüse,** *f.* genital gland (ovary, testicle, gonad). **-gen,** *n.* sex gene. **-glied,** *n.* sex organ. **-krankheit,** *f.* venereal disease. **-pflanze,** *f.* phanerogam. **-reife,** *f.* puberty.

**geschlechtsreizend,** *p.a.* aphrodisiac.

**geschlichen,** *p.p.* (of schleichen) slunk, etc.

**geschliffen,** *p.p.* (of schleifen) ground, etc.

**geschlissen,** *p.p.* (of schleissen) slit, split, etc.

**geschlossen,** *p.p.* (of schliessen) closed, etc.

**Geschlossenheit,** *f.* closeness; completeness.

**geschlungen,** *p.p.* (of schlingen) wound, etc.

**Geschmack,** *m.* taste; flavor; liking.

**geschmacklos,** *a.* tasteless; insipid.

**Geschmacklosigkeit,** *f.* tastelessness.

**Geschmacks-muster,** *n.* registered design or model. **-sinn,** *m.* sense of taste.

**Geschmeide,** *n.* jewelry.

**geschmeidig,** *a.* pliable, flexible, supple; (of metals) soft, ductile, malleable; versatile.

**Geschmeidigkeit,** *f.* pliability, etc. (see geschmeidig).

**Geschmiedehitze,** *f.* forging heat.

**geschmissen,** *p.p.* (of schmeissen) thrown, etc.

**geschmolzen,** *p.p.* (of schmelzen) melted, etc.

**geschnitten,** *p.p.* (of schneiden) cut, etc.

**geschoben,** *p.p.* (of schieben) shoved, etc.

**Geschöpf,** *n.* creature.

**geschoren,** *p.p.* (of scheren) shorn, etc.

**Geschoss,** *n.* projectile, missile; story, floor; (plant) shoot.

**Geschossbahn,** *f.* path of a projectile, trajectory.

**geschossen,** *p.p.* (of schiessen) shot, etc.

**Geschossfüllung,** *f.* shell filling.

**geschosstreibend,** *p.a.* ballistic.

**Geschrei,** *n.* cry, outcry; rumor; disrepute.

**geschrieben,** *p.p.* (of schreiben) written, recorded.

**geschrieen,** *p.p.* (of schreien) cried.

**geschritten,** *p.p.* (of schreiten) stepped, proceeded.

**geschroben,** *p.p.* (of schrauben) screwed.

**geschult,** *a.* trained, skilled.

**geschunden,** *p.p.* (of schinden) skinned.

**Geschür,** *n.* (*Metal.*) dross, scoria.

**Geschütz,** *n.* gun, cannon; ordnance, artillery.

-bronze, *f.*, -guss, *m.*, -metall, *n.* gun metal. -rohr, *n.* cannon bore; gun barrel; gun, cannon.

**geschützt,** *p.p.* (of schützen) protected, etc.

**geschwefelt,** *p.p.* (of schwefeln) sulfurized, etc.

**geschweigen,** *v.t.* not mention, omit. — **geschweige denn,** not to mention.

**geschweisst,** *p.p.* (of schweissen) welded.

**geschwiegen,** *p.p.* (of schweigen) been silent; (of geschweigen) omitted.

**geschwind,** *a.* fast, quick, immediate, prompt.

**Geschwindigkeit,** *f.* velocity, speed, rate; quickness, despatch.

**Geschwindigkeits-messer,** *m.* speed indicator. **-verteilung,** *f.* velocity distribution.

**Geschwister,** *pl.* brother(s) and sister(s).

**geschwollen,** *p.p.* (of schwellen) swollen.

**geschwommen,** *p.p.* (of schwimmen) swum.

**geschworen,** *p.p.* (of schwären) festered; (of schwören) sworn.

**Geschwulst,** *f.* swelling; tumor; new growth.

**geschwunden,** *p.p.* (of schwinden) shrunk, etc.

**geschwungen,** *p.p.* (of schwingen) swung, etc.

**Geschwür,** *n.* ulcer, abscess.

**Gesell, Geselle,** *m.* mate, comrade; journeyman.

**gesellen,** *v.t.* & *r.* join, unite.

**gesellig,** *a.* social, sociable.

**Gesellschaft,** *f.* society, association; company, corporation; partnership; club; community; party.

**Gesellschaftswissenschaft,** *f.* sociology.

**Gesenk, Gesenke,** *n.* slope; hollow; pit; sump; die; swage. **-schmieden,** *n.* drop forging. **-stahl,** *m.* die steel.

**gesessen,** *p.p.* (of sitzen) sat, seated, etc.

**Gesetz,** *n.* law; rule; precept. **-entwurf,** *m.* (legislative) bill.

**gesetzgebend,** *p.a.* legislative.

**Gesetzgebung,** *f.* legislation.

**gesetzlich,** *a.* lawful, legal. — *adv.* lawfully, legally. — — **geschützt,** protected by law (patented, copyrighted, registered).

**Gesetzlichkeit,** *f.* conformity to law, lawfulness, legality.

**gesetzmässig,** *a.* conformable to law, regular; lawful.

**Gesetzmässigkeit,** *f.* conformity to law, regularity; lawfulness.

**gesetzt,** *p.p.* and *p.a.* see setzen.

**Gesetzvorschlag,** *m.* bill; motion.

**ges. gesch.,** *abbrev.* (gesetzlich geschützt) protected by law, patented.

**gesichert,** *p.p.* and *p.a.* see sichern.

**Gesicht,** *n.* sight; face, countenance, look; vision.

**Gesichts-.** visual; facial. **-achse,** *f.* visual axis. **-druck,** *m.* visual impression. **-feld,** *n.*, **-kreis,** *m.* field of vision, field of view, range of vision. **-krem,** *m.* face cream. **-linie,** *f.* visual line; facial line. **-maske,** *f.* face shield, face piece. **-puder,** *m.* face powder. **-punkt,** *m.* visual point, point of sight; viewpoint. **-sinn,** *m.* sense of vision. **-strahl,** *m.* visual ray. **-winkel,** *m.* visual angle, optic angle; facial angle.

**Gesims,** *n.* molding, cornice; shelf; ledge.

**Gesinnung,** *f.* mind, disposition, opinion.

**Gesinter,** *n.* agglomerate.

**gesittet,** *a.* mannered, bred; polite; civilized; moral.

**gesogen,** *p.p.* (of saugen) sucked, etc.

**gesondert,** *a.* separate.

**gesonnen,** *p.a.* (of sinnen) inclined.

**gesotten,** *p.p.* (of sieden) boiled, etc.

**gespannt,** *p.p.* and *p.a.* see spannen.

**Gespenst,** *n.* specter, ghost, phantom.

**Gesperr(e),** *n.* locking device, catch, ratchet.

**gespieen,** *p.p.* (of speien) spat; vomited.

**Gespinst,** *n.* spun yarn; spun goods; thread; (textile) fabric; web; cocoon. **-faser,** *f.* textile fiber. **-pflanze,** *f.* textile plant; fiber plant.

**gesplissen,** *p.p.* (of spleissen) split; spliced.

**gesponnen,** *p.p.* (of spinnen) spun.

**Gespräch,** *n.* talk, conversation; (telephone) call.

**gesprenkelt,** *p.p.* (of sprenkeln) sprinkled, etc.

**gesprochen,** *p.p.* (of sprechen) spoken.

**gesprossen,** *p.p.* (of spriessen) sprouted.

**gesprungen,** *p.p.* (of springen) burst, etc.

**gest.,** *abbrev.* (gestorben) died, deceased.

**gestachelt,** *a.* thorny, spiny, prickly.

**Gestade,** *n.* shore, coast.

**Gestalt,** *f.* form; shape, figure, configuration; design; aspect; manner. **-änderung,** *f.* = Gestaltveränderung.

**gestalten,** *v.t.* form, shape, mold, fashion.

**Gestaltfestigkeit,** *f.* stability of form.

**gestaltlos,** *a.* amorphous, formless, shapeless.

**Gestaltlosigkeit,** *f.* amorphousness, formlessness, shapelessness.

**Gestaltung,** *f.* configuration, formation, shaping, form, state, design; construction.

**Gestaltveränderung,** *f.* change of form or shape; transformation; metamorphosis.

**gestanden,** *p.p.* of stehen and gestehen.

**Geständnis,** *n.* confession, acknowledgment.

**Gestänge,** *n.* poles, rods, bars, pipes, etc.

**Gestank,** *m.* stench, stink, bad smell.

**gestatten,** *v.t.* permit, allow, consent to.

**Geste,** *f.* gesture.

**gestehen,** *v.i.* coagulate, congeal, clot. — *v.t.* confess, admit.

**Gestehungs-kosten,** *f.pl.* working costs, prime cost. **-preis,** *m.* cost price.

**Gestein,** *n.* rock; stone. **-art,** *f.* (kind of) rock

**gesteinbildend,** *a.* rock-forming.

**Gestein-kunde, -lehre,** *f.* petrology; mineralogy; geognosy.
**Gesteins-bildung,** *f.* rock formation. **-gang,** *m.* (*Geol., Mining*) dike. **-mantel,** *m.* (*Geol.*) lithosphere. **-rest,** *m.* (*Ceram.*) rock residue. **-schicht,** *f.* layer of rock or stone. **-schutt,** *m.* rock debris, talus. **-sprengmittel,** *n.* (rock) blasting explosive. **-unterlage,** *f.* rocky subsoil.
**Gestell,** *n.* frame, stand, support, base, rack, bed, mount; (of a blast furnace) hearth.
**gestern,** *adv.* yesterday.
**gesternt,** *a.* starred.
**Gestiebe,** *n.* dust, powder.
**gestiegen,** *p.p.* (of steigen) risen, etc.
**Gestirn,** *n.* star; constellation.
**gestirnt,** *a.* starred, starry; browed.
**gestoben,** *p.p.* (of stieben) scattered.
**Gestöber,** *n.* shower; snowstorm; dust storm.
**gestochen,** *p.p.* (of stechen) stuck, etc.
**gestockt,** *p.p.* (of stocken) stopped, etc. — *a.* (of hides) plump.
**gestohlen,** *p.p.* (of stehlen) stolen.
**gestorben,** *p.p.* (of sterben) died, dead.
**gestört,** *p.p.* (of stören) disturbed, etc.
**gestrahlt,** *p.p.* (of strahlen) radiated.
**Gesträuch,** *n.* bushes, shrubbery, thicket.
**gestreckt,** *p.a.* see strecken.
**gestreift,** *p.p.* (of streifen) striped, etc.
**gestrichelt,** *p.a.* (from stricheln) streaked; shaded; (of lines) broken, dashed(- - - -).
**gestrichen,** *p.p.* (of streichen) stroked, etc.
**gestrig,** *a.* of yesterday.
**gestritten,** *p.p.* (of streiten) disputed, etc.
**Gestrüpp,** *n.* thicket, underbrush, scrub.
**Gestübbe, Gestübe,** *m.* (*Metal.*) brasque; (*Coal*) culm, slack.
**gestunken,** *p.p.* (of stinken) stunk.
**gestürzt,** *p.p.* (of stürzen) hurled, etc.
**Gesuch,** *n.* request, demand; petition.
**gesucht,** *p.a.* (from suchen) sought for, in demand.
**gesund,** *a.* sound, healthy, wholesome.
**Gesundbrunnen,** *m.* mineral spring; spa.
**gesunden,** *v.i.* recover.
**Gesundheit,** *f.* health, soundness, salubrity.
**gesundheitlich,** *a.* sanitary, hygienic.
**Gesundheits-amt,** *n.* board of health. **-pflege,** *f.* sanitation, hygiene.
**gesundheitsschädlich,** *a.* injurious to health.
**Gesundheitswesen,** *n.* sanitary affairs.
**gesungen,** *p.p.* (of singen) sung.
**gesunken,** *p.p.* (of sinken) sunk, etc.
**Getäfel,** *n.* wainscoting; inlaying; paneling.
**getan, gethan,** *p.p.* (of tun, thun) done; made, performed; put.
**geteilt,** *p.p.* (of teilen) divided, etc.
**getönt,** *p.p.* (of tönen) toned, tinted, etc.
**Getränk,** *n.* beverage, drink, liquor.
**getränkt,** *p.p.* (of tränken) steeped, etc.
**getrauen,** *v.t.* dare, venture.
**Getreide,** *n.* grain; cereals; crops. **-art,** *f.* kind of grain; *pl.* cereals. **-branntwein,** *m.* whisky from grain. **-brennerei,** *f.* grain distillery. **-frucht,** *f.* cereal. **-kleie,** *f.* bran. **korn,** *n.* grain. **-krebs,** *m.* grain weevil. **kümmel,** *m.* kümmel (the spirit of which is made from grain). **-prober,** *m.* grain tester. **-prüfer,** *m.* grain tester. **-schnaps,** *m.* whisky from grain. **-stein,** *m.* = Bierstein **-stroh,** *n.* cereal straw, straw.
**getrennt,** *p.p.* (of trennen) separated, etc. — *p.a.* separate.
**getreu,** *a.* faithful, true.
**Getriebe,** *n.* driving, drive, working; (driving) gear, gearing; transmission; pinion. **-fett,** *n.* gear grease, pinion grease. **-lehre,** *f.* kinematics; kinetics.
**getrieben,** *p.p.* (of treiben) driven, etc.
**Getriebe-öl,** *n.* gear oil. **-rad,** *n.* gear wheel, gear.
**getrocknet,** *p.p.* (of trocknen) dried.
**getroffen,** *p.p.* (of treffen) hit, found, etc.; (of triefen) dropped, dripped, etc.
**getrogen,** *p.p.* (of trügen) deceived.
**getrost,** *a.* confident, courageous.
**getrübt,** *p.a.* see trüben.
**getrunken,** *p.p.* (of trinken) drunk.
**Getterspiegel,** *m.* getter patch, getter film.
**geübt,** *p.a.* (from üben) practiced, skilled.
**Geviert, Gevierte,** *n.* square; quadrat.
**gew.,** *abbrev.* (gewöhnlich) usual; usually.
**Gew.,** *abbrev.* (Gewicht) weight, gravity.
**Gew.-%,** *abbrev.* (Gewichtsprozent) per cent by weight.
**Gewächs,** *n.* plant; growth; growing; vintage.
**gewachsen,** *p.a.* see wachsen.
**Gewächs-haus,** *n.* greenhouse, conservatory. **-kunde, -lehre,** *f.* botany. **-reich,** *n.* vegetable kingdom.
**gewahr,** *a.* aware.
**Gewähr,** *f.* surety, security; guarantee.
**gewahren,** *v.t.* perceive.
**gewähren,** *v.t.* give, furnish, afford, grant.
**gewährleisten,** *v.t.* guarantee, warrant, vouch for, assure.
**gewahrt,** *p.p.* (of wahren) kept, preserved.
**Gewalt,** *f.* power, force; authority; violence.
**gewaltig,** *a.* powerful, forcible; huge, vast.
**gewaltsam,** *a.* violent; forceful, in force.
**gewalzt,** *p.p.* (of walzen) rolled, milled.
**Gewand,** *n.* garment, clothing, dress.
**gewandt,** *p.p.* of wenden (which see).
**Gewandtheit,** *f.* dexterity, cleverness, skill.
**gewann,** *pret.* (of gewinnen) obtained, etc.
**gewärtig,** *a.* expectant.
**gewaschen,** *p.p.* (of waschen) washed.
**Gewässer,** *n.* waters.

**Gewebe,** *n.* tissue; texture; (textile) fabric; web; netting.
**Gewebe-.** textile; tissue, histological, histo-.
**gewebeähnlich,** *a.* web-like, webby.
**Gewebe-draht,** *m.* gauze wire. **-farbstoff,** *m.* histohematin.
**gewebefeindlich,** *a.* tissue-destroying.
**Gewebe-flüssigkeit,** *f.* tissue fluid. **-industrie,** *f.* textile industry. **-lehre,** *f.* histology. **-züchtung,** *f.* tissue culture.
**Gewebs-.** = Gewebe-. **-brei,** *m.* (*Bact.*) tissue pulp. **-lehre,** *f.* histology. **-waren,** *f.pl.* textile goods, textiles.
**Gewehr,** *n.* (small) arms, gun, rifle. **-geschoss,** *n.* bullet. **-granate,** *f.* rifle grenade. **-munition,** *f.* small-arms ammunition. **-pulver,** *n.* rifle powder.
**gewehrschusssicher,** *a.* bullet-proof.
**Gewehrsprenggranate,** *f.* high-explosive rifle grenade.
**Geweih,** *n.* horns, antlers.
**gewellt,** *a.* wavy, undulated, corrugated.
**Gewerb, Gewerbe,** *n.* trade, occupation, vocation, profession; industry.
**Gewerbe-ausstellung,** *f.* industrial exposition. **-museum,** *n.* industrial museum. **-salz,** *n.* industrial salt (common salt fit only for industrial use). **-schule,** *f.* technical school, industrial school. **-treibende**(r), *m.* artisan.
**Gewerb-fleiss,** *m.* industrial activity, industry. **-kunde,** *f.* technology.
**gewerb-kundlich,** *a.* technological. **-lich, -tätig,** *a.* industrial.
**Gewerk,** *n.* trade; factory; work. **-genossenschaft,** *f.* trade union, labor union. **-schaft,** *f.* trade union; (mining) company. **-verein,** *m.* trade union, labor union.
**gewesen,** *p.p.* (of sein) been.
**gewichen,** *p.p.* (of weichen) soaked, etc.
**Gewicht,** *n.* weight; gravity. **ins — fallen,** be of weight, be important.
**gewichtig,** *a.* heavy; weighty.
**Gewichts-abgang,** *m.* deficiency in weight; loss of weight. **-abnahme,** *f.* decrease in weight. **-analyse,** *f.* gravimetric analysis.
**gewichtsanalytisch,** *a.* gravimetric. — *adv.* gravimetrically.
**Gewichts-änderung,** *f.* change in weight. **-bestimmung,** *f.* determination of weight. **-einheit,** *f.* unit of weight. **-konstanz,** *n.* constancy of weight, constant weight. **-last,** *f.* dead weight. **-leder,** *n.* heavy leather.
**gewichtsmässig,** *a.* & *adv.* by weight.
**Gewichts-menge,** *f.* amount by weight, weight. **-prozent,** *n.* per cent by weight.
**gewichtsprozentig,** *a.* per cent by weight, weight-per-cent.
**Gewichts-satz,** *m.* set of weights. **-stück,** *n.* weight. **-teil,** *m.* part by weight. **-unterschied,** *m.* difference in weight. **-verhältnis,** *n.* proportion by weight. **-verlust,** *m.* loss in weight. **-verminderung,** *f.* decrease in weight. **-zunahme,** *f.* increase in weight. **-zusammensetzung,** *f.* composition by weight.
**gewiesen,** *p.p.* (of weisen) shown, etc.
**gewillt,** *a.* willing, inclined, disposed.
**Gewinde,** *n.* winding, coil; skein; thread (of a screw); worm. **-glas,** *n.* glass tube with screw cap. **-schneidöl,** *n.* screw-cutting oil. **-steigung,** *f.* screw pitch.
**gewinkelt,** *a.* angled, angular.
**Gewinn,** *m.* yield; winning, gain, profit, proceeds.
**gewinnbar,** *a.* obtainable; exploitable.
**gewinnen,** *v.t.* obtain, get; extract, produce, recover (metals, etc.); prepare (chemicals); win, gain, acquire.
**Gewinnung,** *f.* obtaining, etc. (see gewinnen); recovery; produce.
**Gewinnungsweise,** *f.* manner or way of obtaining, etc. (see gewinnen).
**Gewirr**(e), *n.* tangle, confusion, chaos.
**gewiss,** *a.* sure, certain, fixed. — *adv.* certainly, indeed.
**Gewissen,** *n.* conscience.
**gewissenhaft,** *a.* conscientious.
**gewissermassen,** *adv.* in a certain degree, to some extent, as it were.
**Gewissheit,** *f.* certainty; proof.
**Gewitter,** *n.* thunderstorm; storm.
**gewoben,** *p.p.* (of weben) woven.
**gewogen,** *p.p.* (of wägen) weighed; poised; (of wiegen) weighed; rocked. — *a.* well-disposed.
**gewöhnen,** *v.t.* accustom, habituate; familiarize; domesticate.
**Gewohnheit,** *f.* custom, usage, habit, fashion.
**gewöhnlich,** *a.* usual, customary; common, ordinary; trivial. — *adv.* usually, etc.
**gewöhnlicherweise,** *adv.* usually, customarily.
**gewohnt,** *a.* accustomed; customary.
**Gewöhnung,** *f.* habituation, etc. (see gewöhnen).
**Gewölbe,** *n.* vault, arch; dome; roof, crown (of a furnace); store, storehouse.
**gewölbt,** *a.* vaulted, arched, domed; dished.
**gewönne,** *pret. subj.* of gewinnen.
**gewonnen,** *p.p.* (of gewinnen) obtained, etc.
**geworben,** *p.p.* (of werben) advertized, etc.
**geworden,** *p.p.* (of werden) become.
**geworfen,** *p.p.* (of werfen) thrown, etc.
**Gew.T.,** *abbrev.* (Gewichtsteil) part by weight.
**Gewühl,** *n.* crowd; turmoil.
**gewunden,** *p.p.* (of winden) wound, coiled.
**gewürfelt,** *p.p.* (of würfeln) checkered, checked.
**Gewürm,** *n.* worms, creeping things, vermin.
**Gewürz,** *n.* spice, spices, aromatics; condiment, seasoning.

**gewürzartig,** *a.* spicy, aromatic.
**Gewürzessig,** *m.* aromatic vinegar.
**gewürzhaft,** *a.* spicy, aromatic.
**Gewürz-haftigkeit,** *f.* spiciness, aromatic quality. **-handel,** *m.* spice trade, grocers' trade.
**gewürzig,** *a.* spicy, aromatic.
**Gewürz-kraut,** *n.* spice plant. **-nelke,** *f.* clove. **-nelkenöl,** *n.* oil of cloves, clove oil. **-pulver,** *n.* (*Pharm.*) aromatic powder. **-stoff,** *m.* aromatic. **-strauch,** *m.* allspice (any of several aromatic plants).
**gewürzt,** *p.a.* (from würzen) spiced, aromatic.
**Gewürz-tinktur,** *f.* aromatic tincture. **-waren,** *f.pl.* spices, groceries. **-wein,** *m.* spiced wine.
**gewusst,** *p.p.* (of wissen) known.
**gezackt,** *p.p.* (of zacken) jagged, toothed, etc.
**Gezäh, Gezähe,** *n.* tools, implements.
**gezahnt,** *p.a.* see zahnen.
**gezähnt,** *a.* toothed, dentated, jagged, notched, serrated.
**gezeichnet,** *p.p.* (of zeichnen) drawn, etc.
**Gezeit,** *f.* tide.
**Gezelt,** *n.* pavilion, tent; sensorium.
**Gezeug,** *n.* utensils, tools, implements.
**geziemen,** *v.i. & r.* become, befit.
**gezinkt,** *a.* zincked, covered with zinc.
**gezogen,** *p.p.* (of ziehen) drawn, etc.
**gezweiteilt,** *p.a.* bipartite.
**gezwungen,** *p.p.* (of zwingen) forced; etc.
**gg.,** *abbrev.* (gegen) against, opposite.
**Ggw.,** *abbrev.* (Gegenwart) presence.
**Gheddasäure,** *f.* gheddic acid.
**gibt,** *pr. 3 sing.* (of geben) gives, etc. — **es gibt,** there is, there are.
**Gicht,** *f.* top, mouth, throat (of a furnace or crucible); charge (for a furnace); (*Med.*) gout.
**gicht-artig,** *a.* gouty, arthritic. **-brüchig,** *a.* paralytic.
**Gicht-gas,** *n.* gas from the top of a blast furnace, blast-furnace gas; top gas, exit gas. **-mittel,** *n.* remedy for gout. **-rauch,** *m.* top smoke (of a blast furnace). **-rose,** *f.* peony; rhododendron. **-rübe,** *f.* bryony. **-schwamm,** *m.* incrustation near a furnace top; (*Zinc*) tutty. **-staub,** *m.* blast-furnace dust; flue dust.
**Gichtung,** *f.* charging (of a furnace).
**gichtwidrig,** *a.* antiarthritic.
**giebt,** *pr. 3. sing.* (of geben) = gibt.
**Giemen,** *n.* panting, gasping, dyspnea. — *f.pl.* râles.
**Giemsa-Lösung,** *f.* (*Micros.*) Giemsa('s) stain.
**Gier,** *f.* avidity, eagerness; greed.
**gierig,** *a.* greedy, covetous; eager (for).
**Giessarbeit,** *f.* casting, founding.
**giessbar,** *a.* capable of being poured or cast.
**Giessbecken-.** arytenoid.
**Giessbett,** *n.* (*Metal.*) casting bed, pig bed.
**giessen,** *v.t.* pour; cast, found, mold, teem; coat (a photographic film).
**Giesser,** *m.* founder, caster, molder; melter, smelter; pourer; a vessel for pouring, as a water jug or pot.
**Giesserei,** *f.* foundry, casting house; founding, casting. **-betrieb,** *m.* foundry practice. **-eisen,** *n.* foundry iron, foundry pig. **-koks,** *m.* foundry coke. **-roheisen,** *n.* foundry pig iron, foundry pig. **-wesen,** *n.* founding, foundry matters.
**Giesserschwärze,** *f.* (*Founding*) black wash.
**giessfähig,** *a.* capable of being poured or cast.
**Giessfähigkeit,** *f.* pourability, castability.
**giessfertig,** *a.* ready for pouring or casting.
**Giess-form,** *f.* (casting) mold. **-harz,** *n.* casting resin; cast resin. **-haus,** *n.*, **-hütte,** *f.* foundry, casting house. **-kanne,** *f.* sprinkling can. **-kasten,** *m.* casting mold. **-kelle,** *f.* casting ladle. **-koks,** *m.* foundry coke. **-kunst,** *f.* founding. **-ling,** *m.* casting. **-löffel,** *m.* pouring cup, casting ladle. **-mutter,** *f.* matrix, mold. **-ofen,** *m.* founding furnace. **-pfanne,** *f.* casting ladle. **-probe,** *f.* pour test. **-sand,** *m.* molding sand. **-topf,** *m.* a pot or jar with a lip, for pouring. **-trichter,** *m.* (*Founding*) pouring gate. **-zement,** *m.* a quick-setting alumina cement.
**Gift,** *n.* poison; toxin; venom, virus; malice.
**gift-abtreibend,** *p.a.* antitoxic, antidotal. **-artig,** *a.* poisonous.
**Gift-arznei,** *f.* antidote. **-äscher,** *m.* (*Leather*) arsenic lime. **-blase,** *f.* venom sac. **-drüse,** *f.* poison gland. **-dunst,** *m.* poisonous vapor. **-erz,** *n.* arsenic ore. **-fang,** *m.* = Giftturm; poison fang.
**gift-fest,** *a.* immune to poison. **-frei,** *a.* free from poison, non-poisonous.
**Giftgas,** *n.* poison gas, toxic gas. **-krieg,** *m.* poison-gas warfare.
**Giftgruppe,** *f.* toxin group.
**gifthaltig,** *a.* containing poison, poisonous, toxic.
**Gift-heber,** *m.* siphon for poisons. **-hütte,** *f.* arsenic works.
**giftig,** *a.* poisonous; toxic; virulent; venomous; malicious.
**Giftigkeit,** *f.* poisonousness, toxicity.
**Gift-jasmin,** *m.* Carolina jasmine (*Gelsemium sempervirens*). **-kies,** *m.* arsenopyrite. **-kobalt,** *m.* native arsenic. **-kraut,** *n.* poisonous plant. **-kunde,** *f.* toxicology. **-lattich,** *m.* strong-scented lettuce (*Lactuca virosa*). **-lehre,** *f.* toxicology.
**giftlos,** *a.* nonpoisonous.
**Gift-mehl,** *n.* crude powdered arsenic trioxide. **-mittel,** *n.* antidote. **-nebel,** *m.* (*Mil.*) toxic smoke. **-nebelkerze,** *f.* (*Mil.*) toxic smoke candle. **-nebelwolke,** *f.* (*Mil.*) toxic

gas cloud. **-pille,** *f.* poison pill; antidotal pill. **-pulver,** *n.* = Giftmehl; antidotal powder. **-rauch,** *m.* sublimed arsenic trioxide; (*Mil.*) poisonous smoke, irritant smoke. **-rauchkerze,** *f.* (*Mil.*) toxic smoke candle. **-regen,** *m.* (*Mil.*) aerial gas spray. **-regenangriff,** *m.* (*Mil.*) spray attack. **-schlange,** *f.* poisonous snake. **-schutz,** *m.* protection against poison. **-schwamm,** *m.* poisonous fungus. **-sekret,** *n.* poisonous secretion. **-stein,** *m.* white arsenic. **-stoff,** *m.* poisonous matter, toxic agent, poison, virus. **-sumach,** *m.* poison ivy (*Rhus toxicodendron*). **-turm,** *m.* (*Metal.*) poison tower (for catching arsenic fumes). **-wende,** *f.* swallowwort (*Cynanchum vincetoxicum*).

**giftwidrig,** *a.* antitoxic; antidotal.

**Gift-wirkung,** *f.* poisonous action or effect. **-wurzel,** *f.* contrayerva; = Giftwende.

**Gilbe,** *f.* yellow or yellowish color; yellow substance; yellowing agent; yellow ocher; dyer's rocket (*Reseda luteola*).

**gilben,** *v.i.* turn yellow, yellow; impart a yellowish tone.

**gilbig,** *a.* ocherous.

**Gilb-kraut,** *n.* yellowweed, dyer's rocket (*Reseda luteola*). **-wurzel,** *f.* turmeric.

**gilt,** *pr. 3 sing.* (of gelten) is worth, etc.

**giltig,** *a.* = gültig (valid, binding, etc.).

**Giltigkeit,** *f.* = Gültigkeit (validity, etc.).

**ging,** *pret.* (of gehen) went.

**Ginster,** *m.* (*Bot.*) broom (*Genista*).

**Gipfel,** *m.* top, summit, apex; climax. **-höhe,** *f.* (*Aero.*) ceiling.

**gipfeln,** *v.i.* & *r.* culminate.

**Gipfelung,** *f.* culmination.

**Gipfelwert,** *m.* top (or peak) value, maximum.

**Gips,** *m.* gypsum; calcium sulfate; plaster of Paris. **-abdruck, abguss,** *m.* plaster cast. **-arbeiter,** *m.* plasterer.

**gipsartig,** *a.* gypseous.

**Gips-brei,** *m.* paste of plaster (Paris). **-brennen,** *n.* gypsum burning. **-brennerei,** *f.* calcination of gypsum; plaster kiln. **-brennofen,** *m.* plaster kiln.

**gipsen,** *v.t.* plaster. — *a.* gypseous.

**Gipser,** *m.* plasterer.

**Gips-erde,** *f.* earthy gypsum; gypseous soil. **-form,** *f.* plaster (Paris) mold. **-gu(h)r,** *m.* earthy gypsum. **-guss,** *m.* plaster casting, plaster cast.

**gipshaltig,** *a.* containing gypsum or calcium sulfate, gypsiferous.

**Gips-härte,** *f.* hardness due to calcium sulfate. **-kalk,** *m.* plaster lime. **-kitt,** *m.* gypsum cement. **-lösung,** *f.* calcium sulfate solution. **-mehl,** *n.* powdered gypsum; powdered plaster. **-mergel,** *m.* gypseous marl. **-mörtel,** *m.* plaster, stucco. **-niederschlag,** *m.* calcium sulfate precipitate. **-ofen,** *m.* plaster kiln. **-spat,** *m.* sparry gypsum, selenite. **-stein,** *m.* gypseous stone, plaster stone; hard deposit of calcium sulfate. **-teer,** *m.* mixture of plaster of Paris and tar.

**gischen,** *v.i.* foam, froth; ferment.

**Gischt,** *m.* foam, froth; fermentation.

**Gitter,** *n.* grating; (as in *Cryst.*) lattice; (latticed) screen; grid. **-ableitung,** *f.* grid leak. **-anordnung,** *f.* (*Cryst.*) lattice structure, crystal structure.

**gitter-artig,** *a.* lattice-like, latticed, grated.

**Gitter-ebene,** *f.* (*Cryst.*) lattice plane. **-elektron,** *n.* lattice electron. **-energie,** *f.* (*Cryst.*) lattice energy. **-farbe,** *f.* grating color.

**gitter-förmig,** *a.* = gitterartig. **-fremd,** *a.* (*Cryst.*) foreign to the lattice.

**Gitter-konstante,** *f.* lattice constant; grating constant. **-loch,** *n.* (*Cryst.*) lattice hole, lattice void. **-masche,** *f.* grid mesh. **-spannung,** *f.* (*Elec.*) grid voltage. **-spektrograph,** *m.* grating spectrograph. **-strom,** *m.* grid current. **-typus,** *m.* lattice type. **-werk,** *n.* latticework, lattice; checkerwork; grating, grid. **-widerstand,** *m.* (*Elec.*) grid resistance. **-zusammenhang,** *m.* (*Cryst.*) lattice structure.

**Gl.,** *abbrev.* (Gleichung) equation.

**glacégar,** *a.* (*Leather*) alum-tanned.

**Glacé-karton,** *m.* (*Paper*) glazed board. **-leder.** *n.* glacé leather. **-papier,** *n.* glazed paper.

**glacieren,** *v.t.* gloss, glaze; freeze.

**glandern,** *v.t.* calender.

**Glanz,** *m.* luster; glitter, polish, gloss; glance (in names of minerals); brightness, brilliancy; (of diamonds, etc.) water.

**Glanz-.** shiny, glossy, polished, glazed, glazing, brilliant; glancing, grazing. **-arsenikkies,** *m.* löllingite. **-blech,** *n.* polished sheet metal. **-blende,** *f.* alabandite. **-braunstein,** *m.* hausmannite. **-brenne,** *f.* (*Metal.*) burnishing bath. **-decklack,** *m.* gloss coating varnish.

**Glänze,** *f.* polishing material; glaze, size.

**Glanz-effekt,** *m.* gloss, luster. **-einfall,** *m.* grazing incidence. **-eisen,** *n.* silvery iron. **eisenerz,** *n.*, **-eisenstein,** *m.* specular iron ore (hematite).

**glänzen,** *v.i.* shine, glisten, glitter. — *v.t.* gloss, glaze, polish, luster. — **glänzend,** *p.a.* shining, lustrous, glossy, glittering, brilliant.

**Glanz-erz,** *n.* argentite; graphite. **-farbe,** *f.* brilliant color; glazing varnish; gloss ink.

**glanzfein,** *a.* brilliant.

**Glanz-firnis,** *m.* glazing varnish. **-gold,** *n.* burnished gold; (*Ceram.*) brilliant gold; (imitation) gold foil. **-karton,** *m.* glazed (paste)board. **-kattun,** *m.* glazed calico. **-kobalt,** *m.* glance cobalt, cobaltite; smaltite. **-kohle,** *f.* glance coal; vitrain; lustrous carbon. **-kopf,** *m.* hematite. **-lack,** *m.* glazing varnish; brilliant varnish. **-leder,** *n.* patent leather, enameled leather. **-leinwand,** *f.* glazed linen; buckram.

**glanzlos,** *a.* lusterless, dull, dim, dead, mat.

**Glanz-losigkeit,** *f.* lusterlessness, dullness. **-manganerz,** *n.* (*Min.*) manganite. **-messer,** *m.* glossmeter. **-messing,** *n.* polished brass. **-metall,** *n.* speculum metal. **-mittel** (also Glänzmittel), *n.* lustering agent, polishing agent. **-öl,** *n.* gloss oil. **-papier,** *n.* glazed paper. **-pappe,** *f.* glazed (paper) board. **-paste,** *f.* polishing paste. **-platin,** *n.* burnished platinum. **-polieren,** *n.* polishing, burnishing.

**glanzreich,** *a.* lustrous, brilliant.

**Glanz-rot,** *n.* colcothar. **-russ,** *m.* a lustrous form of soot.

**glanzschleifen,** *v.t.* polish, burnish.

**Glanz-silber,** *n.* polished silver; (*Min.*) silver glance, argentite. **-stahl,** *m.* polished steel. **-stärke,** *f.* gloss starch. **-stoff,** *m.* trade name of a cuprammonium rayon; glazed or glossy fabric.

**glanzvoll,** *a.* brilliant, splendid.

**Glanz-weiss,** *n.* brilliant white; talc. **-wichse,** *f.* polishing wax. **-winkel,** *m.* glancing angle.

**Glänzwirkung,** *f.* polishing or glazing action or effect.

**Glas,** *n.* glass. **-abfall,** *m.* glass waste, cullet. **-achat,** *m.* obsidian.

**glas-ähnlich, -artig,** *a.* glass-like, glassy, vitreous.

**Glas-artigkeit,** *f.* glassiness, vitreousness. **-ätzkunst,** *f.* art of etching glass. **-ballon,** *m.* glass carboy; glass balloon flask; glass bulb. **-becher,** *m.* glass beaker. **-bereitung,** *f.* glassmaking. **-biegen,** *n.* glass bending. **-bild,** *n.* picture on glass, transparency, lantern slide. **-bildner,** *m.* glass former, vitrifier. **-bildung,** *f.* formation of glass, vitrification. **-birne,** *f.* glass bulb or globe. **-blase,** *f.* bubble in glass. **-blasen,** *n.* glassblowing. **-bläser,** *m.* glassblower. **-bläserei,** *f.* glassblowing. **-bläserlampe,** *f.* glassblower's lamp. **-bläseröhre,** *f.* blowpipe, blow tube (for glass). **-brennen,** *n.* annealing of glass. **-brocken,** *m.pl.*, **-bruch,** *m.* glass waste, cullet.

**Gläschen,** *n.* little glass, small glass vessel or tube.

**Glas-dicke,** *f.* glass thickness. **-dose,** *f.* glass box (esp. of flat cylindrical form). **-düse,** *f.* glass nozzle. **-elektrizität,** *f.* vitreous (positive) electricity.

**glasen,** *v.t.* glaze.

**Glaser,** *m.* glazier.

**Gläser,** *n.pl.* (of Glas) glasses.

**Glaserde,** *f.* vitrifiable earth, siliceous earth.

**Glaserkitt,** *m.* (glazier's) putty.

**gläsern,** *a.* glass, of glass; glassy, vitreous.

**Gläsernheit,** *f.* glassiness, vitreousness.

**Glas-erz,** *n.* argentite. **-fabrik,** *f.* glassworks, glass factory. **-fabrikation,** *f.* glass manufacture, glassmaking. **-faden,** *m.* glass thread; thread-like defect in glass. **-farbe,** *f.* glass color. **-färben,** *n.* glass staining.

**glasfarbig,** *a.* glassy, hyaline.

**Glas-fehler,** *m.* defect or flaw in glass. **-feuchtigkeit,** *f.* vitreous humor. **-flasche,** *f.* glass bottle, glass flask. **-fluss,** *m.* glass flux; paste (for imitation of gems); enamel. **-flüssigkeit,** *f.* vitreous humor.

**glasförmig,** *a.* glass-like, vitriform.

**Glas-fritte,** *f.* glass frit. **-galle,** *f.* glass gall, sandiver. **-gefäss,** *n.* glass vessel. **-gerät,** *n.*, **-geräte,** *n.pl.* glass apparatus, glass utensils. **-gespinst,** *n.* spun glass; glass thread; glass cloth. **-gewebe,** *n.* glass cloth. **-glanz,** *m.* vitreous luster; pounded glass, frost.

**glasglänzend,** *p.a.* of vitreous luster, glassy.

**Glasglocke,** *f.* glass bell, bell glass, bell jar.

**glasgrün,** *a.* bottle-green.

**Glas-hafen,** *m.* glass pot. **-hahn,** *m.* glass cock.

**glashart,** *a.* hard as glass, brittle.

**Glas-härte,** *f.* glass hardness (highest temper of steel); chilling (of steel). **-härten,** *n.* tempering of glass. **-haube,** *f.* glass cap. **-haut,** *f.* a product similar to cellophane; vitreous film; hyaline membrane.

**glashell,** *a.* clear as glass.

**Glashütte,** *f.* glass factory, glass house.

**glasicht,** *a.* glassy, vitreous, hyaline.

**glasieren,** *v.t.* glaze; enamel; varnish; vitrify.

**Glasierung,** *f.* glazing; enameling; varnishing; vitrifying; glaze; enamel; varnish.

**glasig,** *a.* glassy, vitreous, hyaline.

**Glas-isolator,** *m.* glass insulator. **-kalk,** *m.* glass gall. **-kasten,** *m.* glass box (of rectangular form), glass case. **-kattun,** *m.* glass cloth. **-keil,** *m.* glass prism. **-kitt,** *m.* glass cement; putty.

**glasklar,** *a.* clear as glass, transparent.

**Glas-klotz,** *m.* glass block. **-kolben,** *m.* glass flask. **-kopf,** *m.* (**roter, eigentlicher**) hematite (fibrous or reniform); (**brauner, gelber**) limonite; (**schwarzer**) psilomelane; a kind of hard brick. **-körper,** *m.* vitreous humor. **-kraut,** *n.* wall pellitory (*Parietaria officinalis*); glasswort (*Salicornia herbacea*). **-kugel,** *f.* glass bulb; glass ball. **-kügelchen,** *n.* small glass bulb; glass bead. **-kühlen,** *n.* annealing of glass. **-lack,** *m.* glass varnish. **-lava,** *f.* volcanic glass, specif. obsidian; hyalite. **-löffel,** *m.* glass spoon. **-machen,** *n.* glassmaking. **-macherseife,** *f.* glassmaker's soap (as manganese dioxide). **-malerei,** *f.* glass painting. **-malz,** *n.* brittle malt. **-masse,** *f.* (*Glass*) metal; (**rohe**) frit. **-mehl,** *n.* glass powder. **-messer,** *n.* glass knife, glass cutter. **-nutsche,** *f.* glass suction filter. **-ofen,** *m.* glass furnace. **-opal,** *m.* hyalite. **-papier,** *n.* glass paper. **-pech,** *n.* hard pitch, stone pitch. **-perle,** *f.* glass bead; glass pearl. **-pinsel,** *m.* glass brush (for acids, etc.). **-platte,** *f.* glass plate; glass slide. **-porzellan,** *n.* vitreous porcelain. **-pulver,** *n.* glass powder. **-quarz,** *m.* hyaline quartz, transparent quartz. **-rohr,** *n.*, **-röhre,** *f.* glass tube. **-röhrchen,** *n.* little glass tube. **-salz,** *n.* glass gall. **-satz,** *m.* glass composition, batch. **-schale,** *f.* glass dish. **-schaum,** *m.* glass gall, sandiver. **-scheibe,** *f.* pane of glass; glass plate. **-scherben,** *f.pl.* broken glass, cullet. **-schlacke,** *f.* glass gall. **-schliff,** *m.* glass grinding; ground-glass joint. **-schmelz,** *m.* enamel. **-schmelzofen,** *m.* (*Glass*) ash furnace. **-schmutz,** *m.* glass gall. **-schneider,** *m.* glass cutter. **-schörl,** *m.* axinite. **-schreibtinte,** *f.* ink for writing on glass. **-schweiss,** *m.* glass gall. **-seife,** *f.* glass soap (as manganese dioxide). **-sorte,** *f.* sort or grade of glass. **-spatel,** *m.* glass spatula. **-splitter,** *m.* glass splinter or fragment. **-stab,** *m.*, **-stange,** *f.* glass rod. **-staub,** *m.* glass dust, powdered glass. **-stein,** *m.* axinite; paste (for imitating gems); glass brick. **-stopfen,** *n.*, **-stöpsel,** *m.* glass stopper. **-stöpselflashe,** *f.* glass-stoppered bottle (or, less often, flask).

**glastechnisch,** *a.* pertaining to glass technology.

**Glas-tiegel,** *m.* glass crucible, glass pot. **-träne,** *f.* glass tear, Prince Rupert's drop. **-trichter,** *m.* glass funnel.

**Glasur,** *f.* glaze, glazing; varnish; enamel; gloss (of leather); frosting, icing. **-blau,** *n.* zaffer. **-brand,** *m.* (*Ceram.*) glaze baking.

**glasuren,** *v.t.* glaze; enamel.

**Glasur-erz,** *n.* alquifou. **-farbe,** *f.* overglaze color. **-ofen,** *m.* glaze kiln, glost oven. **-stein,** *m.* vitrified brick.

**Glas-verbindung,** *f.* glass connection, glass joint. **-wanne,** *f.* glass trough. **-waren,** *f.pl.* glassware. **-watte,** *f.* glass wadding. **-wolle,** *f.* glass wool, spun glass.

**glatt,** *a.* smooth; even, plain, flat; flush; glossy, polished, glazed. — **glatte Wurfmine,** (*Mil.*) projector drum.

**Glättanfrischen,** *n.* reduction of litharge.

**glättbar,** *a.* smoothable, etc. (see glätten).

**Glattbrand,** *m.* (*Ceram.*) glost burn, glaze burn.

**glattbrennen,** *v.t.* subject to the glost burn.

**Glatt-brennen,** *n.* (*Ceram.*) firing on the glaze. **-brennofen,** *m.* (*Ceram.*) glaze kiln.

**Glätte,** *f.* smoothness, polish; litharge.

**Glatteis,** *n.* smooth ice, slippery ice.

**glätten,** *v.t.* smooth; polish, burnish, plane, planish; glaze (paper, gunpowder); calender (cloth).

**Glatt-färberei,** *f.* plain dyeing. **-feuer,** *n.* (*Ceram.*) sharp fire, full fire.

**Glättfrischen,** *n.* reduction of litharge.

**Glattheit,** *f.* smoothness, etc. (see glatt).

**Glättmaschine,** *f.* (*Textiles,* etc.) calender.

**Glatt-masse,** *f.* smoothing (or polishing) compound. **-ofen,** *m.* (*Ceram.*) glost kiln, finishing kiln.

**glattrandig,** *a.* smooth-edged.

**Glattscherbe,** *f.* potsherd.

**Glättungsmittel,** *n.* smoothing or polishing agent.

**Glattwalze,** *f.* smooth roll(er), plain roll.

**Glättwalze,** *f.* glazing roll.

**Glattwasser,** *n.* (*Brewing*) last run of wort.

**Glättwerk,** *n.* glazing machine.

**Glaube,** *m.* belief, faith, credit.

**glauben,** *v.t.* believe; think.

**Glaubersalz,** *n.* Glauber's salt (sodium sulfate decahydrate).

**gläubig,** *a.* believing; credulous.

**Gläubiger,** *m.* creditor.

**glaublich,** *a.* believable, credible, likely.

**glauch,** *a.* glaucous; (of ore, etc.) poor; clear, bright.

**Glaucherz,** *n.* poor ore.

**glaukonitisch,** *a.* glauconitic.

**Glazialzeit,** *f.* glacial period.

**glazieren,** *v.t.* glaze.

**gleich,** *a.* equal, like, alike, similar; same, constant. — *adv.* equally, like; directly, at once, quickly.

**gleich-, Gleich-.** equal, like, similar, constant, iso-, homo-, equi-, co-.

**gleich-achsig,** *a.* equiaxial; coaxial. **-artig,** *a.* of the same kind; alike; similar; homogeneous.

**Gleichartigkeit,** *f.* similarity; homogeneity.

**gleich-bedeutend,** *p.a.* equivalent; synonymous. **-berechtigt,** *a.* of equal rights. **-bleiben,** *v.i.* remain constant. **-bleibend,** *p.a.* constant, invariable. **-deutig,** *a.* synonymous, equivalent; tautomeric.

**Gleich-deutigkeit,** *f.* synonymy; equivalence; tautomerism. **-druck,** *m.* constant pressure. **-drucklinie,** *f.* isobar.

**gleichen,** *v.i.* be equal; be like. — *v.t.* make like or alike, equalize, smooth, level; liken.

**gleich-entfernt,** *a.* equidistant. **-erweise,** *adv.* likewise, in like manner. **-falls,** *adv.* likewise, also. **-farbig,** *a.* of the same color, isochromatic.

**Gleich-feld,** *n.* constant field. **-flügler,** *m.pl.* (*Zoöl.*). Homoptera.

**gleichförmig,** *a.* uniform, even; conformable; similar; homogeneous; monotonous.

**Gleichgang,** *m.* synchronism.

**gleich-gekörnt,** *a.* even-grained. **-gerichtet,** *a.* (*Elec.*) rectified, unidirected; of like orientation. **-gestaltet, -gestaltig,** *a.* (*Cryst.*) isomorphous.

**Gleichgewicht,** *n.* equilibrium; balance.

**Gleichgewichts-bedingung,** *f.* condition of equilibrium. **-gesetz,** *n.* law of equilibrium. **-konstante,** *f.* equilibrium constant. **-lage,** *f.* equilibrium position. **-lehre,** *f.* statics. **-mischung,** *f.* equilibrium mixture. **-störung,** *f.* displacement (or disturbance) of equilibrium. **-verhältnis,** *n.* equilibrium ratio. **-verschiebung,** *f.* displacement (or shifting) of equilibrium. **-zustand,** *m.* state or condition of equilibrium.

**gleich-gross,** *a.* equally large, equal. **-gültig,** *a.* indifferent; immaterial.

**Gleich-gültigkeit,** *f.* indifference. **-heit,** *f.* equality; parity; likeness; sameness; constancy; uniformity.

**gleich-ionig,** *a.* of like ion (or ions), having a common ion. **-kommen,** *v.i.* be equal (to), equal.

**Gleichlauf,** *m.* synchronism.

**gleichlaufend,** *p.a.* running alike; synchronized; (of lines) parallel.

**Gleich-machen,** *n.*, **-machung,** *f.* equalization; leveling; stabilizing.

**gleichmachen,** *v.t.* equalize; level.

**gleich-mässig,** *a.* proportionate, symmetrical, uniform, homogeneous, similar, equal, even. **-mittig,** *a.* concentric. **-molar,** *a.* equimolar.

**Gleichmut,** *m.* equanimity.

**gleichnamig,** *a.* of the same name or kind, like.

**Gleichnis,** *n.* simile; parable.

**gleichphasig,** *a.* of like phase, cophasal.

**Gleichraum,** *m.* constant volume.

**gleichrichten,** *v.t.* arrange in the same way, unidirect; (*Elec.*) rectify.

**Gleichrichter,** *m.* (*Elec.*) rectifier.

**Gleichrichtung,** *f.* unidirection; (*Elec.*) rectifying.

**gleich-sam,** *adv.* so to say; as it were; almost. **-schenkelig,** *a.* (*Geom.*) isosceles. **-schwer,** *a.* of equal weight; equally difficult. **-seitig,** *a.* equilateral; (of fabrics) double-faced. **-setzen,** *v.t.* make equal, equate.

**Gleichspannung,** *f.* (*Elec.*) direct-current voltage, also steady voltage.

**gleich-stellen,** *v.t.* equalize; coordinate; synchronize; compare. **-stoffig,** *a.* homogeneous.

**Gleichstoffigkeit,** *f.* homogeneity.

**Gleichstrom,** *m.* (*Elec.*) continuous current, direct current. **-leitung,** *f.* direct-current line.

**gleichteilig,** *a.* homogeneous; of equal parts; isomeric.

**Gleichteilung,** *f.* equipartition.

**Gleichung,** *f.* equation; equalization.

**gleichverhaltend,** *p.a.* of similar properties or behavior.

**Gleichverteilung,** *f.* equipartition, equidistribution.

**gleich-viel,** *adv.* & *a.* just as much, just as many, equally, all the same. **-weit,** *a.* of uniform width; equidistant.

**Gleichwert,** *m.* equivalent.

**gleichwertig,** *a.* equivalent.

**Gleichwertigkeit,** *f.* equivalence, equivalency.

**gleich-winklig,** *a.* equiangular. **-wohl,** *conj.* yet, however. **-zeitig,** *a.* simultaneous, contemporary, synchronous, isochronous. **-zellig,** *a.* like-celled, homocellular. **-zusammengesetzt,** *p.a.* of like composition.

**Gleis,** *n.* track.

**Gleit-.** glide, gliding, slide, sliding. **-bahn,** *f.* slide, slide way, shoot; gliding plane. **-bombe,** *f.* (*Mil.*) glider bomb. **-ebene,** *f.* gliding plane, slip plane.

**gleiten,** *v.i.* glide, slide, slip, skid.

**Gleiter,** *m.* (*Aero.*) glider.

**gleitfähig,** *a.* capable of gliding or sliding.

**Gleit-fähigkeit,** *f.* gliding or sliding property. **-fläche,** *f.* gliding plane, slip plane; (*Mach.*) sliding surface, slide.

**gleitfrei,** *a.* nongliding, nonslipping.

**Gleit-lager,** *n.* slide bearing, friction bearing, plain bearing. **-linie,** *f.* (*Metal.*) slip band. **-mass,** *n.* modulus of elasticity in shear. **-masse,** *f.* (*Pharm.*) lubricating jelly. **-mittel,** *n.* lubricant. **-modul,** *m.* = Gleitmass. **-reibung,** *f.* sliding friction. **-schiene,** *f.* slide bar, slide rail. **-schutz,** *m.* protection against slipping. **-sitz,** *m.* (*Mach.*) sliding fit. **-skale,** *f.* sliding scale.

**Gleitung,** *f.* gliding, sliding, slipping, slip.

**Gleitungsfläche,** *f.* sliding surface, gliding plane.

**Gletscher,** *m.* glacier. **-boden,** *m.* glacial soil. **-salz,** *n.* Epsom salt. **-schutt,** *m.* glacial drift.

**glich,** *pret.* (of gleichen) equaled, etc.

**Glied,** *n.* member; (*Math.*) term; limb, joint; link (of a chain); degree; unit, section, element.

**Glieder-füssler,** *m.pl.* (*Zoöl.*) Arthropoda. **-gicht,** *f.* arthritic gout.

**-gliederig,** *a.* -membered; -limbed.

**gliedern,** *v.t.* organize, arrange, classify; articulate, joint, segment.

**Gliederung,** *f.* organization, etc. (see gliedern); system.

**Gliederzahl,** *f.* number of members.

**Glied-nummer,** *f.* number of a member (in a series).

**-gliedrig,** *a.* -membered; -limbed.

**Gliedwasser,** *n.* synovial fluid.

**glimmen,** *v.i.* glimmer, glow feebly; smolder.

**Glimmentladung,** *f.* glow discharge.

**Glimmer,** *m.* mica; glimmer, glow.

**glimmerartig,** *a.* micaceous.
**Glimmer-blatt,** *n.* mica sheet. **-blättchen,** *n.* mica scale or lamina. **-erde,** *f.* micaceous earth.
**glimmerführend,** *a.* micaceous.
**Glimmergestein,** *n.* micaceous rock.
**glimmerhaltig,** *a.* micaceous.
**Glimmer-kalk,** *m.* micaceous lime. **-kerze,** *f.* mica spark plug.
**glimmern,** *v.i.* glimmer, glitter.
**Glimmer-plättchen,** *n.* (small) mica plate. **-platte,** *f.* mica plate.
**glimmerreich,** *a.* rich in mica.
**Glimmer-sand,** *m.* micaceous sand. **-schiefer,** *m.* micaceous schist, mica slate. **-ton,** *n.* micaceous clay.
**Glimm-lampe,** *f.* glow (discharge) lamp. **-licht,** *n.* faint light, glimmer; glow-discharge light. **-lichtrohr,** *n.*, **-lichtröhre,** *f.* glow-discharge tube. **-röhre,** *f.* vacuum discharge tube.
**glimpflich,** *a.* moderate, gentle, mild.
**glitt,** *pret.* (of gleiten) glided, slid, slipped.
**glitzern,** *v.i.* glisten, glitter.
**Gln.,** *abbrev.* (Gleichungen) equations.
**Glöckchen,** *n.* little bell or bell jar.
**Glocke,** *f.* bell; bell jar, bell glass; bubble cap; socket; (of an air pump) receiver; clock.
**Glocken-boden,** *m.* bubble plate, bubble tray. **-bronze,** *f.*, **-erz,** *n.* bell metal. **-filter,** *n.* bell-jar filter.
**glocken-form, -förmig,** *a.* bell-shaped; bell-mouthed.
**Glocken-giesser,** *m.* bell founder. **-gut, -metall,** *n.*, **-speise,** *f.* bell metal. **-trichter,** *m.* bell funnel (as on a thistle tube). **-verfahren,** *n.* bell process, bell method. **-wäscher,** *m.* bell-type scrubber.
**glomm,** *pret.* (of glimmen) glimmered.
**glotzen,** *v.i.* stare.
**Glover-säure,** *f.* Glover acid (acid from the Glover tower). **-turm,** *m.* Glover tower.
**Glucinerde,** *f.* glucina (beryllia).
**Glück,** *n.* happiness, good luck, fortune, success.
**glucken,** *v.i.* cluck; gurgle.
**glücken,** *v.i.* succeed, prosper.
**glücklich,** *a.* fortunate, lucky, happy. **-erweise,** *adv.* fortunately, happily.
**Glüh-asche,** *f.* glowing ashes, embers. **-behandlung,** *f.* (*Metal.*) annealing.
**glühbeständig,** *a.* stable at red heat.
**Glüh-birne,** *f.* incandescent bulb. **-draht,** *m.* glowing wire, hot wire; incandescent filament; annealed wire.
**Glühe,** *f.* glowing, glow; (*Iron*) chafery.
**Glüheisen,** *n.* glowing iron, red-hot iron.
**glühelektrisch,** *a.* thermionic.
**Glühelektronen-abgabe,** *f.* thermionic emission. **-entladung,** *f.* thermionic discharge.
**glühen,** *v.i.* glow. — *v.t.* cause to glow, glow, ignite; calcine; anneal; mull (wine). — **glühend,** *p.a.* glowing, incandescent; ardent.
**Glühen,** *n.* glowing, etc. (see glühen); incandescence.
**Glüh-faden,** *m.* incandescent filament. **-farbe,** *f.* glowing-red color; temper color. **-frischen,** *n.* (*Iron*) malleableizing (in an oxidizing medium). **-gut,** *n.* material to be annealed. **-hitze,** *f.* glowing heat, red (or white) heat; annealing heat. **-kasten,** *m.*, **-kiste,** *f.* annealing box. **-kolben,** *m.* retort. **-kopf,** *m.* (*Mach.*) hot bulb. **-körper,** *m.* incandescent body; specif., incandescent mantle or filament. **-lampe,** *f.* incandescent lamp.
**Glühlicht,** *n.* incandescent light. **-brenner,** *m.* incandescent burner. **-körper, -strumpf,** *m* incandescent mantle.
**Glüh-masse,** *f.* incandescing material, specif. crude strontium oxide. **-ofen,** *m.* glowing furnace, annealing furnace; (*Ceram.*) hardening-on kiln. **-phospat,** *n.* calcined phosphate. **-ring,** *m.* ring support for ignitions. **-rohr, -röhrchen,** *n.* ignition tube. **-rückstand,** *m.* residue on ignition. **-sand,** *m.* refractory sand. **-schälchen,** *n.* igniting dish, incinerating capsule. **-schale,** *f.* roasting dish; cupel. **-schiffchen,** *n.* combustion boat. **-span,** *m.* iron scale. **-stahl,** *m.* malleable cast iron. **-stoff,** *m.* incandescent material. **-strumpf,** *m.* incandescent mantle. **-temperatur,** *f.* (*Metal.*) annealing temperature. **-topf,** *m.* (*Metal.*) annealing pot, annealing box, also cementing box.
**Glühung,** *f.* glowing, etc. (see glühen).
**Glüh-verlust,** *m.* loss on ignition. **-wachs,** *n.* gilder's wax. **-wein,** *m.* mulled wine. **-zone,** *f.* zone of incandescence. **-zünder,** *m.* electric igniter.
**Glukonsäure,** *f.* gluconic acid.
**Glukosid,** *n.* glucoside, glycoside. See Glykosid.
**Glukosurie,** *f.* glucosuria, glycosuria.
**Glut,** *f.* glow, incandescence; (*Ceram.*) glow heat; (fig.) fire.
**Glutaminsäure,** *f.* glutamic acid.
**Glutarsäure,** *f.* glutaric acid.
**Glutasche,** *f.* embers.
**glutflüssig,** *a.* molten, fused (by high heat).
**Gluthitze,** *f.* glowing heat.
**glutinös,** *a.* glutinous.
**Glutmesser,** *m.* pyrometer.
**glutrot,** *a.* glowing red.
**Gluzinium,** *n.* glucinum (beryllium).
**Gluzinsäure,** *f.* glucic acid.
**Glyc-.** see also Glyk-, Glyz-.
**Glycerin-galle,** *f.* glycerinated bile. **-leim,** *m.* glycerin jelly.
**glycerinphosphorsauer,** *a.* of or pertaining to glycerophosphoric acid, glycerophosphate of.

**Glycerin-phosphorsäure,** *f.* glycerophosphoric acid. **-säure,** *f.* glyceric acid. **-seife,** *f.* glycerin soap.

**Glycin,** *n.* glycine; glucina (beryllia). **-erde,** *f.* glucina (beryllia).

**Glycium,** *n.* glucinum (beryllium).

**Glycosid,** *n.* = Glykosid.

**Glyk-.** glyc-; (when referring to glucose or its derivatives) gluc-.

**Glyko-cholsäure,** *f.* glycocholic acid. **-gallussäure,** *f.* glucogallic acid.

**Glykokoll,** *n.* glycocoll, glycine.

**Glykol-säure,** *f.* glycolic acid. **-schwefelsäure,** *f.* glycolsulfuric acid. **-ursäure,** *f.* glycoluric acid.

**Glykolyse,** *f.* glycolysis.

**glykolytisch,** *a.* glycolytic.

**Glykosämie,** *f.* glucemia.

**Glykose,** *f.* glucose.

**Glykosid,** *n.* glycoside, glucoside. (Preferably, "glycoside" is the general term, "glucoside" denotes a glucose derivative.)

**Glykoson,** *n.* glucosone.

**Glykosurie,** *f.* glycosuria, glucosuria.

**Glykuronsäure,** *f.* glucuronic acid.

**Glyoxalsäure,** *f.* glyoxalic acid.

**Glyoxylsäure,** *f.* glyoxylic (glyoxalic) acid.

**Glysantin,** *n.* glysantine (an antifreeze).

**Glyz-.** = Glyc-.

**Glyzerid,** *n.* glyceride.

**Glyzerin,** *n.* glycerol, glycerin. (For compounds see Glycerin-.)

**Glyzerol,** *n.* glycerol.

**Glyzid,** *n.* glycide. **-säure,** *f.* glycidic acid.

**Glyzin,** *n.* glycine.

**G.M.** *abbrev.* (Goldmark) gold mark.

**G.m.b.H.** *abbrev.* (Gesellschaft mit beschränkter Haftpflicht *or* Haftung) limited company.

**Gmelinsches Salz, Gmelins Salz.** Gmelin's salt, potassium ferricyanide.

**Gnade,** *f.* grace, mercy, pardon, favor.

**Gnaden-geld,** *n.* pension, allowance. **-kraut,** *n.* hedge hyssop (*Gratiola*). **-stoss,** *m.* finishing blow.

**gnädig,** *a.* gracious, merciful, favorable.

**Gneis,** *m.* gneiss; seborrhea.

**gneisig,** *a.* gneissic.

**Gneist,** *m.* (*Leather*) scud, scurf.

**Goapulver,** *n.* Goa powder.

**gold-ähnlich, -artig,** *a.* gold-like, golden.

**Gold-anstrich,** *m.* gilding. **-äther,** *m.* gold chloride in ether. **-auflösung,** *f.* gold solution. **-bad,** *n.* (*Photog.*) gold (toning) bath. **-belag, -beleg,** *m.* gold coating, gold plating; gold foil. **-beryll,** *m.* chrysoberyl. **-blatt,** *n.* gold leaf, gold foil. **-blick,** *m.* flash or "blick" of gold. **-bromür,** *n.* aurous bromide, gold(I) bromide. **-chlorid,** *n.* gold chloride, specif. auric chloride, gold(III) chloride. **-chlorür,** *n.* aurous chloride, gold(I) chloride. **-chlorwasserstoff,** *m.*, **-chlorwasserstoffsäure,** *f.* chloroauric acid. **-cyanid,** *n.* gold cyanide, specif. auric cyanide, gold(III) cyanide. **-cyanür,** *n.* aurous cyanide, gold(I) cyanide. **-doublé,** *n.* rolled gold. **-draht,** *m.* gold wire. **-erde,** *f.* auriferous earth. **-erz,** *n.* gold ore. **-farbe,** *f.* gold color.

**gold-farben, -farbig,** *a.* gold-colored.

**Gold-firnis,** *m.* gold varnish, gilding varnish. **-flitter,** *m.* gilt tinsel; gold spangle. **-folie,** *f.* gold foil.

**goldführend,** *a.* gold-bearing, auriferous.

**Goldgehalt,** *m.* gold content.

**goldgelb,** *a.* golden-yellow.

**Gold-gelbbraun,** *n.* golden brown. **-gewicht,** *n.* gold weight; weight of gold; troy weight. **-glanz,** *m.* golden luster.

**goldglänzend,** *a.* shining like gold.

**Gold-glätte,** *f.* a kind of litharge. **-glimmer,** *m.* yellow mica. **-grube,** *f.* gold mine. **-grund,** *m.* gold size.

**gold-haltig,** *a.* auriferous. **-hell,** *a.* bright as gold, bright golden.

**Gold-hydroxyd,** *n.* gold hydroxide, specif. auric hydroxide, gold(III) hydroxide. **-jodid,** *n.* gold iodide, specif. auric iodide, gold(III) iodide. **-jodür,** *n.* aurous iodide, gold(I) iodide. **-käfer,** *m.* gold beetle.

**goldkäfergrün,** *a.* beetle-green.

**Gold-kaliumbromür,** *n.* potassium aurobromide, potassium bromoaurate(I). **-kaliumcyanür,** *n.* potassium aurocyanide, potassium cyanoaurate(I). **-kalk,** *m.* gold calx, gold oxide. **-kies,** *m.* auriferous pyrites; auriferous sand or gravel. **-klee,** *m.* yellow trefoil. **-klumpen,** *m.* gold nugget. **-könig,** *m.* regulus of gold. **-krätze,** *f.* gold dross, sweepings, etc. **-kupfer,** *n.* Mannheim gold (a form of brass). **-küste,** *f.* Gold Coast. **-lack,** *m.* gold varnish; aventurine; wallflower (*Cheiranthus cheiri*). **-legierung,** *f.* gold alloy. **-leim,** *m.* gold size. **-lösung,** *f.* gold solution. **-macherkunst,** *f.* alchemy. **-natriumchlorid,** *n.* sodium chloroaurate. **-natriumchlorür,** *n.* sodium aurochloride, sodium chloroaurate(I). **-niederschlag,** *m.* gold precipitate. **-ocher, ocker,** *m.* finest yellow ocher.

**Goldoxyd,** *n.* gold oxide, specif. auric oxide, gold(III) oxide. **-ammoniak,** *n.* fulminating gold. **-salz,** *n.* auric salt, gold(III) salt; aurate.

**Goldoxydul,** *n.* aurous oxide, gold(I) oxide. **-verbindung,** *f.* aurous compound. gold(I) compound.

**Gold-oxydverbindung,** *f.* auric compound, gold(III) compound. **-papier,** *n.* gilt paper, gold paper.

**goldplattiert,** *p.a.* gold-plated.

**Gold-plattierung,** *f.* gold plating. **-probe,** *f.* gold assay, gold test; sample of gold. **-purpur,** *m.* gold purple, purple of Cassius. **-quarz,** *m.* auriferous quartz. **-regen,** *m.* laburnum.

**goldreich,** *a.* rich in gold.

**Gold-rot,** *n.* a kind of rouge. **-rubinglas,** *n.* ruby glass in which gold is used as a colorant. **-rute,** *f.* goldenrod. **-salpeter,** *m.* gold nitrate. **-salz,** *n.* gold salt; specif., sodium chloroaurate(III), $NaAuCl_4$.

**goldsauer,** *a.* of or combined with auric acid, aurate of.

**Gold-säure,** *f.* auric acid. **-schale,** *f.* gold dish, gold cup; cupel. **-schaum,** *m.* gold leaf; imitation gold leaf, Dutch foil; (*Metal.*) gold crust. **-scheiden,** *n.* gold parting, gold refining. **-scheider,** *m.* gold refiner, gold parter. **-scheidewasser,** *n.* aqua regia. **-scheidung,** *f.* gold parting, gold refining. **-schlag,** *m.* gold leaf, gold foil. **-schläger,** *m.* goldbeater. **-schlägerhaut,** *f.* goldbeater's skin. **-schlich,** *m.* gold slimes, gold schlich. **-schmied,** *m.* goldsmith. **-schnitt,** *m.* gilt edge. **-schwefel,** *m.* gold sulfide; golden sulfide of antimony ($Sb_2S_5$). **-seife,** *f.* (*Mining*) gold-bearing alluvium. **-siegellack,** *m.* gold sealing wax; aventurine. **-silber,** *n.* electrum. **-staub,** *m.* gold dust. **-stein,** *m.* auriferous stone; touchstone; goldstone (aventurine). **-streichen,** *n.* gold (streak) test. **-stück,** *n.* gold piece, gold coin. **-sulfür,** *n.* aurous sulfide, gold(I) sulfide. **-thioschwefelsäure,** *f.* aurothiosulfuric acid, thiosulfatoauric acid. **-tropfen,** *m.pl.* (*Pharm.*) ethereal tincture of ferric chloride. **-verbindung,** *f.* gold compound. **-vitriol,** *m.* gold sulfate. **-zahl,** *f.* gold number, gold figure. **-zyanid,** *n.* = Goldcyanid. **-zyanür,** *n.* aurous cyanide, gold(I) cyanide.

**Golf,** *m.* gulf.

**gölte,** *pret. subj.* (of gelten) would be worth, etc.

**Gondel,** *f.* gondola; car, nacelle, basket.

**goniometrisch,** *a.* goniometric.

**gönnen,** *v.t.* wish; grant.

**Gönner,** *m.* well-wisher, patron, supporter.

**Goochtiegel,** *m.*, **Gooch'scher Tiegel.** Gooch crucible.

**gor,** *pret.* (of gären) fermented.

**goss,** *pret.* (of giessen) poured, etc.

**Gosse,** *f.* gutter, drain.

**Gott,** *m.* God, god.

**Götter-baum,** *m.* tree of heaven (*Ailanthus glandulosus*). **-fabel, -lehre,** *f.* mythology. **-speise,** *f.* ambrosia. **-trank,** *m.* nectar.

**Gottesgnadenkraut,** *n.* hedge hyssop (*Gratiola officinalis*).

**Göttin,** *f.* goddess.

**Goudron,** *n.* a soft asphalt or mixture of asphalt with high-boiling mineral oil.

**Goudronnépapier,** *n.* tarred paper.

**gr.,** *abbrev.* (Gramm, Gramme) gram, grams, g.; (granuliert) granulated; (gross) large.

**Grab,** *n.* grave, tomb.

**graben,** *v.t.* dig; engrave, cut.

**Graben,** *n.* ditch, drain, trench. **-krieg,** *m.* trench warfare. **-mörser,** *m.* trench mortar.

**Gräber,** *m.* digger.

**Grab-legung,** *f.* burying, interment. **-scheit,** *n.* spade, shovel. **-schrift,** *f.* epitaph. **-stichel,** *m.* graver, graving tool, chisel.

**Grad,** *m.* degree; grade, rank; order; stage; rate.

**Grad-, grad-.** See also Gerad-, gerad-.

**Grad-abteilung,** *f.* graduation, scale. **-bogen,** *f.* graduated arc. **-einteilung,** *f.* graduation, scale.

**gradfaserig,** *a.* straight-fibered, straight-grained.

**Gradflügler,** *m.pl.* (*Zoöl.*) Orthoptera.

**gradieren,** *v.t.* graduate; test with a hydrometer.

**Gradierhaus,** *n.* (*Salt*) graduation house.

**Gradierung,** *f.* graduation, etc. (see gradieren).

**Gradier-wa(a)ge,** *f.* brine gage. **-werk,** *n.* graduation apparatus or works (for concentrating a solution by exposing a large surface to the air).

**-gradig, -grädig,** *a.* having (certain) degrees.

**Gradigkeit, Grädigkeit,** *f.* number of degrees, concentration, density or the like (expressed in degrees); per cent purity (as of soda).

**Gradkreis,** *m.* graduated circle or arc, limb.

**gradlinig,** *a.* rectilinear, straight-line.

**Grad-messer,** *m.* graduator; protractor; index. **-teiler,** *m.* vernier. **-teilung,** *f.* graduation, scale.

**graduell,** *a.* gradual.

**graduieren,** *v.t.* graduate.

**Graduierung,** *f.* graduation.

**Gradverwandtschaft,** *f.* graduated affinity, degree of affinity.

**gradweise,** *adv.* by degrees, gradually.

**Graf,** *m.* count; (in England) earl.

**grafisch,** *a.* graphic.

**Grafit,** *n.* graphite.

**Gram-Färbung,** *f.* (*Bact.*) Gram staining.

**Gramm-äquivalent,** *n.* gram equivalent. **-bruchteil,** *n.* fraction of a gram.

**Grammenflasche,** *f.* gram bottle, specific-gravity bottle.

**Gramm-grad,** *m.* gram degree. **-ion,** *n.* gram ion.

**Grammmol,** *n.* mole, gram molecule.

**Grammmolekül-gewicht,** *n.* gram-molecular weight. **-volumen,** *n.* gram-molecular volume.

**Gramsche Färbung.** (*Bact.*) Gram staining.

**Gran,** *n.* & *m.* grain.
**Granadilholz,** *n.* granadilla wood.
**Granalien,** *pl.* granulated metal; shot.
**Granat,** *m.* garnet; (in combination) pomegranate; shrimp. **-apfel,** *m.* pomegranate.
**granatartig,** *a.* garnet-like.
**Granat-baum,** *m.* pomegranate tree. **-dodekaeder,** *n.* rhombic dodecahedron.
**Granate,** *f.* shell; grenade; garnet; pomegranate.
**Granat-füllung,** *f.* shell filling. **-gestein,** *n.* garnet rock.
**Granatill-holz,** *n.* granadilla wood. **-öl,** *n.* physic-nut oil. **-samen,** *n.* physic nut.
**Granatoeder,** *n.* rhombic dodecahedron.
**Granatrinde,** *f.* pomegranate bark.
**granatrot,** *a.* garnet-red, garnet.
**Granat-ton,** *m.* garnet shade. **-trichter,** *m.* shell hole, shell crater. **-werfer,** *m.* trench mortar. **-werfergeschoss,** *n.* mortar shell. **-wurzelrinde,** *f.* pomegranate root bark.
**Grand,** *m.* coarse sand or fine gravel; (*Brewing*) underback.
**granieren,** *v.t.* granulate, grain.
**granit-ähnlich,** *a.* granitoid. **-artig,** *a.* granite-like, granitic.
**graniten,** *a.* granite, granitic.
**granitfarbig,** *a.* granite-colored.
**Granit-fels, -felsen,** *m.* granitic rock.
**granitförmig,** *a.* granitiform.
**granitisch,** *a.* granite, granitic.
**Granitpapier,** *n.* jaspé paper, mottled paper.
**Granne,** *f.* awn, beard, arista.
**granulieren,** *v.t.* granulate.
**Granulierung,** *f.* granulation.
**granulös,** *a.* granular.
**Gränze,** *f.* = Grenze.
**Grapen,** *m.* (iron) mixing pot, pot.
**graphisch,** *a.* graphic. — **graphische Farbe,** printing ink.
**graphit-artig, -ähnlich,** *a.* graphite-like, graphitoidal.
**Graphitbildung,** *f.* graphite formation, graphitization.
**graphithaltig,** *a.* containing graphite, graphitic.
**graphitieren,** *v.t.* graphitize; blacklead.
**graphitisch,** *a.* graphitic.
**graphitisieren,** *v.t.* graphitize.
**Graphit-kohle,** *f.* graphitic carbon. **-masse,** *f.* graphite paste. **-pulver,** *n.* graphite powder.
**graphitreich,** *a.* rich in graphite.
**Graphit-säure,** *f.* graphitic acid. **-schmelztiegel,** *m.* graphite crucible. **-schmiere,** *f.*, **-schmiermittel,** *n.* graphite lubricant. **-schmierung,** *f.* graphite lubrication. **-schwärze,** *f.* black-lead wash, graphite blacking. **-spitze,** *f.* (of an arc lamp) carbon. **-staub,** *m.* graphite dust. **-stein,** *m.* graphite brick. **-stift,** *m.* lead pencil; pencil lead. **-tiegel,** *m.* graphite crucible.
**Gras,** *n.* grass.
**grasartig,** *a.* grassy, gramineous.
**Grasebene,** *f.* grassy plain, prairie, savanna.
**grasen,** *v.i.* graze; cut grass.
**Gräser,** *n.pl.* grasses, (*Bot.*) Poaceae.
**gras-fressend,** *p.a.* graminiverous, herbiverous. **-grün,** *a.* grass-green.
**grasig,** *a.* grassy, grassgrown.
**Gras-leinen,** *n.* grass cloth. **-narbe,** *f.* turf, sod. **-öl,** *n.* grass oil, specif. citronella oil.
**grassieren,** *v.i.* rage, spread.
**Graswurzel,** *f.* couch grass (*Agropyron repens*); (*Pharm.*) triticum; grass root.
**Grat,** *m.* edge, ridge, bur, fin; (roof) groin.
**Gräte,** *f.* fishbone; edge, ridge, spine.
**gratfrei,** *a.* free from protrusions, smooth.
**grau,** *a.* gray. — **graue Quecksilbersalbe,** *f.* mercurial ointment.
**Grau,** *n.* gray.
**grau-blau,** *a.* gray-blue. **-braun,** *a.* gray-brown, dun.
**Grau-braunstein,** *m.* (*Min.*) manganite. **-braunsteinerz,** *n.* pyrolusite. **-eisen,** *n.* gray iron. **-eisenerz,** *n.* marcasite.
**grauen,** *v.i.* grow gray; dawn; be in dread.
**Grauerz,** *n.* galena.
**grau-farben, -farbig,** *a.* gray-colored. **-gelb,** *a.* grayish-yellow.
**Grau-glanzoxydbad,** *n.* a bath for coloring metals with a film of arsenic or antimony. **-golderz,** *n.* nagyagite.
**graugrün,** *a.* gray-green.
**Grau-gültigerz,** *n.* tetrahedrite. **-guss,** *m.* gray cast iron, gray iron; gray-iron casting. **-kalk,** *m.* gray lime (inferior in quality); gray chalk; crude calcium acetate. **-keil,** *m.* (*Optics*) gray wedge, neutral wedge. **-keilbelichtung,** *f.* (*Photog.*) gray-scale exposure. **-kobalterz,** *n.* gray cobalt ore, jaipurite. **-kupfererz,** *n.* chalcocite; tennantite; tetrahedrite. **-leiter,** *m.* (*Optics*) gray scale.
**graulich, gräulich,** *a.* grayish.
**Graumanganerz,** *n.* gray manganese ore, manganite; (**lichtes**) polianite.
**graumeliert,** *a.* gray-mottled.
**Graumetall,** *n.* gray metal, specif. gray pewter.
**Graumontsamen,** *m.* pumpkin seed.
**Graupappe,** *f.* pasteboard, mill board.
**Graupe,** *f.* peeled grain, esp. of barley; grain, granule; knot (in cotton). — *pl.* **Graupen,** pearl barley; groats.
**Graupel, Gräupel,** *f.* sleet.
**graupeln,** *v.i.* sleet.
**Graupen-erz,** *n.* granular ore. **-kobalt,** *m.* smaltite. **-schleim,** *m.* barley water. **-schörl,** *m.* aphrizite (a black tourmaline).

**graupig,** *a.* granular.
**graurötlich,** *a.* gray-reddish, roan.
**Graus,** *m.* small fragments, smalls; horror; shudder.
**grausam,** *a.* horrible, inhuman, cruel.
**Grauschleier,** *m.* (*Photog.*) gray fog, chemical fog.
**grauschwarz,** *a.* grayish-black.
**Grau-spiegel,** *m.* gray spiegeleisen. **-spiessglanz,** *m.*, **-spiessglanzerz, -spiessglaserz,** *n.* gray antimony ore, stibnite. **-stein,** *m.* (*Petrog.*) graystone.
**grauviolett,** *a.* gray-violet.
**Grauwacke,** *f.* (*Petrog.*) graywacke.
**grauweiss,** *a.* gray-white.
**Graveur,** *m.* engraver.
**gravieren,** *v.t.* engrave; aggravate.
**gravimetrisch,** *a.* gravimetric.
**Gravitationskraft,** *f.* gravitational force.
**Gravur,** *f.* engraving.
**Grazie,** *f.* grace, charm.
**greifbar,** *a.* graspable, seizable, tangible.
**greifen,** *v.t. & i.* grasp, seize, grip, catch. — *v.i.* mat, felt, cake.
**Greifer,** *m.* seizer, gripper, catcher, grab, claw.
**greifhaft,** *a.* graspable, seizable, tangible.
**Greif-zange,** *f.* gripping tongs. **-zirkel,** *m.* calipers.
**greis,** *a.* gray with age, old.
**Greisen,** *m.* (*Petrog.*) greisen (a quartz-mica rock).
**Greisen-.** senile. **-alter,** *n.* old age.
**grell,** *a.* bright, dazzling, glaring; shrill. — **grelles Roheisen,** white pig iron.
**Grenadillholz,** *n.* granadilla wood.
**Grenz-.** limit (in *Org. Chem.* designating saturated aliphatic compounds); limiting, terminal, marginal; (*Elec.*) aperiodic. **-alkohol,** *m.* limit alcohol, paraffin alcohol, alkanol. **-bedingung,** *f.* limiting condition.
**Grenze,** *f.* limit, boundary, bound, end; edge, border; frontier; limitation.
**grenzen,** *v.i.* border (on), be next (to). — *v.t.* bound, limit, define.
**Grenzenlinie,** *f.* boundary line.
**grenzenlos,** *a.* unlimited, boundless, infinite.
**Grenz-fall,** *m.* limiting case; borderline case. **-fläche,** *f.* boundary surface, surface of contact, interface.
**Grenzflächen-erscheinung,** *f.* interfacial phenomenon. **-katalyse,** *f.* contact catalysis. **-spannung,** *f.* interfacial tension.
**Grenz-gesetz,** *n.* limit law (one which natural phenomena approximate but never actually fulfill). **-kohlenwasserstoff,** *m.* any hydrocarbon of the methane series, alkane, paraffin, limit hydrocarbon. **-kurve,** *f.* limiting curve, limit curve. **-last,** *f.* limit load, maximum load. **-leistung,** *f.* peak performance, maximum output. **-linie,** *f.* boundary line. **-reglung,** *f.* demarcation. **-scheide,** *f.* boundary. **-scheidung,** *f.* demarcation. **-schicht,** *f.* boundary layer; marginal layer. **-spannung,** *f.* limiting stress. **-strahl,** *m.* borderline ray. **-stromdichte,** *f.* (*Elec.*) limit current density. **-verbindung,** *f.* terminal compound, end compound, end member; saturated aliphatic compound. **-wellenlänge,** *f.* threshold wavelength. **-wert,** *m.* limiting value, limit; (*Biol.*) threshold value. **-winkel,** *m.* critical angle. **-zahl,** *f.* limit value, limit figure. **-zustand,** *m.* limiting state.
**greulich,** *a.* abominable, detestable, horrible.
**Greze, Grezseide,** *f.* raw silk.
**Grieben,** *f.pl.* greaves, cracklings; residue (as from sifting sugar).
**Griechenland,** *n.* Greece.
**griechisch,** *a.* Greek. — **griechisches Heu,** fenugreek.
**Gries,** *m.* = Griess.
**grieselig, griesig,** *a.* gritty, gravelly.
**Griess,** *m.* grit, gravel, coarse sand; granules, coarse powder; grits, groats, semolina; small coal; (*Med.*) gravel. **-bildung,** *f.* formation of grit or gravel. **-holz,** *n.* (*Pharm.*) nephritic wood. **-kohle,** *f.* (*Coal*) smalls, small coal, pea coal. **-mittel,** *n.* remedy for gravel. **-stein,** *m.* urinary calculus, gravel; jade. **-wurzel,** *f.* (*Pharm.*) pareira.
**griff,** *pret.* (of greifen) grasped, etc.
**Griff,** *m.* grip, grasp; handle, knob, pull; touch, feel.
**Griffel,** *m.* style, stylus; slate pencil, pencil; (*Bot.*) style.
**griffelförmig,** *a.* styloid, styliform.
**griffig,** *a.* of good feel, of good handle.
**Griffstopfen,** *m.* stopper with thumb piece.
**grignardieren,** *v.t.* subject to the Grignard reaction, grignardize.
**Grignardierung,** *f.* grignardization.
**Grille,** *f.* cricket; whim, crotchet.
**Grimmdarm,** *m.* (*Med.*) colon. **-entzündung,** *f.* colitis.
**grimmen,** *v.i.* gripe.
**Grimmen,** *n.* griping, colic.
**Grind,** *m.* scab, scurf, crust; mange.
**grindig,** *a.* scabby, scurfy, scaly.
**Grindwurzel,** *f.* bitterdock root.
**grinsen,** *v.i.* grin; (of colors) stare; (of metals) begin to melt.
**grithaltig,** *a.* containing grit, gritty.
**grob,** *a.* coarse; thick, heavy, rough; large, gross; ill-bred, rude.
**Grob-ätzung,** *f.* coarse etching, macro-etching. **-blech,** *n.* (*Metal.*) thick plate, heavy plate. **-bruch,** *m.* coarse-grained fracture. **-einstellung,** *f.* coarse adjustment. **-eisen,** *n.* merchant iron. **-erz,** *n.* coarse ore.

**grob-fädig,** *a.* coarse-threaded. **-faserig,** *a.* coarse-fibered, coarse-grained.
**Grob-feile,** *f.* coarse file. **-gefüge,** *n.* coarse structure, macrostructure.
**grobgepulvert,** *p.a.* coarsely powdered.
**Grob-gewicht,** *n.* gross weight. **-kalk,** *m.* coarse limestone. **-keramik,** *f.* ordinary ceramic ware. **-kies,** *m.* coarse gravel. **-kohle,** *f.* coarse or lump coal; open-burning coal. **-korn,** *n.* coarse grain, large grain. **-korneisen,** *n.* coarse-grained iron.
**grob-körnig,** *a.* coarse-grained, large-grained, coarsely granular. **-kristallinisch,** *a.* coarsely crystalline.
**gröblich,** *a.* rather coarse. — *adv.* coarsely, grossly.
**grob-maschig,** *a.* wide-meshed. **-mechanisch,** *a.* macromechanical, large-scale.
**Grobmörtel,** *m.* coarse mortar, concrete.
**grobporig,** *a.* coarsely porous, large-pored.
**Grob-sand,** *m.* coarse sand. **-schrot,** *n.* & *m.* coarse groats; (*Brewing*) coarsely ground malt. **-schutt,** *m.* coarse refuse, coarse debris. **-sieb,** *n.* coarse (wide-meshed) sieve, **-spiegel,** *m.* coarse spiegeleisen.
**grobstrahlig,** *a.* coarsely radiated, coarsely fibrous.
**Grobstruktur,** *f.* coarse structure, macrostructure. **-analyse,** *f.* macrostructure analysis.
**Grobzerkleinerung,** *f.* coarse division, coarse crushing.
**Grönland,** *n.* Greenland.
**gross,** *a.* great; large, big, tall; capital (letter). — **im grossen,** on a large scale; in bulk. — **im grossen und ganzen,** on the whole, generally.
**grossartig,** *a.* grand, sublime.
**Grossbetrieb,** *m.* operation on a large scale; wholesale trade.
**gross-blätterig,** *a.* coarsely foliated or laminated; large-leaved. **-britannisch,** *a.* British.
**Grösse,** *f.* quantity; magnitude; amount, bulk, volume, size, largeness, greatness.
**Grössenlehre,** *f.* mathematics; geometry.
**grössenmässig,** *a.* according to size or amount.
**Grössen-nummer,** *f.* size (expressed as a number). **-ordnung,** *f.* order of magnitude; arrangement by size or value.
**grössenordnungsmässig,** *a.* in order of size or value.
**grossenteils,** *adv.* in large part, mostly.
**Grössenverteilungskurve,** *f.* distribution curve.
**Grosserzeugung,** *f.* mass production.
**Grossfabrikation,** *f.* large-scale manufacture.
**grossfaserig,** *a.* large-fibered, coarse-fibered.
**Gross-feuer,** *n.* conflagration; (*Ceram.*) full fire. **-filter,** *n.* coarse filter. **-gewerbe,** *n.* manufacture on a large scale. **-handel,** *m.* wholesale business. **-händler,** *m.* wholesaler.
**grossherzig,** *a.* magnanimous.
**Gross-hirn,** *n.* cerebrum. **-hirnrinde,** *f.* cerebral cortex. **-industrie,** *f.* = Grossgewerbe.
**grossjährig,** *a.* of age.
**Gross-koks,** *m.* large-sized coke, (blast) furnace coke. **-kraftwerk,** *n.* large power station.
**gross-luckig,** *a.* coarsely porous; coarse-grained. **-mütig,** *a.* magnanimous, generous.
**Gross-ofen,** *m.* large furnace. **-spore,** *f.* (*Biol.*) macrospore.
**grossstückig,** *a.* in large pieces, lumpy.
**Grosstechnik,** *f.* large-scale technology or industry.
**grosstechnisch,** *a.* large-industrial, large-scale.
**grösstenteils,** *adv.* for the most part, mainly.
**grösstmöglich,** *a.* greatest possible.
**Grösstwert,** *m.* largest value, maximum value.
**Gross-verkauf,** *m.* wholesale. **-versuch,** *m.* large-scale experiment. **-zahlforschung, -zahluntersuchung,** *f.* statistical research or analysis.
**grosszügig,** *a.* large-scale.
**Grotte,** *f.* grotto.
**grub,** *pret.* (of graben) dug; engraved.
**Grübchen,** *n.* little hole or opening, small pit; dimple; (*Biol.*) lacuna.
**Grube,** *f.* mine; quarry; hole, cavity; pit; ditch.
**grübeln,** *v.i.* ponder, brood.
**Gruben-abfall,** *m.* mine waste. **-bau,** *m.* mine digging, underground working. **-betrieb,** *m.* mining. **-brand,** *m.* mine fire. **-dampf,** *m.* choke damp.
**grubenfeucht,** *a.* green, freshly mined.
**Gruben-feuchte, -feuchtigkeit,** *f.* pit moisture (as in coal or sand).
**grubengar,** *a.* (*Leather*) pit-tanned.
**Gruben-gas,** *n.* mine gas, specif. marsh gas, methane; firedamp (explosive mixture of methane and air). **-gasanzeiger,** *m.* methanometer. **-gerbung,** *f.* pit tanning. **-gut,** *n.* (*Mining*) minerals. **-klein,** *n.* (*Mining*) smalls, slack. **-kohle,** *f.* pit coal, (mineral) coal; pit charcoal. **-lampe,** *f.*, **-licht,** *n.* miner's lamp. **-pulver,** *n.* miner's powder, blasting powder. **-sand,** *m.* pit sand, dug sand. **-verkohlung,** *f.* pit burning (of charcoal). **-wasser,** *n.* pit water, mine water. **-wetter,** *n.* mine damp, specif. firedamp.
**Grude,** *f.* hot ashes, embers; = Grudekoks.
**Grudekoks,** *m.* a granular coke from lignite.
**grün,** *a.* green. — **grüne Erde** = Grünerde.
**Grün,** *n.* green.
**grünblau,** *a.* greenish-blue.
**Grünbleierz,** *n.* green lead ore, green pyromorphite (or green mimetite).
**grünbraun,** *a.* greenish-brown.

**Grund,** *m.* ground (in various senses); soil; grounds, sediment; bottom; foundation, base, basis. — **im Grunde,** at bottom, on the whole, after all. — **zu Grunde gehen,** be ruined, fail. — **zu Grunde legen,** take as a basis, start out from. — **zu Grunde liegen,** be at the bottom of, be the basis of (or for).

**Grund-.** ground, bottom, foundation, fundamental, base, basic, basal, primary, elementary; (before *adjs.*, **grund-**) thoroly, radically. **-anstrich,** *m.* ground coat, priming coat. **-bahn,** *f.* ground orbit. **-bau,** *m.* foundation. **-bedingung,** *f.* fundamental condition. **-begriff,** *m.* fundamental conception or notion, basic idea. **-besitz,** *m.* landed property, real estate. **-besitzer,** *m.* landowner. **-bestandteil,** *m.* elementary constituent, element; fundamental constituent; base (as for ointment). **-düngung,** *f.* fertilization of the ground. **-eigenschaft,** *f.* fundamental property or characteristic. **-einheit,** *f.* fundamental unit.

**gründen,** *v.t.* ground, found, establish; groove.

**Gründer,** *m.* founder, establisher, promoter.

**grundfalsch,** *a.* radically false.

**Grund-farbe,** *f.* primary color; ground color, priming color; (*Dyeing*) bottom color. **-färbung,** *f.* bottom dyeing. **-faser,** *f.* elementary fiber. **-feuchtigkeit,** *f.* soil moisture. **-firnis,** *m.* priming varnish. **-fläche,** *f.* basal surface, base; area. **-flüssigkeit,** *f.* (*Colloids*) suspending liquid. **-form,** *f.* primary or fundamental form, type. **-formel,** *f.* fundamental formula. **-gebirge,** *n.* primitive rock, basement (rocks). **-gesetz,** *n.* fundamental law. **-gestein,** *n.* primitive rock; underlying rock. **-gewebe,** *n.* primary tissue, ground tissue or texture. **-gleichung,** *f.* fundamental equation. **-heil,** *n.* (*Pharm.*) mountain parsley (*Peucedanum oreoselinum*).

**Grundierbad,** *n.* bottoming bath.

**grundieren,** *v.t.* ground, prime; (*Gilding*) size; (*Paper*) stain; (*Dyeing*) bottom, also impregnate; (*Calico*) prepare.

**Grundier-farbe,** *f.* priming color, primer. **-farbstoff,** *m.* (*Dyeing*) bottoming color or dye. **-firnis,** *m.* priming varnish, filler. **-flotte,** *f.* bottoming bath. **-lack,** *m.* priming varnish, filler. **-salz,** *n.* preparing salt (sodium stannate). **-schicht,** *f.* priming coat.

**Grundierung,** *f.* grounding, priming, etc. (see grundieren); (*Paper*) texture.

**Grundierungs-bad,** *n.* (*Dyeing*) impregnation bath. **-mittel,** *n.* (*Paint*) grounding, primer, surfacer.

**Grund-immunität,** *f.* primary immunity. **-kapital,** *n.* (original) stock. **-konstante,** *f.* fundamental constant. **-körper,** *m.* fundamental or parent substance. **-kraft,** *f.* primary force, primitive force. **-kreis,** *m.* (*Mech.*) base circle.

**gründl.,** *abbrev.* of gründlich.

**Grund-lack,** *m.* base coat, base varnish or lacquer. **-ladung,** *f.* (*Expl.*) base charge. **-lage,** *f.* foundation, groundwork, base; basis, principle; matrix; basement; (*Old Chem.*) radical base.

**grundlegend,** *a.* fundamental.

**Grundlehre,** *f.* fundamental doctrine.

**gründlich,** *a.* fundamental; profound; thoro. — *adv.* fundamentally; thoroly.

**Grundlinie,** *f.* ground line, base line, basis; outline.

**grundlos,** *a.* groundless, baseless.

**Grund-mass,** *n.* fundamental unit or standard of measurement. **-masse,** *f.* (*Petrog.*) groundmass, matrix; (*Paint*) filler, bottoming paste; (*Anat.*) stroma. **-material,** *n.* base material; matrix. **-mischung,** *f.* base mixture, base stock. **-molekül,** *n.* base molecule, (of a polymer) repeating unit or monomeric unit. **-mörtel,** *m.* concrete. **-niveau,** *n.* ground level. **-platte,** *f.* base plate, bed plate. **-problem,** *n.* fundamental problem. **-reaktion,** *f.* essential reaction. **-regel,** *f.* principle, axiom. **-riss,** *m.* ground plan; sketch, outline. **-satz,** *m.* principle, axiom.

**grundsätzlich,** *a.* fundamental, based on principles.

**Grund-schicht,** *f.* primary layer, fundamental layer; ground course. **-stein,** *m.* foundation stone, cornerstone; lower (mill) stone. **-stock,** *m.* matrix. **-stoff,** *m.* element; raw material; base; (*Paper*) ground pulp. **-stoffindustrie,** *f.* basic industry. **-stoffwechsel,** *m.* basal metabolism. **-strich,** *m.* first coat, priming; down stroke. **-stück,** *m.* premises, (real) property. **-substanz,** *f.* element; basic substance; (*Anat.*) ground substance, matrix. **-teil,** *m.* element, principle; basic part. **-teilchen,** *n.* fundamental particle. **-ton,** *m.* fundamental tone, primary tone. **-umsatz,** *m.* (*Biol.*) basal metabolism.

**Gründung,** *f.* foundation; first coat, priming.

**Grün-düngen,** *n.* (*Agric.*) green manuring. **-dünger,** *m.* (*Agric.*) green manure.

**Grundursache,** *f.* primary cause.

**grundverschieden,** *a.* fundamentally different.

**Grund-versuch,** *m.* fundamental experiment. **-wasser,** *n.* (under)ground water. **-wasserspiegel,** *m.* ground-water level, water table. **-zahl,** *f.* unit; base number, base; cardinal number. **-zug,** m. leading feature, characteristic; (*pl.*) outline. **-zustand,** *m.* ground (level) state.

**Grüne,** *f.* green, greenness.

**Grüneisen-erde,** *f.*, **-erz, -stein,** *m.* green iron ore, dufrenite.

**grünempfindlich,** *a.* sensitive to green.
**grünen,** *v.r. & i.* become green, green.
**Grün-erde,** *f.* green earth (glauconite, also celadonite). **-erdelack,** *m.* green-earth lake. **-feuer,** *n.* green fire. **-frucht,** *f.* green crop(s).
**grün-gelb,** *a.* greenish-yellow. **-gesalzen,** *a.* (*Leather*) green-salted, green-cured. **-grau,** *a.* greenish-gray.
**Grün-holz,** *n.* green heartwood; greenheart. **-kalk,** *m.* gas lime. **-kreuz,** *n.*, **-kreuzkampfstoff,** *m.* "green cross" shell filling (trichloromethyl chloroformate or other lung irritant).
**grünlich,** *a.* greenish. **-blau,** *a.* greenish-blue. **-gelb,** *a.* greenish-yellow. **-grau,** *a.* greenish-gray. **-weiss,** *a.* greenish-white.
**Grün-malz,** *n.* green malt. **-mist,** *m.* green manure. **-öl,** *n.* green oil (anthracene oil). **-rost,** *m.* verdigris.
**grünrostig,** *a.* (a)eruginous.
**Grünsand, -stein,** *m.* (*Geol.*) greensand.
**grünschwarz,** *a.* greenish-black.
**Grünspan,** *m.* verdigris.
**grünspanähnlich,** *a.* like verdigris, (a)eruginous.
**Grünspan-blumen,** *f.pl.* crystals of verdigris. **-essig, -geist, -spiritus,** *m.* spirit of verdigris (see Kupfergeist).
**Grün-spat,** *m.* a variety of diopside. **-star,** *m.* glaucoma. **-stein,** *m.* (*Geol.*) greenstone. **-stich,** *m.* greenish tinge or cast. **-stift,** *m.* green pencil. **-sucht,** *f.* chlorosis.
**Gruppe,** *f.* group; cluster, clump, set.
**Gruppen-erscheinung,** *f.* group phenomenon. **-geschwindigkeit,** *f.* group velocity. **-reagens,** *n.* group reagent. **-schaltung,** *f.* (*Elec.*) series-parallel connection.
**gruppenweise,** *adv.* in groups, by groups.
**gruppieren,** *v.t.* group.
**Gruppierung,** *f.* grouping.
**Grus,** *m. & n.* small fragments, smalls, fines; specif., small coal, slack; breeze; fine gravel; debris. **-boden,** *m.* soil from rock debris. **-kakao,** *m.* cacao husks. **-kohle,** *f.* small coal, slack. **-koks,** *m.* coke fines, coke breeze.
**Gruss,** *m.* greeting, salutation.
**grüssen,** *v.t.* greet, salute.
**Grütz-.** of or like grits, pulpy, (*Med.*) sebaceous, atheromatous. **-brei,** *m.* porridge, mush.
**Grütze,** *f.* grits, groats; porridge.
**Grützschleim,** *m.* gruel.
**G-Säure,** *f.* G-acid (2-naphthol-6,8-disulfonic acid).
**G.T.,** *abbrev.* (Gewichtsteil) part by weight.
**Guaj-.** guai-.
**Guajac, Guajac-.** = Guajak, Guajak-.
**Guajadol,** *n.* guaiadol.
**Guajak,** *m.* guaiacum. **-blau,** *n.* guaiacum blue. **-gelb,** *n.* guaiacum yellow. **-harz,** *n.* guaiacum resin, guaiacum. **-harzsäure,** *f.* guaiaretic acid. **-holz,** *n.* guaiacum wood. **-insäure,** *f.* guaiacinic acid. **-ol,** *n.* guaiacol. **-onsäure,** *f.* guaiaconic acid. **-säure,** *f.* guaiacic acid. **-seife,** *f.* guaiac soap.
**Guajen,** *n.* guaiene. **-chinon,** *n.* guaienequinone.
**Guajol,** *n.* guaiol.
**Guäthol,** *n.* guaethol (*o*-ethoxyphenol).
**gucken,** *v.i.* look, peep.
**Guckloch,** *n.* peep hole, sighthole.
**Guhr,** *f.* = Gur.
**Gulden,** *m.* gulden, florin.
**guldig, güldig,** *a.* golden; auriferous.
**Güldisch,** *n.* auriferous silver.
**Gülle,** *f.* liquid manure (esp., a kind formed by the decomposition of animal refuse).
**gültig,** *a.* valid, binding, in force, legal, good, current; applicable; available; (*Mining*) specif., auriferous.
**Gültigkeit,** *f.* validity, binding force, applicability, availability.
**Gummi,** *n.* gum; (India) rubber, caoutchouc. (For compounds see also under Kautschuk-.) **-abfälle,** *m.pl.* scrap rubber. **-arabicum,** gum arabic. **-art,** *f.* variety of gum, gum; kind of rubber.
**gummiartig,** *a.* gum-like, gummous, gummy; rubber-like, rubbery.
**Gummi-artikel,** *m.* rubber article or goods. **-auflösung,** *f.* = Gummilösung. **-auskleidung,** *f.* rubber lining or covering. **-ballon,** *m.* rubber balloon; rubber bulb. **-band,** *n.* rubber band; elastic. **-baum,** *m.* gum tree; rubber tree. **-blase,** *f.* rubber bulb. **-chemiker,** *m.* rubber chemist. **-chromverfahren,** *n.* bichromated gum process.
**gummicht,** *a.* gummy, gummous.
**Gummi-dichtung,** *f.* rubber packing, rubber gasket. **-druck,** *m.* offset printing. **-druckball,** *m.* rubber (pressure) bulb. **-drucklack,** *m.* gum printing varnish.
**Gummi elasticum** (or **elastikum**). rubber.
**gummieren,** *v.t.* gum; (*Gilding*) size; rubberize.
**Gummi-ersatz, -ersatzstoff,** *m.* rubber substitute, specif. factice. **-erz,** *n.* (*Min.*) gummite. **-fahne,** *f.* rubber flag or "policeman" (for precipitates). **-fichte,** *f.* balsam fir. **-finger,** *m.* rubber finger stall. **-flasche,** *f.* rubber bottle.
**gummig,** *a.* gummy, gummous.
**Gummi-gärung,** *f.* mucous fermentation. **-gebläse,** *n.* rubber bellows, rubber bulb. **-gift,** *n.* rubber poison. **-gut, -gutt,** *n.* gamboge.
**gummihaltig,** *a.* containing gum, gummy; containing rubber.
**Gummi-handschuh,** *m.* rubber glove. **-harz,** *n.* gum resin; rubber resin.
**gummiharzig,** *a.* of or pertaining to a gum resin.
**Gummi-hütchen,** *n.* (small) rubber cap. **-iso-**

**lierung,** *f.* rubber insulation. **-käppchen,** *n.* (small) rubber cap. **-kappe,** *f.* rubber cap. **-kneter,** *m.* rubber masticator, dough mill. **-lack,** *m.* gum-lac; rubber varnish. **-lösung,** *f.* gum solution; rubber solution. **-lösungsbenzin,** *n.* (*Petroleum*) rubber solvent. **-maske,** *f.* rubber (gas) mask. **-milch,** *f.* (rubber) latex. **-packung,** *f.* rubber packing. **-papier,** *n.* gummed paper. **-pflaster,** *n.* rubber paving. **-pfropf, -pfropfen,** *m.* rubber stopper or plug. **-platte,** *f.* rubber plate. **-puffer,** *m.* rubber buffer. **-rahmen,** *m.* rubber gasket. **-reifen,** *m.* rubber tire. **-riemen,** *m.* rubber belt(ing). **-ring,** *m.* rubber ring. **-rohr,** *n.*, **-röhre,** *f.* rubber tube. **-sauger,** *m.* rubber suction bulb. **-säure,** *f.* gummic acid (arabic acid). **-scheibe,** *f.* rubber disk. **-schicht,** *f.* layer of rubber (or of gum). **-schlauch,** *m.* rubber tube, rubber tubing, rubber hose. **-schleim,** *m.* mucilage (made from gum), (*Pharm.*) mucilage of acacia. **-schwamm,** *m.* rubber sponge, sponge rubber. **-sirup,** *m.* (*Pharm.*) sirup of acacia. **-stein,** *m.* hyalite. **-stempel,** *m.* rubber stamp. **-stoff,** *m.* gum substance; gummy matter; rubber cloth; (*Min.*) gummite. **-stopfen, -stöpsel,** *m.* rubber stopper. **-tragant,** *m.* gum tragacanth. **-überzug,** *m.* rubber (or gum) coating or film. **-verbindung,** *f.* rubber connection. **-verdickung,** *f.* gum thickening. **-waren,** *f.pl.* rubber goods. **-wasser,** *n.* gum water. **-wischer,** *m.* rubber wiper, rubber "policeman." **-zahl,** *f.* (*Paper*) gum number. **-zucker,** *m.* arabinose.

**gummös,** *a.* gummous, gummy.

**Gundelrebe,** *f.*, **Gundermann,** *m.* ground ivy (*Glecoma hederacea*).

**Gunst,** *f.* favor, kindness. — **zu Gunsten** *or* **zu gunsten,** in favor (of), for the benefit (of).

**günstig,** *a.* favorable; convenient; propitious.

**günstigst,** *a.* most favorable, optimum.

**Gur,** *f.* guhr (pulverulent mineral deposit); specif., kieselguhr; fermentation.

**Guranuss,** *f.* guru nut, cola nut.

**Gurdynamit,** *m. & n.* guhr dynamite.

**Gurgel,** *f.* throat, gullet. **-ader,** *f.* jugular vein. **-mittel,** *n.* gargle.

**gurgeln,** *v.t. & i.* gargle; gurgle.

**Gurgelwasser,** *n.* (*Pharm.*) gargle.

**Gurke,** *f.* cucumber.

**Gurkenkraut,** *n.* borage.

**Gurt,** *m.* girdle, girth; belt, strap; flange.

**Gürtel,** *m.* belt, girdle, band; zone.

**gürten,** *v.t.* gird, girdle.

**Gurtförderer,** *m.* belt conveyer.

**Guss,** *m.* casting, founding; cast iron; gate (of a mold); gutter; pouring; jet (of liquid); font (of type); (*Brewing*) mash liquor, mash water. **-aluminium,** *n.* cast aluminum.

**gussbar,** *a.* = giessbar.

**Guss-beton,** *m.* cast (or poured) concrete. **-blase,** *f.* flaw in a casting, blowhole. **-blei,** *n.* cast lead. **-block,** *m.* ingot. **-bruch,** *m.* broken castings, cast-metal scrap; specif., cast-iron scrap.

**Gusseisen,** *n.* cast iron; pig iron. **-rohr,** *n.*, **-röhre,** *f.* cast-iron pipe.

**guss-eisern,** *a.* cast-iron. **-fähig,** *a.* castable.

**Guss-fehler,** *m.* casting flaw. **-flasche,** *f.* molding flask. **-form,** *f.* (casting) mold; (*Soap*) frame. **-haut,** *f.* skin (of a casting). **-kasten,** *m.* casting box, molding box. **-legierung,** *f.* casting alloy. **-masse,** *f.* substance for pouring or casting; (*Aero.*) dope. **-messing,** *n.* cast brass. **-metall,** *n.* cast metal; casting metal. **-mörtel,** *m.* concrete, cement. **-naht,** *f.* (*Founding*) burr, seam. **-pfanne,** *f.* (*Metal.*) ladle. **-rohr,** *n.*, **-röhre,** *f.* cast-iron pipe. **-schlicker,** *m.* (*Ceram.*) casting slip. **-schrott,** *m.* cast-iron scrap. **-späne,** *m.pl.* cast-iron chips or borings. **-stahl,** *m.* cast steel.

**gussstählern,** *a.* cast-steel.

**Guss-stahltiegel,** *m.* cast-steel crucible. **-stein,** *m.* sink; drain. **-stück,** *n.* cast, casting. **-wachs,** *n.* casting wax. **-waren,** *f.pl.* castings, foundry goods; specif., cast-iron goods. **-zink,** *m. & n.* cast zinc.

**gut,** *a.* good. — *adv.* well.

**Gut,** *n.* good; (valuable or useful) material, possession, property, goods, ware; estate; (in combination) goods or material to be treated; as, *Farbgut,* goods to be dyed. — *pl.* **Güter,** goods, wares, commodities.

**Gutachten,** *n.* expert opinion, judgment; decision, verdict.

**gutartig,** *a.* good-natured; mild.

**Gutbefund,** *m.* approval.

**Güte,** *f.* goodness, worth, quality; grade, class. **-einteilung,** *f.* classification by quality, grading. **-grad,** *m.* quality, grade; efficiency.

**gütemässig,** *adv.* in (regard to) quality.

**Gütemesser,** *m.* eudiometer.

**güten,** *v.t.* improve, (a)meliorate.

**Güter,** *n.pl.* see Gut. **-wagen,** *m.* freight car, goods wagon; truck, lorry, van. **-zug,** *m.* freight train, goods train.

**Güte-verhältnis,** *n.* efficiency. **-wert,** *m.*, **-zahl,** *f.* index of quality, quality factor.

**Gut-gewicht,** *n.* fair weight; allowance (as for moisture). **-haben,** *n.* balance, credit.

**gütig,** *a.* good, kind, gracious.

**gut-sagen,** *v.i.* be responsible (for). **-schliessend,** *a.* (of corks, etc.) tight-fitting.

**Gut-schmecker,** *m.* gastronomist, epicure. **-schrift,** *f.* credit.

**Gutti,** *n.* gamboge.
**Gütung,** *f.* improvement, (a)melioration.
**gut-willig,** *a.* willing, obliging; voluntary. **-ziehend,** *p.a.* well-drawing, with a good draft.
**Gymnasium,** *n.* (German) gymnasium, a classical school preparing for the universities.
**Gynocard-insäure,** *f.* gynocardinic acid. **-säure,** *f.* gynocardic acid (chaulmoogric acid).
**Gyps, Gyps-.** see Gips, Gips-.

# H

**h.**, *abbrev.* (hochschmelzend) high-melting; (heiss) hot; (hoch) high, great; (heilig) holy, sacred.

**H.**, *abbrev.* (Härte) hardness; (Höhe) altitude; (Haben) credit; (Hoheit) Highness.

**Haar**, *n.* hair; filament.

**Haar-.** capillary. **-alaun**, *m.* capillary alum.

**haarartig**, *a.* hair-like, capillary.

**Haar-balg**, *m.* hair follicle. **-balgdrüse**, *f.* sebaceous gland. **-beize**, *f.* depilatory. **-bleiche**, *f.* hair bleaching. **-blutgefäss**, *n.* (*Anat.*) capillary. **-draht**, *m.* extremely thin wire, capillary wire. **-drüse**, *f.* sebaceous gland.

**haardünn**, *a.* hair-thin, capillary.

**Haar-erz**, *n.* capillary ore. **-erzeugungsmittel**, *n.* hair restorer. **-farbe**, *f.*, **-färbemittel**, **-färbungsmittel**, *n.* hair dye. **-faser**, *f.* capillary filament; hair fiber.

**haarfaserig**, *a.* filamentous; capillary.

**Haarfeder**, *f.* hairspring; (*Zoöl.*) filoplume.

**haar-fein**, *a.* fine as a hair. **-förmig**, *a.* capillary, hair-shaped.

**Haargefäss**, *n.* capillary vessel.

**haargenau**, *a.* extremely exact or accurate.

**haarig**, *a.* hairy; pilose; (of fabrics) nappy.

**Haar-kies**, *m.* capillary pyrites, millerite. **-kraft**, *f.* capillarity. **-kupfer**, *n.* capillary copper.

**Haarlemer Öl.** (*Pharm.*) Dutch drops.

**Haarlockerungsmittel**, *n.* depilatory.

**haarlos**, *a.* hairless, bald; (of fabrics) napless.

**Haar-losmachen**, *n.* (*Leather*) unhairing. **-nadel**, *f.* hairpin. **-pinsel**, *m.* camel's-hair brush or pencil. **-riss**, *m.* hair crack, craze.

**haarrissig**, *a.* crazed. — **— werden**, craze.

**Haar-rohr**, **-röhrchen**, *n.* capillary tube. **-röhrchenkraft**, *f.* capillarity. **-röhre**, *f.* capillary tube. **-röhrenanziehung**, *f.* capillary attraction. **-sack**, *m.*, **-säckchen**, *n.* hair follicle. **-salbe**, *f.* pomade, pomatum. **-salz**, *n.* hair salt (fibrous form of alunogen, halotrichite, or epsomite).

**haarscharf**, *a.* very sharp; extremely precise or accurate.

**Haar-schärfe**, *f.* extreme precision. **-schwefel**, *m.* capillary sulfur. **-schweif**, *m.* coma (of a comet). **-seite**, *f.* hair side, grain side. **-silber**, *n.* capillary silver. **-spalte**, *f.* hair crack, fine fissure. **-sprung**, *m.* hair crack. **-stern**, *m.* comet. **-strang**, *m.* (*Bot. & Pharm.*) peucedanum; hair cord. **-vertilgungsmittel**, *n.* depilatory. **-vitriol**, *m.* capillary epsomite. **-wachs**, *n.* pomatum, pomade. **-waschmittel**, **-wasser**, *n.* hair wash. **-wurzel**, *f.* fibrous root; hair root. **-zelle**, *f.* hair cell, capillary cell.

**Habe**, *f.* property.

**haben**, *v.t.* have.

**Haben**, *n.* (*Com.*) credit; creditor.

**Haberverfahren**, *n.* Haber process.

**Habicht**, *m.* hawk.

**Habichtskraut**, *n.* hawkweed (*Hieracium*).

**Habilitationsschrift**, *f.* inaugural dissertation.

**habituell**, *a.* habitual, chronic.

**Habitus**, *m.* habit.

**Habsucht**, *f.* avidity; greed.

**hachieren**, *v.t.* hatch, shade.

**Hacke**, *f.* hoe; mattock; pick; hatchet; ax.

**hacken**, *v.t.* hack, chop; mince; hoe.

**Hacken**, *m.* heel.

**Hacker**, *m.* chopper; hacker; hoer.

**Hack-fleisch**, *m.* chopped meat, minced meat. **-früchte**, *f.pl.* hoed vegetables, esp. potatoes, turnips, and cabbage. **-kultur**, *f.* truck gardening. **-maschine**, *f.* chopper; chipper; hoer. **-messer**, *n.* chopping knife, chopper. **-salz**, *n.* salt for minced meat. **-schnitzel**, *n.pl.* (*Lumber*) hogged chips.

**Häcksel**, *m.* & *n.* chopped straw.

**Hackspan**, *m.* chip.

**Hader**, *m.* rag; dispute.

**haderig**, *a.* (of iron) short, (also) lacking weldability.

**Hadern-brei**, *m.* (*Paper*) rag pulp. **-halbstoff**, *m.* (*Paper*) rag half stuff, rag pulp. **-kocher**, *m.* (*Paper*) rag boiler. **-lade**, *f.* rag chest. **-papier**, *n.* rag paper. **-schneider**, *m.* rag chopper, rag cutter. **-surrogat**, *n.* (*Paper*) rag substitute.

**hadrig**, *a.* = haderig.

**Hafen**, *m.* pot; harbor, port. **-ofen**, *m.* (*Glass*) pot furnace.

**Hafer**, *m.* oats. **-flocken**, *f.pl.* rolled oats. **-malz**, *n.* oat malt. **-mehl**, *n.* oatmeal. **-schleim**, *m.* oat gruel. **-stärke**, *f.* oat starch. **-wurz**, **-wurzel**, *f.* salsify.

**Hafner**, *m.* potter. **-erz**, *n.* potter's ore (fine galena).

**Haft**, *m.* hold; adhesiveness, tenacity; fastener (hook, clasp, etc.); keeping, custody.

**-haft.** partaking of the nature of, -ish, -ous, -ose, -y, -ly, -ful; as, *schmerzhaft*, painful, grievous.

**haftbar,** *a.* liable, responsible.
**Haftdruck,** *m.* solution pressure; adhesion pressure.
**haften,** *v.i.* adhere, cling, stick; be liable.
**Haften,** *n.* adhering, adhesion, etc. (see haften). **-bleiben,** *n.* adherence, adhesion.
**Haft-fähigkeit,** *f.* adhesiveness, adhesion; cohesiveness, cohesion. **-festigkeit,** *f.* adhesiveness; cohesiveness; tenacity; firmness of attachment. **-fläche,** *f.* surface of adhesion. **-heit,** *f.* = Haftigkeit.
**Haftigkeit,** *f.* adhesiveness, adhesion; cohesiveness, cohesion.
**Haft-intensität,** *f.* intensity of adhesion or cohesion; solution pressure; affinity. **-kraft,** *f.* adhesive or cohesive force or power. **-mittel,** *n.* adhesive. **-pflicht,** *f.* liability. **-reibung,** *f.* static (or adhesive) friction. **-sitz,** *m.* (*Mach.*) tight fit or force fit. **-spannung,** *f.* adhesive or cohesive stress.
**Haftung,** *f.* adhesion; cohesion; (sometimes) adsorption; liability.
**Haftvermögen,** *n.* adhesive or cohesive power.
**Hag,** *m.* hedge; clamp, pile (of tiles or bricks); bush; enclosure; grove; meadow.
**Hage-buche,** *f.* hornbeam. **-butte,** *f.* hip (rosebush pseudocarp). **-dorn,** *m.* hawthorn.
**Hagel,** *m.* hail; small shot.
**hageln,** *v.i.* hail.
**hager,** *a.* haggard, thin; (of soils) lean, unproductive.
**Hahn,** *m.* cock, stopcock; tap, faucet, spigot; cock, rooster.
**Hahnen-fett,** *n.* stopcock grease. **-fuss,** *m.* *lit.*, cock's foot; (*Ceram.*) cockspur; (*Bot.*) crowfoot, ranunculus.
**Hahn-hülse,** *f.* (stop)cock shell or barrel. **-kegel,** *m.*, **-küken, -kücken,** *n.* (stop)cock plug or stopper. **-messer,** *m.* flowmeter. **-schlüssel,** *m.* cock wrench, cock spanner. **-sitz,** *m.* (stop)cock seating or seat. **-stopfen,** *n.*, **-stöpsel,** *m.* (stop)cock stopper or plug. **-trichter,** *m.* funnel with stopcock.
**Hai, Haifisch,** *m.* shark.
**Haifisch-leder,** *n.* shark leather. **-tran,** *m.* shark-liver oil.
**Hain,** *m.* grove, wood, thicket.
**Häkchen,** *n.* little hook, hooklet, clasp, catch; apostrophe.
**Häkelgarn,** *n.* crochet thread.
**häkeln,** *v.t.* crochet; hook.
**Haken,** *m.* hook; clasp, catch; (*Puddling*) rabble.
**hakenförmig,** *a.* hooked, unciform.
**Haken-kreuz,** *n.* swastika, hooked cross. **-probe,** *f.* (*Sugar*) hook test. **-wurm,** *m.* hookworm.
**hakig,** *a.* hooked; hackly (fracture).
**halb,** *a.* & *adv.* half.
**Halb-, halb-.** half, semi-, hemi-, demi-. sub-, medium.
**Halb-acetal,** *n.* hemiacetal. **-alaun,** *m.* impure alum. **-aldehyd,** *m.* & *n.* hemialdehyde, semialdehyde. **-anthrazit,** *m.* semianthracite. **-art,** *f.* subspecies. **-ätze,** *f.* (*Calico*) half discharge.
**halb-automatisch,** *a.* semiautomatic. **-beständig,** *a.* metastable. **-beweglich,** *a.* semiportable.
**Halb-bleiche,** *f.* half bleach; cream color. **-chlorschwefel,** *m.* sulfur subchloride (monochloride).
**halb-cylindrisch,** *a.* semicylindrical. **-dauernd,** *a.* semipermanent. **-deckend,** *a.* semiopaque.
**Halb-decker, -deckflügler,** *m.pl.* (*Zoöl.*) Hemiptera. **-dunkel,** *n.* semidarkness, twilight.
**halbdurchlässig,** *a.* semipermeable.
**Halbdurchmesser,** *m.* semidiameter, radius.
**halbdurch-scheinend,** *a.* translucent. **-sichtig,** *a.* semitransparent.
**Halb-durchsichtigkeit,** *f.* semitransparency. **-edelstein,** *m.* semiprecious stone.
**halbeirund,** *a.* semioval.
**Halbelement,** *n.* (*Elec.*) half-cell, half-element.
**halben,** *v.t.* halve.
**halber, halben,** *prep.* (following its object). in behalf of, on account of.
**Halb-erzeugnis, -fabrikat,** *n.* intermediate product, semimanufacture. **-fertigwaren,** *f.pl.* semifinished goods.
**halb-fest,** *a.* semisolid; semifixed; semipermanent. **-fett,** *a.* (*Coal*) semibituminous; (of oil varnish) medium. **-flächig,** *a.* (*Cryst.*) hemihedral.
**Halb-flächner,** *m.* hemihedron. **-flügler,** *m.pl.* (*Zoöl.*) Hemiptera.
**halbflüssig,** *a.* semiliquid, semifluid.
**Halbfranzband,** *m.* half-calf binding; volume bound in half calf.
**halb-gefüllt,** *a.* half-filled, half-full. **-geleimt,** *p.a.* half-sized. **-gesättigt,** *a.* half-saturated. **-gesäuert,** *a.* semi-acidified. **-geschmolzen,** *a.* half-melted, semifused.
**Halb-gold,** *n.* imitation gold (as similor). **-gut,** *n.* (*Metal.*) tin containing much lead.
**halbhart,** *a.* half-hard, semihard, medium.
**Halb-harz,** *n.* crude resin; resinoid. **-heit,** *f.* imperfection; halfway state; indecision. **-holländer,** *m.* (*Paper*) washing engine.
**halbieren,** *v.t.* halve; bisect; mottle.
**Halbinsel,** *f.* peninsula.
**halb-jährlich,** *a.* semiannual. **-klassisch,** *a.* semiclassical.
**Halb-kochen,** *n.* partial boiling, parboiling. **-koks,** *m.* semicoke. **-kokung,** *f.* semicoking, partial carbonization. **-kolloid,** *n.* semicolloid.
**halbkonvergent,** *a.* semiconvergent.

**Halbkreis,** *m.* semicircle.
**halbkreis-förmig, -rund,** *a.* semicircular.
**halbkristallisiert,** *a.* semicrystalline.
**Halbkugel,** *f.* hemisphere.
**halb-kugelig,** *a.* hemispherical. **-lasierend,** *a.* (of colors) semitransparent.
**Halb-lederband,** *m.* half-leather binding (or a volume so bound). **-leinen,** *n.*, **-leinwand,** *f.* half-linen; half-cloth (binding). **-leiter,** *m.* (*Elec.*) semiconductor. **-literkolben,** *m.* half-liter flask. **-mahlen,** *n.* breaking in.
**halbmatt,** *a.* half-mat, semimat, slightly dull.
**Halb-mattglanz,** *m.* semimat luster or glaze. **-mattglasur,** *f.* (*Ceram.*) semimat glaze. **-messer,** *m.* radius. **-metall,** *n.* semimetal. **-metallglanz,** *m.* submetallic luster.
**halbmetallisch,** *a.* semimetallic.
**Halbmikro-.** semimicro-.
**halbmonatlich,** *a.* semimonthly.
**Halbmond,** *m.* half-moon, crescent.
**halbmondförmig,** *a.* crescent-shaped, lunate.
**Halbnitril,** *n.* seminitrile.
**halbnormal,** *a.* half-normal, seminormal.
**Halb-öl,** *n.* (*Paint*) half-oil, thinned oil. **-opal,** *m.* semiopal. **-orthooxalsäure,** *f.* semiorthoöxalic acid.
**halbpolar,** *a.* semipolar.
**Halb-porzellan,** *n.* semiporcelain. **-prisma,** *n.* (*Cryst.*) hemiprism.
**halbracemisch,** *a.* semiracemic.
**Halb-reduktion,** *f.* semireduction, partial reduction. **-reserve,** *f.* (*Calico*) half-resist.
**halb-rund,** *a.* half-round, semicircular, semicylindrical, hemispherical. **-sauer,** *a.* semiacid.
**Halb-schatten,** *m.* half-shade, half-shadow; (*Astron.*) penumbra. **-schwefeleisen,** *n.* iron hemisulfide (supposedly $Fe_2S$). **-schwefelkupfer,** *n.* cuprous sulfide, copper(I) sulfide. **-seide,** *f.* half-silk. **-seite,** *f.* half-page.
**halb-seitig,** *a.* relating to one side or half, unilateral; half-page. **-selbsttätig,** *a.* semiautomatic. **-sicher,** *a.* metastable. **-spezifisch,** *a.* semispecific.
**Halbstahl,** *m.* semisteel.
**halbstarr,** *a.* semirigid.
**Halbstoff,** *m.* (*Paper*) half stuff. **-erzeugung,** *f.* half-stuff production. **-holländer,** *m.* breaker. **-werk,** *n.* half-stuff mill.
**halb-symmetrisch,** *a.* hemisymmetric(al). **-teigig,** *a.* semiplastic; half-pasty. **-tief,** *a.* of half the depth, shallow.
**Halbton-.** (*Photog.*) half-tone.
**halb-tragbar,** *a.* semiportable. **-trocken,** *a.* half-dry, semidry. **-trocknend,** *a.* semidrying.
**Halb-verkokung,** *f.* semicoking. **-vitriolblei,** *n.* lanarkite ($Pb_2SO_5$).
**halbwalzig,** *a.* hemicylindrical.
**Halbwassergas,** *n.* semiwater gas.
**halb-wegs, -wege,** *adv.* halfway, tolerably. **-weich,** *a.* half-soft, partly soft.
**Halb-weiss,** *n.* (*Textiles*) half-bleach. **-wertdruck,** *m.* half-value pressure. **-wertsbreite,** *f.* width at half of maximum intensity (of a spectral line or band). **-wertzeit,** *f.* half-life period. **-wolle,** *f.* half-wool, union. **-wollfärberei,** *f.* union dyeing. **-wüste,** *f.* semidesert.
**halbzahlig,** *a.* half-integral.
**Halb-zeit,** *f.* half-life period. **-zeitkonstante,** *f.* half-life constant. **-zellstoff,** *n.* hemicellulose; (*Paper*) half stuff. **-zeug,** *n.* semifinished or semifabricated product; (*Paper*) half-stuff. **-zinn,** *n.* = Halbgut. **-zirkel,** *m.* semicircle.
**Halde,** *f.* heap (of refuse), dump; hillock; slope.
**Halden-erz,** *n.* waste-heap ore. **-koks,** *m.* stock coke. **-schlacke,** *f.* discarded slag.
**half,** *pret.* (of helfen) helped.
**Halfa,** *f.* esparto.
**Hälfte,** *f.* half; (*Leather*) side.
**hälften,** *v.t.* halve; bisect.
**Hälftflächner,** *m.* (*Cryst.*) hemihedron.
**Hall,** *m.* sound, peal; resonance.
**Halle,** *f.* hall; porch; hangar.
**hallen,** *v.i.* sound, resound, reverberate.
**Halm,** *m.* stalk, culm, haulm; straw; fuze. **-früchte,** *f.pl.* cereals.
**Halo-bildung,** *f.* halo formation, halation. **-chemie,** *f.* chemistry of salts, halochemistry.
**halochemisch,** *a.* halochemical.
**Halochromie,** *f.* halochromism, halochromy.
**Halogen-.** halogen, halo- (as in *Halogenbenzoesäure*, *Halogenpyridin*, etc.), halide of (as in *Halogensilber*, silver halide). **-alkyl,** *n.* alkyl halide. **-aryl,** *n.* aryl halide.
**Halogenid,** *n.* halide.
**halogenierbar,** *a.* capable of being halogenated.
**halogenieren,** *v.t.* halogenate, halogenize.
**Halogenierung,** *f.* halogenation.
**Halogen-kohlenstoff,** *m.* carbon halide. **-metall,** *n.* metallic halide. **-quecksilber,** *n.* mercury halide. **-säure,** *f.* halogen acid. **-schwefel,** *m.* sulfur halide. **-silber,** *n.* silver halide.
**halogensubstituiert,** *p.a.* halogen-substituted or, better, halo- (as *halogensubstituierte Chinone*, haloquinones).
**Halogen-überträger,** *m.* halogen carrier. **-ür,** *n.* (ous) halide. *Cf.* Chlorür. **-verbindung,** *f.* halogen compound.
**Halogenwasserstoff,** *m.* hydrogen halide. **-säure,** *f.* halogen hydracid, hydrohalic acid (general name for hydrochloric acid, hydrobromic acid, etc.). **-verbindung,** *f.* hydrogen halide.

**Haloid, -salz,** *n.* halide, haloid, haloid salt. **-wasserstoff,** *m.* hydrogen halide.

**Hals,** *m.* neck; throat; stem (of a thermometer, etc.).

**Hals-.** (*Anat.*) cervical. **-band,** *n.* neck ribbon; necklace; collar. **-bein,** *n.* collar bone. **-blutader,** *f.* jugular vein. **-bräune,** *f.* throat affection (applied to various diseases, as diphtheria, croup, etc.). **-drüse,** *f.* cervical gland. **-mandel,** *f.* tonsil. **-röhre,** *f.* trachea.

**Halt,** *m.* hold, holding; halt, stop; firmness; yield. — **— machen,** stop, halt.

**hält,** *pr. 3 sing.* (of halten) holds, etc.

**haltbar,** *a.* stable; lasting, durable; fast, permanent (colors).

**haltbaren,** *v.t.* preserve, conserve.

**Haltbar-keit,** *f.* stability, etc. (see haltbar); keeping quality; endurance. **-machen,** *n.*, **-machung,** *f.* making stable, etc. (see haltbar); stabilizing; preserving, conserving.

**Haltbarung,** *f.* preservation, conservation.

**Haltekraft,** *f.* holding or keeping power; cohesion.

**halten,** *v.t.* hold; keep; consider; take (a journal); give (a talk). — *v.r.* hold on, remain; keep, last. — *v.i.* hold, keep, last; stop, halt.

**Haltepunkt,** *m.* halting point, arrest point; critical point; (in a curve) break.

**Halter,** *m.* holder; support; clamp; handle; hold; keeper.

**Hälter,** *m.* holder; reservoir.

**Halterarm,** *m.* supporting arm, support.

**Halterung,** *f.* holder, support, mounting.

**Haltezeit,** *f.* halt, pause.

**haltig, hältig,** *a.* rich (ore); (as a suffix) containing, holding, yielding, bearing, -ferous (as *zinnhaltig,* containing tin, stanniferous).

**haltlos,** *a.* unstable, unsteady, infirm, loose; (of paper) tender.

**Haltung,** *f.* holding, etc. (see halten); attitude, bearing, behavior, state, position; harmony; principle.

**Haltware,** *f.* preserved food (cf. Konserve); (*Pharm.*) conserve, electuary.

**Häm-.** hem-, haem-. **-alaun,** *m.* (*Micros.*) hemalum (a hematoxylin-alum stain).

**Hämatin,** *n.* hematin, haematin.

**Hämatit,** *m.* hematite. **-eisen,** *n.* hematite iron. **-erz,** *n.* hematite ore. **-roheisen,** *n.* hematite pig iron.

**Hamburgerweiss,** *n.* Hamburg white.

**Hämin,** *n.* hemin, haemin.

**Hammatsch.** (*Brewing*) sodium bicarbonate.

**Hammel,** *m.* wether, (male) sheep; mutton. **-fett,** *n.* mutton fat. **-fleisch,** *n.* mutton, **-klauenöl,** *n.* sheep's-foot oil. **-talg,** *m.* mutton tallow.

**hämmerbar,** *a.* malleable; forgeable.

**Hämmerbarkeit,** *f.* malleability; forgeability.

**Hammereisen,** *n.* wrought iron.

**hammergar,** *a.* (*Copper*) tough-pitch, tough.

**hämmern,** *v.t.* hammer, forge.

**Hammer-schlacke,** *f.* hammer scale, forge scale. **-schlag,** *m.* hammer scale, forge scale; hammer blow. **-werk,** *n.* hammer mill.

**Hämo-, hämo-.** hemo-, haemo-.

**Hämo-chininsäure,** *f.* hemoquinic acid. **-globinurie,** *f.* hemoglobinuria. **-lyse,** *f.* hemolysis, haemolysis.

**hämolytisch,** *a.* hemolytic, haemolytic.

**Hämopyrrol,** *n.* hemopyrrole.

**hämorrhagisch,** *a.* hemorrhagic.

**Hand-arbeit,** *f.* hand work; manual labor; handiwork. **-aufgabe,** *f.* hand feed(ing). **-ausgabe,** *f.* pocket edition. **-betrieb,** *m.* hand drive or operation. **-buch,** *n.* manual, handbook, compendium. **-einstellung,** *f.* hand adjustment.

**Handel,** *m.* commerce, trade; traffic; business, affair; quarrel.

**handeln,** *v.i.* act; proceed; trade, deal. — **— um,** treat, be about. — **es handelt sich um . . . ,** it is a matter of . . . , the question is as to . . .

**Handels-.** commercial. **-amt,** *n.* board of trade. **-analyse,** *f.* commercial analysis. **-artikel,** *m.* article of commerce, commodity. **-benzol,** *n.* commercial benzene, benzol. **-betrieb,** *m.* traffic. **-bezeichnung,** *f.* trade name; trademark. **-blatt,** *n.* trade journal. **-chemiker,** *m.* commercial chemist, (commercial) analytical chemist. **-dünger,** *m.* commercial fertilizer. **-eigenschaft,** *f.* commercial value. **-eisen,** *n.* merchant iron.

**handelsgängig,** *a.* of commerce, commercial.

**Handels-gesellschaft,** *f.* (trading) company. **-gewicht,** *n.* commercial weight; specif., avoirdupois weight. **-harz,** *n.* commercial rosin (or resin). **-harzleim,** *m.* commercial rosin size. **-kautschuk,** *m.* commercial rubber. **-kupfer,** *n.* commercial copper, merchant copper. **-laboratorium,** *n.* commercial laboratory. **-leute,** *pl.* tradespeople, tradesmen. **-mann,** *m.* tradesman. **-marke,** *f.* trade-mark, commercial brand. **-name,** *m.* trade name. **-öl,** *n.* commercial oil. **-oxyd,** *n.* commercial oxide; specif., antimony trioxide, antimony(III) oxide. **-silber,** *n.* commercial silver (containing impurities). **-sorte,** *f.* commercial form or variety, market grade.

**handelsüblich,** *a.* customary in commerce or trade, commercial.

**Handels-verein,** *m.* commercial association, commercial union. **-ware,** *f.* commercial article, article of commerce, merchandise. **-wert,** *m.* commercial value. **-zeichen,** *n.* trade-mark. **-zink,** *n.* commercial zinc, spelter. **-zweck,** *m.* commercial purpose. **-zweig,** *m.* branch of commerce or trade.

**Hand-fertigkeit,** *f.* manual skill or dexterity. **-feuerung,** *f.* hand firing. **-gebläse,** *n.* hand blowpipe. **-gebrauch,** *m.* daily use; manual use. **-gelenk,** *n.* wrist, wrist joint. **-granate,** *f.* hand grenade.

**handgreiflich,** *a.* obvious, palpable, downright.

**Hand-griff,** *m.* handle; grasp; hand hold; knack, trick; manipulation. **-habe,** *f.* handle; hold, grip; means.

**handhaben,** *v.t.* handle; manipulate; operate.

**Handhabung,** *f.* handling; manipulation; operation.

**handhabungssicher,** *a.* safe for handling.

**Handhebel,** *m.* hand lever.

**handheiss,** *a.* of the temperature of the hand, lukewarm.

**Händler,** *m.* dealer, retailer.

**Handlexikon,** *n.* abridged lexicon.

**handlich,** *a.* handy, manageable.

**Handlichkeit,** *f.* handiness.

**Handlung,** *f.* trade, commerce; (commercial) establishment; action; plot.

**Handlungsweise,** *f.* way of dealing, procedure.

**Hand-lupe,** *f.* hand lens, magnifying glass. **-mulde,** *f.* hand basin, hand bowl. **-muster,** *n.* hand specimen, small sample. **-probe,** *f.* hand (or small) test or sample.

**handpuddeln,** *v.t.* puddle by hand.

**Hand-regel,** *f.* rough rule. **-reibe,** *f.* hand grater. **-scheidung,** *f.* separation (or sorting) by hand. **-schmierung,** *f.* hand lubrication. **-schrift,** *f.* handwriting; manuscript. **-schuh,** *m.* glove; (**ohne Finger**) mitten. **-strich,** *m.* (*Ceram.*) hand molding. **-stück,** *n.* specimen (of ore or the like, of the size conveniently held in the hand), hand specimen. **-tuch,** *n.* towel. **-verkauf,** *m.* retail. **-versuch,** *m.* small-scale experiment or test. **-voll,** *f.* handful. **-wa(a)ge,** *f.* hand balance.

**handwarm,** *a.* warm to the touch; lukewarm, tepid.

**Hand-wärme,** *f.* heat (or warmth) of the hand. **-werfer,** *m.* (*Mil.*) mortar. **-werk,** *n.* handicraft, trade; guild. **-werker,** *m.* mechanic, artisan, workman.

**handwerksmässig,** *a.* workman-like; mechanical.

**Hand-werkszeug,** *n.* tools, instruments. **-wörterbuch,** *n.* abridged dictionary. **-wurzel,** *f.* wrist; carpus; wrist joint.

**Hanf,** *m.* hemp.

**hanfartig,** *a.* hemp-like, hempen.

**Hanf-dichtung,** *f.* hemp packing. **-faden,** *m.* hemp fiber; hemp twine. **-korn,** *n.* hempseed.

**hanfkorngross,** *a.* of the size of hempseed.

**Hanf-nessel,** *f.*, **-nesselkraut,** *n.* hemp nettle (*Galeopsis*). **-öl,** *n.* hemp (seed) oil. **-papier,** *n.* hemp paper. **-samen,** *n.*, **-saat,** *f.* hempseed. **-säure,** *f.* linoleic acid. **-seil,** *n.* hemp rope, hemp cord.

**Hang,** *m.* slope, incline, declivity; inclination, propensity, bent.

**Hänge,** *f.* place where things are hung to dry, drying house, loft; (*Dyeing*) ager.

**Hänge-.** hanging, suspension, suspended, pendent, overhead. **-bahn,** *f.* suspension (or overhead) track or cable way. **-farbe,** *f.* (*Leather*) suspender.

**hängen, hangen,** *v.i.* hang; cling, adhere; (in a furnace) scaffold. — **hängend, hangend,** *p.a.* hanging, suspended, pendent; drooping.

**hängen,** *v.i.* hang, suspend; attach.

**Hängenbleiben,** *n.* (in a furnace) scaffolding.

**Hänge-rahmen,** *m.* suspension frame. **-tropfen,** *m.* hanging drop.

**Hansagelb,** *n.* Hansa yellow.

**Hansel,** *m.* (*Brewing*) return wort.

**Hantel,** *f.* dumbbell.

**hantelförmig,** *a.* dumbbell-shaped.

**Hantelmodell,** *n.* dumbbell model.

**hanthaben,** *v.t.* = hantieren, *v.t.*

**hantieren,** *v.t.* work, handle, manipulate, operate; manage. — *v.i.* be busy, be occupied.

**Hantierung,** *f.* manipulation, etc. (see hantieren); occupation.

**Härchen,** *n.* little hair; cilium.

**Harfe,** *f.* harp.

**Häring,** *m.* herring.

**Harke,** *f.* rake.

**harken,** *v.t.* rake.

**harmlos,** *a.* unharmed; harmless.

**harmonieren,** *v.i.* harmonize.

**harmonisch,** *a.* harmonic; harmonious.

**Harn,** *m.* urine. **-absatz,** *m.* urinary sediment. **-absonderung,** *f.* urinary secretion.

**harnabtreibend,** *a.* diuretic.

**Harn-analyse,** *f.* urine analysis, urinalysis. **-apparat,** *m.* urinary apparatus.

**harnartig,** *a.* urinous, urinose.

**Harn-ausscheidung,** *f.* excretion of urine. **-bad,** *n.* urine bath. **-benzoesäure,** *f.* hippuric acid. **-bildung,** *f.* formation of urine. **-blase,** *f.* (urinary) bladder.

**Harnblasen-.** (*Anat.*) vesical, vesico-. **-gang,** *m.* (*Anat.*) urethra.

**Harnblau,** *n.* (*Biochem.*) indican.

**harnen,** *v.i.* urinate.

**harnfähig,** *a.* (*Biochem.*) capable of passage into the urine.

**Harn-farbstoff,** *m.* urinary pigment. **-gärung,** *f.* fermentation of urine. **-geist,** *m.* ammonium chloride (old name).

**harnig,** *a.* uric; urinous, urinose.

**Harnisch,** *m.* (*Geol.*) slickenside; harness.

**Harn-kolloid,** *n.* urinary colloid. **-kraut,** *n.* a diuretic plant, specif. (1) dyer's rocket (*Reseda luteola*), (2) *Herniaria* species. **-lehre,** *f.* urinology. **-leiter,** *m.* ureter; catheter. **-messer,** *m.* urinometer. **-mittel,** *n.* diuretic. **-niederschlag,** *m.* urinary deposit. **-oxyd,** *n.* xanthic oxide (xanthine). **-phosphor** *m.* urinary phosphorus. **-probe,** *f.* test for urine; sample of urine. **-prüfung,** *f.* testing of urine, urine analysis. **-röhre,** *f.* urethra.

**Harnröhren-.** urethral, urethro-.

**Harn-rosa,** *f.* urorosein. **-ruhr,** *f.* diabetes. **-salz,** *n.* microcosmic salt; (any) salt found in urine. **-sand,** *m.* (urinary) gravel. **-satz,** *m.* urinary deposit.

**harnsauer,** *a.* of or combined with uric acid, urate of.

**Harn-säure,** *f.* uric acid. **-säurestein,** *m.* uric acid calculus. **-stein,** *m.* urinary calculus. **-stoff,** *m.* urea. **-stoffgärung,** *f.* fermentation of urea. **-stoffstickstoff,** *m.* urea nitrogen. **-stoffvergiftung,** *f.* urea poisoning, uremia.

**harntreibend,** *p.a.* diuretic.

**Harn-untersuchung,** *f.* investigation of urine, urinalysis. **-wa(a)ge,** *f.* urinometer. **weg,** *m.* urinary passage. **-zucker,** *m.* sugar in urine.

**harren,** *v.i.* wait, stay.

**hart,** *a.* hard; hardy; (*Mining*) refractory. — *adv.* hardly, hard. — **— an,** close by.

**härtbar,** *a.* hardenable; temperable.

**Härtbarkeit,** *f.* hardenability; temperability.

**Hart-blei,** *n.* hard lead (applied to crude lead hardened by antimony and other impurities, and to an alloy of lead and antimony). **-borst,** *m.*, **-borste,** *f.* (*Steel*) crack formed during hardening. **-brandstein,** *m.* hard-burned brick. **-braunstein,** *m.* braunite.

**hartbrennen,** *v.t.* burn hard, hard-burn.

**Härte,** *f.* hardness; hardening; tempering; callosity; hardiness. **-bad,** *n.* hardening bath; (*Metal.*) tempering bath.

**härtebeständig,** *a.* (*Textiles*) unaffected by hard water.

**Härte-bestimmung,** *f.* determination of hardness. **-bildner,** *m.* (*Water*) a salt causing hardness; (*Metal.*) hardening constituent. **-flüssigkeit,** *f.* tempering liquid. **-grad,** *m.* degree of hardness; temper (of steel).

**Harteisen,** *n.* hard iron.

**Härte-messer,** *m.* hardness gage. **-messung,** *f.* measurement of hardness. **-mittel,** *n.* hardening or tempering agent.

**härten,** *v.t.* harden; temper (steel). — *v.i.* & *r.* harden; congeal.

**Härte-ofen,** *m.* tempering furnace, hardening furnace. **-öl,** *n.* (*Steel*) hardening oil. **-probe,** *f.* hardness test. **-prüfer,** *m.* hardness tester. **-prüfung,** *f.* hardness test(ing). **-pulver,** *n.* (*Metal.*) cementing powder.

**Härter,** *m.* hardener.

**Härte-riss,** *m.* = Hartborst. **-salz,** *n.* salt causing hardness; (*Metal.*) carburizing salt. **-skala,** *f.* scale of hardness. **-stufe,** *f.* (*Min.*) (degree of) hardness. **-temperatur,** *f.* hardening temperature. **-tiefe,** *f.* depth of hardening. **-trog,** *m.* hardening trough. **-verfahren,** *n.* hardening (or tempering) process. **-wasser,** *n.* hardening water, tempering water. **-wert,** *m.* hardness value. **-zahl,** *f.* hardness number.

**Hart-faser,** *f.* hard fiber. **-fett,** *n.* hard fat, solid fat. **-feuerporzellan,** *n.* hard porcelain. **-filter,** *m.* hard filter, hardened filter. **-floss,** *n.* spiegeleisen. **-flügler,** *m.pl.* Coleoptera.

**hart-gebrannt,** *a.* hard-burned. **-gefroren,** *a.* hard-frozen. **-gelötet,** *p.p.* (of hartlöten) hard-soldered, brazed. **-gesotten,** *a.* hard-boiled.

**Hartgewebe,** *n.* indurated fabric.

**hartgiessen,** *v.t.* chill-cast.

**Hart-glas,** *n.* hard glass; hardened glass. **-glasbecher,** *m.* hard-glass beaker. **-gummi,** *n.* hard rubber, vulcanite, ebonite. **-guss,** *m.* chill casting; chilled casting. **-harz,** *n.* hard resin, solid resin. **-heu,** *n.* St.-John's-wort. **-holz,** *n.* hard wood, hardwood; laminated wood. **-kautschuk,** *m.* & *n.* hard rubber. **-kies,** *m.*, **-kobalterz,** *n.*, **-kobaltkies,** *m.* skutterudite. **-kupfer,** *n.* hard copper.

**hartleibig,** *a.* costive.

**Härtling,** *m.* (*Metal.*) hard slag, also salamander.

**Hartlot,** *n.* hard solder.

**hartlöten,** *v.t.* hard-solder, braze.

**Hart-machen,** *n.* hardening. **-manganerz,** *n.* psilomelane; braunite. **-metall,** *n.* hard metal; specif., (1) metal carbide, hard carbide, (2) hard pewter.

**hartnäckig,** *a.* obstinate, persistent.

**Hart-papier,** *n.* hard paper, specif.: (1) bank paper, (2) kraft paper, (3) a plastic-impregnated paper. **-pappe,** *f.* fiberboard. **-pech,** *n.* hard pitch, dry pitch. **-porzellan,** *n.* hard porcelain. **-riegel,** *m.* privet (*Ligustrum vulgare*); cornel; dogwood. **-salz,** *n.* hard salt (an impure sylvite).

**hartschalig,** *a.* hard-shelled.

**Hart-spat,** *m.* andalusite. **-spiritus,** *m.* solid alcohol. **-stahl,** *m.* hard steel. **-steingut,** *n.* (*Ceram.*) hard white ware, feldspathic ware. **-trockenöl,** *n.* hard-drying oil.

**Härtung,** *f.* hardening; (of steel) tempering.

**härtungsfähig,** *a.* hardenable; temperable.

**Härtungs-kohle,** *f.* hardening carbon. **-mittel,** *n.* hardening agent. **-verfahren,** *n.* hardening process.

**Hart-verchromung,** *f.* hard chromium plating.

**-vernickelung,** *f.* hard nickel plating. **-wachs,** *n.* hard wax. **-waren,** *f.pl.* hardware. **-weizen,** *m.* hard wheat, durum wheat. **-werden,** *n.* hardening. **-zerkleinerung,** *f.* crushing of hard material. **-zinn,** *n.* (hard) pewter.

**Harz,** *n.* resin; rosin.

**harz-ähnlich, -artig,** *a.* resin-like, resinous, rosiny, resinoid.

**Harz-alkohol,** *m.* resin alcohol. **-austauscher,** *m.* ion-exchange resin. **-baum,** *m.* pitch tree (applied to various conifers). **-bildung,** *f.* resin (or rosin) formation, (of gasoline) gumming. **-brei,** *m.* a viscous material trapped in the pores of a synthetic plastic, resin magma. **-cerat,** *n.* (*Pharm.*) rosin cerate. **-elektrizität,** *f.* resinous (negative) electricity.

**harzen,** *v.i.* be resinous or sticky; gather resin. — *v.t.* resin; extract resin from.

**Harz-essenz,** *f.* rosin spirit. **-ester,** *m.* resin ester; rosin ester. **-esterlack,** *m.* gum lacquer. **-fett,** *n.* rosin grease. **-fichte,** *f.* pitch pine. **-firnis,** *m.* resin varnish. **-fleck,** *m.* (*Paper*) resin (or rosin) spot. **-fluss,** *m.* resinous exudation, oleoresin.

**harz-flüssig,** *a.* gummy, viscous. **-förmig,** *a.* resiniform, resinous. **-frei,** *a.* free from resin (or rosin), nonresinous.

**Harz-galle,** *f.* resin deposit (in wood), resin gall. **-gang,** *m.* (*Bot.*) resin duct. **-gas,** *n.* resin gas.

**harz-gebend,** *p.a.* yielding resin, resiniferous. **-gebunden,** *a.* resin-bonded.

**Harz-gehalt,** *m.* resin (or rosin) content. **-geist,** *m.* rosin spirit, pinolin.

**harzgeleimt,** *a.* (*Paper*) rosin-sized.

**Harz-geruch,** *m.* resinous odor. **-glanz,** *m.* resinous luster.

**harzhaltig,** *a.* containing resin, resiniferous.

**Harzholz,** *n.* resinous wood.

**harzig, harzicht,** *a.* resinous, resiny. — **— machen,** resinify.

**Harz-karbollösung,** *f.* (*Paper*) solution of rosin in carbolic acid. **-kernseife,** *f.* rosin curd soap, rosin soap. **-kiefer,** *f.* pitch pine. **-kitt,** *m.* resinous cement. **-kocher,** *m.* (*Paper*) rosin boiler. **-kohle,** *f.* bituminous coal. **-körper,** *m.* resin(ous) substance. **-lack,** *m.* resin lake; resin varnish. **-leim,** *m.* (*Paper*) rosin size. **-leimung,** *f.* (*Paper*) sizing with rosin. **-leimverseifung,** *f.* rosin-size "cutting."

**harzliefernd,** *a.* resiniferous.

**Harz-masse,** *f.* resinous mass or composition; (*Paper*) rosin size. **-milch,** *f.* a suspension of resin or rosin. **-naphta,** *f.* resin oil. **-öl,** *n.* resin oil; rosin oil. **-pech,** *n.* resinous pitch, rosin.

**harzreich,** *a.* rich in resin or rosin.

**Harz-reserve,** *f.* (*Calico*) resin resist. **-röhre,** *f.* resin duct. **-saft,** *m.* resinous juice. **-salbe,** *f.* (*Pharm.*) rosin cerate. **-salz,** *n.* resinate.

**harzsauer,** *a.* of or combined with a resinic acid, resinate of.

**Harz-säure,** *f.* resin acid, resinic acid. **-seife,** *f.* resin soap; rosin soap. **-sikkativ,** *n.* rosin drier. **-spiritus,** *m.* rosin spirit. **-spur,** *f.* trace of resin or rosin. **-stippe,** *f.* (*Paper*) rosin speck, rosin spot. **-stoff,** *m.* resinous substance. **-talgseife,** *f.* tallow-rosin soap, yellow household soap. **-tanne,** *f.* pitch fir. **-teer,** *m.* resinous tar. **-wasser,** *n.* resin water. **-zahl,** *f.* resin number; rosin number. **-zement,** *m.* resinous cement.

**haschen,** *v.t. & i.* catch, seize.

**haschieren,** *v.t.* hatch; hash, mince.

**Haschisch,** *n.* hashish.

**Hase,** *m.* hare; coward.

**Hasel,** *f.* hazel; dace. **-nuss,** *f.* hazelnut.

**haselnussbraun,** *a.* hazel(nut) brown, hazel.

**Haselwurz,** *f.* asarum, asarabacca.

**Hasen-klee,** *m.* rabbit-foot clover, hare's-foot trefoil. **-kohl,** *m.* wood sorrel. **-öhrlein,** *n.* hare's-ear (*Bupleurum*). **-schwanz,** *m.* hare's-tail grass.

**Haspe, Häspe,** *f.* hasp, staple; clamp; cramp.

**Haspel,** *m.* reel; spool; paddle wheel; windlass. **-äscher,** *m.* (*Leather*) paddle lime **-farbe,** *f.* (*Leather*) paddle liquor.

**haspeln,** *v.t.* reel, wind.

**Hass,** *m.* hate, hatred.

**hassen,** *v.t.* hate.

**Hast,** *f.* haste, hurry.

**hastig,** *a.* hasty.

**hat,** *pr. 3 sing.* (of haben) has.

**hatte,** *pret.* (of haben) had.

**Hau,** *m.* cut, cutting, hewing.

**Haube,** *f.* hood, cap; (of a furnace) dome; bonnet.

**Haubenlerche,** *f.* crested lark; (*Ceram.*) cone protector.

**Haubitze,** *f.* (*Mil.*) howitzer.

**Haubitzzünder,** *m.* howitzer fuse.

**Hauch,** *m.* breath, breathing, respiration; condensed moisture; haze; tinge.

**hauchen,** *v.t. & i.* breathe.

**Haue,** *f.* hoe; mattock; pick.

**hauen,** *v.t.* hew, chop; cut; strike (with a stick or the like).

**Hauer,** *m.* hewer, cutter; pickman.

**Häufchen,** *n.* little heap; little mass, clump.

**Haufe, Haufen,** *m.* heap; pile; great amount or number, mass; (*Brewing*) couch, piece, floor, batch; agglomeration, clump, cluster.

**häufen,** *v.t.* heap; pile; accumulate, amass. — *v.r.* increase.

**Haufen-führen,** *n.* (*Brewing*) couching, flooring. **-röstung,** *f.* (*Metal.*) heap roasting.

-**verkohlung,** *f.* charcoal burning in long rectangular piles.

**häufig,** *a.* frequent; numerous; abundant. — *adv.* frequently, often; abundantly.

**Häufigkeit,** *f.* frequency; abundance.

**Häufigkeits-kurve,** *f.* frequency curve. **-verteilung,** *f.* frequency distribution.

**Häufung,** *f.* heaping, etc. (see häufen); congestion.

**Häufungspunkt,** *m.* point of accumulation.

**Haufwerk,** *n.* aggregate; run of mine, mine run.

**Hauhechel,** *f* restharrow (*Ononis*).

**Haupt,** *n.* head; chief.

**Haupt-.** principal, chief, main, primary, parent; cephalic. **-abteilung,** *f.* principal division. **-achse,** *f.* principal axis. **-agens,** *n.* principal agent. **-amt,** *n.* chief office, main office. **-anteil,** *m.* chief or principal constituent; main or principal portion. **-bedingung,** *f.* chief condition. **-bedürfnis,** *n.* chief requirement. **-bestandteil,** *m.* chief constituent. **-bindung,** *f.* principal union or bond. **-brennpunkt,** *m.* principal focus. **-brennweite,** *f.* principal focal distance (or length). **-erzeugnis,** *n.* principal product. **-farbe,** *f.* primary color; principal color. **-form,** *f.* chief or principal form; master mold. **-gärung,** *f.* principal or primary fermentation. **-gesetz,** *n.* fundamental law. **-gitter,** *n.* (*Cryst.*) parent lattice. **-kette,** *f.* principal chain. **-klasse,** *f.* principal or chief class. **-leitung,** *f.* (*Elec.*, etc.) main. **-linie,** *f.* principal line. **-mann,** *m.* captain; chieftain. **-menge,** *f.* principal amount, bulk. **-merkmal,** *n.* leading feature, main characteristic. **-nährstoff,** *m.* chief nutrient; chief food. **-nenner,** *m.* common denominator. **-ölbad,** *n.* (*Dyeing*) white steeping. **-patent,** *n.* master patent. **-pflaster,** *n.* (*Pharm.*) opium plaster. **-platz,** *m.* principal place, center, seat. **-postamt,** *n.* general post office. **-punkt,** *m.* principal point. **-quantenzahl,** *f.* principal or total quantum number. **-quelle,** *f.* chief source. **-reaktion,** *f.* principal reaction. **-redakteur,** *m.* chief editor. **-register,** *n.* general index. **-reihe,** *f.* principal series. **-rohr,** *n.* main tube or pipe, main.

**Hauptsache,** *f.* chief matter, main point. — **in der —,** mainly, chiefly.

**hauptsächlich,** *a.* chief, main, principal. — *adv.* chiefly, principally, especially.

**Haupt-satz,** *m.* fundamental principle or law; main theorem; axiom. **-schalter,** *m.* main (or master) switch. **-schlagader,** *f.* main artery; aorta. **-schluss,** *m.* (*Elec.*) main circuit. **-schlüssel,** *m.* master key. **-schnitt,** *m.* principal section. **-schwingung,** *f.* principal vibration. **-serie,** *f.* principal series. **-sicherung,** *f.* (*Elec.*) main fuse, main cutout. **-spule, -spirale,** *f.* primary coil. **-stadt,** *f.* metropolis, capital. **-strom,** *m.* (*Elec.*) primary current. **-stück,** *n.*, **-teil,** *m.* principal part, body. **-typus,** *m.* principal type. **-unterschied,** *m.* chief difference. **-ursache,** *f.* chief cause, principal reason. **-valenz,** *f.* chief valence, principal valence, primary valence. **-verwendungsgebiet,** *n.* chief field of use. **-vorkommen,** *n.* principal occurrence. **-wert,** *m.* chief value. **-wirkung,** *f.* chief action or effect. **-wissenschaft,** *f.* fundamental science. **-würze,** *f.* (*Brewing*) first wort. **-zahl,** *f.* cardinal number. **-zug,** *m.* main or principal feature.

**Haus,** *n.* house; home; family.

**Haus-.** house, home, family, domestic. **-arznei,** *f.* domestic remedy. **-besitzer,** *m.* house owner, landlord. **-brand,** *m.* domestic fuel; domestic use (of fuels).

**hausen,** *v.i.* reside; keep house; behave badly.

**Hausen,** *m.* sturgeon. **-blase,** *f.* isinglass.

**Haus-gebrauch,** *m.* home use, domestic use. **-gerät,** *n.* household furniture or utensils. **-halt,** *m.* household; housekeeping; budget. **-hälter,** *m.* housekeeper, steward; economist. **-halt(s)-farbe,** *f.* household color or dye. **-haltsseife,** *f.* household soap. **-haltung,** *f.* household; housekeeping. **-lauch, -lauf,** *m.* houseleek.

**häuslich,** *a.* domestic; economical.

**Haus-mittel,** *n.* household remedy. **-müll,** *n.* household refuse. **-schwamm,** *m.* dry rot. **-seife,** *f.* household soap, specif. common curd soap; home-made soap.

**Haustein,** *m.* ashlar.

**Haus-wanze,** *f.* bedbug. **-wäsche,** *f.* domestic wash(ing). **-wirtschaft,** *f.* housekeeping, household.

**hauswirtschaftlich,** *a.* household, housekeeping.

**Hauswurz,** *f.* houseleek.

**Haut,** *f.* skin; hide; membrane; film; pellicle; crust; bloom. — **durchsichtige —,** cornea. — **harte —,** sclerotic coat.

**Haut-.** cutaneous, membranous.

**hautätzend,** *a.* attacking the skin.

**Haut-ausschlag,** *m.* skin eruption. **-bildung,** *f.* skin (or film) formation. **-bräune,** *f.* croup

**Häutchen,** *n.* thin skin, film, pellicle, membrane.

**häuten,** *v.t.* skin. — *v.r.* cast the skin, molt.

**Haut-entgiftungsmittel,** *n.* skin decontaminant. **-entgiftungssalbe,** *f.* decontaminating ointment. **-farbe,** *f.* color of the skin. **-farbstoff,** *m.* skin pigment. **-gift,** *n.* (*Mil.*) skin poison, vesicant.

**häutig,** *a.* cutaneous, membranous; skinny.

**Haut-krankheit,** *f.* skin disease. **-krebs,** *m.* cancer of the skin, epithelioma. **-lehre,** *f.* dermatology. **-leim,** *m.* glue (or size) from hides. **-pulver,** *n.* hide powder. **-reaktion,** *f.*

skin (or cutaneous) reaction. **-reibung,** *f.* skin friction.

**hautreinigend,** *p.a.* skin-cleansing.

**Hautreiz,** *m.* skin irritant; skin irritation.

**hautreizend,** *a.* irritating to the skin.

**Haut-salbe,** *f.* sebaceous matter; skin ointment. **-substanz,** *f.* hide substance. **-talg,** *m.* sebaceous matter.

**Häutung,** *f.* skinning; shedding of the skin, desquamation, molting.

**Haut-verhinderungsmittel,** *n.* (*Paint*) anti-skinning agent. **-wirkung,** *f.* skin effect. **-wolle,** *f.* pulled wool, skin wool.

**H.D.,** *abbrev.* (Hochdruck) high pressure.

**hebärztlich,** *a.* obstetric.

**Hebe-.** lifting, raising, hoisting. **-arm,** *m.* lever. **-baum,** lever, crowbar. **-daumen,** *m.* cam, tappet. **-eisen,** *n.* crowbar. **-kraft,** *f.* lifting power.

**Hebel,** *m.* lever. **-kraft,** *f.* leverage. **-schalter,** *m.* (*Elec.*) lever switch. **-wa(a)ge,** *f.* lever scale, beam scale. **-werk,** *n.* system of levers. **-wirkung,** *f.* lever action, leverage.

**heben,** *v.t.* lift, raise, elevate; further; remove; (*Math.*) reduce. — *v.r.* rise; go; cancel.

**Hebe-pumpe,** *f.* lift pump, lifting pump. **-punkt,** *m.* fulcrum.

**Heber,** *m.* siphon; pipet(te); syringe; lifter; lever; jack; (*Anat.*) levator. **-barometer,** *m.* siphon barometer. **-haarrohr,** *n.* capillary siphon.

**hebern,** *v.t.* siphon; pipet(te).

**Heber-pumpe,** *f.* siphon pump. **-rohr,** *n.* siphon tube or pipe, siphon. **-säuremesser,** *m.* syringe hydrometer for acids. **-schreiber,** *m.* siphon recorder.

**Hebe-vorrichtung,** *f.* lifting apparatus; lever. **-werk, -zeug,** *n.* lifting apparatus, hoisting device, gin, whim, screw jack, etc.

**Hebling,** *m.* (*Mach.*) tappet.

**Hebung,** *f.* lifting, etc. (see heben).

**hecheln,** *v.t.* comb, hatchel, heckle; criticize.

**Hecht,** *m.* pike (fish).

**Heck,** *n.* stern; tail; rear.

**Hecke,** *f.* hedge; hatch, brood.

**Hede,** *f.* tow; oakum.

**Hederich,** *m.* hedge mustard, specif. *Sisymbrium officinale.*

**Heer,** *n.* army; armed forces; host.

**Heeresgerät,** *n.* army material or equipment.

**Heerstrasse,** *f.* highway; military road.

**Hefe,** *f.* yeast; (*Brewing*) barm; lees, dregs, sediment. **-apparat,** *m.* (*Brewing*) yeast propagator. **-art,** *f.* kind or variety of yeast. **-bier,** *n.* rest beer. **-brühe,** *f.* liquid yeast. **-ernte,** *f.* crop of yeast. **-form,** *f.* yeast mold, yeast press. **-gabe,** *f.* (*Brewing*) quantity of yeast for a pitching. **-geben,** *n.* (*Brewing*) adding yeast to the wort, pitching. **-gift,** *n.* yeast poison. **-gut,** *n.* leaven. **-keim,** *m.* yeast germ. **-kühler,** *m.* yeast cooler or refrigerator. **-mehl,** *n.* yeast powder.

**hefenähnlich,** *a.* yeast-like, yeasty.

**Hefe-nährmittel,** *n.* yeast food, yeast nutrient. **-nahrung,** *f.* yeast food.

**Hefenart,** *f.* variety of yeast.

**hefenartig,** *a.* yeast-like, yeasty.

**Hefenartigkeit,** *f.* yeastiness.

**Hefen-keim,** *m.* yeast germ. **-pflanze,** *f.* yeast plant. **-pilz,** *m.* = Hefepilz. **-pulver,** *n.* yeast powder; baking powder.

**hefentrüb,** *a.* yeasty, muddy (from yeast).

**Hefe-nukleinsäure,** *f.* nucleic acid of yeast. **-pilz,** *m.* yeast fungus; yeast plant. **-presssaft,** *m.* yeast press juice. **-rasse,** *f.* race, breed or type of yeast. **-reinzucht,** *f.* pure yeast culture. **-satz,** *m.* yeast sediment. **-trieb,** *m.* (*Brewing*) yeasty head. **-vermehrung,** *f.* yeast multiplication, yeast growth. **-wanne,** *f.* yeast trough. **-zelle,** *f.* yeast cell. **-zucht, -zuchtung,** *f.* yeast culture.

**hefig,** *a.* yeasty, yeast-like; dreggy.

**Hefnerkerze,** *f.* Hefner candle.

**Heft,** *n.* part, number (of a book or periodical); stitched book; booklet; handle, hilt.

**heften,** *v.t.* fasten, hook, pin; stitch, sew. — **geheftet,** *p.a.* (of printed matter) stitched but not bound (or only in paper).

**heftig,** *a.* violent, severe; vigorous, lively.

**Heftigkeit,** *f.* violence; intensity; ardor.

**Heft-klammer,** *f.* clip or staple (for papers). **-pflaster,** *n.* adhesive plaster.

**heftweise,** *adv.* in parts or numbers, serially.

**hegen,** *v.t.* enclose; cherish; entertain, feel.

**Hehl,** *n.* secrecy.

**hehlen,** *v.t.* conceal.

**hehr,** *a.* sublime, grand.

**Heide,** *f.* heath; heather. — *m.* heathen, pagan.

**heideähnlich,** *a.* (*Bot.*) ericaceous.

**Heidekorn,** *n.* buckwheat (*Fagopyrum*).

**Heidelbeere,** *f.* whortleberry; bilberry.

**Heidetorf,** *m.* peat.

**heikel,** *a.* critical; delicate.

**heil,** *a.* whole, sound, well. — **— werden,** heal, become well.

**Heil,** *n.* welfare, health, safety.

**Heil-.** healing, curative, therapeutic, medical. **-anstalt,** *f.* hospital, sanatorium.

**heilbar,** *a.* curable.

**Heilbrunnen,** *m.* mineral spring or well.

**Heilbutt,** *m.* halibut.

**heilen,** *v.t.* heal, cure.

**heilfähig,** *a.* curable.

**Heil-formel,** *f.* (*Med.*) prescription. **-gerät,** *n.* therapeutic apparatus.

**heilig,** *a.* holy; solemn, sacred.

**heiligen,** *v.t.* hallow, sanctify; consecrate.

**Heiligen-harz,** *n.* guaiacum (resin). **-holz,** *n.*

holy wood (a variety of lignum vitae). **-stein,** *m.* (*Pharm.*) lapis divinus, cuprum aluminatum.

**Heilkraft,** *f.* curative power.

**heilkräftig,** *a.* curative, healing, therapeutic.

**Heil-kraut,** *n.* officinal plant, medicinal herb. **-kunde, -kunst,** *f.* medicine, therapeutics, "healing art." **-mittel,** *n.* remedy, medicament. **-mittellehre,** *f.* pharmacology, pharmacy. **-pflanze,** *f.* officinal or medicinal plant.

**Heilpflaster,** *n.* healing plaster. — **englisches —,** court plaster.

**Heil-quell,** *m.*, **-quelle,** *f.* medicinal spring or well, mineral spring or well. **-salbe,** *f.* healing ointment.

**heilsam,** *a.* wholesome.

**Heil-serum,** *n.* antitoxic serum. **-stoff,** *m.* curative, remedy. **-stofflehre,** *f.* pharmacology, pharmacy.

**Heilung,** *f.* healing, curing, cure.

**Heilungsvorgang,** *m.* healing process.

**Heil-verfahren,** *n.* healing process. **-wasser,** *n.* curative water, mineral water. **-wert,** *m.* therapeutic value. **-wesen,** *n.* medical affairs. **-wirkung,** *f.* curative effect. **-wissenschaft,** *f.* medical science.

**Heim,** *n.* home, dwelling.

**Heimat,** *f.* native place or country; habitat.

**heimisch,** *a.* native, domestic, indigenous.

**heimlich,** *a.* secret; private.

**Heimlauf,** *m.* return course or stroke.

**Heirat,** *f.* marriage, wedding, match.

**heiraten,** *v.t.* & *i.* marry, wed.

**heischen,** *v.t.* demand, require.

**heiser,** *a.* hoarse, husky.

**heiss,** *a.* hot; ardent, burning; torrid.

**Heiss-bearbeitung,** *f.* hot-working. **-blasegas,** *n.* hot blast gas. **-blasen,** *n.* (*Water Gas*) blow, air blow.

**heiss-blütig,** *a.* warm-blooded; hot-blooded. **-brüchig,** *a.* hot-short. **-brühen,** *v.t.* scald.

**Heissdampf,** *m.* superheated steam.

**Heisse,** *f.* (*Metal.*) charge.

**heissen,** *v.t.* call; bid, order. — *v.i.* be called; mean, be. — **es heisst,** it says, they say; it is called.

**heiss-erblasen,** *a.* (*Iron*) hot-blast. **-gar,** *a.* (*Metal.*) too hot; (of iron) kishy.

**Heissgas,** *n.* hot gas.

**heissgrädig,** *a.* (of ores) difficultly fusible.

**Heiss-kühlung,** *f.* cooling by evaporation; cooling with glycol or similar liquid. **-lauf,** *m.* (*Metal.*) hot run.

**heisslaufen,** *v.i.* (*Mach.*) heat, overheat.

**Heiss-leiter,** *m.* (*Elec.*) hot conductor. **-lösen,** *n.* hot dissolving.

**Heissluft-.** hot-air. **-bad,** *n.* hot-air bath. **-kammer,** *f.* hot-air chamber. **-trichter,** *m.* hot-air funnel. **-trockenraum,** *m.* hot-air drying room. **-trocknung,** *f.* hot-air drying.

**heissverformbar,** *a.* shapable or workable when hot, hot-forming.

**Heisswasser-behälter,** *m.* hot-water tank or container. **-heizung,** *f.* hot-water heating. **-trichter,** *m.* hot-water funnel.

**Heiss-werden,** *n.* becoming hot, heating. **-wind,** *m.* hot blast, hot-air blast. **-windofen,** *m.* hot-blast furnace.

**-heit.** A suffix attached to adjectives to form abstract nouns (as *Trockenheit,* dryness), and to nouns to form collectives (as *Menschheit,* mankind); -hood, -ness, -dom.

**heiter,** *a.* clear, fair; cheerful, bright.

**Heiz-.** heating, calorific. **-apparat,** *m.* heating apparatus. **-bad,** *n.* heating bath. **-band,** *n.* heating tape, heating band.

**heiz-bar,** *a.* heatable. **-beständig,** *a.* heat-resistant.

**Heiz-dampf,** *m.* steam for heating. **-draht,** *m.* heating wire; hot filament.

**Heize,** *f.* (*Steel*) charge of pig.

**Heiz-effekt,** *m.* heating effect. **-einrichtung,** *f.* heating arrangement, heating system.

**heizen,** *v.t.* & *i.* heat; fire, stoke.

**Heizer,** *m.* fireman, stoker.

**Heiz-faden,** *m.* heating filament. **-fähigkeit,** *f.* heating capacity. **-fläche,** *f.* heating surface. **-gas,** *n.* gas for heating, fuel gas; (*pl.*) combustion gases. **-gerät,** *n.* heating apparatus. **-kammer,** *f.* heating chamber; fire box. **-kessel,** *m.* kettle, boiler, cauldron. **-körper,** *m.* heating body, heating element; heater, radiator. **-kraft,** *f.* heating power, calorific power. **-kranz,** *m.* ring burner. **-lampe,** *f.* heating lamp. **-loch,** *n.* fire door, stoke hole. **-luftmotor,** *m.* hot-air motor. **-mantel,** *m.* heating jacket. **-material, -mittel,** *n.* fuel. **-oberfläche,** *f.* heating surface. **-ofen,** *m.* heating furnace or oven or stove. **-öl,** *n.* fuel oil. **-platte,** *f.* hot plate. **-raum,** *m.* heating space; combustion chamber; fireplace. **-rohr,** *n.*, **-röhre,** *f.* heating tube or pipe; fire tube. **-röhrenkessel,** *m.* fire-tube boiler. **-schlange,** *f.* heating coil. **-schrank,** *m.* heating chamber, oven. **-spule,** *f.* heating coil. **-stoff,** *m.* fuel. **-strom,** *m.* (*Elec.*) heating current. **-tisch,** *m.* (*Micros.*) heating stage, warm stage.

**Heizung,** *f.* heating, firing; fuel.

**Heizungs-anlage,** *f.* heating plant. **-vorrichtung,** *f.* heating apparatus or contrivance.

**Heiz-verlust,** *m.* loss of heat. **-vermögen,** *n.* heating power or capacity. **-vorgang,** *m.* heating process. **-vorrichtung,** *f.* heating apparatus, heating device.

**Heizwert,** *m.* heating value, calorific value. **-bestimmung,** *f.* determination of heating

value. **-messer,** *m.* calorimeter. **-untersuchung,** *f.* calorimetric investigation.
**Heiz-widerstand,** *m.* heating resistance. **-wirkung,** *f.* heating effect. **-wirkungsgrad,** *m.* heating efficiency. **-zeit,** *f.* heating period. **-zug,** *m.* heating flue. **-zweck,** *m.* heating purpose(s).
**Hektographentinte,** *f.* hectographic ink.
**hektographieren,** *v.t.* (copy with the) hectograph.
**Held,** *m.* hero.
**helfen,** *v.i.* help, assist; be of use, avail.
**Helfer,** *m.* helper, assistant.
**Helio-echtrot,** *n.* (*Dyes*) helio fast red. **-farbstoff,** *m.* helio dye.
**Helium-entwicklung,** *f.* evolution of helium. **-gehalt,** *m.* helium content. **-kern,** *m.* helium nucleus.
**hell,** *a.* bright, brilliant; light, pale; clear, transparent, limpid; loud, shrill. **-blau,** *a.* light blue. **-bläulich,** *a.* light bluish. **-braun,** *a.* light brown.
**Helle,** *f.* brightness, luminosity; clearness, transparency; vermeil (the varnish).
**hellen,** *v.t.* make clear, clarify; treat with vermeil.
**Heller,** *m.* heller ($\frac{1}{100}$ krone); farthing.
**hellfarbig,** *a.* light-colored.
**Hellfeldbeleuchtung,** *f.* bright-field illumination.
**hell-gelb,** *a.* light yellow, bright yellow. **-getönt,** *a.* light-toned. **-grau,** *a.* light gray. **-grün,** *a.* light green.
**Helligkeit,** *f.* brightness, luminosity; clearness, transparency.
**Helligkeitswert,** *m.* luminosity value.
**hell-matt,** *a.* slightly dull, semidull, semimat. **-rot,** *a.* bright red; light red. **-rotglühend,** *a.* bright-red-hot.
**Hellrotglut,** *f.* bright red heat (about 950°C.).
**hellrotwarm,** *a.* bright-red-hot.
**Helltran,** *m.* a clear, light yellow fish oil.
**hellweiss,** *a.* clear white, bright white.
**Helm,** *m.* helmet; helm; (of a still) head. **-kolben,** *m.* distilling flask. **-rohr,** *n.*, **-schnabel,** *m.* (of a still) beak, nose.
**Hemd,** *n.* shirt; chemise; (of a blast furnace) shell.
**Hemellit(h)säure,** *f.* hemellitic acid.
**Hemi-eder,** *n.* hemihedron, hemihedral form or crystal. **-edrie,** *f.* hemihedrism.
**hemiedrisch,** *a.* hemihedral.
**Hemimellit(h)säure,** *f.* hemimellitic acid.
**hemitrop,** *a.* (*Cryst.*) hemitrope, twinned.
**Hemme,** *f.* hindrance, restraint, impediment, obstruction; arrest; brake.
**hemmen,** *v.t.* stop, check, arrest, inhibit, restrain; retard; brake; clog.
**Hemmnis,** *n.* obstruction, check.
**Hemmung,** *f.* stopping, etc. (see hemmen); hindrance, restraint; check, arrest; escapement.
**Hemmungskörper,** *m.* inhibiting or restraining substance, inhibitor, decelerator.
**Heneikosan,** *n.* heneicosane.
**Hengst,** *m.* stallion; jack; (*Brewing*) old piece.
**Henkel,** *m.* handle, lug, ear. **-schale,** *f.* casserole.
**Henne,** *f.* hen.
**hepatisch,** *a.* hepatic.
**heptacarbocyclisch,** *a.* heptacarbocyclic.
**Heptanaphten,** *n.* heptanaphthene.
**her,** *adv.* here, hither; since, ago. — **von je —,** always.
**herab,** *adv.* down, downwards. **-drücken,** *v.t.* press down, depress. **-fliessen,** *v.i.* flow down, run down. **-hängend,** *a.* hanging down, pendent. **-lassen,** *v.t.* let down, lower. — *v.r.* condescend. **-mindern,** *v.t.* diminish, lessen. **-rieseln,** *v.i.* trickle down. **-setzen,** *v.t.* lower; reduce, step down; degrade; undervalue; disparage.
**Herabsetzung,** *f.* lowering, etc. (see herabsetzen).
**herab-steigen,** *v.i.* descend. **-transformieren,** *v.t.* (*Elec.*) step down. **-tropfen,** *v.i.* drop down, drip down.
**Heraldik,** *f.* heraldry.
**heran,** *adv.* on, up, near, along(side). **-bilden,** *v.t.* bring up, educate. **-wachsen,** *v.t.* grow up. **-ziehen,** *v.t.* draw on; attract; call upon; refer to, consult. — *v.i.* draw near.
**herauf,** *adv.* up, up here.
**heraus,** *adv.* out, out here, forth. **-arbeiten,** *v.t.* work out. **-bekommen,** *v.t.* get back; get out, elicit, solve. **-bilden,** *v.t.* develop, elaborate. **-bringen,** *v.t.* get out, turn out, draw out; perplex. **-destillieren,** *v.t.* distill out. **-drehen,** *v.t.* turn out, twist out. **-fordern,** *v.t.* challenge; provoke.
**Herausgabe,** *f.* editing, edition, editorship; publication; issue; giving up.
**herausgeben,** *v.t.* edit; publish, issue; give out or up; give back (change).
**Herausgeber,** *m.* editor; publisher.
**heraus-greifen,** *v.t.* single out, choose at random. **-heben,** *v.t.* lift out, raise; bring out. **-holen,** *v.t.* draw out, take out, extract. **-kommen,** *v.i.* come out, get out, be edited, be published, result, amount. **-laugen,** *v.t.* leach out. **-lösen,** *v.t.* dissolve out. **-nehmbar,** *a.* removable. **-nehmen,** *v.t.* take out, remove; choose. **-oxydieren,** *v.t.* oxidize off. **-pipettieren,** *v.t.* remove with a pipet(te), pipet out. **-pressen,** *v.t.* press out, squeeze out. **-ragen,** *v.i.* project, protrude. **-schlagen,** *v.t.* beat out; strike (sparks); make (money). **-schleudern,** *v.t.* throw out, fling out; spatter.

**-spritzen,** *v.i.* spurt out, spout out. **-stellen,** *v.r.* turn out, prove. **-treiben,** *v.t.* drive out, expel. **-treten,** *v.i.* protrude; emerge; step out. **-ziehen,** *v.t.* draw out, pull out, extract.

**herb, herbe,** *a.* harsh, sharp, tart, rough, raw.

**herbei,** *adv.* here, hither, near, on. **-führen,** *v.t.* bring; bring about, cause. **-schaffen,** *v.t.* bring up, collect, procure, furnish.

**Herberge,** *f.* inn; shelter.

**herblich,** *a.* sourish, subacid; somewhat harsh.

**Herbst,** *m.* autumn. **-rose,** *f.* hollyhock. **-zeitlose,** *f.* meadow saffron.

**Herd,** *m.* hearth; forge; center, focus, seat; (*Mining*) buddle.

**Herd-.** (*Med.*) focal, localized. **-asche,** *f.* hearth ashes. **-auskleidung,** *f.* (*Metal.*) hearth lining. **-blei,** *n.* furnace lead. **-brücke,** *f.* fire bridge.

**Herde,** *f.* herd, flock, drove; crowd.

**Herdformerei,** *f.* open sand molding.

**Herdfrisch-arbeit,** *f.* (*Iron*) refinery process. **-eisen,** *n.* iron treated by the refinery process.

**Herdfrischen,** *n.* hearth refining; (*Iron*) refinery process; (*Steel*) open-hearth process; (*Lead*) reduction of litharge.

**Herdfrisch-prozess,** *m.* = Herdfrischen. **-roheisen,** *n.* pig iron for refining. **-schlacke,** *f.* refinery cinder (or slag). **-stahl,** *m.* fined steel(charcoal hearth); open-hearth steel. **-verfahren,** *n.* = Herdfrischen.

**Herd-futter,** *n.* hearth lining or fettling. **-glas,** *n.* glass that has run down from the pot into the hearth. **-guss,** *m.* open sand casting. **-ofen,** *m.* hearth furnace. **-raum,** *m.* heating chamber. **-schlacke,** *f.* (*Metal.*) hearth cinder. **-sohle,** *f.* hearth bottom, hearth bed, sole. **-stahl,** *m.* = Herdfrischstahl.

**herein,** *adv.* in; come in. **-ziehen,** *v.t.* draw in.

**herführen,** *v.t.* lead on; refresh (yeast); usher in.

**Hergang,** *m.* affair, circumstances.

**hergeben,** *v.t.* deliver, yield.

**hergebracht,** *p.a.* established, conventional.

**herhalten,** *v.t.* hold out; suffer, pay.

**Hering,** *m.* herring.

**Herings-öl,** *n.*, **-tran,** *m.* herring oil.

**herkommen,** *v.i.* come; come here, come on.

**Herkommen,** *n.* origin, descent; usage, custom.

**herkömmlich,** *a.* conventional, traditional.

**Herkunft,** *f.* origin, source; arrival.

**herleiten,** *v.t.* derive; deduce; conduct.

**Hermelin,** *n.* ermine.

**Hermesfinger,** *m.* (*Pharm.*) hermodactyl.

**hermetisch,** *a.* hermetic. — **hermetische Wissenschaft,** hermetic science, alchemy.

**hernach,** *adv.* afterwards, hereafter, then.

**Herr,** *m.* master, lord; gentleman; Mr.

**herrichten,** *v.t.* prepare, arrange, adjust; season (wood).

**herrlich,** *a.* magnificent, grand, excellent.

**Herrlichkeit,** *f.* grandeur, splendor, excellence.

**herrschen,** *v.i.* rule, reign; prevail.

**herrühren,** *v.i.* proceed, be due (to), come (from), originate.

**hersagen,** *v.t.* recite, repeat.

**herschieben,** *v.t.* shove along, shove this way.

**Herst.,** *abbrev.* (Herstellung) production.

**herstellbar,** *a.* capable of being produced, etc. (see herstellen).

**herstellen,** *v.t.* produce, prepare, make, manufacture; restore.

**Hersteller,** *m.* producer, maker, manufacturer.

**Herstellung,** *f.* production, preparation, manufacture; restoration, recovery.

**Herstellungs-mittel,** *n.* restorative. **-verfahren,** *n.* method of production, manufacturing process.

**Hertz,** *n.* hertz (frequency of one cycle per second), c.p.s.

**herüber,** *adv.* over (here).

**herum,** *adv.* round, about. **-spritzen,** *v.i. & t.* squirt (spurt, spatter, etc.) about.

**herunter,** *adv.* down (here); low. **-blasen,** *v.t.* blow down. **-drücken,** *v.t.* lower, depress. **-kommen,** *v.i.* come down; decay. **-kühlen,** *v.t.* cool down. **-lassen,** *v.t.* let down, lower; (*Brewing*) strike out (wort). **-schwemmen,** *v.t.* wash down. **-setzen,** *v.t.* reduce; undervalue. **-trocknen,** *v.t.* dry down, reduce by drying. **-ziehen,** *v.t.* take off; (*Textiles*) strip.

**hervor,** *adv.* forth, forward, out. **-bringen,** *v.t.* produce, cause; bring forth. **-gehen,** *v.i.* arise, result; go forth. **-heben,** *v.t.* make prominent, emphasize; raise. **-ragen,** *v.i.* project; stand out, be prominent. **-ragend,** *p.a.* projecting; outstanding, signal, prominent. **-rufen,** *v.t.* call forth, bring about, produce; develop (a photographic image). **-stechen,** *v.i.* stick out, stand out. **-stechend,** *p.a.* prominent, conspicuous. **-stehend,** *p.a.* prominent, projecting, standing out. **-treten,** *v.i.* step forward; stand out, be prominent. **-tun,** *v.r.* distinguish oneself.

**Herz,** *n.* heart; core, kernel, etc.

**Herz-.** heart, cardiac; cardioid. **-arznei,** *f.* cardiac remedy. **-bahn,** *f.* cardioid path. **-beutel,** *m.* pericardium.

**Herzbeutel-.** pericardial.

**Herzbräune,** *f.* angina pectoris.

**Herzens-.** cardiac; of the heart; darling; inmost.

**Herz-entzündung,** *f.* carditis. **-fell,** *n.* pericardium.

**herzförmig,** *a.* heart-shaped, cordate.

**Herz-fraktion,** *f.* middle fraction, heart cut (in

distilling petroleum). **-gekröse,** *n.* mesocardium. **-gespann,** *n.* motherwort (*Leonurus cardiaca*). **-gift,** *n.* cardiac poison.

**herzhaft,** *a.* hearty; brave; strong (taste).

**Herzhaut,** *f.* (äussere) pericardium; (**innere**) endocardium.

**herzig,** *a.* hearty; dear, lovely.

**Herz-kammer,** *f.* ventricle. **-klappe,** *f.* cardiac valve. **-kurve,** *f.* (*Math.*) cardioid. **-leiden,** *n.* heart disease.

**herzlich,** *a.* heartfelt, hearty, cordial; loving. — *adv.* heartily; extremely.

**Herzmittel,** *n.* cardiac remedy.

**Herzog,** *m.* duke.

**Herz-pulver,** *n.* cardiac powder. **-reiz,** *m.* cardiac stimulant or irritant. **-sack,** *m.* pericardium. **-schlag,** *m.* heart beat; cardiac paralysis.

**herzu,** *adv.* here, hither, near. **-kommen,** *v.i.* come near, approach.

**Herz-vorhof,** *m.*, **-vorkammer,** *f.* auricle. **-wasser,** *n.* pericardial fluid.

**Hessenfliege,** *f.* Hessian fly.

**hessisch,** *a.* Hessian.

**Hessischpurpur,** *n.* (*Dyes*) Hessian purple.

**hetero-atomig,** *a.* heteratomic. **-cyclisch,** *a.* heterocyclic. **-gen,** *a.* heterogeneous.

**Heterogenität,** *f.* heterogeneity.

**heterolog,** *a.* heterologous.

**Hetero-polysäure,** *f.* heteropoly acid. **-ringbildung,** *f.* formation of a ring (or rings) composed of atoms of different kinds. **-zimtsäure,** *f.* heterocinnamic acid.

**heterozygotisch,** *a.* heterozygotic, -zygous.

**heterozyklisch,** *a.* heterocyclic.

**Heterozyklus,** *m.* heterocycle.

**Heu,** *n.* hay.

**heuer,** *adv.* this year, this season.

**heuern,** *v.t.* hire.

**heulen,** *v.i.* howl, yell, roar.

**Heupferd,** *n.* grasshopper.

**heurig,** *a.* of this year, current.

**Heu-schrecke,** *f.* locust. **-schreckenbaum,** *m.* locust tree.

**heute,** *adv.* to-day. — **— abend,** this evening; **— nacht,** to-night.

**heutig,** *a.* of to-day; present; modern.

**heutzutage,** *adv.* at present, nowadays.

**Heveabaum,** *m.* hevea tree, rubber tree.

**hexacyclisch,** *a.* hexacyclic.

**Hexaeder,** *n.* hexahedron.

**hexaedrisch,** *a.* hexahedral.

**Hexa-naphten,** *n.* hexanaphthene (cyclohexane). **-vanadinsäure,** *f.* hexavanadic acid.

**hexazyklisch,** *a.* hexacyclic.

**Hexe,** *f.* witch; hag.

**Hexen-kraut,** *n.* mandragora, mandrake; enchanter's nightshade (*Circaea*). **-mehl,** **-pulver,** *n.* lycopodium, witch meal. **-meister,** *m.* sorcerer, wizard. **-schuss,** *m.* lumbago.

**Hexonsäure,** *f.* hexonic acid.

**HF, Hf.,** *abbrev.* (Hochfrequenz) high frequency.

**Hg-Bogen,** *m.* mercury arc.

**Hg-Druck,** *m.* mercurial pressure.

**hieb,** *pret.* (of hauen) hewed, chopped, etc.

**Hieb,** *m.* stroke, cut, slash.

**hiebei,** *adv.* = hierbei.

**hielt,** *pret.* (of halten) held, kept, etc.

**hier,** *adv.* here.

**hieran,** *adv.* hereon, hereat, at this, on this.

**hierauf,** *adv.* hereupon, upon this.

**hieraus,** *adv.* from this, hence.

**hierbei,** *adv.* hereby, herewith, herein.

**hierdurch,** *adv.* thru here; by this means, hereby, thus; herewith, inclosed.

**hierfür,** *adv.* for this, for it.

**hierher,** *adv.* hither, here, now.

**hierhin,** *adv.* hither, this way.

**hiermit,** *adv.* herewith, with it.

**hiernach,** *adv.* hereafter, according to this.

**Hiersein,** *n.* presence.

**hierüber,** *adv.* over here, regarding this, on this account.

**hierum,** *adv.* hereabout, concerning this.

**hierzu,** *adv.* hereto, to this, moreover.

**hiesig,** *a.* of this place, in this place.

**hiess,** *pret.* (of heissen) was called, etc.

**Hilfe,** *f.* help, assistance; relief; remedy.

**hilf-los,** *a.* helpless. **-reich,** *a.* helpful.

**Hilfs-.** assistant, auxiliary, subsidiary, accessory. **-apparat,** *m.* accessory (apparatus); stand-by. **-arbeiter,** *m.* assistant, helper. **-behälter,** *m.* auxiliary container; reserve tank. **-beize,** *f.* (*Dyeing*) auxiliary mordant, also assistant. **-brennstoff,** *m.* auxiliary fuel. **-buch,** *n.* manual, primer, textbook. **-dünger,** *m.* auxiliary fertilizer. **-elektrode,** *f.* auxiliary electrode. **-geld,** *n.* subsidy. **-grösse,** *f.* (*Math.*) auxiliary or subsidiary quantity, auxiliary. **-kondensator,** *m.* auxiliary condenser. **-leitung,** *f.* auxiliary line (piping, conduit, circuit, etc.). **-massnahme,** *f.* remedial measure; first aid. **-mittel,** *n.* help, aid, expedient, auxiliary agent; (*Med.*) adjuvant. **-quelle,** *f.* resource, expedient. **-stativ,** *n.* auxiliary stand or support. **-stoff,** *m.* adjuvant substance, auxiliary or accessory material or agent. **-strom,** *m.* (*Elec.*) auxiliary current. **-teilung,** *f.* auxiliary graduation. **-vorrichtung,** *f.* auxiliary contrivance or appliance.

**Himbeere,** *f.* raspberry.

**Himbeer-essig,** *m.* raspberry vinegar. **-spat,** *m.* rhodochrosite. **-wein,** *m.* raspberry wine.

**Himmel,** *n.* sky; heaven; canopy.

**himmelblau,** *a.* sky-blue, azure.

**Himmel-blau,** *n.* cerulean blue, ceruleum. **-brot,** *n.* manna.

**Himmels-gegend,** *f.* quarter of the heavens, point of the compass. **-gerste,** *f.*, **-korn,** *n.* naked barley. **-körper,** *m.* celestial body. **-kunde,** *f.* astronomy. **-luft,** *f.* ether. **-mehl,** *n.* earthy gypsum. **-richtung,** *f.* cardinal point. **-schlüssel,** *m.* primrose. **-strich,** *m.* zone, climate.

**himmlisch,** *a.* celestial, heavenly.

**hin,** *adv.* there, thither, away, out, along, gone. — **— under her,** hither and thither, to and fro, back and forth. — **— und wieder,** now and again.

**hinab,** *adv.* down there, down. **-wandern,** *v.i.* migrate downward.

**hinauf,** *adv.* up.

**hinaufsetzen,** *v.t.* set up, put up; superscribe. — **hinaufgesetzter Index,** superscript.

**hinauftransformieren,** *v.t.* (*Elec.*) step up.

**hinaufwandern,** *v.i.* migrate upward.

**hinaus,** *adv.* out; beyond. **-schieben,** *v.t.* push out, expel. **-waschen,** *v.t.* wash out.

**Hinblick,** *m.* look, view, regard.

**hinbringen,** *v.t.* carry; pass (time).

**hinderlich,** *a.* obstructive, troublesome.

**hindern,** *v.t.* hinder, prevent, check, stop.

**Hindernis,** *n.* hindrance, obstacle, bar.

**Hinderung,** *f.* hindrance; prevention.

**hindeuten,** *v.i.* point (at or to).

**hindurch,** *adv.* thru, thruout. **-dringen,** *v.t. & i.* penetrate; permeate. **-fallen,** *v.i.* fall thru, pass thru. **-leiten,** *v.t* lead thru, conduct thru. **-saugen,** *v.t.* suck thru, draw thru.

**hinein,** *adv.* in, inside. **-bringen,** *v.t.* bring in, take in. **-dringen,** *v.i.* penetrate. **-ziehen,** *v.t.* draw in, drag in; incorporate; implicate, involve.

**hinfahren,** *v.i.* go, drive (away or along); pass away, depart.

**hinfällig,** *a.* decaying, perishable, weak.

**hinfliessen,** *v.i.* flow (in or toward).

**hinfort,** *adv.* henceforth.

**hing,** *pret.* (of hängen) hung, etc.

**hingeben,** *v.t.* give up.

**hingegen,** *adv.* on the contrary.

**hingehen,** *v.i.* go, pass. — **hin- und hergehen,** (*Mech.*) reciprocate.

**hinhalten,** *v.t.* hold out; hold off; delay.

**hinken,** *v.i.* limp, be lame; be imperfect.

**hinkommen,** *v.i.* come, go, arrive.

**hinlänglich,** *a.* sufficient, adequate.

**hinreichen,** *v.i.* suffice, do. — **hinreichend,** *p.a.* sufficient.

**hinreissen,** *v.t.* tear away, carry away.

**hinrichten,** *v.t.* turn, direct; execute; spoil.

**hinschreiben,** *v.t.* write, write down.

**Hinsicht,** *f.* respect, regard, view.

**hinsichtlich,** *adv.* with regard to.

**hinstellen,** *v.t.* put down; put or bring forward.

**hintan,** *adv.* behind, after, back.

**hinten,** *adv.* behind, after, in the rear.

**hinter,** *prep.* behind, after. — *adv.* behind, back.

**Hinter-.** hind, posterior, back, rear. **-ansicht,** *f.* rear view, back view. **-asien,** *n.* Eastern Asia. **-bliebene,** *m. & f.* survivor.

**hinterbringen,** *v.t.* give information of.

**Hinterdarm,** *m.* rectum.

**hintereinander,** *adv.* one after another, in succession; (*Elec.*) in series.

**Hinter-einanderschaltung,** *f.* (*Elec.*) connection in series. **-grund,** *m.* background. **-halt,** *m.* reserve; ambush. **-haupt,** *n.* occiput (back part of head).

**Hinterhaupts-.** occipital.

**hinterher,** *adv.* behind, after, afterward.

**Hinterkopf,** *m.* occiput.

**hinter-lassen,** *v.t.* leave behind, leave. **-legen,** *v.t.* deposit; file; consign.

**Hinterleib,** *m.* hindquarters; back, dorsum.

**hinterst,** *a.* hindmost, last.

**hinüber,** *adv.* over, across, beyond. **-reissen,** *v.t.* carry over (as in distillation).

**Hinundherbewegung,** *f.* to-and-fro motion, reciprocating motion, oscillation.

**hin- und hergehend,** *a.* (*Mach.*) reciprocating.

**hinunter,** *adv.* down (there), below.

**hinuntersetzen,** *v.t.* put down, put below. — **hinuntergesetzter Index,** subscript.

**hinweg,** *adv.* off, away.

**Hinweg,** *m.* way there.

**Hinweis,** *m.* hint; reference, indication.

**hinweisen,** *v.t.* refer, direct, indicate. — *v.i.* point (to).

**hinwelken,** *v.i.* wither away, fade away.

**hinwerfen,** *v.t.* throw, throw down; jot down; drop (remarks).

**hinziehen,** *v.t.* draw, draw along; draw out, protract; attract. — *v.i.* go.

**hinzu,** *adv.* besides, to it, towards, near. **-addieren,** *v.t.* add, add further. **-fügen,** *v.t.* add.

**Hinzufügung,** *f.* addition.

**hinzu-geben,** *v.t.* add. **-giessen,** *v.t.* pour in, add. **-kommen,** *v.i.* come to, come toward, be added. — **-kommend,** *p.a.* additional, adventitious. **-setzen,** *v.t.* add. **-träufeln,** *v.t.* add by dropping.

**Hinzutritt,** *m.* approach; appearance; accession.

**hinzu-tropfen,** *v.t.* drop (on or in), add by dropping. **-tun,** *v.t.* add.

**hippursauer,** *a.* of or combined with hippuric acid, hippurate of.

**Hippursäure,** *f.* hippuric acid.

**Hirn,** *n.* brain.

**Hirn-.** cerebral; (of wood) crosscut. (For compounds see also Gehirn-.) **-anhang,** *m.*

pituitary body or gland, hypophysis. **-fett,** *n.* cerebrin. **-holz,** *n.* wood cut across the grain. **-mark,** *n.* medullary brain substance. **-rinde,** *f.* cerebral cortex. **-säure,** *f.* cerebric acid. **-schädel,** *m.*, **-schale,** *f.* skull, cranium. **-schnitt,** *m.* cross section.

**Hirsch,** *m.* stag, deer. **-dorn,** *m.* buckthorn (*Rhamnus cathartica*).

**Hirschhorn,** *n.* hartshorn. **-geist,** *m.* spirits of hartshorn (aqua ammoniae). **-salz,** *n.* salt of hartshorn (commercial ammonium carbonate). **-schwarz,** *n.* hartshorn black (fine boneblack). **-spiritus,** *m.* = Hirschhorngeist.

**Hirsch-leder,** *n.* deerskin leather; buckskin. **-talg,** *m.* deer tallow. **-zunge,** *f.* (*Bot.*) hart's-tongue.

**Hirse,** *f.* millet. **-erz,** *n.* oölitic hematite. **-fieber,** *n.* miliaria. **-korn, Hirsenkorn,** *n.* millet seed.

**Hirsen-eisenstein,** *m.*, **-erz,** *n.*, **Hirsestein,** *m.* oölitic hematite.

**Hirt, Hirte,** *m.* shepherd, herdsman.

**Hirten-tasche,** *f.*, **-täschchen, -täschlein,** *n.* shepherd's-purse (*Capsella bursa-pastoris*).

**Histo-chemie,** *f.* histochemistry (chemistry of the tissues). **-genese,** *f.* histogenesis.

**histologisch,** *a.* histological.

**historisch,** *a.* historic(al).

**Hitzdraht,** *m.* (*Elec.*) hot wire.

**Hitze,** *f.* heat; hotness; ardor, passion. — **in der — erhärtend,** thermosetting.

**Hitze-altern,** *n.* heat aging. **-ausgleich,** *m.* heat balance.

**hitzebeständig,** *a.* stable on heating, heat-resistant, thermostable; (of colors) fast to ironing or hot-pressing; (of brick, etc.) refractory.

**Hitze-einheit,** *f.* heat unit, thermal unit. **-einwirkung,** *f.* action or influence of heat.

**hitzeempfindlich,** *a.* sensitive to heat.

**Hitzeerzeugung,** *f.* heat generation.

**hitzefest,** *a.* resistant to heat.

**Hitze-gegenwert,** *m.* heat equivalent. **-grad,** *m.* degree of heat.

**hitzehärtbar,** *a.* thermosetting, heat-setting.

**Hitze-härtung,** *f.* thermosetting. **-messer,** *m.* pyrometer. **-messung,** *f.* pyrometry.

**hitzempfindlich,** *a.* sensitive to heat.

**hitzen,** *v.t.* heat. — **hitzend,** *p.a.* heating, calorific.

**Hitze-probe,** *f.* heat test. **-strahlung,** *f.* heat radiation. **-wirkung,** *f.* action of heat, heat effect, thermal effect. **-wirkungsgrad,** *m.* thermal efficiency.

**hitzig,** *a.* hot; heating; inflammatory; acute; passionate.

**Hk., HK.,** *abbrev.* (Hefnerkerse, -en). Hefner candle(s).

**Hl.,** *abbrev.* (Halbleder) half-leather.

**Hlw.,** *abbrev.* (Halbleinwand) half-cloth.

**hob,** *pret.* (of heben) lifted, etc.

**Hobbock, Hobbok.** drum; large can; keg.

**Hobel,** *m.* plane.

**hobeln,** *v.t.* plane; smooth.

**Hobelspäne,** *m.pl.* shavings.

**hoch,** *a.* high; tall; (of colors) intense, bright, deep; (of numerals, etc.) superior; great, sublime. — *adv.* highly, high, deeply, greatly. **-aktiv,** *a.* highly active. **-angeregt,** *p.a.* highly excited. **-atomar,** *a.* high-atomic. **-atomig,** *a.* containing a large number of atoms.

**Hoch-ätzung,** *f.* relief engraving. **-behälter,** *m.* overhead container or tank. **-bild,** *n.* relief.

**hoch-bildsam,** *a.* highly plastic; highly flexible. **-blau,** *a.* bright blue, light blue, azure. **-bleichbar,** *a.* highly bleachable. **-brisant,** *a.* highly brisant, high-explosive. **-dispers,** *a.* highly dispersed.

**Hochdruck,** *m.* high pressure; relief printing. **-dampf,** *m.* high-pressure steam. **-dampfkocher,** *m.* high-pressure steam cooker. **-gebläse,** *n.* high-pressure blast or blower. **-kessel,** *m.* high-pressure boiler. **-kocher,** *m.* high-pressure cooker. **-rohr,** *n.*, **-röhre,** *f.* high-pressure tube or pipe. **-sauerstoff,** *m.* compressed oxygen. **-schlauch,** *m.* high-pressure hose or tubing. **-verfahrung,** *f.* high-pressure process.

**Hoch-ebene,** *f.* tableland, plateau. **-email,** *n.* embossed enamel.

**hochempfindlich,** *a.* highly sensitive.

**Hochempfindlichkeit,** *f.* great sensitiveness.

**hoch-erhitzt,** *a.* highly heated. **-evakuiert,** *a.* highly evacuated. **-explosiv,** *a.* highly explosive.

**Hochexplosivstoff,** *m.* high explosive.

**hoch-farbig,** *a.* high-colored, intensely colored **-fein,** *a.* superfine, choice. **-fest,** *a.* (*Steel*) high-strength, high-tensile. **-feuerfest,** *a.* highly fireproof; highly refractory. **-flüchtig,** *a.* highly volatile.

**Hochfrequenzgrenze,** *f.* high-frequency limit.

**hochfrequenzmässig,** *a.* relating to high frequency.

**Hochfrequenzstrom,** *m.* (*Elec.*) high-frequency current.

**hoch-gekohlt,** *a.* (*Metal.*) high-carbon. **-geladen,** *p.a.* (*Elec.*) highly charged. **-gespannt,** *p.a.* at high tension, highly superheated, etc. (see spannen).

**Hochglanz,** *m.* high polish or luster, brilliancy. **-kalander,** *m.* supercalender. **-lack,** *m.* high-gloss varnish or lacquer. **-papier,** *n.* enameled paper.

**hochglanzpolieren,** *v.t.* polish extra bright, burnish, planish.

**Hoch-glanzpolitur,** *f.* high-luster polish. **-glühen,** *n.* (*Metal.*) grain-coarsening anneal.

**hoch-gradig, -grädig,** *a.* in or of high degree; high-grade; (of acids, etc.) concentrated; intense. **-grün,** *n.* bright green. **-haltig,** *a.* of high content, high-grade, rich. **-herzig,** *a.* noble-minded, high-spirited.

**Hochkante,** *f.* edge (of a brick or the like).

**hoch-kantig,** *a. & adv.* on edge, edgewise. **-klassig,** *a.* high-grade, high-class. **-komprimiert,** *a.* highly compressed.

**hochkonz.,** *abbrev.* of hochkonzentriert.

**hochkonzentriert,** *a.* highly concentrated, high-concentration.

**Hochleistungs-.** (*Mach.*) high-capacity, heavy-duty.

**hoch-lichtstark,** *a.* (*Photog.*) high-speed, ultraspeed. **-molekular,** *a.* of high molecular weight. **-mütig,** *a.* haughty, proud; arrogant, insolent.

**Hochofen,** *m.* blast furnace. **-anlage,** *f.* blast-furnace plant. **-betrieb,** *m.* blast-furnace operation. **-gas,** *n.* blast-furnace gas. **-guss,** *m.* blast-furnace cast iron. **-koks,** *m.* blast-furnace coke, metallurgical coke. **-schlacke,** *f.* blast-furnace slag. **-schmelze,** *f.* blast-furnace smelting. **-verfahren,** *n.* blast-furnace process.

**hoch-orange,** *a.* bright or deep orange. **-phosphorhaltig,** *a.* high in phosphorus. **-plastisch,** *a.* highly plastic. **-poliert,** *a.* highly polished. **-polymer,** *a.* highly polymerized, high-polymer.

**Hochpolymer,** *n.* high polymer.

**hoch-prozentig,** *a.* high-per-cent, high-percentage. **-quantig,** *a.* of high quantum number. **-rot,** *a.* bright red. **-rund,** *a.* convex.

**Hochscharlach,** *m.* cochineal scarlet.

**hochschmelzend,** *p.a.* high-melting.

**Hochschule,** *f.* a German higher school (college, institution, etc.; *not* high school as used in U. S. A.).

**hoch-selig,** *a.* late, deceased. **-sensibel,** *a.* highly sensible (or sensitive). **-siedend,** *p.a.* high-boiling. **-siliziert,** *a.* high in silicon.

**Hochspannung,** *f.* high tension.

**Hochspannungs-erzeuger,** *m.* (*Elec.*) high-voltage generator. **-leitung,** *f.* (*Elec.*) high-tension line or circuit.

**hochspannungssicher,** *a.* proof against high tension.

**Hochspannungsstrom,** *m.* (*Elec.*) high-tension (or high-voltage) current.

**höchst,** *a.* highest; maximum; utmost. — *adv.* most highly, extremely.

**Höchst-belastung,** *f.* maximum load, peak load. **-besetzungszahl,** *f.* maximum number of electrons in a shell. **-betrag,** *m.* maximum amount. **-druck,** *m.* highest pressure, maximum pressure.

**höchstempfindlich,** *a.* extremely sensitive.

**höchstens,** *adv.* at most, at best.

**Höchst-fall,** *m.* maximum case. **-last,** *f.* maximum load. **-leistung,** *f.* maximum performance or output.

**höchstprozentig,** *a.* highest-percentage, of or at the maximum per cent.

**Hochstrom,** *m.* (*Elec.*) heavy current.

**höchstsiedend,** *a.* highest-boiling.

**Höchst-spannung,** *f.* maximum tension. **-temperatur,** *f.* highest temperature, maximum temperature.

**höchstwahrscheinlich,** *a.* most likely, most probable.

**Höchst-wert,** *m.* highest value, maximum value. **-zahl,** *f.* highest number, maximum number.

**hoch-tonerdehaltig,** *a.* high in alumina, highly aluminous. **-trabend,** *p.a.* pompous, bombastic. **-treiben,** *v.t.* drive or raise high, work or refine highly, etc. (see treiben).

**Hochvakuum,** *n.* high vacuum.

**hochvergärend,** *p.a.* (of yeast) high-attenuating; (also of yeast) top-fermenting.

**Hochvergärung,** *f.* high attenuation (of wort); top fermentation.

**hoch-viskos,** *a.* highly viscous. **-voluminös,** *a.* highly voluminous.

**Hoch-wald,** *m.* (high) forest, timber forest. **-wärmeverkohlung,** *f.* high-temperature carbonization.

**hoch-weiss,** *a.* very white. **-wertig,** *a.* of high value or quality, high-grade; of high valence. **-wirksam,** *a.* highly active; highly effective.

**Hochzeit,** *f.* wedding.

**Höcker,** *m.* hump, bump, protuberance; cam; huckster.

**höckerig,** *a.* knotty, knobby, rough, humpy.

**Hode,** *f.*, **Hoden,** *m.*, **Hodendrüse,** *f.* testicle.

**Hodensack,** *m.* scrotum.

**Hof,** *m.* areola; halo; court; yard; farm; residence.

**hoffen,** *v.t. & i.* hope for, hope.

**hoffentlich,** *adv.* it is to be hoped, as I hope.

**Hoffnung,** *f.* hope.

**höflich,** *a.* civil, courteous, polite.

**hohe, hoher,** etc. case forms of hoch, *a.*

**Höhe,** *f.* height, altitude; head (of water); intensity (of color); amount; summit; latitude. — **in der —,** on high. — **in die —,** up.

**Hoheit,** *f.* highness; sovereignty; greatness.

**Höhen-gas,** *n.* (*Aero.*) high-altitude gas. **-lage,** *f.* height, altitude, level. **-messer,** *m.* altimeter; hypsometer. **-sonne,** *f.* a kind of sunlight lamp. *T.N.* **-strahlen,** *m.pl.* high-altitude rays, specif. cosmic rays. **-strahlung,** *f.* high-altitude (specif., cosmic) radiation.

**höhensymmetrisch,** *a.* (*Cryst.*) symmetrical about the vertical axis.
**Höhepunkt,** *m.* high point, maximum, peak.
**hoher,** *a.* high, etc. (see hoch).
**höher,** *a.* higher; superior. **-quantig,** *a.* of higher quantum number. **-wertig,** *a.* of higher valence, multivalent.
**hohes,** *a.* high, etc. (see hoch).
**hohl,** *a.* hollow; concave; (of sound) dull, boomy.
**Hohldrüse,** *f.* (*Anat.*) follicle.
**Höhle,** *f.* cave, cavern; hole, cavity.
**höhlen,** *v.t.* hollow, excavate.
**hohl-erhaben,** *a.* concavo-convex. **-geschliffen,** *p.a.* hollow-ground, concave.
**Hohl-gitter,** *n.* concave grating. **-glas,** *n.* hollow glassware (bottles, tumblers, etc.); concave glass. **-granate,** *f.* hollow shell. **-guss,** *m.* hollow casting, cored work. **-hand,** *f.* palm (of the hand).
**höhlig,** *a.* containing cavities, cavernous, honeycombed, blebby.
**Hohl-körper,** *m.* hollow body or piece. **-kugel,** *f.* hollow sphere or ball. **-ladung,** *f.* (*Expl.*) hollow charge. **-linse,** *f.* concave lens. **-mass,** *n.* measure of capacity. **-prisma,** *n.* hollow prism. **-raum,** *m.* hollow space, empty space, cavity. **-raumbildung,** *f.* cavitation. **-raumschiessen,** *n.* cushioned blasting. **-raumvolumen,** *n.* pore space. **-rührer,** *m.* hollow stirrer.
**hohlrund,** *a.* concave.
**Hohl-schicht,** *f.* air space. **-spat,** *m.* chiastolite. **-spiegel,** *m.* concave mirror. **-tiere,** *n.pl.* (*Zoöl.*) Coelenterata.
**Höhlung,** *f.* cavity, hollow, excavation.
**Hohl-vene,** *f.* (*Anat.*) vena cava. **-walze,** *f.* hollow cylinder or roll. **-welle,** *f.* hollow shaft. **-zahn,** *m.* (*Bot.*) hemp nettle. **-ziegel,** *m.* hollow brick (or tile). **-zirkel,** *m.* inside calipers. **-zylinder,** *m.* hollow cylinder.
**hold,** *a.* kind, friendly, lovely, charming.
**Holder,** *m.* = Holunder.
**holen,** *v.t.* fetch, go for, get.
**holl.,** *abbrev.* (holländisch) Dutch.
**Holländer,** *m.* (*Paper*, etc.) hollander, engine.
**holländern,** *v.t.* beat in a hollander.
**Holländerweiss,** *n.* Dutch white.
**holländisch,** *a.* Dutch. — **holländisches Geschirr,** (*Paper*) hollander. — **holländisches Öl, holländische Flüssigkeit,** ethylene chloride.
**Hölle,** *f.* hell.
**Höllen-öl,** *n.* curcas oil (from *Jatropha curcas*); castor oil; worst grade of olive oil. **-stein,** *m.* lapis infernalis, lunar caustic (silver nitrate).
**Holl.P.,** *abbrev.* (holländisches Patent) Dutch patent.
**Hollunder,** *m.* = Holunder.
**Holm,** *m.* spar; beam; stringer; handle. **-firnis,** *m.* spar varnish.
**Holo-eder,** *n.* holohedral form or crystal. **-edrie,** *f.* holohedrism.
**holoedrisch,** *a.* holohedral.
**holperig, holprig,** *a.* uneven, rough.
**Holunder,** *m.* elder. — **spanischer** (or **türkischer**) **—,** lilac.
**Holunder-beere,** *f.* elderberry. **-blüte,** *f.* elder blossom. **-wein,** *m.* elder(berry) wine.
**Holz,** *n.* wood; timber; forest; thicket. **-abfall,** *m.*, **-abfälle,** *m.pl.* wood waste.
**holzähnlich,** *a.* wood-like, ligneous.
**Holz-alkohol,** *m.* wood alcohol. **-amiant,** *m.* ligneous asbestos. **-apfel,** *m.* crab apple. **-apfelwein,** *m.* crab cider. **-art,** *f.* kind or species of wood.
**holzartig,** *a.* woody, ligneous, xyloid.
**Holz-asbest,** *m.* ligneous asbestos. **-asche,** *f.* wood ashes. **-aschenlauge,** *f.* lye from wood ashes.
**Holzäther,** *m.* methyl ether. — **essigsaurer —,** methyl acetate.
**Holz-bearbeitung,** *f.* woodworking. **-beize,** *f.* mordant for staining wood. **-beizen,** *n.* wood staining. **-blau,** *n.* logwood blue, logwood. **-bottich,** *m.* wooden vat, tub, or tank. **-branntwein,** *m.* wood spirit. **-brei,** *m.* wood pulp. **-büchse,** *f.* wooden box or case. **-cassie,** *f.* = Holzkassie. **-chemie,** *f.* chemistry of wood.
**Hölzchen,** *n.* splinter, splint; match.
**Holz-dämpfer,** *m.* (*Paper*) digester (for wood). **-deckel,** *m.* wooden cover or lid. **-destillation,** *f.* wood distillation. **-destillieranlage,** *f.* wood-distilling plant.
**hölzern,** *a.* wooden; ligneous.
**Holzessig,** *m.*, **-säure,** *f.* wood vinegar, pyroligneous acid. **-geist,** *m.* = Holzgeist.
**holzessigsauer,** *a.* of or combined with pyroligneous acid, pyrolignite of. — **holzessigsaures Eisen,** iron liquor.
**holzfarbig,** *a.* of the color of wood.
**Holzfarbstoff,** *m.* wood dye.
**Holzfaser,** *f.* wood fiber, ligneous fiber; wood pulp; = Holzfaserstoff. **-papier,** *n.* wood-pulp paper. **-stoff,** *m.* lignin; cellulose; lignocellulose.
**Holz-fäule, -fäulnis,** *f.* dry rot. **-feuer,** *n.* wood fire. **-firnis,** *m.* wood varnish.
**holzfrei,** *a.* (*Paper*) without wood (pulp).
**Holz-fuss,** *m.* wooden base or foot; wooden stand. **-gas,** *n.* wood gas. **-gattung,** *f.* kind of wood. **-geist,** *m.* wood spirit, wood alcohol.
**holzgeistig,** *a.* containing wood alcohol.
**Holz-gerbstoff,** *m.* wood tannin. **-gestell,** *n.* wooden stand, wooden frame **-gewächs,** *n.*

woody plant. **-gewebe**, *n.* woody tissue, ligneous tissue; texture of wood. **-griff,** *m.* wooden handle. **-grundierfarbe,** *f.* (*Paint*) wood primer. **-gummi,** *n.* wood gum, xylan. **-handel,** *m.* timber trade, lumber trade. **-harz,** *n.* wood resin; wood rosin.

**holzicht, holzig,** *a.* woody, ligneous.

**Holz-kalk,** *m.* pyrolignite of lime (crude calcium acetate). **-karton,** *m.* wood-pulp board. **-kassie,** *f.* cassia lignea, coarse cassia bark. **-kasten,** *m.* wooden box, case or vat. **-kirsche,** *f.* wild cherry. **-kistchen,** *n.* wooden box. **-kitt,** *m.* wood cement, joiner's putty. **-klotz,** *m.* wooden block, wood block. **-kocher,** *m.* (*Paper*) digester (for wood). **-kohle,** *f.* charcoal (from wood).

**Holzkohlen-brennerei,** *f.* charcoal burner. **-brennofen,** *m.* charcoal furnace. **-eisen,** *n.* charcoal iron. **-feuer,** *n.* charcoal fire. **-klein,** *n.*, **-lösche,** *f.* charcoal dust, charcoal smalls. **-meiler,** *m.* charcoal mound (cf. Meiler). **-ofen,** *m.* charcoal oven. **-pulver,** *n.* powdered charcoal. **-roheisen,** *n.* charcoal pig iron. **-staub,** *m.* charcoal dust. **-teer,** *m.* charcoal tar.

**Holz-konservierung,** *f.* wood preservation. **-konservierungsmittel,** *n.* wood preservative. **-körper,** *m.* woody tissue, xylem. **-kugel,** *f.* wooden ball. **-kupfer, -kupfererz,** *n.* wood copper (fibrous olivenite). **-lack,** *m.* wood lacquer or varnish; stick-lac. **-mangold,** *m.* (*Bot.*) pyrola. **-masse,** *f.* wood paste. **-mehl,** *n.* wood powder, wood meal, wood flour; sawdust. **-melasse,** *f.* wood molasses. **-naphta,** *n.* wood naphtha, (crude) wood spirit. **-öl,** *n.* wood oil (any of various oils found in certain woods, also an oil obtained by destructive distillation); (sometimes) wood tar oil. **-öllack,** *m.* wood oil varnish. **-opal,** *m.* wood opal. **-papier,** *n.* paper from wood pulp, wood paper. **-pappe,** *f.* (*Paper*) board made from wood pulp. **-pech,** *n.* wood pitch. **-pflanze,** *f.* woody plant. **-pflaster,** *n.* wood pavement or paving. **-pulver,** *n.* = Holzmehl. **-reif, -reifen,** *m.* wooden ring, wooden hoop. **-rot,** *n.* redwood extract; hematoxylin. **-russ,** *m.* wood soot.

**holzsauer,** *a.* = holzessigsauer.

**Holz-säure,** *f.* pyroligneous acid. **-schleifer,** *m.* (*Paper*) woodpulp grinder. **-schliff,** *m.* mechanical wood pulp. **-schnitt,** *m.* wood engraving, woodcut. **-schutzmittel,** *n.* wood preservative. **-schwarz,** *n.* wood black. **-span,** *m.* wood shaving, chip, or boring. **-spiritus,** *m.* wood spirit, wood alcohol. **-stativ,** *n.* wooden stand or support. **-stein,** *m.* petrified wood. **-steinkohle,** *f.* lignite. **-stich,** *m.* wood engraving, woodcut. **-stoff,** *m.* wood pulp, specif. mechanical wood pulp; lignin (*Obs.*?).

**holzstoff-frei,** *a.* (*Paper*) free from wood pulp. **-haltig,** *a.* (*Paper*) containing wood pulp.

**Holz-stoffmasse,** *f.* wood pulp. **-substanz,** *f.* wood substance, lignocellulose. **-tafel,** *f.* board. **-tee,** *m.* (*Pharm.*) wood drink.

**Holzteer,** *m.* wood tar. **-öl,** *n.* wood-tar oil. **-pech,** *n.* wood-tar pitch.

**Holz-teil,** *m.* (*Bot.*) xylem. **-terpentinöl,** *n.* wood turpentine (oil). **-trank,** *m.* (*Pharm.*) wood drink. **-tränkung,** *f.* wood pickling. **-trocknung,** *f.* wood drying. **-ung,** *f.* cutting (of wood). **-vergasung,** *f.* wood distillation. **-verkohlung,** *f.* carbonization of wood, charcoal burning. **-verzuckerung,** *f.* saccharification (hydrolysis) of wood. **-watte, -wolle,** *f.* wood wool; excelsior. **-zellstoff,** *m.* chemical wood pulp. **-zeug,** *n.* wood pulp.

**holzzerstörend,** *a.* wood-destroying.

**Holz-zimt,** *m.* = Holzkassie. **-zinn, -zinnerz,** *n.* wood tin (fibrous cassiterite). **-zucker,** *m.* wood sugar (now usually, a mixture of carbohydrates from hydrolysis of wood; sometimes, xylose).

**Homo-brenzcatechin,** *n.* homopyrocatechol. **-campher,** *m.* homocamphor. **-camphersäure,** *f.* homocamphoric acid.

**homo-chrom,** *a.* of uniform color, homochromous; (*Dyeing*) monogenetic. **-cyklisch,** *a.* homocyclic. **-edrisch,** *a.* (*Cryst.*) homohedral.

**Homogallusaldehyd,** *n.* homogallaldehyde.

**homogen,** *a.* homogeneous.

**homogenisieren,** *v.t.* homogenize.

**Homogenität, Homogeneität,** *f.* homogeneity.

**Homogen-kohle,** *f.* solid carbon. **-stahl,** *m.* homogeneous steel.

**Homo-kaffeesäure,** *f.* homocaffeic acid. **-kamphersäure,** *f.* homocamphoric acid

**homolog,** *a.* homologous.

**Homo-loge,** *n.* homolog. **-logie,** *f.* homology.

**homöomorph,** *a.* homeomorphous.

**Homöomorphie,** *f.* (*Cryst.*) homeomorphism.

**homöopolar,** *a.* homopolar, homeopolar.

**Homo-phtalsäure,** *f.* homophthalic acid. **-pinocamphersäure,** *f.* homopinocamphoric acid. **-veratrumaldehyd,** *n.* homoveratraldehyde. **-veratrumsäure,** *f.* homoveratric acid.

**homo-zygotisch,** *a.* (*Biol.*) homozygous. **-zyklisch,** *a.* homocyclic.

**Honig,** *m.* honey.

**honig-ähnlich, -artig,** *a.* honey-like, melleous.

**Honig-biene,** *f.* honeybee. **-essig,** *m.* oxymel.

**honig-farbig,** *a.* honey-colored. **-gelb,** *a.* honey-yellow.

**Honig-geruch,** *m.* odor of honey. **-geschmack,** *m.* taste of honey.

**honighaltig,** *a.* containing honey, honeyed.

**Honig-harnruhr,** *f.* diabetes mellitus. **-klee,** *m.* sweet clover, melilot. **-saft,** *m.* nectar. **-säure,** *f.* (*Pharm.*) oxymel; mellitic acid. **-scheibe,** *f.* honeycomb. **-seim,** *m.* liquid honey. **-stein,** *m.* honeystone, mellite. **-steinsäure,** *f.* mellitic acid.

**honigsüss,** *a.* honey-sweet.

**Honig-tau,** *m.* honeydew. **-trank,** *m.* mead. **-wabe,** *f.* honeycomb. **-wasser,** *n.* hydromel. **-wein,** *m.* mead; mulse.

**Honorar,** *n.* honorarium, fee.

**hopfen,** *v.t.* hop, add hops to.

**Hopfen,** *m.* hop, hops. **-abkochung,** *f.* hop decoction.

**hopfen-ähnlich, -artig,** *a.* like hops.

**Hopfen-aufguss,** *m.* infusion of hops. **-baum,** *m.* hop tree (*Ptelea trifoliata*). **-bitter,** *n.* hop bitter, lupulin. **-bittersäure,** *f.* hop bitter acid. **-bitterstoff,** *m.* hop bitter substance. **-darre,** *f.*, **-darrofen,** *m.* hop kiln. **-drüse,** *f.* (*Bot.*) lupulinic gland; (*pl.*) (crude) lupulin. **-harz,** *n.* hop resin. **-klee,** *m.* black medic (*Medicago lupulina*). **-mehl,** *n.* lupulin, hop dust. **-mehltau,** *m.* hop blight. **-öl,** *n.* hop oil; (**spanisches**) origanum oil. **-staub,** *m.* hop dust, lupulin. **-stopfen,** *n.* (*Brewing*) dry hopping. **-treber,** *pl.* spent hops. **-trieb,** *m.* (*Brewing*) frothy head, first stage of fermentation.

**Hör-.** hearing, auditory. **-apparat,** *m.* hearing apparatus; (telephone) receiver.

**hörbar,** *a.* audible.

**Hörbarkeit,** *f.* audibility.

**horchen,** *v.i.* listen, hearken; eavesdrop.

**Horchgerät,** *n.* listening device; sound locator.

**Horde,** *f.* hurdle, wickerwork; lattice; (*Brewing*) kiln floor; horde, band.

**hören,** *v.t. & i.* hear.

**Hörer,** *m.* hearer; (telephone) receiver.

**Hörfrequenz,** *f.* audio frequency.

**Horizont,** *m.* horizon; level.

**Horizontale,** *f.* horizontal (line).

**Horizontierung,** *f.* leveling.

**Hormonabsonderung,** *f.* hormone secretion.

**hormonartig,** *a.* of hormone nature, hormonal, hormone-like.

**Hormondrüse,** *f.* hormone gland, hormonal gland.

**hormonhaltig,** *a.* hormone-containing.

**Hornabfall,** *m.* horn waste (chippings, etc.).

**horn-ähnlich, -artig,** *a.* horn-like, horny.

**Horn-blatt,** *n.* horn blade (for cleaning mortars); horn sheet. **-blei, -bleierz,** *n.* phosgenite. **-blendeschiefer,** *m.* hornblende schist. **-chlorsilber,** *n.* horn silver (cerargyrite).

**hörnern,** *a.* of horn, horny.

**Hörnerv,** *m.* auditory nerve.

**Horn-erz,** *n.* horn silver (cerargyrite). **-gewebe, -gebilde,** *n.* horny tissue. **-gummi,** *n.* hard rubber. **-haut,** *f.* cornea; horny layer of the skin.

**Hornhaut-.** corneal; horny, callous.

**hornig,** *a.* horn-like, horny, callous.

**hornisieren,** *v.t.* hornify; vulcanize.

**Hornisse, Hornis,** *f.* hornet.

**Horn-klee,** *m.* bird's-foot trefoil (*Lotus corniculatus*). **-kobalt,** *n.* asbolite. **-löffel,** *m.* horn spoon. **-mohn,** *m.* horn poppy (*Glaucium*). **-quecksilber,** *n.* horn quicksilver (native mercurous chloride). **-schicht,** *f.* horny layer, specif. epidermis. **-silber,** *n.* horn silver (cerargyrite). **-spatel,** *m.* horn spatula. **-stein,** *m.* hornstone (variety of quartz).

**hornsteinartig,** *a.* hornstone-like, cherty.

**Horn-stoff,** *m.*, **-substanz,** *f.* keratin; horny substance.

**Hörsaal,** *m.* lecture room, auditorium.

**Hörstein,** *m.* otolith, ear stone.

**Hortensienblau,** *n.* Prussian blue.

**Hosenrohr,** *n.* siphon pipe (of a hot-blast oven).

**hrsg.,** *abbrev.* (herausgegeben) edited, published, issued.

**h.s.l.,** *abbrev.* (heiss sehr löslich) very soluble hot.

**H-Strahlen,** *m.pl.* H rays (proton particles).

**Huaco,** *m.* (*Bot.*) guaco.

**Huano,** *m.* guano.

**hub,** *pret.* (of heben) lifted, raised, etc.

**Hub,** *m.* lift, lifting; (*Mach.*) stroke, throw.

**Hübel,** *m.* hillock, mound.

**Hub-kraft,** *f.* lifting power; buoyancy. **-rad,** *n.* lifting wheel.

**hübsch,** *a.* pretty, handsome.

**Hub-schnecke,** *f.* lifting screw. **-schraube,** *f.* (*Aero.*) lifting propeller.

**Hubschrauber,** *m.* helicopter, autogiro.

**Hub-vermögen,** *n.* lifting power. **-werk,** *n.* (*Mach.*) hoisting gear.

**Huf,** *m.* hoof. **-eisen,** *n.* horseshoe.

**hufeisenförmig,** *a.* horseshoe-shaped.

**Huf-eisenfuss,** *m.* horseshoe base. **-fett,** *n.* neat's-foot oil; hoof ointment. **-lattich, -lattig,** *m.* coltsfoot. **-nagel,** *m.* horseshoe nail; hobnail. **-schlag,** *m.* hoof beat; horseshoeing.

**Hüft-bein,** *n.* hip bone. **-gelenk,** *n.* hip joint.

**Hüfte,** *f.* hip; haunch.

**Huftier,** *n.* hoofed animal, ungulate.

**Hüft-loch,** *n.* obturator foramen. **-nerv,** *m.* sciatic nerve.

**Hufträger,** *m.* hoofed animal, ungulate.

**Hügel,** *m.* hill, hillock; knob, nodule; barrier.

**Huhn,** *n.* hen; fowl.

**Hühnchen,** *n.* chicken, pullet.

**Hühner-auge,** *n.* corn (the callosity). **-eiweiss,** *n.* white of egg.

**hühnereiweissartig,** *a.* like white of egg, albuminous.

**Hühner-fett,** *n.* chicken fat. **-kot, -mist,** *m.* chicken manure.
**Huld,** *f.* grace; kindness, favor.
**huldigen,** *v.i.* pay homage, devote oneself.
**Hülfe,** etc. see Hilfe, etc.
**Hülle,** *f.* sheath, cover, covering, case, casing, jacket, wrapper, envelope; (of electrons) envelope, sheath, also shell.
**hüllen,** *v.t.* cover, wrap.
**Hüllen-elektron,** *n.* sheath electron, shell electron. **-stoff,** *m.* cover material; specif., balloon fabric.
**Hüllrohr,** *n.* encasing tube, jacket.
**Hülse,** *f.* hull, husk, pod, shell; case; cartridge case; (*Mach.*) socket, collar, sleeve, etc.; vial; capsule; spool, bobbin.
**hülsenartig,** *a.* like a hull, socket, etc. (see Hülse); leguminous.
**Hülsen-baum,** *m.* locust tree. **-frucht,** *f.* legume.
**hülsen-fruchtartig, -früchtig,** *a.* leguminous.
**Hülsen-früchtler,** *m.pl.* (*Bot.*) Leguminosae. **-gewächs,** *n.* leguminous plant, legume. **-mutter,** *f.* sleeve nut. **-pflanze,** *f.* = Hülsengewächs. **-schliff,** *m.* concave part of a ground joint. **-träger,** *m.* = Hülsengewächs.
**Humat,** *n.* humate.
**Humin-säure,** *f.* humic acid. **-stoff,** *m.*, **-substanz,** *f.* humic (or humous) substance.
**Hummel,** *f.* bumblebee.
**Hummer,** *m.* lobster.
**humös,** *a.* humous.
**humpeln,** *v.i.* hobble.
**Humulo-chinon,** *n.* humuloquinone. **-hydrochinon,** *n.* humulohydroquinone.
**Humus-bildung,** *f.* humus formation. **-decke,** *f.* covering of humus. **-erde,** *f.* humus; humous soil.
**humusreich,** *a.* rich in humus.
**Humus-säure,** *f.* humic acid. **-schicht,** *f.* layer of humus. **-stoff,** *m.* humus substance.
**Hund,** *m.* dog; hound; (*Mach.*) rammer, monkey; (*Mining*) car.
**Hundekot,** *m.* canine feces, album graecum.
**hundert,** *a.* hundred.
**Hundertel,** *n.* hundredth; per cent.
**hundert-gradig,** *a.* centigrade. **-prozentig,** *a.* hundred-percent.
**Hundertsatz,** *m.* percentage.
**Hundertstel,** *n.* hundredth.
**hundertteilig,** *a.* centesimal, centigrade.
**Hundezahnspat,** *m.* dogtooth spar (variety of calcite).
**Hunds-kamille,** *f.* dog's camomile, mayweed (*Anthemis cotula*). **-wut,** *f.* rabies. **-zahnspat,** *m.* = Hundezahnspat. **-zunge,** *f.*, **-zungenkraut,** *n.* hound's-tongue (*Cynoglossum*).
**Hungerkorn,** *n.* ergot.
**hungern,** *v.i.* hunger, be hungry.
**Hungersnot,** *f.* famine.
**Hunger-stein,** *m.* salt-pan scale (sulfates of calcium and sodium, etc.). **-stoffwechsel,** *m.* starvation metabolism. **-tod,** *m.* (death from) starvation.
**hungrig,** *a.* hungry.
**Hupe,** *f.* horn, trumpet, siren.
**hüpfen,** *v.i.* hop, jump.
**Hürde,** *f.* hurdle, wickerwork, lattice; rack, shelf.
**Hürdentrockner,** *m.* tray drier.
**hurtig,** *a.* quick, nimble, speedy.
**husten,** *v.i.* cough.
**Hustenmittel,** *n.* cough remedy.
**Hut,** *m.* hat; cap, cover, lid, top; (*Bot.*) pileus; loaf (of sugar); scum (of wine); layer of spent tanbark; (*Mining*) gossan. —*f.* guard; pasture.
**Hütchen,** *n.* cap; capsule; (*Bot.*) pileus; small hat.
**hüten,** *v.t.* watch, guard, keep. — *v.r.* take care.
**Hut-filz,** *m.* hatter's felt. **-lack,** *m.* hat varnish. **-pilz,** *m.* pileate fungus, agaricaceous fungus, mushroom.
**Hütte,** *f.* (metallurgical or glass) works, mill, smelting house, foundry; hut, cabin, cottage, shed.
**Hütten-abfall,** *m.* (*Metal.*) waste. **-after,** *m.* residue or refuse from a foundry or the like. **-arbeit,** *f.* smelting, founding; foundry work (distinguished from blast-lamp work, in glass). **-blei,** *n.* smelter lead. **-glas,** *n.* (*Glass*) pot metal. **-herr,** *m.* owner of a smeltery or the like. **-katze,** *f.* lead colic. **-koks, -kok,** *m.* metallurgical coke. **-kunde,** *f.* metallurgy. **-kundiger,** *m.* metallurgist. **-kupfer,** *n.* smelter copper, pig copper. **-mann,** *m.* metallurgist; smelter, founder, etc.
**hüttenmännisch,** *a.* metallurgical.
**Hütten-mehl,** *n.* white-arsenic powder. **-nichts,** *n.* nihilum album, white tutty (impure zinc oxide). **-probierkunst,** *f.* metallurgical assaying. **-produkt,** *n.* metallurgical product. **-prozess,** *m.* metallurgical process. **-prüfer,** *m.* metallurgical assayer. **-rauch,** *m.* smelter smoke; flue dust; white arsenic. **-reise,** *f.* (*Metal.*) campaign. **-speise,** *f.* material to be smelted. **-trichter,** *m.* conical funnel (the common form). **-werk,** *n.* smelting works, foundry, mill, plant, works (where smelting, founding, rolling, etc. are carried on). **-wesen,** *n.* smelting, metallurgy. **-zink,** *n.* smelter zinc, spelter. **-zinn,** *n.* (*Metal.*) grain tin.
**Hutze,** *f.* hood; scoop.
**hutzenartig,** *a.* hood-like.
**Hut-zinn,** *n.* cap tin, Malacca tin. **-zucker,** *m.* loaf sugar.

**h.w.l.,** *abbrev.* (heiss wenig löslich) not very soluble hot.
**Hyacinthgranat,** *m.* essonite.
**Hyänasäure,** *f.* hyenic acid.
**Hyäne,** *f.* hyena.
**Hyazinthe,** *f.* hyacinth.
**Hyazinthgranat,** *m.* essonite.
**Hybridrohöl,** *n.* mixed-base crude oil.
**Hydantoinsäure,** *f.* hydantoic acid.
**Hydnocarpussäure,** *f.* hydnocarpic acid.
**hydrat.,** *abbrev.* (hydratiert, hydratisiert) hydrated.
**Hydrat,** *n.* hydrate; hydroxide.
**Hydratation,** *f.* hydration.
**Hydratationswärme,** *f.* heat of hydration.
**Hydratbildung,** *f.* hydrate formation, hydration.
**hydrathaltig,** *a.* hydrated.
**hydratieren,** *v.t.* hydrate.
**Hydrationswärme,** *f.* heat of hydration.
**hydratisch,** *a.* hydrated.
**hydratisieren,** *v.t.* hydrate. — *v.r.* become hydrated.
**Hydratisierung,** *f.* hydration.
**Hydratisierungsgrad,** *m.* degree of hydration.
**Hydratropa-aldehyd,** *n.* hydratropaldehyde. **-alkohol,** *m.* hydratropic alcohol. **-säure,** *f.* hydratropic acid.
**Hydratwasser,** *n.* water of hydration.
**hydratwasserhaltig,** *a.* containing water of hydration.
**Hydrat-zellulose,** *f.* hydrate cellulose. **-zustand,** *m.* state of hydration.
**Hydraulik,** *f.* hydraulics.
**hydraulisch,** *a.* hydraulic.
**Hydrazo-benzol,** *n.* hydrazobenzene. **-körper,** *m.*, **-verbindung,** *f.* hydrazo compound.
**Hydrid,** *n.* hydride, esp. a higher hydride, as contrasted with Hydrür.
**Hydrieranlage,** *f.* hydrogenation plant.
**hydrieren,** *v.t.* hydrogenize, hydrogenate; hydrate.
**Hydrierrückstand,** *m.* hydrogenation residue.
**Hydrierung,** *f.* hydrogenation; hydration.
**Hydrierwerk,** *n.* hydrogenation work or plant.
**hydroaromatisch,** *a.* hydroaromatic.
**Hydrobromsäure,** *f.* hydrobromic acid.
**Hydrochin-.** hydroquin-.
**Hydro-chinon,** *n.* hydroquinone. **-chinoxalin,** *n.* hydroquinoxaline. **-chlorsäure,** *f.* hydrochloric acid. **-cumaron,** *n.* hydrocoumarone, hydrocumarone. **-cumarsäure,** *f.* hydrocoumaric (or -cumaric) acid. **-cyansäure,** *f.* hydrocyanic acid.
**hydroelektrisch,** *a.* hydroelectric.
**hydrogenieren,** *v.t.* hydrogenize, hydrogenate.
**Hydrogenisation,** *f.* hydrogenation.
**hydrogenisieren,** *v.t.* = hydrogenieren.
**Hydrogenschwefel,** *m.* hydrogen sulfide.
**Hydro-jodid,** *n.* hydriodide. **-jodsäure,** *f.* hydriodic acid. **-kaffeesäure,** *f.* hydrocaffeic acid. **-karbür,** *n.* hydrocarbon. **-kautschuk,** *m.* hydrorubber. **-kette,** *f.* (*Elec.*) hydrocell, hydroelement.
**hydrolis-.** see hydrolys-.
**Hydrolyse,** *f.* hydrolysis.
**hydrolysierbar,** *a.* hydrolyzable.
**hydrolysieren,** *v.t.* hydrolyze.
**Hydrolysierung,** *f.* hydrolyzation, hydrolysis.
**Hydrolysierungsfähigkeit,** *f.* hydrolyzing power; hydrolyzability.
**Hydrolysierzahl,** *f.* hydrolyzation number.
**hydro-lytisch,** *a.* hydrolytic. **-metrisch,** *a.* hydrometric.
**Hydro-peroxyd,** *n.* hydrogen peroxide. **-persulfid,** *n.* hydrogen persulfide.
**hydro-phil,** *n.* hydrophile, hydrophil(ic). **-phob,** *a.* hydrophobe, hydrophobic.
**Hydrophobie,** *f.* hydrophobic (water-repellent) property; (*Med.*) hydrophobia, rabies.
**Hydro-phtalsäure,** *f.* hydrophthalic acid. **-polysulfid,** *n.* hydrogen polysulfide.
**hydro-schweflig,** *a.* hydrosulfurous. **-skopisch,** *a.* hydroscopic. **-statisch,** *a.* hydrostatic.
**Hydrosulfit-ätze,** *f.* hydrosulfite discharge. **-küpe,** *f.* hydrosulfite vat.
**Hydro-thionsäure,** *f.* hydrosulfuric acid, hydrogen sulfide. **-verbindung,** *f.* hydro compound (compound formed by the addition of hydrogen).
**Hydroxyd,** *n.* hydroxide.
**Hydroxydul,** *n.* (-ous) hydroxide.
**hydroxylhaltig,** *a.* containing hydroxyl.
**hydroxylieren,** *v.t.* hydroxylate.
**Hydrozellulose,** *f.* hydrocellulose.
**Hydrozimt-, Hydrozimmt-.** hydrocinnamic. **-säure,** *f.* hydrocinnamic acid.
**Hydrür,** *n.* hydride, specif. a lower hydride as contrasted with Hydrid.
**Hygienik,** *f.* hygienics, hygiene.
**hygienisch,** *a.* hygienic.
**hygro-metrisch,** *a.* hygrometric. **-skopisch,** *a.* hygroscopic.
**Hygroskopizität,** *f.* hygroscopicity.
**hylotrop,** *a.* hylotropic.
**Hyper-ämie,** *f.* hyperemia. **-bel,** *f.* hyperbola. **-bahn,** *f.* hyperbolic orbit or path.
**hyperbolisch,** *a.* hyperbolic.
**Hyper-chlorat,** *n.* perchlorate. **-chlorid,** *n.* perchloride. **-chlorsäure,** *f.* perchloric acid.
**hyper-eutektisch,** *a.* hypereutectic. **-eutektoidisch,** *a.* hypereutectoid. **-fein,** *a.* hyperfine.
**Hyper-glukämie,** *f.* hyperglycemia. **-jodat,** *n.* periodate. **-jodsäure,** *f.* periodic acid.
**hypermangansauer,** *a.* = übermangansauer.

**Hyper-mangansäure,** *f.* permanganic acid. **-oxyd,** *n.* hyperoxide (peroxide).

**hypersensibilisieren,** *v.t.* hypersensitize.

**Hypochloritlauge,** *f.* hypochlorite liquor, hypochlorite solution.

**hypoeutektisch,** *a.* hypoeutectic.

**Hypo-gäasäure,** *f.* hypogeic acid. **-hirnsäure,** *f.* hypocerebric acid. **-jodit,** *n.* hypoiodite.

**hypophosphorig,** *a.* hypophosphorous.

**Hypophyse,** *f.* (*Anat.*) hypophysis, pituitary body.

**Hypothek,** *f.* mortgage, security.

**Hypothese,** *f.* hypothesis.

**hypothetisch,** *a.* hypothetical.

**Hysterese,** *f.* hysteresis.

**H.Z., HZ,** *abbrev.* (Hydrolysierzahl) hydrolyzation number; (Hertzzahl) Hertz unit, hertz (cycle per second).

# I

**i.**, *abbrev.* (in) in; (im) in the; (ist) is; (imido) imino, imido.

**i.A.**, *abbrev.* (im Allgemeinen) in general; (im Auftrag) by, per (in signatures).

**Ia.**, *abbrev.* (prima) first-class, prime.

**i. allg.**, *abbrev.* (im allgemeinen) in general.

**Iatro-chemie**, *f.* iatrochemistry. **-chemiker**, *m.* iatrochemist.

**iatrochemisch**, *a.* iatrochemical.

**i.B. auf**, *abbrev.* (in Bezug auf) in relation to, referred to; (in Berechnung auf) calculated on the basis of.

**ich**, *pron.* I.

**-icht.** A suffix used with verb roots to form collective nouns (as Feil*icht*, filings, from feilen) and with nouns to form adjectives of quality, as öl*icht*, oily. In the latter sense the ending *-ig* is more common. See *-ig*, and adjectives ending in -ig.

**Ichthyolseife**, *f.* ichthyol soap.

**i.D.**, *abbrev.* (in Dampf) in steam; (in Dampfform) in vapor form; (im Durchschnitt) on the average; (im Dunkeln) in the dark.

**-id.** -ide. (There is American authority for chlor*id*, am*id*, etc., but these spellings are not used by the American or London chemical societies. Translation should be uniform, not -ide for some compounds and -id for others.)

**Ideallösung**, *f.* ideal solution.

**Idee**, *f.* idea, notion, conception.

**ideell**, *a.* ideal.

**Ideenverbindung**, *f.* association of ideas.

**identifizieren**, *v.t.* identify.

**Identifizierung**, *f.* identification.

**identisch**, *a.* identical.

**Identität**, *f.* identity.

**Idit**, *n.* iditol, idite.

**Idozuckersäure**, *f.* idosaccharic acid

**Idrisöl**, *n.* lemongrass oil.

**I.E.**, *abbrev.* (Immunisierungseinheit) immunization unit.

**I-echt**, *a.* (*Dyeing*) of best fastness.

**-ieren**, -ate, -ize, etc. (the infinitive ending of a large number of verbs, mostly of non-German origin, the meaning of which can often be easily guessed).

**-ierung**, *f.* -ation, -ization, etc. Cf. -ieren.

**IG, I.G.**, *abbrev.* (Interessengemeinschaft) community of interests, pool, trust; specif., Interessengemeinschaft Farbenindustrie Aktien-Gesellschaft, "I.G. Farben" (the German dye trust).

**-ig.** An adjective suffix denoting quality or relation; -y, -ous, -ed, -ful; as, *ölig*, oily; *flüchtig*, volatile, flying; *zweiseitig*, two-sided; 5%*ig*, 5 per cent; specif., in names of chemical compounds, -ous; as, *schweflig*, sulfurous.

**Igamid**, *n.* a nylon-like polyamide. *T.N.*

**Igedur**, *n.* an aluminum alloy. *T.N.*

**Igel**, *m.* hedgehog; porcupine; (*Agr.*) harrow.

**Igelit**, *n.* a polyvinyl plastic. *T.N.*

**-igen.** A termination of causative verbs formed from adjectives and nouns; as, rein*igen* (make pure) from rein; end*igen* (make an end of) from Ende.

**Igevin**, *n.* a polyvinyl ether plastic. *T.N.*

**Ignatiusbohne**, *f.* St.-Ignatius's-bean.

**ihm**, *pron.* to him, to it.

**ihn**, *pron.* him, it. — **ihnen**, to them.

**Ihnen**, *pron.* to you.

**ihr**, *pron.* you; to her; her; their.

**Ihr**, *pron.* your.

**ihrer**, *pron.* of her; of them; hers; theirs.

**Ihrer**, *pron.* of you.

**ihrerseits**, *adv.* for its, her, or their part, in turn, again.

**ihresgleichen**, *pron.* their like, its like, her like.

**ihresteils**, *adv.* on her part, on their part.

**ihrige**, *pron.* hers; theirs.

**Ihrige**, *pron.* yours.

**i.J.**, *abbrev.* (im Jahre) in the year.

**I.K.**, *abbrev.* (Immunkörper) immune body.

**Ikositetraeder**, *n.* icositetrahedron.

**i.L.**, *abbrev.* (in Liter) in a liter, per liter.

**-il.** (*Org. Chem.*) -il; as, *anil*, *carbostyril*, etc. Nitril (translated nitrile) is an exception.

**illuminieren**, *v.t.* illuminate.

**illusorisch**, *a.* illusory.

**illustrieren**, *v.t.* illustrate.

**Iltis**, *m.* polecat, fitchet (*Putorius*).

**im**, *abbrev.* (in dem) in the.

**imaginär**, *a.* imaginary.

**im allg., im allgem.**, *abbrev.* (im allgemeinen) in general.

**Imber**, *m.* ginger. See Ingwer.

**imbibieren**, *v.t.* imbibe.

**Imbiss**, *m.* light meal, lunch.

**Imido-.** imido-, imino- (should be translated imido- only when the compound is of imide nature, otherwise imino-). **-äther**, *m.* imido ester. **-gruppe**, *f.* imido group; imino

group. **-säure,** *f.* imido acid. **-sulfonsäure,** *f.* imidosulfonic acid (imidodisulfuric acid, $HN(SO_3H)_2$). **-thioäther,** *m.* imido thio ester.
**imitieren,** *v.t.* imitate.
**Imme,** *f.* (honey)bee.
**Immedial-farbe,** *f.* immedial dye. **-schwarz,** *n.* immedial black.
**Immediatanalyse,** *f.* proximate analysis.
**immer,** *adv.* always, ever. — **— noch,** still.
**immer-fort,** *adv.* always, constantly. **-grün,** *a.* evergreen.
**Immergrün,** *n.* periwinkle, myrtle (*Vinca*).
**immerhin,** *adv.* still, after all, at any rate.
**Immersionsflüssigkeit,** *f.* immersion liquid.
**immer-während,** *p.a.* everlasting, perpetual. **-zu,** *adv.* always; *imperative,* go on!
**Immobilien,** *n.pl.* real property, real estate.
**immunisieren,** *v.t.* immunize.
**Immunisierung,** *f.* immunization.
**Immunität,** *f.* immunity.
**Immunkörper,** *m.* immune body.
**Immunochemie,** *f.* immunochemistry.
**Impf-.** inoculation, vaccination.
**impfbar,** *a.* inoculable.
**impfen,** *v.t.* inoculate; vaccinate; (of plants) graft.
**Impf-flüssigkeit,** *f.* inoculation lymph, vaccine lymph. **-kristall,** *m.* seed crystal. **-mittel,** *n.* inoculating agent, inoculum, inoculant; vaccine. **-stift,** *m.* inoculating pencil. **-stoff,** *m.* inoculating material, inoculum; vaccine.
**Impfung,** *f.* inoculation, vaccination.
**Impfversuch,** *m.* inoculation experiment.
**imponieren,** *v.i.* impose, impress.
**importieren,** *v.t.* import.
**Imprägnierbad,** *n.* impregnating bath.
**imprägnierbar,** *a.* impregnable.
**imprägnieren,** *v.t.* impregnate.
**Imprägnier-lack,** *m.* impregnation lacquer. **-mittel,** *n.* impregnating agent. **-öl,** *n.* impregnating oil.
**Imprägnierung,** *f.* impregnation; impregnating agent.
**Imprägnierungs-mittel,** *n.* impregnating agent. **-öl,** *n.* impregnating oil.
**Imprägnierverfahren,** *n.* impregnation process or method.
**improvisieren,** *v.t.* improvise.
**Impuls,** *m.* impulse; impulsion; pulse; momentum. **-gabe,** *f.* impulse giving, impulsing, pulsing. **-quantenzahl,** *f.* spin quantum number. **-satz,** *m.* momentum principle.
**imstande,** *a.* able, capable.
**in,** *prep.* in, at; into, to.
**-in.** (1) A suffix used to form a feminine (as *Wirtin,* hostess, landlady). (2) (as a chemical ending) -ine, when the compound is a base; -in, when it is not. Names of alcohols and phenols are preferably translated so as to end in -ol (as *Resorcin,* resorcinol).
**inaktiv,** *a.* inactive.
**inaktivieren,** *v.t.* inactivate.
**Inaktivierung,** *f.* inactivation.
**Inaktivität,** *f.* inactivity.
**Inangriffnahme,** *f.* beginning, attack.
**Inanspruchnahme,** *f.* requisition, claim; occupation; use.
**inanspruchnehmen,** *v.t.* lay claim to; occupy.
**Inaug. Diss.,** *abbrev.* inaugural dissertation.
**Inbegriff,** *m.* total, sum, inclusion; summary.
**inbegriffen,** *p.a.* included; inclusive; implied.
**Inbetriebsetzung,** *f.* setting in motion, starting.
**inbezug auf.** with regard (or relation) to.
**Inbringer,** *m.* conveyor.
**incarnat,** *a.* flesh-colored.
**inchromieren,** *v.t.* (*Metal.*) chromize.
**Indanthren-blau,** *n.* indanthrene blue. **-gelb,** *n.* indanthrene yellow.
**indem,** *conj.* while, when, as; since, because. (*Indem* is often conveniently translated *by* or *on,* with a participial construction, e.g. *indem man behandelt,* by treating, on treating.)
**indessen, indes,** *adv.* meanwhile; however.
**Index-strich,** *m.* index mark, index line. **-zahl, -ziffer,** *f.* index number or figure. **-zeiger,** *m.* indicator needle, pointer.
**indianisch,** *a.* Indian (usually, American Indian).
**Indianischrot,** *n.* Indian red.
**Indicatorpapier,** *n.* indicator paper.
**Indien,** *n.* India.
**indifferent,** *a.* indifferent (inert; passive; neutral).
**Indig,** *m.* indigo. **-blau,** *n.* indigo blue. **-blauschwefelsäure,** *f.* = Indigoblauschwefelsäure.
**indigen,** *a.* indigenous.
**Indigkraut,** *n.* indigo plant.
**indigoartig,** *a.* indigoid.
**Indigo-auszug,** *m.* indigo extract. **-blau,** *n.* indigo blue. **-blauschwefelsäure,** *f.* indigosulfuric acid, sulfindigotic acid (indigosulfonic or indigodisulfonic acid). **-druck,** *m.* indigo printing; indigo print. **-farbe,** *f.* indigo color.
**indigofarbig,** *a.* indigo(-colored).
**Indigo-farbstoff,** *m.* indigo blue, indigotin. **-küpe,** *f.* indigo vat, blue vat (solution of indigo white). **-leim,** *m.* indigo gelatin, indigo gluten.
**indigoliefernd,** *a.* yielding indigo.
**Indigo-lösung,** *f.* indigo solution. **-messung,** *f.* indigometry. **-purpur,** *m.* indigo purple. **-rot,** *n.* indigo red (indirubin). **-salz,** *n.* indigo salt, indigotate. **-säure,** *f.* indigotic acid. **-schwefelsäure,** *f.* = Indigoblauschwe-

felsäure. **-stein,** *m.* = Indigstein. **-stoff,** *m.* indigo blue, indigotin. **-sulfosäure,** *f.* indigosulfonic acid. **-weiss,** *n.* indigo white.
**Indig-rot,** *n.* = Indigorot. **-stein,** *m.* indicolite (blue tourmaline). **-weiss,** *n.* indigo white.
**Indikator-folie,** *f.* indicator foil. **-lösung,** *f.* indicator solution. **-papier,** *n.* indicator paper.
**Indioxyd,** *n.* indium oxide, $In_2O_3$.
**Indisch,** *a.* (East) Indian. — **indischer Balsam,** balsam of Peru. — **indische Bohne,** St.-Ignatius's-bean. — **indische Feige,** prickly pear. — **indischer Flachs,** jute. — **indisches Grasöl,** palmarosa oil. — **indisches Rohr,** rattan. — **indischer Safran,** turmeric.
**Indisch-gelb,** *n.* Indian yellow. **-hanftinktur,** *f.* tincture of Indian hemp. **-rot,** *n.* Indian red.
**Indisulfid, Indiumsulfid,** *n.* indium (sesqui)-sulfide, indium(III) sulfide.
**Indiumsulfür,** *n.* indium monosulfide, indium(II) sulfide.
**individuell,** *a.* individual.
**Individuum,** *n.* (*pl.* **Individuen**). individual.
**Indizes,** *m.pl.* indices.
**indizieren,** *v.t.* indicate.
**Indochinolin,** *n.* indoquinoline.
**Indol-bildung,** *f.* indole formation. **-gruppe,** *f.* indole group. **-körper,** *m.* indole substance, member of the indole group.
**Indoxylschwefelsäure,** *f.* indoxylsulfuric acid.
**induktionsfrei,** *a.* noninductive.
**Induktions-härten,** *n.*(*Metal.*) induction hardening. **-ofen,** *m.* induction furnace. **-rolle, -spule,** *f.* induction coil. **-strom,** *m.* induction current. **-vermögen,** *n.* inductive capacity. **-wirkung,** *f.* inductive effect. **-zeit,** *f.* period of induction.
**Induktivität,** *f.* (*Elec.*) inductance.
**Induktorium,** *n.* (*Elec.*) induction coil.
**indurieren,** *v.t.* indurate, harden.
**Industrie-abfallstoff,** *m.* industrial waste material. **-abwasser,** *n.* industrial waste water or waste liquor. **-erzeugnis,** *f.* industrial product. **-gas,** *n.* industrial gas. **-gerät,** *n.*, **-geräte,** *n.pl.* industrial apparatus.
**industriell,** *a.* industrial.
**Industrielle(r),** *m.* industrial, manufacturer.
**Industrie-ofen,** *m.* industrial furnace. **-wasser,** *n.* industrial water. **-zweig,** *m.* branch of industry.
**induzieren,** *v.t.* induce.
**Induzierung,** *f.* induction; inductance.
**inegal,** *a.* unequal.
**ineinander,** *adv.* in(to) each other, in(to) one another. **-fliessen,** *v.i.* flow or run into one another. **-greifen,** *v.i.* interlock, mesh, engage. **-passen,** *v.i.* fit into each other, fit together. **-stellen,** *v.t.* put one within the other.
**Inertie,** *f.* inertia; inertness.
**inertmachen,** *v.t.* render inert, deactivate.
**Infanterie,** *f.* infantry.
**Infektions-herd,** *m.* focus of infection. **-krankheit,** *f.* infectious disease. **-quelle,** *f.* source of infection. **-träger,** *m.* carrier of infection.
**infektionswidrig,** *a.* opposing infection.
**infektiös,** *a.* infectious.
**infiltrieren,** *v.t.* & *i.* infiltrate.
**infizieren,** *v.t.* infect; inoculate (with crystals).
**Infizierung,** *f.* infection; (crystal) inoculation.
**infökund,** *a.* sterile.
**infolge,** *prep.* on account of, owing to. — **-dessen,** consequently.
**informieren,** *v.t.* inform; instruct.
**infrarot,** *a.* infra-red.
**Infraschall-.** infrasonic.
**Infundier-apparat,** *m.* infusion apparatus. **-büchse,** *f.* infusion vessel, digester.
**infundieren,** *v.t.* infuse.
**Infusionstierchen,** *n.pl.* infusoria.
**Infusorienerde,** *f.* infusorial earth (kieselguhr).
**Ing.,** *abbrev.* (Ingenieur) engineer.
**Ingangsetzung,** *f.* (*Mach.*) starting.
**Ingber,** *m.* ginger. See Ingwer.
**Ingebrauchnahme,** *f.* putting into operation or use.
**Ingenieur, Ingeniör,** *m.* engineer. **-Chemiker,** *m.* chemical engineer (graduate in chemistry of a Technikum). **-wesen,** *n.* engineering.
**ingeniös,** *a.* ingenious.
**Ingotstahl,** *m.* ingot steel.
**Ingrediens,** *n.*, **Ingredienz,** *f.* ingredient.
**Inguss,** *m.* ingot; ingot mold.
**Ingwer,** *m.* ginger; (**gelber**) turmeric.
**ingwerartig,** *a.* like ginger, gingery.
**Ingwer-bier,** *n.* ginger beer. **-gewürz,** *n.* ginger (the spice). **-gras,** *n.* ginger grass. **-öl,** *n.* ginger oil. **-wurzel,** *f.* ginger root, ginger.
**Inh.,** *abbrev.* Inhalt; Inhaber.
**Inhaber,** *m.* holder, owner, proprietor.
**inhalieren,** *v.t.* inhale.
**Inhalt,** *m.* content, contents; (of a surface) area; (of a body) volume; (of a vessel) capacity; index.
**Inhaltsangabe,** *f.* table of contents; summary.
**inhalts-leer,** *a.* empty. **-reich,** *a.* meaningful, significant.
**Inhalts-übersicht,** *f.* = Inhaltsangabe. **-verzeichnis,** *n.* table of contents; index.
**inhärent,** *a.* inherent.
**inhibieren,** *v.t.* inhibit, stay, stop.
**inhomogen,** *a.* inhomogeneous.
**Inhomogenität,** *f.* inhomogeneity.
**Initiale,** *f.* initial; (*Expl.*) primer.
**Initial-explosivstoff, -sprengstoff,** *m.* initiating or priming explosive, primer, priming. **-zünder,** *m.* primer. **-zündsatz,** *m.* priming

composition. **-zündung,** *f.* (*Expl.*) initiation, priming.
**initiieren,** *v.t.* initiate; (*Expl.*) explode.
**Injektionsspritze,** *f.* injection syringe.
**injizieren,** *v.t.* inject.
**inkarnat,** *a.* flesh-colored.
**Inkarnatklee,** *m.* crimson clover.
**inkl.,** *abbrev.* (inklusive) inclusive(ly). — **bis inkl.,** up to and including.
**Inkohärens,** *f.* incoherence.
**Inkohlung,** *f.* conversion into coal, coalification, carbonization.
**Inkompressibilität,** *f.* incompressibility.
**inkrustieren,** *v.t.* incrust. — *v.i.* become incrusted.
**Inkrustierung,** *f.* incrustation.
**Inländer,** *m.* inlander; native.
**inländisch,** *a.* native, indigenous; internal, domestic; inland.
**inliegend,** *a.* enclosed, inclosed.
**inmitten,** *adv.* in the midst.
**inne,** *adv.* in. **-haben,** *v.t.* hold, occupy, keep. **-halten,** *v.t.* keep within; keep in. — *v.i.* stop; pause.
**innen,** *adv.* within, in, inside; at home.
**Innen-.** internal, interior, inside, inner. **-ansicht,** *f.* interior view. **-aufnahme,** *f.* interior photograph(y). **-druck,** *m.* internal pressure. **-durchmesser,** *m.* inside diameter. **-feuerung,** *f.* internal furnace. **-fläche,** *f.* inner surface. **-gewinde,** *n.* internal (or female) thread. **-haut,** *f.* inner or internal membrane or skin. **-heizung,** *f.* internal heating or firing. **-hütchen,** *n.* (*Expl.*) inner capsule. **-konus,** *m.* inner cone (as a cock plug); inside taper. **-lack,** *m.* inside (or interior) varnish. **-leitung,** *f.* interior wiring, piping, etc.; inner circuit.
**innenliegend,** *a.* lying within, inside.
**Innen-mass,** *n.* inside measure. **-raum,** *m.* interior space, interior. **-rinde,** *f.* inner rind, bark, or crust. **-taster,** *m.* inside calipers. **-tränkung,** *f.* soaking in, penetration. **-wand, -wandung,** *f.* inner wall. **-weite,** *f.* inside diameter. **-widerstand,** *m.* internal resistance. **-winkel,** *m.* (*Math.*) interior angle.
**inner,** *a.* internal; interior, inward, inner; intrinsic. — **innere Reibung,** internal friction. — **innere Verschmelzung,** internal seal.
**inneratomar,** *a.* intra-atomic.
**Innere, Inneres,** *n.* interior, inside, midst; core, heart, etc.
**inner-halb,** *adv.* & *prep.* within, inside. **-lich,** *a.* inner, internal, interior; heartfelt. — *adv.* inwardly, internally; earnestly. — **-lich ausgeglichen,** internally compensated. **-molekular,** *a.* intramolecular. **-sekretorisch,** *a.* of internal secretion.
**innerst,** *a.* innermost, inmost.
**innewohnend,** *p.a.* inherent.
**innig,** *a.* intimate; cordial, earnest, sincere.
**Innigkeit,** *f.* intimacy; warmth, sincerity
**inokulieren,** *v.t.* inoculate.
**Inosinsäure,** *f.* inosic acid.
**Inosit,** *n.* inositol, inosite.
**in praxi.** in practice.
**Insass, Insasse,** *m.* inhabitant; inmate; occupant; passenger.
**insbesondere,** *adv.* especially, particularly.
**Inschrift,** *f.* inscription, legend.
**insektenfressend,** *a.* insectivorous.
**Insekten-kunde, -lehre,** *f.* entomology. **-mittel,** *n.* insecticide. **-pulver,** *n.* insect powder. **-vertilgungsmittel,** *n.* insecticide. **-vertreibungsmittel,** *n.* insectifuge. **-wachs,** *n.* insect wax.
**Insektizid,** *n.* insecticide.
**Insel,** *f.* island.
**Inselt,** *n.* tallow; suet.
**Inserat,** *n.* advertisement; insertion.
**inserieren,** *v.t.* advertise; insert.
**insgemein,** *adv.* in general, generally.
**insgesamt,** *adv.* all together, collectively, totally.
**insofern,** *conj.* so far as, inasmuch as.
**Insolator,** *m.* insulator.
**insolieren,** *v.t.* insulate.
**Insolierung,** *f.* insulation.
**insoweit,** *conj.* so far as, inasmuch as.
**Inspizient,** *m.* inspector.
**inspizieren,** *v.t.* inspect.
**instabil,** *a.* unstable.
**Instabilität,** *f.* instability.
**installieren,** *v.t.* install.
**Instandhaltung,** *f.* maintenance.
**inständig,** *a.* earnest, urgent.
**Instandsetzung,** *f.* reconditioning, repairing; enabling.
**instruieren,** *v.t.* instruct.
**Instrumentenkunde,** *f.* knowledge of instruments.
**Integral-ausdruck,** *m.* integral expression. **-rechnung,** *f.* integral calculus.
**Integrationsweg,** *m.* (*Math.*) path of integration.
**integrierbar,** *a.* integrable.
**integrieren,** *v.t.* integrate. — **integrierend,** *p.a.* integrating, integrant.
**Intensität,** *f.* intensity.
**intensiv,** *a.* intensive, intense.
**Intensivität,** *f.* intensiveness, intensity.
**interessant,** *a.* interesting.
**Interesse,** *f.* interest.
**Interessengemeinschaft,** *f.* See IG.
**Interessent,** *m.* person interested (or concerned).
**interessieren,** *v.t.* interest.
**Interesterifizierung,** *f.* inter-esterification.

**Interferenz-bild,** *n.* interference figure. **-erscheinung,** *f.* interference phenomenon. **-farbe,** *f.* interference color.
**interferieren,** *v.t.* interfere.
**interimistisch,** *a.* interimistic, temporary.
**interionisch,** *a.* interionic.
**inter-mediär,** *a.* intermediary, intermediate. **-mittierend,** *p.a.* intermittent. **-polieren,** *v.t.* interpolate. **-ponieren,** *v.t.* insert, interpolate. **-punktieren,** *v.t.* punctuate.
**intern,** *a.* internal.
**intervenieren,** *v.i.* intervene, interfere.
**intim,** *a.* intimate.
**intra-atomar,** *a.* intra-atomic. **-magmatisch,** *a.* intramagmatic. **-perlitisch,** *a.* intrapearlitic. **-venös,** *a.* intravenous.
**Intrusivgestein,** *n.* intrusive rock.
**Intumeszenz,** *f.* intumescence.
**Invarstahl,** *m.* invar steel.
**Inventar,** *n.* inventory.
**Inventur,** *f.* inventory; stocktaking.
**Inversionsgeschwindigkeit,** *f.* rate of inversion.
**invertieren,** *v.t.* invert.
**Invertierung,** *f.* inversion.
**Invertzucker,** *m.* invert sugar.
**investieren,** *v.t.* invest.
**inwärts,** *adv.* inwards.
**inwendig,** *a.* inward, interior, internal.
**inwiefern, inwieweit,** *adv.* to what extent, how far.
**inwohnend,** *p.a.* inherent.
**inzidieren,** *v.t.* incise.
**Inzision,** *f.* incision.
**Inzucht,** *f.* inbreeding.
**inzwischen,** *adv.* meantime.
**Iod,** *n.* iodine. For compounds see Jod-.
**Ionen-art,** *f.* kind of ion. **-austausch,** *m.* ion exchange. **-beweglichkeit,** *f.* ionic mobility.
**ionenbildend,** *a.* ion-forming.
**Ionen-bildung,** *f.* formation of ions. **-bindung,** *f.* ionic linkage, ionic bond. **-dichte,** *f.* ionic density. **-falle,** *f.* ion trap. **-farbe,** *f.* ionic color. **-gehalt,** *m.* ionic content. **-geschwindigkeit,** *f.* ionic velocity. **-gitter,** *n.* ionic lattice. **-gleichung,** *f.* ionic equation. **-leitfähigkeit,** *f.* ionic conductivity. **-leitungsstrom,** *m.* ionic-conduction current. **-produkt,** *n.* ionic product. **-reaktion,** *f.* ionic reaction. **-reibung,** *f.* ionic friction. **-reihe,** *f.* ionic series. **-rumpf,** *m.* core of an ion, ionic core. **-spaltung,** *f.* ionic cleavage, ionization. **-spreizung,** *f.* ionic spread (of flocculation ratios). **-stärkemesser,** *m.* ionometer. **-stoss,** *m.* ionic collision. **-theorie,** *f.* ionic theory. **-wanderung,** *f.* ionic migration. **-wolke,** *f.* ionic cloud, ionic atmosphere. **-zustand,** *m.* ionic state.
**Ionisations-.** See Ionisierungs-.
**Ionisator,** *m.* ionizer.
**ionisch,** *a.* ionic.
**ionisierbar,** *a.* ionizable.
**ionisieren,** *v.t.* ionize.
**Ionisierung,** *f.* ionization.
**Ionisierungs-arbeit,** *f.* work of ionization. **-kammer,** *f.* ionization chamber. **-mittel,** *n.* ionizing agent. **-spannung,** *f.* ionization potential. **-störung,** *f.* ionic interference; disturbance of ionization. **-stufe,** *f.* stage of ionization. **-vermögen,** *n.* ionizing power. **-wärme,** *f.* heat of ionization. **-zustand,** state of ionization.
**ionometrisch,** *a.* ionometric.
**Ionosphäre,** *f.* ionosphere, Heaviside layer.
**I.P.,** *abbrev.* (italienisches Patent) Italian patent.
**Ipecacuanhasäure,** *f.* ipecacuanhic acid.
**I.P.S.,** *abbrev.* (indizierte Pferdestärke) indicated horsepower.
**Ipser Tiegel,** *a.* kind of graphite crucible.
**irden,** *a.* earthen. — **irdenes Geschirr,** earthenware.
**Irdenware,** *f.* earthenware.
**irdisch,** *a.* terrestrial; earthly; perishable.
**-iren.** = **-ieren.**
**irgend,** *adv.* any, at all, some. — **— ein, — -ein,** *a.* any, some.
**irgend-welcher,** *pron.* someone, anyone, some, any. **-wie,** *adv.* anyhow, somehow. **-wo,** *adv.* anywhere, somewhere.
**iridisieren,** *v.t. & i.* = irisieren.
**iridisierend,** *p.a.* iridescent.
**Irisation,** *f.* irisation, iridescence.
**Irisblende,** *f.* iris diaphragm.
**irisch,** *a.* Irish.
**Iris-druck,** *m.* (*Textiles*) iris print. **-fond,** *m.* (*Dyeing*) rainbow ground.
**irisieren,** *v.t.* irisate, iridize. — *v.i.* iridesce. — **irisierend,** *p.a.* iridescent.
**Irisierung,** *f.*, **Irisieren,** *n.* iridescence.
**Irisöl,** *n.* iris oil, orris oil.
**Irland,** *n.* Ireland.
**irländisch,** *a.* Irish.
**Iron,** *n.* irone.
**irre,** *a. & adv.* astray, wrong.
**Irre,** *f.* wandering; error; labyrinth. — *m. & f.* lunatic.
**irreduzibel,** *a.* irreducible.
**irreführend,** *p.a.* misleading, confusing.
**irremachen,** *v.t.* confuse, perplex.
**irren,** *v.i.* err, be wrong; be insane or delirious. — *v.r.* be mistaken. — *v.t.* mislead; puzzle; disturb.
**Irrenarzt,** *m.* alienist, psychiatrist.
**Irresein,** *n.* insanity.
**irreversibel,** *a.* irreversible.
**Irr-fahrt,** *f.* wandering, vagary. **-gang, -garten,** *m.* labyrinth.

**irrig,** *a.* erroneous, false.

**Irr-lehre,** *f.* false teaching, heresy. **-licht,** *n.* will-o'-the-wisp. **-sinn,** *m.* insanity; delirium. **-strom,** *m.* (*Elec.*) stray current. **-tum,** *m.* error; mistake, fault.

**irrtümlich,** *a.* erroneous. — *adv.* erroneously. **-erweise,** *adv.* erroneously.

**Irrung,** *f.* error, mistake; disagreement.

**isabellen, -farbig, isabellfarbig,** *a.* cream-colored, light buff.

**Isabellfarbe,** *f.* cream color, light buff.

**Isäthionsäure,** *f.* isethionic acid.

**Isatropasäure,** *f.* isatropic acid.

**-isch.** An adjective suffix equivalent to -ish (as *weibisch,* womanish) and also used to form adjectives from proper names and foreign words (as *Schiff'sche* Basen, Schiff bases; *chemisch,* chemical).

**ischämisch,** *a.* ischemic, locally anemic.

**isen-trop, -tropisch,** *a.* isentropic.

**-isieren.** -ize. (infinitive verb ending).

**Isländer Doppelspat.** Iceland spar.

**isländisch,** *a.* Iceland, Icelandic. — **isländischer Doppelspat,** Iceland spar.

**Iso-bare,** *f.* isobar. **-bernsteinsäure,** *f.* isosuccinic acid. **-buttersäure,** *f.* isobutyric acid. **-chinolin,** *n.* isoquinoline.

**iso-chrom, -chromatisch,** *a.* isochromatic. **-chron, -chronisch,** *a.* isochronal, isochronous, isochronic.

**Iso-crotonsäure,** *f.* isocrotonic acid. **-cumarin,** *n.* isocoumarin, isocumarin. **-cyansäure,** *f.* isocyanic acid. **-cyanursäure,** *f.* isocyanuric acid.

**iso-cyclisch,** *a.* isocyclic. **-elektrisch,** *a.* isoelectric.

**Isoferulasäure,** *f.* isoferulic acid.

**isohydrisch,** *a.* isohydric.

**Isokamphersäure,** *f.* isocamphoric acid.

**Isolation,** *f.* isolation; insulation.

**Isolations-.** See Isolier-.

**Isolator,** *m.* (*Elec.*) insulator.

**Isolier-anstrich,** *m.* insulating paint, varnish, or coat. **-band,** *n.* insulating tape.

**isolierbar,** *a.* capable of being isolated or insulated.

**isolieren,** *v.t.* isolate; (*Elec.*) insulate. — **isolierte Färbung,** (*Micros.*) differential staining.

**Isolier-fähigkeit,** *f.* insulating ability or property. **-farbe,** *f.* insulating paint. **-fehler,** *m.* defect in insulation. **-firnis,** *m.* insulating varnish. **-flasche,** *f.* insulating bottle, vacuum flask. **-flüssigkeit,** *f.* insulating liquid. **-gewebe,** *n.* insulating fabric. **-hülle,** *f.* insulating covering. **-kitt,** *m.* insulating cement. **-lack,** *m.* insulating varnish. **-masse,** *f.*, **-material,** *n.* insulating material. **-mittel,** *n.* insulating agent, insulator. **-öl,** *n.* insulating oil. **-rohr,** *n.*, **-röhre,** *f.* (*Elec.*) insulating tube or pipe, conduit. **-schicht,** *f.* insulating layer. **-schlauch,** *m.* (flexible) insulating tube. **-stoff,** *m.* insulating substance, insulator.

**Isolierung,** *f.* isolation; insulation.

**Isolier-vermögen,** *n.* insulating power. **-werkstoff,** *m.* insulating material. **-zustand,** *m.* state of insulation or isolation.

**isolog,** *a.* isologous.

**isomer,** *a.* isomeric.

**Isomerie,** *f.* isomerism. **-fall,** *m.* case of isomerism. **-möglichkeit,** *f.* possibility of isomerism.

**isomerisch,** *a.* isomeric.

**isomerisieren,** *v.t.* isomerize.

**Isomerisierung,** *f.* isomerization.

**Isomerismus,** *m.* isomerism.

**iso-metrisch,** *a.* isometric. **-morph,** *a.* isomorphous.

**Iso-morphie,** *f.*, **-morphismus,** *m.* isomorphism. **-ölsäure,** *f.* isoöleic acid.

**Isop,** *m.* hyssop.

**Iso-phtalsäure,** *f.* isophthalic acid. **-pikrinsäure,** *f.* isopicric acid.

**Isopöl,** *n.* hyssop oil.

**Iso-polysäure,** *f.* isopoly acid. **-purpurinsäure,** *f.* isopurpuric acid. **-saccharinsäure,** *f.* isosaccharinic acid.

**isosmotisch,** *a.* isosmotic.

**iso-therm, -thermisch,** *a.* isothermal.

**Iso-therme,** *f.* isotherm. **-thiocyanat, -thiocyanid,** *n.* isothiocyanate. **-thiocyansäure,** *f.* isothiocyanic acid. **-tonie,** *f.* isotonicity.

**iso-tonisch,** *a.* isotonic. **-top,** *a.* isotopic.

**Isotopieverschiebung,** *f.* isotopic shift.

**isotrop,** *a.* isotropic.

**Isotropie,** *f.* isotropy, isotropism.

**isotropisch,** *a.* isotropic.

**Iso-valeriansäure,** *f.* isovaleric acid. **-xylol,** *n.* isoxylene. **-xylylsäure,** *f.* isoxylic acid. **-zimmtsäure,** *f.* isocinnamic acid. **-zuckersäure,** *f.* isosaccharic acid.

**isozyklisch,** *a.* isocyclic.

**isst,** *pr. 2 & 3 sing.* (of essen) eatest, eats.

**ist,** *pr. 3 sing.* (of sein) is.

**Ist-.** real, actual, effective. **-mass,** *n.* actual size.

**I-Stoss,** *m.* butt joint.

**Istrien,** *n.* Istria.

**Istwert,** *m.* actual value.

**-it.** -ite. When it seems desirable to retain the exact spelling of a German name ending in *-it,* quotation marks should be used; as, thermite or "thermit" (or Thermit). Names of alcohols ending in *-it* are preferably translated so as to end in *-ol* (as mannitol).

**Itaconsäure,** *f.* itaconic acid.
**Italien,** *n.* Italy.
**italienisch,** *a.* Italian.
**-ität.** A suffix used to form abstract nouns from adjectives; -ity, -ness.
**iterieren,** *v.t.* iterate, repeat.
**i.V.,** *abbrev.* (im Vakuum) in vacuo; (in Vertretung) by, per.
**Iva-kraut,** *n.* musk milfoil (*Achillea moschata*). **-öl,** *n.* musk milfoil oil.
**i.W.,** *abbrev.* (innere Weite) inside diameter; (in Worten) in words.

# J

**J,** symbol for iodine, I.
**J.,** *abbrev.* Jahresbericht der Chemie; (Jahr) year.
**ja,** *adv.* yes; indeed; certainly, by all means.
**Jagarazucker,** *m.* jaggery.
**Jagd,** *f.* chase, hunt, hunting; pursuit; huntsmen; game; hubbub.
**Jagd-.** hunting, sporting, game; (*Aero.*) fight, fighter, pursuit.
**Jagdpulver,** *n.* sporting powder.
**jagen,** *v.t.* hunt, chase; drive. — *v.i.* hunt; rush.
**Jäger,** *m.* hunter; light infantryman; fighter plane; forest ranger.
**jäh,** *a.* steep, abrupt; hasty, sudden.
**jählings,** *adv.* headlong; abruptly.
**Jahr,** *n.* year. **-buch,** *n.* yearbook, annual; almanac; annal.
**jahrelang,** *a.* lasting, permanent. — *adv.* for years.
**Jahres-ausbeute,** *f.* year's yield, annual yield. **-bericht,** *m.* annual report. **-frist,** *f.* space of a year. **-schrift,** *f.* annual publication. **-tag,** *m.* anniversary; birthday. **-wechsel,** *m.* new year. **-zeit,** *f.* season.
**jahreszeitlich,** *a.* seasonal.
**Jahreszuwachs,** *m.* annual growth.
**Jahrg.,** *abbrev.* of Jahrgang.
**Jahr-gang,** *m.* year's course, year's set, year; year's growth; vintage. **-hundert,** *n.* century.
**jährlich,** *a.* yearly, annual.
**Jahr-tausend,** *n.* millennium, a thousand years. **-zehnt,** *n.* decade.
**jahrzeitlich,** *a.* seasonal.
**Jakobskraut,** *n.* groundsel (*Senecio*).
**Jalape, Jalappe,** *f.* jalap.
**Jalapinsäure,** *f.* jalapic acid.
**Jalap(p)en-harz,** *n.* jalap resin, jalapin. **-wurzel,** *f.* jalap root, jalap.
**jammern,** *v.i.* lament. — *v.t.* move to pity.
**Janusgrün,** *n.* Janus green.
**Japanholz,** *n.* sapanwood.
**japanieren,** *v.t.* japan.
**japanisch,** *a.* Japanese, Japan. — **japanische Erde,** catechu. — **japanische Gelatine,** Japanese gelatin (agar-agar). — **japanisches Wachs,** Japan wax.
**Japan-kampher,** *m.* Japan camphor. **-lack,** *m.* Japan lacquer, Japan varnish. **-leder,** *n.* japanned leather, patent leather. **-leim,** *m.* agar-agar. **-papier,** *n.* rice paper; Japan paper. **-säure,** *f.* japonic acid. **-schwarz,** *n.* Japan black, black japan. **-wachs, -talg,** *n.* Japan wax.
**Jasmin,** *m.* jasmine. jessamine. — **gemeiner —, wilder —,** syringa.
**Jasmin-blütenöl,** *n.* jasmine-flower oil. **-öl,** *n.* jasmine oil.
**Jaspachat,** *m.* jasper agate, jasper.
**jaspiert,** *p.a.* marbled, jaspé.
**Jaspis,** *m.* jasper. **-gut,** *n.* jasper ware. **-porzellan,** *n.* jasperated china. **-steingut,** *n.* jasper ware.
**Jaspopal,** *m.* jasper opal.
**jäten,** *v.t.* weed.
**jatro-, Jatro-.** see Iatro-.
**Jauche,** *f.* dung water, liquid manure; (*Med.*) ichor.
**javanisch,** *a.* Javanese, Java. — **javanisches Wachs,** gondang wax, Java wax.
**Javazimt,** *m.* Java cinnamon.
**Javelle'sche Lauge.** Javelle water.
**jawohl,** *adv.* yes indeed.
**Jb.,** *abbrev.* (Jahrbuch) yearbook.
**Jber.,** *abbrev.* (Jahresbericht) annual report.
**je,** *adv.* always, ever; every; apiece; each time. — **— nach,** according to. — **— nachdem,** according as, according to. — **— . . . —,** the . . . the. — **— . . . um so,** the . . . the.
**jedenfalls,** *adv.* in any case, by all means.
**Jeder,** *pron.* every, each, any; everyone, everybody, each. **-mann,** *pron.* everybody, anybody. **-seits,** *adv.* on each side. **-zeit,** *adv.* at any time, always.
**jedesmal,** *adv.* every time.
**jedesmalig,** *a.* of that time, then being.
**jedoch,** *adv.* however, yet, nevertheless.
**jeglicher,** *pron.* every, any, everything.
**jeher,** *adv.* — **von —,** ever since, all along.
**jemals,** *adv.* ever, at any time.
**jemand,** *pron.* somebody, someone, anybody, anyone.
**Jenaer Glas.** Jena glass.
**jenaisch, jenesisch,** *a.* Jena, of Jena.
**jener,** *pron.* that, the other; that one, that person, the former.
**jenseit, jenseits,** *prep.* beyond, on the other side of.
**jenseitig,** *a.* farther, opposite.
**Jesuiten-rinde,** *f.* Jesuit bark (cinchona bark). **-tee,** *m.* Mexican tea (*Chenopodium ambrosioides*).
**jettschwarz,** *a.* jet-black.
**jetzig,** *a.* present.

**jetzt,** *adv.* now, at present.

**Jetzt-wert,** *m.* present value. **-zeit,** *f.* present time.

**jeweilen,** *adv.* for the time being; at times.

**jeweilig,** *a.* for the time being; respective, particular, under consideration.

**jeweils,** *adv.* for the time being; at times.

**Jg.,** *abbrev.* (Jahrgang) year's set, year.

**Joch,** *n.* yoke; section; joch, 0.576 hectare (Austrian).

**Joch-.** yoke; (*Anat.*) zygomatic, zygo-, jugal. **-baum,** *m.* hornbeam.

**Jod,** *n.* iodine.

**Jod-.** iodine, iodide of, iodo-, iodated. **-alkyl,** *n.* alkyl iodide. **-allyl,** *n.* allyl iodide. **-ammon,** *m.*, **-ammonium,** *n.* ammonium iodide. **-amyl,** *n.* amyl iodide. **-amylum,** *n.* starch iodide. **-antimon,** *n.* antimony iodide. **-arsen,** *n.*, **-arsenik,** *m.* arsenic iodide.

**jodartig,** *a.* iodine-like.

**Jodat,** *n.* iodate.

**Jod-äther,** *m.* iodo ether. **-äthyl,** *n.* ethyl iodide, iodoethane.

**Jodation,** *f.* iodination. — *n.* iodate ion.

**Jod-azid,** *n.* iodine azide. **-baryum,** *n.* barium iodide. **-benzin,** *n.* iodized benzine. **-benzoesäure,** *f.* iodobenzoic acid. **-benzol,** *n.* iodobenzene ($C_6H_5I$ or, in general, any iodine derivative of benzene; cf. Jodobenzol). **-blei,** *n.* lead iodide. **-bromchlorsilber,** *n.* (*Min.*) iodobromite. **-bromid,** *n.* iodine bromide. **-bromür,** *n.* iodine monobromide, iodine(I) bromide. **-cadmium,** *n.* cadmium iodide. **-calcium,** *n.* calcium iodide. **-chinolin,** *n.* iodoquinoline. **-chlor,** *n.* iodine chloride. **-chlorid,** *n.* iodine chloride, esp. iodine trichloride, iodine(III) chloride. **-chlorür,** *n.* iodine monochloride, iodine(I) chloride. **-cyan,** *n.* cyanogen iodide. **-dampf,** *m.* iodine vapor. **-eisen,** *n.* iron iodide. **-eiweiss,** *n.* (*Pharm.*) iodated albumen. **-essigester,** *m.* iodoacetic ester. **-gehalt,** *m.* iodine content. **-gold,** *n.* gold iodide. **-gorgosäure,** *f.* iodogorgoic acid (diiodotyrosine). **-grün,** *n.* iodine green.

**jod-haltend, -haltig,** *a.* containing iodine. iodiferous.

**Jod-hydrat,** *n.* hydriodide. **-hydrin,** *n.* iodohydrin.

**Jodid,** *n.* iodide (esp., an -ic iodide, as contrasted with Jodür). **-chlorid,** *n.* iodochloride, iodide chloride.

**jodierbar,** *a.* capable of being iodinated or iodized.

**jodieren,** *v.t.* iodinate; iodize, iodate.

**jodig,** *a.* iodous.

**Jodijodat,** *n.* iodine iodate.

**jodimetrisch,** *a.* iodometric.

**Jodinrot,** *n.* iodine scarlet (red $HgI_2$).

**Jod-ion,** *n.* iodine ion. **-ismus,** *m.* iodism.

**Jodit,** *m.* iodite (iodyrite, AgI).

**Jodiverbindung,** *f.* iodic compound.

**Jod-jodkaliumlösung,** *f.* solution of iodine in aqueous potassium iodide. **-kadmium,** *n.* cadmium iodide. **-kalium, -kali,** *n.* potassium iodide. **-kaliumlösung,** *f.* potassium iodide solution. **-kaliumpapier,** *n.* potassium iodide paper. **-kaliumstärkepapier,** *n.* potassium-iodide-starch paper. **-kalzium,** *n.* calcium iodide. **-kohlenstoff,** *m.* carbon (tetra)iodide. **-kupfer,** *n.* copper iodide. **-lebertran,** *m.* iodated cod-liver oil. **-lithium,** *n.* lithium iodide. **-lösung,** *f.* iodine solution. **-magnesium,** *n.* magnesium iodide. **-mangan,** *n.* manganese iodide. **-menge,** *f.* amount of iodine. **-messung,** *f.* iodometry. **-metall,** *n.* metallic iodide. **-methode,** *f.* iodine method. **-methyl,** *n.* methyl iodide, iodomethane. **-methylat,** *n.* methiodide. **-mittel,** *n.* iodiferous remedy. **-natrium,** *n.* sodium iodide. **-natron,** *n.* sodium hypoiodite.

**Jodo-.** iodoxy- ($IO_2$); iodo-. **-benzoesäure,** *f.* iodoxybenzoic acid. **-benzol,** *n.* iodoxybenzene ($C_6H_5IO_2$). **-form,** *n.* iodoform. **-formgaze,** *f.* iodoform gauze. **-formprobe,** *f.* iodoform test.

**Jodol,** *n.* iodol.

**Jodometrie,** *f.* iodometry.

**jodometrisch,** *a.* iodometric.

**Jodonaphtalin,** *n.* iodoxynaphthalene.

**Jodonium,** *n.* iodonium.

**Jodoso-.** iodoso-. **-benzol,** *n.* iodosobenzene ($C_6H_5IO$).

**Jodoxy-.** iodohydroxy-. **-naphtochinon,** *n.* hydroxyiodonaphthoquinone, $C_{10}H_4O_2(OH)I$.

**Jod-papier,** *n.* iodized paper. **-phosphonium,** *n.* phosphonium iodide. **-phosphor,** *m.* phosphorus iodide. **-phtalsäure,** *f.* iodophthalic acid. **-präparat,** *n.* iodine preparation. **-probe,** *f.* iodine test. **-quecksilber,** *n.* mercury (esp. mercuric) iodide. **-quecksilberoxyd,** *n.* mercuric iodide, mercury(II) iodide. **-quecksilberoxydul,** *n.* mercurous iodide, mercury(I) iodide. **-radium,** *n.* radium iodide. **-salbe,** *f.* iodine ointment. **-salz,** *n.* iodine salt, specif. iodide.

**jodsauer,** *a.* of or combined with iodic acid, iodate of.

**Jod-säure,** *f.* iodic acid. **-schwefel,** *m.* sulfur iodide. **-serum,** *n.* iodized serum. **-silber,** *n.* silver iodide. **-silizium,** *n.* silicon iodide. **-stärke,** *f.* starch iodide, iodized starch. **-stärkepapier,** *n.* starch iodide paper. **-stickstoff,** *m.* nitrogen iodide. **-thymol,** *n.* (*Pharm.*) thymol iodide. **-tinktur,** *f.* tincture of iodine. **-toluol,** *n.* iodotoluene. **-überträger,** *m.* iodine carrier.

**Jodür,** *n.* (-ous) iodide. Cf. Chlorür.

**Jod-verbindung,** *f.* iodine compound. **-vergiftung,** *f.* iodine poisoning, iodism. **-wasser,** *n.* iodine water.

**Jodwasserstoff,** *m.* hydrogen iodide; hydriodic acid. **-äther,** *m.* ethyl iodide.

**jodwasserstoffsauer,** *a.* iodide of; hydriodide of.

**Jodwasserstoffsäure,** *f.* hydriodic acid.

**Jodwismut,** *m.* & *n.* bismuth iodide.

**Jodyrit,** *m.* iodyrite.

**Jod-zahl,** *f.* iodine number. **-zim(m)tsäure,** *f.* iodocinnamic acid. **-zink,** *n.* zinc iodide. **-zinkstärkepapier,** *n.* zinc iodide starch paper. **-zinn,** *n.* tin iodide. **-zinnober,** *m.* red mercuric iodide.

**Joggelung,** *f.* joggling.

**Joghurt,** *n.* yoghurt (a fermented milk).

**Johannis-beere,** *f.* currant. **-beerwein,** *m.* currant wine. **-brot,** *n.* St.-John's-bread, carob bean, locust bean. **-brotkernmehl,** *n.* carob (or locust) bean flour. **-brotverdickung,** *f.* carob (or locust) bean thickening. **-kraut,** *n.* St.-John's-wort. **-wurzel,** *f.* male fern, (*Pharm.*) aspidium.

**Johimberinde,** *f.* yohimbé bark.

**Johimbin,** *n.* yohimbine.

**Jon,** *n.* ion (for compounds see Ion-).

**Jonan,** *n.* ionan.

**Jonen,** *n.* ionene. — *n.pl.* ions (for compounds see Ionen-).

**Jonidin,** *n.* ionidine.

**Jonium,** *n.* ionium.

**Jonol,** *n.* ionol.

**Jonon,** *n.* ionone. **-säure,** *f.* iononic acid.

**Josefpapier, Josephpapier,** *n.* a kind of tissue paper.

**Jubel,** *m.* jubilation; jubilee. **-band,** *m.* jubilee volume. **-feier,** *f.*, **-fest,** *n.* jubilee.

**Jubiläum,** *n.* jubilee.

**Jucht, Juchten, Juchtenleder,** *n.* Russia leather.

**Juchten-öl,** *n.* birch-tar oil, birch oil. **-rot,** *n.* Janus red.

**juchtenrot,** *a.* red like Russia leather.

**jucken,** *v.t.* & *i.* itch. — *v.r.* scratch, rub.

**Jucken,** *n.* itching, pruritus.

**Juckstoff,** *m.* (*Mil.*) urticant, nettle gas.

**Jude,** *m.* Jew.

**Juden,** *m.pl.* Jews; (*Metal.*) refinery scraps. **-dornbeere,** *f.* jujube, zizyphus. **-harz,** *n.* = Judenpech. **-kirsche,** *f.* alkekengi (*Physalis*). **-pech,** *n.* Jew's pitch (asphalt). **-pilz, -schwamm,** *m.* a species of *Boletus.*

**jüdisch,** *a.* Jewish.

**Jugend,** *f.* youth; adolescence.

**jugendlich,** *a.* youthful, young, juvenile.

**Jugoslawien,** *n.* Yugoslavia.

**Juli,** *m.* July.

**jung,** *a.* young; fresh, early; new (wine or beer); overpoled (copper).

**Jungbier,** *n.* new beer.

**Junge,** *m.* boy, lad, youth; apprentice; young (of animals), cub, etc.

**Jünger,** *m.* disciple, follower, votary.

**Jungfer,** *f.* virgin, maid; iron ladle; rammer.

**Jungfern-, Jungfer-.** virgin; native.

**Jungfern-blei,** *n.* first lead from a furnace. **-erde,** *f.* virgin soil. **-geburt,** *f.* parthenogenesis. **-glas,** *n.* selenite (transparent gypsum). **-metall,** *n.* native metal. **-öl,** *n.* virgin oil. **-pergament,** *n.* vellum. **-quecksilber,** *n.* native mercury. **-schwefel,** *m.* virgin sulfur, native sulfur. **-wachs,** *n.* virgin wax. **-wein,** *m.* wine from unpressed grapes. **-zeugung,** *f.* parthenogenesis.

**Jungfrau,** *f.* virgin, maid; (*Geog.*) Jungfrau.

**jungfräulich,** *a.* virgin.

**Jungholz,** *n.* sapwood.

**jüngst,** *a.* youngest, last, latest. — *adv.* lately, recently.

**jungvulkanisch,** *a.* (*Geol.*) young volcanic.

**jungzeitlich,** *a.* of recent time, recent.

**Juni,** *m.* June.

**Jura-.** (*Geol.*) Jura, Jurassic.

**jurassisch,** *a.* (*Geol.*) Jurassic.

**Jurazeitalter,** *n.* Jurassic period.

**just,** *adv.* just, just now; exactly. — *a.* right, safe.

**justierbar,** *a.* adjustable.

**Justiereinrichtung,** *f.* adjusting device.

**justieren,** *v.t.* adjust; justify (type).

**Justier-schraube,** *f.* adjusting screw, set screw. **-tisch,** *m.* adjusting table. **-ung,** *f.* adjustment; justification. **-wa(a)ge,** *f.* adjusting balance.

**Justiz,** *f.* justice. **-wesen,** *n.* the law, legal affairs.

**Jute-faden,** *m.* jute fiber; jute twine. **-faser,** *f.* jute fiber. **-leinwand,** *f.* gunny cloth, gunny. **-stoff,** *m.* jute cloth, jute material.

**Juwel,** *n.* jewel.

**Juwelier,** *m.* jeweler. **-arbeiten,** *f.pl.* jewelry. **-borax,** *m.* octahedral borax.

**Jux,** *m.* filth; spree, lark.

**J.Z.,** *abbrev.* (Jodzahl) iodine number.

# K

**k** (as symbol). constant. **k.,** *abbrev.* (kalt) cold; (kaiserlich) imperial; (königlich) royal.

**-k.,** *abbrev.* (-keit) -ness.

**K.,** *abbrev.* (elektrische Dissociationskonstante) electric dissociation constant; (kaiserlich) imperial; (königlich) royal.

**K.a.A.,** *abbrev.* (Kommanditgesellschaft auf Aktien) stock company with general partners.

**Kabel,** *n.* cable. **-ausgussmasse,** *f.* cable compound.

**Kabeljau,** *m.* cod, codfish. **-lebertran, -tran,** *m.* cod-liver oil.

**Kabel-lack,** *m.* cable dope. **-litze,** *f.* (*Elec.*) cable strand. **-mischung,** *f.* (*Rubber*) cable stock. **-öl,** *n.* cable oil. **-schmiere,** *f.* cable compound. **-teer,** *m.* cable tar. **-vergussmasse,** *f.* cable compound. **-wachs,** *n.* cable wax.

**Kabine,** *f.* cabin.

**Kabliau,** *m.* = Kabeljau.

**Kachel,** *f.* (Dutch) tile.

**Kachu,** *n.* catechu.

**Kaddig, Kaddich,** *m.* cade (*Juniperus oxycedrus*).

**Kaddigöl,** *n.* oil of cade.

**Kadeöl, Kadinöl, Kadiöl,** *n.* oil of cade.

**kadmieren,** *v.t.* treat or plate with cadmium, cadmiumize, cadmiate.

**Kadming,** *n.* (proposed term for) cadmium.

**Kadmium,** *n.* cadmium. **-beize,** *f.* (*Dyeing*) cadmium mordant. **-chromgelb,** *n.* cadmium chrome yellow. **-gehalt,** *m.* cadmium content. **-gelb,** *n.* cadmium yellow.

**kadmiumhaltig,** *a.* containing cadmium, cadmiferous.

**Kadmium-jodid,** *n.* cadmium iodide. **-legierung,** *f.* cadmium alloy. **-oxydhydrat,** *n.* cadmium hydroxide.

**kadmiumplattiert,** *a.* cadmium-plated.

**Kadmium-rhodanid,** *n.* cadmium thiocyanate. **-salz,** *n.* cadmium salt.

**Käfer,** *m.* beetle, coleopter.

**käferartig,** *a.* coleopterous.

**Kaff,** *n.* chaff.

**Kaffalsäure,** *f.* coffalic acid, caffalic acid.

**Kaffee,** *m.* coffee.

**kaffeeähnlich,** *a.* coffee-like.

**Kaffee-auszug,** *m.* coffee extract. **-baum,** *m.* coffee tree. **-bohne,** *f.* coffee bean.

**kaffeebraun,** *a.* coffee-brown, coffee-colored.

**Kaffee-ersatzstoff,** *m.* coffee substitute. **-gerbsäure,** *f.* caffetannic acid. **-kanne,** *f.* coffee pot. **-öl,** *n.* coffee oil. **-satz,** *m.* coffee grounds. **-säure,** *f.* caffeic acid. **-surrogat,** *n.* coffee substitute.

**Kaffein,** *n.* caffeine.

**Käfig,** *m.* cage, birdcage.

**Kahinkawurzel,** *f.* cahinca root.

**kahl,** *a.* bald; bare; barren; (of fabrics) napless; mere, poor. — **— gehen,** (*Metal.*) need no flux.

**Kahlheit,** *f.* baldness, etc. (see kahl).

**Kahm,** *m.* mold (on wine, etc.).

**kahmen,** *v.i.* mold.

**Kahmhaut,** *f.* pellicle of mold.

**kahmicht, kahmig,** *a.* moldy, stale, (of wine) ropy.

**Kahmpilz,** *m.* mold fungus, mold, mycoderm.

**Kahn,** *m.* boat; lighter, barge, canoe, etc.

**kahnförmig,** *a.* boat-shaped, scaphoid.

**Kai,** *m.* quay, wharf.

**Kaiman,** *m.* cayman, (one kind of) alligator.

**Kaïnkawurzel,** *f.* cahinca root.

**Kaiser,** *m.* emperor.

**Kaiser-.** imperial; Caesarean. **-blau,** *n.* smalt. **-gelb,** *n.* mineral yellow. **-grün,** *n.* imperial green (Paris green).

**kaiserlich,** *a.* imperial.

**Kaiser-öl,** *n.* a kind of kerosene. **-reich,** *n.* empire. **-rot,** *n.* colcothar; imperial red (a dye). **-schnitt,** *m.* (*Med.*) Caesarean section. **-wasser,** *n.* aqua regia. **-wurz,** *f.* masterwort (specif., *Imperatoria ostruthium*).

**Kajaputöl, Kajeputöl,** *n.* cajuput oil.

**Kakao,** *m.* cacao; cocoa. **-baum,** *m.* cacao, cacao tree. **-bohne,** *f.* cacao bean, cocoa bean. **-butter,** *f.* cacao butter, cocoa butter. **-masse,** *f.* cocoa paste. **-öl,** *n.* cocoa (cacao) oil or butter. **-pulver,** *n.* cocoa powder.

**Kakaorin,** *n.* cacaorine.

**Kakaorot,** *n.* cocoa red.

**Kakodyl,** *n.* cacodyl.; **-säure,** *f.* cacodylic acid. **-wasserstoff,** *m.* cacodyl hydride.

**Kakothelin,** *n.* cacotheline.

**Kakoxen,** *n.* (*Min.*) cacoxene, cacoxenite.

**Kaktus,** *m.* cactus.

**Kal.,** *abbrev.* (Kalorie) large or kilogram calorie, Cal.

**Kalabarbohne,** *f.* Calabar bean.

**Kalamin,** *m.* calamine.

**Kalander,** *m.* calender.

**kalandern, kalandrieren,** *v.t.* calender.

**Kalb,** *n.* calf.

**Kälber-lab,** *n.*, **-magen,** *m.* rennet.
**Kalb-fell,** *n.* calfskin. **-fleisch,** *n.* veal. **-lackleder,** *n.* patent calf (leather). **-leder,** *n.* calf (leather).
**Kalbs-magen,** *m.* rennet; calf's stomach. **-pergament,** *n.* vellum.
**kalcinieren,** *v.t.* calcine.
**Kalcinierung,** *f.* calcination.
**Kalcit,** *m.* calcite.
**Kalcium,** *n.* calcium. See Calcium-.
**Kaldaune,** *f.* tripe; (*pl.*) guts.
**Kalender,** *m.* calendar; almanac.
**Kaleszenz,** *f.* calescence.
**kalfatern,** *v.t.* calk.
**Kali,** *n.* potash, in the following senses: (1) potassium carbonate, $K_2CO_3$ ("kohlensaures Kali"); (2) potassium hydrogen carbonate, $KHCO_3$ ("doppeltkohlensaures Kali"); (3) potassium hydroxide or caustic potash, KOH, usually called "Ätzkali"; (4) in older names, potassium oxide, $K_2O$ (as in "schwefelsaures Kali," potassium sulfate); saltwort (*Salsola kali*). — **-ätzendes —,** caustic potash. **-alaun,** *n.* potash alum. **-ammonsalpeter,** *m.* a material made by mixing potassium chloride and ammonium nitrate. **-apparat,** *m.* potash apparatus.
**Kaliaturholz,** *n.* caliatour wood.
**Kaliber,** *n.* caliber, bore, gage.
**Kali-bergwerk,** *n.* potash mine. **-blau,** *n.* Prussian blue. **-bleiglas,** *n.* potash lead glass.
**kalibrieren,** *v.t.* calibrate; groove (a roll).
**Kalibrierpipette,** *f.* calibrating pipet(te).
**Kalibrierung,** *f.* calibration.
**-kalibrig,** *a.* -caliber(ed), -bore.
**kalibrisch,** *a.* in calibration, calibrated.
**Kali-düngemittel,** *n.*, **-dunger,** *m.* potash manure, potash fertilizer. **-düngesalz,** *n.* potassium salt for fertilizing. **-eisenalaun,** *m.* potash iron alum. **-eisencyanür,** *n.* potassium ferrocyanide. **-endlauge,** *f.* (*Paper*) black liquor. **-feldspat,** *m.* potash feldspar. **-form,** *f.* potash mold.
**kalifornisch,** *a.* California.
**kalifrei,** *a.* potash-free.
**Kali-glas,** *n.* potash glass. **-glimmer,** *m.* potash mica, muscovite.
**kalihaltig,** *a.* containing potash.
**Kali-hydrat,** *n.* potassium hydroxide. **-hydratlösung,** *f.* potassium hydroxide solution, potash lye. **-kalk,** *m.* potash lime.
**Kalikodruck,** *m.* calico printing.
**Kali-kugel,** *f.* potash bulb. **-lauge,** *f.* potash lye, caustic potash solution. **-lösung,** *f.* potash solution. **-metall,** *n.* (metallic) potassium. **-olivenölseife,** *f.* potash olive oil soap. **-präparat,** *n.* potash (or potassium) preparation. **-reihe,** *f.* (*Petrog.*) potash series. **-rohsalz,** *n.* crude potassium salt. **-salpeter,** *m.* saltpeter, potassium nitrate. **-salz,** *n.* potash salt, potassium salt. **-salzlager,** *n.* bed or deposit of potash salts. **-schmelze,** *f.* potash fusion; potash melt. **-schwefelleber,** *f.* (*Pharm.*) sulfurated potassa, liver of sulfur (impure potassium sulfide). **-seife,** *f.* potash soap. **-siederei,** *f.* potash works. **-sulfat,** *n.* potassium sulfate. **-tonerde,** *f.* potassium aluminate.
**Kalium,** *n.* potassium. **-alaun,** *m.* potassium alum. **-azetat,** *n.* potassium acetate. **-borfluorid,** *n.* potassium fluoborate. **-brechweinstein,** *m.* antimonyl potassium tartrate, tartar emetic.
**Kalium bromatum.** (*Pharm.*) potassium bromide.
**Kaliumbromid,** *n.* potassium bromide.
**Kalium chloratum.** (*Pharm.*) potassium chloride.
**Kalium chloricum.** (*Pharm.*) potassium chlorate.
**Kalium-chlorid,** *n.* potassium chloride. **-chromalaun,** *m.* potassium chromium alum. **-eisencyanid,** *n.* potassium ferricyanide. **-eisencyanür,** *n.* potassium ferrocyanide. **-ferrisulfat,** *n.* ferric potassium sulfate. **-ferrocyanat, -ferrocyanür,** *n.* potassium ferrocyanide. **-gehalt,** *m.* potassium content. **-goldbromür,** *n.* potassium bromoaurite. **-goldchlorid,** *n.* potassium chloroaurate. **-goldcyanid,** *n.* potassium cyanoaurate; specif., potassium cyanoaurate(III), potassium auricyanide. **-goldcyanür,** *n.* potassium cyanoaurate(I), potassium aurocyanide. **-halogen,** *n.* potassium halide.
**kaliumhaltig,** *a.* containing potassium.
**Kalium-hydrat,** *n.* potassium hydroxide. **-hydrid,** *n.* potassium hydride (KH). **-hydroxyd,** *n.* potassium hydroxide. **-hydrür,** *n.* potassium subhydride ($K_2H$ or $K_4H_2$). **-iridichlorid,** *n.* potassium chloroiridate. **-jodat,** *n.* potassium iodate.
**Kalium jodatum.** (*Pharm.*) potassium iodide.
**Kalium-jodid,** *n.* potassium iodide. **-jodidlösung,** *f.* potassium iodide solution. **-jodidstärke,** *f.* potassium iodide starch. **-jodidstärkepapier,** *n.* potassium iodide starch paper. **-kobaltnitrit,** *n.* potassium cobaltinitrite. **-kohlenoxyd,** *n.* potassium carboxide, potassium hexacarbonyl. **-nitrat,** *n.* potassium nitrate.
**Kalium nitricum.** (*Pharm.*) potassium nitrate.
**Kalium nitrosum.** (*Pharm.*) potassium nitrite.
**Kalium-oxyd,** *n.* potassium oxide. **-oxydhydrat,** *n.* potassium hydroxide. **-permanganat,** *n.* potassium permanganate. **-platinchlorid,** *n.* potassium chloroplatinate, potassium chloroplatinate(IV). **-platinchlorür,** *n.* potassium chloroplatinite, potassium chloroplatinate (II). **-platincyanür,** *n.* potassium cyanoplatinite, potassium cyanoplatinate(II).

**-platinochlorid,** *n.* potassium chloroplatinite, potassium chloroplatinate(II). **-platinzyanür,** *n.* = Kaliumplatincyanür. **-quecksilberjodid,** *n.* potassium mercury iodide. **-rhodanat, -rhodanid,** *n.* potassium thiocyanate. **-salz,** *n.* potassium salt. **-seife,** *f.* potassium soap. **-sulfat,** *n.* potassium sulfate. **-sulfhydrat,** *n.* potassium sulfhydrate (potassium hydrosulfide). **-sulfozyanat, -sulfozyanid,** *n.* potassium thiocyanate. **-verbindung,** *f.* potassium compound. **-wasserstoff,** *m.* potassium hydride. **-wolframat,** *n.* potassium tungstate. **-zelle,** *f.* (*Elec.*) potassium cell. **-zyanid,** *n.* potassium cyanide.

**Kali-verbindung,** *f.* potash compound. **-wasserglas,** *n.* potash water glass (potassium silicate). **-werk,** *n.* potash works.

**Kalk,** *m.* lime (equivalent, in old names of salts, to calcium; as, **phosphorsauerer Kalk,** phosphate of lime, calcium phosphate); limestone; (*Old Chem.*) calx. — **ätzender —,** caustic lime, quicklime. — **gelöschter —,** slaked lime. — **gebrannter —,** quicklime.

**Kalk-.** lime, calc-, calci-, calcareous, calcium, limestone. **-ablagerung,** *f.* lime deposit, calcareous deposit. **-abscheidung,** *f.* separation or deposit of lime; lime scum. **-algen,** *f.pl.* calcareous algae. **-ammonsalpeter,** *m.* calcium ammonium nitrate. **-anlagerung,** *f.* (*Physiol.*) calcification. **-ansammlung,** *f.* accumulation of lime. **-ansatz,** *m.* lime deposit, lime crust. **-anstrich,** *m.* whitewash.

**kalkarm,** *a.* deficient in lime.

**Kalkarsen,** *n.* calcium arsenite.

**kalkartig,** *a.* calcareous, limy.

**Kalk-artigkeit,** *f.* calcareousness. **-äscher,** *m.* (*Soap*) lixiviated ashes, soap waste; (*Leather*) lime pit. **-ausscheidung,** *f.* = Kalkabscheidung. **-back,** *m.* (*Sugar*) lime back. **-bad,** *n.* lime bath. **-baryt,** *m.* (*Min.*) calcareous barite. **-behändlung,** *f.* lime treatment, liming. **-beize,** *f.* (*Dyeing*) lime mordant.

**kalkbeständig,** *a.* lime-resistant, unaffected by lime.

**Kalk-beständigkeit,** *f.* resistance or fastness to lime. **-bestimmung,** *f.* determination of lime. **-beton,** *m.* lime concrete. **-beuche,** *f.* (*Bleaching*) lime boil. **-bewurf,** *m.* coat of plaster, plastering. **-blau,** *n.* blue verditer. **-boden,** *m.* lime soil, calcareous soil. **-borat,** *n.* calcium borate. **-brei,** *m.* lime paste, lime cream. **-brennen,** *n.* lime burning. **-brennerei,** *f.* lime kiln; lime burning. **-brennofen,** *m.* lime kiln. **-bruch,** *m.* limestone quarry. **-brühe,** *f.* milk of lime; lime liquor; whitewash. **-chromgelb,** *n.* calcium chrome yellow. **-düngung,** *f.* manuring with lime.

**Kälke,** *f.* (*Leather*) lime pit, lime.

**kalkecht,** *a.* fast to lime.

**Kalk-echtheit,** *f.* fastness to lime. **-einlagerung,** *f.* calcareous deposit. **-eisengranat,** *m.* lime-iron garnet, andradite. **-eisenstein,** *m.* ferruginous limestone.

**kalkempfindlich,** *a.* sensitive to lime.

**Kalkempfindlichkeit,** *f.* sensitiveness to lime.

**kalken, kälken,** *v.t.* lime.

**Kalkentartung,** *f.* calcareous degeneration.

**Kalkerde,** *f.* lime, calcium oxide; calcareous earth.

**kalkerdig,** *a.* calcareous.

**Kalk-erz,** *n.* limy ore. **-fällung,** *f.* precipitation of lime. **-farbe,** *f.* lime color, lime paint. **-fass,** *n.* (*Leather*) lime pit. **-feldspat,** *m.* lime feldspar, anorthite.

**kalk-frei,** *a.* free from lime. **-führend,** *a.* lime-bearing, calciferous.

**Kalk-gebirge,** *n.* limestone mountains. **-gehalt,** *m.* lime content. **-glas,** *n.* lime glass. **-glimmer,** *m.* (*Min.*) margarite. **-granat,** *m.* lime garnet (grossularite). **-grube,** *f.* lime pit. **-guss,** *m.* thin lime mortar, grout.

**kalk-haft,** *a.* limy, calcareous. **-haltig,** *a.* containing lime, calcareous.

**Kalk-haltigkeit,** *f.* calcareousness. **-härte,** *f.* hardness due to lime. **-harz,** *n.* hardened rosin.

**kalkhold,** *a.* (of plants) lime-loving.

**Kalk-hütte,** *f.* lime kiln. **-hydrat,** *n.* hydrate of lime (calcium hydroxide).

**Kalkier-leinwand,** *f.* tracing cloth. **-papier,** *n.* tracing paper.

**kalkig,** *a.* limy, calcareous.

**Kalk-kitt,** *m.* lime cement, calcareous cement. **-körperchen,** *n.* (*Physiol.*) calcareous body. **-lack,** *m.* calcium lake. **-lager,** *n.* lime deposit, calcareous deposit; lime store. **-lauge,** *f.* lime lye (calcium hydroxide solution). **-licht,** *m.* lime light, calcium light.

**kalkliebend,** *a.* (of plants) lime-loving.

**Kalk-löschen,** *n.* lime slaking. **-löschtrommel,** *f.* lime-slaking drum. **-lösung,** *f.* solution of lime (calcium hydroxide). **-malerei,** *f.* fresco painting. **-mangel,** *m.* lack or deficiency of lime. **-mehl,** *n.* lime powder (air-slaked lime).

**kalkmeidend,** *a.* (of plants) avoiding lime.

**Kalk-menge,** *f.* amount of lime. **-mergel,** *m.* lime marl, calcareous marl. **-messer,** *m.* calcimeter (for determination of carbon dioxide in limestone, etc.). **-milch,** *f.* milk of lime. **-mörtel,** *m.* lime mortar. **-niederschlag,** *m.* lime precipitate. **-ofen,** *m.* lime kiln. **-pflanze,** *f.* calcareous plant. **-pulver,** *n.* lime powder. **-rahm,** *m.* cream of lime.

**kalkreich,** *a.* rich in lime.

**Kalk-saccharat,** *n.* calcium sucrate. **-salpeter,** *m.* calcium nitrate. **-salz,** *n.* lime salt, calcium salt. **-sand,** *m.* lime sand, calcareous sand. **-sandstein,** *m.* calcareous sandstone; (*Ceram.*) sand-lime brick. **-sandziegel,** *m.* sand-lime brick. **-sauerbad,** *n.* (*Bleaching*) lime sour. **-schaum,** *m.* lime froth or scum.

**kalkscheu,** *a.* (of plants) avoiding lime.

**Kalk-schicht,** *f.* layer of lime or limestone or chalk. **-schiefer,** *m.* calcareous slate (or schist). **-schlacke,** *f.* lime slag. **-schlamm,** *m.* lime sludge, lime mud. **-schwarz,** *n.* lime black. **-schwefelleber,** *f.* (*Pharm.*) sulfurated lime, lime hepar. **-seife,** *f.* lime soap, calcium soap. **-seifenbildung,** *f.* formation of calcium soap. **-seifenniederschlag,** *m.* calcium-soap precipitate. **-silo,** *n.* (*Metal.*) limestone bin. **-sinter,** *m.* calcareous sinter. **-spalt,** *m.* (*Leather*) limed split. **-spat,** *m.* calc-spar, calcite. **-stein,** *m.* limestone. **-steinablagerung,** *f.* limestone deposit. **-steingut,** *n.* (*Ceram.*) calcareous white ware. **-steinzuschlag,** *m.* limestone flux; addition of limestone. **-stickstoff,** *m.* (crude) calcium cyanamide, "lime-nitrogen." **-sulfat,** *n.* sulfate of lime (calcium sulfate). **-talkspat,** *m.* dolomite. **-tiegel,** *m.* lime crucible. **-tropfstein,** *m.* calcareous dripstone. **-tuff,** *m.* calcareous tufa. **-tünche,** *f.* (lime) whitewash.

**kalkulatorisch,** *a.* calculating, calculated. — *adv.* by calculation.

**kalkulieren,** *v.t.* & *i.* calculate.

**Kalk-untergrund,** *m.* (*Dyeing*) lime ground. **-verbindung,** *f.* lime compound, calcium compound. **-verseifung,** *f.* saponification with lime. **-wasser,** *n.* limewater. **-weinstein,** *m.* calcareous tartar. **-werk,** *n.* lime works. **-zementmörtel,** *m.* lime-cement mortar. **-zufuhr,** *f.* addition or supply of lime. **-zuschlag,** *m.* lime(stone) flux.

**kallös,** *a.* callous.

**Kalmie,** *f.* mountain laurel (*Kalmia latifolia*).

**Kalmus,** *m.* calamus. **-öl,** *n.* calamus oil. **-wurzel,** *f.* calamus root.

**Kalorescenz,** *f.* calorescence.

**Kaloriengehalt,** *m.* calorie content.

**Kalorifer,** *m.* heater, radiator.

**Kalorimetrie,** *f.* calorimetry.

**kalorimetrisch,** *a.* calorimetric.

**kalorisch,** *a.* caloric.

**kalorisieren,** *v.t.* calorize.

**kaloritieren,** *v.t.* (*Metal.*) calorize, aluminize.

**Kalotte,** *f.* cap, calotte; cup.

**kalt,** *a.* cold, cool. — **kalter Satz,** (*Brewing*) cold-water extract of malt.

**Kalt-absetzen,** *n.* cold settling or sedimentation. **-aushärtung,** *f.* (*Metal.*) age hardening at room temperature; cold tempering. **-bad,** *n.* cold bath. **-bearbeitung,** *f.* cold-working.

**kalt-bildsam,** *a.* plastic or ductile (when cold). **-bläsig,** *a.* (*Metal.*) refractory.

**Kalt-bleiche,** *f.* cold bleaching. **-blüter,** *m.* cold-blooded animal. **-bruch,** *m.* cold-shortness.

**kaltbrüchig,** *a.* cold-short.

**Kaltbrüchigkeit,** *f.* cold-shortness.

**Kälte,** *f.* cold, coldness, chill. **-anlage,** *f.* refrigerating plant. **-anwendung,** *f.* employment of cold, refrigeration. **-bad,** *n.* cold bath, cooling bath.

**kältebeständig,** *a.* resistant to cold; antifreezing, antifreeze.

**Kälte-beständigkeit,** *f.* resistance to cold. **-chemie,** *f.* chemistry of cold, cryochemistry. **-einheit,** *f.* unit of cold, frigorie.

**kälteempfindlich,** *a.* sensitive to cold.

**Kälteempfindung,** *f.* sensation of cold.

**kälteerzeugend,** *p.a.* refrigerating, cryogenic, frigorific.

**Kälte-erzeuger,** *m.* refrigerator. **-erzeugung,** *f.* production of cold, refrigeration.

**kältefest,** *a.* resistant to cold.

**Kälte-festigkeit,** *f.* resistance to cold. **-grad,** *m.* degree of cold, degree below zero. **-industrie,** *f.* refrigerating industry. **-leistung,** *f.* refrigerating capacity. **-maschine,** *f.* refrigerating machine. **-mischung,** *f.* freezing mixture. **-mittel,** *n.* refrigerating agent.

**kälten,** *v.t.* chill, refrigerate.

**Kälte-probe,** *f.* cold test. **-punkt,** *m.* (*Oils*) solidifying point.

**kalterblasen,** *a.* (*Iron*) cold-blast.

**Kälte-regler,** *m.* cryostat. **-schutzmittel,** *n.* protective agent against cold. **-starre,** *f.* stiffness (or rigidity or rigor) due to cold. **-stoff,** *m.* freezing mixture. **-träger,** *m.* cooling medium. **-verfahren,** *n.* cold process; cold storage.

**Kalt-färben,** *n.* cold-dyeing. **-gebläse,** *n.* cold blast.

**kalt-gerührt,** *a.* cold-stirred. **-gewalzt,** *p.a.* cold-rolled. **-gezogen,** *p.a.* cold-drawn. **-giessen,** *v.t.* cast cold. **-gründig,** *a.* (of soil) cold.

**Kaltguss,** *m.* spoiled casting.

**kalthämmerbar,** *a.* malleable.

**kalthämmern,** *v.t.* cold-hammer, cold-forge.

**Kalt-hefe,** *f.* wild yeast. **-lack,** *m.* cold varnish. **-lagerung,** *f.* cold storage.

**kaltlegen,** *v.t.* blow out, stop ( a furnace).

**Kaltleim,** *m.* cold glue.

**kalt-liegen,** *v.i.* (*Metal.*) be out of operation. **-lösen,** *v.t.* dissolve (in the) cold.

**Kalt-luft,** *f.* cold air. **-luftgas,** *n.* carbureted water gas. **-nachverdichten,** *n.* (*Metal.*) cold working following heat treatment. **-schliff,** *m.* (*Paper*) cold-ground pulp. **-sprödigkeit,** *f.* cold-shortness.

**kaltverformen,** *v.t.* form (when) cold, work cold.

**Kaltvulkanisat,** *n.* (*Rubber*) cold-cured goods.

**kaltvulkanisiert,** *a.* (*Rubber*) cold-cured.
**kaltwalzen,** *v.t.* cold-roll.
**Kaltwasser-bad,** *n.* cold-water bath. **-farbe,** *f.* cold-water color or paint. **-probe,** *f.* cold-water test. **-strom,** *m.* stream or current of cold water.
**Kaltwerden,** *n.* becoming cold, cooling.
**kaltziehen,** *v.t.* cold-draw.
**kalz.,** *abbrev.* (kalziniert) calcined.
**Kalzi-, kalzi-,** calci-.
**Kalzinator,** *m.* calciner.
**kalzinieren,** *v.t.* calcine.
**Kalzinierofen,** *m.* calcining furnace or kiln.
**Kalzinierung,** *f.* calcination.
**Kalzit,** *n.* calcite.
**Kalzium,** *n.* calcium. (For compounds see Calcium-.).
**kam,** *pret.* (of kommen) came, etc.
**Kambaholz, Kambalholz,** *n.* camwood.
**Kambodscha,** *n.* Cambodia.
**kambrisch,** *a.* Cambrian.
**Kamee,** *f.* cameo.
**Kamel,** *n.* camel. **-haarpinsel,** *m.* camel's-hair brush.
**Kamelie,** *f.* camellia.
**Kamera,** *f.* camera; chamber.
**Kamerad,** *m.* comrade, fellow.
**Kamfer,** *m.* camphor. See Kampher-.
**Kamholz,** *n.* camwood.
**kamig, kamicht,** *a.* moldy.
**Kamille,** *f.* camomile.
**Kamillenöl,** *n.* camomile oil.
**Kamin,** *m.* chimney, stack; fireplace. **-brenner,** *m.* burner with a chimney. **-haube,** *f.* chimney hood. **-russ,** *m.* chimney soot.
**Kamm,** *m.* comb; cog (of a wheel); cam; ridge, crest. **-abfall,** *m.* combings.
**kämmen,** *v.t.* comb; card; notch.
**Kammer,** *f.* chamber; room; compartment; ventricle (of the heart); camera.
**Kämmerchen,** *n.* little chamber, closet.
**Kammer-kristall,** *m.* chamber crystal. **-ofen,** *m.* chamber oven; compartment kiln; (*Coke*) by-product oven. **-prozess,** *m.* chamber process. **-säure,** *f.* chamber acid. **-schlamm,** *m.* chamber sludge. **-sohle,** *f.* chamber floor. **-tuch,** *n.* cambric. **-wasser,** *n.* (*Anat.*) aqueous humor. **-wesen,** *n.* finances.
**Kammfett,** *n.* horse grease.
**kammförmig,** *a.* comb-shaped.
**Kamm-garn,** *n.* worsted (yarn). **-gras,** *n.* dog's-tail. **-kies,** *m.* cockscomb pyrites (variety of marcasite). **-muschel,** *f.* scallop. **-rad,** *n.* cog wheel. **-wolle,** *f.* combing wool, long wool. **-zug,** *m.* (*Textiles*) combed material, (of wool) slubbing.
**Kamomille,** *f.* camomile.
**Kampagne,** *f.* campaign, (working) season.
**Kampane,** *f.* bell jar.
**Kampescheholz,** *n.* campeachy wood (logwood).
**Kampf,** *m.* combat, conflict, battle, fight, warfare.
**Kampfen,** *n.* camphene.
**kämpfen,** *v.i.* battle, contend, fight.
**Kampfer,** *m.* camphor. (For compounds see Kampher-.)
**Kämpfer,** *m.* combatant, fighter.
**Kämpferid,** *n.* kaempferide.
**Kämpferin,** *n.* kaempferin.
**Kämpferol,** *m.* kaempferol.
**Kampfgas,** *n.* gas used in warfare, war gas.
**Kampfin,** *n.* camphine.
**Kampfor,** *m.* camphor. See Kampher-.
**Kampfplatz,** *m.* field of battle, arena.
**Kampfstoff,** *m.* war material, esp. a chemical warfare agent. **-beschuss,** *m.* chemical-shell fire. **-bombe,** *f.* chemical bomb, gas bomb. **-gehalt,** *m.* (*Mil.*) gas concentration. **-schwaden,** *m.* (*Mil.*) chemical fumes, gas fumes. **-sperre,** *f.* (*Mil.*) chemical obstacle. **-verwendung,** *f.* (*Mil.*) use of chemical warfare agents. **-zerstäuber,** *m.* (*Mil.*) chemical spray apparatus.
**Kampfwagen,** *m.* (*Mil.*) tank, also combat car.
**Kamphen,** *n.* camphene.
**Kampher,** *m.* camphor. **-art,** *f.* (variety of) camphor.
**kampherartig,** *a.* camphor-like, camphoraceous.
**Kampher-baum,** *m.* camphor tree. **-chinon,** *n.* camphorquinone. **-essig,** *m.* camphorated vinegar. **-geist,** *m.* spirit of camphor.
**kampher-haltig,** *a.* containing camphor, camphorated. **-ieren,** *v.t.* camphorate.
**kamphern,** *v.t.* camphorate.
**Kampher-öl,** *n.* camphor oil; (*Pharm.*) camphorated oil. **-phoron,** *n.* camphorphorone. **-säure,** *f.* camphoric acid. **-säuresalz,** *n.* camphorate. **-spiritus,** *m.* spirit of camphor. **-wein,** *m.* camphorated wine.
**Kamphorsäure,** *f.* camphoric acid.
**kanadisch,** *a.* Canadian, Canada.
**Kanadischbalsam,** *m.* Canada balsam.
**Kanal,** *m.* canal; channel; conduit; sewer; flue; tunnel. **-gas,** *n.* sewer gas.
**Kanalisation,** *f.* sewerage; canalization.
**Kanalisations-rohr,** *n.*, **-röhre,** *f.* sewer pipe, water pipe, gas pipe, or electric conduit.
**Kanal-jauche,** *f.* (liquid) sewage. **-ofen,** *m.* tunnel kiln. **-rohr,** *n.* = Kanalisationsrohr. **-strahl,** *m.* canal ray. **-trockner,** *m.* tunnel drying oven. **-wasser,** *n.* sewage.
**Kanarien-.** canary. **-farbe,** *f.* canary color; canarin.
**kanarien-farbig,** *a.* canary-colored, canary. **-gelb,** *a.* canary-yellow.
**Kanarien-hirse,** *f.* canary seed. **-holz,** *n.* canary wood. **-samen,** *m.* canary seed. **-vogel,** *m.* canary bird, canary.

**kandeln,** *v.t.* channel, flute, groove.
**kandieren,** *v.t.* candy; coat (seed).
**Kandis, -zucker,** *m.* sugar candy. **-störzel,** *m.* mother liquor from sugar candy.
**Kanditen-.** candy.
**Kaneel, Kanel,** *m.* cinnamon; (**weisser**) canella; clove cassia; (**brauner**) Ceylon cinnamon. **-bruch,** *m.* broken cinnamon. **-granat, -stein,** *m.* cinnamon stone (essonite).
**Kanellarinde,** *f.* canella bark.
**Kanevas,** *m.* canvas.
**Känguruh,** *n.* kangaroo. **-leder,** *n.* kangaroo leather.
**Kaninchen,** *n.* rabbit.
**kann,** *pr. 1 & 3 sing.* (of können) can.
**Kännchen,** *n.* small can.
**Kanne,** *f.* can; canister; jug, pot, liter.
**kannelieren,** *v.t.* channel, flute, groove.
**Kannelierung,** *f.* channeling, fluting.
**Kannelkohle,** *f.* cannel coal.
**Kannenzinn,** *n.* pewter.
**kannte,** *pret.* (of kennen) knew.
**Kanone,** *f.* cannon, gun.
**Kanonen-bronze,** *f.* gun metal. **-gut, -metall,** *n.* gun metal. **-ofen,** *m.* bomb furnace. **-pulver,** *n.* cannon powder. **-rohr,** *n.*, **-röhre,** *f.* bomb-furnace tube; gun barrel.
**kanonisch,** *a.* canonical.
**Känozoikum,** *n.* (*Geol.*) Cenozoic.
**Kansasstein,** *m.* Arkansas stone (a kind of novaculite).
**Kante,** *f.* edge; border, margin, brim; lace.
**kanten,** *v.t.* edge, border; square (stones); cant, tilt; turn on edge; bend. **-weise,** *adv.* edgewise, on edge.
**Kanthar-.** See also Canthar-.
**Kantharide(n),** *f.* (*Pharm.*) cantharides, Spanish fly
**Kantholz,** *n.* squared timber.
**kantig,** *a.* edged, angular, squared, beveled.
**-kantig.** -edged; -angled.
**Kantille,** *f.* gold or silver wire, purl.
**Kantine,** *f.* canteen.
**Kanüle,** *f.* cannula, tubule, small tube.
**Kanzlei,** *f.* office (esp., for records); chancery. **-papier,** *n.* (*Paper*) legal cap, foolscap. **-tinte,** *f.* record ink.
**kaolinisieren,** *v.t.* kaolinize.
**Kaolinisierung,** *f.* kaolinization.
**Kaolinlager,** *n.* kaolin deposit.
**Kaoutschuk,** *m.* caoutchouc, rubber. See Kautschuk-.
**Kap,** *n.* cape, promontory.
**Kap.,** *abbrev.* (Kapitel) chapter.
**Kapaun,** *m.* capon.
**Kapazitanz,** *f.* (*Elec.*) capacitance.
**Kapazität,** *f.* capacity.
**kapazitätsarm,** *a.* of low capacity.
**kapazitiv,** *a.* capacitive.

**Kapelle,** *f.* cupel; sand bath; subliming dish; capsule; priming cap; chapel; band.
**Kapellen-abfall,** *m.* loss in cupellation. **-asche,** *f.* bone ash. **-form,** *f.* cupel mold. **-gold,** *n.* fine gold. **-kläre,** *f.* = Kapellenpulver. **-ofen,** *m.* cupelling furnace, assay furnace; sublimation furnace. **-probe,** *f.* cupel test, cupellation. **-pulver,** *n.* cupel dust, bone ash. **-raub,** *m.* loss in cupellation. **-silber,** *n.* fine silver. **-träger,** *m.* cupel holder. **-zug,** *m.* = Kapellenraub.
**kapellieren,** *v.t.* cupel.
**Kaper,** *f.* (*Bot.*) caper.
**Kapgranat,** *m.* Cape ruby (pyrope).
**kapillar,** *a.* capillary.
**Kapillar,** *n.* capillary. **-affinität,** *f.* capillary affinity.
**kapillaraktiv,** *a.* active in lowering surface tension, surface-active.
**Kapillar-analyse,** *f.* capillary analysis. **-anziehung,** *f.* capillary attraction. **-chemie,** *f.* capillary chemistry. **-druck,** *m.* capillary pressure.
**Kapillare,** *f.* capillary, capillary tube.
**Kapillar-flasche,** *f.* capillary bottle or flask. **-fläschchen,** *n.* small capillary bottle or flask.
**kapillarförmig,** *a.* capillary, capillaceous.
**Kapillar-gang,** *m.* capillary passage. **-gefäss,** *n.* capillary vessel.
**kapillar-inaktiv,** *a.* not lowering surface tension, surface-inactive. **-isieren,** *v.t.* investigate by capillary analysis.
**Kapillarität,** *f.* capillarity.
**Kapillaritätsanziehung,** *f.* capillary attraction.
**Kapillar-kraft,** *f.* capillary force. **-kreislauf,** *n.* capillary circulation. **-rohr, -röhrchen,** *n.*, **-röhre,** *f.* capillary tube. **-spannung,** *f.* capillary tension. **-strömung,** *f.* capillary flow. **-versuch,** *m.* capillary test or experiment. **-wirkung,** *f.* capillary action.
**Kapir,** *m.* kefir.
**Kapitel,** *n.* chapter; section; topic.
**Kapocköl, Kapoköl,** *n.* kapok oil.
**Kapotte,** *f.* hood, cap.
**Kappe,** *f.* cap; hood; top, dome, crown, etc.
**kappeln,** *v.t.* top.
**kappen,** *v.t.* top (trees); cut; caponize.
**Kappenflasche,** *f.* bottle with cap.
**kappenförmig,** *a.* cap-shaped, hood-shaped.
**Kappenpfeffer,** *m.* Guinea pepper.
**Kapper,** *f.* caper.
**Kapphahn,** *m.* capon.
**Kaprinsäure,** etc. see Caprinsäure, etc.
**Kapsel,** *f.* capsule; case, box; cap; bubble cap; priming cap; (*Founding*) chill, mold; (*Ceram.*) sagger.
**kapselartig,** *a.* capsular.
**Kapsel-blitz,** *m.* (*Photog.*) flashlight capsule.

**-boden,** *m.* bubble plate, bubble tray. **-färbung,** *f.* (*Micros.*) capsule staining.
**kapselförmig,** *a.* capsular.
**Kapsel-frucht,** *f.* (*Bot.*) capsule. **-guss,** *m.* casting in chills; chilled work. **-lack,** *m.* capping lacquer, capsule lacquer. **-mutter,** *f.* cap nut, box nut; screw cap.
**kapseln,** *v.t.* enclose, incase, capsulate; cap.
**Kapselton,** *m.* sagger clay.
**Kapselung,** *f.* enclosing, incasing, capsulation; capping.
**kaputt,** *a.* broken, ruined, done for.
**Kapuze,** *f.* hood, cowl.
**Kapuziner,** *m.* Capuchin. **-kresse,** *f.* Indian cress, nasturtium.
**Kap-wein,** *m.* Cape wine. **-wolle,** *f.* Cape wool.
**Kapyr,** *n.* kefir.
**Karabinerhaken,** *m.* snap hook, spring catch.
**Karaghenmoos,** *n.* carrageen, Irish moss.
**karaibisch,** *a.* Caribbean.
**karamelisieren,** *v.t.* caramelize.
**Karapöl,** *n.* carap oil, carapa oil.
**Karat-gewicht,** *n.* troy weight. **-gold,** *n.* alloyed gold.
**karatieren,** *v.t.* alloy (gold or silver).
**Karatierung,** *f.* alloying (of gold or silver).
**-karatig, -karätig,** *a.* -carat (as *achtzehn-karatig,* eighteen-carat).
**Karb-.** see Carb-.
**Karbe,** *f.* caraway.
**Kardamom,** *m.* cardamom. **-öl,** *n.* cardamom oil.
**Kardangelenk,** *n.* Cardan joint, universal joint.
**kardieren,** *v.t.* card (wool, etc.).
**kardinalrot,** *a.* cardinal(-red).
**Kardobenedikt,** *m.* blessed thistle.
**Karfunkel,** *m.* carbuncle. **-stein,** *m.* garnet, esp. almandite.
**karg,** *a.* stingy, close; poor (soil).
**kargen,** *v.i.* be sparing, be stingy.
**kärglich,** *a.* sparing, spare, scanty.
**karibisch,** *a.* Caribbean.
**karieren,** *v.t.* checker, check; crosshatch.
**Kariteöl,** *n.* karite oil, shea butter.
**Karmalaun,** *m.* (*Micros.*) carmalum.
**Karmelitergeist,** *m.* Carmelite water (an old toilet water made from balm mint).
**karmesin,** *a.* crimson.
**Karmesinbeeren,** *f.pl.* kermes berries, kermes.
**karmesin-farbig,** *a.* crimson-colored. **-rot,** *a.* crimson-red, crimson.
**Karmin,** *m.* carmine. **-blau,** *n.* indigo carmine. **-farbe,** *f.* carmine color, carmine.
**karminfarben,** *a.* carmine.
**Karminlack,** *m.* carmine lake.
**Karminochinon,** *n.* carminoquinone.
**karminrot,** *a.* carmine-red, carmine.
**Karmin-rot,** *n.* carmine red. **-säure,** *f.* carminic acid. **-spat,** *m.* (*Min.*) carminite. **-stoff,** *m.* carminic acid.
**karmoisin,** *a.* crimson.
**karmoisinrot,** *a.* crimson, crimson-red.
**Karnallit,** *m.* carnallite.
**Karnauba-.** = Carnauba-.
**Karneol,** *m.* carnelian.
**kärntisch, kärntnerisch,** *a.* Carinthian.
**Karo,** *n.* check, checker, square.
**Karobe,** *f.* carob, carob bean.
**Karosserie,** *f.* body (of a vehicle)
**Karotide,** *f.* carotid (artery).
**Karotin,** *n.* carotene, (formerly) carotin.
**Karotte,** *f.* carrot.
**Karpfen,** *m.,* **Karpfe,** *f.* carp.
**Karraghenmoos,** *n.* carrageen, Irish moss.
**Karre,** *f.* wheelbarrow; cart, car, truck.
**Karren,** *m.* cart; wheelbarrow; truck; car.
**karriert,** *a.* checkered, checked.
**Karst,** *m.* mattock, hoe; (*Geog.*) Karst, karst.
**Kartäuser-likör,** *m.* chartreuse. **-pulver,** *n.* Carthusian powder (kermes mineral). **-tee,** *m.* Mexican tea (*Chenopodium ambrosioides*).
**Karte,** *f.* card; ticket; map; chart; menu; charter.
**Kartei,** *f.* card index, card file. **-karte,** *f.* index card, filing card. **-karton,** *m.* cardboard, index board. **-wesen,** *n.* card indexing, card indexes.
**Kartell,** *n.* cartel, trust.
**Karten-blatt,** *n.* card. **-papier,** *n.* cardboard; map paper. **-pappe,** *f.* cardboard, index board.
**kartesisch,** *a.* Cartesian.
**Karthäuser-.** = Kartäuser-.
**kartieren,** *v.t.* sketch, trace, map.
**Kartoffel,** *f.* potato. **-beizung,** *f.* potato disinfection. **-branntwein,** *m.* potato spirits. **-brei,** *m.* mashed potatoes. **-fuselöl,** *n.* fusel oil from potatoes. **-kraut,** *n.* potato plant; potato tops. **-krebs,** *m.* (*Agric.*) potato wart. **-mehl,** *n.* potato flour. **-nährboden,** *m.* potato culture medium. **-pulpe,** *f.* potato pulp. **-sirup,** *m.* glucose sirup from potato starch. **-spiritus,** *m.* potato spirits. **-stärke,** *f.* potato starch. **-walzmehl,** *n.* roller-mill potato flour. **-zucker,** *m.* potato sugar (glucose from potato starch).
**Karton,** *m.* carton, (paper)board, boxboard; carton, paper-board box.
**Kartonage,** *f.* = Kartonnage.
**kartonieren,** *v.t.* bind in boards.
**Kartonnage,** *f.* paper board, pasteboard, cardboard; paper-board box, carton.
**Kartonnagen-fabrikation,** *f.* paper-board making; carton making. **-leim,** *m.* boxmakers' glue.
**Kartonpapier,** *n.* paper board.

**Kartothek,** *f.* card collection, card catalog or index.
**Kartusche,** *f.* cartridge; cartouche.
**Kartuschpapier,** *n.* cartridge paper.
**Karub,** *m.*, **Karube,** *f.* carob.
**Karyokinese,** *f.* (*Biol.*) karyokinesis.
**Karzinom,** *n.* (*Med.*) carcinoma.
**karzinomatös,** *a.* carcinomatous.
**kaschieren,** *v.t.* cover, coat, line, back; hide, conceal.
**Kaschierpapier,** *n.* lining paper.
**Kaschierung,** *f.* covering, etc. (see kaschieren).
**Kaschmir,** *m.* cashmere.
**Kaschu,** *n.* catechu, cutch.
**kaschutieren,** *v.t.* dye with catechu or cutch.
**Käse,** *m.* cheese; cheese-shaped object, as a disk of fireclay used as a crucible stand.
**käseartig,** *a.* cheesy, caseous.
**Käse-bildung,** *f.* cheese formation; caseation. **-firnis,** *m.* (*Med.*) vernix caseosa.
**käseförmig,** *a.* cheese-shaped, flat-cylindrical.
**Kasein,** *n.* casein. (See Casein-.) **-farbstoff,** *m.* casein paint. **-seide,** *f.* casein silk, casein rayon.
**Käse-lab,** *n.* rennet. **-leim,** *m.* casein glue.
**käsen,** *v.i.* curd, curdle.
**Käse-pappel,** *f.* wild mallow (*Malva sylvestris*). **-rei,** *f.* cheese factory; cheese making. **-reifung,** *f.* cheese ripening or curing.
**käsesauer,** *a.* lactate of.
**Käse-säure,** *f.* lactic acid. **-stoff,** *m.* casein.
**Kasette,** *f.* little case.
**Käsewasser,** *n.* whey.
**käsig,** *a.* cheesy, caseous, curdy.
**Kasimir,** *m.* (*Textiles*) cassimere.
**Kaskadenschaltung,** *f.* (*Elec.*) cascade connection.
**Kaskarillenrinde,** *f.* cascarilla bark.
**kaspisch,** *a.* Caspian.
**Kassaunzucker,** *m.* raw or muscovado sugar, cassonade.
**Kassawa,** *f.* cassava. **-mehl,** *n.* cassava starch, cassava.
**Kasse,** *f.* (money) box, chest, safe; cash; pay office, ticket office, etc.
**Kasseler Braun.** Cassel brown.
**Kasseler Erde.** Cassel earth.
**Kasseler-gelb,** *n.* Cassel yellow. **-grün,** *n.* Cassel green.
**Kasserolle,** *f.* casserole.
**Kassette,** *f.* sagger, casket, coffer; box; (*Photog.*) plate (or film) holder.
**Kassia, Kassie,** *f.* cassia. **-öl,** *n.* cassia oil.
**Kassien-blüten,** *f.pl.* cassia buds. **-rinde,** *f.* cassia bark.
**kassieren,** *v.t.* cancel, annul; cashier; cash.
**Kassierer,** *m.* cashier, treasurer, ticket agent.
**Kassiopeium,** *n.* cassiopeium (lutecium).
**Kassiuspurpur,** *m.* purple of Cassius.
**Kassler Braun.** Cassel brown.
**Kastanie,** *f.* chestnut.
**Kastanienauszug,** *m.* chestnut extract.
**kastanienbraun,** *a.* chestnut-brown, chestnut.
**Kastanienholz,** *n.* chestnut wood.
**Kästchen,** *n.* little chest, casket; alveolus.
**Kasten,** *m.* chest, box, case, trunk, safe, cabinet; crate, frame; vat, back, beck, tank; crucible (of a furnace); (*Founding*) flask; (*Ceram.*) sagger; (*Jewelry*) collet. **-blau,** *n.* pencil blue (indigo blue produced by vat dyeing). **-mälzerei,** *f.* box malting, compartment malting.
**Kastoröl,** *n.* castor oil.
**kastrieren,** *v.t.* castrate.
**Katabolismus,** *m.* catabolism.
**katalanisch,** *a.* Catalan.
**Katalase,** *f.* catalase.
**Katalisator,** *m.* catalyst.
**katalogisieren,** *v.t.* catalog, list.
**katalonisch,** *a.* Catalan.
**Katalysator,** *m.* catalyst.
**Katalysatorengift,** *n.* catalyst poison.
**katalysatorisch,** *a.* catalytic.
**Katalyse, Katalysis,** *f.* catalysis.
**katalysieren,** *v.t.* catalyze.
**katalytisch,** *a.* catalytic.
**Kataphorese,** *f.* cataphoresis.
**katarrhalisch,** *a.* catarrhal.
**Katechin,** *n.* catechol, catechin. **-gerbstoff,** *m.* catechol tan. **-säure,** *f.* catechuic acid (catechol).
**Katechu,** *n.* catechu, cashoo. **-braun,** *n.* catechu brown, catechu, cutch (the color). **-gerbsäure,** *f.* catechutannic acid. **-säure,** *f.* catechuic acid (catechol).
**kathartisch,** *a.* cathartic.
**Kathete,** *f.* (*Geom.*) cathetus.
**Kathoden-dichte,** *f.* cathode density. **-fläche,** *f.* cathode surface. **-licht,** *n.* cathode glow. **-niederschlag,** *m.* cathode deposit. **-raum,** *m.* cathode space, space around the cathode. **-röhre,** *f.* cathode-ray tube. **-strahl,** *m.* cathode ray. **-strahlenbündel,** *n.* cathode beam. **-strahlröhre,** *f.* cathode-ray tube. **-strahlung,** *f.* cathode radiation. **-strom,** *m.* cathode current. **-zerstäubung,** *f.* cathode sputtering.
**kathodisch,** *a.* cathodic.
**kathodochemisch,** *a.* cathodochemical.
**Katholyt,** *m.* catholyte.
**Kation,** *n.* cation, kation.
**Kattun,** *m.* calico, cotton (cloth). **-druck,** *m.* calico printing. **-druckerei,** *f.* calico printing; calico printery. **-fabrik,** *f.* calico factory, cotton mill. **-färberei,** *f.* cotton (cloth) dyeing or dye works. **-presse,** *f.* calico press.
**Kätzchen,** *n.* kitten; catkin.

**Katze,** *f.* cat; (*Paper*) thread in the stuff; (*Mach.*) trolley.

**Katzen-auge,** *f.* cat's-eye; reflector; bull's-eye (lens). **-bahn,** *f.* trolley track. **-baldrian,** *m.* (common) valerian. **-darm,** *m.* catgut. **-glimmer,** *m.*, **-gold,** *n.* cat gold (yellow mica); pyrite. **-kraut,** *n.* cat thyme. **-minze, -münze,** *f.* catnip. **-minzöl,** *n.* catnip oil. **-silber,** *n.* cat silver (colorless mica).

**Kau-.** chewing, masticating, masticatory.

**kaubar,** *a.* masticable.

**kauen,** *v.t.* & *i.* chew, masticate.

**Kauf,** *m.* purchase; bargain. — **in den — nehmen,** be content with, accept. **-blei,** *n.* merchant lead, commercial lead.

**kaufen,** *v.t.* buy, purchase; deal in.

**Käufer,** *m.* buyer, purchaser, customer.

**Kauf-gut,** *n.* merchandise. **-handel,** *m.* trade, commerce. **-laden,** *m.* store, shop. **-leute,** *pl.* merchants, tradesmen.

**käufl.,** *abbrev.* of käuflich.

**käuflich,** *a.* commercial, of commerce; merchantable, purchasable.

**Kaufmann,** *m.* merchant, tradesman.

**kaufmännisch,** *a.* mercantile, commercial; business-like.

**Kauf-muster,** *n.* commercial sample. **-zink,** *n.* commercial zinc.

**Kaugummi,** *n.* chewing gum.

**kaum,** *adv.* scarcely, hardly.

**Kau-magen,** *m.* gizzard. **-mittel,** *n.* masticatory. **-pfeffer,** *m.* betel.

**Kaupren,** *n.* cauprene.

**Kauprobe,** *f.* mastication test.

**Kauri-harz,** *n.* kauri resin, kauri. **-nuss,** *f.* kauri nut. **-öl,** *n.* kauri oil.

**kaustifizieren,** *v.t.* causticize, caustify.

**Kaustifizierung,** *f.* causticization, caustification.

**kaustisch,** *a.* caustic.

**kaustizieren,** *v.t.* causticize.

**Kaustizierung,** *f.* causticization.

**Kaustizität,** *f.* causticity.

**Kautabak,** *m.* chewing tobacco.

**Kautel,** *f.* precaution.

**Kauter,** *m.* (*Med.*) cautery.

**Kauterien,** *n.pl.* (*Med.*) cauteries.

**kauterisieren,** *v.t.* cauterize.

**kautschen,** *v.t.* couch.

**Kautschin,** *n.* caoutchene (dipentene).

**Kautschucin,** *n.* caoutchoucin, rubber oil.

**Kautschuk,** *m.* & *n.* caoutchouc, rubber. (For compounds see also Gummi-.) **-ballon,** *m.* rubber balloon; rubber bulb. **-baum,** *m.* rubber tree. **-block,** *m.* cake of rubber. **-feigenbaum,** *m.* rubber fig (*Ficus elastica*). **-firnis,** *m.* rubber varnish. **-füllung,** *f.* rubber filling or filler. **-gewebe,** *n.* rubber fabric. **-gift,** *n.* rubber poison. **-kitt,** *m.* rubber cement. **-kuchen,** *m.* cake of rubber. **-lack,** *m.* rubber varnish. **-lösung,** *f.* rubber solution. **-milch,** *m.* rubber latex. **-pflanze,** *f.* rubber(-yielding) plant. **-rohr,** *n.*, **-röhre,** *f.* rubber tube. **-saft,** *m.* rubber latex. **-schlauch,** *m.* rubber tube, rubber tubing, rubber hose. **-schnur,** *f.* rubber cord. **-stopfen,** *m.* rubber stopper. **-surrogat,** *n.* rubber substitute. **-waren,** *f.pl.* rubber goods.

**Kaverne,** *f.* cavity; cavern.

**Kawa-pfeffer,** *m.* kava. **-säure,** *f.* kavaic acid.

**kcal.,** *abbrev.* kilogram calorie.

**keck,** *a.* bold.

**Kefirkörner,** *n.pl.* kefir grains.

**Kegel,** *m.* cone; bevel, taper; pin, skittle.

**Kegel-.** conical. **-brenner,** *m.* cone burner. **-fläche,** *f.* conical surface. **-flasche,** *f.* conical flask (as an Erlenmeyer flask).

**kegelförmig,** *a.* cone-shaped, conical, coniform, tapered.

**Kegel-glas,** *n.* conical glass; conical flask. **-hahn,** *m.* stopcock (with tapered plug).

**kegelig,** *a.* conical, cone-shaped.

**Kegel-mühle,** *f.* cone mill. **-rad,** *n.* bevel wheel, bevel gear; cone wheel. **-schnitt,** *m.* conic section. **-stumpf,** *m.* truncated cone. **-ventil,** *n.* conical valve.

**keglich,** *a.* conical, cone-shaped.

**Kehl-ader,** *f.* jugular vein. **-deckel,** *m.* epiglottis. **-drüse,** *f.* thyroid gland.

**Kehle,** *f.* throat, larynx; channel, flute, groove.

**kehlen,** *v.t.* groove, channel, flute.

**Kehl-entzündung,** *f.* laryngitis. **-kopf,** *m.* larynx.

**Kehlkopf-.** laryngeal.

**Kehrbild,** *n.* inverted image; (*Photog.*) negative.

**Kehre,** *f.* turn, turning; direction.

**kehren,** *v.t.* sweep, brush; turn. — *v.r.* & *i.* turn.

**Kehricht,** *m.* & *n.* sweepings, rubbish, garbage. **-ofen,** *m.* incinerator.

**Kehr-salpeter,** *f.* saltpeter sweepings. **-salz,** *n.* salt sweepings. **-seite,** *f.* other side, reverse; wrong side. **-wert,** *m.* reciprocal value, reciprocal. **-wolle,** *f.* wool sweepings.

**Keil,** *m.* wedge; cuneus; key, cotter; gore.

**keil-ähnlich, -artig,** *a.* wedge-shaped, cuneiform, sphenoid.

**Keilbein,** *n.* sphenoid bone; cuneiform bone.

**keilen,** *v.t.* wedge; key.

**keilförmig,** *a.* = keilähnlich.

**Keil-nut,** *f.* wedge-shaped groove; keyway. **-paar,** *n.* pair of wedges, double wedge. **-riemen,** *m.* V-belt.

**Keim,** *m.* germ; embryo; (of crystallization) nucleus, seed; sprout, shoot.

**Keim-.** embryonic, germinal, germination. **-apparat,** *m.* germinating apparatus.

**keimbar,** *a.* germinable.
**Keim-bildung,** *f.* formation of nuclei. **-blatt,** *n.* cotyledon; germinal layer.
**keim-blätterig,** *a.* cotyledonous. **-blattlos,** *a.* acotyledonous.
**Keim-dauer,** *f.* duration of germination. **-drüse,** *f.* (*Biol.*) germ gland, gonad. **-drüsenhormon,** *n.* germ gland hormone, sex hormone.
**keimen,** *v.i.* germinate.
**Keimentwickelung,** *f.* development of the germ.
**keimfähig,** *a.* capable of germinating, germinable.
**Keimfähigkeit,** *f.* capability of germinating, germinating power.
**keimfrei,** *a.* free from germs (or from nuclei), sterile.
**Keim-freiheit,** *f.* freedom from germs, sterility. **-gift,** *n.* poison from germs, bacterial toxin; poison for germs.
**keimhaltig,** *a.* containing germs (or nuclei).
**Keim-haut,** *f.* blastoderm. **-kern,** *m.* (*Biol.*) germinal nucleus. **-kraft,** *f.* germinating power. **-kristall,** *m.* seed crystal, crystal nucleus. **-ling,** *n.* germ, embryo; seed crystal; seedling.
**keimlos,** *a.* germless; free from nuclei.
**Keim-plasma,** *n.* germ plasm(a). **-probe, -prüfung,** *f.* germination test. **-stoff,** *m.*, **-substanz,** *f.* germinal matter, blastema.
**keimtötend,** *p.a.* germicidal. — **keimtötendes Mittel,** germicide.
**Keim-töter,** *m.* germ killer, sterilizer. **-träger,** *m.* carrier of germs. **-trommel,** *f.* germinating drum.
**keimunfähig,** *a.* incapable of germinating.
**Keimung,** *f.* germination.
**Keimungs-dauer,** *f.* duration of germination. **-fähigkeit,** *f.* = Keimfähigkeit.
**Keimversuch,** *m.* germination test.
**keimvoll,** *a.* full of germs (or of nuclei).
**Keim-wirkung,** *f.* germ action; (of crystallization) action of nuclei. **-zählung,** *f.* bacterial count. **-zelle,** *f.* germ cell.
**kein,** *a.* no, not a.
**keiner,** *pron.* no one, none, neither.
**keinerlei,** *a.* of no sort, not any.
**keinesfalls,** *adv.* in no case.
**keineswegs,** *adv.* by no means.
**keinmal,** *adv.* not once, never.
**-keit.** A suffix used like *-heit* (which see); -ness, -hood, -dom.
**Keks, Kek,** *m.* small cake, cookie.
**Kelch,** *m.* cup; calyx; infundibulum. **-blatt,** *n.* sepal.
**kelchförmig,** *a.* cup-shaped.
**Kelch-glas,** *n.* cup-shaped test glass. **-mensur,** *f.* measuring cup.
**Kelen,** *n.* (*Pharm.*) kelene (ethyl chloride).
**Kelle,** *f.* ladle; scoop; trowel.
**kellen,** *v.t.* ladle.
**Keller,** *m.* cellar.
**Kellerei,** *f.* cellarage; brewery.
**Keller-geschoss,** *n.* basement. **-hals,** *m.* mezereon (*Daphne mezereum*).
**Kelter,** *f.* winepress.
**keltern,** *v.t.* press (grapes).
**Kelterwein,** *n.* wine from expressed juice.
**Keltium,** *n.* celtium.
**Kenn-.** characteristic, distinctive, indicative.
**kennbar,** *a.* knowable, distinguishable; remarkable.
**kennen,** *v.t.* know.
**Kenner,** *m.* connoisseur, expert, professional.
**Kenn-grösse,** *f.* characteristic quantity. **-linie,** *f.* characteristic line, characteristic, graph, curve. **-linienknick,** *m.* break or knee in a characteristic or graph. **-marke,** *f.* identification mark. **-merkmal,** *n.* characteristic; criterion. **-nummer,** *f.* identification number.
**kenntlich,** *a.* knowable, distinguishable; distinctive; distinct, clear. — **— machen,** make known, characterize, mark.
**Kenntnis,** *f.* knowledge; information, notice.
**Kennung,** *f.* = Kennzeichen.
**Kenn-wort,** *n.* identifying word, code word. **-zahl,** *f.* characteristic value or number, coefficient, constant. **-zeichen,** *n.* mark, sign, signal, indication; characteristic; specifications; criterion; symptom.
**kennzeichnen,** *v.t.* mark, denote; distinguish; identify; characterize. — **kennzeichnend,** *p.a.* indicative, characteristic.
**Kennzeichnung,** *f.* marking, etc. (see kennzeichnen); character; mark, sign.
**Kennzeichnungsfarbe,** *f.* sighting color.
**Kennziffer,** *f.* characteristic (of a logarithm); index; code number.
**Keph-.** ceph-.
**Keramik,** *f.* ceramics.
**Keramiker,** *m.* ceramist.
**keramisch,** *a.* ceramic.
**Kerargyrit,** *m.*, **Kerat,** *n.* cerargyrite.
**Kerbe,** *f.*, **Kerb,** *m.* notch, nick, groove, slit, slot, indentation.
**Kerbel,** *m.* (*Bot.*) chervil.
**kerben,** *v.t.* notch, indent, groove, nick.
**kerbig,** *a.* notched, indented; grooved; jagged.
**Kerbschlag,** *m.*, **-probe,** *f.*, **-versuch,** *m.* notched-bar impact test.
**Kerb-tier,** *n.* insect. **-tierkunde,** *f.* entomology. **-zähigkeit,** *f.* (*Metal.*) notch toughness, impact resistance or strength (in notched-bar test).
**Kerf,** *m.* insect; = Kerbe. **-kunde,** *f.* entomology.
**Kermes-beeren,** *f.pl.* kermes berries, kermes;

(vegetabilische) pokeberries. **-körner,** *n.pl.* kermes grains, kermes.

**kermesrot,** *a.* scarlet.

**Kermes-rot,** *n.* kermes red, scarlet. **-scharlach,** *m.* kermes scarlet, French scarlet. **-schildlaus,** *f.* kermes insect.

**Kern,** *m.* nucleus; kernel, pip, stone; pith; core; heart; gist; (*Soap*) curd.

**Kern-.** nuclear; pithy, choice. **-abstand,** *m.* internuclear distance. **-anregung,** *f.* nuclear excitation. **-aufbau,** *m.* nuclear structure; nuclear synthesis. **-bewegung,** *f.* nuclear motion. **-bildung,** *f.* nucleation. **-bindemittel,** *n.* (*Founding*) core binder.

**kern-chloriert,** *a.* chlorinated in the nucleus. **-echt,** *a.* true to type.

**Kern-eisen,** *n.* mottled white pig iron; (*Elec.*) core iron. **-eiweisskörper, -eiweisstoff,** *m.* nucleoprotein. **-farbe,** *f.*, **-färbemittel,** *n.*, **-farbstoff,** *m.* nuclear stain. **-färbung,** *f.* (*Micros.*) nuclear staining. **-faser,** *f.* nuclear fiber or filament.

**kern-faul,** *a.* rotten at the core or heart. **-fern,** *a.* (of electrons) outer, peripheral. **-frisch,** *a.* quite fresh. **-gebunden,** *p.a.* united to a (or the) nucleus.

**Kern-gehalt,** *m.* nuclear content; nuclear concentration. **-gehäuse,** *n.* core. **-guss,** *m.* (*Founding*) cored work.

**kernhaltig,** *a.* containing a nucleus or kernel, nucleate(d).

**Kern-hefe,** *f.* seed yeast. **-höhle,** *f.* (*Biol.*) nuclear vacuole. **-holz,** *n.* heart wood.

**kernig,** *a.* strong, stout, solid, firm, vigorous; (of liquors) full; (of leather) compact; kernelly; pithy.

**-kernig.** -nuclear.

**Kernigkeit,** *f.* strength, etc. (see kernig); (*Leather*) fullness, body.

**Kern-isomer,** *n.* nuclear isomer, ring isomer. **-isomerie,** *f.* nucleus (or nuclear) isomerism. **-körper,** *m.*, **-körperchen,** *n.* nucleolus. **-ladung,** *f.* nuclear charge; main charge. **-ladungszahl,** *f.* nuclear-charge number, atomic number. **-leder,** *n.* butt or bend leather.

**kernlos,** *a.* without a nucleus, anucleate; coreless.

**Kern-mehl,** *n.* best grade of flour, firsts. **-membran,** *f.* nuclear membrane. **-milch,** *f.* buttermilk.

**kernnah,** *a.* close to the nucleus.

**Kern-obst,** *n.* stone fruit, pip fruit. **-öl,** *n.* kernel oil, specif. palm kernel oil; (*Founding*) core oil. **-physik,** *f.* nuclear physics. **-polymerie,** *f.* nuclear polymerism. **-probe,** *f.* core sample. **-pulver,** *n.* progressive burning powder. **-punkt,** *m.* nucleus; essential point. **-rückfeinen,** *n.* (*Metal.*) core refining. **-saft,** *m.* (*Biol.*) nuclear fluid. **-salz,** *n.* rock salt. **-sand,** *m.* core sand. **-schatten,** *m.* complete shadow, umbra. **-schliff,** *m.* convex part of a ground joint. **-schwarz,** *n.* a carbon black from fruit kernels; (*Micros.*) nucleus black. **-schwingung,** *f.* nuclear vibration. **-seife,** *f.* curd soap, grain soap. **-spaltung,** *f.* nuclear fission. **-spin,** *m.* nuclear spin. **-stäbchen,** *n.* (*Biol.*) chromosome. **-stoff,** *m.* nuclear substance; nuclein. **-synthese,** *f.* nuclear synthesis. **-teilung,** *f.* nuclear division. **-theorie,** *f.* nuclear theory. **-tinktion,** *f.* nuclear staining.

**kerntrocken,** *a.* thoroly dry.

**Kern-umwandlung,** *f.* nuclear transformation, transmutation. **-verknüpfung,** *f.* linkage to a nucleus. **-verschmelzung,** *f.* nuclear fusion. **-wechselwirkung,** *f.* nuclear interaction. **-werkstoff,** *m.* core material. **-wolle,** *f.* prime wool. **-zahl,** *f.* number of nuclei. **-zelle,** *f.* nuclear cell. **-zerfall,** *m.* nuclear disintegration. **-zerplatzen,** *n.* nuclear explosion or disintegration.

**Kerosin,** *n.* kerosene.

**Kerze,** *f.* candle; (*Mach.*) spark plug.

**Kerzen-docht,** *m.* candle wick. **-filter,** *n.* candle filter, filter candle. **-masse,** *f.* candle composition. **-nuss,** *f.* candlenut. **-nussöl,** *n.* candlenut oil. **-stärke,** *f.* candle power. **zündung,** *f.* electric ignition.

**Kessel,** *m.* kettle, caldron, copper; boiler; tank; kier; still; basin, reservoir; kennel. **-asche,** *f.* potash (potassium carbonate). **-betrieb,** *m.* boiler operation. **-blech,** *n.* boiler plate, boiler iron. **-dampf,** *m.* boiler steam, live steam. **-druck,** *m.* boiler pressure. **-fabrik,** *f.* boiler factory. **-färberei,** *f.* kettle dyeing.

**kesselförmig,** *a.* kettle-shaped.

**Kessel-gas,** *n.* boiler flue gas. **-haus,** *n.* boiler house. **-hausbetrieb,** *m.* boiler-house operation or management. **-kochung,** *f.* (*Textiles*) kier boiling. **-kohle,** *f.* boiler coal, steam coal.

**kesseln,** *v.t.* (*Expl.*) chamber.

**Kessel-niederschlag,** *m.* deposit in a kettle, boiler or reservoir. **-ofen,** *m.* pot furnace; crucible furnace. **-rohr,** *n.* boiler tube. **-spannung,** *f.* boiler pressure. **-speisewasser,** *n.* boiler feed water. **-speisung,** *f.* boiler feeding, boiler feed.

**Kesselstein,** *m.* boiler scale; compass brick. **-ablagerung,** *f.* deposit(ion) of boiler scale. **-beseitigung,** *f.* removal of boiler scale. **-beseitigungsmittel,** *n.* (boiler) scale remover, disincrustant. **-bilder, -bildner,** *m.* (boiler) scale former. **-bildung,** *f.* (boiler) scale formation, incrustation. **-gegenmittel,** *n.* boiler compound, disincrustant. **-kruste,** *f.* incrustation of boiler scale. **-lösemittel, -lösungsmittel,** *n.* (boiler) scale solvent, disincrustant. **-mittel,** *n.* boiler compound, disincrustant, anti-incrustant. **-schicht,** *f.* layer of (boiler) scale. **-verhütung,** *f.* (boiler) scale prevention. **-verhütungsmittel,** *n.* boiler compound, anti-incrustant.

**Kessel-wagen,** *m.* tank car; tank truck or wagon. **-wand,** *f.* boiler wall. **-wasser,** *n.* boiler water.

**Ketogruppe,** *f.* keto group.

**Keton,** *n.* ketone.

**ketonartig,** *a.* ketonic; ketone-like.

**Keton-säure,** *f.* ketonic acid, keto acid. **-spaltung,** *f.* ketonic cleavage. **-zucker,** *m.* ketonic sugar.

**Ketoverbindung,** *f.* keto compound, ketonic compound.

**Kettdruck,** *m.* (*Calico*) warp print(ing).

**Kette,** *f.* chain; train, series; warp (of a fabric); bondage; (*Elec.*) cell, element, also circuit, and network.

**ketten,** *v.t.* link, join, connect; chain. **-artig,** *a.* of the nature of a chain, chain-like.

**Ketten-bruch,** *m.* (*Math.*) continued fraction. **-druck,** *m.* warp printing. **-färberei,** *f.* warp dyeing. **-fläche,** *f.* (*Geom.*) catenoid.

**kettenförmig,** *a.* having the form of a chain, chain.

**Ketten-glied,** *n.* link (or member) of a chain. **-isomerie,** *f.* chain isomerism. **-kokken,** *m.pl.* streptococci. **-linie,** *f.* catenary (curve). **-molekül,** *n.* chain molecule, linear molecule. **-polymer,** *n.* chain polymer, linear polymer. **-rad,** *n.* sprocket wheel. **-reaktion,** *f.* chain reaction. **-trieb,** *m.* chain drive.

**keuchen,** *v.i.* gasp, pant.

**Keuchhusten,** *m.* whooping cough.

**Keule,** *f.* pestle; club; leg, joint (of meat).

**keulenförmig,** *a.* club-shaped, clavate, claviform.

**kfm.,** *abbrev.* (kaufmännisch) mercantile, commercial.

**K.G.,** *abbrev.* (Kommanditgesellschaft) limited partnership, commandite.

**kgl.,** *abbrev.* (königlich) royal.

**Khakifarbe,** *f.* khaki color.

**khakifarben,** *a.* khaki-colored.

**Khakistoff,** *m.* khaki cloth.

**KHz,** *abbrev.* (Kilohertz) kilocycle(s) per second.

**Kicher, -erbse,** *f.* chick-pea.

**Kid-leder,** *n.* kid leather. **-öl,** *n.* (*Leather*) kid oil.

**Kiefer,** *m.* jawbone, jaw, maxilla.

**Kiefer,** *f.* pine, esp. Scotch pine (*Pinus sylvestris*).

**Kiefer-.** maxillary.

**Kiefer-, Kiefern-.** pine. **-harz,** *n.* pine resin, rosin. **-holz,** *n.* pine(wood). **-nadel,** *f.* pine needle. **-nadelöl,** *n.* pine-needle oil. **-sperre,** *f.* lockjaw. **-teer,** *m.* pine tar. **-teeröl,** *n.* pine-tar oil. **-zapfen,** *m.* pine cone.

**Kiel,** *m.* quill; keel.

**Kieme,** *f.* gill, branchia.

**Kiemen-.** branchial.

**Kien,** *m.* resinous pine. **-apfel,** *m.* pine cone. **-baum,** *m.* pine tree. **-harz,** *m.* pine resin, rosin. **-holz,** *n.* (resinous) pine wood, pine. **-holzöl,** *n.* pine wood oil.

**kienig,** *a.* piny, resinous.

**Kien-öl,** *n.* pine oil, oil of turpentine. **-pech,** *n.* pine pitch. **-russ,** *m.* pine soot (form of lampblack). **-stock,** *m.* (*Metal.*) carcass. **-teer,** *m.* pine tar.

**Kies,** *m.* pyrites; gravel; shingle; sand, grit. **-abbrand,** *m.* roasted pyrites, purple ore.

**kies-ähnlich,** *a.* pyritous; gravelly. **-artig,** *a.* pyritic; gravelly, gritty.

**Kies-boden,** *m.* gravelly soil. **-brenner,** *m.* pyrites burner.

**Kiesel,** *m.* flint; silica, silex; pebble.

**Kiesel-.** siliceous; silicic. **-algen,** *f.pl.* diatoms.

**kieselartig,** *a.* flinty, siliceous.

**Kiesel-chlorid,** *n.* silicon (tetra)chloride. **-effekt,** *m.* (*Leather*, etc.) pebble effect. **-erde,** *f.* silica; flinty earth. **-erdegel,** *n.* silica gel.

**kieselerdehaltig,** *a.* siliceous, siliciferous.

**Kiesel-erdehydrat,** *n.* hydrated silica. **-fluorbaryum,** *n.* barium fluosilicate. **-fluorblei,** *n.* lead fluosilicate. **-fluorid,** *n.* silicon (tetra)-fluoride. **-fluorkalium,** *n.* potassium fluosilicate. **-fluornatrium,** *n.* sodium fluosilicate. **-fluorsalz,** *n.* fluosilicate. **-fluorsäure,** *f.* fluosilicic acid. **-fluorverbindung,** *f.* fluosilicate. **-fluorwasserstoff,** *m.*, **-fluorwasserstoffsäure,** *f.* fluosilicic acid. **-fluss,** *m.* siliceous flux. **-flus(s)säure,** *f.* fluosilicic acid. **-galmei,** *m.* siliceous calamine (hydrous zinc silicate). **-gestein,** *n.* siliceous rock. **-gips,** *m.* vulpinite (variety of anhydrite). **-glas,** *n.* flint glass; siliceous calamine. **-gur, -guhr,** *m.* diatomaceous earth, kieselguhr. **-gurstein,** *m.* kieselguhr brick.

**kiesel-haltig,** *a.* siliceous, siliciferous. **-hart,** *a.* hard as flint.

**Kieselhärte,** *f.* hardness of flint.

**kieselig,** *a.* siliceous; flinty; pebbly, gravelly.

**Kieselkalk,** *m.* siliceous limestone. **-eisen,** *n.* ilvaite.

**kieselkalkhaltig,** *a.* silicicalcareous.

**Kiesel-kalkspat,** *m.* wollastonite. **-kalkstein,** *m.* flinty or cherty limestone. **-knolle,** *f.* flint nodule, flint. **-körper,** *m.* siliceous body. **-kreide,** *f.* siliceous chalk. **-kristall,** *m.* crystal of silica, rock crystal. **-kupfer,** *n.* chrysocolla. **-mangan,** *n.* rhodonite. **-metall,** *n.* silicon. **-papier,** *n.* flint paper. **-pulver,** *n.* pebble powder.

**kieselreich,** *a.* siliceous; flinty; pebbly.

**Kieselsandstein,** *m.* siliceous sandstone.
**kieselsauer,** *a.* of or combined with silicic acid, silicate of.
**Kieselsäure,** *f.* silicic acid. **-anhydrid,** *n.* silicic anhydride, silicon dioxide. **-düngung,** *f.* fertilization with silica or silicates. **-gallerte,** *f.* silica jelly, silica gel. **-gehalt,** *m.* silicic acid content, silica content. **-gel,** *n.* silica gel.
**kieselsäure-haltig,** *a.* containing silicic acid, siliceous. **-reich,** *a.* rich in silicic acid.
**Kieselsäure-salz,** *n.* silicate. **-seife,** *f.* silicated soap. **-verbindung,** *f.* silicic-acid compound.
**Kiesel-schiefer,** *m.* siliceous schist. **-schwamm,** *m.* siliceous sponge. **-sinter,** *m.* siliceous sinter. **-spat,** *m.* albite. **-stein,** *m.* pebble, gravelstone, flint. **-ton,** *m.* clay slate, argillite. **-tuff,** *m.* siliceous sinter. **-verbindung,** *f.* silicate. **-wasserstoff,** *m.* hydrogen silicide. **-wasserstoffsäure,** *f.* hydrosilicic acid. **-wismut,** *m.* bismuth silicate. **-wolframsäure,** *f.* silicotungstic acid. **-zinkerz,** *n.*, **-zinkspat,** *m.* siliceous calamine; willemite. **-zuschlag,** *m.* siliceous flux.
**Kiesfilter,** *n.* gravel filter.
**kieshaltig,** *a.* pyritiferous; gravelly.
**kiesig,** *a.* gravelly, gritty; pyritic.
**Kies-lager,** *n.* pyrites deposit, sulfide deposit; gravel deposit. **-lagerstätte,** *f.* (*Min.*) pyrites deposit, sulfide deposit. **-ofen,** *m.* pyrites burner, pyrites kiln. **-sand,** *m.* gravelly sand; grit.
**Kiff,** *m.* tan, tanbark
**Kilo-hertz,** *n.* kilocycle per second. **-wattstunde,** *f.* (*Elec.*) kilowatt-hour.
**Kimme,** *f.* notch; edge, border.
**Kind,** *n.* child.
**Kinder-balsam,** *m.* soothing sirup. **-ernährung,** *f.* infant feeding; child nutrition. **-lähmung,** *f.* infantile paralysis. **-mehl,** *n.* (powdered) infant food. **-nährmittel,** *n.* infant food. **-pech,** *n.* meconium. **-pulver,** *n.* (*Pharm.*) compound powder of rhubarb. **-schleim,** *m.*, **-schmiere,** *f.* vernix caseosa. **-seife,** *f.* nursery soap.
**Kindespech,** *n.* meconium.
**Kindeswasser,** *n.* amniotic fluid.
**Kindheit,** *f.* childhood, infancy.
**Kindspech,** *n.* meconium.
**Kinefilm,** *n.* motion-picture film.
**kinematisch,** *a.* kinematic.
**kinematographisch,** *a.* cinematographic.
**Kinetik,** *f.* kinetics.
**kinetisch,** *a.* kinetic.
**Kinn,** *n.* chin. **-backen,** *m.* jaw, jawbone. **-lade,** *f.* jaw.
**Kino,** *n.* motion pictures, cinema; motion-picture theater; kino. **-gerbsäure,** *f.* kinotannic acid. **-maschine,** *f.* motion-picture machine. **-tinktur,** *f.* tincture of kino.
**Kipp-.** tilting, tipping, dumping, tripping.
**kippbar,** *a.* tiltable, tilting, tippable.
**Kippbewegung,** *f.* tilting or tipping motion.
**Kippe,** *f.* tilt; hinge; edge. — **auf der —,** atilt; on the verge of disaster.
**kippelig,** *a.* unstable, labile, unsteady.
**kippen,** *v.t.* tilt, tip, tip over, dump, trip.
**Kipper,** *m.* tipping device, tipper, tipple.
**Kippkessel,** *m.* tilting basin, swivel pan.
**kipplig,** *a.* unstable, labile, unsteady.
**Kippofen,** *m.* tilting furnace.
**Kipp'scher Apparat.** Kipp apparatus.
**kippsicher,** *a.* stable, steady.
**Kipp-spiegel,** *m.* tilting mirror; oscillating mirror. **-verrichtung,** *f.* tipping device, tipper.
**Kirche,** *f.* church.
**kirnen,** *v.t.* churn.
**kirr, kirre,** *a.* tame.
**Kirsch-baum,** *m.* cherry tree. **-branntwein,** *m.* kirsch (see Kirschwasser); cherry brandy.
**kirschbraun,** *a.* cherry-brown.
**Kirsche,** *f.* cherry; small bulb; pellet.
**Kirschengummi,** *n.* cherry gum.
**kirsch-farben, -farbig,** *a.* cherry-colored.
**Kirsch-geist,** *m.* kirsch (see Kirschwasser). **-glut,** *f.* cherry-red heat. **-gummi, -harz,** *n.* cherry gum. **-kernöl,** *n.* cherry-kernel oil. **-lorbeer,** *m.* cherry laurel.
**kirschrot,** *a.* cherry-red.
**Kirschrotglut,** *f.* cherry-red heat (about 850° C.).
**kirschrotwarm,** *a.* cherry-red (hot).
**Kirsch-saft,** *m.* cherry juice. **-wasser,** *n.* kirsch, kirschwasser (a liquor distilled from fermented cherry juice); bitter-almond water. **-wurzelkraut,** *n.* athamanta (*Peucedanum oreoselinum*).
**Kissen,** *n.* cushion; pillow, bolster; pad.
**Kistchen,** *n.* small chest, box or case.
**Kiste,** *f.* chest, box, case.
**Kistenzucker,** *m.* muscovado.
**Kitt,** *m.* cement; lute; mastic; putty.
**kitt-artig,** *a.* cement-like; putty-like. **-bar,** *a.* capable of being cemented or luted.
**kitten,** *v.t.* cement; lute, putty, glue.
**Kitt-erde,** *f.* luting clay; pozzuolana. **-harz,** *m.* (*Zoöl.*) propolis, bee glue. **-masse,** *f.* cementing composition; (*Anat.*) cement substance. **-öl,** *n.* putty oil. **-substanz,** *f.* cement substance, cement.
**Kitzel,** *m.* tickling; itching; longing, desire.
**kitzeln,** *v.t.* tickle.
**Kjeldahlkolben,** *m.* Kjeldahl flask.
**K.K., k.k.,** *abbrev.* (kaiserlich-königlich) imperial-royal.
**k.kal.,** *abbrev.* (kleine Kalorie) small calorie.
**kl.,** *abbrev.* (kaum löslich) scarcely soluble; (klein) small.
**Kl.,** *abbrev.* (Klasse) class.

**Kladstein,** *m.* place brick (brick not fully burned).

**klaffen,** *v.i.* gape, yawn; split.

**kläffen,** *v.i.* bark; clamor.

**Klafter,** *f.* cord (of wood); fathom.

**Klage,** *f.* complaint, grievance; claim; suit, accusation; lament.

**klagen,** *v.i.* lament; complain; sue.

**Klai,** *m.* clay.

**klamm,** *a.* tight, close, narrow; clammy.

**Klammer,** *f.* clamp, clasp, cramp, clip; parenthesis; (**eckige**) bracket; brace. **-ausdruck,** *m.* parenthetical expression.

**klammern,** *v.t.* cramp, clamp, rivet, fasten.

**Klampe,** *f.* clamp, cramp, clasp, clip; cleat.

**klang,** *pret.* (of klingen) sounded, rang.

**Klang,** *m.* sound, ring, clang; timbre. **-farbe,** *f.* tone color, timbre. **-lehre,** *f.* acoustics.

**klanglos,** *a.* soundless, mute, dumb.

**Klangzinn,** *n.* fine tin, sonorous tin.

**Klapp-.** hinged, folding, tilting, swinging.

**klappbar,** *a.* hinged; collapsible, folding.

**Klappdeckel,** *m.* hinged cover.

**Klappe,** *f.* flap, trap, lid; damper; (clack) valve; stop.

**klappen,** *v.t.* clap, flap, click. — *v.i.* clap, strike, clatter; fit, work.

**Klappen-.** valvular. **-ventil,** *n.* clack valve, flap valve.

**klappern,** *v.i.* rattle, clatter, chatter.

**Klapper-rose,** *f.* corn poppy. **-schlange,** *f.* rattlesnake. **-stein,** *m.* eaglestone (nodular clay ironstone).

**Klappmesser,** *n.* clasp knife, pocket knife.

**klapsen,** *v.t.* clap, smack, slap.

**klar,** *a.* clear. — **— ausziehen,** (*Dyeing*) exhaust completely.

**Klär-.** clearing, clarifying, fining, settling. **-anlage,** *f.* clarifying plant; (*Sewage*) purification plant. **-apparat,** *n.* settling or clarifying apparatus. **-bad,** *n.* clearing bath. **-bassin,** *n.* settling tank or reservoir. **-becken,** *n.* settling basin or vessel; filter bed. **-behälter,** *m.* settling tank or vessel.

**klarblickend,** *a.* clear-sighted.

**Klärbottich,** *m.* clearing tub, settling vat, cleansing vat.

**Klare,** *f.* clear liquid.

**Kläre,** *f.* clearness; clarifier; clear (clarified) liquid; coal dust; boneash.

**klären,** *v.t.* clear, clarify, purify, defecate. — *v.r.* clear, clear up.

**Klären,** *n.* clarification, clarifying, clearing.

**Klär-fass,** *n.* clearing cask or tub, clarifier, settler; (*Brewing*) cleansing cask; (*Vinegar*) fining tun. **-filter,** *n.* filter. **-flasche,** *f.* decanting bottle (or flask). **-gefäss,** *n.* (*Sugar*) clarifier. **-gelatine,** *f.* isinglass. **-grube,** *f.* settling pit; clearing tank.

**Klarheit,** *f.* clearness, clarity.

**klarieren,** *v.t.* clear; (*Sugar*) clear, purge.

**Klär-kasten,** *m.* (*Paper*) settler. **-kessel,** *m.* (*Sugar*, etc.) clarifier.

**klarkochen,** *v.t.* boil till clear.

**Klar-kohle,** *f.* small coal, slack. **-lack,** *m.* clear varnish or lacquer.

**klarlegen,** *v.t.* make clear, explain, state (a case).

**Klärlösung,** *f.* clearing solution.

**Klär-mittel,** *n.* clarifying or clearing agent, clarifier, fining. **-pfanne,** *f.* (*Sugar*) clearing pan, clarifier, defecating pan.

**klarschleifen,** *v.t.* grind smooth.

**Klärsel,** *n.* (*Sugar*) clear(ing) liquor, fine liquor, clear, clairce.

**Klarsichtsalbe,** *f.* antidim compound.

**Klärstaub,** *m.* boneash.

**klarstellen,** *v.t.* clear up, explain.

**Klärung,** *f.* clarification, clarifying, clearing.

**Klärungs-fass,** *n.* = Klärfass. **-mittel,** *n.* = Klärmittel. **-prozess,** *m.* clarification process. **-salz,** *n.* clearing salt.

**Klarwerden,** *n.* clearing up, becoming clear.

**Klasse,** *f.* class; grade, sort, etc.

**Klassenordnung,** *f.* classification.

**klassieren,** *v.t.* classify (as ore), grade, sort.

**Klassifikator,** *m.* classifier.

**klassifizieren,** *v.t.* classify.

**Klassiker,** *m.* classic.

**klassisch,** *a.* classic, classical.

**klastisch,** *a.* clastic.

**Klatsch,** *m.* clap, pop, slap, dab, etc.; gossip.

**klatschen,** *v.t.* clap, pop, slap. — *v.i.* clap, pop, slap, flap; chat; gossip.

**Klatsch-präparat,** *n.* (*Micros.*) a smear preparation made by pressing the material between two cover glasses and sliding them apart. **-rose,** *f.* corn poppy.

**klauben,** *v.t.* pick, sort (esp., by hand).

**Klaue,** *f.* claw; paw; hoof; prong; pawl; clutch.

**Klauen-fett,** *n.*, **-öl,** *n.* oil from the feet of animals, specif. neat's-foot oil. **-mehl,** *n.* hoof meal.

**Klause,** *f.* cell; closet; chamber; sink.

**Klaviatur,** *f.* keys, keyboard.

**Klavier,** *n.* piano. **-draht,** *m.* piano wire.

**Kleb-, Klebe-.** adhesive, adherent, sticking.

**Kleb-äther,** *m.* collodion. **-band,** *n.* adhesive tape.

**Klebe,** *f.* dodder. **-band,** *n.* adhesive tape. **-fähigkeit,** *f.* adhesiveness.

**klebefrei,** *a.* free from stickiness or tackiness.

**Klebe-korn,** *n.* (*Biol.*) microsome. **-material,** *n.* adhesive material. **-mittel,** *n.* adhesive, agglutinant, cement.

**kleben,** *v.i.* stick, adhere. — *v.t.* stick, glue, gum, paste, cement. — **klebend,** *p.a.* adherent, adhesive, glutinative, agglutinant; tacky, sticky.

**Klebepflaster,** *n.* adhesive plaster.

**Kleber,** *m.* gluten; adhesive; sticker, gluer. **-brot,** *n.* gluten bread. **-griess,** *m.* gluten grits.

**kleber-haltig,** *a.* containing gluten, glutinous. **-ig,** *a.* sticky, adhesive, viscid, glutinous.

**Kleberigkeit,** *f.* viscidity, viscosity.

**Kleber-leim,** *m.* gluten glue. **-mehl,** *n.* aleurone grains, aleurone.

**Kleberolle,** *f.* (roll of) gummed tape or adhesive tape.

**Kleberprotein,** *n.* gluten protein.

**kleberreich,** *a.* rich in gluten.

**Kleberschicht,** *f.* (*Bot.*) aleurone layer.

**Klebe-stoff,** *m.* adhesive substance, cement; adhesive; binder. **-streifen,** *m.* adhesive tape. **-taffet,** *m.* court plaster. **-wachs,** *n.* adhesive wax, sticking wax. **-zettel,** *m.* gummed label, sticker.

**klebfähig,** *a.* adhesive.

**Klebfähigkeit,** *f.* adhesiveness.

**klebfrei,** *a.* free from tackiness.

**Kleb-kraft,** *f.* adhesive power. **-kraut,** *n.* cleavers (*Galium*). **-lack,** *m.* adhesive lacquer. **-material,** *n.* adhesive material. **-mittel,** *n.* adhesive, agglutinant; binder. **-pflaster,** *n.* adhesive plaster.

**klebrig, klebricht,** *a.* = kleberig.

**Klebrigkeit,** *f.* stickiness, viscidity, tackiness.

**Kleb-sand,** *m.* (*Ceram.*) luting sand, daubing sand. **-schiefer,** *m.* (*Petrog.*) adhesive slate or shale. **-schmutz,** *m.* adhering dirt. **-stoff,** *m.* = Klebestoff. **-wachs,** *n.* adhesive wax, sticking wax. **-zwecken,** *m.pl.* adhesive purposes.

**klecken,** *v.i.* blot; blur; daub.

**Klecks,** *m.* blot, blotch, splotch, spot.

**Klee,** *m.* clover, trefoil. — **ewiger —, Luzerner —,** alfalfa, lucern. — **spanischer —, türkischer —,** sainfoin.

**Klee-baum,** *m.* hop tree (*Ptelea trifoliata*). **-futter, -heu,** *n.* clover hay.

**kleerot,** *a.* clover-red, purplish-red.

**Klee-salz,** *n.* salt of sorrel (potassium hydrogen oxalate). **-samenöl,** *n.* cloverseed oil.

**kleesauer,** *a.* of or combined with oxalic acid, oxalate of.

**Klee-säure,** *f.* oxalic acid. **-seide,** *f.* dodder.

**Klei,** *m.* clay; clay soil. **-absudbad,** *n.* (*Dyeing*) bran decoction.

**Kleid,** *n.* garment, dress, clothing, garb.

**kleiden,** *v.t.* dress, clothe; fit.

**Kleider-färberei,** *f.* garment dyeing. **-motte,** *f.* clothes moth. **-stoff,** *m.* garment material.

**Kleidung,** *f.* clothing, dressing, costume.

**Kleie,** *f.* bran.

**kleienartig,** *a.* branny, furfuraceous.

**Kleien-bad,** *n.*, **-beize,** *f.* bran drench, bran steep. **-brot,** *n.* bran bread. **-essig,** *m.* bran vinegar.

**kleienförmig,** *a.* bran-like, branny.

**Kleien-mehl,** *n.* pollard. **-sucht,** *f.* (*Med.*) pityriasis. **-wasser,** *n.* bran water.

**Kleierde,** *f.* clay earth.

**kleiig,** *a.* clayey; branny.

**klein,** *a.* small, little; short. — **kleinstes Lebewesen,** microörganism.

**Klein,** *n.* (*Mining*) smalls. **-asien,** *n.* Asia Minor. **-bessemerei,** *f.* small Bessemer plant; small-scale Bessemerizing. **-betrieb,** *m.* work on a small scale; small business. **-bildphotographie,** *f.* microphotography. **-birne,** *f.* (*Metal.*) small converter. **-eisenwaren,** *f.pl.* small ironware, hardware.

**kleinen,** *v.t.* pulverize, comminute.

**kleinern,** *v.t.* make smaller; reduce (fractions).

**Klein-färber,** *m.* clothes dyer. **-filter,** *n.* fine filter. **-gärmethode,** *f.* micro fermentation method. **-gefüge,** *n.* fine structure, microstructure.

**kleingepulvert,** *a.* finely powdered.

**Klein-handel,** *m.* retail trade. **-heit,** *f.* smallness, minuteness. **-hirn,** *n.* cerebellum. **-hirnrinde,** *f.* cerebellar cortex.

**kleinieren,** *v.t.* make small, reduce.

**Kleinigkeit,** *f.* trifle.

**Klein-kohle,** *f.* small-sized coal, buckwheat coal, pea coal; small coal, slack. **-koks,** *m.* small-sized coke, nut coke.

**klein-körnig,** *a.* small-grained, fine-grained. **-kristallinisch,** *a.* finely crystalline, in small crystals.

**Klein-lader,** *m.* (*Elec.*) trickle charger. **-lebewesen,** *n.* microörganism.

**kleinlich,** *a.* petty, paltry, mean.

**Kleinlichtbildkunst,** *f.* microphotography.

**klein-luckig,** *a.* finely porous; close-grained. **-maschig,** *a.* fine-meshed.

**Klein-messer,** *m.* micrometer. **-mühle,** *f.* pulverizing mill.

**Kleinod,** *n.* jewel, gem, ornament.

**Kleinröhre,** *f.* little tube, miniature tube.

**kleinschuppig,** *a.* in (or having) small scales, finely scaly.

**Kleinspore,** *f.* (*Biol.*) microspore.

**kleinst,** *a.* smallest, least, minimal.

**kleinstädtisch,** *a.* provincial.

**Kleinsteller,** *m.* bypass (in Bunsen burner).

**kleinstmöglich,** *a.* smallest possible.

**kleinstückig,** *a.* in small pieces, small-sized.

**Kleinstwert,** *m.* minimum value, minimum.

**Klein-verkauf,** *m.* retailing, retail. **-versuch,** *m.* small-scale experiment or test.

**Kleister,** *m.* paste; size (thin paste). **-bildung,** *f.* formation of paste.

**kleisterig,** *a.* pasty, sticky.

**kleistern,** *v.t.* paste; size (with paste).
**Kleisterzähigkeit,** *f.* viscidity (or glutinousness) of starch.
**kleistrig,** *a.* pasty, sticky.
**Klemmbacke,** *f.* (*Mach.*) jaw, clamp.
**Klemme,** *f.* clamp; clip; nippers, tongs, forceps; vise; (*Elec.*) terminal; dilemma.
**klemmen,** *v.t.* clamp, grip, pinch, squeeze, bind, jam.
**Klemmenspannung,** *f.* (*Elec.*) terminal voltage.
**Klemmer,** *m.* pinchcock; nose glasses.
**Klemm-mutter,** *f.* lock nut. **-schraube,** *f.* binding screw, set screw; screw clamp; (*Elec.*) binding post, terminal. **-verbindung,** *f.* clamp connection; screw fastening.
**Klempner,** *m.* tinner, tinsmith; brazier; plumber.
**Klette,** *f.* bur; burdock.
**Kletten-bombe,** *f.* (*Mil.*) adhesive bomb. **-erz,** *n.* bur ore. **-wurzel,** *f.* (*Pharm.*) lappa, burdock root. **-wurzelöl,** *n.* burdock oil.
**klettern,** *v.i.* climb.
**Kletterpflanze,** *f.* (*Bot.*) climber, creeper.
**Klima,** *n.* climate. **-anlage,** *f.* air-conditioning plant. **-kunde, -lehre,** *f.* climatology.
**klimatisch,** *a.* climatic.
**Klimatisierung,** *f.* air conditioning.
**klimmen,** *v.i.* climb.
**klimpern,** *v.i.* jingle, tinkle, strum; grate.
**Klinge,** *f.* blade; sword.
**Klingel,** *f.* (small) bell. **-draht,** *m.* bell wire.
**klingeln,** *v.i.* ring; tinkle, jingle.
**Klingelschnur,** *f.* bell cord.
**klingen,** *v.i.* sound, resound, ring, clink.
**Kling-glas,** *n.* flint glass. **-stein,** *m.* clinkstone (phonolite).
**klinisch,** *a.* (*Med.*) clinical.
**Klinke,** *f.* latch; pawl; catch; (door) handle.
**Klinker,** *m.* clinker, (hard) brick. **-pflaster,** *n.* brick paving.
**Klino-achse,** *f.* (*Cryst.*) clino axis. **-edrit,** *n.* (*Min.*) clinohedrite. **-klas,** *m.* clinoclase, clinoclasite.
**Klippe,** *f.* cliff, rock, crag; bluff; reef.
**Klippfisch,** *m.* stockfish, dried fish.
**klirren,** *v.i.* clink, clatter, rattle, scratch.
**Klischee,** *n.* engraved plate, stereotype, cliché, electrotype, electro.
**klischieren,** *v.t.* stereotype; electrotype.
**Klistier,** *n.* (*Med.*) enema, clyster.
**klitschig,** *a.* soggy, doughy.
**Kloake,** *f.* cloaca, sewer; sink; cesspool.
**Kloaken-gas,** *n.* sewer gas. **-wasser,** *n.* sewage.
**Kloben,** *m.* pulley, block; vise; pincers; log.
**klomm,** *pret.* (of klimmen) climbed.
**klonisch,** *a.* (*Med.*) clonic.
**klopfen,** *v.t.* & *i.* beat, knock, tap; scale (a boiler); drive (a nail); break (stone).
**Klopffeind,** *m.* antiknock, antiknock agent.
**klopffest,** *a.* knockproof, antiknock.
**Klopf-festigkeit,** *f.* resistance to knocking, antiknock quality. **-festigkeitswert,** *m.* antiknock value. **-gegenmittel,** *n.* antiknock agent. **-grenze,** *f.* knocking (or detonation) limit (point of incipient knocking). **-holz,** *n.* mallet, beater. **-neigung,** *f.* knocking tendency. **-sieb,** *n.* shaking or tapping sieve. **-wert,** *m.* antiknock value, octane rating.
**Klöppel,** *m.* beater, knocker, clapper, etc ; (lace) bobbin.
**Klosettpapier,** *n.* toilet paper.
**Kloss,** *m.* clod, lump; dumpling.
**Kloster,** *n.* cloister.
**Klotz,** *m.* block, log, stump. **-artikel,** *m.* (*Calico*) padded style. **-bad,** *n.* slop-pad liquor, padding liquor. **-druck,** *m.* slop-pad printing.
**klotzen,** *v.t.* (*Calico*) slop-pad, pad.
**Klotz-farbe,** *f.* (*Dyeing*) padding color. **-färbung,** *f.* padded dyeing, slop-pad, pad. **-flotte,** *f.* padding liquor. **-reserveartikel,** *m.* padded resist style. **-schwarz,** *n.* (*Dyeing*) slop-pad black.
**Klotzung,** *f.* (*Calico*) (slop-)padding, pad.
**Kluft,** *f.* cleft, fissure; chasm; tongs.
**klüften,** *v.t.* cleave, split.
**klüftig,** *a.* split, cracked, creviced.
**Klüftung,** *f.* cleaving, segmentation.
**klug,** *a.* clever, knowing, wise, skilful.
**Klümpchen,** *n.* little lump, etc. (see Klumpen); particle; nodule.
**Klumpen,** *m.* lump, mass; ingot; bloom; nugget; clot; clump; clod. **-bildung,** *f.* formation of lumps, clots, clumps, etc. (see Klumpen).
**klumpig, klümperig, klümprig,** *a.* clotted, clotty; lumpy; cloddy.
**Kluppe,** *f.* pincers, nippers, tongs; clip, clamp; diestock; calipers.
**Kluppzange,** *f.* forceps.
**Klystier,** *n.* (*Med.*) enema, clyster.
**k.M.,** *abbrev.* (kommenden Monats) of the coming month, of next month.
**Knabbelkoks,** *m.* crushed coke, nut coke.
**knabbern,** *v.t.* & *i.* gnaw, nibble.
**Knabe,** *m.* boy.
**knacken,** *v.i.* crack; crackle, crepitate; click. — *v.t.* crack.
**Knagge,** *f.* cam, catch, tappet; dog; knot, snag.
**Knall,** *m.* detonation; explosion, report, crack, pop.
**Knall-.** detonating; fulminating, fulminate of. **-aufsatz,** *m.* (*Expl.*) initiator. **-blei,** *n.* fulminating lead.
**knallen,** *v.i.* detonate, fulminate; crack, pop, go off.
**Knallerbse,** *f.* (*Fireworks*) torpedo.
**knallfähig,** *a.* detonating, explosive.
**Knallflamme,** *f.* oxyhydrogen flame.

**Knallgas,** *n.* detonating gas, specif. an explosive mixture of hydrogen and oxygen, oxyhydrogen gas. **-flamme,** *f.* oxyhydrogen flame. **-gebläse,** *n.* oxyhydrogen blowpipe. **-licht,** *n.* oxyhydrogen light. **-lötapparat,** *m.* oxyhydrogen blowpipe.

**Knall-gebläse,** *n.* oxyhydrogen blast. **-glas,** *n.* Rupert's drop; anaclastic glass. **-gold,** *n.* fulminating gold. **-korken,** *m.* explosive cap. **-körper,** *m.* detonator. **-kraft,** *f.* explosive force or power. **-luft,** *f.* detonating gas; explosive air. **-pulver,** *n.* detonating powder. **-pyrometer,** *n.* explosion pyrometer. **-quecksilber,** *n.* fulminating mercury (mercuric fulminate). **-salpeter,** *m.* ammonium nitrate. **-satz,** *m.* detonating composition.

**knallsauer,** *a.* of or combined with fulminic acid, fulminate of.

**Knall-säure,** *f.* fulminic acid. **-silber,** *n.* fulminating silver. **-welle,** *f.* explosion wave, shock wave. **-zucker,** *m.* (*Expl.*) nitrosaccharose. **-zünder,** *m.* detonator. **-zündmittel,** *n.* detonating priming.

**knapp,** *a.* close, tight, narrow; scanty; exact.

**Knappe,** *m.* miner.

**Knappheit,** *f.* tightness; conciseness; scarcity.

**Knarre,** *f.* ratchet; rattle.

**knarren,** *v.i.* crackle, rattle, creak, squeak.

**Knast,** *m.* knot (in wood), nob, snag.

**knattern,** *v.i.* rattle, crackle; (*Motors*) knock.

**Knäuel, Knauel,** *m.* ball, coil (of thread, etc.); convolution. **-drüse,** *f.* sweat gland.

**knäuelförmig,** *a.* convoluted, coiled; globular.

**knäueln, knaueln,** *v.t.* coil up; tangle; agglomerate.

**Knauf,** *m.* knob, stud; capital.

**Knäulchen,** *n.* little (wound) ball or coil.

**Knebel,** *m.* stick; crossbar; (*Bot.*) slip. **-gelenk,** *n.* toggle joint.

**Knecht,** *m.* (man) servant; trestle, horse.

**kneifen,** *v.t.* nip, squeeze, pinch, gripe.

**Kneifzange,** *f.* nippers.

**Kneipe,** *f.* pincers, nippers; beer party; tavern, pub.

**kneipen,** *v.t.* nip, pinch, squeeze, gripe; drink (beer).

**knetbar,** *a.* kneadable, plastic.

**kneten,** *v.t.* knead; masticate, mill; work; (*Ceram.*) pug.

**Knet-gummi,** *n.* a soft cleaning composition, art gum. **-holz,** *n.* plastic wood. **-legierung,** *f.* wrought alloy. **-maschine, -mühle,** *f.* kneading machine, malaxator; masticator; (*Ceram.*) pug mill.

**Knick,** *m.* break (in curves, etc.); sharp bend, knee; crack, flaw.

**knicken,** *v.t.* & *i.* crack; break; buckle; collapse.

**Knick-festigkeit,** *f.* breaking strength; (of metals) buckling strength. **-punkt,** *m.* (in a curve) break. **-spannung,** *f.* breaking stress; buckling stress. **-stelle,** *f.* (in a curve) break, knee.

**Knickung,** *f.* cracking, etc. (see knicken); rupture.

**Knie,** *n.* knee; angle, elbow; sharp bend.

**knieen,** *v.i.* kneel.

**knieförmig,** *a.* knee-shaped, geniculate.

**Knie-gelenk,** *n.* knee joint; elbow joint; toggle joint. **-kehle,** *f.* popliteal space. **-rohr,** *n.*, **-röhre,** *f.* elbow (tube or pipe), bent tube. **-scheibe,** *f.* kneepan, patella. **-stück,** *n.* (*Mach.*) elbow; knee, angle.

**kniff,** *pret.* (of kneifen) nipped, etc.

**Kniff,** *m.* pinch; crease; trick, device.

**knipsen,** *v.t.* & *i.* clip, punch, snap, click.

**knirschen,** *v.i.* crackle, grate, crunch, rustle.

**Knirschpulver,** *n.* a kind of coarse gunpowder.

**Knistergold,** *n.* Dutch metal, Dutch gold.

**knistern,** *v.i.* crackle, decrepitate, crepitate; (of silk) rustle.

**Knistersalz,** *n.* decrepitating salt.

**Knitter,** *m.* crease, fold, wrinkle.

**knitter-fest, -frei,** *a.* creaseproof, noncreasing.

**Knittergold,** *n.* = Knistergold.

**knitterig,** *a.* creased, crumpled, wrinkled; crackling.

**knittern,** *v.t.* & *r.* crumple, crease. — *v.i.* = knistern.

**Knitter-papier,** *n.* crinkled paper. **-zahl,** *f.* fold-test (or crease-test) value.

**knittrig,** *a.* = knitterig.

**Knoblauch,** *m.* garlic.

**knoblauchartig,** *a.* garlic-like, garlicky.

**Knoblauch-erz,** *n.* (*Min.*) scorodite. **-gamander,** *m.* water germander. **-öl,** *n.* garlic oil.

**Knöchel,** *m.* knuckle; ankle; (*pl.*) dice.

**Knochen,** *m.* bone.

**Knochen-.** bone, bony, osseous, osteo-. **-abfall,** *m.* bone waste, waste bone.

**knochen-ähnlich, -artig,** *a.* bone-like, bony, osseous.

**Knochen-asche,** *f.* bone ash. **-band,** *n.* (*Anat.*) ligament.

**knochenbildend,** *p.a.* bone-forming.

**Knochen-bildung,** *f.* bone formation. **-bruch,** *m.* (bone) fracture. **-dämpfapparat,** *m.* bone steamer. **-dünger,** *m.* bone manure. **-dungmehl,** *n.* (*Agric.*) bone meal. **-düngung,** *f.* manuring with bone. **-erde,** *f.* bone earth (bone ash). **-fett,** *n.* bone fat, bone grease. **-gallerte,** *f.* bone gelatin; ossein. **-geist,** *m.* bone spirit. **-gewebe,** *n.* bony tissue. **-haut,** *f.* periosteum. **-kohle,** *f.* boneblack. **-kohleglühofen,** *m.* boneblack furnace. **-leim,** *m.* bone glue, osteocolla. **-mark,** *n.* bone marrow. **-masse,** *f.* osseous material. **-mehl,** *n.*

bone meal, bone dust. **-öl,** *n.* bone oil, Dippel's oil. **-porzellan,** *n.* bone porcelain, bone china. **-säure,** *f.* phosphoric acid. **-schrot,** *n.* & *m.* crushed bone. **-schwarz,** *n.* boneblack. **-teeröl,** *n.* bone oil.

**knochentrocken,** *a.* bone-dry.

**knöchern,** *a.* of bone, bony, osseous.

**knochig,** *a.* bony, osseous.

**Knöllchen,** *n.* nodule, little knob, small lump.

**Knolle,** *f.*, **Knollen,** *m.* lump, knob, nodule; tuber; tubercle; tumor.

**knollig,** *a.* knobby, knotty, bulbous, tuberous; lumpy, in lumps, in balls.

**Knopf,** *m.* button; stud, head, knob; knot.

**Knöpfchen,** *n.* small button or knob.

**Knopfdeckel,** *m.* knobbed cover.

**knopfförmig,** *a.* button-shaped, knobbed.

**Knopper,** *f.* (nut)gall, gallnut.

**Knorpel,** *m.* cartilage, gristle.

**knorpel-ähnlich, -artig,** *a.* cartilaginous, gristly.

**Knorpelhaut,** *f.* (*Anat.*) perichondrium.

**knorpelig,** *a.* cartilaginous, gristly.

**Knorpel-leim,** *m.* chondrin. **-tang,** *m.* carrageen, (*Pharm.*) chondrus.

**knorplich,** *a.* cartilaginous.

**Knorren,** *n.* protuberance, excrescence, knot, gnarl, snag.

**knorrig,** *a.* gnarled, knotty, knobby.

**Knöspchen,** *n.* budlet, plumule, gemmule.

**Knospe,** *f.* bud.

**knospen,** *v.i.* bud.

**Knötchen,** *n.* little knot; nodule; tubercle; pimple.

**Knoten,** *m.* knot; node; nodule; tubercle; ganglion; knob; plot.

**knoten,** *v.t.* knot, tie in knots.

**Knoten-linie,** *f.* nodal line. **-punkt,** *m.* nodal point; junction. **-wurz,** *f.* figwort, (*Pharm.*) scrophularia. **-zahl,** *f.* nodal number; number of nodes.

**Knöterich,** *m.* knotgrass (*Polygonum* sp.).

**knotig,** *a.* knotty, nodular, tubercular, nobby; jointed; caddish.

**knüpfen,** *v.t.* knit, tie, unite, attach.

**Knüppel,** *m.* billet; club; (*Aero.*) control stick.

**knurren,** *v.i.* snarl, growl, rumble.

**knusperig,** *a.* crisp.

**koachsial,** *a.* coaxial.

**Koagulat,** *n.* coagulum, clot.

**Koagulations-.** see Koagulierungs-.

**Koagulatmasse,** *f.* coagulum.

**koagulierbar,** *a.* coagulable.

**koagulieren,** *v.t.* & *i.* coagulate.

**Koagulierung,** *f.* coagulation.

**Koagulierungsbad,** *n.* coagulating bath.

**koagulierungs-beständig,** *a.* resisting coagulation. **-empfindlich,** *a.* liable to coagulation. **-fähig,** *a.* coagulable.

**Koagulierungs-fähigkeit,** *f.* coagulability. **-flüssigkeit,** *f.* coagulating liquid. **-mittel,** *n.* coagulating agent, coagulant. **-schutzwirkung,** *f.* anticoagulating effect. **-wärme,** *f.* heat of coagulation.

**koaleszieren,** *v.i.* coalesce.

**koalisieren,** *v.i.* coalesce.

**Kobalt,** *m.* cobalt. **-ammin, -amin,** *n.* cobaltammine. **-bad,** *n.* cobalt bath. **-beize,** *f.* (*Dyeing*) cobalt mordant. **-beschlag,** *m.* (*Min.*) cobalt bloom, erythrite. **-blau,** *n.* cobalt blue. **-bleierz,** *n.*, **-bleiglanz,** *m.* (*Min.*) clausthalite. **-blüte, -blume,** *f.* cobalt bloom (erythrite). **-braun,** *n.* cobalt brown. **-chlorür,** *n.* cobaltous chloride, cobalt(II) chloride. **-erde,** *f.* (*Min.*) cobalt crust. **-erz,** *n.* cobalt ore. **-farbe,** *f.* cobalt pigment; powder blue. **-firnis,** *m.* cobalt varnish. **-flasche,** *f.* cobalt-glass bottle. **-gehalt,** *m.* cobalt content. **-gelb,** *n.* cobalt yellow. **-glanz,** *m.* cobalt glance (cobaltite). **-grün,** *n.* cobalt green.

**kobalthaltig,** *a.* cobaltiferous.

**Kobalti-.** cobaltic, cobalti-, cobalt(III).

**Kobaltiak,** *n.* cobaltiac, cobaltammine. **-salz,** *n.* cobaltiac salt, cobaltammine salt.

**Kobalti-chlorid,** *n.* cobaltic chloride, cobalt(III) chloride. **-cyankalium,** *n.* potassium cobalticyanide. **-cyanwasserstoff,** *m.*, **-cyanwasserstoffsäure,** *f.* cobalticyanic acid.

**kobaltieren,** *v.t.* coat or plate with cobalt.

**Kobalti-kaliumnitrit,** *n.* potassium cobaltinitrite. **-oxyd,** *n.* cobaltic oxide, cobalt(III) oxide. **-sulfid,** *n.* cobaltic sulfide, cobalt(III) sulfide. **-verbindung,** *f.* cobaltic compound, cobalt(III) compound. **-zyankalium,** *n.* potassium cobalticyanide, potassium cyanocobaltate(III).

**Kobalt-kies,** *m.* cobalt pyrites (linnaeite). **-manganerz,** *n.* asbolite. **-nickelkies,** *m.* (*Min.*) linnaeite.

**Kobalto-.** cobaltous, cobalto-, cobalt(II). **-chlorid,** *n.* cobaltous chloride, cobalt(II) chloride. **-cyanwasserstoff,** *m.*, **-cyanwasserstoffsäure,** *f.* cobaltocyanic acid. **-nitrat,** *n.* cobaltous nitrate, cobalt(II) nitrate. **-oxyd,** *n.* cobaltous oxide, cobalt(II) oxide. **-salz,** *n.* cobaltous salt, cobalt(II) salt. **-sulfat,** *n.* cobaltous sulfate, cobalt(II) sulfate. **-sulfid,** *n.* cobaltous sulfide, cobalt(II) sulfide. **-verbindung,** *f.* cobaltous compound, cobalt(II) compound.

**Kobaltoxyd,** *n.* cobalt oxide, specif. cobaltic oxide, cobalt(III) oxide. **-hydrat,** *n.* cobalt hydroxide. **-oxydul,** *n.* cobaltocobaltic oxide, cobalt(II,III) oxide.

**Kobaltoxydul,** *n.* cobaltous oxide, cobalt(II) oxide. **-oxyd,** *n.* cobaltocobaltic oxide, cobalt(II,III) oxide. **-verbindung,** *f.* cobaltous compound. cobalt(II) oxide.

**Kobaltoxydverbindung,** *f.* cobaltic compound, cobalt(III) compound.

**Kobaltozyankalium,** *n.* potassium cobaltocyanide, potassium cyanocobaltate(II).

**Kobalt-rosa,** *n.* cobalt red. **-salz,** *n.* cobalt salt. **-spat,** *m.* (*Min.*) sphaerocobaltite. **-speise,** *f.* cobalt speiss. **-trockner,** *m.* cobalt drier. **-verbindung,** *f.* cobalt compound. **-vitriol,** *m.* cobalt vitriol (cobaltous sulfate, cobalt(II) sulfate).

**Kober,** *m.* basket.

**Koch,** *m.* cook. **-abschnitt,** *m.* period of boiling or cooking. **-apparat,** *m.* cooking apparatus. **-becher,** *m.* beaker.

**kochbeständig,** *a.* stable on boiling or cooking; (of dyes) fast to boiling.

**Koch-brenner,** *m.* boiling (or cooking) burner. **-dauer,** *f.* duration of boiling.

**kochecht,** *a.* fast to boiling (in water).

**Kochechtheit,** *f.* fastness to boiling.

**kochen,** *v.t.* boil; cook. — *v.i.* boil.

**Kochen,** *n.* boiling, boil, ebullition; cooking, cookery.

**kochend,** *p.a.* boiling, at the boil. — **— heiss,** boiling hot, just under boiling.

**Kocher,** *m.* boiler, cooker, digester; hot plate. **-ausbeute,** *f.* cooker yield, yield on cooking or boiling.

**Kocherei,** *f.* boiling; cooking.

**Kocherlauge,** *f.* cooking liquor, cooker liquor.

**Koch-flasche,** *f.* boiling flask. **-fleck,** *m.* (*Textiles*) kier mark, kier stain. **-flüssigkeit,** *f.* liquid for boiling, cooking liquor. **-gefäss,** *n.* boiling vessel, boiler; cooking vessel; (*Paper,* etc.) bucking keir. **-gerät,** *n.* boiling or cooking apparatus. **-geschirr,** *n.* boiling or cooking vessel(s).

**kochheiss,** *a.* boiling hot.

**Koch-hitze,** *f.* boiling heat. **-kessel,** *m.* boiling kettle, boiler; (*Paper*) pulp boiler, pulp digester. **-kläre,** *f.* (*Sugar*) filtered liquor (or sirup). **-kölbchen,** *n.* small boiling flask, fractional distillation flask. **-kolben,** *m.* boiling flask. **-lauge,** *f.* boiling lye. **-periode,** *f.* boiling period, boil. **-platte,** *f.* cooking plate, hot plate. **-probe,** *f.* boiling test. **-prozess,** *n.* boiling process, cooking process. **-puddeln,** *n.* slag puddling, pig boiling. **-punkt,** *m.* boiling point. **-punktmesser,** *m.* boiling-point apparatus; specif., ebullioscope. **-rohr,** *n.*, **röhre,** *f.* boiling tube, distilling tube.

**Kochsalz,** *n.* common salt (sodium chloride). **-bad,** *n.* (common) salt bath; brine bath. **-flamme,** *f.* sodium chloride flame.

**kochsalzhaltig,** *a.* containing (common) salt, salted.

**Kochsalz-lauge,** *f.* brine (of common salt). **-lösung,** *f.* (common) salt solution.

**kochsalzsauer,** *a.* chloride (or hydrochloride) of.

**Kochsalzsäure,** *f.* hydrochloric acid.

**Koch-stadium,** *n.* stage of boiling or cooking. **-topf,** *m.* boiler; cooker.

**Kochung,** *f.* boiling; cooking.

**Koch-vergütung,** *f.* (*Metal.*) artificial aging. **-wasser,** *n.* boiling water. **-zeit,** *f.* period of boiling or cooking. **-zucker,** *m.* brown sugar; powdered sugar.

**Kockels-beere,** *f.*, **-korn,** *n.* cocculus indicus.

**Kodäthylin,** *n.* codethyline.

**Kodein,** *n.* codeine.

**Köder,** *m.* bait; lure; decoy.

**Kodöl,** *n.* cod-liver oil; rosin oil.

**Kodzufaser,** *f.* kodzu fiber, tapa fiber.

**Koeffizient,** *m.* coefficient.

**Koenzym,** *n.* coenzyme.

**koerzibel,** *a.* coercible.

**Koerzitivkraft,** *f.* coercive force.

**koexistieren,** *v.i.* coexist.

**Koffein,** *n.* caffeine.

**Koffer,** *m.* trunk, coffer, box; (travel) bag. **-lack,** *m.* trunk varnish or lacquer. **-pappe,** *f.* (*Paper*) panel board.

**Kognak,** *m.* cognac. **-öl,** *n.* oil of cognac, oil of wine ("oenanthic ether").

**kohärent,** *a.* coherent.

**Kohärenz,** *f.* coherence, coherency.

**kohärieren,** *v.i.* cohere.

**Kohäsion,** *f.* cohesion.

**Kohäsionsvermögen,** *n.* cohesive power.

**kohäsiv,** *a.* cohesive.

**Kohl,** *m.* cabbage.

**Kohle,** *f.* coal; charcoal; carbon.

**kohlebeheizt,** *a.* heated with coal, coal-fired.

**Kohle-chemie,** *f.* coal(tar) chemistry. **-druck,** *m.* (*Photog.*) carbon print. **-fadenlampe,** *f.* carbon-filament lamp. **-feuerung,** *f.* heating with coal; coal furnace.

**kohlefrei,** *a.* carbon-free.

**Kohle-gehalt,** *m.* carbon content. **-hydrat,** *n.* carbohydrate. **-klemme,** *f.* (*Elec.*) carbon terminal. **-korn,** *n.* carbon granule. **-lampe,** *f.* carbon lamp. **-lichtbogen,** *m.* (*Elec.*) carbon arc.

**kohlen,** *v.t.* char; carbonize, carburize. — *v.i.* char.

**Kohlen-abbrand,** *m.* (*Elec.*) carbon loss. **-ablagerung,** *f.* carbon deposition, carbonization.

**kohlen-ähnlich, -artig,** *a.* coal-like, carbon-like, carbonaceous.

**Kohlen-asche,** *f.* coal ash, coal ashes. **-aufbereitung,** *f.* coal dressing. **-becken,** *n.* (*Geol.*) coal basin. **-benzin,** *n.* benzene, benzol. **-bergbau,** *m.* coal mining. **-bergwerk,** *n.* coal mine, colliery. **-beule,** *f.* (*Med.*) carbuncle. **-bleispat,** *m.* cerussite. **-bleivitriolspat,** *m.* lanarkite. **-blende,** *f.* anthracite. **-bogenlampe,** *f.* carbon arc lamp. **-bohrer,** *m.* charcoal borer. **-braun,** *n.* Cologne brown. **-brennen,** *n.* charcoal burning; coal burning. **-brennerei,** *f.* charcoal works; charcoal burning. **-dampf,** *m.* gases from burning coal. **-dioxyd,** *n.* carbon dioxide. **-dioxydstrom,** *m.* current of carbon dioxide. **-disulfid,** *n.* carbon disulfide. **-dithiolsäure,** *f.* dithiolcarbonic acid. **-drucksäule,** *f.* carbon pile. **-dunst,** *m.* vapor from coals (containing carbon monoxide as a poisonous ingredient). **-eisen,** *n.* iron carbide. **-eisenstein,** *m.* blackband (carbonaceous iron carbonate). **-entgasung,** *f.* coal carbonization or distillation. **-faden,** *m.* carbon filament. **-filter,** *n.* charcoal filter; boneblack filter. **-flöz,** *n.* coal seam, coal measure. **-futter,** *n.* carbonaceous lining. **-gas,** *n.* coal gas; carbon monoxide. **-gestein,** *n.* (*Geol.*) carbonaceous rock. **-gestübbe,** *n.* coal slack; brasque. **-griess,** *m.* small coal, slack; carbon granules. **-grube,** *f.* coal mine. **-grus,** *m.* small coal, slack.

**kohlenhaltig,** *a.* carbonaceous, carboniferous.

**Kohlenhaufe(n),** *m.* coal pile, coal heap.

**Kohlenhydrat,** *n.* carbohydrate. **-abbau,** *m.* carbohydrate degradation, specif. carbohydrate catabolism. **-stoffwechsel,** *m.* carbohydrate metabolism. **-verwertung,** *f.* carbohydrate utilization.

**Kohlenkalk,** *m.* carboniferous limestone. **-spat,** *m.* anthraconite. **-stein,** *m.* carboniferous limestone.

**Kohlen-karbonit,** *n.* kohlencarbonite (trade name of an explosive). **-klein,** *n.* small coal. **-klemme,** *f.* (*Elec.*) carbon terminal. **-korn,** *n.* carbon granule. **-licht,** *n.* carbon light. **-lösche,** *f.* coal dust or slack. **-mehl,** *n.* coal dust, powdered coal. **-meiler,** *m.* charcoal pile. **-monoxyd,** *n.* carbon monoxide. **-mulm,** *m.* coal dust, slack; charcoal dust. **-ölsäure,** *f.* carbolic acid. **-oxychlorid,** *n.* carbon oxychloride, carbonyl chloride.

**Kohlenoxyd,** *n.* carbon monoxide. **-eisen,** *n.* iron carbonyl. **-gas,** *n.* carbon monoxide gas. **-hämoglobin,** *n.* compound of carbon monoxide with hemoglobin. **-kalium,** *n.* potassium carboxide, potassium hexacarbonyl. **-knallgas,** *n.* explosive mixture of carbon monoxide and oxygen. **-nickel,** *m.& n.* nickel carbonyl.

**kohlenoxydreich,** *a.* rich in carbon monoxide.

**Kohlen-oxydvergiftung,** *f.* carbon monoxide poisoning. **-oxysulfid,** *n.* carbon oxysulfide. **-papier,** *n.* carbon paper. **-pres(s)stein,** *m.* coal briquet. **-pulver,** *n.* coal powder, powdered coal; charcoal powder, powdered charcoal. **-puppe,** *f.* (*Elec.*) carbon rod. **-rückstand,** *m.* carbon residue. **-sandstein,** *m.* carboniferous sandstone.

**kohlensauer,** *a.* of or combined with carbonic acid, carbonate of.

**Kohlensäure,** *f.* carbonic acid; carbon dioxide. **-anhydrid,** *n.* carbonic anhydride (carbon dioxide). **-ausscheidung,** *f.* (*Physiol.*) carbon dioxide excretion. **-bestimmer,** *m.* apparatus for determining carbon dioxide. **-brot,** *n.* aerated bread. **-chlorid,** *n.* carbonyl chloride. **-entwickelung,** *f.* evolution of carbon dioxide. **-ester,** *m.* carbonic ester. **-flasche,** *f.* carbon dioxide cylinder. **-gas,** *n.* carbonic acid gas (carbon dioxide). **-gehalt,** *m.* carbon dioxide content.

**kohlensäurehaltig,** *a.* containing carbonic acid, carbonated.

**Kohlensäure-messer,** *m.* instrument or apparatus for measuring carbon dioxide, anthracometer, carbonometer. **-salz,** *n.* carbonate. **-schnee,** *m.* carbon dioxide snow, dry ice. **-strom,** *m.* stream or current of carbon dioxide. **-verflüssigung,** *f.* liquefaction of carbon dioxide. **-verlust,** *m.* loss (or escape) of carbon dioxide. **-wäsche,** *f.* carbon dioxide washer. **-wasser,** *n.* carbonated water, soda water.

**Kohlen-schiefer,** *m.* bituminous shale; coal-bearing shale. **-schlacke,** *f.* cinder, clinker. **-schlichte,** *f.* (*Founding*) black wash.

**kohlenschwarz,** *a.* coal-black.

**Kohlen-schwarz,** *n.* carbon black; charcoal black. **-schwefelwasserstoffsäure,** *f.* (tri)-thiocarbonic acid ($H_2CS_3$). **-spat,** *m.* anthraconite; whewellite. **-spitze,** *f.* carbon point. **-staub,** *m.* coal dust; charcoal dust. **-stickstoff,** *m.* cyanogen. **-stickstoffsäure,** *f.* carbazotic acid (picric acid). **-stoff,** *m.* carbon.

**kohlenstoffarm,** *a.* poor in carbon, low-carbon.

**Kohlenstoff-art,** *f.* variety of carbon. **-ausscheidung,** *f.* separation of carbon. **-bestimmung,** *f.* carbon determination. **-bindung,** *f.* carbon linkage. **-eisen,** *n.* iron carbide. **-entziehung,** *f.* removal of carbon, decarbonization, decarburization.

**kohlenstof(f)frei,** *a.* free from carbon.

**Kohlenstoff-gehalt,** *m.* carbon content. **-gehaltverhältnis,** *n.* (*Petroleum*) carbon ratio. **-gerüst,** *n.* carbon skeleton.

**kohlenstoffhaltig,** *a.* carbonaceous, carboniferous.

**Kohlenstoff-hydrat,** *n.* carbohydrate. **-kalium,** *n.* potassium carbide. **-kern,** *m.* carbon nucleus. **-kette,** *f.* carbon chain. **-legierung,** *f.* carbon alloy. **-metall,** *n.* carbide.

**kohlenstoffreich,** *a.* rich in carbon.

**Kohlenstoff-silicium,** *n.* carbon silicide. **-skelett,** *n.* carbon skeleton. **-stahl,** *m.* carbon steel. **-stein,** *m.* carbon brick. **-stickstofftitan,** *n.* titanium carbonitride. **-sulfid,** *n.*

carbon disulfide. **-verbindung,** *f.* carbon compound.

**Kohlen-suboxyd,** *n.* carbon suboxide. **-sulfid,** *n.* carbon disulfide. **-sulfidsalz,** *n.* thiocarbonate. **-technik,** *f.* coal technology. **-teer,** *m.* coal tar. **-teerfarbe,** *f.* coal-tar color. **-teeröl,** *n.* coal-tar oil. **-teerpech,** *n.* coal-tar pitch. **-teerseife,** *f.* coal-tar soap. **-tiegel,** *m.* carbon crucible; charcoal crucible; crucible with carbonaceous lining. **-verbrauch,** *m.* coal consumption. **-verflüssigung,** *f.* coal liquefaction. **-vergasung,** *f.* gasification of coal, coal distillation. **-verschwelung,** *f.* low-temperature carbonization of coal. **-vorkommen,** *n.* occurrence of coal, coal deposit.

**Kohlenwasserstoff,** *m.* hydrocarbon. **-gas,** *n.* hydrocarbon gas; (**leichtes**) methane; (**schweres**) ethylene. **-gemisch,** *n.* hydrocarbon mixture.

**kohlenwasserstoff-haltig,** *a.* containing hydrocarbons, hydrocarbonaceous. **-löslich,** *a.* soluble in hydrocarbons.

**Kohlen-wasserstofföl,** *n.* hydrocarbon oil. **-wasserstoffverbindung,** *f.* hydrocarbon. **-wertstoff,** *m.* coal product (esp., a by-product). **-wertstoffbetrieb,** *m.*, **-wertstoffgewinnungsanlage,** *f.* coal by-product plant. **-ziegel,** *m.* coal briquet.

**Kohlepapier,** *n.* carbon paper.

**Köhler,** *m.* charcoal burner.

**Köhlerei,** *f.* charcoal burning; charcoal works.

**Kohle-rohr,** *n.*, **-röhre,** *f.* carbon tube. **-schwelung,** *f.* coal distillation. **-stab,** *m.* carbon rod. **-stahl,** *m.* carbon steel, ordinary steel. **-staub,** *m.* coal dust; charcoal dust.

**Kohlholz,** *n.* wood for charcoal.

**kohlig,** *a.* like coal, coaly, coal-bearing, carbonaceous.

**Kohl-palme,** *f.* cabbage palm. **-palmöl,** *n.* cabbage-palm oil. **-rabi,** *m.* kohlrabi, turnip cabbage. **-raps,** *m.* rape, rapeseed. **-rübe,** *f.* rutabaga. **-saat,** *f.* colza, rapeseed. **-saatöl,** *n.* colza oil, rape oil. **-schwarz,** *n.* charcoal black; coal black.

**kohlschwarz,** *a.* coal-black.

**Kohlsprossen,** *f.pl.* Brussels sprouts.

**Kohlung,** *f.* charring; carbonization, carburization; cementation.

**Kohlungs-mittel,** *n.* carbonizing (or carburizing) agent. **-stahl,** *m.* cementation steel.

**kohobieren,** *v.t.* cohobate, distil repeatedly.

**Kohunennuss,** *f.* cohune nut. **-öl,** *n.* cohune nut oil.

**koinzidieren,** *v.i.* coincide.

**Kok,** *m.* coke.

**Koka,** *f.* coca. **-blätter,** *n.pl.* coca leaves.

**Kokaïn,** *n.* cocaine. **-vergiftung,** *f.* cocaine poisoning.

**Koke,** *m.* & *f.* coke.

**Koker,** *m.* sagger.

**Kokerei,** *f.* coke plant, coke works; coking, coking practice. **-gas,** *n.* coke-oven gas. **-ofen,** *m.* coke oven. **-teer,** *m.* coke-oven tar, coke tar.

**Kokes-.** see Koks-.

**Kokille,** *f.* ingot mold; (*Founding*) chill, chill mold.

**Kokillenguss,** *m.* chill casting.

**Kokkelskorn,** *n.* cocculus indicus.

**Kokken,** *m.pl.* (*Bact.*) cocci. **-ketten,** *f.pl.* (*Bact.*) streptococci.

**Kokkus,** *m.* coccus.

**Kokon,** *m.* cocoon. **-faden,** *m.* cocoon fiber, cocoon thread.

**Kokos, -baum,** *m.* coco, coco palm, coconut tree. **-butter,** *f.* coconut butter (coconut oil). **-faser,** *f.* coco fiber, coir (fiber from the husk of the coconut). **-fett,** *n.* coconut oil. **-garn,** *n.* coir yarn.

**Kokosnuss,** *f.* coconut. **-bast,** *m.* coconut bast, coco fiber. **-fett,** *n.* coconut oil. **-milch,** *f.* coconut milk. **-öl,** *n.* coconut oil. **-ölseife,** *f.* coconut-oil soap. **-talg,** *m.* coconut oil.

**Kokos-öl,** *n.* coconut oil. **-ölseife,** *f.* coconut-oil soap. **-palme,** *f.* coco palm. **-seife,** *f.* coconut-oil soap. **-talg,** *m.* coconut oil. **-talgsäure,** *f.* cocinic acid (formerly supposed to exist as an ester in coconut oil).

**Koks,** *m.* & *m.pl.* coke. **-abfall,** *m.* refuse coke.

**koksähnlich,** *a.* coke-like.

**Koks-asche,** *f.* coke ash(es). **-ausbeute,** *f.* yield of coke. **-bereitung,** *f.* coke making, coking. **-brennen,** *n.* coke burning, coking. **-erzeugung,** *f.* coke production. **-filter,** *m.* coke filter. **-gas,** *n.* gas from coke, specif. blue water gas; coke-oven gas. **-gicht,** *f.* charge of coke. **-grus,** *m.* small coke, coke breeze. **-heizung,** *f.* heating with coke. **-hochofen,** *m.* coke blast furnace. **-klein,** *n.* small coke, coke breeze, coke dust. **-kohle,** *f.* coking coal. **-lösche,** *f.* coke dust. **-mehl,** *n.* coke dust, powdered coke. **-ofen,** *m.* coke oven. **-ofenteer,** *m.* coke-oven tar. **-roheisen,** *n.* coke pig iron. **-schicht,** *f.* layer of coke. **-staub,** *m.* coke dust. **-stein,** *m.* coke brick. **-teer,** *m.* coke tar, coke-oven tar.

**Kokung,** *f.* coking.

**Kolanuss,** *f.* cola nut.

**Kolatorium,** *n.* colatorium, strainer.

**Kölbchen,** *n.* little flask, etc. (see Kolben).

**Kolben,** *m.* flask; butt, butt end; (*Mach.*) piston, plunger; soldering iron; ram; (*Metal.*) bloom; (*Old Chem.*) bolthead, matrass, cucurbit; (*Bot.*) head, spike; (corn)cob; club.

**kolbenförmig,** *a.* bulb-shaped; club-shaped, clavate.

**Kolben-hals,** *m.* neck of a flask. **-hub,** *m.* piston

stroke. **-schimmel,** *m.* club mold (*Aspergillus* sp.). **-stange,** *f.* piston rod. **-stoss,** *m.* (*Mach.*) piston stroke. **-träger,** *m.* flask support, flask stand.
**kolbig,** *a.* knobby, clubby, knotty; club-shaped.
**Kolibazillus,** *m.* colon bacillus.
**kolieren,** *v.t.* filter, percolate, strain.
**Kolier-rahmen,** *m.* filtering frame. **-tuch,** *n.* filtering cloth.
**Koli-gruppe,** *f.* colon bacillus group. **-reinkultur,** *f.* colon bacillus pure culture.
**Kolleg,** *n.* (course of) lectures; college.
**Kollege,** *m.* colleague.
**Kollegium,** *n.* board, council, staff.
**Kollektor,** *m.* (*Elec.*) commutator.
**Koller-gang,** *m.*, **-mühle,** *f.* edge mill, edge runner.
**kollern,** *v.i.* rumble; gobble; rave; roll. — *v.t.* grind (in an edge mill).
**Kolli,** *n.& m.* = Kollo.
**kollidieren,** *v.i.* collide.
**Kollidin,** *n.* collidine.
**kolligativ,** *a.* colligative.
**Kollo,** *n.* parcel, bale, bundle.
**kollodisieren,** *v.t.* collodionize.
**Kollodium,** *n.* collodion. **-ersatz,** *m.* collodion substitute. **-faden,** *m.* collodion filament. **-fasermasse,** *f.* collodion cotton. **-haut,** *f.*, **-häutchen,** *n.* collodion film. **-lösung,** *f.* collodion solution. **-seide,** *f.* collodion silk (nitrate rayon). **-überzug,** *m.* coat or skin of collodion. **-verfahren,** *n.* collodion process or method. **-wolle,** *f.* collodion cotton, soluble guncotton, pyroxylin.
**kolloid, kolloidal,** *a.* colloid, colloidal.
**Kolloidal-lösung,** *f.* colloidal solution. **-stoff,** *m.*, **-substanz,** *f.* colloidal substance, colloid. **-zustand,** *m.* colloidal state.
**kolloidarm,** *a.* poor in colloids.
**Kolloid-chemie,** *f.* colloid chemistry, chemistry of colloids. **-chemiker,** *m.* colloid chemist.
**kolloidchemisch,** *a.* colloidochemical.
**Kolloidität,** *f.* colloidal quality.
**Kolloid-lösung** *f.* colloid(al) solution. **-mühle,** *f.* colloid mill. **-stoff,** *m.*, **-substanz,** *f.* colloid substance, colloid. **-teilchen,** *n.* colloid(al) particle. **-zustand,** *m.* colloid(al) state.
**Köln,** *n.* Cologne.
**kölner, kölnisch,** *a.* Cologne. — **kölner Braun,** Cologne brown. — **kölner Erde, kölnische Erde,** Cologne earth.
**Kölnerwasser,** *n.* cologne, Cologne water.
**kölnisch,** *a.* see kölner.
**Kölnischbraun,** *n.* Cologne brown.
**Kolombowurzel,** *f.* calumba root, calumba.
**Kolonial-waren,** *f.pl.* colonial products; groceries. **-zucker,** *m.* muscovado; cane sugar.
**Kolonie,** *f.* colony.
**Kolonne,** *f.* column; tower; gang, crew.
**Kolonnen-apparat,** *m.* column apparatus. **-turm,** *m.* fractionating tower; absorption tower.
**Kolophan,** *n.* colophane.
**Kolophoneisenerz,** *m.* pitticite.
**Kolophonium,** *n.* colophony, rosin. **-ester,** *m.* rosin ester, ester gum. **-lack,** *m.* rosin varnish. **-seife,** *f.* rosin soap.
**Kolophonsäure,** *f.* colophonic acid.
**Koloquinte,** *f.* colocynth.
**Koloquintin,** *n.* colocynthin.
**kolorieren,** *v.t.* color.
**Kolorimetrie,** *f.* colorimetry.
**kolorimetrisch,** *a.* colorimetric.
**koloristisch,** *a.* coloristic, colouristic.
**Kolorit,** *n.* coloring, color, hue.
**Kolostralmilch,** *f.* colostrum.
**Kolumbin,** *n.* columbin.
**Kolumbowurzel,** *f.* calumba root, calumba.
**Kolzaöl,** *n.* colza oil, rape oil.
**Komansäure,** *f.* comanic acid.
**Kombinations-bleiche,** *f.* combined bleach. **-druck,** *m.* combination printing. **-färbung,** *f.* combination dyeing; (*Micros.*) differential staining. **-gerbung,** *f.* combination tanning. **-schwarz,** *n.* (*Dyeing*) combination black.
**kombinieren,** *v.t. & i.* combine.
**Kombinierfarbstoff,** *m.* compound dye(stuff).
**kombustibel,** *a.* combustible.
**Komensäure,** *f.* comenic acid.
**komisch,** *a.* comic, funny.
**Komisstuch,** *n.* army cloth.
**kommaförmig,** *a.* comma-shaped.
**kommandieren,** *v.t.* command.
**Kommanditgesellschaft,** *f.* limited partnership, commandite. — — **auf Aktien,** stock company with general partners.
**Kommando-.** control; signal; command.
**kommen,** *v.i.* come; happen; be, come out.
**Kommentar,** *m.* commentary.
**kommentieren,** *v.t.* comment on, annotate.
**Kommerz,** *m.* commerce.
**Kommis,** *m.* clerk.
**Kömmling,** *m.* new product; newcomer.
**Kommode,** *f.* chest of drawers.
**kommunizieren,** *v.i.* communicate.
**kommutieren,** *v.t.* commute; (*Elec.*) commutate.
**Kommutierung,** *f.* commutation.
**Komödie,** *f.* comedy.
**kompakt,** *a.* compact, solid, firm, rugged.
**Kompendium,** *n.* compendium, abridgment, summary, abstract.
**Kompensationsfarbe,** *f.* complementary color.
**kompensieren,** *v.t.* compensate.
**komplementär,** *a.* complementary.
**Komplementärfarbe,** *f.* complementary color.
**Komplement-bindung, -fixierung,** *f.* complement fixation. **-winkel,** *m.* complementary angle.

**komplett,** *a.* complete.
**komplettieren,** *v.t.* complete.
**Komplex-erz,** *n.* complex ore. **-ion,** *n.* complex ion. **-salz,** *n.* complex salt. **-stahl,** *m.* complex alloy steel. **-verbindung,** *f.* complex compound.
**kompliziert,** *p.a.* complicated.
**Kompliziertheit,** *f.* complication.
**Komposition,** *f.* composition; (*Dyeing*) tin composition (solution of tin in aqua regia); hard lead.
**Kompositionsmetall,** *n.* composition metal (a copper alloy).
**Kompostdünger,** *m.* (*Agric.*) compost.
**kompostieren,** *v.t.* compost.
**Kompott,** *n.* compote (preserved or stewed fruit).
**kompoundieren,** *v.t.* compound.
**Kompoundöl,** *n.* (*Petroleum*) compounded oil.
**kompr.,** *abbrev.* (komprimiert) compressed.
**kompressibel,** *a.* compressible.
**Kompressibilität,** *f.* compressibility.
**Kompressions-wärme,** *f.* heat of compression. **-welle,** *f.* compression wave.
**Kompressoröl,** *n.* compressor oil.
**komprimierbar,** *a.* compressible.
**Komprimierbarkeit,** *f.* compressibility.
**komprimieren,** *v.t.* compress.
**kompromittieren,** *v.t.* compromise.
**Konchylien,** *f.pl.* shells, shellfish.
**Kondensapparat,** *m.* condensing apparatus, condenser.
**Kondensat,** *n.* condensate.
**Kondensations-apparat,** *m.* condensing apparatus, condenser. **-druck,** *m.* condensation pressure. **-ergebnis,** *n.* condensation product. **-gefäss,** *n.* condensation vessel, receiver. **-harz,** *n.* condensation resin, synthetic resin. **-kammer,** *f.* condensing chamber. **-mittel,** *n.* condensing agent. **-punkt,** *m.* condensation point. **-raum,** *m.* condensation space, condensing chamber. **-rohr,** *n.*, **-röhre,** *f.* condensing tube; adapter. **-turm,** *m.* condensing tower, cooling tower. **-verlust,** *m.* loss from condensation. **-vorrichtung,** *f.* condensing apparatus, condenser. **-wärme,** *f.* heat of condensation. **-wasser,** *n.* = Kondenswasser.
**Kondensator,** *m.* condenser. **-röhre,** *f.* condenser tube.
**kondensierbar,** *a.* condensable.
**Kondensierbarkeit,** *f.* condensability.
**kondensieren,** *v.t. & i.* condense.
**Kondensierung,** *f.* condensation.
**Kondensor,** *m.* condenser.
**Kondens-rohr,** *n.* condenser tube. **-topf,** *m.* condensing pot; steam trap. **-wasser,** *n.* condensation water, condensed water, condensing water.
**Konditionieranstalt,** *f.* conditioning plant or house.
**konditionieren,** *v.t.* condition.
**Konditor,** *m.* confectioner.
**Konditorei,** *f.* confectionery.
**Konditorfarbe,** *f.* confectionery color.
**Konfekt,** *n.* confectionery.
**Konfektion,** *f.* ready-made clothing or its manufacture.
**Konferenz,** *f.* conference, meeting.
**konferieren,** *v.i.* confer.
**Konfitüren,** *pl.* confectionery, sweets.
**konform,** *a.* conformable.
**konfus,** *a.* confused.
**kongelieren,** *v.i.* congeal.
**Kongo-.** see Congo-.
**kongruieren,** *v.i.* be congruent.
**Konidie,** *f.* conidium.
**Konifere,** *f.* conifer.
**Koniferenholz,** *n.* conifer wood, softwood.
**König,** *m.* regulus; king.
**Königin,** *f.* queen. **-metall,** *n.* queen's metal (a tin alloy).
**königlich,** *a.* kingly, regal, royal.
**König-reich,** *n.* kingdom, realm. **-salbe,** *f.* (*Pharm.*) rosin cerate, basilicon ointment.
**Königs-blau,** *n.* king's blue (a name for cobalt blue and for smalt). **-chinarinde,** *f.* calisaya bark, (yellow) cinchona. **-farbe,** *f.* = Königsblau. **-gelb,** *n.* king's yellow ($As_2S_3$); chrome yellow; massicot. **-grün,** *n.* Paris green. **-holz,** *n.* kingwood, violet wood. **-kerze,** *f.* (common) mullen. **-krankheit,** *f.* king's evil, scrofula. **-pulver,** *n.* perfuming powder. **-salbe,** *f.* basilicon, resin ointment. **-säure,** *f.*, **-wasser,** *n.* aqua regia.
**Koniin,** *n.* conine, coniine.
**konisch,** *a.* conic, conical, coniform.
**Konizität,** *f.* conicity, angle of taper.
**konjugiert,** *p.a.* conjugate.
**Konjunktur,** *f.* conjuncture; (*Com.*) market turn or condition. **-tafel,** *f.* (*Com.*) price chart.
**konkav,** *a.* concave.
**Konkavgitter,** *n.* concave grating.
**Konkavität,** *f.* concavity.
**Konkavspiegel,** *m.* concave mirror.
**Konkrement,** *n.* concrement, concretion.
**konkret,** *a.* concrete.
**Konkurrenz,** *f.* competition.
**konkurrenzlos,** *a.* without competition, noncompetitive.
**konkurrieren,** *v.i.* compete. — **konkurrierend,** *p.a.* competing; concurrent.
**Konkurs,** *m.* bankruptcy, failure; assignment.
**Konkussionszünder,** *m.* concussion fuse.
**können,** *v.t.* be able, can; may.
**Können,** *n.* ability.
**Konnossement,** *n.* bill of lading.
**konnte,** *pret.* (of können) was able, could, might.

**konphas,** *a.* in phase, cophasal.
**konsequent,** *a.* consequent; consistent; congruous.
**Konserve,** *f.* preserved food (as canned fruit or meat, preserves, pickles); (*Pharm.*) confection, electuary.
**Konserven-büchse,** *f.* can, tin (for food). **-büchsenlack,** *m.* lacquer for cans or tins. **-dose,** *f.* can, tin (for food). **-dosenlack,** *m.* lacquer for cans or tins. **-fabrik,** *f.* cannery, preserve factory, etc. **-ring,** *m.* (*Rubber*) jar ring.
**konservieren,** *v.t.* preserve.
**Konservierung,** *f.* preservation; conservation.
**Konservierungs-firnis,** *m.* preserving varnish. **-mittel,** *n.* preservative. **-verfahren,** *n.* preserving process or method.
**konsistent,** *a.* consistent; firm, solid.
**Konsistenz,** *f.* consistency; firmness, solidity; (of paint, etc.) body. **-messer,** *m.* consistometer; viscosimeter. **-probe,** *f.* consistency test.
**Konsole,** *f.* bracket, console.
**konsolidieren,** *v.t.* consolidate.
**Konsortium,** *n.* syndicate (properly, a less permanent combination than Syndikat).
**konspergieren,** *v.t.* sprinkle, strew.
**Konspergiermittel,** *n.* sprinkling (or dusting) agent.
**konst.,** *abbrev.* (konstant) constant.
**konstant,** *a.* constant. — **konstante Härte,** (*Water*) permanent hardness.
**Konstante,** *f.* constant.
**konstant(er)halten,** *v.t.* keep constant, maintain.
**Konstant(er)haltung,** *f.* keeping constant, maintenance.
**Konstanz,** *n.* constancy.
**konstatieren,** *v.t.* ascertain, establish, verify.
**Konstellation,** *f.* constellation; configuration, arrangement (as in microstructure).
**konstituieren,** *v.t.* constitute.
**Konstitutions-formel,** *f.* constitutional formula. **-wasser,** *n.* water of constitution.
**konstruieren,** *v.t.* construct; construe.
**konstruktiv,** *a.* constructive; structural.
**konsultieren,** *v.t.* consult.
**Konsum,** *m.* consumption.
**Konsument,** *m.* consumer.
**konsumieren,** *v.t.* consume.
**kontagiös,** *a.* contagious.
**Kontagium,** *n.* contagion.
**Kontakt-(ab)druck,** *m.* contact print(ing). **-fläche,** *f.* surface of contact. **-gift,** *n.* contact poison. **-körper,** *m.* contact body (as a catalyst pellet); contact substance, catalyst. **-mittel,** *n.* contact agent, catalyst. **-oberfläche,** *f.* contact surface. **-russ,** *m.* contact black. **-schraube,** *f.* contact screw. **-substanz,** *f.* contact substance, catalyst. **-verfahren,** *n.* contact process. **-wirkung,** *f.* contact action, catalysis.
**Konter-.** counter-, reverse, inverse. **-mutter,** *f.* lock nut, jam nut. **-spülung,** *f.* counterwashing, reverse circulation.
**Kontinue-.** continuous. **-betrieb,** *m.* continuous operation. **-küpe,** *f.* (*Dyeing*) continuous vat. **-verfahren,** *n.* continuous process.
**kontinuierlich,** *a.* continuous.
**Kontinuität,** *f.* continuity.
**Konto,** *n.* account.
**Kontor,** *n.* (business) office.
**kontrahieren,** *v.i.* & *t.* contract.
**kontrainsulär,** *a.* opposing the action of insulin.
**kontrapolarisieren,** *v.t.* counterpolarize.
**konträr,** *a.* contrary.
**Kontrast-farbe,** *f.* contrast color. **-färbung,** *f.* contrast staining.
**kontrastieren,** *v.i.* contrast.
**kontrastreich,** *a.* rich in contrasts, contrasty.
**Kontrastwirkung,** *f.* contrast effect.
**Kontravalenz,** *f.* contravalence.
**Kontroll-ablesung,** *f.* control reading, check reading. **-analyse,** *f.* control (or check) analysis. **-bestimmung,** *f.* control determination.
**Kontrolle,** *f.* control; check.
**Kontroll-gerät,** *n.* control apparatus, controlling device. **-hahn,** *m.* test cock, tester cock; regulator tap.
**kontrollierbar,** *a.* controllable.
**kontrollieren,** *v.t.* control, check, supervise.
**Kontroll-kolben,** *m.* control flask. **-lampe,** *f.* pilot lamp. **-messung,** *f.* control measurement, check measurement. **-muster,** *n.* control sample, check sample. **-probe,** *f.* control sample or test. **-versuch,** *m.* control test, control experiment.
**Kontur,** *f.* outline, contour.
**Konturenschwarz,** *n.* (*Dyeing*) black for outlines.
**Konus,** *m.* cone. **-hahn,** *m.* conical cock (or plug), taper cock (or plug). **-spülung,** *f.* conical rinsing.
**Konvektionsstrom,** *m.* convection current.
**konventionell,** *a.* conventional.
**Konvergenz,** *f.* convergence.
**konvergieren,** *v.i.* converge. — **konvergierend,** *p.a.* convergent.
**Konversions-artikel,** *m.* (*Calico*) conversion style. **-farbe,** *f.* conversion color. **-salpeter,** *m.* converted saltpeter (sodium nitrate converted into potassium nitrate by double decomposition with potassium chloride).
**Konverter-birne,** *f.* (*Metal.*) converter. **-futter,** *n.* converter lining. **-stahl,** *m.* converter steel, Bessemer steel. **-werk,** *m.* converter mill, Bessemer plant.
**konvertierbar,** *a.* convertible.
**konvertieren,** *v.t.* convert.

**Konvertierung,** *f.* conversion.
**Konvexität,** *f.* convexity.
**konz.,** *abbrev.* (konzentriert) concentrated.
**Konz.,** *abbrev.* (Konzentration) concentration.
**Konzentrat,** *n.* concentrate.
**Konzentrations-änderung,** *f.* change in concentration. **-apparat,** *m.* concentrating apparatus, concentrator. **-gefäll(e),** *n.* concentration gradient. **-spannung,** *f.* (*Elec.*) concentration potential. **-stein,** *m.* (*Copper*) white metal. **-verhältnis,** *f.* ratio of concentration.
**Konzentrattrübe,** *f.* (*Metal.*) concentrate pulp.
**konzentrieren,** *v.t.* concentrate.
**konzentriert,** *p.a.* concentrated. — **konzentrierter Alaun,** concentrated alum (aluminum sulfate).
**Konzentrierung,** *f.* concentration.
**konzentrisch,** *a.* concentric.
**Konzept,** *n.* (rough) draft, sketch; concept. **-papier,** *n.* scratch paper, scribbling paper.
**Koordinaten-netz,** *n.* (*Math.*) coördinate system. **-papier,** *n.* coördinate paper. **-zahl,** *f.* coördination number.
**Koordinations-lehre,** *f.* coördination theory. **-zahl,** *f.* coördination number.
**Kopaiva-.** see Copaiva-.
**Kopal-baum,** *m.* copal tree. **-brecher,** *m.* copal disintegrator. **-firnis,** *m.* copal varnish. **-harz, -gummi,** *n.* copal resin, copal. **-insäure,** *f.* copalinic acid.
**Kopalkerinde,** *f.* copalche (or copalchi) bark.
**Kopal-lack,** *m.* copal varnish. **-luftlack,** *m.* airproof copal varnish. **-mattlack,** *m.* dull copal varnish. **-öl,** *n.* copal oil. **-säure,** *f.* copalic acid.
**Köper,** *m.* cotton twill, twilled cotton.
**köpern,** *v.t.* twill.
**Kopf,** *m.* head (in various senses); top.
**Kopf-.** head; top; main, principal; cephalic; mental. **-decke,** *f.* scalp. **-drüse,** *f.* cephalic gland. **-düngung,** *f.* (*Agric.*) top-dressing.
**köpfen,** *v.t.* top; truncate; behead.
**Kopf-füss(l)er,** *m.pl.* (*Zoöl.*) Cephalopoda, cephalopods. **-haut,** *f.* scalp.
**-köpfig.** -headed.
**Kopfkissen,** *n.* pillow.
**kopflos,** *a.* headless, acephalous; silly.
**Kopf-rechnen,** *n.* mental calculation. **-ring,** *m.* (*Zinc*) nozzle block. **-rose,** *f.* erysipelas. **-salat,** *m.* head lettuce. **-schimmel,** *m.* any mold of the genus *Mucor*. **-schmerz,** *m.* headache. **-schraube,** *f.* cap screw; cap bolt. **-steuer,** *f.* poll tax. **-titel,** *m.* main title, main heading. **-überschrift,** *f.* principal heading. **-waschpulver,** *n.* hair wash, head wash. **-wasser,** *n.* hair wash; head wash. **-wassersucht,** *f.* hydrocephalus. **-weh,** *n.* headache. **-zünder,** *m.* (*Expl.*) nose fuse.

**Kopie,** *f.* copy; (*Photog.*) print.
**kopieren,** *v.t.* copy; (*Photog.*) print.
**Kopierdruckfarbe,** *f.* copying ink.
**kopierfähig,** *a.* copiable.
**Kopier-farbe,** *f.* copying ink. **-leinwand,** *f.* copying cloth, tracing cloth. **-mine,** *f.* copying lead (for pencils). **-papier,** *n.* copying paper, duplicating paper. **-presse,** *f.* copying press. **-stift,** *m.* copying pencil. **-tinte,** *f.* copying ink.
**koppeln,** *v.t.* couple.
**köppeln,** *v.i.* (*Brewing*) froth in afterfermentation.
**Koppelung,** *f.* coupling; linkage.
**Koppelwirtschaft,** *f.* rotation of crops.
**Kopra-öl, -fett,** *n.* coconut oil.
**Koprolith,** *m.* coprolite.
**Koprosterin,** *n.* coprosterol.
**Kopsfärbung,** *f.* cop dyeing.
**kor,** *pret.* (of küren) chose, elected.
**kor.,** *abbrev.* (korrigiert) corrected.
**Koralle,** *f.* coral.
**korallenartig,** *a.* coral-like, coralloid.
**Korallen-kalk,** *m.* (*Geol.*) coral rag. **-rot,** *n.* coral red. **-wurzel,** *f.* (*Pharm.*) polypody root.
**Korb,** *m.* basket; hamper, crate, canister; cage; (*Mining*) corf, cage. **-flasche,** *f.* carboy; demijohn. **-warenlack,** *m.* basketmaker's varnish.
**Kordel,** *f.* twine, string, cord. **-griff,** *m.* milled (or knurled) knob.
**kordeln, kordieren,** *v.t.* knurl.
**Kordit,** *n.* cordite.
**Kordofangummi,** *n.* Kordofan gum.
**Korduan,** *n.* cordovan, Cordovan leather.
**Korianderöl,** *n.* coriander oil.
**Korinthe,** *f.* (dried) currant.
**kork-ähnlich,** *a.* cork-like, suberose. **-artig,** *a.* of the nature of cork, corky.
**Kork-asbest,** *m.* mountain cork, rock cork. **-baum,** *m.* cork tree. **-bohrer,** *m.* cork borer. **-bohrerschärfer,** *m.* cork borer sharpener. **-dichtung,** *f.* cork packing. **-eiche,** *f.* cork oak, cork tree.
**korken,** *v.t.* cork.
**Korken,** *m.* cork, cork stopper. **-zieher,** *m.* corkscrew.
**korkig,** *a.* corky, of the nature of cork.
**Kork-isolation,** *f.* cork insulation. **-kohle,** *f.* cork charcoal, burnt cork. **-mehl,** *n.* cork powder. **-messer,** *n.* cork knife. **-propfen,** *m.* cork stopper, cork. **-säure,** *f.* suberic acid. **-schrot,** *m. & n.* granulated cork. **-schwarz,** *n.* cork black. **-spund,** *m.* cork stopper, cork. **-staub,** *m.* cork dust, cork powder. **-stein,** *m.* cork board; cork brick. **-stoff,** *m.* suberin. **-stopfen, -stöpsel,** *m.* cork stopper, cork. **-substanz,** *f.* suberin. **-teppich,** *m.* linoleum.

-**verbindung,** *f.* cork connection. -**wachssäure,** *f.* (*Org. Chem.*) ceric acid. -**zieher,** *m.* corkscrew.

**Korn,** *n.* grain; granule; seed, kernel; particle; bead; fineness, standard (of coins); corn; (of flax) boon; (*Assaying*) button. -**alkohol,** *m.* grain alcohol. -**art,** *f.* (kind of) grain.

**kornartig,** *a.* grainy, granulated.

**Korn-bildung,** *f.* (*Sugar*) granulation, crystallization. -**bildungspunkt,** *m.* (*Sugar*) granulation point.

**kornblau,** *a.* cornflower-blue.

**Korn-blei,** *n.* grain lead (finely granulated lead for use in assaying). -**blume,** *f.* bluebottle, cornflower (*Centaurea cyanus*). -**blumenblau,** *n.* cornflower blue. -**brand,** *m.* blight, smut (of grain). -**branntwein,** *m.* grain spirits, whisky. -**brennerei,** *f.* grain (or corn) distillery or distilling. -**bürste,** *f.* (*Assaying*) button brush.

**Körnchen,** *n.* little grain, granule.

**Korn-dichte,** *f.* closeness of grain. -**eisen,** *n.* iron of granular fracture.

**Kornelkirsche,** *f.* cornelian cherry.

**körneln,** *v.t.* granulate.

**Körnelung,** *f.* granulation.

**körnen,** *v.t.* granulate; grain; corn (gunpowder). — **gekörnt,** *p.a.* granulated, granular.

**Körner,** *n.pl.* of Korn (which see); grain, corn (collectively); kermes; shot. — *m.* center.

**Körner-.** granular, grained, in grains. -**asant,** *m.* asafetida in grains. -**form,** *f.* granular form or shape. -**frucht,** *f.* cereal, grain. -**futter,** *n.* grain feed, grain. -**lack,** *m.* seed-lac. -**leder,** *n.* grained leather.

**körnerreich,** *a.* full of grains, grainy.

**Körner-spitze,** *f.* (*Mach.*) dead center. -**zinn,** *n.* grain tin, granular tin.

**Körnezähler,** *m.* grain counter.

**Kornfeinheit,** *f.* fineness of grain.

**korn-förmig,** *a.* in the form of grains, granular. -**frei,** *a.* free from grains or granules.

**Korn-fuselöl,** *n.* fusel oil from grain. -**gefüge,** *n.* grain structure. -**grenze,** *f.* grain boundary. -**grösse,** *f.* grain size, particle size. -**grössenverteilung,** *f.* particle-size distribution.

**Körnhaus,** *n.* (*Explosives*) corning house, granulating house.

**körnig,** *a.* granular, granulated; grainy, gritty; grained, showing a grain; brittle (malt).

**Körnigkeit,** *f.* granularity, graininess.

**Körnigkeitsmesser,** *m.* granulometer.

**körnigkristallinisch,** *a.* granular-crystalline.

**Korn-käfer,** *m.* grain weevil. -**kluft,** *f.* assayer's tongs. -**kochen,** *n.* (*Sugar*) boiling to grain. -**kupfer, Körnkupfer,** *n.* granulated copper. -**leder,** *n.* grain leather, -**mutter,** *f.* ergot. -**prüfer,** *m.* grain tester. -**puddeln,** *n.* puddling of fine-grained iron. -**pulver,** *n.* granulated powder, powder in grains. -**schnaps,** *m.* grain spirits, whisky. -**sieb,** *n.* granulating sieve; grain sieve. -**stahl,** *m.* granulated steel. -**struktur,** *f.* grain structure, granular structure.

**Kornung,** *f.* granulation, grain.

**Körnung,** *f.* granulation; graining; grain; pitting.

**Korn-vergröberung, -vergrösserung,** *f.* coarsening of grain. -**wa(a)ge,** *f.* button balance, assay balance; grain scales. -**wachstum,** *n.* grain growth, crystalline growth. -**wurm,** *m.* grain weevil. -**zange,** *f.* assayer's tongs. -**zinn,** *n.* (*Metal.*) grain tin. -**zucker,** *m.* granulated sugar. -**zusammensetzung,** *f.* grain composition.

**Körper,** *m.* body; substance, compound; (*Elec.*) earth, ground. (Careful modern usage avoids the translation "body" for chemical substances.)

**Körper-.** body, bodily, corpor(e)al, physical; solid. -**bau,** *m.* bodily structure, build. -**beschaffenheit,** *f.* constitution. -**chen,** *n.* corpuscle; particle. -**farbe,** *f.* body color; pigment, covering color. -**flüssigkeit,** *f.* body fluid. -**fülle,** *f.* corpulence. -**gehalt,** *m.* solid content (as of a lacquer). -**gewicht,** *n.* body weight. -**gruppe,** *f.* group of substances (or bodies), -**klasse,** *f.* class of substances (or bodies).

**körperlich,** *a.* bodily, corporeal, material, physical; corpuscular; solid.

**Körper-mass,** *n.* solid measure, cubic measure. -**oberfläche,** *f.* body surface. -**pflegemittel,** *n.* cosmetic. -**schaft,** *f.* corporation. -**stoff,** *m.* organic matter; matter. -**teil,** *m.* part of the body. -**teilchen,** *n.* particle, specif. molecule. -**verbindung,** *f.* (*Elec.*) ground connection, ground. -**wärme,** *f.* body heat. -**zusammensetzung,** *f.* composition of the body.

**Korpuskel,** *n.* corpuscle.

**korr.,** *abbrev.* (korrigiert) corrected.

**Korrektionsmittel, Korrektivmittel,** *n.* corrective agent, corrigent.

**Korrektur,** *f.* correction; proof.

**Korrelat,** *n.* correlative.

**korrigieren,** *v.t.* correct; soften (water).

**korrodierbar,** *a.* corrodible.

**Korrodierbarkeit,** *f.* corrodibility.

**korrodieren,** *v.t.* & *i.* corrode. — **korrodierend,** *p.a.* corroding, corrosive.

**korrosionsbeständig,** *a.* resisting corrosion, corrosionproof, stainless, rustless.

**Korrosions-beständigkeit,** *f.* corrosion resistance. -**bildner,** *m.* corrosive agent.

**korrosions-empfindlich,** *a.* sensitive to corrosion. -**fest,** *a.* resisting corrosion, corrosionproof.

**Korrosionsfestigkeit,** *f.* resistance to corrosion.

**korrosions-fördernd,** *a.* promoting corrosion. **-frei,** *a.* free from corrosion, noncorrodible, stainless, rustless. **-hemmend,** *a.* inhibiting corrosion.

**Korrosions-mittel,** *n.* corrosive. **-schutz,** *m.* protection against corrosion. **-wirkung,** *f.* corrosive effect.

**Korund,** *m.* corundum.

**Koschenille,** *f.* cochineal.

**Kosekante,** *f.* cosecant.

**Kosinus,** *m.* cosine.

**Kosmetikum,** *n.* cosmetic.

**kosmetisch,** *a.* cosmetic.

**kosmisch,** *a.* cosmic.

**Kosoblüten,** *f.pl.* (*Pharm.*) cusso.

**Kost,** *f.* food, fare, diet, board.

**kostbar,** *a.* costly, expensive, precious.

**kosten,** *v.i.* cost. — *v.t.* taste; try.

**Kosten,** *f.pl.* costs, expenses, charges. **-anschlag,** *m.* estimate (of cost). **-aufwand,** *m.* expenditure.

**kosten-frei, -los,** *a.* free of charge, free.

**köstlich,** *a.* costly, dainty, excellent.

**kostspielig,** *a.* expensive.

**Kot,** *m.* feces, excrement; mud; sludge; dirt.

**Kot-.** fecal. **-abgang,** *m.* defecation.

**kot-artig,** *a.* fecal, feculent, excremental. **-ausführend, -ausleerend,** *p.a.* purgative, cathartic, aperient.

**Kot-ausleerung,** *f.* evacuation of feces. **-bad,** *n.* dung bath. **-beize,** *f.* (*Leather*) dung bate.

**koten,** *v.t.* dung.

**Kotgeruch,** *m.* fecal odor.

**kotig,** *a.* fecal, stercoraceous; dirty, filthy.

**kotonisieren,** *v.t.* cottonize; degum (silk).

**Kotorinde,** *f.* coto bark.

**Kot-porphyrin,** *n.* coproporphyrin. **-stein,** *m.* fecal concretion.

**kottonisieren,** *v.t.* cottonize.

**Kötzer,** *m.* (*Textiles*) cop.

**Kouvert,** *n.* envelope; cover.

**Kovolum, Kovolumen,** *n.* covolume.

**Kp.,** *abbrev.* (Kochpunkt) boiling point, b.p.

**kpl.,** *abbrev.* (komplett) complete.

**Krabbe,** *f.* crab; shrimp.

**krabbecht,** *a.* fast to crabbing.

**krabbeln,** *v.t.* tickle. — *v.i.* itch; crawl.

**krabben,** *v.t.* (*Textiles*) crab.

**Krach,** *m.* crack, crash.

**krachen,** *v.i.* crack, crash, crackle; (of silk) rustle, scroop.

**Krackbenzin,** *n.* cracked gasoline (or petrol).

**kracken,** *v.t.* crack (as petroleum).

**Krack-gas,** *n.* gas from cracking. **-prozess,** *m.* cracking (process).

**Krackung,** *f.* cracking.

**Krackverfahren,** *n.* cracking (process).

**Krad,** *abbrev.* (Kraftrad) motorcycle.

**kraft,** *prep.* on the strength of, by virtue of.

**Kraft,** *f.* force; power; strength, vigor, energy; worker, help. **-anlage,** *f.* power plant, power station. **-antrieb,** *m.* (*Mach.*) power drive. **-aufwand,** *m.* expenditure of energy. **-äusserung,** *f.* manifestation of force or energy. **-bedarf,** *m.* power demand, power requirement.

**kraftbetätigt,** *a.* power-operated.

**Kraft-brühe,** *f.* strong broth; (*Tech.*) strong liquor. **-eck,** *n.* (*Mech.*) polygon of forces.

**kräftefrei,** *a.* force-free.

**Kräftegleichgewicht,** *n.* equilibrium of forces.

**Kraft-einheit,** *f.* unit of force. **-erzeugung,** *f.* power production.

**Kräfte-vieleck,** *n.* (*Mech.*) polygon of forces. **-zerlegung,** *f.* (*Mech.*) resolution of forces. **-zusammensetzung,** *f.* (*Mech.*) composition of forces.

**Kraftfahrzeug,** *n.* motor vehicle.

**Kraft-feld,** *n.* (*Physics*) field of force. **-futter, -futtermittel,** *n.* concentrated feed.

**Kraftgas,** *n.* power gas, fuel gas, esp. producer gas. **-anlage,** *f.* power gas plant; gas producer. **-erzeuger,** *m.* gas producer.

**kräftig,** *a.* strong; vigorous; firm; effective; valid; nourishing; (of hides) plump; (of dyeing) full, heavy.

**kräftigen,** *v.t.* strengthen.

**Kraft-lehre,** *f.* dynamics. **-leitung,** *f.* (*Elec.*) power circuit. **-linie,** *f.* line of force.

**kraftlos,** *a.* forceless, powerless, feeble.

**Kraft-mehl,** *n.* starch, amylum. **-messer,** *m.* dynamometer. **-mittel,** *n.* forceful means; powerful remedy; tonic. **-packpapier,** *n.* kraft (wrapping) paper. **-papier,** *n.* kraft paper, kraft. **-papierstoff,** *m.* kraft pulp. **-quelle,** *f.* source of power. **-rad,** *n.* motorcycle. **-röhre,** *f.* (*Physics*) tube of force. **-sammler,** *m.* accumulator. **-sitz,** *m.* (*Mach.*) forced fit. **-speicher,** *m.* accumulator. **-spiritus,** *m.* motor spirit. **-stoff,** *m.* power fuel, motor fuel; (*Paper*) kraft pulp. **-stoffgemisch,** *n.* fuel mixture. **-stoffverbrauch,** *m.* fuel consumption. **-stoffwirtschaft,** *f.* fuel economy. **-strom,** *m.* (*Elec.*) power current. **-übertragung,** *f.* power transmission. **-verbrauch,** *m.* power consumption. **-verkehr,** *m.* motor traffic.

**kraftvoll,** *a.* powerful, strong, vigorous.

**Kraft-wagen,** *m.* automobile, motor car, motor truck. **-wagenfett,** *n.* automobile grease. **-wagenlack,** *m.* automobile varnish. **-wechsel,** *m.* energy exchange. **-werk,** *n.*, **-zentrale,** *f.* power station. **-wirkung,** *f.* (dynamic) effect, action (of a force).

**Kragen,** *m.* collar; cape; flange. **-kolben,** *m.* flanged flask.

**Krähe,** *f.* crow.

**Krähenaugen,** *pl.* (*Pharm.*) nux vomica.
**Krahle,** *f.* rake, rabble.
**Krahn,** *m.* cock, faucet; crane.
**Krain,** *n.* Carniola.
**Kralle,** *f.* claw; clutch.
**Kram,** *m.* retail; store, shop; retail articles; stuff, lot.
**Krämer,** *m.* retailer, storekeeper, tradesman. **-gewicht,** *n.* avoirdupois.
**Krampe,** *f.* cramp, cramp iron; staple; clip.
**Krampf,** *m.* cramp, spasm, convulsion. **-ader,** *f.* varicose vein.
**krampf-ähnlich, -artig,** *a.* convulsive, spasmodic.
**Krampf-arznei,** *f.* antispasmodic. **-gift,** *n.* convulsive poison.
**krampfhaft,** *a.* spasmodic, convulsive.
**Krampf-mittel,** *n.* antispasmodic. **-wurzel,** *f.* valerian root.
**Kran,** *m.* cock, faucet; crane.
**Kranewitbeere,** *f.* juniper berry.
**krängen,** *v.i.* (of ships, etc.) heel, list.
**Kranich,** *m.* crane.
**krank,** *a.* ill, sick; (of wood) rotten.
**kränkeln,** *v.i.* be ailing, be sickly.
**Kranken-anstalt,** *f.* hospital. **-haus,** *n.* hospital. **-heilanstalt,** *f.* sanatorium, hospital. **-kost,** *f.* sick diet.
**krankhaft,** *a.* diseased; morbid.
**Krankheit,** *f.* disease; illness, sickness.
**krankheitserregend,** *a.* disease-producing, pathogenic.
**Krankheitserreger,** *m.* excitant of disease, pathogenic agent. **-erscheinung,** *f.* pathological symptom or phenomenon.
**krankheitserzeugend,** *p.a.* pathogenic.
**Krankheits-keim,** *m.* disease germ. **-kunde, -lehre,** *f.* pathology. **-stoff,** *m.* morbid or contagious matter. **-verlauf, -vorgang,** *m.* course of a disease.
**krankheitswiderständig,** *a.* disease-resistant.
**kränklich,** *a.* sickly, in poor health.
**Kranz,** *m.* wreath; crown; corona; ring; border, rim, brim; lid (of a furnace); rim (of a wheel).
**Kranz-.** (*Anat.*) coronary, coronal. **-brenner,** *m.* ring burner, crown burner.
**Kränzchen,** *n.* little wreath; (social) circle.
**Krapp,** *m.* madder. **-artikel,** *m.* (*Calico*) madder style. **-bad,** *n.* madder bath.
**krappen,** *v.t.* (*Dyeing*) madder.
**Krapp-farbe,** *f.* madder color, madder dye. **-färben,** *n.* madder dyeing. **-farbstoff, -färbestoff,** *m.* alizarin. **-gelb,** *n.* madder yellow, xanthin. **-lack,** *m.* madder lake. **-rot,** *n.* madder red, alizarin. **-stoff,** *m.* alizarin. **-wurzel,** *f.* madder root.
**Kraterbildung,** *f.* crater formation; pitting.
**Kratte,** *f.* crate
**Kratz,** *m.* scratch.
**Krätzblei,** *n.* slag lead.
**Kratzbürste,** *f.* stiff brush, scraper; cross person.
**Kratze,** *f.* scraper; rabble; rake; skimmer; card (for wool, etc.); scrapings.
**Krätze,** *f.* waste metal (dross, cuttings, sweepings, etc.); (*Med.*) itch.
**Kratzeisen,** *n.* scraping iron, scraper, doctor.
**kratzen,** *v.t.* scrape, scratch; rake; card (wool, etc.); (*Metal.*) rabble. — *v.i.* scratch, grate; be harsh (in taste). — **kratzend,** *p.a.* harsh, irritating (of taste).
**Kratzer, Krätzer,** *m.* scraper, scratcher, rake, raker, skimmer.
**Krätzfrischen,** *n.* (*Metal.*) refining of waste.
**krätzig,** *a.* itchy; scabby; (*Glass*) fibrous.
**Krätz-kupfer,** *n.* copper from waste. **-messing,** *n.* brass cuttings. **-wurzel,** *f.* white hellebore (root).
**kraus,** *a.* crisp; curly, curled; crinkly; nappy.
**Kräuschung,** *f.* crinkling.
**kräuseln,** *v.t.* curl, crisp, crimp, crinkle, crepe; mill (coins).
**Krauseminze,** *f.* curled mint (*Mentha crispa*); spearmint (*Mentha spicata*).
**Kräusen,** *f.pl.* (*Brewing*) head, specif. rocky head.
**Kraus-gummi,** *n.* crêpe rubber. **-putz,** *m.* rough plaster, rough cast. **-tabak,** *m.* shag.
**Kraut,** *n.* (*pl.* **Kräuter**). herb, plant; weed; top (of beets, etc.); cabbage.
**krautartig,** *a.* herbaceous.
**Kräuter-essig,** *m.* aromatic vinegar. **-mittel,** *n.* vegetable remedy. **-salz,** *n.* vegetable salt. **-tee,** *m.* herb tea. **-wein,** *m.* medicated wine. **-zucker,** *m.* (*Pharm.*) conserve, confection.
**Kreatin,** *n.* creatine.
**Kreatinin,** *n.* creatinine.
**Krebs,** *m.* cancer; crayfish; grain, hard particle (in clay, etc.); knot (in ore, etc.); wart; canker; crab; crustacean.
**krebsartig,** *a.* cancerous; crab-like; crustaceous.
**Krebs-behandlung,** *f.* treatment of cancer. **-gewebe,** *n.* cancerous tissue.
**krebsig,** *a.* cancerous; cankered.
**Krebs-kohlenwasserstoff,** *m.* cancerogenic hydrocarbon. **-milch,** *f.* (*Med.*) cancer juice. **-tiere,** *n.pl.* (*Zoöl.*) Crustacea. **-wurz,** *f.* beechdrops (*Leptamnium virginianum*). **-wurzel,** *f.* bistort; squawroot (*Conopholis americana*).
**Kreide,** *f.* chalk.
**kreideartig,** *a.* chalky, cretaceous.
**Kreide-bad,** *n.* chalk bath. **-boden,** *m.* chalky soil. **-flotte,** *f.* chalk liquor. **-grund,** *m.* chalk ground. **-gur,** *f.* agaric mineral (earthy calcium carbonate).

**kreidehaltig,** *a.* containing chalk, cretaceous.
**Kreidemehl,** *n.* powdered chalk.
**kreiden,** *v.t.* chalk.
**Kreide-papier,** *n.* enameled paper, art paper. **-paste,** *f.* a cement of chalk and glue. **-pulver,** *n.* chalk powder. **-stein,** *m.* chalkstone. **-stift,** *m.* crayon.
**kreidig,** *a.* chalky, cretaceous.
**Kreis,** *m.* circle; circuit; orbit; district; range. **-abschnitt,** *m.* segment (of a circle).
**kreisartig,** *a.* circular.
**Kreis-ausschnitt,** *m.* sector. **-bahn,** *f.* circular path; orbit. **-bewegung,** *f.* circular motion, rotation, revolution. **-blende,** *f.* (*Photog.*) iris diaphragm. **-bogen,** *m.* arc of a circle; circular arch.
**kreischen,** *v.i.* shriek, scream, (of fat) sizzle, (of bending tin) cry.
**Kreisel,** *m.* top; gyroscope. **-bewegung,** *f.* motion of a top, gyroscopic motion. **-brecher,** *m.* rotary crusher. **-elektron,** *n.* spinning electron.
**kreiselförmig,** *a.* top-shaped, turbinate.
**Kreisel-gang,** *m.* circular motion, rotation, revolution. **-gebläse,** *n.* turboblower. **-mischer,** *m.* rotary mixer. **-molekül,** *n.* spinning molecule.
**kreiseln,** *v.i.* & *r.* spin like a top, rotate with precession.
**Kreisel-pumpe,** *f.* centrifugal pump; rotary pump. **-rad,** *n.* turbine; turbine rotor, turbine impeller. **-verdichter,** *m.* turbocompressor.
**kreisen,** *v.i.* circle, revolve, rotate, circulate.
**Kreisfläche,** *f.* circular area.
**kreisförmig,** *a.* circular; round.
**Kreis-frequenz,** *f.* angular frequency or velocity. **-gang,** *m.* revolution. **-grad,** *m.* degree of arc, angular degree. **-lauf,** *m.* cycle; circulation (of liquid or gas); circular course, circuit; revolution; rotation.
**kreislaufend,** *p.a.* circulatory.
**Kreis-laufgas,** *n.* recycle gas. **-linie,** *f.* circular line, circumference. **-ordnung,** *f.* district regulation. **-prozess,** *m.* cyclic process, cycle. **-pumpe,** *f.* circulating pump.
**kreisrund,** *a.* circular.
**Kreis-säge,** *f.* circular saw. **-schicht,** *f.* circular layer, (of a tree) annual ring. **-umfang,** *m.* circumference, periphery. **-umlauf,** *m.* circulation, cycle.
**Krem,** *m.* cream. **-farbe,** *f.* cream color.
**Kremnitzerweiss,** *n.* Kremnitz white.
**Krempe,** *f.* rim; flange; brim.
**Krempel-.** (*Textiles*) card, carding, carded.
**krempeln,** *v.t.* card.
**Kremserweiss,** *n.* Kremnitz white.
**Krensäure,** *f.* crenic acid.
**Kreo-sol,** *n.* creosol. **-sot,** *n.* creosote.
**kreosotieren,** *v.t.* creosote.
**Kreosotöl,** *n.* creosote oil.
**krepieren,** *v.i.* burst; explode. — *v.t.* vex.
**krepitieren,** *v.i.* crepitate, crackle.
**kreponieren,** *v.t.* crêpe.
**Kreponstoff,** *m.* crepon material, crepon.
**Krepp,** *m.* crêpe.
**kreppen,** *v.t.* crêpe, crimp, frieze.
**Krepp-flüssigkeit,** *f.* crêping liquor. **-kautschuk,** *m.* & *n.* crêpe rubber. **-papier,** *n.* crêpe paper.
**Kresol,** *n.* cresol. **-harz,** *n.* cresylic resin. **-natron,** *n.* sodium cresylate. **-säure,** *f.* cresylic acid (cresol). **-seife,** *f.* cresol soap.
**Kresorcin,** *n.* cresorcinol.
**Kresotinsäure,** *f.* cresotic acid, cresotinic acid.
**Kresse,** *f.* cress.
**Kresyl,** *n.* cresyl ($HOC_6H_4CH_2$ or $CH_3C_6H_4$; in the latter case better translated tolyl). **-säure,** *f.* cresylic acid (cresol).
**Kreuz,** *n.* cross; loins; rump. **-beeren,** *f.pl.* = Kreuzdornbeeren. **-befruchtung,** *f.* cross-fertilization. **-bein,** *n.* sacrum. **-bestäubung,** *f.* cross-pollination. **-blume,** *f.* milkwort (*Polygala*). **-blütler,** *m.* (*Bot.*) crucifer. **-dorn,** *m.* buckthorn (*Rhamnus*). **-dornbeeren,** *f.pl.* buckthorn berries, Persian berries.
**kreuzen,** *v.t.* cross; intersect.
**Kreuzer,** *m.* cruiser; kreutzer, farthing.
**kreuzförmig,** *a.* cross-shaped, cruciform, cruciate.
**Kreuzgelenk,** *n.* universal joint.
**kreuzgeschichtet,** *a.* cross-bedded.
**Kreuz-gitter,** *n.* cross grating; surface lattice. **-hahn,** *m.* four-way cock. **-kopf,** *m.* (*Mach.*) crosshead. **-kraut,** *n.* groundsel (*Senecio*). **-kümmel,** *m.* cumin. **-punkt,** *m.* intersection. **-schichtung,** *f.* (*Geol.*) cross-bedding. **-schlagmühle,** *f.* hammer mill. **-schmerz,** *m.* lumbago.
**kreuzschraffieren,** *v.t.* cross-hatch.
**Kreuz-stein,** *m.* cross-stone (chiastolite, harmotome, staurolite). **-stück,** *n.* crosspiece; four-way cross(piece). **-tisch,** *m.* (*Micros.*) mechanical stage.
**Kreuzung,** *f.* crossing; intersection.
**Kreuzungspunkt,** *m.* intersection.
**Kreuzverweisung,** *f.* cross reference.
**kreuzweise,** *a.* & *adv.* crosswise, transverse(ly).
**Kreuzwinkel,** *m.* T-square.
**kribbeln, kriebeln,** *v.t.* tickle, irritate.
**kriechen,** *v.i.* creep, crawl; leak.
**Kriech-festigkeit,** *f.* creep(ing) strength. **-pflanze,** *f.* creeping plant, creeper. **-strom,** *m.* (*Elec.*) surface leakage (current).
**Krieg,** *m.* war; warfare.
**kriegen,** *v.t.* seize, get. — *v.i.* make war.
**Kriegführung,** *f.* warfare.
**Kriegs-ersatzstoff,** *m.* war substitute, war-time

substitute. **-gerät,** *n.* war material. **-mittel,** *n.* warfare agent, war material.
**krimpen,** *v.t.* shrink (cloth).
**krimpfähig,** *a.* shrinking, shrinkable.
**Krimpfähigkeit,** *f.* property of shrinking; (of wool) felting property.
**krimpfrei,** *a.* nonshrinking.
**Kringel,** *m.* cracknel.
**Krippe,** *f.* crib, manger.
**krisch,** *pret.* (of kreischen) shrieked, etc.
**Krise,** *f.* crisis.
**krisenhaft,** *a.* critical.
**krispelig,** *a.* grained, pebbled; blistered.
**krispeln,** *v.t.* grain, pebble (leather).
**krist.,** *abbrev.* of kristallisiert, kristallinisch.
**Krist.,** *abbrev.* of Kristalle, Kristallisation, Kristallographie.
**Kristall,** *m.* crystal. **-abscheidung,** *f.* separation of crystals. **-achse,** *f.* crystal axis, crystallographic axis.
**kristallähnlich,** *a.* crystal-like, crystalloid.
**Kristallanschuss,** *m.* crop of crystals; crystalline growth.
**kristallartig,** *a.* crystal-like, crystalline.
**Kristall-aufbau,** *m.* crystal structure. **-ausscheidung,** *f.* separation of crystals. **-bau,** *m.* crystal structure. **-baufehler,** *m.* defect in crystal structure. **-baustein,** *m.* unit of crystal structure, crystal unit. **-benzol,** *n.* benzene of crystallization. **-bildung,** *f.* formation of crystals, crystallization, (*Sugar*) granulation. **-bildungspunkt,** *m.* (*Sugar*) granulating pitch. **-brei,** *m.* (moist) crystal mass, crystal sludge, crop of crystals.
**Kriställchen,** *n.* little crystal.
**Kristall-chloroform,** *n.* chloroform of crystallization. **-druse,** *f.* crystal druse, crystal cluster. **-ebene,** *f.* crystal plane, crystal face. **-ecke,** *f.* (solid) crystal angle.
**kristallelektrisch,** *a.* piezoelectric.
**kristallen,** *a.* crystalline.
**Kristall-fabrik,** *f.* glass works. **-feuchtigkeit,** *f.* crystalline humor (vitreous humor). **-fläche,** *f.* crystal face.
**kristallförmig,** *a.* crystalline, crystalloid.
**Kristall-gitter,** *n.* crystal lattice; crystal grating. **-glasur,** *f.* (*Ceram.*) crystalline glaze. **-grenze,** *f.* crystal boundary.
**kristallhaltig,** *a.* containing crystals, crystalliferous.
**Kristall-haufwerk,** *n.* crystal aggregate. **-haut,** *f.* crystalline crust. **-häutchen,** *n.* crystalline film.
**kristallhell,** *a.* crystal-clear, transparent.
**Kristallierschale,** *f.* crystallizing dish or basin.
**kristallinisch,** *a.* crystalline.
**Kristallinität,** *f.* crystallinity.
**Kristallinse,** *f.* (*Anat.*) crystalline lens.
**Kristallisationsbassin,** *n.* crystallizing basin, tank, or cistern.
**kristallisationsfähig,** *a.* crystallizable.
**Kristallisationsfähigkeit,** *f.* crystallizability.
**kristallisationsfreudig,** *a.* readily crystallizable.
**Kristallisations-gefäss,** *n.* crystallizing vessel, crystallizer. **-kern,** *m.*, **-korn,** *n.* crystal nucleus. **-schale,** *f.* crystallizing dish. **-vermögen,** *n.* crystallizing power. **-wärme,** *f.* heat of crystallization.
**Kristallisator,** *m.* crystallizer, (for paraffin) chiller.
**kristallisch,** *a.* crystalline.
**kristallisierbar,** *a.* crystallizable.
**Kristallisier-barkeit,** *f.* crystallizability. **-behälter,** *m.* crystallizing receptacle, crystallizing tank.
**kristallisieren,** *v.t. & i.* crystallize.
**Kristallisier-gefäss,** *n.* crystallizing vessel, crystallizer. **-schale,** *f.* crystallizing dish or basin.
**Kristallisierung,** *f.* crystallization, crystallizing.
**Kristallisierungsgefäss,** *n.* crystallization vessel.
**Kristall-kante,** *f.* crystal edge. **-keim,** *m.* crystal nucleus, seed crystal. **-kern,** *m.* nucleus of crystallization. **-korn,** *n.* crystal grain. **-lack,** *m.* crystallizing lacquer. **-lehre,** *f.* crystallography. **-linse,** *f.* (*Anat.*) crystalline lens. **-mehl,** *m.* crystal powder; crystal sand. **-messung,** *f.* crystallometry. **-nädelchen,** *n.* crystal needle, acicular crystal. **-oberfläche,** *f.* crystal surface.
**kristallogenisch,** *a.* crystallogenic.
**Kristallographie,** *f.* crystallography.
**kristallographisch,** *a.* crystallographic.
**Kristall-pulver,** *n.* crystal powder. **-säure,** *f.* fuming sulfuric acid of high strength, forming a crystalline solid. **-schnitt,** *m.* crystal cut or section. **-schwingung,** *f.* crystal vibration. **-soda,** *f.* soda crystals ($Na_2CO_3 \cdot 10H_2O$). **-stein,** *m.* rock crystal. **-wachstum,** *n.* crystal growth. **-waren,** *f.pl.* (crystal) glassware. **-wasser,** *n.* crystal water, water of crystallization.
**kristallwasser-frei,** *a.* free from water of crystallization. **-haltig,** *a.* containing crystal water.
**Kristall-winkel,** *m.* crystal angle. **-zucker,** *m.* refined sugar in crystals.
**Kristfm.,** *abbrev.* (Kristallform) crystal form.
**Kriterium,** *n.* criterion.
**Kritik,** *f.* criticism; critique, review.
**Kritiker,** *m.* critic.
**kritisch,** *a.* critical.
**kritisieren,** *v.t. & i.* criticize.
**kritteln,** *v.i.* carp at, criticize.
**kritzeln,** *v.i.* scribble; scratch.
**Kroatien,** *n.* Croatia.
**kroch,** *pret.* (of kriechen) crept, crawled.
**Krokonsäure,** *f.* croconic acid.

**Krokuspapier,** *n.* crocus paper.
**Krone,** *f.* crown; corolla; corona; wreath; crest, top.
**kronenartig,** *a.* like a crown, coronal; (*Anat.*) coronary.
**Kronen-aufsatz,** *m.* column (of a still); (of a burner) crown top. **-brenner,** *m.* crown burner, ring burner. **-gold,** *n.* crown gold.
**Kron-glas,** *n.* crown glass. **-kümmel,** *m.* cumin.
**Kropf,** *m.* goiter; enlargement; craw, crop; bend; (*Paper*) breasting. **-drüse,** *f.* thyroid gland.
**kröpfen,** *v.t.* bend at right angles, bend; crank, offset.
**Kropf-rohr,** *m.*, **-röhre,** *f.* bent tube, bent pipe. **-wurz,** *f.* figwort. **-wurzel,** *f.* polypody root. **-zylinder,** *m.* a glass cylinder with a wider upper part, hydrometer jar.
**kröseln,** *v.t.* crumble (glass); groove.
**Kröte,** *f.* toad.
**Kroton-.** see Croton-.
**Krücke,** *f.* crutch; rake, rabble, scraper, etc. (of crutch shape); crowbar.
**Krug,** *m.* pitcher; jug, mug, jar, pot.
**Kruke,** *f.* earthenware pot, jar or pitcher.
**krüllen,** *v.t.* crumple.
**Krulltabak,** *m.* shag.
**Krümchen,** *n.* (small) crumb, bit.
**Krume,** *f.* crumb, bit; black earth.
**krümelig,** *a.* crumbly, crumbling, friable.
**krümeln,** *v.i.* crumble, crumb. — *v.a.* crumble.
**Krümel-torf,** *m.* lump peat. **-zucker,** *m.* (dextro)glucose, dextrose.
**krumm,** *a.* crooked, curved, bent.
**Krummachse,** *f.* crank.
**krummblätterig,** *a.* in curved or bent leaflets; (*Bot.*) curvifoliate.
**Krummdarm,** *m.* ileum.
**krümmen,** *v.t.* curve, bend, crook. — *v.r.* bend; warp.
**Krümmer,** *m.* bent piece, bend, elbow. **-verbindung,** *f.* elbow joint.
**krummfaserig,** *a.* cross-grained.
**Krummholz,** *n.* crooked or curved piece of wood; = Krummholzbaum. **-baum,** *m.*, **-fichte, -kiefer,** *f.* knee pine (*Pinus montana pumilio*). **-öl,** *n.* templin oil (from knee pine).
**krummlinig,** *a.* curvilinear, curved.
**Krümmung,** *f.* curvature; curve, bend, turn, sinuosity; crookedness.
**Krümmungshalbmesser,** *m.* radius of curvature.
**Krumm-werden,** *n.* warping, bending, buckling. **-zirkel,** *m.* calipers.
**krumös,** *a.* friable, crumbly.
**krümpeln,** *v.t.* crumple, pucker, crinkle.
**krumpen, krumpfen,** *v.t.* shrink; crimp.
**Krümpfe,** *pl.* coal fines, coal slack.
**krumpffrei,** *a.* nonshrinking.
**Krupp,** *m.* croup.
**krüppelhaft, krüppelig,** *a.* crippled, deformed, stunted.
**Kruste,** *f.* crust, incrustation; scab, scale.
**krusten-artig,** *a.* crust-like, crusty. **-bildend,** *a.* crust-forming, incrusting.
**Krusten-bildung,** *f.* crust formation, incrustation. **-tier,** *n.* crustacean.
**krustieren,** *v.t.* crust, incrust.
**krustig,** *a.* crusty, crusted.
**Kryochemie,** *f.* cryochemistry.
**kryohydratisch,** *a.* cryohydric.
**Kryo-lith,** *m.* cryolite. **-phor,** *n.* cryophorus. **-skopie,** *f.* cryoscopy.
**kryoskopisch,** *a.* cryoscopic.
**Kryptogame,** *f.* cryptogam.
**Krystall,** *m.* crystal (or compounds see Kristall-).
**k.s.l.,** *abbrev.* (kalt sehr löslich) very soluble cold.
**Kubaholz,** *n.* Cuba wood (fustic).
**Kubebe,** *f.* cubeb.
**Kübel,** *m.* vat, tub, pail, bucket.
**kub. Gew.,** *abbrev.* (kubisches Gewicht) specific gravity, sp.gr.
**kubieren,** *v.t.* cube.
**Kubik-gehalt,** *m.* solid content, volume. **-inhalt,** *m.* cubic contents. **-mass,** *n.* cubic measure. **-wurzel,** *f.* cube root. **-zahl,** *f.* cube.
**kubisch,** *a.* cubic, cubical. **-raumzentriert, -zentriert,** *a.* (*Cryst.*) cubic body-centered.
**kubizieren,** *v.t.* calculate the volume of; cube.
**Küblerware,** *f.* cooper's wares, casks, tubs, etc.
**Kubus,** *m.* cube.
**Küche,** *f.* kitchen; cooking, cookery.
**Kuchen,** *m.* cake.
**kuchenbildend,** *a.* cake-forming, caking.
**Kuchen-erz,** *n.* cake ore. **-form,** *f.* form of a cake.
**Küchen-gewächs,** *n.* kitchen herb; vegetable. **-salz,** *n.* common salt. **-schelle,** *f.* pasque flower (*Pulsatilla*).
**Kücken,** *n.* = Küken.
**Kufe,** *f.* vat, tun, tub, beck, tank; sled; skid, ski, runner; pad.
**Küfer,** *m.* cooper.
**Kugel,** *f.* bulb; ball, sphere, globe; shot; bead.
**Kugel-.** spherical, ball, globular, bulb. **-abschnitt,** *m.* (*Geom.*) spherical segment.
**kugelähnlich,** *a.* spheroidal; ball-like.
**Kugelapparat,** *m.* bulb apparatus (*e.g.*, potash bulbs).
**kugelartig,** *a.* spherical, globular, spheroidal.
**Kugel-ausschnitt,** *m.* (*Geom.*) spherical sector. **-bakterien,** *n.pl.* spherical bacteria.
**Kügelchen,** *n.* small bulb; globule; spherule; pellet; small ball.
**Kugel-diorit,** *m.* globular diorite. **-dreieck,** *n.* (*Geom.*) spherical triangle. **-druckprobe,** *f.* ball pressure test (for hardness), Brinell

test. **-eisenstein,** *m.* spherosiderite. **-fallmethode,** *f.* falling-ball method.

**kugelfest,** *a.* bulletproof.

**Kugel-fläche,** *f.* spherical surface or area. **-flasche,** *f.* balloon flask, spherical flask.

**kugelförmig,** *a.* globular, spherical, globose.

**Kugel-funktion,** *f.* spherical harmonic. **-gelenk,** *n.* ball-and-socket joint. **-gestalt,** *f.* spherical form. **-hahnpipette,** *f.*, **-hahnstechheber,** *m.* pipet(te) with globe stopcock. **-hefe,** *f.* spherical yeast.

**kugelig,** *a.* globular, spherical, globose.

**Kugel-kocher,** *m.* spherical boiler. **-körperchen,** *n.* spherical particle; (*Cryst.*) globulite. **-kühler,** *m.* ball condenser, spherical condenser. **-kupplung,** *f.* ball-and-socket joint. **-lack,** *m.* lac or lake in balls. **-lager,** *n.* ball bearing. **-linse,** *f.* spherical lens. **-mikroskop,** *n.* ball-stage microscope. **-mühle,** *f.* ball mill.

**kugeln,** *v.t. & i.* roll; form into a ball.

**Kugel-packung,** *f.* packing of spheres. **-probe,** *f.* ball test. Cf. Kugeldruckprobe. **-probehahn,** *m.* ball gage cock. **-rohr,** *n.*, **-röhre,** *f.* bulb tube (tube with one or more bulbar enlargements). **-rührer,** *m.* bulb (or ball) stirrer. **-schale,** *f.* spherical shell; ball cup. **-schliff,** *m.* ground ball-and-socket joint.

**kugelsicher,** *a.* bulletproof.

**Kugel-spiegel,** *m.* spherical mirror. **-stopfen,** *m.* bulb stopper, globular stopper. **-symmetrie,** *f.* spherical symmetry.

**kugelsymmetrisch,** *a.* spherosymmetric.

**Kugel-tee,** *m.* gunpowder tea. **-tisch,** *m.* (*Micros.*) ball stage. **-ventil,** *n.* ball valve. **-vorlage,** *f.* spherical (or globular) receiver. **-welle,** *f.* spherical wave.

**kuglig,** *a.* globular, spherical, globose.

**Kuh,** *f.* cow. **-dünger,** *m.* cow dung. **-euter,** *n.* cow udder; Bredt adapter for vacuum distillation. **-haut,** *f.* cowhide. **-kot,** *m.* cow dung. **-kotbad,** *n.* cow-dung bath. **-kotsalz,** *n.* (*Dyeing*) dung salt.

**kuhkoten,** *v.t.* dung (with cow dung).

**kühl,** *a.* cool.

**Kühl-anlage,** *f.* cooling plant, refrigerating plant. **-apparat,** *m.* cooling apparatus; cooler; refrigerator; condenser. **-bottich,** *m.* cooling tub, cooler.

**Kühle,** *f.* coolness; cooler.

**kühlen,** *v.t.* cool, chill, refrigerate; (*Glass*) anneal.

**Kühler,** *m.* condenser; cooler; refrigerator; (of an automobile) radiator. **-gestell,** *n.* condenser stand, condenser support. **-halter,** *m.* condenser holder or clamp. **-mantel,** *m.* condenser jacket. **-retorte,** *f.* condenser retort. **-stativ,** *n.* condenser stand or support.

**Kühl-fass,** *n.* cooling vessel, cooling vat, cooling tub. **-fläche,** *f.* cooling surface. **-flüssigkeit,** *f.* cooling liquid, coolant. **-gefäss,** *m.* cooling vessel, cooler; refrigerator; condenser. **-geläger,** *n.* (*Brewing*) wort sediment, dregs. **-haus,** *n.* cold-storage house. **-kammer,** *f.* cooling chamber. **-kasten,** *m.* cooling box, cooler. **-mantel,** *m.* cooling jacket or mantle. **-maschine,** *f.* refrigerating machine, refrigerator. **-mittel,** *n.* cooling agent, coolant, refrigerant. **-ofen,** *m.* cooling oven, annealing furnace. **-öl,** *n.* cooling oil, (*Mach.*) cutting oil, (*Metal.*) quenching oil. **-pfanne,** *f.* cooling pan, cooler; (*Glass*) leer pan. **-raum,** *m.* cooling chamber, chill room, cold-storage room or space. **-rippe,** *f.* cooling fin or vane or flange. **-rohr,** *n.*, **-röhre,** *f.* cooling tube or pipe; condenser tube. **-salz,** *n.* refrigerating salt. **-schiff,** *n.* (*Brewing*) cooling back, cooler; refrigerator ship. **-schlange, -schnecke,** *f.* worm (for distilling), cooling coil, condenser coil. **-schrank,** *m.* refrigerator. **-spirale,** *f.* cooling spiral, spiral condenser. **-tasche,** *f.* cooling chamber. **-turm,** *n.* cooling tower.

**Kühlung,** *f.* cooling, refrigeration.

**Kühlungsgrad,** *m.* degree of cooling; rate of cooling.

**Kühl-verfahren,** *n.* cooling or refrigerating method or process. **-vorrichtung,** *f.* cooling or refrigerating device or apparatus. **-wagen,** *m.* refrigerator car (truck, etc.). **-wasser,** *n.* cooling water; (*Pharm.*) lead water. **-werk,** *n.* cooling or refrigerating plant or apparatus. **-wirkung,** *f.* cooling effect. **-zylinder,** *m.* condenser; cooling cylinder.

**Kuh-milch,** *f.* cow's milk. **-mist,** *m.* cow dung. **-mistbad,** *n.* cow-dung bath.

**kuhmisten,** *v.t.* (*Leather*) cow-dung.

**kühn,** *a.* bold.

**Kuhpocken-gift,** *n.* vaccine virus. **-impfung,** *f.* vaccination.

**Kukabrühe,** *f.* (*abbrev.* for *Ku*pfer-*Ka*lk-Brühe) Bordeaux mixture.

**Küken,** *n.* (stop)cock plug or stopper; (sometimes) stopcock; chicken, chick. **-hahn,** *m.* stopcock.

**Kukuruz,** *m.* corn, maize.

**Külbchen,** *n.* (*Glass*) ball, piece, lump.

**Kulilawanöl,** *n.* culilawan oil.

**kulinarisch,** *a.* culinary.

**Kulisse,** *f.* coulisse (something that slides).

**kulminieren,** *v.i.* culminate.

**kultivierbar,** *a.* cultivable, tillable.

**kultivieren,** *v.t.* cultivate.

**Kultivierung,** *f.* cultivation, culture.

**Kultur,** *f.* civilization; culture; cultivation.

**kulturell,** *a.* cultural.

**kulturfähig,** *a.* cultivable, tillable; civilizable.

**Kultur-flasche,** *f.* culture flask. **-geräte,** *n.pl.*

agricultural implements. **-hefe,** *f.* culture yeast. **-kolben,** *m.* culture flask. **-medien,** *n.pl.* culture media. **-pflanze,** *f.* cultivated plant. **-röhre,** *f.* culture tube. **-schale,** *f.* culture dish. **-staat,** *m.* civilized state (or nation). **-stufe,** *f.* stage of civilization. **-versuch,** *m.* cultivation experiment.

**Kumar-.** coumar- (or cumar-). See Cumar-.

**Kuminsäure,** *f.* cumic acid, cuminic acid.

**Kümmel,** *m.* caraway; (**römischer**) cumin; kümmel (the liqueur). **-branntwein, -likör,** *m.* kümmel (the liqueur). **-öl,** *n.* caraway oil; cumin oil; (*Org. Chem.*) carvone.

**Kummer,** *m.* sorrow, trouble.

**Kümmer-.** below-normal. **-form,** *f.* degenerate form.

**kümmern,** *v.t.* trouble, concern. — *v.i.* be in trouble.

**Kumol,** *n.* cumene.

**Kumpe,** *f.* (*Dyeing*) basin, vessel.

**kümpeln,** *v.t.* dish, flange.

**kumulieren,** *v.t.* accumulate.

**Kumys,** *m.* kumiss.

**kund,** *a.* known, public. — **— und zu wissen sei,** be it known, take notice.

**Kunde,** *f.* knowledge, information, science; notice; news. — *m.* customer; client.

**kundgeben,** *v.t.* make known, manifest, declare.

**kundig,** *a.* learned, expert, skilful, intelligent.

**kündigen,** *v.t.* give notice of; recall.

**Kündigung,** *f.* notice, warning.

**Kundschaft,** *f.* notice, information, knowledge; custom, patronage.

**künftig,** *a.* future, coming, to be.

**Kunst,** *f.* art; profession; skill; work (of art).

**Kunst-.** artificial; synthetic; technical; art. **-asphalt,** *m.* pitch. **-ausdruck,** *m.* technical term. **-baumwolle,** *f.* artificial cotton. **-benzin,** *n.* synthetic gasoline. **-bronze,** *f.* art bronze. **-butter,** *f.* artificial butter, oleomargarine. **-darm,** *m.* artificial gut, synthetic sausage casing. **-druck,** *m.* art printing. **-dünger,** *m.* artificial manure, fertilizer. **-eis,** *n.* artificial ice. **-faden,** *m.*, **-faser,** *f.* artificial fiber, synthetic fiber.

**kunstfertig,** *a.* (technically) skilled, skilful.

**Kunst-fertigkeit,** *f.* technical skill. **-fett,** *n.* artificial fat (or grease). **-feuer, -feuerwerk,** *n.* firework(s). **-feuerwerkerei,** *f.* pyrotechnics. **-fleiss,** *m.* industry. **-gärtnerei,** *f.* horticulture; nursery. **-gewerbe,** *n.* useful art, applied art. **-gewerbeschule,** *f.* arts-and-crafts school, polytechnic school. **-glanz,** *m.* artificial luster. **-griff,** *m.* artifice, trick, device. **-gummi,** *n.* (usually) artificial rubber, synthetic rubber; artificial gum. **-guss,** *m.* art casting. **-harz,** *n.* synthetic resin. **-harzbindung,** *f.* plastic bond, (often) bakelite bond. **-harzpressmasse,** *f.*, **-harzpressstoff,** *m.* synthetic plastic molding composition. **-harzstoff,** *m.* synthetic resin. **-hefe,** *f.* artificial yeast. **-heilmittel,** *n.* artificial remedy, synthetic remedy. **-holz,** *n.* artificial wood; laminated wood. **-honig,** *m.* artificial honey. **-horn,** *n.* artificial horn; specif., a casein-formaldehyde plastic (*T.N.*). **-keramik,** *f.* art ceramics. **-kohle,** *f.* artificial coal or carbon. **-korund,** *m.* artificial corundum, fused alumina. **-leder,** *n.* artificial leather. **-lehre,** *f.* technology, technics.

**Künstler,** *m.* artist; artificer. **-farbe,** *f.* artist's color.

**künstlerisch,** *a.* artistic.

**künstlich,** *a.* artificial; synthetic; artistic; artful, ingenious. — **— kunstlicher Zug,** forced draft.

**Kunst-licht,** *n.* artificial light. **-masse,** *f.* artificial composition, specif. synthetic plastic. **-mist,** *m.* compost. **-mittel,** *n.* artificial means. **-öl,** *n.* artificial or synthetic oil. **-papier,** *n.* art paper, enameled paper. **-porzellan,** *n.* art porcelain. **-produkt,** *n.* synthetic product, artificial product. **-richter,** *m.* critic. **-schmalz,** *n.* artificial lard, compound lard. **-seide,** *f.* artificial silk, rayon. **-seideverarbeitung,** *f.* rayon processing. **-spinnfaser,** *f.* artificial textile fiber; specif., staple fiber, staple rayon. **-spinnstoff,** *m.* artificial spinning material, specif. material reclaimed from old fabrics. **-sprache,** *f.* technical language. **-stein,** *m.* artificial stone; earthenware. **-stoff,** *m.* artificial or synthetic substance or material, specif. plastic. **-stoffmasse,** *f.* synthetic composition, specif. plastic base. **-stück,** *n.* feat, trick.

**kunstvoll,** *a.* skilful; artistic; artful.

**Kunst-werk,** *n.* work of art. **-wolle,** *f.* artificial wool, specif. wool reclaimed from old fabrics, shoddy. **-wort,** *n.* technical word, technical term.

**kunterbunt,** *a.* party-colored; topsy-turvy.

**Kuoxam,** *n.* cuprammonium solution.

**Küpe,** *f.* vat; boiler, copper.

**kupellieren,** *v.t.* cupel.

**küpen,** *v.t.* vat-dye, vat.

**Küpen-alkali,** *n.* vat alkali. **-ansatz,** *m.* (*Dyeing*) setting of the vat. **-artikel,** *m.* (*Calico*) vat style. **-bad,** *n.* dye liquor. **-blau,** *n.* vat blue, indigo blue. **-buntätze,** *f.* (*Dyeing*) colored vat discharge. **-einsatz,** *m.* (*Dyeing*) dipping frame. **-färber,** *m.* vat dyer. **-färberei,** *f.* vat dyeing.

**küpenfarbig,** *a.* vat-colored, vat-dyed.

**Küpen-farbstoff,** *m.* vat dye. **-färbung,** *f.* vat dyeing. **-flotte,** *f.* vat liquor. **-geruch,** *m.* vat odor. **-schlamm,** *m.* vat sediment.

**Kupfer,** *n.* copper. **-abfall,** *m.* waste copper. **-alaun,** *m.* (*Pharm.*) cuprum aluminatum, lapis divinus. **-ammoniaklösung,** *f.* cupr(o)-ammonium solution. **-ammonium,** *n.* cupr(o)ammonium, Schweitzer's reagent. **-antimonglanz,** *m.* chalcostibite.

**kupferartig,** *a.* coppery, copper-like, cupreous.

**Kupfer-asche,** *f.* copper scale. **-azetat,** *n.* copper acetate. **-azetylen,** *n.* copper acetylide. **-bad,** *n.* copper bath. **-barre,** *f.* copper bar; copper ingot. **-beize,** *f.* copper mordant. **-blatt,** *n.* copper foil. **-blau,** *n.* blue verditer, azurite. **-blech,** *n.* sheet copper, copper foil. **-blei,** *n.* copper-lead alloy. **-bleiglanz,** *m.* (*Min.*) cuproplumbite. **-bleivitriol,** *m.* linarite. **-blende,** *f.* tennantite. **-blüte,** *f.* copper bloom (capillary cuprite). **-braun,** *n.* tile ore (earthy ferruginous cuprite).

**kupferbraun,** *a.* copper-brown.

**Kupfer-bromid,** *n.* copper bromide, specif. cupric bromide, copper(II) bromide. **-bromür,** *n.* cuprous bromide, copper(I) bromide. **-chlorid,** *n.* copper chloride, specif. cupric chloride, copper(II) chloride. **-chlorür,** *n.* cuprous chloride, copper(I) chloride. **-cyanid,** *n.* copper cyanide, specif. cupric cyanide, copper(II) cyanide. **-cyanür,** *n.* cuprous cyanide, copper(I) cyanide. **-dorn,** *m.* slag from liquated copper. **-draht,** *m.* copper wire. **-drahtnetz,** *n.* copper gauze. **-drehspäne,** *m.pl.* copper turnings. **-druck,** *m.* copperplate (printing). **-druckfarbe,** *f.* copperplate ink, specif. Frankfort black. **-druckschwarz,** *n.* (copper)plate black. **-eisenvitriol,** *n.* copper iron sulfate; specif., pisanite. **-elektrode,** *f.* copper electrode.

**kupferempfindlich,** *a.* sensitive to copper.

**Kupfer-erz,** *n.* copper ore. **-fahlerz,** *n.* tetrahedrite; tennantite. **-farbe,** *f.* copper color; copper pigment.

**kupfer-farben, -farbig,** *a.* copper-colored.

**Kupfer-federerz,** *n.* = Kupferblüte. **-feilicht,** *n.*, **-feilspäne,** *m.pl.* copper filings. **-folie,** *f.* copper foil. **-formiat,** *n.* copper formate.

**kupferführend,** *a.* copper-bearing, cupriferous.

**Kupfer-gare,** *f.*, **-garmachen,** *n.* copper refining. **-gefäss,** *n.* copper vessel. **-gehalt,** *m.* copper content. **-geist,** *m.* spirit of verdigris (mixture of acetic acid and acetone obtained by distilling verdigris). **-gewebe,** *n.* copper gauze. **-gewinnung,** *f.* extraction of copper. **-giesserei,** *f.* copper foundry; copper founding. **-glanz,** *m.* copper glance (chalcocite); coppery luster. **-glas, -glaserz,** *n.* (*Min.*) chalcocite. **-glimmer,** *m.* chalcophyllite; micaceous copper (copper made brittle by the presence of foreign oxides, formed in refining). **-glühspan,** *m.* copper scale. **-gold,** *n.* a copper alloy imitating gold, as Mannheim gold or similor. **-grün,** *n.* copper green (verditer; verdigris); (*Min.*) chrysocolla. **-guss,** *m.* copper casting; cast copper.

**kupferhaltig,** *a.* containing copper, cupriferous, cupreous.

**Kupfer-hammerschlag,** *m.* copper scale. **-hochofen,** *m.* copper blast furnace. **-hütte,** *f.* copper smeltery. **-hydrat,** *n.* copper hydroxide. **-hydroxyd,** *n.* copper hydroxide, specif. cupric hydroxide, copper(II) hydroxide. **-hydroxydul,** *n.* cuprous hydroxide, copper(I) hydroxide.

**kupferig,** *a.* coppery, copper-like, cupreous.

**Kupfer-indig, -indigo,** *m.* indigo copper (covellite). **-jodid,** *n.* copper iodide, specif. cupric iodide, copper(II) iodide. **-jodür,** *n.* cuprous iodide, copper(I) iodide. **-kalk,** *m.* copper calx, copper oxide; (*Agric.*) Bordeaux mixture. **-kalkbrühe,** *f.* (*Agric.*) Bordeaux mixture. **-kapsel,** *f.* copper capsule, copper cup; copper (priming) cap.

**Kupferkies,** *m.* copper pyrites (chalcopyrite). — **bunter —,** bornite.

**kupferkieshaltig,** *a.* containing copper pyrites.

**Kupfer-kohle,** *f.* coppered carbon. **-könig,** *m.* copper regulus. **-kunstseide,** *f.* cuprammonium rayon. **-lasur,** *f.* azurite. **-lauge,** *f.* copper solution. **-laugung,** *f.* copper leaching. **-legierung,** *f.* copper alloy. **-lösung,** *f.* copper solution. **-lot,** *n.* copper solder. **-mangan,** *n.* cupromanganese. **-metall,** *n.* copper metal, metallic copper. **-münze,** *f.* copper coin.

**kupfern,** *v.t.* treat with copper, copper. — *a.* copper, coppery, copper-colored.

**Kupfer-nickel,** *m.* copper-nickel (niccolite). **-niederschlag,** *m.* copper precipitate or deposit. **-ocher, -ocker,** *m.* = Kupferbraun.

**Kupferoxyd,** *n.* cupric oxide, copper(II) oxide. **-ammoniak,** *n.* ammoniacal copper oxide, cuprammonium. **-ammoniakkunstseide, -ammoniakzellulose,** *f.* cuprammonium rayon. **-hydrat,** *n.* cupric hydroxide, copper(II) hydroxide. **-salz,** *n.* cupric salt, copper(II) salt.

**Kupferoxydul,** *n.* cuprous oxide, copper(I) oxide. **-hydrat,** *n.* cuprous hydroxide, copper(I) hydroxide. **-salz,** *n.* cuprous salt, copper(I) salt. **-verbindung,** *f.* cuprous compound, copper(I) compound.

**Kupfer-oxydverbindung,** *f.* cupric compound, copper(II) compound. **-pecherz,** *n.* = Kupferbraun. **-platte,** *f.* copper plate, copperplate.

**kupferplattiert,** *a.* copper-plated.

**Kupfer-pol,** *m.* (*Elec.*) copper pole (positive pole). **-präparat,** *n.* copper preparation. **-probe,** *f.* copper assay, test for copper. **-raffination,** *f.* copper refining. **-rauch,** *m.* copper smoke, copper fumes; white vitriol. **-regen,** *m.* = Streukupfer.

**kupferreich,** *a.* rich in copper, high-copper.

**Kupfer-reinigung,** *f.* copper refining. **-reserve,** *f.* (*Calico*) copper resist. **-rhodanat, -rhodanid,** *n.* copper thiocyanate, specif. cupric thiocyanate, copper(II) thiocyanate. **-rhodanür,** *n.* cuprous thiocyanate, copper(I) thiocyanate. **-rohr,** *n.*, **-röhre,** *f.* copper tube, copper pipe. **-rohstein,** *m.* raw copper mat(te). **-rost,** *m.* copper rust, verdigris (greenish coating on exposed copper).

**kupferrot,** *a.* copper-red, copper-colored.

**Kupfer-rot,** *n.* red copper (cuprite). **-salpeter,** *m.* copper nitrate. **-salz,** *n.* copper salt. **-sammeterz, -samterz,** *n.* velvet copper ore (cyanotrichite). **-säure,** *f.* cupric acid. **-schachtofen,** *m.* copper shaft furnace. **-schaum,** *m.* (*Metal.*) copper scum; (*Min.*) tyrolite. **-scheibe,** *f.* copper disk. **-schiefer,** *m.* copper(-bearing) schist or shale. **-schlacke,** *f.* copper slag. **-schlag,** *m.* copper scale. **-schlange,** *f.* copper coil. **-schwamm,** *m.* copper sponge; (*Min.*) tyrolite. **-schwärze,** *f.* black copper (melaconite). **-schwefel,** *m.* copper sulfide. **-seide,** *f.* cuprammonium rayon. **-silberglanz,** *m.* stromeyerite. **-sinter,** *m.* copper scale; copper pyrites. **-smaragd,** *m.* emerald copper (dioptase). **-spat,** *m.* malachite. **-spiritus,** *m.* = Kupfergeist. **-stahl,** *m.* copper steel. **-stechen,** *n.* copper engraving.

**Kupferstein,** *m.* copper mat(te). — **blasiger —,** pimple metal.

**Kupfer-stich,** *m.* copper engraving. **-streckseide,** *f.* stretched cuprammonium rayon, Lilienfeld rayon. **-sulfat,** *n.* copper sulfate, cupric sulfate, copper(II) sulfate. **-sulfid,** *n.* copper sulfide, specif. cupric sulfide, copper-(II) sulfide. **-sulfozyanür,** *n.* cuprous thiocyanate, copper(I) thiocyanate. **-sulfür,** *n.* cuprous sulfide, copper(I) sulfide. **-überzug,** *m.* copper coating or covering or plating. **-verbindung,** *f.* copper compound. **-vergiftung,** *f.* copper poisoning. **-verhüttung,** *f.* copper smelting. **-vitriol,** *m.* blue vitriol, copper sulfate. **-wasser,** *n.* copperas (*Obs.*); (*Mining*) copper water, cement water. **-wasserstoff,** *m.* copper hydride. **-wismuterz,** *n.* klaprotholite; wittichenite. **-wismutglanz,** *m.* emplectite. **-zahl,** *f.* copper number, copper value. **-ziegelerz,** *n.* = Kupferbraun. **-zuschlag,** *m.* copper flux. **-zyanid,** *n.* = Kupfercyanid. **-zyanür,** *n.* cuprous cyanide, copper(I) cyanide.

**kupfrig,** *a.* copper-like, coppery.

**Kupol-hochofen,** *m.* cupola blast furnace. **-ofen,** *m.* cupola furnace or kiln, cupola.

**Kuppe,** *f.* top, summit, tip, head; meniscus.

**Kuppel,** *f.* cupola, dome; arch (of a furnace).

**kuppelartig,** *a.* dome-like, dome-shaped, arched.

**kuppeln,** *v.t. & i.* couple; (*Dyeing*) develop; (*Mach.*) engage, connect.

**Kuppelofen,** *m.* = Kupolofen.

**Kuppelung,** *f.* coupling; connection; (*Dyeing*) developing; (of an automobile) clutch.

**Kuppelungs-bad,** *n.* (*Dyeing*) developing bath. **-farbstoff,** *m.* coupling dye. **-färbung,** *f.* coupled dyeing. **-flotte,** *f.* (*Dyeing*) developing liquor. **-verfahren,** *n.* coupling process.

**Kuppler,** *m.* coupler; (*Dyeing*) developer.

**Kupplung,** *f.* = Kuppelung.

**Kupplungs-.** = Kuppelungs-.

**Kupri-.** see Cupri-.

**Kuprit,** *m.* cuprite.

**Kupro-.** see Cupro-.

**Küpung,** *f.* vat dyeing, vatting.

**Kupüre,** *f.* (*Calico*) reduction.

**Kur,** *f.* cure, treatment.

**Kurbel,** *f.* crank, winch. **-gehäuseöl,** *n.* crank-case oil.

**kurbeln,** *v.t.* crank, turn, wind.

**Kurbel-pumpe,** *f.* reciprocating pump. **-welle,** *f.* crankshaft.

**Kürbis,** *m.* gourd; pumpkin. **-baum,** *m.* gourd tree, calabash tree. **-gewächse,** *n.pl.* Cucurbitaceae. **-korn,** *n.*, **-kern, -samen,** *m.* pumpkin seed; gourd seed.

**küren,** *v.t.* choose, elect.

**Kurkuma,** *f.* curcuma, turmeric. **-gelb,** *n.* curcumin. **-papier,** *n.* turmeric paper. **-säure,** *f.* curcumic acid. **-wurzel,** *f.* turmeric.

**Kuromojiöl,** *n.* curomoji oil.

**Kurort,** *m.* health resort.

**Kurrent-buchstaben,** *m.pl.*, **-schrift,** *f.* script.

**Kurs,** *m.* exchange; circulation; course.

**Kürschner,** *m.* furrier, fellmonger. **-waren,** *f.pl.* furs, skins.

**kursieren,** *v.i.* be current.

**kursiv,** *a.* italic.

**Kursivschrift,** *f.* italics.

**Kursstativ,** *n.* (*Micros.*) class microscope.

**Kursus,** *m.* course.

**Kurswert,** *m.* exchange value.

**Kurve,** *f.*, curve.

**Kurven-ast,** *m.* branch of a (or the) curve. **-bild,** *n.* curve; diagram, graph. **-blatt,** *n.* graph. **-darstellung,** *f.* graphic representation. **-eck,** *n.* angle in a curve. **-gipfel,** *m.* apex of a curve. **-lineal,** *n.* curved ruler, curved rule, French curve.

**kurvenmässig,** *a.* diagrammatic.

**Kurven-schar,** *f.* group or system of curves. **-schreiber,** *m.* curve tracer. **-zacke,** *f.* jag (sharp change in direction) in a curve. **-zeichnen,** *n.* curve plotting. **-zug,** *m.* curve.

**kurz,** *a.* short, brief. — **binnen kurzem,** within a short time. — **kurze Flotte,** concentrated dye liquor. — **vor kurzem,** recently.

**kurz-armig,** *a.* short-armed, short-arm, short-beam (balance). **-brennweitig,** *a.* (*Opt.*) short-focus. **-brüchig,** *a.* short, brittle. **-dauernd,** *a.* short(-lived), brief, transient.

**Kürze,** *f.* shortness, brevity.

**kürzen,** *v.t.* shorten; abridge.

**kurz-faserig,** *a.* short-fiber(ed). **-flammig,** *a.* short-flame, short-flaming. **-gefasst,** *a.* brief, concise, compendious. **-geschlossen,** *a.* (*Elec.*) short-circuited. **-haarig,** *a.* short-haired; (of wool) short-staple. **-halsig,** *a.* short-necked. **-lebig,** *a.* short-lived.

**kürzlich,** *a.* late, recent.

**Kurzprüfung,** *f.* short test, accelerated test.

**kurz-säulig,** *a.* (*Min.*) short-columnar. **-schliessen,** *v.t.* (*Elec.*) short-circuit.

**Kurzschliffhalskolben,** *m.* flask with short ground neck.

**Kurzschluss,** *m.* (*Elec.*) short circuit. **-ofen,** *m.* short-circuit furnace. **-strom,** *m.* short-circuit current.

**Kurzschrift,** *f.* shorthand, stenography.

**kurz-sichtig,** *a.* near-sighted, short-sighted. **-skalig,** *a.* short-scale(d).

**Kurzstäbchen,** *n.* bacillus.

**kurzstapelig,** *a.* (of fibers) short-staple(d).

**kurzum,** *adv.* in short, in brief.

**Kürzung,** *f.* shortening, abbreviation, cut.

**Kurzungs-fett,** *n.*, **-fette,** *n.pl.* shortening.

**Kurz-versuch,** *m.* short test, quick test. **-waren,** *f.pl.* small wares, esp. hardware.

**kurzweg,** *adv.* shortly, curtly, offhand.

**Kurzwelle,** *f.* short wave.

**kurzwellig,** *a.* of short wave length, short-wave.

**Kurz-wolle,** *f.* short wool fibers, noils. **-wort,** *n.* abbreviation. **-zeichen,** *n.* symbol.

**kurzzeitig,** *a.* short-time, temporary, brief.

**küssen,** *v.t.* kiss.

**Kussin,** *n.* kosin.

**Kusso,** *m.* (*Pharm. & Bot.*) cusso.

**Küste,** *f.* coast, shore.

**Kustos,** *m.* keeper, custodian.

**kutan,** *a.* cutaneous.

**Kuteragummi,** *n.* kutira gum.

**Kutsche,** *f.* coach, carriage.

**Kutschenlack,** *m.* carriage (or coach) varnish.

**Kuvert,** *n.* envelope; cover.

**kuvertieren,** *v.t.* enclose in an envelope.

**Kuvertpapier,** *n.* envelope paper.

**Kuvette, Küvette,** *f.* bulb; cell, vessel; trough; (dental) flask.

**Küvettenverschluss,** *m.* (*Opt.*) cell cover.

**Kux,** *m.* mining share.

**K.W.,** *abbrev.* (Kohlenwasserstoff) hydrocarbon.

**k.w.l.,** *abbrev.* (kalt wenig löslich) not very soluble cold.

**Kwst.,** *abbrev.* (Kilowattstunde) kilowatt-hour.

**KW-stoff,** *abbrev.* (Kohlenwasserstoff) hydrocarbon.

**Kyanäthin,** *n.* cyanethine, kyanethine.

**Kyanidin,** *n.* cyanidine, kyanidine.

**kyanisieren,** *v.t.* kyanize.

**Kyanisierung,** *f.* kyanizing, kyanization.

**Kyaphenin,** *n.* cyaphenine, kyaphenine.

**Kynurensäure,** *f.* kynurenic acid.

**Kyste,** *f.* cyst.

**KZ.,** *abbrev.* (Kernzahl) number of (crystal) nuclei.

# L

**l.,** *abbrev.* (löslich) soluble; (lies) read; liter; (links) left; (linksdrehend) levorotatory.
**L.,** *abbrev.* lira, lire.
**-l.,** *abbrev.* -lich. See -lich.
**Lab, Laab,** *n.* rennet.
**lab.,** *abbrev.* (labil) labile.
**Labdan-gummi, -harz,** *n.* labdanum, ladanum.
**Labdrüse,** *f.* peptic gland.
**laben,** *v.t.* curdle with rennet; refresh.
**Laberdan,** *m.* salted codfish.
**Lab-essenz,** *f.* rennet extract, rennet. **-ferment,** *n.* rennet ferment, rennin.
**labil,** *a.* labile, unstable.
**Labilität,** *f.* lability, instability.
**Labkraut,** *n.* galium.
**Laborant,** *m.* (male) laboratory helper, technician. **-in,** *f.* (female) laboratory helper, technician.
**Laborationstaxe,** *f.* tax on chemists.
**Laboratorien,** *n.pl.* laboratories.
**Laboratorium,** *n.* laboratory.
**Laboratoriums-tisch,** *m.* laboratory table or bench. **-versuch,** *m.* laboratory experiment or test. **-zweck,** *m.* laboratory purpose.
**laborieren,** *v.i.* practice chemistry; work in a laboratory; labor.
**Lab-probe,** *f.* curd test. **-pulver,** *n.* rennet powder.
**Labrador-isieren,** *n.* play of colors (as on labradorite), iridescence. **-stein,** *m.* Labrador stone, labradorite.
**Labsaft,** *m.* gastric juice.
**Lache,** *f.* cut, incision; pool; laugh.
**lächeln,** *v.i.* smile.
**lachen,** *v.i.* laugh.
**lächerlich,** *a.* laughable, ludicrous.
**Lachgas,** *n.* laughing gas (nitrous oxide).
**Lachs,** *m.* salmon. **-farbe,** *f.* salmon color, salmon shade.
**lachs-farben, -farbig,** *a.* salmon-colored.
**Lachsöl,** *n.* salmon oil.
**lachsrot,** *a.* salmon-pink.
**Lacht,** *m.* slag, finery slag.
**Lack,** *m.* lacquer, japan; varnish; lake (the pigment); lac. **-abbeizmittel,** *n.* varnish remover. **-anstrich,** *m.* coat of lacquer or varnish.
**lackartig,** *a.* lake-colored; varnish-like, (*Bot.*) vernicose.
**Lack-auflösungsmittel,** *n.* varnish remover. **-aufstrich,** *m.* = Lackanstrich. **-beize,** *f.* varnish remover. **-benzin,** *n* (*Paints*) mineral spirits, white spirit. **-bildner,** *m.* lake former. **-bildung,** *f.* lake formation; varnish (or lacquer) formation. **-bindemittel,** *n.* lacquer binding medium. **-draht,** *m.* lacquered wire.
**lacken,** *v.t.* = lackieren.
**Lackfarbe,** *f.* lake; lac dye; varnish color, color varnish.
**lackfarbig,** *a.* lake-colored, laky, laked.
**Lack-farbstoff,** *m.* dye for lake making. **-firnis,** *m.* lac varnish, lacquer; lake varnish; varnish. **-firnislack,** *m.* lac lake. **-fläche,** *f.* varnish surface; lacquer coat. **-harz,** *n.* varnish gum, varnishing resin, esp. copal; gum lac. **-haut,** *f.* lacquer (or varnish) film.
**lackierecht,** *a.* fast to overvarnishing, nonbleeding.
**lackieren,** *v.t.* lacquer, japan; varnish; paint.
**lackierfähig,** *a.* lacquerable; varnishable.
**Lackier-ofen,** *m.* japanning stove. **-ung,** *f.* lacquering; varnishing; dope paint.
**Lack-industrie,** *f.* (paint and) varnish industry. **-lack,** *m.* lac lake. **-lasurfarbe,** *f.* transparent varnish color. **-laus,** *f.* lac insect. **-lausfarbstoff,** *m.* lac dye. **-leder,** *n.* japanned leather, patent leather. **-leinöl,** *n.* linseed oil for varnish. **-lösungsmittel,** *n.* lacquer solvent.
**Lackmus,** *m.*, **-farbstoff,** *m.* litmus. **-flechte,** *f.* litmus lichen, archil. **-lösung,** *f.* litmus solution. **-papier,** *n.* litmus paper.
**lackmussauer,** *a.* acid to litmus.
**Lackmustinktur,** *f.* litmus tincture.
**Lack-papier,** *n.* lacquered paper, varnished paper. **-pigment,** *n.* lake pigment. **-rohstoff,** *m.* raw material for lacquer or varnish.
**lacksauer,** *a.* of pertaining to laccaic acid, laccaate of.
**Lack-säure,** *f.* laccaic acid. **-schicht,** *f.* coat or film of lacquer or varnish. **-sieder,** *m.* varnish boiler. **-siegel,** *n.* wax seal. **-sud,** *m.* varnish boiling. **-überzug,** *m.* = Lackanstrich. **-verdünner,** *m.* lacquer (or varnish) thinner. **-waren,** *f.pl.* lacquered goods, japanned goods.
**Lacmus,** *m.* litmus. See Lackmus-.
**Lactar-insäure,** *f.* lactarinic acid. **-säure,** *f.* lactaric acid (stearic acid).
**Lacton-bindung,** *f.* lactonic linkage. **-säure,** *f.* lactonic acid, lactone acid (a compound which is both an acid and a lactone); lactonic acid, D-galactonic acid.
**Ladan, -gummi,** *n.* labdanum, ladanum.

**Lade,** *f.* chest, box, case; (*Founding*) flask. **-anlage,** *f.* loading plant, filling plant. **-dichte,** *f.* (*Elec.*) charge density. **-löffel,** *m.* (*Expl.*) loading plate.
**laden,** *v.t.* load, charge; summon, invite; (*Elec.*) charge.
**Laden,** *m.* store, shop; shutter; plank.
**Ladenburgkolben,** *m.* Ladenburg flask.
**Ladenpreis,** *m.* retail price.
**Lader,** *m.* loader, charge, filler.
**Lade-raum,** *m.* exploding chamber; loading space. **-spannung,** *f.* (*Elec.*) charging voltage. **-strom,** *m.* charging current. **-widerstand,** *m.* (*Elec.*) charging resistance.
**lädieren,** *v.t.* hurt, injure, damage.
**Ladung,** *f.* charge; load; cargo; charging, loading.
**Ladungs-dichte,** *f.* density of charge, charge density. **-einheit,** *f.* unit of charge. **-flasche,** *f.* Leyden jar. **-gemisch,** *n.* charge mixture, mixed charge. **-sinn,** *m.* (*Elec.*) nature of a charge, sign. **-träger,** *m.* carrier of a charge. **-vermögen,** *n.* (*Elec.*) electrostatic capacity. **-werfer,** *m.* (*Mil.*) projector. **-wolke,** *f.* charge cloud.
**lag,** *pret.* (of liegen) lay, etc.
**Lage,** *f.* layer, stratum, bed, deposit; coat, coating; state, position, situation, location; condition; attitude; quire (of paper); (*Textiles*) lap. — **in — sein,** be in a position, be able.
**lagefest,** *a.* stable (in position).
**Lagefestigkeit,** *f.* stability (of position).
**Lägel,** *n.* barrel, keg.
**lagenförmig,** *a.* layered, bedded, banded.
**Lagentextur,** *f.* (*Geol.*) banded structure.
**lagenweise,** *adv.* in layers or beds.
**Lager,** *n.* bed, layer, stratum; store, stock; storehouse; sediment, deposit; camp; bed, couch; lair; stand (for casks); (*Mach.*) bearing, bush. **-bestand,** *m.* stock, inventory.
**lagerbeständig,** *a.* stable in storage.
**Lager-beständigkeit,** *f.* stability in storage. **-bock,** *m.* (*Mach.*) pedestal. **-buchse, -büchse,** *f.* (*Mach.*) bush, bushing. **-butter,** *f.* cold-storage butter.
**lagerecht,** *a.* fast to storing, stable in storage.
**Lager-fähigkeit,** *f.* storability, stability in storage; storage capacity. **-fass,** *n.* storage vat or cask. **-festigkeit,** *f.* stability in storage.
**lagerförmig,** *a.* in beds or layers or strata.
**Lager-gang,** *m.* (*Geol.*) bedded vein, sheet, sill. **-haus,** *n.* warehouse, storehouse. **-keller,** *m.* storage cellar. **-legierung,** *f.* bearing alloy. **-metall,** *n.* bush metal, bearing metal.
**lagern,** *v.i & r.* lie stored; be deposited; lie, remain; lie down; camp. — *v.t.* store; lay down, deposit; season, age; support, seat.
**Lager-platz,** *m.* storage place, depot; camp site. **-prozess,** *m.* storage process. **-raum,** *m.* store room, warehouse room. **-reibung,** *f.* (*Mach.*) bearing friction.
**lagerreif,** *a.* aged.
**Lager-schale,** *f.* (*Mach.*) bush, bushing. **-stätte,** *f.* (*Geol.*) deposit, bed.
**Lagerstätten-kunde, -lehre,** *f.* science of mineral deposits, economic geology.
**Lagerung,** *f.* arrangement; stratification, bedding; bed; grain (of a stone); (*Cryst.*) orientation; (*Mach.*) seating, support, bearing; storage; lying down; encampment.
**Lagerwein,** *m.* wine seasoned by storage.
**Lagerweissmetall,** *n.* white bearing metal, Babbitt metal.
**lageweise,** *adv.* in layers, in strata.
**lahm,** *a.* lame; paralyzed.
**lähmen,** *v.t.* paralyze, cripple, lame, disable.
**Lähmung,** *f.* lameness; paralysis.
**Lahn,** *m.* flattened wire; tinsel.
**Laib,** *m.* loaf.
**Laich,** *m.* spawn.
**Laie,** *m.* layman; novice.
**Lake,** *f.* brine, pickle.
**Laken,** *n.* linen; cloth; sheet.
**Lakmus,** *m.* litmus. See Lackmus-.
**Lakritze,** *f.*, **Lakritz, Lakriz,** *m.* licorice.
**Lakritzensaft,** *m.* extract of licorice.
**Laktat,** *n.* lactate.
**Lakton,** *n.* lactone.
**Lambertsnuss,** *f.* filbert.
**Lamelle,** *f.* lamella; lamina; leaf, sheet, plate, vane.
**lamellenförmig,** *a.* lamelliform.
**Lamellenstruktur,** *f.* lamellar structure.
**lamellieren,** *v.t.* laminate.
**Lamellierung,** *f.* lamination.
**laminieren,** *v.t.* laminate; (*Spinning*) draw.
**Lamm,** *n.* lamb.
**Lämmerwolle, Lammwolle,** *f.* lamb's wool.
**Lämpchen,** *n.* small lamp.
**Lampe,** *f.* lamp; burner, torch, light.
**Lampen-arbeit,** *f.* (*Glass*) blast-lamp work, as distinguished from foundry work. **-brennstunde,** *f.* lamp hour. **-docht,** *m.* lamp wick. **-faden,** *m.* lighting filament. **-fassung,** *f.* (*Elec.*) lamp socket. **-russ,** *m.*, **-schwarz,** *n.* lampblack. **-säure,** *f.* lampic acid. *Obs.*
**Land,** *n.* land; ground; country.
**Land-.** land, country, rural, farm, agricultural, provincial; (*Med.*) epidemic, also endemic. **-bau,** *m.* agriculture, farming.
**Lande-.** (*Aero.*) landing.
**landen,** *v.i.* land.
**Landenge,** *f.* isthmus.
**Landes-.** state, national, of a country; native, home; land; agricultural. **-erzeugnis,** *n.* agricultural product; native product.

**Land-gut,** *n.* estate. **-karte,** *f.* map. **-krankheit,** *f.* epidemic or endemic disease.
**land-kundig,** *a.* notorious. **-läufig,** *a.* customary, current.
**ländlich,** *a.* rural; rustic.
**Land-mann,** *m.* farmer, countryman. **-messer,** *m.* surveyor. **-polizei,** *f.* rural police. **-schaft,** *f.* province, district, state; landscape. **-see,** *m.* lake. **-seuche,** *f.* epidemic. **-stadt,** *f.* inland town, country town. **-strasse,** *f.* highway, road. **-strich,** *m.* district; climate. **-sturm,** *m.* general levy (of troops), reserves. **-tag,** *m.* diet, legislature. **-ung,** *f.* landing. **-vogt,** *m.* governor.
**landw.,** *abbrev.* of landwirtschaftlich.
**Land-wehr,** *f.* first home reserve, militia. **-wirt,** *m.* farmer. **-wirtschaft,** *f.* agriculture.
**landwirtschaftlich,** *a.* agricultural.
**lang,** *a.* long; tall; (of wine, etc.) ropy. — **lange Flotte,** dilute dye liquor. — **seit langem,** for a long time.
**lang-anhaltend,** *a.* long-lasting; continuous. **-brennweitig,** *a.* long-focus. **-dauernd,** *a.* long-continued, lasting.
**lange,** *adv.* long; far.
**Länge,** *f.* length; longitude; tallness. **-bruch,** *m.* longitudinal fracture. — **der Länge nach,** lengthwise.
**langeiförmig,** *a.* of extended oval shape.
**langen,** *v.i.* suffice; reach. — *v.t.* seize, take.
**längen,** *v.t.* lengthen, extend.
**Längen-.** longitudinal; linear. **-ausdehnung,** *f.* linear expansion. **-bruch,** *m.* longitudinal fracture. **-durchschnitt,** *m.* longitudinal section. **-einheit,** *f.* unit of length. **-grad,** *m.* degree of longitude. **-mass,** *n.* linear measure. **-schnitt,** *m.* longitudinal cut or section.
**länger,** *a.* longer, etc. (see lang).
**Langerhanssche Inseln.** (*Anat.*) islands of Langerhans.
**längern,** *v.t.* = verlängern.
**längerwellig,** *a.* of greater wavelength.
**lang-faserig,** *a.* long-fibered, long-staple(d). **-flammig,** *a.* long-flame, long-flaming. **-flurig,** *a.* (*Textiles*) long-haired, long-piled. **-fristig,** *a.* long-time. **-gestielt,** *p.a.* long-handled; long-stalked. **-gestreckt,** *p.a.* extended, elongated. **-gezogen,** *a.* long-drawn-out, elongated, extended. **-haarig,** *a.* long-haired; flossy (silk); long-staple (wool). **-halsig,** *a.* long-necked.
**langj.,** *abbrev.* of langjährig.
**lang-jährig,** *a.* of many years, long-term. **-kettig,** *a.* long-chain. **-lebig,** *a.* long-lived.
**länglich,** *a.* longish, elongated; oblong. **-rund,** *a.* elliptical; oval.
**Lang-loch,** *n.* oblong hole, slot. **-mut,** *f.* patience, forbearance.
**langrund,** *a.* oval, elliptical.
**längs,** *prep.* along.
**Längs-.** longitudinal. **-achse,** *f.* longitudinal axis.
**langsam,** *a.* slow. — *adv.* slowly.
**Langsam-binder,** *m.* slow-setting cement. **-gang,** *m.* slow speed. **-keit,** *f.* slowness.
**langsamlaufend,** *a.* slow-running, slow-speed.
**Längsbruch,** *m.* longitudinal fracture.
**Langschliff,** *m.* long-fibered mechanical pulp.
**Längs-durchschnitt,** *m.* longitudinal section. **-ebene,** *f.* longitudinal plane.
**Langsein,** *n.* (of wine) ropiness.
**Längsfaser,** *f.* longitudinal fiber.
**Langsieb,** *n.* (*Paper*) endless wire, Fourdrinier web. **-maschine,** *f.* (*Paper*) Fourdrinier machine.
**längslaufend,** *a.* longitudinal, lengthwise.
**Längs-richtung,** *f.* longitudinal direction. — **in der —,** lengthwise. **-schnitt,** *m.* longitudinal section. **-schwingung,** *f.* longitudinal vibration.
**längsseit,** *adv.* alongside.
**Längsstreifen,** *m.* longitudinal stripe or stria.
**längst,** *a.* longest. — *adv.* long ago.
**Langstäbchen,** *n.* bacillus.
**langstapelig,** *a.* long-staple(d).
**längstens,** *adv.* at the longest.
**lang-stielig,** *a.* long-stemmed, long-stalked; long-handled. **-strahlig,** *a.* (*Cryst.*) long and radiating, radiating-acicular.
**Längswelle,** *f.* longitudinal wave.
**Längung,** *f.* elongation, extension.
**Languste,** *f.* spiny lobster (*Palinurus vulgaris*).
**langweilen,** *v.t.* tire, bore.
**Langwelle,** *f.* (*Physics*) long wave (esp. 100–1500 kc.).
**lang-wellig,** *a.* of long wavelength, long-wave. **-wierig,** *a.* protracted, wearisome, tedious.
**Lanthan,** *n.* lanthanum. **-salz,** *n.* lanthanum salt. **-schwefelsäure,** *f.* lanthanumsulfuric acid (lanthanum hydrogen sulfate).
**Lanze,** *f.* lance.
**lanzenförmig,** *a.* lance-shaped, lanceolate.
**lanzieren,** *v.t.* launch.
**Lapisdruck,** *m.* (*Calico*) lapis style.
**Läppchen,** *n.* lobe; flap, rag.
**Lappen,** *m.* flap; tab; flange; rag; lobe.
**läppen,** *v.t.* lap, (fine-)polish.
**Läppenmittel,** *n.* lapping abrasive.
**lappig,** *a.* lobed, lobate; flabby, flaccid, spongy.
**Läpp-pulver,** *n.* lapping abrasive.
**Lärche,** *f.* larch.
**Lärchen-baum,** *m.* larch. **-baumharz, -harz,** *n.* larch resin, Venetian turpentine. **-holzöl,** *n.* larch-wood oil. **-pech,** *n.* larch pitch. **-pilz, -schwamm,** *m.* purging agaric (*Polyporus officinalis*). **-stoff,** *m.* coniferin. **-terpentin,** *m.* larch turpentine, Venetian turpentine.
**Lardöl,** *n.* lard oil.

**Laricinsäure,** *f.* laricinic acid, maltol.
**Larixinsäure,** *f.* larixinic acid, laricic acid.
**Lärm,** *m.* noise; din; clamor.
**Larve,** *f.* larva; mask.
**larvizid,** *a.* larvicidal.
**las,** *pret.* (of lesen) read; gathered.
**Lasche,** *f.* (*Mech.*) fish, fishplate, strap; flap.
**lasieren,** *v.t.* glaze. — **lasierend,** *p.a.* glazing, transparent.
**Lasierfarbe,** *f.* glazing color, glazing.
**Läsion,** *f.* lesion.
**lassen,** *v.t.* let, leave, yield, allow; cause, have (something done). — *v.i.* desist; look, suit. — **gelassen,** *p.a.* patient, calm. — **es lässt sich sehen,** it can be seen.
**lässig,** *a.* negligent, lazy.
**lässt,** *pr. 2 & 3 sing.* (of lassen) lets, etc.
**Last,** *f.* load, burden, weight; freight, cargo; stress. **-auto,** *n.* (motor) truck, (motor) lorry.
**lasten,** *v.i.* weigh. — *v.t.* load, burden.
**Laster,** *m.* truck, lorry.
**lästig,** *a.* burdensome, irksome, troublesome.
**Lastwagen,** *m.* truck, lorry; freight car.
**Lasur,** *f.* azure; azurite; glazing, glaze. — *m.* lapis lazuli.
**lasurblau,** *a.* azure, sky-blue.
**Lasur-blau,** *n.* ultramarine. **-farbe,** *f.* azure; glazing color; ultramarine.
**lasurfarben,** *a.* azure, sky-blue.
**Lasurit,** *m.* azurite; lapis lazuli.
**Lasur-lack,** *m.* transparent varnish. **-schleiflack,** *m.* transparent flatting varnish. **-spat,** *m.* lazulite.
**Lasurstein,** *m.* lapis lazuli. — **unechter —,** false lapis lazuli, chessylite.
**lateinisch,** *a.* Latin; roman (letters).
**Latenz,** *f.* latency. **-zeit,** *f.* latent period.
**Laterne,** *f.* lantern; lamp.
**Laternen-bild,** *n.* lantern slide. **-ofen,** *m.* a lantern-shaped oven made by winding resistance wire around a frame of porcelain rods.
**latexführend,** *a.* latex-bearing, laticiferous.
**Latex-gummi,** *n.* latex rubber. **-mischung,** *f.* latex mixture.
**Latsche, Latschen-kiefer,** *f.* knee pine (*Pinus montana pumilio*). **-öl,** *n.* templin oil.
**Latte,** *f.* lath; strip, slat, board, batten.
**Latten-kiste,** *f.* crate. **-verschlag,** *m.* latticework; crate.
**Lattich,** *m.* lettuce. **-säure,** *f.* lactucic acid.
**Latwerge,** *f.* (*Pharm.*) electuary, confection.
**lau,** *a.* tepid, lukewarm; mild.
**Laub,** *n.* foliage, leaves.
**laubartig,** *a.* foliaceous.
**Laube,** *f.* arbor, bower; hall.
**Laub-erde,** *f.* leaf mold. **-grün,** *n.* a kind of chrome green.
**laubgrün,** *a.* leaf-green.
**Laub-holz,** *n.* leaved trees, deciduous trees; wood of deciduous trees, hardwood. **-holzkohle,** *f.* hardwood charcoal. **-holzzellstoff,** *m.* (*Paper*) hardwood cellulose or pulp.
**laubverlierend, laubwechselnd,** *a.* deciduous.
**Lauch,** *m.* leek.
**lauch-artig,** *a.* like or of the nature of leeks. **-grün,** *a.* leek-green.
**laudieren,** *v.t.* gloss (cloth).
**Laue-fleck, -punkt,** *m.* Laue spot.
**Lauer,** *m.* (*Distilling*) low wine, singlings.
**Lauf,** *m.* course, path, track; running, run, race; flow; current; circulation; passage; (gun) barrel. **-bahn,** *f.* track, runway, run; orbit; career; racecourse.
**Laufbild,** *n.* motion picture. **-fänger,** *m.*, **-kammer,** *f.* motion-picture camera. **-werfer,** *m.* motion-picture projector.
**laufen,** *v.i.* run; go, move, turn; leak. — **laufend,** *p.a.* running, current; continuous; consecutive (numbers). — **laufendes Bad,** (*Dyeing*) standing bath.
**Läufer,** *m.* runner; muller; rammer; slider; traveler; rotor. **-gewicht,** *n.* sliding weight. **-mühle,** *f.* edge mill.
**Lauf-fläche,** *f.* bearing surface; (*Mach.*) journal; (of tires) tread. **-gewicht,** *n.* sliding weight. **-glasur,** *f.* (*Ceram.*) flow glaze. **-gummi,** *n.* tread (of a rubber tire).
**-läufig.** running, moving.
**Lauf-katze,** *f.* trolley; crane carriage. **-kran,** *m.* traveling crane. **-nummer,** *f.* serial number. **-pass,** *m.* dismissal. **-pfanne,** *f.* (*Sugar*) cooler. **-rad,** *n.* running wheel (trailing wheel, bogie wheel, landing wheel, rotor, etc.). **-richtung,** *f.* direction of motion. **-rolle,** *f.* (*Mach.*) roller, roll. **-term,** *m.* variable term. **-werk,** *n.* running gear, works, mechanism. **-zahl,** *f.* variable number, running variable. **-zeit,** *f.* running time, transmission time, transit time. **-zeitschwingung,** *f.* electron oscillation.
**laugartig,** *a.* = laugenartig.
**Laugasche,** *f.* leached ashes.
**laugbar,** *a.* leachable.
**Lauge,** *f.* lye; lixivium; (in many technical phrases) liquor; wash; suds; (*Metal.*, etc.) leach; (*Bleaching*) buck; (*Elec.*) electrolyte. **-anlage,** *f.* lixiviation plant, leaching plant. **-behälter,** *m.* leaching vat or tub or tank.
**laugebeständig,** *a.* alkali-resistant.
**Laugebottich,** *m.* leaching vat or tub or tank.
**lauge-empfindlich,** *a.* sensitive to alkali. **-fähig,** *a.* leachable.
**Laugemittel,** *n.* leaching agent.
**laugen,** *v.t.* lye, steep in lye; buck; leach, lixiviate. — **gelaugte Säure,** (*Paper*) tower liquor to which has been added liquor from the cookers (in the sulfite process).

**laugenartig,** *a.* of the nature of, or resembling, lye, alkaline, (*Old Chem.*) lixivial.

**Laugen-asche,** *f.* leached ashes. **-bad,** *n.* lye bath, lye, liquor. **-bottich,** *m.* lye vat, liquor vat.

**laugenecht,** *a.* fast to (caustic) lye.

**Laugen-eiweiss,** *n.* alkali albumin(ate). **-essenz,** *f.* caustic soda (or potash) solution. **-fass,** *n.* lye vat, leaching tub, etc.

**laugenfest,** *a.* lyeproof.

**Laugenflüssigkeit,** *f.* liquor.

**laugenhaft,** *a.* like lye, alkaline.

**Laugen-lösung,** *f.* leaching solution. **-messer,** *m.* alkalimeter. **-probe,** *f.* lye (or liquor) test or sample. **-rückstand,** *m.* residue from leaching.

**Laugensalz,** *n.* (*Old Chem.*) alkaline salt, lixivial salt. — **flüchtiges —,** sal volatile (commercial ammonium carbonate). — **mineralisches —,** sodium carbonate. — **vegetabilisches —,** potassium carbonate. — **bernsteinsaures —,** potassium succinate.

**laugensalzig,** *a.* (*Old Chem.*) alkaline, lixivial.

**Laugen-turm,** *m.* lye tower, liquor tower. **-wa(a)ge,** *f.* lye or liquor hydrometer; (*Salt*) brine gage. **-wasser,** *n.* weak lye or liquor. **-zusatz,** *m.* addition of lye or liquor.

**Laugerei,** *f.* leaching, lixiviation; leaching plant.

**Laugerückstand,** *m.* residue from lixiviation or extraction.

**Laugflüssigkeit,** *f.* (*Metal.*, etc.) liquor.

**laugig,** *a.* = laugenartig.

**Laugrückstand,** *m.* = Laugerückstand.

**Laugung,** *f.* lyeing, bucking; leaching.

**laugungsfähig,** *a.* leachable.

**Laugungsmittel,** *n.* leaching agent.

**Laune,** *f.* humor, temper.

**launisch,** *a.* capricious, erratic; mean.

**Laurin-fett,** *n.* laurin. **-säure,** *f.* lauric acid.

**Laus,** *f.* louse; (*Tech.*) a fault of some kind, as a knot in wool or a light spot on a dyed fabric.

**lauschen,** *v.i.* listen.

**Läuse-körner,** *n.pl.* stavesacre seed; cocculus indicus; sabadilla seed. **-pulver,** *n.* insect powder. **-samen,** *m.pl.* = Läusekörner.

**laut,** *a.* loud; public. — *prep.* according to, in accordance with.

**Laut,** *m.* sound; tone.

**Lautal,** *n.* a light-metal alloy. *T. N.*

**lautbar,** *a.* audible; public; notorious.

**Laute,** *f.* lute; (*Dyeing*) crutch.

**lauten,** *v.i.* sound; run, read.

**läuten,** *v.t. & i.* ring.

**lauter,** *a.* pure; clear; genuine, unalloyed; mere, only.

**Läuter,** *m.* = Lauer. **-batterie,** *f.* (*Brewing*) underlet.

**Lauterbeize,** *f.* (in turkey red dyeing) white liquor.

**Läuter-boden,** *m.* (*Brewing*) false bottom, strainer. **-bottich,** *m.* (*Brewing*) straining vat, clarifying tub.

**Läuterer,** *m.* purifier, etc. (see läutern).

**Läuter-feuer,** *n.* refining fire. **-flasche,** *f.* wash(ing) bottle.

**Lauter-keit,** *f.* purity; clarity; genuineness. **-maische,** *f.* (*Brewing*) liquid part of mash.

**läutern,** *v.t.* purify, refine, clear, clarify, rectify, defecate, wash; strain.

**Läuter-ofen,** *m.* refining furnace (or kiln). **-pfanne,** *f.* clearing pan, clarifier; defecator. **-trommel,** *f.* washing drum.

**Läuterung,** *f.* purification, etc. (see läutern).

**Läuterungs-bad,** *n.* clearing bath. **-kessel,** *m.* melting pot; refining boiler (as for saltpeter); clarifier. **-mittel,** *n.* purifying agent.

**Läutervorrichtung,** *f.* purifying apparatus.

**Lautheit,** *f.* loudness.

**lautlos,** *a.* soundless, noiseless, silent.

**Laut-sprecher,** *m.* loud-speaker; megaphone. **-stärke,** *f.* loudness, sound intensity. **-verstärker,** *m.* (sound) amplifier. **-verstärkung,** *f.* amplification (of sound).

**lauwarm,** *a.* lukewarm, tepid.

**Laven,** *f.pl.* lavas.

**Lavendel,** *m.* lavender. **-blüte,** *f.* lavender flower. **-farbe,** *f.* lavender color, lavender.

**lavendel-farben, -farbig,** *a.* lavender-colored, lavender.

**Lavendel-öl,** *n.* lavender oil. **-wasser,** *n.* lavender water.

**Lavezstein,** *m.* potstone.

**Lävo-.** levo-, laevo-. **-glukosan,** *n.* levoglucosan.

**lävogyr,** *a.* levorotatory.

**Lavör,** *m.* washer.

**Lävulin,** *n.* levulin. **-säure,** *f.* levulinic acid.

**Lavulkan,** *n.* a kind of synthetic rubber. *T. N.*

**Lävulose,** *f.* levulose, D-fructose.

**Lawine,** *f.* avalanche; surge.

**Laxanz,** *f.* laxative, purgative.

**laxieren,** *v.t.* purge. — **laxierend,** *p.a.* purging, laxative.

**Laxiermittel,** *n.* laxative, purgative.

**Laxiersalz,** *n.* purging or laxative salt. — **englisches —,** Epsom salt.

**Lazarett,** *n.* hospital.

**Lazur, Lazur-.** = Lasur, Lasur-.

**L.B.,** *abbrev.* Landolt-Börnstein Tabellen.

**l.c.,** *abbrev.* (loco citato) in the place cited.

**Leben,** *n.* life.

**leben,** *v.i.* live. — **lebend,** *p.a.* living, live. — **lebender Kalk,** quicklime.

**lebendig,** *a.* living, live, active; vital. — **lebendige Kraft,** vis viva, kinetic energy. — **lebendiger Kalk,** quicklime.

**Lebendigkeit,** *f.* liveness, life, vitality.

**Lebens-.** life, vital, biological, bio-. **-alter,** *n.* period of life, age. **-art,** *f.* way of living, life;

(*pl.*) behavior, manners. **-baum,** *m.* arborvitae. **-dauer,** *f.* life period; life, lifetime; longevity; durability.

**lebensfähig,** *a.* capable of living; (*Med.*) viable.

**Lebens-fähigkeit,** *f.* capacity for living, vitality; viability. **-funktion,** *f.* vital function.

**lebensgefährlich,** *a.* dangerous to life.

**Lebens-haltung,** *f.* standard of living. **-holz,** *n.* lignum vitae. **-kraft,** *f.* vital force; vitality. **-kunde, -lehre,** *f.* biology. **-luft,** *f.* (*Old Chem.*) vital air (oxygen). **-luftmesser,** *m.* eudiometer.

**Lebensmittel,** *n.pl.* provisions, victuals; food; nourishment, sustenance. **-farbe,** *f.* food color, food dye. **-gewerb(e),** *n.* foodstuff industry. **-untersuchung,** *f.* investigation of foods, food research.

**Lebens-ordnung,** *f.* regimen, diet. **-prozess,** *m.* vital process. **-saft,** *m.* vital fluid; (*Bot.*) latex. **-substanz,** *f.* vital substance. **-tätigkeit,** *f.* vital activity. **-träger,** *m.* (*Biol.*) biophore.

**lebensunfähig,** *a.* incapable of life, nonviable.

**Lebens-unterhalt,** *m.* living, subsistence. **-verrichtung,** *f.* vital function. **-versicherung,** *f.* life insurance. **-vorgang,** *m.* vital process. **-wandel,** *m.* life, conduct. **-wasser,** *n.* aqua vitae (spirits). **-weise,** *f.* mode of life.

**lebenswichtig,** *a.* vital, essential.

**Leber,** *f.* liver; hepar.

**Leber-.** hepatic. **-blende,** *f.* reniform sphalerite. **-blume,** *f.*, **-blümchen,** *n.* hepatica, liverwort.

**leberbraun,** *a.* liver-brown, liver-colored.

**Leber-brei,** *m.* liver pulp. **-eisenerz,** *n.* pyrrhotite. **-erz,** *n.* hepatic ore, esp. hepatic cinnabar (liver-brown cinnabar). **-farbe,** *f.* liver color.

**leberfarben,** *a.* liver-colored, liver-brown.

**Leber-galle,** *f.* hepatic bile. **-kies,** *m.* pyrrhotite. **-klette,** *f.* agrimony (*Agrimonia eupatoria*). **-kraut,** *n.* liverwort, hepatica. **-mittel,** *n.* liver remedy. **-nucleinsäure,** *f.* nucleic acid of liver. **-opal,** *m.* menilite (brown opaque opal). **-schwefel,** *m.* liver of sulfur, hepar. **-stärke,** *f.* glycogen. **-stein,** *m.* hepatite (fetid variety of barite); biliary calculus, gallstone. **-tran,** *m.* fish-liver oil, specif. cod-liver oil. **wurst,** *f.* liver sausage.

**Lebe-wesen,** *n.* living being, organism. **-wohl,** *n.* farewell.

**lebhaft,** *a.* lively, brisk, active; vivacious; bright, vivid, gay (colors).

**Lebhaftigkeit,** *f.* liveliness, etc. (see lebhaft).

**leblos,** *a.* lifeless, inanimate; inactive, dull, dead.

**Lebzeit,** *f.* lifetime, life.

**Lecanorsäure,** *f.* lecanoric acid.

**Lech,** *m.* (*Metal.*) regulus, mat(te), metal.

**leck,** *a.* leaking, leaky.

**Leck,** *m.* & *n.* leak; leakage.

**Leckage,** *f.*, **Lecken,** *n.* leaking, leakage, leak.

**lecken,** *v.i.* leak, drop out, trickle out. — *v.t.* & *i.* lick.

**lecker,** *a.* dainty, nice.

**Leckerei,** *f.* dainty, sweetmeat; daintiness.

**Leck-salz,** *n.* (*Agric.*) salt in block form. **-schaden,** *m.* damage or loss from leaking. **-strom,** *m.* leakage current. **-verlust,** *m.* loss from leaking, leakage.

**Leder,** *n.* leather. **-abfall,** *m.*, **-abfälle,** *m.pl.* leather waste, leather cuttings, scrap leather. **-abschnitt,** *m.* leather cutting.

**leder-ähnlich, -artig,** *a.* leather-like, leathery, coriaceous.

**Lederband,** *m.* leather binding.

**lederbeschlagen,** *a.* leather-covered, leather-lined.

**Leder-etui,** *n.* leather case. **-farbe,** *f.* leather color, buff.

**leder-farben, -farbig,** *a.* leather-colored, buff.

**Lederfett,** *n.* leather grease, dubbing.

**ledergelb,** *a.* buff.

**Leder-gummi,** *n.* = Lederharz. **-handel,** *m.* leather trade. **-harz,** *n.* (India) rubber. **-haut,** *n.* true skin, corium. **-kitt,** *m.* leather cement. **-kohle,** *f.* charcoal from leather. **-lack,** *m.* leather varnish. **-leim,** *m.* glue from leather waste. **-mehl,** *n.* leather powder, ground leather.

**ledern,** *a.* of leather, leathern.

**Leder-öl,** *n.* oil for dressing leather. **-pappe,** *f.* leather board. **-pflegemittel,** *n.* leather dressing. **-riemen,** *m.* leather belt or strap. **-schmiere,** *f.*, **-schmiermittel,** *n.* (*Leather*) dégras, dubbing. **-schnur,** *f.* leather cord, leather string. **-wichse,** *f.* leather polish. **-zucker,** *m.* marshmallow paste; **(brauner)** licorice paste.

**ledig,** *a.* exempt; devoid; vacant; unmarried.

**lediglich,** *adv.* only, solely, merely, entirely.

**leer,** *a.* empty; blank; void; vacant; weak, flat. — **leerer Raum,** empty space, vacuum.

**Leerdarm,** *m.* jejunum.

**Leere,** *f.* vacuum; emptiness, void; vacancy; gage, pattern.

**leeren,** *v.t.* empty, evacuate.

**Leer-fass,** *n.* (*Paper*) emptying vat. **-gang, -lauf,** *m.* (*Mach.*) idle motion, running without load, also backlash. **-gewicht,** *n.* weight empty, tare.

**leerlaufen,** *v.i.* run empty, run idle, idle.

**Leer-raum,** *m.* empty space, vacuum. **-stelle,** *f.* empty place, empty spot.

**Leerung,** *f.* emptying, evacuation.

**Leerversuch,** *m.* blank experiment or test; no-load test.

**Lefze,** *f.* lip.

**Leg.,** *abbrev.* (Legierung) alloy.

**lege artis.** (Latin) by the rules of art.
**legen,** *v.t.* lay; put, place, deposit, plant. — *v.r.* lie down; abate; devote oneself.
**Legg.,** *abbrev.* (Legierungen) alloys.
**legierbar,** *a.* alloyable.
**Legierbarkeit,** *f.* alloyability.
**legieren,** *v.t.* alloy; mix; bequeath.
**Legierung,** *f.* alloy; alloying.
**Legierungs-bestandteil,** *m.* alloy constituent. **-stahl,** *m.* alloy steel. **-zusatz,** *m.* alloying addition.
**Leguminose,** *f.* legume; pea meal.
**Lehm,** *m.* loam; clay; mud.
**lehmartig,** *a.* = lehmig.
**Lehm-formguss,** *m.* loam casting. **-gelb,** *n.* clay yellow. **-grube,** *f.* loam pit, clay pit. **-guss,** *m.* loam casting.
**lehmhaltig,** *a.* = lehmig.
**lehmig,** *a.* loamy; clayey, argillaceous.
**Lehm-kalk,** *m.* argillocalcite (argillaceous limestone). **-kern,** *m.* loam core. **-kitt,** *m.* loam lute, clay lute. **-mergel,** *m.* loamy marl; clay marl. **-schmierung,** *f.* luting with loam or clay. **-stein,** *m.* unburnt brick, adobe. **-ziegel,** *m.* clay brick, loam brick.
**Lehne,** *f.* slope; support; back (of a chair); railing.
**lehnen,** *v.i.* lean.
**Lehnerseide,** *f.* nitrate (or Chardonnet) rayon.
**Lehr-anstalt,** *f.* educational institution. **-buch,** *n.* textbook.
**Lehre,** *f.* teaching, instruction, doctrine, theory, science, -ology; lesson; apprenticeship; pattern; gage; balance; centering.
**lehren,** *v.t.* teach, instruct; gage, caliper. — **gelehrt,** *p.a.* learned.
**lehrenhaltig,** *a.* true to gage.
**Lehrentoleranz,** *f.* gage tolerance.
**Lehrer,** *m.* teacher, instructor.
**Lehr-fach,** *n.* teaching; branch of study. **-kursus,** *m.* course of study. **-ling,** *m.* apprentice. **-mittel,** *n.* instruction material, means of instruction. **-plan,** *m.* curriculum; syllabus.
**lehrreich,** *a.* instructive.
**Lehr-satz,** *m.* theorem; doctrine. **-stelle,** *f.* teaching position.
**Leib,** *m.* body; belly, abdomen; womb; waist.
**Leibesfrucht,** *f.* fetus.
**leiblich,** *a.* bodily, corporal; (*Med.*) somatic. — *adv.* corporally; personally, in person.
**Leichdorn,** *m.* corn (callosity).
**Leiche,** *f.* corpse, cadaver.
**Leichen-alkaloid,** *n.* putrefactive alkaloid, ptomaine. **-base,** *f.* putrefactive base, ptomaine. **-fett,** *n.* adipocere. **-gift,** *n.* cadaveric poison, ptomaine. **-verbrennung,** *f.* cremation. **-wachs,** *n.* adipocere.
**Leichnam,** *m.* corpse, cadaver.
**leicht,** *a.* light; easy; slight. — *adv.* easily, readily, lightly, slightly. **-aschig,** *a.* (*Coal*) giving a light ash.
**Leicht-benzin,** *n.* light gasoline, light petrol. **-benzol,** *n.* light benzol(e).
**leichtbeweglich,** *a.* (of liquids) very mobile.
**Leichtbrennstoff,** *m.* light fuel.
**leicht-entzündlich,** *a.* easily (in)flammable. **-flüchtig,** *a.* readily volatile. **-flüssig,** *a.* easily fusible; easily liquefiable; thinly liquid; mobile.
**Leicht-flüssigkeit,** *f.* easy fusibility; easy liquefiability; high fluidity; mobility. **-frucht,** *f.* light grain (as oats, emmer).
**leichtgläubig,** *a.* credulous.
**Leichtigkeit,** *f.* lightness; facility, ease.
**leichtl.,** *abbrev.* of leichtlöslich.
**Leichtlegierung,** *f.* light alloy.
**leichtlich,** *adv.* easily.
**leichtlöslich,** *a.* easily soluble.
**Leicht-metall,** *n.* light metal (of sp. gr. less than 5; sometimes, specif., an alkali or alkaline-earth metal); light alloy. **-öl,** *n.* light oil.
**leicht-schmelzbar,** *a.* easily fusible. **-schmelzend, -schmelzlich,** *a.* low-melting. **-siedend** *a.* low-boiling.
**Leicht-spat,** *m.* gypsum. **-stoff,** *m.* light (-weight) material.
**leichtverbrennlich,** *a.* easily combustible, free-burning.
**Leid,** *n.* sorrow, pain; wrong, harm; mourning.
**leiden,** *v.t.* suffer; undergo; permit. — *v.i.* suffer.
**Leiden,** *n.* suffering, distress; ailment, disease.
**Leidener Flasche.** Leyden jar.
**Leidenschaft,** *f.* passion.
**leider,** *adv.* unfortunately; alas.
**leidig,** *a.* fatal; evil; tiresome.
**leidlich,** *a.* tolerable, passable, fair.
**leihen,** *v.t.* lend; borrow.
**Leim,** *m.* glue; size. — **farbloser —, weisser —,** gelatin. — **pflanzlicher —,** gluten.
**Leimanstrich,** *m.* coat of glue or size.
**leimartig,** *a.* gluey, glutinous, gelatinous.
**Leim-aufstrich,** *m.* coat of glue or size. **-bottich,** *m.* (*Textiles*) sizing beck. **-druck,** *m.* size printing (as for wallpaper); collotype.
**leimen,** *v.t.* glue; size. — **leimend,** *p.a.* adhesive, agglutinative. — **ganz —,** (*Paper*) hard-size.
**Leim-fabrik,** *f.* glue factory. **-farbe,** *f.* distemper; (*Paper*) size color. **-fass,** *n.* (*Paper*) size tank, glue tank. **-festigkeit,** *f.* bonding strength; (*Paper*) resistance (imperviousness) due to sizing. **-flüssigkeit,** *f.* size. **-galle,** *f.* (*Paper*) a dark precipitate from rosin size. **-gallerte,** *f.* gelatin jelly.
**leimgebend,** *p a.* yielding glue, gelatigenous.
**Leim-gewebe,** *n.* collagen; (*Bot.*) collenchyma.

**-glanz,** *m.* (*Leather*) size. **-gut,** *n.* material for making glue, glue stock.

**leimig,** *a.* gluey, glutinous, adhesive.

**Leim-kitt,** *m.* joiner's cement. **-küche,** *f.* glue cooking. **-kufe,** *f.* (*Textiles*) sizing beck. **-leder,** *n.* leather (or hide) scraps for making glue. **-lösung,** *f.* glue solution. **-niederschlag,** *m.* (*Soap*) = Leimsiederniederschlag. **-pflaster,** *n.* adhesive plaster. **-prober,** *m.* glue tester. **-pulver,** *n.* glue powder, powdered glue. **-rohstoff,** *m.* = Leimgut. **-seife,** *f.* filled soap (in which the glycerin and lye are allowed to remain). **-sieder,** *m.* glue boiler. **-siederniederschlag,** *m.* the solution of soap in salt lye which forms as an under layer in making curd soap. **-stoff,** *m.* sizing material; gluten. **-substanz,** *f.* gelatigenous substance. **-süss,** *n.* glycine, glycocoll. **-tiegel, -topf,** *m.* glue pot. **-trog,** *m.* (*Paper*) sizing vat.

**Leimung,** *f.* gluing; sizing; distempering. — **— in der Masse,** (*Paper*) engine sizing.

**Leim-wasser,** *n.* glue water; size. **-werk,** *n.* glue factory. **-zucker,** *m.* glycine, glycocoll.

**-lein.** little, small, -let, -kin.

**Lein,** *m.* flax; linseed. **-dotter,** *f.* gold-of-pleasure, dodder seed (*Camelina sativa*, the seeds of which yield an oil); sometimes, dodder (*Cuscuta*). **-dotteröl,** *n.* cameline oil.

**Leine,** *f.* line, cord.

**leinen,** *a.* linen.

**Leinen,** *n.* linen; cloth. **-faden,** *m.* linen fiber; linen thread. **-stoff,** *m.* linen cloth.

**Lein-firnis,** *m.* linseed varnish (thickened linseed oil). **-kraut,** *n.* toadflax. **-kuchen,** *m.* linseed cake, oil cake. **-mehl,** *m.* linseed meal.

**Leinöl,** *n.* linseed oil. **-ersatz,** *m.* linseed-oil substitute. **-fettsäure,** *f.* fatty acid of linseed oil. **-firnis,** *m.* linseed oil varnish, boiled linseed oil. **-harzlack,** *m.* linseed oil resin varnish. **-kuchen,** *m.* linseed cake, oil cake.

**leinölsauer,** *a.* linoleate of.

**Leinöl-säure,** *f.* linoleic acid. **-schlichte,** *f.* linseed-oil size. **-trockenprozess,** *m.* drying of linseed oil.

**Lein-pflanze,** *f.* flax. **-saat,** *f.* linseed.

**Leinsamen,** *m.* flaxseed, linseed. **-abkochung,** *f.* decoction of linseed. **-mehl,** *n.* flaxseed meal, linseed meal. **-öl,** *n.* linseed oil. **-schleim,** *m.* linseed (or flaxseed) mucilage.

**Leinschmalz,** *n.* hydrogenated linseed oil.

**Leinwand,** *f.* linen; cloth; (painter's) canvas. **-band,** *m.* cloth binding.

**Leiogomm(e),** *n* leiocome (dextrin).

**leise,** *a.* low, soft; slight. — *adv.* low, softly.

**Leiste,** *f.* ledge, border, lath, strip, molding; ridge; list, selvage; (*Anat.*) groin.

**leisten,** *v.t.* do, perform, accomplish, effect; render, pay, give.

**Leisten-.** (*Anat.*) inguinal.

**leistenförmig,** *a.* lath-shaped.

**leistig,** *a.* listed.

**Leistung,** *f.* work, performance, output; capacity; (mechanical, etc.) power; efficiency; service; doing, rendering.

**leistungsfähig,** *a.* serviceable, productive, capable, efficient.

**Leistungs-fähigkeit,** *f.* serviceability, power, ability; productivity; capacity; (*Mech.*) efficiency. **-faktor,** *m.* (*Elec.*) power factor.

**leistungslos,** *a.* (*Elec.*) wattless.

**Leistungsmesser,** *m.* power meter; (*Elec.*) wattmeter.

**leistungsunfähig,** *a.* unserviceable, inefficient.

**Leistungszeiger,** *m.* (*Elec.*) wattmeter.

**Leitbahn,** *f.* transit path. **-bewegung,** *f.* transit-path motion. **-welle,** *f.* transit-path oscillation.

**Leitblech,** *n.* guide plate, baffle plate.

**leiten,** *v.t.* conduct; lead; direct; guide; govern; preside over.

**Leiter,** *m.* conductor; leader, guide, director, etc. — *f.* ladder. **-tafel,** *f.* nomogram.

**Leitfaden,** *m.* clue; guide, manual.

**leitfähig,** *a.* conducting, conductive.

**Leitfähigkeit,** *f.* conductivity.

**Leitfähigkeits-gefäss,** *n.* conductivity cell. **-messung,** *f.* conductivity measurement. **-wasser,** *n.* conductivity water.

**Leit-linie,** *f.* directrix. **-rohr,** *n.*, **-röhre,** *f.* = Leitungsrohr. **-salz,** *n.* conducting salt. **-satz,** *m.* rule, guiding principle. **-stern,** *m.* pole-star; guiding star. **-strahl,** *m.* (*Math.*) radius vector; (*Aero.*) pilot beam, guide beam.

**Leitung,** *f.* conduction, conducting, transmission (as of electricity); (electric) circuit; (electric) wire, cable, lead; conduit, piping, tubing, line, main, supply (as of gas or water); duct; leading, direction, management; guide.

**Leitungs-draht,** *m.* conducting wire. **-elektron,** *n.* conduction electron.

**leitungsfähig,** *a.* conducting, conductive.

**Leitungs-fähigkeit,** *f.* conductivity. **-kraft,** *f.* conducting power. **-messer,** *m.* conductometer. **-netz,** *n.* network of piping or wiring (for gas, etc., or electricity), distribution system. **-rohr,** *n.*, **-röhre,** *f.* conducting tube or pipe; (for gases) delivery tube; conduit pipe, conduit. **-spannung,** *f.* (*Elec.*) line voltage. **-vermögen,** *n.* = Leitvermögen. **-wärme,** *f.* heat of conduction. **-wasser,** *n.* tap water. **-widerstand,** *m.* (*Elec.*) resistance, specif. line resistance.

**Leit-vermögen,** *n.* conducting power, (*Elec.*) conductance; conductivity. **-wert,** *m.* (*Elec.*) conductance, admittance, or susceptance. **-zahl,** *f.* (coefficient of) conductivity.

**Lekanorsäure,** *f.* lecanoric acid.

**Lektion,** *f.* lesson.
**Lektüre,** *f.* reading.
**Lemnische Erde.** Lemnian earth.
**Lemongrasöl,** *n.* lemon-grass oil.
**Lende,** *f.* loin; haunch, hip.
**Lenden-.** lumbar.
**lenkbar,** *a.* dirigible, guidable; tractable.
**lenken,** *v.t.* guide, direct, drive, steer.
**lenksam,** manageable, flexible, tractable.
**Lenz,** *m.* spring.
**Lenzin,** *n.* ground gypsum, annaline.
**Leonecopal-insäure,** *f.* leonecopalinic acid. **-säure,** *f.* leonecopalic acid.
**Lepra,** *f.* leprosy, lepra.
**Lerche,** *f.* lark; larch.
**lernen,** *v.t.* learn. — **kennen —,** become acquainted with. — **gelernt,** *p.a.* skilled.
**Lesart,** *f.* reading; version.
**lesbar,** *a.* legible, readable.
**Lesbarkeit,** *f.* legibility, readability.
**Lese,** *f.* vintage; gathering.
**Lese-buch,** *n.* reader. **-glas,** *n.* reading glass. **-lupe,** *f.* reading lens.
**lesen,** *v.t.* read; gather; cull, sort. — *v.i.* read; lecture.
**leserlich,** *a.* legible.
**Lesestein,** *m.* bog iron ore (form of limonite); boulder.
**leslich,** *a.* legible.
**letal,** *a.* lethal, fatal.
**Letten,** *m.* potter's clay, loam. **-nudel,** *f.* (*Expl.*) clay roll (for tamping). **-schlamm,** *m.* clay slurry, slip.
**Letter,** *f.* letter, character, type.
**Lettern-gut, -metall,** *n.* type metal.
**lettig,** *a.* clayish, clayey, loamy.
**letztangeführt,** *a.* last-mentioned or -quoted.
**letzte,** *a.* last; latest; lowest. — **der (die, das) letztere,** the latter. — **in letzter Zeit,** recently, lately.
**letztgenannt,** *p.a.* last-named, latter.
**letzthin,** *adv.* of late, recently.
**Leuchämie,** *f.* leukemia.
**Leucht-.** illuminating, lighting, luminous. **-bakterien,** *n.pl.* photogenic bacteria. **-beugung,** *f.* diffraction of light. **-bombe,** *f.* (*Mil.*) flash bomb, flare. **-brenner,** *m.* illuminating burner. **-dauer,** *f.* luminous period or duration. **-dichte,** *f.* light density, brightness. **-draht,** *m.* lighting filament.
**Leuchte,** *f.* light; lamp.
**Leuchtelektron,** *n.* emitting electron, optical electron; photo-electron.
**leuchten,** *v.i.* give light, shine, glow, luminesce. — **leuchtend,** *p.a.* luminous, bright, shining.
**Leuchter,** *m.* light source.
**Leucht-erscheinung,** *f.* luminous phenomenon. **-faden,** *m.* luminous filament; glow column; light streamer.
**leuchtfähig,** *a.* capable of luminescence.
**Leuchtfarbe,** *f.* luminous paint or color.
**Leuchtgas,** *n.* illuminating gas, city gas. **-anstalt,** *f.* illuminating-gas plant. **-erzeugung,** *f.* production of illuminating gas.
**Leucht-gebilde,** *n.* luminous pattern. **-geschoss,** *n.* (*Mil.*) star shell. **-granate,** *f.* (a kind of) star shell. **-granatwerfer,** *m.* pyrotechnic projector. **-hülle,** *f.* luminous envelope, (of the sun) photosphere. **-käfer,** *m.* firefly, glowworm. **-kraft,** *f.* illuminating power, luminosity. **-kraftbestimmung, -kraftmessung,** *f.* photometry. **-kraftverstärker,** *m.* phosphorogen. **-kugel,** *f.* (*Mil.*) Very light flare. **-masse,** *f.* luminescent mass or composition. **-material,** *n.* luminescent material, phosphor. **-mittel,** *n.* illuminant; pyrotechnic device. **-munition,** *f.* (*Mil.*) pyrotechnics, also tracer ammunition. **-öl,** *n.* illuminating oil, specif. kerosene. **-patrone,** *f.* signal cartridge, Very cartridge. **-petroleum,** *n.* kerosene. **-pistole,** *f.* signal pistol, Very pistol. **-punkt,** *m.* flash point; luminous point. **-quarz,** *n.* glow crystal. **-rakete,** *f.* (*Mil.*) signal rocket. **-raketengestell,** *n.* (*Mil.*) pyrotechnics projector. **-rohr,** *n.*, **-röhre,** *f.* illuminating tube, specif. fluorescent tube; radiating tube. **-satz,** *m.* (*Mil.*) tracer composition. **-schirm,** *m.* luminescent screen. **-spur,** *f.* light trail, (*Mil.*) tracer trajectory. **-spurgeschoss,** *n.* (*Mil.*) tracer projectile. **-spurgranate,** *f.* (*Mil.*) tracer shell. **-spursatz,** *m.* (*Mil.*) tracer composition. **-stab,** *m.* flashlight. **-stärke,** *f.* brightness; candle power. **-stein,** *m.* phosphorescent stone. **-stoff,** *m.* luminous substance. **-strahl,** *m.* light ray. **-vermögen,** *n.* illuminating power. **-wert,** *m.* illuminating value. **-wurm,** *m.* glowworm. **-zeichen,** *n.* light signal, flare signal.
**leucitführend,** *a.* leucite-bearing, leucitic.
**leugnen,** *v.t.* deny; retract.
**Leuk-, Leuko-.** leuc-, leuco-.
**Leukämie,** *f.* leukemia.
**Leukokörper,** *m.* leuco compound.
**leukokrat,** *a.* (*Petrog.*) leucocratic.
**Leukolyse,** *f.* leucocytolysis.
**Leuko-phan,** *m.* leucophane. **-plast,** *n.* (a kind of) adhesive plaster. **-verbindung,** *f.* leuco compound. **-zyt,** *n.* (*Physiol.*) leucocyte. **-zytenzahl,** *f.* leucocyte count. **-zytose,** *f.* leucocytosis.
**Leuna-salpeter,** *m.* Leuna saltpeter (ammonium sulfate nitrate). **-werk,** *n.* Leuna (fixed-nitrogen) plant.
**Leute,** *pl.* people; persons, men, the world, hands, servants.
**leutselig,** *a.* humane, affable, popular, kind.
**Leuzin,** *n.* leucine.

**Leuzit,** *m.* (*Min.*) leucite.
**levantieren,** *v.t.* (*Leather*), grain, levant.
**levantisch,** *a.* Levantine.
**levigieren,** *v.t.* levigate.
**Levkoje,** *f.* stock, gillyflower.
**lexikalisch,** *a.* lexical, lexicographic.
**Lexikon,** *n.* dictionary, lexicon.
**Leyd(e)ner Blau.** Leyden blue, cobalt blue.
**Leyd(e)ner Flasche.** Leyden jar.
**Lezithin,** *n.* lecithin.
**lfd.,** *abbrev.* (laufend) running, current, consecutive.
**lfd.Nr.,** *abbrev.* (laufende Nummer) serial number, running number.
**Lfg.,** *abbrev.* (Lieferung) issue, number, part.
**lg.,** *abbrev.* (lang) long.
**Lg.,** *abbrev.* ligroin.
**Libelle,** *f.* level (the instrument).
**-lich.** A suffix forming adjectives from nouns (-ly, -ful, -ous), from verb roots (-able, -ible), and from adjectives (-ly, -ish); as, *schadlich*, harmful, *möglich*, possible, *süsslich*, sweetish.
**licht,** *a.* light, pale; bright, luminous; clear; (of widths) in the clear, interior, inside. — **lichte Weite,** inside diameter.
**Licht,** *n.* light; candle.
**Licht-.** light, photo-, luminous, lighting; candle. **-abschluss,** *m.* exclusion of light. **-alterung,** *f.* light aging. **-art,** *f.* kind of light. **-äther,** *m.* luminiferous ether. **-ausschluss,** *m.* exclusion of light. **-bedarf,** *m.*, **-bedürfnis,** *n.* light requirement.
**lichtbeständig,** *a.* stable in light, photostable, (of colors) fast to light.
**Lichtbild,** *n.* photograph. **-kunst,** *f.* photography.
**lichtbilden, lichtbildern,** *v.t.* photograph.
**lichtbildlich,** *a.* photographic. — *adv.* photographically.
**Lichtbildnerei,** *f.* photography.
**Lichtbildung,** *f.* production of light, photogenesis.
**Lichtbild-wesen,** *n.* photographic matters, photography. **-zeichnung,** *f.* photogrammetry.
**lichtblau,** *a.* light blue.
**Licht-blende,** *f.* light shield, light stop, diaphragm. **-blitz,** *m.* flash of light.
**Lichtbogen,** *m.* luminous arc, (electric) arc. **-bildung,** *f.* arc formation, arcing. **-ofen,** *m.* (electric) arc furnace. **-schweissung,** *f.* arc welding. **-zündung,** *f.* arc ignition.
**licht-braun,** *a.* light brown. **-brechend,** *p.a.* refracting, refractive.
**Lichtbrechung,** *f.* refraction of light, optical refraction.
**Lichtbrechungsvermögen,** *n.* (optical) refractive power, refractivity.
**Licht-bündel,** *n.*, **-büschel,** *m.*, beam or pencil of light.
**licht-chemisch,** *a.* photochemical. **-dicht,** *a.* light-tight, light-proof.
**Lichtdruck,** *m.* photomechanical printing; photographic printing. **-gelatine,** *f.* photoengraving gelatin.
**lichtdurchlässig,** *a.* transmitting light.
**Lichtdurchlässigkeit,** *f.* permeability to light, transparency or translucency.
**lichtecht,** *a.* fast to light.
**Licht-echtheit,** *f.* fastness to light. **-effekt,** *m.* luminous effect. **-eindruck,** *m.* luminous impression. **-einstrahlung,** *f.* irradiation (by light). **-einwirkung,** *f.* action or effect of light.
**lichtelektrisch,** *a.* photoelectric.
**Lichtelektron,** *n.* photoelectron.
**lichtempfindlich,** *a.* sensitive to light, optically sensitive.
**Lichtempfindlichkeit,** *f.* sensitivity to light.
**lichten,** *v.t.* clear, thin; expose to light; weigh (anchor).
**lichtentwickelnd,** *a.* emitting light, photogenic.
**Lichtentwick(e)lung,** *f.* evolution of light, photogenesis.
**Lichterfabrik,** *f.* candle factory.
**lichterloh,** *a.* blazing. — *adv.* ablaze.
**Lichterscheinung,** *f.* luminous phenomenon; optical phenomenon; luminosity.
**lichterzeugend,** *p.a.* producing light, photogenic.
**Licht-faden,** *m.* (*Elec.*) light filament. **-farbe,** *f.* color of light.
**licht-farben, -farbig,** *a.* light-colored.
**Licht-farbendruck,** *m.* photomechanical color printing. **-filter,** *n.* light filter, color filter. **-form,** *f.* candle mold. **-fortpflanzung,** *f.* transmission of light.
**licht-freundlich,** *a.* transmitting light; (*Biol.*) photophilic. **-gebend,** *p.a.* giving light, luminous. **-gelb,** *a.* light yellow.
**Licht-genuss,** *m.* (*Biol.*) utilization of light. **-geschmack,** *m.* sun flavor. **-geschwindigkeit,** *f.* velocity of light. **-giessen,** *n.* candle molding. **-glanz,** *m.* brilliant luster, brilliance.
**licht-grau,** *a.* light gray. **-grün,** *a.* light green.
**Licht-güte,** *f.* quality of light. **-haut,** *f.* (*Physics*) cathode glow. **-hof,** *m.* halo. **-hofbildung,** *f.* (*Photog.*) halation.
**licht-hoffrei, -hofsicher,** *a.* (*Photog.*) free from halo, nonhalation, antihalation.
**Licht-hofschutzmittel,** *n.* antihalation agent. **-hülle,** *f.* luminous envelope. **-kegel,** *m.* cone of light, luminous cone. **-kohle,** *f.* (electric-) light carbon. **-korpuskel,** *n.* light corpuscle, photon. **-kranz,** *m.* (*Astron.*) corona. **-kreis,** *m.* circle of light, halo. **-kunde, -lehre,** *f.* optics. **-leimdruck,** *m.* collotypy; collotype. **-leitung,** *f.* (*Elec.*) lighting circuit. **-loch,** *n.* opening for light; pupil (of the eye).

**lichtlos,** *a.* without light, dark.
**Licht-maschine,** *f.* (*Elec.*) dynamo, generator. **-mass,** *n.* clearance. **-menge,** *f.* amount or quantity of light. **-messer,** *m.* photometer. **-messkunst, -messung,** *f.* photometry. **-mikroskop,** *n.* optical microscope. **-mühle,** *f.* radiometer. **-netz,** *n.* lighting system. **-papier,** *n.* photographic paper. **-pause,** *f.* photographic tracing. **-pauspapier,** *n.* photographic paper for blueprints or the like. **-pausverfahren,** *n.* photographic tracing process, esp. blueprinting. **-punkt,** *m.* luminous point, bright spot; focus. **-quant, -quantum,** *n.* light quantum, photon. **-quelle,** *f.* light source, source of light. **-rakete,** *f.* rocket flare. **-raummass,** *n.* clearance.
**lichtreflektierend,** *a.* light-reflecting.
**Licht-reiz,** *m.* light stimulus. **-riss,** *m.* crack due to light, sun crack. **-schalter,** *m.* (*Elec.*) light switch. **-schein,** *m.* gleam, shine, glow, blaze. **-schirm,** *m.* shade, screen.
**licht-schluckend,** *p.a.* light-absorbing, (optically) absorptive.
**Licht-schreiber,** *m.* photographic recorder. **-schutz,** *m.* protection from light, shade, hood.
**lichtschwach,** *a.* (*Optics*) of small intensity.
**Licht-schwingung,** *f.* light vibration. **-spiegler,** *m.* reflector (of light). **-spiel,** *n.* motion picture. **-sprecher,** *m.* optophone. **-spur,** *f.* light track, light trace.
**lichtstark,** *a.* (*Optics*) of strong intensity, powerful, (of lenses) rapid, high-speed.
**Licht-stärke,** *f.* strength or intensity of light; candle power; (of lenses) rapidity, speed. **-stärkemesser,** *m.* photometer. **-stärkemessung,** *f.* photometry. **-steindruck,** *m.* photolithography. **-strahl,** *m.* light ray, ray of light, luminous ray. **-strahlung,** *f.* light radiation. **-strom,** *m.* luminous flux; (*Elec.*) light(ing) current. **-talg,** *m.* candle tallow. **-täuschung,** *f.* optical illusion.
**licht-undurchlässig,** *a.* opaque to light. **-unecht,** *a.* not fast to light, fading. **-unempfindlich,** *a.* insensitive to light.
**Lichtung,** *f.* clearing, etc. (see lichten); opening; (*Biol.*) lumen.
**lichtvoll,** *a.* luminous, lucid.
**Licht-weg,** *m.* path of light. **-weite,** *f.* inside diameter; clearance. **-welle,** *f.* light wave. **-werfer,** *m.* (optical) projector. **-wirkung,** *f.* action of light; luminous effect. **-zelle,** *f.* photoelectric cell; (*Biol.*) visual cell. **-zerstreuung,** *f.* dispersion or diffusion of light. **-ziehen,** *n.* candle dipping. **-zufuhr,** *f.* admission of light.
**licken,** *v.t.* burnish, polish.
**Licker-bad,** *n.* (*Leather*) fat-liquoring bath. **-material,** *n.* (*Leather*) fat liquor.
**lickern,** *v.t.* (*Leather*) fat-liquor.
**Licker-öl,** *n.* leather oil. **-verfahren,** *n.* fat-liquoring process.
**Lid,** *n.* lid, esp. of the eye. **-bindehaut,** *f.* (*Anat.*) conjunctiva.
**lidern,** *v.t.* (*Mach.*) pack.
**Liderung,** *f.* (*Mach.*) packing.
**lieb,** *a.* dear, beloved; agreeable.
**Liebe,** *f.* love; favor.
**lieben,** *v.t.* love; like.
**Liebenswürdigkeit,** *f.* amiability, kindness.
**lieber,** *adv.* rather, sooner, better.
**Liebhaber,** *m.* lover; amateur; buyer.
**Liebigkühler, Liebig'scher Kühler.** Liebig condenser.
**lieblich,** *a.* lovely, sweet, charming.
**Lieblings-.** favorite.
**Lieb-stöckel, -stock,** *m.* lovage (*Levisticum*). **-stöckelöl,** *n.* lovage oil.
**Lied,** *n.* song.
**liederlich,** *a.* careless, disorderly, dissolute.
**lief,** *pret.* (of laufen) ran, went, etc.
**Lieferant,** *m.* purveyor, supplier.
**lieferbar,** *a.* deliverable, available.
**Lieferer,** *m.* purveyor, supplier.
**liefern,** *v.t.* yield, produce; furnish, supply, afford; deliver.
**Lieferung,** *f.* supply; providing; delivery; (of books, etc.) issue, number, part; lot.
**lieferungsweise,** *adv.* in parts or numbers.
**liegen,** *v.i.* lie; be (situated); matter, signify. — **liegend,** *p.a.* lying; extended; horizontal. — **liegende Schrift,** italics. — **gelegen,** *p.a.* situated; convenient; important. — **es liegt auf der Hand,** it is plain (or obvious). — **es liegt nahe,** it is natural, it suggests itself.
**lieh,** *pret.* (of leihen) lent; borrowed.
**liess,** *pret.* (of lassen) let, allowed, etc.
**liest,** *pr. 2 & 3 sing.* (of lesen) reads; gathers.
**Ligand,** *n.* attached atom or group, ligand.
**lignin-haltig,** *a.* containing lignin. **-reich,** *a.* rich in lignin.
**lignitartig,** *a.* lignitic.
**Lignocerinalkohol,** *m.* lignoceric alcohol.
**Likariol,** *n.* licareol (*l*-linaloöl).
**Likör,** *m.* liqueur.
**likörartig,** *a.* liqueur-like.
**Likörwein,** *m.* liqueur wine.
**lila,** *a.* lilac, lilac-colored.
**Lila, Lilak,** *m.* lilac.
**lilablau,** *a.* lilac-blue.
**Lila-farbe,** *f.* lilac color. **-öl,** *n.* lilac oil.
**Lilie,** *f.* lily.
**Liliengewächse,** *n.pl.* (*Bot.*) Liliaceae.
**Lima-bohne,** *f.* Lima bean. **-holz,** *n.* Lima wood (a dyewood).
**Limbus,** *m.* graduated circle or arc, limb.
**Limes,** *m.* limit.
**Limette,** *f.* lime (the fruit).
**Limettenessenz,** *f.* lime juice.

**Limettöl,** *n.* lime oil.
**Limonade,** *f.* lemonade.
**Limone,** *f.* citron; (süsse) lime; (**saure, eigentliche**) lemon.
**Limonen,** *n.* limonene. — *f.pl.* of Limone. **-grasöl,** *n.* lemon-grass oil. **-öl,** *n.* lemon oil.
**Limongras,** *n.* lemon grass. **-öl,** *n.* lemon-grass oil.
**Linaloë-holz,** *n.* linaloa (wood). **-öl,** *n.* linaloa oil.
**lind, linde,** *a.* soft, mild; (of silk) scoured.
**Linde,** *f.* linden, lime (the tree).
**Linden-blüte,** *f.* linden flower. **-gewächse,** *n.pl.* (*Bot.*) Tiliaceae. **-holz,** *n.* linden wood, basswood. **-kohle,** *f.* linden charcoal.
**lindern,** *v.t.* alleviate, soften, relieve. — **linderned,** *p.a.* soothing, palliative, lenitive.
**Linderungsmittel,** *n.* palliative, lenitive.
**Lineal,** *n.* ruler, rule; specif., straightedge.
**linealisch,** *a.* lineal, linear, lineate.
**Linearmass,** *n.* linear measure.
**-ling.** A suffix used to denote a person or thing described, or connected with the idea conveyed, by the original word (as, *Abkömmling,* derivative, descendant; *Jüngling,* youth).
**Linie,** *f.* line. — **in erster —,** first of all.
**Linienanordnung,** *f.* arrangement of lines.
**linienförmig,** *a.* linear.
**Linien-gebild(e),** *n.* system of lines. **-kern,** *m.* nucleus (central part) of a line. **-mitte,** *f.* middle of a line. **-paar,** *n.* pair of lines. **-papier,** *n.* ruled paper. **-raster,** *m.* ruled screen, line screen.
**linienreich,** *a.* rich in lines.
**Linien-spannung,** *f.* (*Elec.*) line tension, line voltage. **-spektrum,** *n.* line spectrum. **-verschiebung,** *f.* displacement of lines. **-zahl,** *f.* number of lines. **-zug,** *m.* line, trace (in a graph).
**linieren, liniieren,** *v.t.* rule.
**Linierfarbe, Liniierfarbe,** *f.* ruling ink.
**-linig.** -linear, -lined.
**link,** *a.* left; wrong (side), back.
**linkisch,** *a.* awkward, clumsy.
**links,** *adv.* to the left, on the left, left.
**links-.** to the left, levo-, counterclockwise.
**linksdr.,** *abbrev.* of linksdrehend.
**linksdrehend,** *p.a.* levorotatory; counterclockwise; left-handed.
**Links-drehung,** *f.* levorotation, left-handed polarization; counterclockwise motion; left turn. **-fruchtzucker,** *m.* levulose, D-fructose.
**linksgängig,** *a.* left-turning, counterclockwise.
**Links-gewinde,** *n.* left-handed thread. **-lauf,** *m.* motion to the left, counterclockwise motion.
**linkslaufend, linksläufig,** *a.* to the left, counterclockwise.
**Links-milchsäure,** *f.* levolactic acid. **-polarisation,** *f.* levopolarization. **-quarz,** *m.* left-handed quartz. **-säure,** *f.* levo acid. **-schraube,** *f.* left-handed screw. **-weinsäure,** *f.* levotartaric acid.
**Linolensäure,** *f.* linolenic acid.
**Linolsäure,** *f.* linoleic acid.
**Linse,** *f.* lens; lentil; bob (of a pendulum).
**Linsen-.** lenticular.
**linsen-ähnlich, -artig,** *a.* lenticular, lens-shaped.
**Linsenerz,** *n.* oölitic limonite.
**linsenförmig,** *a.* lens-shaped, lenticular.
**Linsenglas,** *n.* lens.
**linsengross,** *a.* lentil-sized.
**Linsensatz,** *m.* system of lenses.
**lipidlöslich, lipoidlöslich,** *a.* lipide-soluble.
**Lipolyse,** *f.* lipolysis.
**lipolytisch,** *a.* lipolytic.
**Lippe,** *f.* lip; labium; edge, border.
**Lippen-.** labial, lip. **-stift,** *m.* lipstick.
**Liquatsalz,** *n.* an aluminum salt solution used as a disinfectant and astringent.
**liqueszieren,** *v.i.* liquefy, melt.
**liquidieren,** *v.t.* liquidate, settle.
**lischt,** *pr. 3 sing.* (of löschen) extinguishes, etc.
**Lisseuse,** *f.* (*Textiles*) backwasher.
**lissieren,** *v.t.* (*Textiles*) backwash.
**List,** *f.* device, artifice, trick, cunning.
**Liste,** *f.* list, register, catalog.
**Listenpreis,** *m.* list price, catalog price.
**Lit.,** *abbrev.* (Literatur) literature.
**litauer, litauisch,** *a.* Lithuanian.
**literarisch,** *a.* literary.
**Literaturangaben,** *f.pl.* literature data.
**Liter-inhalt,** *m.* capacity in liters. **-kolben,** *m.* liter flask. **-messkolben,** *m.* liter measuring flask.
**Lithargyrum,** *n.* litharge.
**Lithion,** *n.* lithia. **-glimmer,** *m.* lithia mica. **-hydrat,** *n.* lithium hydroxide.
**lithiumhaltig,** *a.* containing lithium.
**Lithium-jodid,** *n.* lithium iodide. **-metall,** *n.* lithium metal, metallic lithium. **-salz,** *n.* lithium salt.
**Lithografenfirnis,** *m.* lithographic varnish.
**Lithografiertinte,** *f.* lithographic ink.
**litho-grafisch, -graphisch,** *a.* lithographic. **-phil,** *a.* (*Petrog.*) lithophilic.
**Lithurin,** *n.* lithurin (magnesium fluosilicate). *T.N.*
**litt,** *pret.* (of leiden) suffered, underwent.
**Litze,** *f.* braid, lace, cord, string; strand; (*Elec.*) strand wire, flexible conductor, flex wire.
**Litzendraht,** *m.* strand wire, litz.
**Lixiv,** *n.* lixivium; lye.
**Lizenz,** *f.* license. **-gebühr,** *f.* royalty. **-nehmer,** *m.* licensee.
**l.J.,** *abbrev.* (laufenden Jahres) of the current year.

**ll.**, *abbrev.* (leicht löslich) readily soluble.
**Loangocopal-insäure**, *f.* loangocopalinic acid. **-säure**, *f.* loangocopalic acid.
**Lob**, *n.* praise; fame.
**Lobelie**, *f.* lobelia.
**loben**, *v.t.* praise.
**löblich**, *a.* praiseworthy; estimable.
**Lobrede**, *f.* eulogy.
**Loch**, *n.* hole, opening; cavity; eye; pore; prison. **-blende**, *f.* perforated screen or diaphragm. **-eisen**, *n.* puncher, punch.
**lochen**, *v.t.* perforate, punch, pierce.
**löcherig**, *a.* full of holes, perforated, porous.
**Locherstelle**, *f.* open place, gap, hole.
**Loch-frass**, *m.* pitting (as of metals). **-karte**, *f.* punch(ed) card. **-kultur**, *f.* (*Bact.*) stab culture. **-scheibe**, *f.* perforated disk, apertured disk.
**Lochung**, *f.* perforation, punching.
**Lochweite**, *f.* width of opening, inside diameter.
**locken**, *v.t.* entice, induce, attract; curl.
**locker**, *a.* loose; incompact, spongy, porous.
**Lockerheit**, *f.* looseness; sponginess, porosity.
**lockern**, *v.t.* loosen, make loose; disintegrate; release. — *v.r.* slacken, relax.
**Lockerstelle**, *f.* (*Cryst.*) loose place, loose spot.
**Lockerung**, *f.* loosening; disintegration.
**Lockflamme**, *f.* pilot flame.
**Lode**, *f.* shoot, sprig; rag; tuft.
**Loden**, *m.* coarse cloth; tuft.
**lodern**, *v.i.* blaze, flame, flare.
**Löffel**, *m.* spoon; ladle; scoop; bailer; shovel; (*Surgery*) curette. **-bagger**, *m.* power shovel, excavator.
**löffelförmig**, *a.* spoon-shaped, spatular.
**Löffelkraut**, *n.* scurvy grass (*Cochlearia officinalis*).
**löffeln**, *v.t.* & *i.* spoon, ladle, scoop; bail.
**Löffelstiel**, *m.* spoon handle.
**löffelweise**, *adv.* by spoonfuls.
**log**, *pret.* (of lügen) lied, deceived.
**Logarithmentafel**, *f.* logarithm table.
**logarithmisch**, *a.* logarithmic.
**logisch**, *a.* logical. **-erweise**, *adv.* logically.
**loh**, *a.* blazing, burning.
**Loh-beize**, *f.* tan liquor; tanning. **-brühe**, *f.* (*Leather*) bark liquor, ooze. **-brühleder**, *n.* ooze leather.
**Lohe**, *f.* tanbark; tan liquor, ooze; flame, blaze.
**loheartig**, *a.* tan-like.
**Loheiche**, *f.* tanbark oak.
**lohen**, *v.t.* tan, steep in tan liquor. — *v.i.* blaze, flame.
**Lohfarbe**, *f.* tan color.
**loh-farbig, -farben**, *a.* tan-colored, tan, tawny.
**Lohfass**, *n.* tan vat.
**lohgar**, *a.* (bark-)tanned.
**Loh-gare**, *f.* (bark) tanning; dressing. **-gerber**, *m.* (bark) tanner. **-gerberei**, *f.* tanning, bark tanning; tannery. **-grube**, *f.* tan pit. **-messer**, *m.* barkometer.
**Lohn**, *m.* reward; wages, pay. **-arbeiter**, *m.* common workman.
**lohnen**, *v.t.* pay, recompense, reward. — *v.i.* & *r.* pay. — **lohnend**, *p.a.* paying, profitable.
**Lohnfärber**, *m.* job dyer.
**Lohnung, Löhnung**, *f.* pay, payment.
**Loh-probe**, *f.* (*Leather*) bark test. **-prüfer, -prober**, *m.* barkometer. **-pulver**, *n.* tan powder. **-rinde**, *f.* tanbark.
**Lohschmidt'sche Zahl.** Lohschmidt number.
**Lokal**, *n.* locality, place; tavern; shop. **-farbe**, *f.* natural color. **-geschmack**, *m.* local taste.
**lokalisieren**, *v.t.* localize.
**Lokalwirkung**, *f.* local action or effect.
**Lorbeer**, *m.* laurel, bay. **-blatt**, *n.* laurel leaf, bay leaf.
**Lorbeere**, *f.* laurel berry, bayberry.
**Lorbeer-kampher**, *m.* laurin. **-öl**, *n.* laurel oil, bay oil. **-ölsäure**, *f.* lauric acid. **-rose**, *f.* oleander. **-spiritus**, *m.* bay rum.
**Lore, Lori**, *f.* lorry, truck.
**los**, *a.* loose, free. — *adv.* on, up.
**Los**, *n.* lot; share; fate; prize.
**los-.** loose, free, off, un-, de-, dis-.
**-los.** destitute of, -less.
**Lös.**, *abbrev.* (Lösung) solution.
**Losantin**, *n.* a bleaching-powder preparation. *T.N.*
**lösbar**, *a.* soluble; dissoluble, resolvable; detachable.
**Lösbarkeit**, *f.* solubility; dissolubility; (*Math.*) resolvability.
**los-blättern**, *v.i.* exfoliate, defoliate. **-brechen**, *v.t.* & *i.* break loose, break off, break out, burst out.
**losch**, *pret.* (of löschen) extinguished, etc.
**Lösch-arbeit**, *f.* (*Metal.*) charcoal process; unloading. **-blatt**, *n.* sheet of blotting paper.
**Lösche**, *f.* charcoal dust, charcoal bed; coal dust, slack, or culm; coke dust; cinder; clinker; quenching tub or trough; quenching material, quench. **-beton**, *m.* cinder concrete.
**löschen**, *v.t.* extinguish, quench; slake (lime); blot; cancel; erase; discharge; unload. — *v.i.* be extinguished, go out; blot.
**Löscher**, *m.* extinguisher; quencher; slaker; blotter; unloader.
**Lösch-flüssigkeit**, *f.* extinguisher fluid. **-gerät**, *n.* fire extinguisher. **-kalk**, *m.* quicklime; slaked lime. **-karton**, *m.* thick blotting paper. **-kohle**, *f.* quenched charcoal. **-mittel**, *n.* extinguishing or quenching agent. **-papier**, *n.* blotting paper. **-spannung**, *f.* (*Elec.*) extinction potential. **-turm**, *m.* quenching tower.
**Löschung**, *f.* extinguishing, etc. (see löschen).

**Löschwasser,** *n.* quenching water, tempering water.

**losdrücken,** *v.t.* push off; fire off.

**lose,** *a.* loose. — *adv.* loosely.

**Löse-gefäss,** *n.* dissolving vessel. **-geschwindigkeit,** *f.* rate of dissolving. **-kraft,** *f.* solvent power.

**lösekräftig,** *a.* strongly solvent.

**Lösemittel,** *n.* solvent.

**lösen,** *v.t.* dissolve; solve; loosen, untie, release; detach, disconnect; redeem; fire (a gun); make (money). — *v.r.* dissolve; get loose. — **lösend,** *p.a.* dissolving, solvent; expectorant; purgative.

**Löser,** *m.* dissolver, etc. (see lösen); solvent; solubilizer.

**Löse-verlust,** *m.* loss of solution. **-vermögen,** *n.* dissolving power. **-vorgang,** *m.* dissolving process, solvent action. **-wirkung,** *f.* dissolving action, solvent effect.

**losgehen,** *v.i.* become loose, come off, go off.

**Losgehen,** *n.* coming loose, coming off; explosion, discharge.

**los-gelöst,** *p.a.* set free, liberated. **-kitten,** *v.t.* unlute, unseal, etc. **-kuppeln,** *v.t.* disengage, disconnect.

**lösl.,** *abbrev.* of löslich.

**Lösl.,** *abbrev.* of Löslichkeit.

**loslassen,** *v.t.* let go, let loose, set loose. — **losgelassen,** *p.a.* free, uncontrolled.

**löslich,** *a.* soluble.

**Lösliches,** *n.* soluble matter.

**Löslichkeit,** *f.* solubility.

**Löslichkeits-bestimmung,** *f.* solubility determination. **-druck,** *m.* solubility pressure. **-grenze,** *f.* limit of solubility. **-produkt,** *n.* solubility product. **-steigerung,** *f.* increase of solubility. **-unterschied,** *m.* difference in solubility. **-veränderung,** *f.* change in solubility. **-verhältnis,** *n.* solubility relation. **-verminderung,** *f.* decrease of solubility. **-zahl,** *f.* solubility value.

**löslichmachen,** *v.t.* render soluble, solubilize.

**Löslichmachung,** *f.* rendering soluble, solubilization.

**loslösbar,** *a.* separable, detachable.

**los-lösen,** *v.t.* set free, liberate, separate, detach, untie, disengage. **-löten,** *v.t.* unsolder. **-machen,** *v.t.* loosen, undo, disengage, disconnect, set free, release. **-platzen,** *v.i.* explode; burst out. **-reissen,** *v.t.* tear off or away, tear loose.

**Löss,** *m.* loess.

**lossagen,** *v.t.* renounce.

**Lössboden,** *m.* loess ground or soil.

**Losscheibe,** *f.* (*Mach.*) loose pulley.

**los-schrauben,** *v.t.* unscrew. **-sprechen,** *v t.* release; acquit. **-sprengen,** *v.t.* blast loose, burst off.

**Lost,** *n.* mustard gas.

**lostrennen,** *v.t.* separate, detach; tear apart; unstitch.

**Lostvergiftete,** *m.* mustard gas casualty.

**Losung,** *f.* casting of lots; excrement; watchword.

**Lösung,** *f.* solution; discharge (of a gun); loosening; release; separation.

**Lösungs-behälter,** *m.* solution (storage) tank. **-benzin,** *n.* benzine, mineral spirits, white spirit (a petroleum distillate). **-benzol,** *n.* solvent naphtha (a coaltar distillate containing alkylated benzenes). **-dichte,** *f.* concentration. **-druck,** *m.* solution pressure. **-erscheinung,** *f.* phenomenon of solution.

**lösungsfähig,** *a.* capable of solution.

**Lösungs-fähigkeit,** *f.* dissolving capacity. **-flüssigkeit,** *f.* solvent liquid, solvent. **-geschwindigkeit,** *f.* rate of solution. **-koeffizient,** *m.* coefficient of solution. **-kohle,** *f.* (*Metal.*) cementing carbon. **-mittel,** *n.* solvent. **-mitteldampf,** *m.* solvent vapor.

**lösungsmittel-echt,** *a.* fast to solvents. **-frei,** *a.* free from solvent.

**Lösungs-mittelgemisch,** *n.* solvent mixture. **-mittelrückgewinnung,** *f.* recovery of solvent(s). **-stärke,** *f.* strength of solution. **-tendenz,** *f.* tendency to dissolve. **-tension,** *f.* solution tension, solution pressure. **-theorie,** *f.* theory of solution. **-vermittler,** *m.* dissolving intermediary, aid to solution. **-vermögen,** *n.* dissolving power. **-vorgang,** *m.* dissolving process. **-vorschrift,** *f.* direction(s) for dissolving. **-wärme,** *f.* heat of solution. **-wasser,** *n.* solvent water. **-wirkung,** *f.* solvent effect.

**Lot,** *n.* solder; plummet, plumb; a weight (now 10 grams); perpendicular.

**Lötapparat,** *m.* soldering apparatus.

**lötbar,** *a.* solderable.

**Löt-blei,** *n.* lead solder. **-brenner,** *m.* gas blowpipe, soldering burner. **-draht,** *m.* soldering wire.

**Löte,** *f.* solder, soldering.

**loten,** *v.t.* plumb. — *v.i.* sound.

**löten,** *v.t.* solder; braze; seal (glass); agglutinate.

**Löten,** *n.* soldering; brazing; sealing.

**Löt-fett,** *n.* soldering paste. **-flamme,** *f.* blowpipe flame. **-flüssigkeit,** *f.* soldering fluid.

**Loth, löthen,** etc. = Lot, löten, etc.

**Lothringen,** *n.* Lorraine.

**lötig,** *a.* weighing 10 grams; (of ore) containing 10 grams silver per hundredweight; (of silver) fine, pure; (in combination) so many sixteenths fine (as *dreizehnlötiges Silber*, silver 13/16 fine); (in combination) per cent.

**Lötigkeit,** *f.* fineness (of silver).

**Löt-kolben,** *m.* soldering bit, soldering iron.

-**lampe,** *f.* soldering torch, blowtorch. **-masse,** *f.* solder composition. **-material,** *n.* soldering material. **-metall,** *n.* soldering metal. **-mittel,** *n.* solder. **-paste,** *f.* soldering paste. **-probe,** *f.* blowpipe test. **-pulver,** *n.* soldering powder.

**lotrecht,** *a.* perpendicular, vertical.

**Lötrohr,** *n.* blowpipe. **-analyse,** *f.* blowpipe analysis. **-beschlag,** *m.* coating before the blowpipe.

**Lötröhre,** *f.* blowpipe.

**Lötrohr-flamme,** *f.* blowpipe flame. **-fluss,** *m.* blowpipe flux. **-gebläse,** *n.* blast lamp. **-kapelle,** *f.* blowpipe cupel. **-kohle,** *f.* blowpipe charcoal. **-lampe,** *f.* blowpipe lamp. **-probe,** *f.* blowpipe test. **-prüfgerätschaft,** *f.* apparatus for blowpipe testing. **-reagens,** *n.* blowpipe reagent. **-versuch,** *m.* blowpipe experiment or test.

**Löt-salmiak,** *m.* sal ammoniac for soldering. **-salz,** *n.* soldering salt. **-säure,** *f.* soldering acid. **-stelle,** *f.* soldered place; place to be soldered; junction (of a thermocouple).

**Lotte,** *f.* (*Iron*) ball, bloom.

**Lötung,** *f.* soldering; sealing (of glass); agglutination; adhesion.

**Löt-versuch,** *m.* blowpipe test; soldering test. **-wasser,** *n.* soldering fluid. **-zinn,** *n.* soldering tin.

**Loupe,** *f.* magnifying glass.

**Löwe,** *m.* lion.

**Löwenmaul,** *n.* toadflax; snapdragon.

**Löwenzahn,** *m.* dandelion. **-bitter,** *n.* taraxacin. **-wurzel,** *f.* dandelion root.

**Loxachina,** *f.* loxa bark, pale bark.

**L.S.,** *abbrev.* (Luftschutz) air defense.

**Lsg.,** *abbrev.* (Lösung) solution.

**Lsgg.,** *abbrev.* (Lösungen) solutions.

**lt.,** *abbrev.* (laut) in accordance with.

**Lucke,** *f.* (*Metal.*) blister.

**Lücke,** *f.* gap, void, space, interstice, blank, vacancy, deficiency.

**lückenbildend,** *a.* forming voids or gaps.

**Lückenbindung,** *f.* unsaturated linkage.

**lücken-haft,** *a.* having gaps, defective, interrupted, incomplete. **-los,** *a.* without gaps, uninterrupted, continuous; nonporous; flawless.

**Lückensatz,** *m.* vacancy principle.

**luckig,** *a.* (*Metal.*) porous, honeycombed.

**lückig,** *a.* = lückenhaft; = luckig.

**lud,** *pret.* (of laden) loaded, etc.

**Luder,** *n.* carrion.

**Luft,** *f.* air; atmosphere. **-ablass,** *m.* escape of air; air outlet. **-abscheider,** *m.* air separator, deaerator. **-abschluss,** *m.* exclusion of air; air trap. **-abschreckung,** *f.* (*Metal.*) air quenching. **-abwehr,** *f.* air defense, antiaircraft. **-abzug,** *m.* air exhaust, air exhauster.

**luft-ähnlich,** *a.* gaseous, aeriform.

**Luft-anfeuchter,** *m.* air moistener, humidifier. **-angriff,** *m.* air attack, air raid.

**luftartig,** *a.* gaseous, aeriform.

**Luft-aufnahme,** *f.* absorption or occlusion of air; aerial photograph. **-aufnehmer,** *m.* air receiver. **-auftrieb,** *m.* buoyancy of the air; distension. **-ausdehnungsmaschine,** *f.* hot-air engine. **-auslass,** *m.* air outlet, air vent. **-ausschluss,** *m.* exclusion of air. **-bad,** *n.* air bath. **-befeuchter,** *m.* air moistener. **-befeuchtung,** *f.* air moistening. **-behälter,** *m.* air holder, air chamber; lungs. **-beschaffenheit,** *f.* condition of the air.

**luftbeständig,** *a.* stable in air, not affected by the air.

**Luft-beständigkeit,** *f.* stability in air, resistance to air. **-bestandteil,** *m.* constituent of air. **-bild,** *n.* aerial photograph; (*Optics*) aerial image. **-bläschen,** *n.* (small) air bubble. **-blase,** *f.* air bubble; air pocket; air bladder. **-bleiche,** *f.* open-air bleaching. **-bombe,** *f.* aerial bomb. **-brennstoffgemisch,** *n.* fuel-air mixture.

**luftdicht,** *a.* airtight. — *adv.* hermetically.

**Luft-dichte,** *f.* = Luftdichtigkeit. **-dichtemesser,** *m.* densimeter. **-dichtheit,** *f.* air-tightness, impermeability to air. **-dichtigkeit,** *f.* density of the air, atmospheric density.

**luftdichtschliessend,** *a.* forming an airtight seal, hermetic.

**Luftdruck,** *m.* atmospheric pressure; air pressure, pneumatic pressure.

**Luftdruck-.** pneumatic. **-anzeiger,** *m.* air-pressure gage or indicator. **-messer,** *m.* barometer; manometer. **-pumpe,** *f.* pneumatic pump, air compressor. **-unterschied,** *m.* difference in air pressure.

**luftdurchlässig,** *a.* permeable to air.

**Luft-durchlässigkeit,** *f.* permeability to air. **-durchlässigkeitsprüfer,** *m.* (*Paper*) densometer. **-düse,** *f.* air nozzle, air twyer; air vent.

**luftecht,** *a.* fast to air (atmospheric influences).

**Luft-einlass,** *m.* air inlet, air intake. **-einschluss,** *m.* air inclusion or occlusion. **-eintritt,** *m.* entrance of air; air inlet, air intake. **-einwirkung,** *f.* action or effect of air. **-eisenstein,** *n.* aerosiderite, iron meteorite. **-elektrizität,** *f.* atmospheric electricity.

**luftempfindlich,** *a.* sensitive to air.

**lüften,** *v.t.* air; aerate; ventilate; weather; raise, clear.

**luftentzündlich,** *a.* (in)flammable in contact with air, pyrophoric.

**Lüfter,** *m.* ventilator.

**Luft-erhärtung,** *f.* air hardening. **-erhitzer,** *m.* air heater. **-erneuerung,** *f.* ventilation. **-erscheinung,** *f.* atmospheric phenomenon. **-erscheinungslehre,** *f.* meteorology. **-fahrt,** *f.*

aeronautics; aviation; air trip. **-fahrzeug,** *n.* aircraft. **-falle,** *f.* air trap. **-feuchtigkeit,** *f.* atmospheric moisture. **-feuchtigkeitsmesser,** *m.* hygrometer. **-filter,** *n.* air filter. **-förderung,** *f.* air displacement; air transport.

**luft-förmig,** *a.* gaseous, aeriform. **-frei,** *a.* free from air.

**Luft-gang,** *m.* air passage, air duct. **-gas,** *n.* air gas. **-gaskrieg,** *m.* chemical air war.

**luftgefüllt,** *a.* air-filled.

**Luftgehalt,** *m.* air content.

**luft-gekühlt,** *a.* air-cooled. **-gesichtet,** *a.* air-floated. **-getrocknet,** *a.* air-dried.

**Luft-gütemesser,** *m.* eudiometer. **-gütemessung,** *f.* eudiometry. **-hafen,** *m.* airport, airdrome. **-hahn,** *m.* air cock.

**lufthaltig,** *a.* containing air.

**Luft-härten,** *n.*, **-härtung,** *f.* air hardening.

**lufthärtend,** *a.* air-hardening.

**Luft-hefe,** *f.* air yeast, aerial yeast. **-heizung,** *f.* hot-air heating. **-hülle,** *f.* atmosphere.

**luftig,** *a.* light, voluminous; aerial, airy, windy, flighty.

**Luft-inhalt,** *m.* air content. **-ion,** *n.* atmospheric ion. **-kalk,** *m.* air-hardening lime. **-kammer,** *f.* air chamber. **-kampfstoff,** *m.* (*Mil.*) volatile chemical agent. **-kanal,** *m.* air duct. **-kessel,** *m.* air chamber or reservoir. **-kompressor,** *m.* air compressor. **-konditionierung,** *f.* air conditioning. **-kraftmaschine,** *f.* hot-air engine. **-kreis,** *m.* atmosphere. **-kühler,** *m.* air cooler. **-kühlung,** *f.* air cooling. **-lack,** *m.* air-proof varnish; air-drying varnish. **-lauf,** *m.* air passage; air flow.

**luftleer,** *a.* exhausted (of air), void. — **luftleerer Raum,** vacuum.

**Luftleere,** *f.* vacuum; exhaustion (of air). **-messer,** *m.* vacuometer, vacuum gage.

**luftleitend,** *a.* air-conducting.

**Luft-leitung,** *f.* air piping. **-loch,** *n.* air hole, vent hole. **-lücke,** *f.* air space. **-malz,** *n.* air-dried malt. **-mangel,** *n.* lack of air. **-mantel,** *m.* air mantle, air jacket. **-menge,** *f.* amount of air. **-messer,** *m.* aerometer. **-messung,** *f.* aerometry. **-mörtel,** *m.* air mortar, lime mortar (requiring air to harden it). **-nitrit,** *n.* nitrite from atmospheric nitrogen. **-patentieren,** *n.* (*Wire*) patenting with cooling in air. **-pflanze,** *f.* air plant, epiphyte. **-post,** *f.* air mail, air post. **-presser,** *m.* air compressor. **-pressung,** *f.* air compression; air pressure. **-prüfer,** *m.* air tester. **-pumpe,** *f.* air pump, pneumatic pump. **-raum,** *m.* air space; atmosphere. **-reifen,** *m.* pneumatic tire.

**luftreinigend,** *a.* purifying the air.

**Luft-reiniger,** *m.* air purifier. **-rohr,** *n.* air tube or pipe. **-röhre,** *f.* air tube, air pipe; windpipe, trachea.

**Luftröhren-.** tracheal; bronchial. **-entzündung,** *f.* bronchitis.

**Luft-rückstand,** *m.* air residue, residual atmosphere. **-salpetersäure,** *f.* nitric acid from atmospheric nitrogen. **-sättigung,** *f.* saturation of the air. **-sauerstoff,** *m.* atmospheric oxygen. **-saugapparat, -sauger,** *m.*, **-saugpumpe,** *f.* aspirator. **-säule,** *f.* air column. **-säure,** *f.* carbonic acid. **-schicht,** *f.* layer or film of air. **-schiff,** *n.* airship. **-schiffer,** *m.* aeronaut. **-schlag,** *m.* (*Pyro.*) petard. **-schlauch,** *m.* air hose, air tubing; (of a tire) inner tube. **-schöpfen,** *n.* respiration. **-schraube,** *f.* (air) propeller, airscrew. **-schutz,** *m.* air-raid defense. **-schwärmer,** *m.* (*Pyro.*) serpent. **-seide,** *f.* (*lit.*, air silk) a kind of hollow-tubular rayon. **-sog,** *m.* air suction; vacuum. **-spalt,** *m.* air gap. **-spiegelung,** *f.* mirage. **-stählung,** *f.* air hardening. **-stickstoff,** *m.* atmospheric nitrogen. **-störung,** *f.* atmospheric disturbance. **-strahl,** *m.* air jet. **-strecke,** *f.* air gap. **-strom,** *m.*, **-strömung,** *f.* air current, air flow, air blast. **-trennung,** *f.* separation of air.

**lufttrocken,** *a.* air-dry, air-dried, air-seasoned.

**Lufttrocken-gewicht,** *n.* weight when dried by exposure to the air. **-schrank,** *m.* air drying closet.

**lufttrocknen,** *v.t.* dry in air, air-dry.

**Luft-trocknung,** *f.* air drying. **-überschuss,** *m.* excess of air.

**luftundurchlässig,** *a.* impermeable to air.

**Lüftung,** *f.* airing, etc. (see lüften).

**Luft-ventil,** *n.* air valve. **-verdichter,** *m.* air condenser or compressor. **-verdichtung,** *f.* air condensation or compression.

**luftverdorben,** *a.* damaged by air; weathered.

**Luftverdrängung,** *f.* displacement of air.

**luftverdünnt,** *a.* partially exhausted of air.

**Luft-verdünnung,** *f.* rarefaction of air; vacuum. **-verdünnungsmesser,** *m.* vacuum gage. **-verflüssigung,** *f.* liquefaction of air. **-verflüssigungsanlage,** *f.* liquid-air plant. **-vergüten,** *n.*, **-vergütung,** *f.* (*Metal.*) heat treatment using air. **-volumen,** *n.* volume of air. **-vorwärmung,** *f.* preheating of air. **-vulkanisation,** *f.* (*Rubber*) open cure. **-wa(a)ge,** *f.* aerometer. **-waffe,** *f.* (*Mil.*) air force. **-wärme,** *f.* air temperature. **-wechsel,** *m.* ventilation. **-weg,** *m.* airway, air passage, air route. **-wehr,** *f.* air defense. **-welle,** *f.* air wave. **-wichte,** *f.* density of the air. **-widerstand,** *m.* air resistance, atmospheric resistance. **-wirkung,** *f.* action of the air, atmospheric effect. **-wurzel,** *f.* (*Bot.*) aerial root. **-zerstäubung,** *f.* atomization of air. **-ziegel,** *m.* air-dried brick. **-zufluss,** *m.* influx of air. **-zufuhr,** *f.* air supply. **-zuführung,** *f.* air supply; air duct. **-zug,** *m.* draft, current

(of air); air duct. **-zünder,** *m.* pyrophorus (substance inflaming spontaneously in air). **-zurichtung,** *f.* air conditioning. **-zustand,** *m.* atmospheric state.
**Luftzutritt,** *m.* access of air, admission of air. — **unter —,** with access of air, in a stream of air.
**Luftzwischen-kühler,** *m.* air intercooler. **-raum,** *m.* air gap.
**lugen,** *v.i.* look out.
**lügen,** *v.i.* lie (speak falsely); deceive; be affected.
**Luke,** *f.* opening, aperture, window, hatch.
**lullen,** *v.t.* lull.
**Lumineszenz,** *f.* luminescence.
**lumineszieren,** *v.i.* luminesce.
**Lumpen,** *m.* rag; titler (coarse sugar loaf). **-auskohlung,** *f.* carbonization of rags. **-bleiche,** *f.* rag bleaching. **-brei,** *m.* (*Paper*) first stuff, (first) pulp from rags. **-bütte, -butte,** *f.* (*Paper*) rag tub. **-kocher,** *m.* rag boiler. **-papier,** *n.* rag paper. **-reisser,** *m.* (*Paper*) rag cutter, devil. **-stoff,** *m.* (*Paper*) rag pulp. **-wolf,** *m.* rag-tearing machine, willow, devil. **-wolle,** *f.* shoddy. **-zucker,** *m.* titlers (sugar in coarse loaves).
**Lunge,** *f.* lung, lungs.
**Lungen-.** pulmonary. **-entzündung,** *f.* pneumonia. **-gift,** *n.* lung poison, lung irritant. **-kraut,** *n.* lungwort.
**lungenschädigend,** *a.* injuring the lungs.
**Lungen-schützer,** *m.* respirator. **-stein,** *m.* pulmonary concretion. **-sucht,** *f.* lung disease, specif. tuberculosis.
**lungern,** *v.i.* develop cavities, pipe.
**Lunker,** *n.* (*Metal.*) shrinkage cavity, shrinkhole, pipe. **-bildung,** *f.* (*Metal.*) formation of cavities, piping.
**lunkerfrei,** *a.* (*Metal.*) free from cavities, pipeless.
**Lunkerhohlraum,** *m.* (*Metal.*) cavity, pipe.
**lunker-ig,** *a.* (*Metal.*) containing cavities, honeycombed, vesicular, piped. **-los,** *a.* = lunkerfrei.
**lunkern,** *v.i.* develop cavities, pipe.
**Lunkerung,** *f.* (*Metal.*) shrinkage (forming cavities), piping, cavitation.
**lunkrig,** *a.* = lunkerig.
**Lunte,** *f.* slow match, fuse; (*Textiles*) rove, roving; cigaret.
**Lupe,** *f.* magnifying glass, lens.
**Lupenlinse,** *f.* magnifying lens.
**Luppe,** *f.* (*Metal.*) bloom, loop, lump, ball.
**Luppen-eisen,** *n.* ball iron, puddled iron. **-frischfeuer,** *n.* bloomery fire. **-frischhütte,** *f.* bloomery. **-stahl,** *m.* bloom steel, steel in blooms.
**Lupulinsäure,** *f.* lupulic acid, lupulinic acid.
**Lust,** *f.* pleasure, joy, mirth; desire, inclination; lust.
**Lüster,** *m.* luster. **-farbe,** *f.* (*Ceram.*) luster color. **-glanz,** *m.* luster. **-glasur,** *f.* (*Ceram.*) luster glaze. **-stoff,** *m.* luster fabric.
**Lustgas,** *n.* laughing gas (nitrous oxide).
**lustig,** *a.* merry, jolly, gay; funny.
**lustlos,** *a.* listless, lifeless, dull.
**lustrieren, lüstrieren,** *v.t.* luster; glaze (silk).
**Lust-seuche,** *f.* syphilis. **-spiel,** *n.* comedy.
**Luteo-kobaltchlorid,** *n.* luteocobaltic chloride, hexaamminecobalt(III) chloride. **-verbindung,** *f.* luteo compound.
**Lutidinsäure,** *f.* lutidinic acid.
**lutieren,** *v.t.* lute.
**Lutte,** *f.* (*Mining*) air tube, air pipe, ventilator.
**Lutter,** *m.* (*Distilling*) low wine, singlings. **-blase,** *f.* low-wine still.
**luttern,** *v.i.* distil low wine.
**Lutterprober,** *m.* low-wine tester.
**Luxboje,** *f.* flare buoy.
**Luxus,** *m.* luxury.
**Luxus-.** fancy, fine, de luxe, luxury. **-konsumption,** *f.* (*Foods*) excess consumption. **-leder,** *n.* fancy leather. **-papier,** *n.* fine paper, fancy paper.
**Luzerne,** *f.*, **Luzernerklee,** *m.* lucern, alfalfa.
**L.V.St.,** *abbrev.* (Landwirtschaftliche Versuchsstation) agricultural experiment station.
**l.W.,** *abbrev.* (lichte Weite) internal diameter.
**Lw., Lwd.,** *abbrev.* (Leinwand) linen, cloth.
**lydischer Stein.** Lydian stone (touchstone).
**Lymph-bildung,** *f.* lymph formation. **-drüse,** *f.* lymphatic gland.
**Lymphe,** *f.* lymph.
**Lymph-gefäss,** *n.* lymphatic vessel. **-körperchen,** *n.* lymph corpuscle, leucocyte.
**lyo-phil,** *a.* lyophile, lyophil(ic). **-phob,** *a.* lyophobe, lyophobic. **-trop,** *a.* lyotrope, lyotropic.
**Lysalbinsäure,** *f.* lysalbinic acid.
**Lyse,** *f.* lysis.
**lytisch,** *a.* lytic.

# M

**m.,** *abbrev.* (mit) with; (mein, meine, meines) my, of my; minute(s); meter(s).
**M.,** *abbrev.* (Masse) mass; (Monat) month; (Mittelsorte) medium grade; Monatshefte für Chemie; (Mark) mark, marks.
**Maal,** *n.* mole, mark.
**Maass, Maass-.** see Mass, Mass-.
**macerieren,** *v.t.* macerate.
**Maceriergefäss,** *n.* macerater.
**Machart,** *f.* make, type, kind.
**Mache,** *f.* making, make, workmanship.
**Macheeinheit,** *f.* Mache unit (of radioactivity).
**machen,** *v.t.* make; do; cause. — *v.r.* make oneself; procure, get. — *v.i.* deal, trade.
**Macherei,** *f.* making; make.
**Macht,** *f.* might, power, force.
**mächtig,** *a.* mighty, powerful, strong, huge, big, thick; in command (of something).
**Mächtigkeit,** *f.* mightiness, etc. (see mächtig); (*Tech.*) thickness, size, power, etc.
**machtlos,** *a.* powerless, impotent.
**Machwerk,** *n.* poor work; hack work.
**Macis,** *f.* mace. **-öl,** *n.* mace oil, oil of mace.
**Madarwurzel,** *f.* mudar root.
**Mädchen,** *n.* girl; maid.
**Made,** *f.* maggot, mite, worm; grub screw.
**Madenloch,** *n.* wormhole; pinhole.
**madig,** *a.* maggoty, wormy, worm-eaten.
**Mafuratalg,** *m.*, **mafurische Butter.** mafura tallow.
**mag,** *pr. 1 & 3 sing.* (of mögen) may.
**Magazin,** *n.* magazine (storehouse, warehouse, chamber, etc.).
**Magdalarot,** *n.* Magdala red.
**Magen,** *m.* stomach; maw.
**Magen-.** gastric, gastro-, stomach. **-arznei,** *f.* stomachic. **-brei,** *m.* chyme.
**Magendarm-.** gastrointestinal.
**Magen-drüse,** *f.* gastric gland, peptic gland. **-entzündung,** *f.* gastritis. **-flüssigkeit,** *f.* gastric fluid, gastric juice. **-haut,** *f.* lining or coat of the stomach. **-inhalt,** *m.* stomach contents. **-lab,** *n.* rennet. **-labdrüse,** *f.* gastric peptic gland. **-lipase,** *f.* stomach lipase. **-mittel,** *n.* stomachic. **-pförtner,** *m.* pylorus. **-saft,** *m.* gastric juice. **-säure,** *f.* stomach acid or acidity. **-schleimhaut,** *f.* gastric mucosa. **-schlund,** *m.* esophagus. **-schwäche,** *f.* dyspepsia.
**magenstärkend,** *p.a.* stomachic.
**Magen-stärkungsmittel,** *n.* stomachic. **-stein,** *m.* gastric concretion. **-verdauung,** *f.* gastric digestion. **-wand,** *f.* wall or coat of the stomach. **-zwölffingerdarm-.** gastroduodenal.
**mager,** *a.* lean; slender, thin, weak, meager, poor; (of varnish, etc.) low-grade. — **magerer Kalk,** lime that does not slake easily. — **mageres Öl,** mineral oil (as distinguished from a fatty oil). — **magerer Stoff,** (*Paper*) short pulp.
**Mager-beton,** *m.* lean concrete. **-erz,** *n.* lean ore. **-kalk,** *m.* = magerer Kalk. **-keit,** *f.* leanness, thinness. **-keitsanzeiger,** *m.* (*Soils*) indicator of lime exhaustion. **-kohle,** *f.* lean coal. **-milch,** *f.* skim milk.
**magern,** *v. t. & i.* make or grow lean or poor; specif., (*Ceram.*) diminish the plasticity of, shorten.
**Magerton,** *m.* lean clay.
**Magerungsmittel,** *n.* leaning material.
**magisch,** *a.* magic, magical.
**Magisterium,** *n.* magistery.
**magmatisch,** *a.* magmatic.
**Magnesia-beize,** *f.* (*Dyeing*) magnesia mordant. **-gehalt,** *m.* magnesia content. **-glimmer,** *m.* magnesium mica (biotite).
**magnesiahaltig,** *a.* containing magnesia, magnesian.
**Magnesia-härte,** *f.* hardness due to magnesia. **-hydrat,** *n.* magnesium hydroxide. **-kalk,** *m.* magnesian limestone. **-milch,** *f.* milk of magnesia. **-mischung, -mixtur,** *f.* magnesia mixture. **-salz,** *n.* magnesia salt (magnesium salt). **-seife,** *f.* magnesia soap. **-verbindung,** *f.* magnesia (magnesium) compound. **-weiss,** *n.* magnesia white. **-zement,** *m.* magnesia cement.
**Magnesit-mehl,** *n.* ground magnesite. **-spat,** *m.* magnesite. **-stein, -ziegel,** *m.* magnesite brick.
**Magnesium-blitz,** *m.*, **-blitzlicht,** *n.* magnesium flashlight. **-draht,** *m.* magnesium wire. **-gehalt,** *m.* magnesium content.
**magnesiumhaltig,** *a.* containing magnesium.
**Magnesium-jodid,** *n.* magnesium iodide. **-legierung,** *f.* magnesium alloy. **-licht,** *n.* magnesium light, flashlight.
**magnesiumorganisch,** *a.* magnesium-organic, organomagnesium.
**Magnesium-oxydhydrat,** *n.* magnesium hydroxide. **-pulver,** *n.* magnesium powder. **-rhodanid,** *n.* magnesium thiocyanate. **-salz,** *n.* magnesium salt. **-seife,** *f.* magnesium soap **-verbindung,** *f.* magnesium compound.

**Magnet-eisen,** *n.* magnet iron; = Magneteisenerz. **-eisenerz,** *n.*, **-eisenstein,** *m.* magnetic iron ore (magnetite).
**magnetelektrisch,** *a.* magneto-electric.
**Magnetfeld,** *n.* magnetic field.
**magnethaltig,** *a.* magnetic.
**magnetisch,** *a.* magnetic.
**magnetisierbar,** *a.* magnetizable.
**Magnetisierbarkeit,** *f.* magnetizability.
**magnetisieren,** *v.t.* magnetize.
**magnetisierfähig,** *a.* magnetizable.
**Magnetisierfähigkeit,** *f.* magnetizability.
**Magnetisierung,** *f.* magnetizing, magnetization.
**Magnetisierungs-fähigkeit,** *f.* magnetizability. **-strom,** *m.* magnetizing current.
**Magnet-kern,** *m.* magnet core. **-kies,** *m.* magnetic pyrites (pyrrhotite). **-kraft,** *f.* magnetic force. **-messer,** *m.* magnetometer. **-nadel,** *f.* magnetic needle.
**magneto-metrisch,** *a.* magnetometric. **-motorisch,** *a.* magnetomotive. **-optisch,** *a.* magneto-optic.
**Magnet-schale,** *f.* magnetic shell. **-scheider,** *m.* magnetic separator. **-spule,** *f.* field coil, solenoid. **-stab,** *m.* magnetic bar, bar magnet. **-stahl,** *m.* magnet steel. **-stein,** *m.* magnetic iron ore (magnetite). **-zünder,** *m.* magneto. **-zündung,** *f.* magneto ignition.
**Magnolie,** *f.* magnolia.
**Magsamen,** *m.* poppy seed.
**Mahagoni,** *n.* mahogany.
**mahagonibraun,** *a.* mahogany-brown.
**Mahagoni-holzöl,** *n.* mahogany wood oil. **-nuss,** *f.* cashew nut.
**Mahd,** *f.* mowing; hay crop.
**mähen,** *v.t.* mow.
**Mahl,** *n.* meal; banquet; mark; mole.
**Mahlanlage,** *f.* grinding or milling plant.
**mahlen,** *v.t.* grind, mill, crush, pulverize; (*Paper*) beat.
**Mahl-feinheit,** *f.* fineness of grinding. **-gang,** *m.* grinding or milling operation; grinding mill. **-gut,** *n.* material to be ground or milled; (less often) ground material. **-holländer,** *m.* beating engine, beater. **-korn,** *n.* grist. **-rückstand,** *m.* grinding residue.
**Mahlung,** *f.* grinding, milling, crushing.
**Mahlungsgrad,** *m.* degree of fineness.
**Mahl-werk,** *n.* milling plant, grinding mill; grinding, milling. **-wirkung,** *f.* grinding or pulverizing action or effect. **-zahn,** *m.* molar. **-zeit,** *f.* meal, repast.
**mahnen,** *v.t.* remind, urge; dun.
**Mähren,** *n.* Moravia.
**Mai,** *m.* May. **-baum,** *m.* birch. **-blume,** *f.* lily of the valley. **-fisch,** *m.* shad.
**Mais,** *m.* maize, (Indian) corn. **-brand,** *m.* corn smut. **-branntwein,** *m.* corn whisky, whisky from maize.
**Maisch,** *m.* = Maische. **-apparat,** *m.* mashing apparatus, mash machine. **-bottich,** *m.* mash tub, mashing tun.
**Maische,** *f.* mash; grape juice, grape must; (*Sugar*) pulp. — **weingare —,** (*Distilling*) wash. — **zweite —,** aftermash.
**maischen,** *v.t.* mash.
**Maischepumpe,** *f.* (*Brewing*) mash pump.
**Maisch-gitter,** *n.* (*Brewing*) stirrer, rake. **-gut,** *n.* (*Brewing*) mash goods, mash. **-kessel,** *m.* mash copper. **-pfanne,** *f.* mash copper. **-prozess,** *m.* mashing process.
**Maischung,** *f.* mashing; mash.
**Maisch-ventil,** *f.* (*Brewing*) grains valve, trap. **-wasser,** *n.* mash liquor. **-würze,** *f.* mash wort, grain wash.
**Mais-geist,** *m.* = Maisspiritus. **-gelb,** *n.* maize yellow, maize (the color). **-kleber,** *m.* zein. **-kolben,** *m.* corncob. **-korn,** *n.* grain of corn, maize grain. **-krankheit,** *f.* pellagra. **-mehl,** *n.* Indian meal, corn meal. **-mehlkleber,** *m.* zein. **-öl,** *n.* maize oil, corn oil. **-pistille,** *n. pl.* cornsilk, (*Pharm.*) zea. **-schrot,** *m.* crushed maize, crushed corn. **-spiritus,** *m.* spirits from maize, corn spirit. **-stärke,** *f.* maize starch, cornstarch. **-stroh,** *n.* maize straw, corn fodder.
**Mai-wein, -trank,** *m.* white wine flavored with woodruff. **-weinessenz,** *f.* an alcoholic solution of coumarin used for flavoring.
**Maizena.** maize flour.
**Majoran,** *m.* marjoram. **-öl,** *n.* marjoram oil.
**majorenn,** *a.* of age.
**Majuskel,** *f.* capital (letter), majuscule.
**makadamisieren,** *v.t.* macadamize.
**Makadamstrasse,** *f.* macadam road.
**Makassaröl,** *n.* Macassar oil.
**Makel,** *m.* spot, blemish, flaw.
**makellos,** *a.* spotless, flawless, unblemished.
**Maker,** *m.* maul, sledge.
**Makko.** Egyptian cotton.
**Makler, Mäkler,** *m.* broker, jobber; faultfinder.
**Makrele,** *f.* mackerel.
**Makro-achse,** *f.* (*Cryst.*) macro axis. **-analyse,** *f.* macroanalysis. **-elementaranalyse,** *f.* elementary macroanalysis.
**makrogravimetrisch,** *a.* macrogravimetric.
**Makro-mechanik,** *f.* macromechanics. **-molekül, -molekel,** *n.* macromolecule.
**Makrone,** *f.* macaroon.
**makroskopisch,** *a.* macroscopic.
**Makrountersuchung,** *f.* macroinvestigation, macroanalysis.
**Makulatur,** *f.* (*Printing*) waste sheets.
**mal,** *adv.* times, time; once, just.
**Mal,** *n.* time; mark, spot, mole; sign, token; (*Biol.*) stigma.
**mal.,** *abbrev.* maleinoid.

**Malachit-grün,** *n.* malachite green. **-grünnährboden,** *m.* malachite-green nutrient medium. **-kiesel,** *m.* chrysocolla.

**malaiisch,** *a.* Malay, Malayan.

**Malakkanuss,** *f.* Malacca nut, marking nut.

**Malakolith,** *m.* (*Min.*) malacolite.

**malaxieren,** *v.t.* malax, malaxate.

**Malayenstaaten,** *m.pl.* Malay States.

**Malein-aldehyd,** *n.* maleic aldehyde, malealdehyde. **-amidsäure,** *f.* maleamic acid. **-anilsäure,** *f.* maleanilic acid. **-säure,** *f.* maleic acid.

**malen,** *v.t.* paint; depict.

**Maler,** *m.* painter, artist.

**Malerei,** *f.* (artistic) painting.

**Maler-email,** *n.* painter's enamel. **-farbe,** *f.* painter's color, artist's color. **-firnis,** *m.* painter's varnish. **-gold,** *n.* painter's gold, ormolu. **-grundierung,** *f.* painter's priming.

**malerisch,** *a.* picturesque.

**Maler-kolik, -krankheit,** *f.* painter's colic, plumbism. **-leim,** *m.* painter's size. **-leinwand,** *f.* painter's canvas. **-silber,** *n.* painter's silver, silver powder. **-stift,** *m.* artist's pencil. **-tuch,** *n.* canvas.

**-malig.** times; as, *dreimalig*, three times.

**Malleinimpfung,** *f.* mallein inoculation.

**Malonester,** *m.* malonic ester.

**Malonitril,** *n.* malonitrile, malic nitrile; (improperly but commonly) malononitrile, malonic nitrile.

**malonsauer,** *a.* of or combined with malonic acid, malonate of.

**Malonsäure,** *f.* malonic acid. **-äthylester,** *m.* ethyl malonate.

**Malter,** *m.* quarter (grain measure, about 8 bu.).

**Malve,** *f.*, **Malvenkraut,** *n.* mallow.

**Malvenfarbe,** *f.* mauve.

**malvenfarbig,** *a.* mauve.

**Malwe,** *f.* mallow.

**Malz,** *n.* malt. **-aufguss,** *m.* infusion of malt, wort. **-auszug,** *m.* malt extract; wort. **-bottich,** *m.* malt vat, malt tub. **-darre,** *f.* malt kiln. **-eiweiss,** *n.* diastase.

**malzen, mälzen,** *v.t.* malt.

**Malzer, Mälzer,** *m.* maltster, maltman.

**Mälzerei,** *f.* malting; malt house.

**Malz-essig,** *m.* malt vinegar. **-fabrik,** *f.* malt house, malting. **-fabrikation,** *f.* malt manufacture. **-gerste,** *f.* malting barley. **-häufen,** *n.* couching. **-haus,** *n.* malt house. **-keim,** *m.* malt sprout. **-probe,** *f.* malt test, malt testing. **-quetsche,** *f.* malt press. **-schrot,** *n.* crushed malt, malt grist. **-stärke,** *f.* malt starch. **-surrogat,** *n.* malt substitute. **-tenne,** *f.* malt floor. **-treber,** *pl.* spent malt, brewer's grains, spent grains, malt husks.

**Mälzung,** *f.* malting.

**Mälzungsschwand,** *m.* loss in malting, malting shrinkage.

**Malz-wendeapparat, -wender,** *m.* malt turner. **-zucker,** *m.* malt sugar, maltose.

**Mammut,** *n.* mammoth.

**m.A.n.,** *abbrev.* (meiner Ansicht nach) in my opinion.

**man,** *pron.* one, a person, somebody, they, people, we, you.

**manch,** *pron.* many a.

**mancher,** *pron.* many a one, many a thing, many a.

**mancherlei,** *a.* many, various.

**manchmal,** *adv.* often, sometimes.

**Mandarindruck,** *m.* (*Calico*) mandarining.

**Mandarine,** *f.* mandarin orange, mandarin (*Citrus nobilis*).

**Mandarinen-öl,** *n.* mandarin oil. **-schalenöl,** *n.* oil of mandarin peel.

**Mandaringelb,** *n.* mandarin yellow.

**Mandel,** *f.* almond; tonsil; fifteen; shock; (*Geol.*) geode.

**mandelartig,** *a.* almond-like, amygdaline.

**Mandel-blüte,** *f.* almond blossom. **-bräune,** *f.* quinsy. **-drüse,** *f.* tonsil. **-entzündung,** *f.* tonsillitis.

**mandelförmig,** *a.* almond-shaped, amygdaloid.

**Mandel-gummi,** *n.* almond gum. **-kern,** *m.* almond kernel. **-milch,** *f.* almond milk, (*Pharm.*) emulsion of almond. **-öl,** *n.* almond oil. **-säure,** *f.* mandelic acid. **-säureamid,** *n.* mandelamide. **-seife,** *f.* almond soap. **-stein,** *m.* amygdaloid; tonsillar concretion.

**mandelsteinartig,** *a.* amygdaloidal.

**Mandel-stoff,** *m.* amygdalin. **-storax,** *m.* amygdaloid storax.

**Mandschurei,** *f.* Manchuria.

**Mangabeiragummi,** *n.* mangabeira rubber (from *Hancornia speciosa*).

**Mangan,** *n.* manganese. **-alaun,** *m.* manganese alum.

**manganarm,** *a.* poor (or low) in manganese.

**Mangan-beize,** *f.* (*Dyeing*) manganese mordant. **-bister,** *m.* manganese bister, manganese brown. **-blende,** *f.* alabandite. **-braun,** *n.* manganese brown. **-chlorid,** *n.* manganese chloride, specif. manganic chloride, manganese(III) chloride. **-chlorür,** *n.* manganous chloride, manganese(II) chloride. **-dioxyd,** *n.* manganese dioxide, manganese(IV) oxide. **-eisen,** *n.* ferromanganese. **-eisenstein,** *m.* triplite.

**Manganerz,** *n.* manganese ore. — **graues —,** manganite; pyrolusite. — **schwarzes —,** hausmannite.

**Mangan-gehalt,** *m.* manganese content. **-glanz,** *m.* (*Min.*) alabandite. **-granat,** *m.* manganese garnet, spessartite.

**manganhaltig,** *a.* containing manganese, manganiferous.

**Mangan-hartstahl,** *m.* austenitic manganese steel. **-hydroxyd,** *n.* manganic hydroxide, manganese(III) hydroxide. **-hydroxydul,** *n.* manganous hydroxide, manganese(II) hydroxide. **-hyperoxyd,** *n.* manganese peroxide (dioxide), manganese(IV) oxide.

**Mangani-.** manganic. **-chlorid,** *n.* manganic chloride, manganese(III) chloride. **-cyanwasserstoffsäure,** *f.* manganicyanic acid, cyanomanganic(III) acid.

**manganig,** *a.* manganous. **-sauer,** *a.* of or combined with manganous acid, manganite of.

**Manganigsäure,** *f.* manganous acid.

**Mangani-hydroxyd,** *n.* manganic hydroxide, manganese(III) hydroxide. **-phosphat,** *n.* manganic phosphate, manganese(III) phosphate. **-salz,** *n.* manganic salt, manganese(III) salt. **-sulfat,** *n.* manganic sulfate, manganese(III) sulfate. **-verbindung,** *f.* manganic compound, manganese(III) compound.

**Mangan-jodür,** *n.* manganous iodide, manganese(II) iodide. **-karbid,** *n.* manganese carbide. **-kiesel,** *m.* rhodonite. **-kupfer,** *n.* cupromanganese. **-legierung,** *f.* manganese alloy. **-menge,** *f.* amount of manganese.

**Mangano-.** manganous, mangano-. **-azetat,** *n.* manganous acetate, manganese(II) acetate. **-chlorid,** *n.* manganous chloride, manganese(II) chloride. **-cyanwasserstoffsäure,** *f.* manganocyanic acid, cyanomanganic(II) acid. **-ferrum,** *n.* ferromanganese. **-hydroxyd,** *n.* manganous hydroxide, manganese(II) hydroxide. **-ion,** *n.* manganous ion, manganese(II) ion. **-karbonat,** *n.* manganous carbonate, manganese(II) carbonate. **-oxyd,** *n.* manganous oxide, manganese(II) oxide. **-phosphat,** *n.* manganous phosphate, manganese(II) phosphate. **-salz,** *n.* manganous salt, manganese(II) salt. **-sulfat,** *n.* manganous sulfate, manganese(II) sulfate. **-verbindung,** *f.* manganous compound, manganese(II) compound.

**Manganoxyd,** *n.* manganese oxide, specif. manganic oxide, manganese(III) oxide. — **rotes —,** mangano-manganic oxide, manganese(II,III) oxide.

**Manganoxyd-hydrat,** *n.* manganic hydroxide, manganese(III) hydroxide. **-oxydul,** *n.* mangano-manganic oxide, manganese(II,III) oxide. **-salz,** *n.* manganic salt, manganese(III) salt.

**Manganoxydul,** *n.* manganous oxide, manganese(II) oxide. — **schwefelsaures —,** manganous sulfate, manganese(II) sulfate.

**Manganoxydul-hydrat,** *n.* manganous hydroxide, manganese(II) hydroxide. **-oxyd,** *n.* mangano-manganic oxide, manganese (II,III) oxide. **-salz,** *n.* manganous salt, manganese (II) salt. **-verbindung,** *f.* manganous compound, manganese(II) compound.

**Mangan-oxydverbindung,** *f.* manganic compound, manganese(III) compound. **-pecherz,** *n.* triplite. **-peroxyd,** *n.* manganese peroxide (dioxide).

**manganreich,** *a.* rich (or high) in manganese.

**Mangan-reserve,** *f.* (*Calico*) manganese resist. **-salz,** *n.* manganese salt.

**mangansauer,** *a.* of or combined with manganic acid, manganate of.

**Mangan-säure,** *f.* manganic acid. **-säureanhydrid,** *n.* manganic anhydride, manganese trioxide, manganese(VI) oxide. **-schaum,** *m.* bog manganese; wad. **-schlamm,** *m.* Weldon mud (regenerated slime in the Weldon process). **-schwarz,** *n.* manganese black. **-siliziumstahl,** *m.* silicomanganese steel. **-spat,** *m.* rhodochrosite. **-stahl,** *m.* manganese steel. **-sulfat,** *n.* manganese sulfate. **-sulfür,** *n.* manganous sulfide, manganese(II) sulfide. **-superoxyd,** *n.* manganese peroxide (dioxide). **-verbindung,** *f.* manganese compound. **-vitriol,** *m.* manganese vitriol (manganese sulfate).

**Mangel,** *m.* lack, want, deficiency; fault, defect; distress, want. — *f.* mangle.

**mangelhaft,** *a.* deficient, defective, imperfect, incomplete.

**mangeln,** *v.i.* be wanting, lack. — *v.t.* mangle.

**mangels,** *prep.* for want of, failing.

**Mangfutter,** *n.* mixed grain.

**Mangold,** *m.* beet, beetroot; specif., mangelwurzel, mangel.

**Manie,** *f.* mania.

**Manier,** *f.* manner.

**Manila-hanf,** *m.* Manila hemp, abacá. **-papier,** *n.* Manila paper.

**manipulieren,** *v.t. & i.* manipulate.

**Manko,** *n.* shortage, deficiency, deficit.

**Mann,** *m.* man; husband.

**Manna-zucker, -stoff,** *m.* manna sugar, mannitol.

**Männchen,** *n.* little man, mannikin; male.

**Mannesreife,** *f.* puberty.

**mannig-fach, -faltig,** *a.* manifold, various, varied.

**Mannigfaltigkeit,** *f.* manifoldness, variety, diversity, multiplicity; (*Math.*) manifold, aggregate.

**Mannit,** *m.* mannitol, (formerly) mannite.

**männlich,** *a.* male; masculine; manly.

**Männlichkeit,** *f.* male quality, maleness.

**Mannloch,** *n.* manhole.

**Manno-heptit,** *n.* mannoheptitol. **-zuckersäure,** *f.* mannosaccharic acid.

**Mannschaft,** *f.* men, forces, crew.

**Manometerdruck,** *m.* manometer pressure, gage pressure.
**manometrisch,** *a.* manometric.
**Manöver,** *n.* maneuver. **-pulver,** *n.* (*Expl.*) blank-fire powder.
**Manschette,** *f.* cuff; (*Tech.*) flap, collar, sleeve.
**Mantel,** *m.* mantle; casing, jacket, case, sheath, shell; (*Geom.*) surface, nappe, sheet. **-fläche,** *f.* (*Geom.*) generated surface. **-futter,** *n.* casing lining, jacket lining, etc. **-geschoss,** *n.* cased bullet. **-konus,** *m.* casing cone (as a stopcock shell). **-kühlung,** *f.* jacket cooling. **-linie,** *f.* (*Geom.*) director line, directrix. **-rohr,** *n.* casing tube, jacket pipe. **-schicht,** *f.* covering layer, protective layer. **-sprengstoff,** *m.* sheathed explosive. **-tier,** *n.* (*Zoöl.*) tunicate.
**Mantisse,** *f.* (*Math.*) mantissa.
**manuell,** *a.* manual, hand.
**Manufaktur,** *f.* manufacture; manufactory.
**Mappe,** *f.* portfolio; case (for paper, etc.).
**Marantastärke,** *f.* arrowroot.
**Märchen,** *n.* (fairy) tale, story.
**märchenhaft,** *a.* fabulous, legendary, fictitious.
**Märe,** *f.* news, report, story, tradition.
**Margarinekäse,** *m.* margarine cheese.
**margarinsauer,** *a.* of or combined with margaric acid, margarate of.
**Margarinsäure,** *f.* margaric acid.
**Marien-bad,** *n.* water bath. **-distel,** *f.* milk thistle (*Silybum marianum*). **-glas,** *n.* selenite; (**russisches**) mica. **-käfer,** *m.* ladybird. **-körner,** *n.pl.* milk-thistle seed.
**Marine,** *f.* navy. **-blau,** *n.* navy blue. **-legierung,** *f.* admiralty alloy, admiralty brass. **-leim,** *m.* marine glue. **-öl,** *n.* marine oil.
**marinieren,** *v.t.* marinate, pickle.
**Mark,** *n.* marrow; pith; pulp; medulla; core. — *f.* mark (the money); boundary.
**Mark-.** medullary.
**markant,** *a.* striking, remarkable.
**markartig,** *a.* marrow-like, myeloid, medullary; pith-like.
**Markasit,** *m.* marcasite. **-glanz,** *m.* tetradymite.
**Markbildung,** *f.* (*Physiol.*) myelinization.
**Marke,** *f.* mark; stamp; brand; trade name; quality, sort.
**marken,** *v.t.* mark.
**Marken-artikel,** *m.* standard article. **-öl,** *n.* branded oil. **-schutz,** *m.* trade-mark protection. **-werkstoff,** *m.* branded material.
**Markette,** *f.* virgin wax in cake form.
**Markflüssigkeit,** *f.* spinal fluid.
**Markholz,** *n.* pithy wood.
**markieren,** *v.t.* mark, brand, label, stamp.
**Markierung,** *f.* marking, etc. (see markieren); mark, brand.
**Mark-knopf,** *m.* (*Anat.*) medulla oblongata. **-lager,** *n.* medullary layer. **-masse,** *f.* medullary substance. **-saft,** *m.* medullary sap. **-scheide,** *f.* boundary, limit; medullary sheath. **-stoff,** *m.* medullary substance. **-strahl,** *m.* medullary ray. **-substanz,** *f.* medullary substance.
**Markt,** *m.* market, mart, fair.
**markten,** *v.i.* market; bargain.
**markt-fähig,** *a.* marketable. **-gängig,** *a.* market, current.
**Marktpreis,** *m.* market price.
**marktreif,** *a.* ready for market, marketable.
**Markt-reife,** *f.* marketable condition. **-wert,** *m.* market value. **-zettel,** *m.* market report.
**Markung,** *f.* marking.
**Markzelle,** *f.* medullary cell.
**Marmelade,** *f.* marmalade; marmalade tree (*Achras zapota*).
**Marmelos-beere, -frucht,** *f.* fruit of the bel or marmelos (*Aegle marmelos*).
**Marmite,** *f.* kettle, boiler, digester.
**Marmor,** *m.* marble.
**marmor-ähnlich, -artig,** *a.* marble-like, marmoraceous, marmoreal.
**Marmorbruch,** *m.* marble chips or fragments; marble quarry.
**marmorieren,** *v.t.* marble, vein, mottle.
**Marmorierung,** *f.* marbling, veining, mottling.
**Marmor-kalk,** *m.* lime from marble. **-kiesel,** *m.* a kind of hornstone. **-lack,** *m.* marble varnish. **-mehl,** *n.* marble dust. **-papier,** *n.* marbled paper. **-weiss,** *n.* whiting (as a pigment). **-zement,** *m.* marble cement; specif., Keene's cement.
**marode,** *a.* tired, exhausted.
**Marokainpapier,** *n.* morocco paper.
**marokkanisch,** *a.* Moroccan, Morocco.
**Marokko,** *n.* Morocco.
**Marone,** *f.* chestnut, marron.
**Maroquin,** *m.* morocco.
**Marsch,** *f.* marsh. — *m.* march. **-boden,** *m.* marsh land, marshy soil.
**Marseillerseife,** *f.* Marseilles soap.
**Marsgelb,** *n.* Mars yellow.
**Marshische Probe.** Marsh test, Marsh's test.
**martensitisch,** *a.* (*Metal.*) martensitic.
**Martin-.** (*Iron*) Martin, open-hearth. **-flusseisen,** *n.* open-hearth iron. **-fluss-stahl,** *m* open-hearth steel. **-ofen,** *m.* Martin furnace, open-hearth furnace. **-ofenschlacke,** *f.* open-hearth slag. **-roheisen,** *n.* open-hearth pig (iron). **-stahl,** *m.* Martin steel (open-hearth steel). **-stahlofen,** *m.* open-hearth steel furnace. **-verfahren,** *n.* (Siemens-)Martin process, open-hearth process.
**Martitisierung,** *f.* (*Min.*) martitization.
**Martiusgelb,** *n.* Martius yellow.
**März,** *m.* March.
**Masche,** *f.* mesh; stitch; compartment.

**Maschen-draht,** *m.* screen wire, netting wire, **-grösse,** *f.* size of mesh. **-sieb,** *n.* mesh sieve, mesh screen. **-weite,** *f.* width of mesh. **-werk,** *n.* network. **-zahl,** *f.* mesh number, mesh.

**maschig,** *a.* meshed, netted, reticulated.

**Maschine,** *f.* machine; engine; airplane; (atomic) pile. **-lehre,** *f.* engineering.

**maschinell,** *a.* mechanical; automatic.

**Maschinen-bau,** *m.* machine (or engine) building, mechanical engineering. **-bauer,** *m.* machine (or engine) builder, machinist, millwright. **-element,** *n.* machine part, engine part. **-fett,** *n.* machine grease, engine grease, lubricating grease. **-gas,** *n.* engine gas, power gas.

**maschinengefertigt,** *a.* machine-made.

**Maschinen-gewehr,** *n.* machine gun. **-glanz,** *m.*, **-glätte,** *f.* machine finish. **-guss,** *m.* machine casting. **-kunde,** *f.* mechanical science. **-lack,** *m.* machine varnish, engine varnish. **-lager,** *n.* (*Mach.*) bearing. **-lageröl,** *n.* bearing oil.

**maschinenmässig,** *a.* machinelike, mechanical.

**Maschinen-mischung,** *f.* machine mixing, mechanical mixing. **-öl,** *n.* machine oil. **-schmiere,** *f.* lubricating grease. **-schmierung,** *f.* machine lubrication, engine lubrication. **-schreiber,** *m.* typist. **-schrift,** *f.* typewriting. **-sieb,** *n.* wire cloth. **-strom,** *m.* (*Elec.*) generator current. **-torf,** *m.* machine-cut peat. **-werk,** *n.* machinery. **-werkstatt,** *f.* machine shop. **-wesen,** *n.* mechanical affairs; mechanical engineering.

**Masel,** *f.* mark, spot, scar.

**Maser,** *f.* speckle, spot, mark; grain (of wood); (*pl.*) measles.

**Maserholz,** *n.* veined wood, grained wood.

**maserig,** *a.* speckled, mottled, streaked, grained.

**masern,** *v.t.* speckle, mottle, vein, grain.

**Maserpapier,** *n.* speckled (or grained) paper.

**Maserung,** *f.* speckling, mottling, streaking, graining.

**Maske,** *f.* mask.

**maskieren,** *v.t.* mask, cover, disguise.

**mass,** *pret.* (of messen) measured.

**Mass,** *n.* measure; measurement; dimension; size; gage; titer; proportion, extent, degree; manner. **-abweichung,** *f.* deviation from size. **-analyse,** *f.* volumetric analysis.

**massanalytisch,** *a.* volumetric.

**Mass-änderung,** *f.* change in dimension or size. **-beständigkeit,** *f.* permanency of dimension or size. **-bürette,** *f.* measuring buret(te).

**Masse,** *f.* mass; substance; composition; material; stock; batch; assets; (*Founding*) dry sand; (*Ceram.*) paste; (*Paper*) pulp; (*Elec.*) earth, ground; ( = Mass) measure, dimension, manner.

**massefrei,** *a.* (*Elec.*) not grounded.

**Masseherstellung,** *f.* mass production.

**Masseinheit,** *f.* unit of measure.

**Massel,** *f.* (*Metal.*) pig; slab, bloom. **-bett,** *n.* (*Metal.*) pig bed. **-eisen,** *n.* pig iron. **-graben,** *m.* (*Metal.*) sow.

**Massen-analyse,** *f.* volumetric analysis. **-anziehung,** *f.* gravitation. **-bewegung,** *f.* mass motion. **-defekt,** *m.* mass defect. **-dichte,** *f.* mass density. **-einheit,** *f.* unit of mass. **-erzeugung, -fabrikation,** *f.* mass production. **-gestein,** *n.* unstratified rock, massive rock. **-guss,** *m.* dry-sand casting; duplicate casting. **-gut,** *n.*, **-güter,** *n.pl.* mass-production goods; bulk goods.

**massenhaft,** *a.* massive, massy; numerous, abundant. — *adv.* abundantly; in a lump; wholesale.

**Massen-herstellung,** *f.* mass production. **-mittelpunkt,** *m.* center of mass. **-moment,** *n.* moment of inertia. **-platte,** *f.* pasted (battery) plate. **-punkt,** *m.* (*Physics*) mass point (center of mass, also particle). **-rübe,** *f.* common or low-grade beet. **-stahl,** *m.* ordinary low-carbon steel. **-strahler,** *m.* mass radiator. **-teilchen,** *n.* (*Physics*) corpuscle, particle. **-trägheit,** *f.* (*Physics*) inertia. **-verhältnis,** *n.* ratio of masses, mass ratio. **-ware,** *f.* production goods. **-wirkung,** *f.* mass action. **-wirkungsgesetz,** *n.* law of mass action. **-zahl,** *f.* mass number. **-zentrum,** *n.* center of mass. **-zucht,** *f.* (*Agric.*) quantity growing. **-zuwachs,** *n.* increase in mass, mass accretion.

**Masse-schlamm,** *m.* (*Ceram.*) body slip. **-schlicker,** *m.* (*Ceram.*) body paste.

**Mass-flasche,** *f.* measuring flask. **-flüssigkeit,** *f.* standard solution. **-formel,** *f.* (*Pharm.*) standard formula. **-gabe,** *f.* measure, proportion.

**massgebend,** *p.a.* determinative, decisive, authoritative, conclusive, standard.

**Massgefäss,** *n.* measuring vessel; graduate.

**massgerecht,** *a.* of accurate size, true to size.

**Massglas,** *n.* measuring glass, marked glass vessel.

**masshaltig,** *a.* = massgerecht.

**Massholder,** *m.* (field) maple.

**massig,** *a.* massy, massive; compact, solid.

**mässig,** *a.* moderate; temperate; reasonable (in cost). — *adv.* moderately, reasonably, fairly.

**-mässig.** An adjective suffix signifying "in the manner of, in accordance with"; as *verhältnismässig*, proportional.

**mässigen,** *v.t.* moderate, temper. — **gemässigt,** *p.a.* temperate, moderate.

**Mässigkeit,** *f.* moderation; temperance.

**Mässigung,** *f.* moderation.

**Massikot,** *n.* massicot (unfused lead monoxide).

**massiv,** *a.* massive; unalloyed; solid; clumsy.
**Mass-kontrolle,** *f.* gaging. **-kunde,** *f.* metrology.
**massmässig,** *a.* according to measurement.
**Mass-nahme,** *f.* mode of action; precaution. **-regel,** *f.* measure, step, expedient. **-röhre,** *f.* measuring tube, graduated tube, buret(te). **-stab,** *m.* scale; rule, measure; criterion.
**mass-stäblich,** *adv.* to scale; full scale.
**Mass-system,** *n.* system of measurement. **-teil,** *m.* part by measure. **-teilung,** *f.* graduation. **-zeichnung,** *f.* drawing to scale.
**Mast,** *f.* feeding, fattening; mast, nuts. — *m.* pole; mast. **-darm,** *m.* rectum.
**Mastdarm-.** rectal, recto-.
**masten,** *v.t. & i.* fatten, feed well.
**mästen,** *v.t.* feed, fatten.
**Mastfähigkeit,** *f.* fattening capacity.
**Mastix,** *m.* mastic (the resin), gum mastic. **-branntwein,** *m.* mastic (the liquor). **-firnis,** *m.* mastic varnish. **-harz,** *n.* mastic (resin). **-kitt,** *m.* mastic (cement). **-lack,** *m.* mastic varnish. **-lösung,** *f.* mastic solution.
**mastizieren,** *v.t.* masticate.
**Mästung,** *f.* feeding, fattening; fatness.
**Mastvieh,** *n.* fattening cattle.
**Masut,** *n.* mazut, masut.
**Material,** *n.* material, matter. — **Materialien,** *pl.* material(s); groceries; drugs.
**Material-behälter,** *m.* receptacle for material, container. **-eigenschaft,** *f.* property of materials. **-förderung,** *f.* output or transport of material.
**Materialien,** *n.pl.* see Material.
**Material-prüfung,** *f.* testing of materials. **-prüfungsamt,** *n.* bureau for testing materials (often not translated). **-überhitzung,** *f.* overheating of materials. **-untersuchung,** *f.* investigation of materials. **-waren,** *f.pl.* groceries; drugs.
**Materie,** *f.* matter.
**materiell,** *a.* material.
**Materienofen,** *m.* (*Glass*) calcar.
**materieren,** *v.i.* suppurate.
**Materie-teilchen,** *n.* particle of matter. **-welle,** *f.* wave of matter.
**Matern,** *n.* matrix paper, flong.
**Mathematik,** *f.* mathematics.
**mathematisch,** *a.* mathematical.
**Matratze,** *f.* mattress.
**matrisieren,** *v.t.* damp (paper).
**Matrize,** *f.* matrix; die; mold.
**Matrizenpappe,** *f.* (*Paper*) matrix board.
**Matsch,** *m.* pulp, mash; slush, mire.
**matt,** *a.* dull, dead, mat; (of glass) ground; faint, feeble, weak, dull; insipid, flat; (*Metal.*) pasty.
**Matt,** *n.* dullness, deadness of surface. **-anstrich,** *m.* lusterless paint. **-appretur,** *f.* dull finish. **-beize,** *f.* pickle for giving a dull surface.
**mattblau,** *a.* mat blue, dull blue.
**Matt-blech,** *n.* pickled sheet metal. **-brenne,** *f.*, **-brennen,** *n.* dull pickling. **-dekatur,** *f.* (*Textiles*) dull finish.
**Matte,** *f.* mat; matting; meadow.
**Matt-eisen,** *n.* white pig iron.
**Mattenstoff,** *m.* matting.
**Mattfarbe,** *f.* deadening color.
**matt-gelb,** *a.* pale yellow, cream. **-geschliffen,** *p.a.* ground, frosted.
**Matt-glanz,** *m.* dull luster, dull finish. **-glas,** *n.* ground glass, frosted glass. **-glasur,** *f.* (*Ceram.*) mat glaze. **-gold,** *n.* dead gold. **-heit,** *f.* dullness, etc. (see matt).
**mattierbar,** *a.* (of metals) tarnishable.
**mattieren,** *v.t.* give a mat surface to, deluster, dull, deaden; tarnish; frost, grind (glass).
**Mattierung,** *f.* delustering, dulling.
**Mattierungsmittel,** *n.* delustering or dulling agent.
**Mattigkeit,** *f.* fatigue, exhaustion.
**Matt-kohle,** *f.* dull coal. **-kunstseide,** *f.* delustered rayon. **-lack,** *m.* flat (dull, mat) varnish or lacquer.
**mattrosa,** *a.* dull pink.
**mattrot,** *a.* dull red.
**Mattscheibe,** *f.* ground-glass plate, (*Photog.*) focusing screen.
**mattschleifen,** *v.t.* grind, frost (glass).
**Matt-schwarz,** *n.* dead black. **-sein,** *n.* dullness, deadness, dimness. **-vergoldung,** *f.* dead-gilding.
**mattweiss,** *a.* dull white, dead white.
**Matt-weissblech,** *n.* terneplate. **-zurichtung,** *f.* mat finish, dull finish.
**Mauer,** *f.* wall. **-gelb,** *n.* yellow badigeon. **-kalk,** *m.* mortar. **-kraut,** *n.* wall pellitory.
**mauern,** *v.t.* build of masonry; wall in or up.
**Mauer-pfeffer,** *m.* stonecrop (*Sedum acre*). **-salpeter,** *m.*, **-salz,** *n.* wall saltpeter (calcium nitrate). **-stein,** *m.* (building) stone; (building) brick.
**Mauerung,** *f.*, **Mauerwerk,** *n.* masonry, walling.
**Mauerziegel,** *m.* (building) brick.
**mauken,** *v.t.* digest with water; weather; age.
**Mauken,** *n.* (*Ceram.*) fermenting, aging.
**Maul,** *n.* mouth; jaws.
**Maul-beere,** *f.* mulberry. **-esel,** *m.* mule. **-sperre,** *f.* lockjaw. **-tier,** *n.* mule. **-wurf,** *m.* mole (the animal).
**Maurer,** *m.* mason, bricklayer.
**maurisch,** *a.* Moorish.
**Maus,** *f.* mouse.
**Mäuse-dreck,** *m.* mouse dung. **-gift,** *n.* ratsbane, (white) arsenic.
**Mauser,** *f.* molting, molt.
**mausern,** *v.r.* molt.

**maus-fahl, -farben, -farbig, -grau,** *a.* mouse-colored, mouse-gray.
**m.a.W.,** *abbrev.* (mit anderen Worten) in other words, that is to say.
**maximal,** *a.* maximum, maximal.
**Maximal-geschwindigkeit,** *f.* maximum velocity or speed. **-spannung,** *f.* (*Elec.*) maximum voltage. **-strom,** *m.* (*Elec.*) maximum current. **-wert,** *m.* maximum value. **-wertigkeit,** *f.* maximum valence. **-zahl,** *f.* maximum number.
**Maxivalenz,** *f.* maximum valence.
**Mazeration,** *f.* maceration.
**mazerieren,** *v.t.* macerate.
**Mazeriergefäss,** *m.* macerater.
**m.b.H.,** *abbrev.* (mit beschränkter Haftung, or Haftpflicht) with limited liability, Limited, Ltd.
**M.D.,** *abbrev.* (Mitteldruck) medium pressure.
**m.E.,** *abbrev.* (meines Erachtens) in my opinion.
**M.E.,** *abbrev.* (Mache-Einheit) Mache unit; (*Biol.*) (Mäuse-Einheit) mouse unit.
**Mechanik,** *f.* mechanics; mechanism.
**Mechaniker,** *m.* mechanician.
**mechanisch,** *a.* mechanical, mechanic. — *adv.* mechanically. — **mechanisches Gemenge,** mechanical mixture.
**mechanisieren,** *v.t.* mechanize.
**Mechanisierung,** *f.* mechanization.
**Mechanismus,** *m.* mechanism; machinery.
**Meconsäure,** *f.* meconic acid.
**med.,** *abbrev.* (medizinisch) medical, medicinal.
**Medaille,** *f.* medal.
**Medianpapier,** *n.* medium paper.
**Medien,** *n.pl.* mediums, media.
**Mediterranfieber,** *n.* Mediterranean fever, undulant fever.
**Medizin,** *f.* medicine.
**Medizinal-rinde,** *f.* officinal bark. **-ware,** *f.* drug.
**Mediziner,** *m.* medical man or student.
**medizinert,** *p.a.* medicated.
**medizinisch,** *a.* medicinal; medical. **-chemisch,** *a.* medico-chemical.
**Medusa, Meduse,** *f.* jellyfish, medusa.
**Meer,** *n.* sea, ocean. **-ablagerung,** *f.* marine deposit.
**meer-bewohnend,** *a.* marine. **-blau,** *a.* greenish-blue, glaucous.
**Meeres-bildung,** *f.* marine formation. **-boden,** *m.* sea bottom, sea floor. **-fläche,** *f.* sea level; surface of the sea. **-forschung,** *f.* oceanography. **-grund,** *m.* sea bottom. **-höhe,** *f.* sea level; altitude. **-küste,** *f.* seacoast. **-leuchten,** *n.* = Meerleuchten. **-niveau,** *n.* sea level. **-oberfläche,** *f.*, **-spiegel,** *m.* sea level; surface of the sea. **-strand,** *m.* seashore. **-strömung,** *f.* ocean current.
**Meer-farbe,** *f.*, **-grün,** *n.* sea green.
**meergrün,** *a.* sea-green.
**Meer-kohl,** *m.* sea kale. **-leuchten,** *n.* phosphorescence of the sea. **-rettich, -rettig,** *m.* horseradish. **-salz,** *n.* sea salt. **-sand,** *m.* sea sand. **-schaum,** *m.* meerschaum; sea foam. **-schlamm,** *m.* sea ooze. **-schwein,** *n.* porpoise. **-schweinchen,** *n.* guinea pig. **-schweinöl,** *n.*, **-schweintran,** *m.* porpoise oil. **-seide,** *f.* sea silk (fiber from seaweed). **-tang,** *m.* (*Bot.*) tang, seatang (coarse seaweed). **-torf,** *m.* sea peat. **-wachs,** *n.* (*Petroleum*) sea wax. **-wasser,** *n.* sea water.
**meerwasserecht,** *a.* fast to sea water.
**Meerzwiebel,** *f.* squill.
**Megahertz,** *n.* (*Physics*) megacycle(s) per second.
**Megerkraut,** *n.* yellow bedstraw (*Galium verum*).
**Mehl,** *n.* meal; flour; dust, powder.
**mehlartig,** *a.* like meal or flour, farinaceous.
**Mehl-beere,** *f.* haw. **-beutel,** *m.* bolter, sifter. **-fälschung,** *f.* adulteration of flour or meal.
**mehlfein,** *a.* fine as flour.
**Mehl-früchte,** *f.pl.* cereals. **-gips,** *m.* (*Min.*) earthy gypsum.
**mehlhaltig,** *a.* containing flour, farinaceous.
**mehlig,** *a.* mealy, floury, farinaceous.
**Mehligkeit,** *f.* flouriness, mealiness.
**Mehl-kleister,** *m.* flour paste. **-körper,** *m.* endosperm (of grains). **-kreide,** *f.* earthy calcite; kieselguhr. **-prüfer,** *m.* flour tester; specif., aleurometer. **-pulver,** *n.* meal powder. **-sand,** *m.* very fine sand, rock flour. **-speise,** *f.* farinaceous food. **-staub,** *m.* (flour)mill dust. **-stoff,** *m.* farinaceous substance. **-tau,** *m.* mildew. **-taupilz,** *m.* mildew fungus, mildew. **-zucker,** *m.* brown sugar; powdered sugar.
**mehr,** *a.* & *adv.* more. — **immer mehr,** more and more.
**mehr-, Mehr-.** poly, multi-, many-; excess of; additional.
**Mehrarbeit,** *f.* overtime work, extra work.
**mehratomig,** *a.* polyatomic.
**Mehrbadverfahren,** *n.* multiple-bath process.
**mehrbändig,** *a.* of several volumes.
**Mehrbasigkeit,** *f.* polybasicity.
**mehr-basisch, -basig,** *a.* polybasic.
**Mehr-belastung,** *f.* overload, extra load. **-betrag,** *m.* increased amount; surplus, excess. **-deutigkeit,** *f.* ambiguity.
**mehrdimensional,** *a.* many-dimensioned, multidimensional.
**Mehrdrehung,** *f.* multirotation.
**mehren,** *v.t.* increase, multiply.
**mehrere,** *a.* several.
**mehrerlei,** *a.* of several kinds, various.
**mehrfach,** *a.* manifold, multiple, multiplex, repeated.
**Mehrfach-färbung,** *f.* (*Micros.*) multiple stain-

ing. **-zünder,** *m.* multiple fuse, combination fuse.
**mehrfältig,** *a.* = mehrfach.
**Mehrfarbendruck,** *m.* multicolor printing.
**mehrfarbig,** *a.* multicolor(ed), polychromatic; pleochroic.
**Mehrfarbigkeit,** *f.* polychromatism; pleochroism; (*Art*) polychromy.
**mehrflammig,** *a.* having more than one flame.
**Mehr-gehalt,** *m.* excess content. **-gewicht,** *n.* excess weight, overweight.
**mehrgliedrig,** *a.* having several, or more, members.
**Mehrheit,** *f.* majority; plurality; multiplicity.
**mehr-kantig,** *a.* many-sided. **-kernig,** *a.* polynuclear, having more than one nucleus.
**Mehr-körperproblem,** *n.* many-body problem. **-kristall,** *m.* polycrystal. **-linienspektrum,** *n.* many-line spectrum.
**mehr-malig,** *a.* repeated. **-mals,** *adv.* several times, repeatedly.
**Mehrphasen-.** polyphase, multiphase. **-strom,** *m.* (*Elec.*) polyphase current.
**mehr-phasig,** *a.* polyphase, multiphase. **-polig,** *a.* multipolar. **-säurig,** *a.* polyacid. **-schichtig,** *a.* many-layered, multilayered. **-stellig,** *a.* (of numbers) of more than one place.
**Mehrstrahlbrenner,** *m.* multijet burner.
**mehr-stufig,** *a.* of several steps, stages, or grades, multiple-stage, multistage. **-stündig,** *a.* lasting for hours, of several hours' duration. **-tägig,** *a.* of several days' duration. **-teilig,** *a.* of several parts, multiple-part. **-wellig,** *a.* multiwave.
**Mehrwert,** *m.* surplus value.
**mehrwertig,** *a.* multivalent, polyvalent.
**Mehrzahl,** *f.* majority; plurality; plural.
**mehrzellig,** *a.* multicellular.
**Mehrzünder,** *m.* multiple fuse.
**Mehrzweck-.** multipurpose, general-purpose.
**meiden,** *v.t.* avoid, shun.
**Meierei,** *f.* farm, dairy farm.
**Meile,** *f.* mile.
**Meiler,** *m.* circular pile (esp. that used in charcoal burning), mound, stack; (*Brick*) clamp. **-kohle,** *f.* charcoal. **-verfahren,** *n.*, **-verkohlung,** *f.* pile charring. **-verkokung,** *f.* pile coking.
**mein,** *pron.* my, mine.
**meinen,** *v.t. & i.* think; mean.
**meinerseits,** *adv.* for my part.
**meines Erachtens.** in my opinion.
**meinet-halben, -wegen,** *adv.* for my sake; for my part.
**Meinung,** *f.* opinion, idea; meaning, intention.
**Meiran,** *m.* marjoram. **-öl,** *n.* marjoram oil.
**Meisch,** *m.* mash; (unfermented) grape juice, grape must.
**Meissel,** *m.* chisel; cutting tool; bit; stylus; (*Med.*) pledget.
**meisselförmig,** *a.* chisel-shaped.
**meisseln,** *v.t.* chisel, chip.
**Meisselstahl,** *m.* chisel steel.
**meist,** *a.* most. — *adv.* mostly. — **am meisten,** for the most part, mostly.
**meistens, meistenteils,** *adv.* for the most part, generally.
**Meister,** *m.* master; foreman.
**meisterhaft,** *a.* masterly.
**Meister-stück,** *n.* masterpiece; master stroke. **-wurz, -wurzel,** *f.* masterwort (imperatoria) or its rhizome.
**Mekerbrenner,** *m.* Meker burner.
**Mekoninsäure,** *f.* meconinic acid.
**Mekonsäure,** *f.* meconic acid.
**Melangallussäure,** *f.* melanogallic acid, metagallic acid.
**Melange,** *f.* mixture.
**melangieren,** *v.t.* mix.
**Melan-glanz,** *m.* (*Min.*) stephanite. **-glimmer,** *m.* stilpnomelane (in part).
**Melasse,** *f.* molasses.
**Melassen-säure,** *f.* melassic acid. **-spiritus,** *m.* molasses spirit.
**Melasse-schlempe,** *f.* molasses residue. **-sprit,** *m.* molasses spirit.
**Melde-.** registration, recording, record, intelligence; alarm, signal.
**melden,** *v.t.* announce, inform, report, declare, mention. — *v.r.* present oneself, apply.
**meldepflichtig,** *a.* declarable.
**Melder,** *m.* announcer, informer; alarm; indicator; messenger.
**Meldolablau,** *n.* Meldola blue.
**Meldung,** *f.* announcement, information, mention, notification; report; message; alarm.
**melieren,** *v.t.* mix; blend; mottle.
**Melier-farbe,** *f.* (*Paper*) mottling color. **-fasern,** *f.pl.* (*Paper*) mottling fibers. **-papier,** *n.* mottled paper.
**Melierung,** *f.* mixing; blending; mottling.
**Melilote,** *f.*, **Melilotenklee,** *m.* melilot.
**Melilotsäure,** *f.* melilotic acid.
**meliorieren,** *v.t.* meliorate, ameliorate.
**Melis,** *m.* titlers (coarse loaf sugar).
**Melisse,** *f.*, **Melissen-kraut,** *n.* balm, balm mint. **-geist,** *m.* = Karmelitergeist. **-öl,** *n.* balm mint oil. **-spiritus,** *m.*, **-wasser,** *n.* = Karmelitergeist.
**Melissinsäure,** *f.* melissic acid.
**Meliszucker,** *m.* = Melis.
**melken,** *v.t.* milk.
**Mellit(h)säure,** *f.* mellitic acid.
**Mellonwasserstoffsäure,** *f.* hydromellonic acid.
**Melone,** *f.* melon.
**Melonenöl,** *n.* melon (seed) oil.
**Meltau,** *m.* mildew. **-pilz,** *m.* mildew fungus.

**Membran, Membrane,** *f.* membrane; diaphragm.
**Mendelejew.** Mendelyeev, Mendeléeff.
**Mendelsch,** *a.* Mendel's, Mendelian.
**Meng-.** mixing.
**mengbar,** *a.* capable of being mixed, miscible.
**Menge,** *f.* quantity, amount; lot; multitude, crowd; abundance, plenty; (*Math.*) aggregate, set. **-einheit,** *f.* unit of quantity.
**mengen,** *v.t.* mix; blend.
**Mengen-bestimmung,** *f.* quantitative determination. **-lehre,** *f.* (*Math.*) theory of sets.
**mengenmässig,** *a.* quantitative.
**Mengen-messer,** *m.* volume meter, volumeter. **-regelung,** *f.* quantity control. **-untersuchung,** *f.* quantitative examination. **-verhältnis,** *n.* quantitative relation, proportion, composition.
**Meng-futter,** *n.* mixed food or feed. **-gestein,** *n.* conglomerate. **-kapsel,** *f.* mixing capsule. **-korn,** *n.* mixed grain (specif., wheat and rye). **-saat,** *f.* mixed seed. **-spatel,** *m.* mixing spatula. **-teil,** *m.* ingredient of a mixture.
**Mengung,** *f.* mixing, mixture; blending, blend; hybridization.
**Mengungsverhältnis,** *n.* proportion of ingredients.
**Menhadenöl,** *n.* menhaden oil.
**Menisk, Meniskus,** *m.* meniscus.
**meniskenförmig,** *a.* meniscal, meniscoid.
**Meniskuskante,** *f.* meniscus edge.
**Mennig,** *m.*, **Mennige,** *f.* minium, red lead.
**Mennige-ersatz,** *m.* red-lead substitute. **-kitt,** *m.* red-lead cement.
**mennigen,** *v.t.* paint with minium, miniate.
**mennig-farbig, -rot,** *a.* minium-colored, miniaceous.
**Mensch,** *m.* man, human being, person.
**Menschen-.** human.
**menschenähnlich,** *a.* man-like, human-like; anthropoid.
**Menschen-alter,** *n.* generation. **-blut,** *n.* human blood. **-fett,** *n.* human fat. **-freund,** *m.* philanthropist. **-geschlecht,** *n.* mankind, humanity. **-körper,** *m.* human body. **-lehre,** *f.* anthropology; human teaching. **-pocken,** *f.pl.* smallpox.
**Menschheit,** *f.* mankind, human race.
**menschlich,** *a.* human; humane.
**Mensur,** *f.* measure, measuring vessel. **-glas,** *n.* measuring glass, graduated glass.
**Menthakampher,** *m.* mint camphor, menthol.
**Mepasin,** *n.* a mixture of paraffin hydrocarbons about $C_{14}$ to $C_{17}$. *T.N.*
**mephitisch,** *a.* mephitic.
**Mercerisationsgrad,** *m.* degree of mercerization.
**mercerisierecht,** *a.* fast to mercerizing.
**mercerisieren,** *v.t.* mercerize.
**Mercerisier-hilfsmittel,** *n.* mercerizing assistant. **-lauge,** *f.* mercerizing liquor.
**Mercur, Mercur-.** see Merkur, Merkur-.
**Mergel,** *m.* marl. **-art,** *f.* (kind or variety of) marl.
**mergelartig,** *a.* marly.
**Mergel-boden,** *m.* marly soil. **-düngung,** *f.* (*Agric.*) marling. **-erde,** *f.* earthy marl.
**mergelhaltig,** *a.* containing marl, marly.
**mergelig,** *a.* marly.
**Mergelkalk,** *m.* marly limestone.
**mergeln,** *v.t.* marl, treat with marl.
**Mergel-schiefer,** *m.* slaty marl. **-ton,** *m.* marly clay, argillaceous marl.
**Mergelung,** *f.* marling, treating with marl.
**Merinorot,** *n.* (*Dyeing*) Turkey red.
**merkbar,** *a.* perceptible, noticeable.
**Merk-blatt,** *n.* leaflet; pamphlet; memorandum. **-buch,** *n.* notebook.
**merken,** *v.t.* mark, notice, perceive, note.
**merkenswert,** *a.* noteworthy, remarkable.
**Merkfarbe,** *f.* indicator color.
**merklich,** *a.* perceptible, noticeable, appreciable.
**Merkmal,** *n.* characteristic, mark, sign, symbol, indication, index, criterion.
**Merkmalsträger,** *m.* (*Biol.*) gene.
**Merktinte,** *f.* marking ink.
**Merkur,** *m.* mercury. **-blende,** *f.* (*Min.*) cinnabar. **-chlorid,** *n.* mercury chloride, specif. mercuric chloride, mercury(II) chloride. **-chlorür,** *n.* mercurous chloride, mercury(I) chloride. **-gelb,** *n.* mercury yellow, turpeth mineral.
**merkurhaltig,** *a.* containing mercury, mercurial.
**Merkurhornerz,** *n.* (*Min.*) horn quicksilver, calomel.
**Merkuri-.** mercuric, mercuri-, mercury(II).
**Merkurialien,** *pl.* (*Pharm.*) mercurials.
**Merkurialmittel,** *n.* (*Pharm.*) mercurial.
**Merkuri-ammoniumchlorid,** *n.* mercuriammonium chloride. **-azetat,** *n.* mercuric acetate, mercury(II) acetate. **-chlorid,** *n.* mercuric chloride, mercury(II) chloride. **-cyanid,** *n.* mercuric cyanide, mercury(II) cyanide. **-cyanwasserstoffsäure,** *f.* mercuricyanic acid, cyanomercuric(II) acid.
**merkurieren,** *v.t.* mercurize, combine with mercury.
**Merkurierung,** *f.* mercurization.
**Merkuri-jodid,** *n.* mercuric iodide, mercury(II) iodide. **-nitrat,** *n.* mercuric nitrate, mercury-(II) nitrate. **-oxyd,** *n.* mercuric oxide, mercury(II) oxide. **-rhodanid,** *n.* mercuric thiocyanate, mercury(II) thiocyanate. **-salz,** *n.* mercuric salt, mercury(II) salt. **-sulfat,** *n.* mercuric sulfate, mercury(II) sulfate. **-sulfid,** *n.* mercuric sulfide, mercury(II) sulfide. **-sulfozyanid,** *n.* mercuric thiocyanate,

mercury(II) thiocyanate. **-verbindung,** *f.* mercuric compound, mercury(II) compound.

**Merkurjodid,** *n.* mercury iodide.

**Merkuro-.** mercurous, mercury(I). **-azetat,** *n.* mercurous acetate, mercury(I) acetate. **-chlorid,** *n.* mercurous chloride, mercury(I) choride. **-chrom,** *n.* (*Pharm.*) mercurochrome. **-jodid,** *n.* mercurous iodide, mercury(I) iodide. **-nitrat,** *n.* mercurous nitrate, mercury(I) nitrate. **-oxyd,** *n.* mercurous oxide, mercury(I) oxide. **-salz,** *n.* mercurous salt, mercury(I) salt. **-sulfat,** *n.* mercurous sulfate, mercury(I) sulfate. **-sulfid,** *n.* mercurous sulfide, mercury(I) sulfide. **-verbindung,** *f.* mercurous compound, mercury(I) compound.

**Merkur-oxyd,** *n.* mercury oxide, specif. mercuric oxide, mercury(II) oxide. **-silber,** *n.* silver amalgam. **-sulfid,** *n.* mercury sulfide. specif. mercuric sulfide, mercury(II) sulfide.

**merkwürdig,** *a.* noteworthy, remarkable. **-erweise,** *adv.* strange to say.

**Merk-zeichen,** *n.* mark, sign, memorandum. **-zettel,** *m.* memorandum card, data card.

**Mero-chinen,** *n.* meroquinene. **-tropie,** *f.* merotropism, merotropy.

**Mersolat,** *n.* a sodium alkanesulfonate detergent. *T.N.*

**merzen,** *v.t.* = ausmerzen.

**Merzerisationsgrad,** *m.* degree of mercerization.

**merzerisieren,** *v.t.* mercerize.

**Mesonenzerfall,** *m.* meson decay.

**Mesothor,** *n.* mesothorium.

**Mesoweinsäure,** *f.* mesotartaric acid.

**Mesoxalsäure,** *f.* mesoxalic acid.

**mesozoisch,** *a.* (*Geol.*) Mesozoic.

**Mess-.** measuring. **-analyse,** *f.* volumetric analysis. **-apparat,** *m.* measuring apparatus. **-apparatöl,** *n.* (*Petroleum*) meter oil. **-band,** *n.* tape measure.

**messbar,** *a.* measurable.

**Mess-behälter,** *m.* measuring vessel, measuring tank. **-bereich,** *m.* range of measurement. **-brücke,** *f.* (*Elec.*) measuring bridge, Wheatstone bridge. **-bürette,** *f.* graduated buret(te). **-draht,** *m.* slide wire (of a Wheatstone bridge).

**Messe,** *f.* fair, market; (*Mil.*) mess; mass (the rite).

**Mess-einheit,** *f.* unit of measurement. **-einteilung,** *f.* graduation.

**messen,** *v.t.* measure; survey; contain. — **gemessen,** *p.a.* measured, etc.; strict; formal.

**Messer,** *m.* measurer, meter. — *n.* knife; cutter; doctor, wiper.

**Messergebnis,** *n.* result of measurement.

**Messer-klinge,** *f.* knife blade. **-schalter,** *m.* (*Elec.*) knife switch.

**messerscharf,** *a.* sharp as a knife.

**Messer-schneide,** *f.* knife edge. **-spitze,** *f.* knife point. **-stahl,** *m.* knife steel.

**messfähig,** *a.* measurable.

**Mess-fehler,** *m.* error in measurement. **-flasche,** *f.* measuring bottle (or flask). **-flüssigkeit,** *f.* measuring liquid, (frequently) titrating solution. **-gefäss,** *n.* measuring vessel, measure. **-genauigkeit,** *f.* accuracy of measurement. **-geräte,** *n.pl.* measuring apparatus. **-gerätetisch,** *m.* instrument table. **-glas,** *n.* measuring glass, graduated glass vessel, gage glass. **-grenze,** *f.* limit of measurement. **-heber,** *m.* measuring pipet(te). **-holz,** *n.* dimension lumber or timber.

**Messing,** *n.* brass. **-abstrich, -abzug,** *m.* brass scum.

**messingartig,** *a.* like brass, brassy.

**Messing-artigkeit,** *n.* brassiness. **-blatt,** *n.* brass foil. **-blech,** *n.* sheet brass, brass plate. **-blüte,** *f.* aurichalcite. **-brennen,** *n.* brass making. **-draht,** *m.* brass wire.

**messingen,** *a.* of brass, brass.

**messing-farben, -farbig,** *a.* brass-colored.

**Messing-fassung,** *f.* brass casing or mounting. **-folie,** *f.* brass foil. **-gewicht,** *n.* brass weight. **-giesser,** *m.* brass founder. **-giesserei,** *f.* brass foundry; brass founding. **-guss,** *m.* brass casting. **-hartlot,** *n.* = Messinglot. **-lack,** *m.* brass lacquer. **-lot,** *n.* brass solder, spelter solder, brazing spelter. **-netz,** *n.* brass netting, brass gauze. **-rohr,** *n.*, **-röhre,** *f.* brass tube or pipe. **-schlaglot,** *n.* brass solder, hard solder. **-späne,** *m.pl.* brass shavings, brass turnings. **-stange,** *f.* brass rod.

**Mess-instrument,** *n.* measuring instrument. **-keil,** *m.* measuring wedge (inside caliper for tubing). **-kelch,** *m.* measuring cup. **-kölbchen,** *n.* little measuring flask. **-kolben,** *m.* measuring flask. **-kunde,** *f.* metrology. **-kurve,** *f.* calibration curve. **-länge,** *f.* gage length. **-lupe,** *f.* measuring magnifier or lens. **-mikroskop,** *n.* measuring microscope. **-mittel,** *n.* means of measuring, measuring instrument. **-okular,** *n.* micrometric eyepiece. **-pipette,** *f.* graduated pipet(te), scale pipet(te). Cf. Vollpipette. **-reihe,** *f.* series of measurements. **-rohr,** *n.*, **-röhre,** *f.* measuring tube; specif., buret(te). **-röhrenklemme,** *f.* buret clamp. **-schaufel,** *f.* measuring scoop. **-serie,** *f.* series of measurements. **-stab,** *m* measuring rod; (for casks) liquor gage **-strecke,** *f.* measured distance. **-trichter,** *m* measuring funnel or hopper. **-trommel,** *f* graduated drum. **-uhr,** *f.* dial gage; measuring clock.

**Messung,** *f.* measuring, measurement, metering mensuration.

**Messungsergebnis,** *n.* result of measurement

**Mess-verfahren,** *n.* method or process of measurement. **-vorrichtung,** *f.* measuring device or instrument. **-wesen,** *n.* measuring technic, measuring matters. **-winkel,** *m.* measuring angle, reference angle. **-zahl,** *f.* measured (or measuring) value. **-zylinder,** *m.* measuring cylinder. **-zylinderchen,** *n.* small measuring cylinder.

**Met,** *m.* mead.

**metaantimonig,** *a.* metantimonious.

**Metaantimonsäure,** *f.* metantimonic acid.

**metaarsenig,** *a.* metarsenious.

**Meta-arsensäure,** *f.* metarsenic acid. **-bleisäure,** *f.* metaplumbic acid.

**Metabolie,** *f.* metabolism.

**metabolisch,** *a.* metabolic.

**Metabolismus,** *m.* metabolism.

**Meta-borsäure,** *f.* metaboric acid. **-cer,** *n.* metacerium.

**metachromatisch,** *a.* metachromatic.

**Meta-cymol,** *n.* metacymene, *m.* cymene. **-eisenoxyd,** *n.* metaferric oxide. **-ferrihydrat,** *n.* metaferric hydroxide. **-gallussäure,** *f.* metagallic acid. **-kieselsäure,** *f.* metasilicic acid. **-kohlensäure,** *f.* metacarbonic acid (ordinary carbonic acid, $H_2CO_3$).

**Metall,** *n.* metal.

**Metall-.** metallic, metal. **-abfall,** *m.* metal waste, waste metal, scrap metal. **-ablagerung,** *f.* metalliferous deposit. **-ader,** *f.* metallic vein, metalliferous vein.

**metallähnlich,** *a.* metallic, metalline.

**Metallamid,** *n.* metallic amide.

**metall-arm,** *a.* poor in metal. **-artig,** *a.* metallic, metalline.

**Metall-artigkeit,** *f.* metallicity. **-asche,** *f.* metallic ash. **-auftrag,** *m.* metallic coating or plating. **-auskleidung,** *f.* metal coating or covering. **-azid,** *n.* metallic azide. **-bad,** *n.* metallic bath or solution. **-bau,** *m.* metal construction. **-bearbeitung,** *f.* metal working. **-beize,** *f.* metallic mordant. **-beschlag,** *m.* metallic coating or sheathing. **-beschreibung,** *f.* metallography. **-beschwerung,** *f.* (*Textiles*) loading with metallic salts. **-blatt,** *n.* (thin) sheet of metal. **-blättchen,** *n.* metal foil, metal leaf. **-carbid,** *n.* metallic carbide. **-chemie,** *f.* chemistry of metals. **-chlorid,** *n.* metallic chloride. **-chlorwasserstoffsäure,** *f.* an acid composed of hydrogen, chlorine and a metal. **-cyanid,** *n.* metal(lic) cyanide. **-dampf,** *m.* metallic vapor. **-draht,** *m.* metal(lic) wire. **-eigenschaft,** *f.* metallic property. **-einkristall,** *m.* metal single crystal. **-emaillelack,** *m.* metal enamel varnish.

**metallempfindlich,** *a.* sensitive to metal.

**metallen,** *a.* metallic, metalline.

**Metall-erz,** *n.* metallic ore. **-faden,** *m.* metal thread, metal filament. **-fadenlampe,** *f.* metal-filament lamp. **-farbe,** *f.* metallic color; bronze color.

**metallfarbig,** *a.* metal-colored.

**Metall-färbung,** *f.* coloring of metal (specif., metallochrome); metallic coloring. **-fassung,** *f.* metal casing or mounting. **-fläche,** *f.* metallic surface. **-folie,** *f.* metal foil.

**metall-förmig,** *a.* metalliform. **-führend,** *a.* metalliferous.

**Metall-gefäss,** *n.* metal(lic) vessel. **-gehalt,** *m.* metal(lic) content. **-gekrätz,** *n.* metal waste, dross. **-geld,** *n.* metallic currency, coin. **-gemisch,** *n.* metallic mixture, alloy. **-gewebe,** *n.* wire gauze, wire cloth. **-gewinnung,** *f.* extraction of metals, metallurgy. **-gift,** *n.* metallic poison. **-gitter,** *n.* metal grating or grid. **-glanz,** *m.* metallic luster.

**metallglänzend,** *p.a.* having metallic luster.

**Metall-glas,** *n.* enamel. **-gold,** *n.* Dutch gold, Dutch foil. **-guss,** *m.* metal founding, metal casting; nonferrous castings.

**metallhaltig,** *a.* containing metal, metalliferous.

**Metall-hütte,** *f.* smeltery (for nonferrous metals). **-hüttenkunde,** *f.* nonferrous metallurgy. **-hydroxyd,** *n.* metallic hydroxide. **-ion,** *n.* metal(lic) ion.

**metallisch,** *a.* metallic.

**metallisieren,** *v.t.* metallize.

**Metallisierung,** *f.* metallization.

**Metallität,** *f.* metallic nature.

**Metall-kalk,** *m.* metallic calx (oxide). **-karbid,** *n.* metallic carbide. **-karbonyl,** *n.* compound of a metal with carbonyl. **-keramik,** *f.* powder metallurgy. **-kitt,** *m.* metal cement. **-kolloid,** *n.* metallic colloid. **-komplexsalz,** *n.* complex metallic salt. **-komplexsäure,** *f.* complex metallic acid. **-könig,** *m.* metallic regulus or button. **-korn,** *n.* metal grain; *pl.*, granulated metal. **-krätze,** *f.* waste metal. **-kühler,** *m.* metallic condenser or cooler. **-kunde,** *f.* science of metals; metallography. **-lack,** *m.* metal lacquer or varnish. **-legierung,** *f.* metallic alloy. **-lösung,** *f.* metallic solution. **-membran,** *f.* metal diaphragm. **-mikroskop,** *n.* metallurgical microscope. **-mikroskopie,** *f.* metallographic microscopy, microscopic metallography. **-mischung,** *f.* metal mixture, alloy; alloying. **-mischungswa(a)ge,** *f.* alloy balance. **-mohr,** *m.* metallic moiré; = Mineralmohr. **-mutter,** *f.* matrix (of ores). **-nebel,** *m.* metallic fog, metal fog. **-niederschlag,** *m.* metallic precipitate or deposit.

**Metallo-chemie,** *f.* chemistry of metals. **-chromie,** *f.* metallochromy. **-graph,** *m.* metallographer. **-graphie,** *f.* metallography.

**metallographisch,** *a.* metallographic.

**metallorganisch,** *a.* organometallic, metallo-organic.

**Metall-oxyd,** *n.* metallic oxide. **-oxydhydrat,** *n.* metal(lic) hydroxide. **-papier,** *n.* metal(lic) paper. **-poliermittel,** *n.* metal polish. **-probe,** *f.* test for metal, assay. **-putzmittel,** *n.* metal polish. **-rohr,** *n.*, **-röhre,** *f.* metal tube or pipe. **-röhrchen,** *n.* (small) metal tube or pipe. **-rückstand,** *m.* metallic residue. **-safran,** *m.* crocus of antimony. **-salz,** *n.* metallic salt.

**metallsalzbeständig,** *a.* resistant to metallic salts.

**Metall-salzlösung,** *f.* metallic-salt solution. **-säure,** *f.* metallic acid (as $HMnO_4$). **-schlacke,** *f.* metal slag. **-schlauch,** *m.* (flexible) metallic tube, metallic hose. **-schliff,** *m.* ground metal section or surface; metal filings. **-schmelze,** *f.* metallic fusion; metallic melt, fused metal. **-schmelzofen,** *m.* nonferrous melting furnace. **-schwamm,** *m.* metallic sponge. **-seife,** *f.* soap for metals, metal soap. **-silber,** *n.* imitation silver foil. **-späne,** *m.pl.* metal shavings, turnings or chips. **-spektrum,** *n.* spectrum of a metal. **-spiegel,** *m.* metallic mirror. **-spritzen, -spritzverfahren,** *n.* metal spraying, metallization. **-staub,** *m.* metal(lic) dust. **-sulfid,** *n.* metallic sulfide. **-technik,** *f.* technology of metals. **-teil,** *m.* metal part, metallic part. **-teilchen,** *n.* metallic particle. **-tuch,** *n.* wire cloth. **-überziehung,** *f.* metal plating.

**metallüberzogen,** *a.* (metal-)plated; metal-sheathed.

**Metallüberzug,** *m.* metallic coating, plating, wash, or sheathing.

**Metallurg, Metallurge,** *m.* metallurgist.

**Metallurgie,** *f.* metallurgy.

**metallurgisch,** *a.* metallurgic, metallurgical.

**metallverarbeitend,** *a.* metal-working.

**Metall-verarbeitung,** *f.* metal working. **-verbindung,** *f.* metallic compound. **-vergiftung,** *f.* metal(lic) poisoning. **-verlust,** *m.* loss of metal. **-versetzung,** *f.* alloying, alloy. **-waren,** *f.pl.* metal wares, hardware. **-wolle,** *f.* metal wool. **-zapon,** *m.* lacquer for metals.

**metamer,** *a.* metameric.

**Metamerie,** *f.* metamerism, metamery.

**metamerisch,** *a.* metameric.

**Metamerismus,** *m.* metamerism.

**Metamorphie,** *f.* metamorphism.

**metamorphisch,** *a.* metamorphic.

**Metamorphose,** *f.* metamorphosis.

**Metanil-gelb,** *n.* metanil yellow, metaniline yellow. **-säure,** *f.* metanilic acid.

**metantimonig,** *a.* metantimonious.

**Metantimonsäure,** *f.* metantimonic acid.

**meta-phosphorig,** *a.* metaphosphorous. **-phosphorsauer,** *a.* of or combined with metaphosphoric acid, metaphosphate of.

**Meta-phosphorsäure,** *f.* metaphosphoric acid. **-säure,** *f.* meta acid.

**metasomatisch,** *a.* metasomatic.

**meta-stabil,** *a.* metastable. **-ständig,** *a.* in the meta position.

**Metastase,** *f.* metastasis.

**Meta-stellung,** *f.* meta position. **-styrol,** *n.* metastyrene. **-vanadinsäure,** *f.* metavanadic acid. **-verbindung,** *f.* meta compound. **-weinsäure,** *f.* metatartaric acid. **-wolframsäure,** *f.* metatungstic acid. **-xylol,** *n.* metaxylene, *m*-xylene.

**metazentrisch,** *a.* metacentric.

**Meta-zentrum,** *n.* metacenter. **-zinnober,** *m.* (*Min.*) metacinnabarite. **-zinnsäure,** *f.* metastannic acid. **-zirkonsäure,** *f.* metazirconic acid. **-zuckersäure,** *f.* metasaccharic acid.

**Meteoreisen,** *n.* meteoric iron.

**meteorisch,** *a.* meteoric; (*Med.*) meteoristic.

**Meteorolog, Meteorologe,** *m.* meteorologist.

**meteorologisch,** *a.* meteorological.

**Meteor-stahl,** *m.* meteoric steel. **-staub,** *m.* meteoric dust. **-stein,** *m.* meteoric stone, aerolite.

**Meter-kerze,** *f.* (*Optics*) meter candle. **-mass,** *n.* metric measure; meter rule. **-tonne,** *f.* metric ton.

**Methacrylsäure, Methakrylsäure,** *f.* methacrylic acid.

**Methämoglobin,** *n.* methemoglobin.

**Methan,** *n.* methane. **-säure,** *f.* methanoic (formic) acid.

**Methen,** *n.* methene (methylene).

**Methode,** *f.* method.

**Methodik,** *f.* methodics, methodology.

**methodisch,** *a.* methodical.

**Methoxylgruppe,** *f.* methoxyl (or methoxy) group.

**methylalkoholisch,** *a.* methyl-alcoholic, methanolic.

**Methyl-arsonsäure,** *f.* methylarsonic (methanearsonic) acid. **-äther,** *m.* methyl ether. **-blau,** *n.* methyl blue. **-chlorid, -chlorür,** *n.* methyl chloride, chloromethane.

**Methylen-blau,** *n.* methylene blue. **-gruppe,** *f.* methylene group. **-jodid,** *n.* methylene iodide, diiodomethane.

**Methyl-gallusäthersäure,** *f.* *O*-methylgallic acid, methyl ether of gallic acid. **-grün,** *n.* methyl green. **-hydrür,** *n.* methyl hydride, methane.

**methylierbar,** *a.* capable of being methylated.

**methylieren,** *v.t.* methylate.

**Methyl-ierung, -isierung,** *f.* methylation. **-jodid,** *n.* methyl iodide, iodomethane. **-kautschuk,** *m.* methyl rubber.

**Methylostärke,** *f.* methylstarch.

**Methyl-oxydhydrat,** *n.* methyl hydroxide (methanol). **-rot,** *n.* methyl red. **-verbindung,** *f.* methyl compound. **-wasserstoff,** *m.* methyl hydride, methane. **-zahl,** *f.* methyl number, methyl value. **-zinnsäure,** *f.* methylstannic acid.

**Metochinon,** *n.* metoquinone.

**metrisch,** *a.* metric, metrical.

**Metze,** *f.* peck.

**Metzelsuppe,** *f.* meat broth.

**Metzger,** *m.* butcher.

**mexikanisch,** *a.* Mexican.

**m.G.,** *abbrev.* (mit Goldschnitt) with gilt edges.

**M.G.,** *abbrev.* (Molekulargewicht) molecular weight; (Massenwirkungsgesetz) law of mass action.

**MHz,** *abbrev.* (Megahertz) megahertz, megacycle per second.

**Micell,** *n.*, **Micelle,** *f.* micell(e), micella.

**Micellen-.** see Mizellen-.

**mich,** *pron.* me, myself.

**mied,** *pret.* (of meiden) avoided, shunned.

**Miene,** *f.* mien, look, air, feature.

**Miesmuschel,** *f.* (edible) mussel.

**Miete,** *f.* hiring, hire, lease; rent; stack, shock; (*Zoöl.*) mite.

**mieten,** *v.t.* hire, rent, lease.

**Migräne,** *f.* migraine, (sick) headache.

**Mikro-analyse,** *f.* microanalysis. **-analytiker,** *m.* microanalyst. **-arbeit,** *f.* micro work, work on a minute scale. **-aufnahme,** *f.* microphotograph. **-becher,** *m.* micro beaker.

**Mikrobentätigkeit,** *f.* microbial activity.

**Mikrobestimmung,** *f.* microdetermination.

**Mikrobien, Mikroben,** *f.pl.* microbes.

**Mikro-bild,** *n.* micrograph. **-brenner,** *m.* micro burner. **-chemie,** *f.* microchemistry. **-chemiker,** *m.* microchemist.

**mikrochemisch,** *a.* microchemical.

**Mikro-dampfbad,** *n.* micro steam bath. **-druckmesser,** *m.* micromanometer. **-elementaranalyse,** *f.* elementary microanalysis. **-gasbrenner,** *m.* micro gas burner. **-graphie,** *f.* micrography.

**mikrographisch,** *a.* micrographic.

**Mikrohärteprüfer,** *m.* micro hardness tester.

**mikrokanonisch,** *a.* microcanonical.

**Mikroklin,** *n.* microcline.

**mikro-kosmisch,** *a.* microcosmic. **-kristallinisch,** *a.* microcrystalline.

**Mikro-lith,** *m.* microlite. **-lunker,** *n.* microcavity, micropore. **-mechanik,** *f.* micromechanics. **-meterschraube,** *f.* micrometer screw.

**mikrometrisch,** *a.* micrometric.

**Mikro-nutsche,** *f.* micro suction filter, esp. micro Büchner funnel. **-organismen,** *m.pl.* microörganisms.

**mikrophotographisch,** *a.* (properly) microphotographic; (often) photomicrographic.

**Mikro-probe,** *f.* micro test; micro sample. **-schnellbestimmung,** *f.* rapid microdetermination.

**mikroskopieren,** *v.t.* examine with the microscope.

**Mikroskopiker,** *m.* microscopist.

**mikroskopisch,** *a.* microscopic(al).

**Mikroskop-linse,** *f.* microscope lens. **-stativ,** *n.* miscroscope stage.

**Mikro-spatel,** *m.* micro spatula. **-stativ,** *n.* micro stand. **-tomschnitt,** *m.* microtome section. **-trichter,** *m.* micro funnel. **-verbrennung,** *f.* microcombustion.

**mikrovolumetrisch,** *a.* microvolumetric.

**Mikro-wa(a)ge,** *f.* microbalance. **-welle,** *f.* microwave.

**mikrurgisch,** *a.* micrurgic(al).

**Milbe,** *f.* mite.

**Milch,** *f.* milk; emulsion; milt (of fishes).

**Milch-.** milk, lacteal, lacto-, galacto-.

**milch-abscheidend, -absondernd,** *a.* milk-secreting.

**Milchabsonderung,** *f.* milk secretion.

**milchabtreibend,** *p.a.* antigalactic.

**Milch-achat,** *m.* milk-white agate. **-ader,** *f.* lacteal vessel.

**milch-ähnlich,** *a.* milk-like, milky. **-artig,** *a.* milky, lacteal.

**Milch-bestandteil,** *m.* constituent of milk. **-bier,** *n.* kumiss. **-drüse,** *f.* mammary gland; lacteal gland.

**milchen,** *v.i.* & *t.* yield milk or a milky juice; milk; emulsify.

**Milch-erzeugnis,** *f.* dairy product; milk production. **-fälschung,** *f.* adulteration of milk. **-farbe,** *f.* milk color, milk white.

**milchfarbig,** *a.* milk-colored.

**Milch-fett,** *n.* milk fat. **-flasche,** *f.* milk bottle.

**milch-fördernd,** *a.* promoting milk secretion, galactagog(ue). **-führend,** *a.* lactiferous.

**Milch-gang,** *m.* lactiferous duct. **-gärung,** *f.* fermentation of milk. **-gerinnung,** *f.* curdling of milk. **-gewinnung,** *f.* milk production. **-glanz,** *m.* (*Leather*) milk finish. **-glas,** *n.* milk glass; breast glass.

**milchglasartig,** *a.* like milk glass, opalescent.

**Milch-grad,** *m.* milk degree (degree on the galactometer). **-güte,** *f.* quality of milk. **-harnen,** *n.*, **-harnfluss,** *m.* chyluria.

**milchig, milchicht,** *a.* milky, lacteal.

**milchigtrüb(e),** *a.* milky, turbid.

**Milch-kanal,** *m.* lactiferous duct. **-konserve,** *f.* preserved milk (any kind). **-kraut,** *n.* sea milkwort. **-kügelchen,** *n.* milk globule, fat globule in milk. **-kuh,** *f.* milch cow. **-lab,** *n.* rennet. **-leistung,** *f.* milk yield. **-messer,** *m.* galactometer; lactometer. **-porzellan,** *n.* milk glass, glass porcelain. **-prober, -prüfer,** *m.* milk tester (specif., lactometer). **-prüfung,**

*f.* milk testing. **-pulver,** *n.* milk powder. **-quarz,** *m.* milky quartz. **-rahm,** *m.* cream. **-röhre,** *f.* latex tube; lactiferous duct. **-saft,** *m.* milky juice; (*Bot.*) latex; (*Physiol.*) chyle.

**milch-saftführend,** *a.* laticiferous; (*Physiol.*) chyliferous. **-saftig,** *a.* (*Physiol.*) chylous.

**Milchsaftschlauch,** *m.* (*Bot.*) latex tube.

**milchsauer,** *a.* of or combined with lactic acid, lactate of.

**Milchsäure,** *f.* lactic acid. **-ferment,** *n.* lactic ferment. **-gärung,** *f.* lactic fermentation. **-pilz,** *m.* lactic-acid bacillus. **-salz,** *n.* lactate. **-stäbchen,** *n.* lactic acid bacillus.

**Milch-schicht,** *f.* (*Photog.*) emulsion. **-schleuder,** *f.* (cream) separator. **-strasse,** *f.* Milky Way.

**milchtreibend,** *a.* = milchfördernd.

**Milch-untersuchung,** *f.* examination of milk, milk analysis. **-verfälschung,** *f.* adulteration of milk.

**milch-vermehrend,** *p.a.* = milchfördernd. **-vertreibend,** *p.a.* antigalactic.

**Milch-vieh,** *n.* dairy cattle. **-wa(a)ge,** *f.* lactometer. **-wein,** *m.* kumiss.

**milchweiss,** *a.* milk-white.

**Milchwirtschaft,** *f.* dairy; dairying.

**milchwirtschaftlich,** *a.* dairy, dairying.

**Milchwurz,** *f.* milkwort.

**Milchz.,** *abbrev.* of Milchzucker.

**Milch-zelle,** *f.* (*Bot.*) latex cell. **-zentrifuge,** *f.* (cream) separator. **-zersetzung,** *f.* decomposition of milk.

**Milchzucker,** *m.* milk sugar, lactose. **-agar,** *m.* lactose agar. **-säure,** *f.* saccholactic acid (mucic acid).

**mild, milde,** *a.* mild, soft, tender; mellow; gentle, kind.

**mildern,** *v.t.* temper, mitigate, moderate, modify, soften; correct (acidity). — **mildernd,** *p.a.* (*Pharm.*) mitigant, lenitive.

**Milderung,** *f.* tempering, etc. (see mildern).

**Milderungsmittel,** *n.* mitigant, demulcent, lenitive; corrective.

**mildhart,** *a.* moderately hard.

**Militär-, militärisch,** *a.* military.

**Militärzweck,** *m.* military purpose.

**Milliarde,** *f.* milliard (1,000 million, billion).

**millionstel,** *a.* millionth (part of), micro-.

**Miloriblau,** *n.* milori blue (Prussian blue).

**Milz,** *f.* spleen.

**Milz-.** splenic. **-brand,** *m.* anthrax. **-brandgift,** *n.* anthrax virus. **-drüse,** *f.* spleen.

**Mimose,** *f.* mimosa.

**Mimosengummi,** *n.* gum arabic, esp. a fine variety.

**min.,** *abbrev.* minimum, minimal.

**minder,** *a.* less, smaller, inferior, minor. — *adv.* less.

**Minder-druck,** *m.* diminished pressure. **-ertrag,** *m.* decreased yield. **-gehalt,** *m.* decreased content. **-gewicht,** *n.* underweight; short weight.

**minderhaltig,** *a.* inferior, low-grade.

**Minderheit,** *f.* minority.

**minderjährig,** *a.* under age, minor.

**mindern,** *v.t. & i.* diminish, lessen, decrease.

**Minderung,** *f.* diminution, decrease, reduction.

**Minderwert,** *m.* inferior value.

**minderwertig,** *a.* of lower valence; of inferior quality, low-grade.

**Minder-wertigkeit,** *f.* lower valence; inferior quality. **-zahl,** *f.* minority.

**Mindest-.** least, minimum, lowest. **-druck,** *m.* minimum pressure.

**mindestens,** *adv.*, **zum mindesten.** at least, at the least.

**Mindest-erfordernis,** *n.* minimum requirement. **-wert,** *m.* least value, minimum value.

**Mine,** *f.* mine; lead (for pencils).

**Minen-bombe,** *f.* mine bomb, high-explosive bomb. **-gas,** *n.* mine gas. **-granate,** *f.* mine grenade. **-körper,** *m.* (*Mil.*) shell body. **-pulver,** *n.* blasting powder. **-werfer,** *m.* trench mortar.

**Mineral-ablagerung,** *f.* mineral deposit. **-analyse,** *f.* mineral analysis. **-bad,** *n.* mineral bath. **-beize,** *f.* (*Dyeing*) mineral mordant. **-bestandteil,** *m.* mineral (inorganic) constituent. **-bildner,** *m.* mineral former, mineralizer. **-bildung,** *f.* mineral formation, mineralization. **-blau,** *n.* mineral blue. **-brunnen,** *m.* mineral spring (or well). **-chemie,** *f.* mineral chemistry, inorganic chemistry. **-farbe,** *f.* mineral color; mineral dye. **-farbstoff,** *m.* mineral coloring matter; mineral dye. **-fett,** *n.* mineral fat or grease, specif. Vaseline or petroleum jelly, also ozocerite. **-fettwachs,** *n.* = Mineraltalg. **-gang,** *m.* mineral vein. **-gehalt,** *m.* mineral content. **-gelb,** *n.* mineral yellow. **-gerbung,** *f.* mineral tannage. **-grün,** *n.* mineral green.

**Mineralienkunde,** *f.* mineralogy.

**mineralisch,** *a.* mineral. — **mineralisches Leichenwachs,** ozocerite. — **mineralischer Spiritus,** ethyl alcohol made from acetylene.

**mineralisieren,** *v.t.* mineralize.

**Mineral-kermes,** *m.* kermes mineral. **-laugensalz,** *n.* (*Old Chem.*) sodium carbonate. **-mohr,** *m.* ethiops mineral (essentially amorphous HgS).

**Mineralog, Mineraloge,** *m.* mineralogist.

**Mineralogie,** *f.* mineralogy.

**mineralogisch,** *a.* mineralogical.

**Mineral-öl,** *n.* mineral oil; specif., petroleum. **-ölfirnis,** *m.* mineral-oil varnish. **-ölraffinat,** *n.* refined mineral oil. **-pech,** *n.* mineral pitch, asphalt. **-quelle,** *f.* mineral spring or well. **-reich,** *n.* mineral kingdom. **-rot,** *n.* cinnabar.

-**salz,** *n.* mineral salt. -**säure,** *f.* mineral acid. -**schmiermittel,** *n.* mineral lubricant. -**schmieröl,** *n.* mineral lubricating oil. -**schwarz,** *n.* mineral black (ground graphite or graphitic slate). -**seife,** *f.* mineral soap.

**Mineralstoff,** *m.* mineral substance, mineral matter. -**gehalt,** *m.* mineral content. -**wechsel,** *m.* mineral (or inorganic) metabolism. -**zusammensetzung,** *f.* composition of mineral matter.

**Mineral-talg,** *m.* mineral tallow (hatchettite or ozocerite). -**teer,** *m.* mineral tar, maltha. -**trennung,** *f.* separation of minerals. -**turpeth,** *m.* turpeth mineral (basic mercuric sulfate). -**vorkommen,** *n.* mineral occurrence or deposit. -**wachs,** *n.* mineral wax, ozocerite. -**wasser,** *n.* mineral water. -**wasserfabrikant,** *m.* mineral water manufacturer. -**weiss,** *n.* mineral white. -**wolle,** *f.* mineral wool.

**Minetteerz,** *n.* minet(te) ore.

**minieren,** *v.t.* mine.

**Minimal-.** lowest, minimum. -**betrag,** *m.* lowest amount; lowest rate. -**dosis,** *f.* minimum dose. -**gehalt,** *m.* minimum content. -**oberfläche,** *f.* minimum surface. -**wert,** *m.* minimum value. -**zahl,** *f.* minimum number.

**Minimiformel,** *f.* empirical formula.

**Ministerium,** *n.* ministry; administration.

**Minivalenz,** *f.* minimum valence.

**Minuskel,** *f.* small letter, minuscule.

**Minus-leitung,** *f.* (*Elec.*) negative lead. -**pol,** *m.* negative pole. -**zeichen,** *n.* minus sign.

**minutenlang,** *a.* & *adv.* lasting a minute or minutes, for minutes.

**Minutenzeiger,** *m.* minute hand.

**minutlich,** *a.* per minute.

**Minze,** *f.* mint.

**Miocän, Miocen, Miozän,** *n.* (*Geol.*) Miocene.

**Mipolam.** a polyvinyl plastic. *T.N.*

**mir,** *pron.* to me, me.

**Mirban-essenz,** *f.* essence of mirbane (nitrobenzene). -**öl,** *n.* oil of mirbane (nitrobenzene).

**Mirrhe,** *f.* myrrh.

**Mirte,** *f.* myrtle.

**Misch-.** mixed; mixing. -**anlage,** *f.* mixing plant. -**apparat,** *m.* mixing apparatus, mixer.

**mischbar,** *a.* miscible, mixable.

**Misch-barkeit,** *f.* miscibility. -**behälter,** *m.* mixing vessel (tank, drum, etc.), mixer. -**bestand,** *m.* (*Agric.*) mixed stand, mixed crop. -**bleichen,** *n.* mixed bleaching. -**bottich,** *m.* mixing tub or trough. -**dünger,** *m.* mixed fertilizer; compost. -**element,** *n.* mixed element (a mixture of isotopes).

**mischen,** *v.t.* & *r.* mix; mingle. blend; adulterate; alloy (metals); (*Metal.*) fettle; (*Old Chem.*) combine.

**Mischer,** *m.* mixer; mixing vessel; blender; (*Dyeing*) color mixer. -**eisen,** *n.* (*Metal.*) mixer metal.

**Misch-erz,** *n.* mixed ore. -**fähigkeit,** *f.* mixing property, mixability. -**farbe,** *f.* mixed color, combination color.

**misch-farben, -farbig,** *a.* of mixed color.

**Misch-farbstoff,** *m.* mixed coloring matter or dye; component dye. -**färbung,** *f.* (*Micros.*) mixed staining; (*Dyeing*) combination dyeing or shade. -**flasche,** *f.* mixing bottle. -**gärung,** *f.* mixed fermentation. -**gas,** *n.* mixed gas; specif., semiwater gas. -**gefäss,** *n.* mixing vessel. -**gerbung,** *f.* combination tannage. -**glas,** *n.* mixing glass. -**gut,** *n.* material to be mixed. -**hahn,** *m.* mixing cock. -**hefe,** *f.* composite yeast. -**holländer,** *m.* mixing beater, mixing engine. -**infektion,** *f.* mixed infection. -**kammer,** *f.* mixing chamber. -**katalysator,** *m.* mixed catalyst. -**kegel,** *m.* mixing cone (of a burner). -**kessel,** *m.* mixing kettle. -**komponente,** *f.* component of a mixture. -**kraftstoff,** *m.* mixed fuel. -**kristall,** *m.* mixed crystal, crystalline solid solution. -**ling,** *m.* hybrid, crossbreed. -**masch,** *m.* medley, jumble, mixup. -**maschine,** *f.* mixing machine, mixer. -**material,** *n.* (*Rubber*) filler. -**metall,** *n.* mixed metal, alloy; specif., "misch metal" (an alloy of cerium, lanthanum, etc.). -**molekül,** *n.* mixed molecule (loosely bound union of molecules). -**mühle,** *f.* mixing mill, incorporating mill. -**öl,** *n.* mixed oil. -**oxyd,** *n.* mixed oxide (specif., *Metal.*, of lead and zinc). -**pipette,** *f.* mixing pipet(te). -**polymerisat,** *n.* mixed polymerizate. -**raum,** *m.* mixing space or chamber. -**rohr,** *n.*, -**röhre,** *f.* mixing tube, mixer tube. -**rührwerk,** *n.* mixing apparatus, stirrer. -**salz,** *n.* mixed salt. -**säure,** *f.* mixed acid. -**schmelzpunkt,** *m.* mixed melting point. -**spektrum,** *n.* mixed spectrum. -**strom,** *m.* (*Elec.*) undulatory current. -**trommel,** *f.* mixing drum.

**Mischung,** *f.* mixture; mixing; composition; blend; adulteration; (*Old Chem.*) combination, compound.

**Mischungsbestandteil,** *m.* ingredient of a mixture.

**mischungsfähig,** *a.* miscible.

**Mischungs-formel,** *f.* mixing formula. -**gewicht,** *n.* (*Old Chem.*) combining weight. -**kohle,** *f.* (*Soda*) mixing coal. -**lücke,** *f.* miscibility gap. -**probe,** *f.* test or sample of a mixture; mixing test. -**rechnung,** *f.* (*Math.*) alligation. -**regel,** *f.* rule or law of mixtures. -**verhältnis,** *f.* mixing proportion. -**wärme,** *f.* heat of mixing, heat of mixture. -**zusatz,** *m.* addition to a mixture; filler.

**Misch-ventil,** *n.* mixing valve, mixer valve. -**walzwerk,** *n.* (set of) mixing rollers. -**werk,**

*n.* mixing mill, mixer. **-zement,** *m.* & *n.* mixed cement. **-zylinder,** *m.* mixing cylinder, stoppered cylinder.
**Mispel,** *f.* medlar.
**miss-, Miss-.** mis-, dis-, mal-, de-, ill-.
**miss-achten,** *v.t.* disregard; disdain. **-arten,** *v.i.* degenerate.
**Missbildung,** *f.* malformation; deformity.
**missbilligen,** *v.t.* disapprove of, oppose.
**Missbrauch,** *m.* misuse, abuse.
**missen,** *v.t.* miss; dispense with.
**Miss-erfolg,** *m.* failure. **-ernte,** *f.* crop failure.
**miss-fallen,** *v.t.* be displeasing. **-fällig,** *a.* disagreeable, unpleasant. **-farbig,** *a.* discolored; inharmonious in color.
**Miss-färbung,** *f.* discoloration. **-geschick,** *n.* misfortune; mishap.
**miss-gestaltet,** *a.* deformed, misshapen. **-glücken,** *v.i.* fail.
**Missgriff,** *m.* mistake, blunder.
**miss-griffsicher,** *a.* foolproof. **-handeln,** *v.t.* mistreat, maltreat.
**Misshandlung,** *f.* mistreatment, ill treatment.
**miss-lang,** *pret.* (of misslingen) failed. **-lich,** *a.* doubtful, embarrassing, precarious. **-lingen,** *v.i.* fail, miscarry. **-lungen,** *p.a.* (of misslingen) failed; spoiled, faulty. **-raten,** *v.i.* = misslingen.
**Missstand,** *m.* improper state or condition; inconvenience, nuisance, abuse, grievance.
**misst,** *pr. 3 sing.* (of messen) measures.
**misstrauen,** *v.i.* distrust, mistrust.
**Miss-verhältnis,** *n.* disproportion, asymmetry; incongruity; disparity; inadequacy. **-verständnis,** *n.* misunderstanding.
**missverstehen,** *v.t.* misunderstand.
**Misswachs,** *m.* crop failure.
**Mist,** *m.* manure, dung. **-bad,** *n.* dung bath. **-beet,** *n.* hotbed. **-beize,** *f.* (*Leather*) dung bate; (*Dyeing*) gray steeping.
**Mistel,** *f.* mistletoe.
**misten,** *v.t.* manure, dung, fertilize.
**Mist-jauche,** *f.* liquid manure, dung water. **-pulver,** *n.* powdered manure; specif., poudrette.
**mit,** *prep.* with; by, in, at. — *adv.* together, jointly, along, also.
**Mit-.** fellow, joint, common, co-, com-, sym-. **-arbeit,** *f.* collaboration, coöperation.
**mitarbeiten,** *v.i.* collaborate, participate.
**Mitarbeiter,** *m.* fellow worker, coworker, collaborator, contributor, assistant.
**mit-begreifen,** *v.t.* include; comprize. **-bewegt,** *a.* (of the atomic nucleus) in relative motion, moving.
**Mit-bewegung,** *f.* associated movement, comovement; relative motion (as of the atomic nucleus). **-bewerber,** *m.* competitor.
**mit-einander,** *adv.* with one another, together.
**-führbar,** *a.* capable of being carried along or entrained. **-führen,** *v.t.* carry along, take along, entrain.
**Mit-führung,** *f.* carrying along, entrainment; convection. **-gefühl,** *n.* sympathy.
**mitgerissen,** *p.p.* of mitreissen.
**Mitglied,** *n.* member; fellow. **-schaft,** *f.* membership.
**Mithilfe,** *f.* help, assistance, coöperation.
**mithin,** *conj.* therefore, hence; of course.
**Mitisgrün,** *n.* Mitis green, Paris green.
**mit-klingen,** *v.i.* resonate. **-machen,** *v.t.* join in, take part in, conform to. **-nehmen,** *v.t.* take along, take, share; weaken, exhaust, wear; maltreat, criticize.
**Mitnehmer,** *m.* (*Mach.*) driver, dog, catch, carrier.
**Mitnehmer-.** (*Mach.*) driving, carrying, pushing.
**mitniederreissen,** *v.t.* carry down.
**Mitose,** *f.* mitosis.
**mit-reissen, -schleppen,** *v.t.* carry over (in distillation, etc.); carry down (in precipitation); carry, pull or drag along. **-schwingen,** *v.i* covibrate, resonate.
**Mitschwingen,** *n.* covibration; resonance.
**mitt.,** *abbrev.* (mittels) by means of.
**Mitt.,** *abbrev.* (Mitteilung) communication.
**Mittag,** *m.* midday, noon; south.
**Mittags-essen,** *n.* noon meal. **-kreis,** *m.*, **-linie,** *f.* meridian.
**Mitte,** *f.* middle, midst, center; mean.
**mitteilen,** *v.t.* communicate, impart, give.
**Mitteilung,** *f.* communication, etc. (see mitteilen); report, bulletin, note.
**mittel,** *a.* middle, central, mean, average, median, medium, intermediate, middling.
**Mittel,** *n.* middle; medium; means, agent; (*Pharm.*) remedy; (*Math.*) mean; (*Mining*) mass; average; means, capital; mediation.
**Mittel-.** middle, etc. (see mittel); meso-. **-alter,** *n.* Middle Ages.
**mittelalterlich,** *a.* medieval.
**Mittelasien,** *n.* Central Asia.
**mittelbar,** *a.* indirect, mediate.
**Mittel-bauchgegend,** *f.* mesogastric region. **-benzin,** *n.* medium benzine, medium-heavy gasoline or petrol. **-binder,** *m.* medium-setting cement.
**Mittelblech,** *n.* (*Metal.*) light plate.
**mitteldick,** *a.* medium-thick.
**Mittel-ding,** *n.* intermediate, cross. **-druck,** *m.* medium pressure. **-eck,** *n.*, **-ecke,** *f.* (*Cryst.*) lateral summit. **-erz,** *n.* ore of medium value. **-Europa,** *n.* Central Europe.
**mitteleuropäisch,** *a.* Central-European.
**Mittel-farbe,** *f.* intermediate color; secondary color. **-fehler,** *m.* average error, mean error.

**mittelfein,** *a.* medium-fine.

**Mittel-fell,** *n.* mediastinum. **-fleisch,** *n.* perineum.

**mittelflüssig,** *a.* semifluid.

**Mittel-fuss,** *m.* metatarsus. **-gehirn,** *n.* midbrain, mesencephalon. **-geschwindigkeit,** *f.* mean velocity. **-glied,** *n.* intermediate member (of a series); (*Anat.*) middle phalanx.

**mittelgross,** *a.* medium-sized.

**Mittel-grösse,** *f.* medium size. **-hand,** *f.* metacarpus.

**mittelhart,** *a.* medium-hard, moderately hard.

**Mittel-hartpech,** *n.* medium-hard pitch. **-haut,** *f.* middle coat, tunica media. **-hirn,** *n.* midbrain, mesencephalon. **-keim,** *m.* (*Zoöl.*) mesoblast.

**mittelkörnig,** *a.* medium-grained.

**Mittel-kraft,** *f.* resultant force. **-lage,** *f.* middle position.

**mittellang,** *a.* of medium length.

**Mittel-lauf,** *m.* (in distillation) middle fraction. **-lauge,** *f.* weak lye. **-linie,** *f.* median line; center line; bisectrix; axis: equator.

**mittel-los,** *a.* without means. **-mässig,** *a.* middling, mediocre, average.

**Mittel-meer,** *n.* Mediterranean Sea. **-meerfieber,** *n.* Mediterranean fever (undulant fever).

**mitteln,** *v.t.* average, obtain the mean of; = vermitteln.

**Mittel-öl,** *n.* middle oil; medium-heavy oil. **-ost,** *m.* Middle East. **-produkt,** *n.* middle product; intermediate; middlings. **-punkt,** *m.* center, central point.

**mittels,** *prep.* by means of.

**Mittel-saft,** *m.* (*Sugar*) middle sirup. **-salz,** *n.* neutral salt. **-schicht,** *f.* middle or intermediate layer.

**mittelschwer,** *a.* medium heavy, medium-weight, medium; half-weighted.

**Mittelsenkrechte,** *f.* mean perpendicular; perpendicular bisector.

**mittelst,** *prep.* by means of.

**Mittel-stadt,** *f.* medium-sized city. **-stand,** *m.* middle class.

**mittel-ständig,** *a.* occupying a middle position, middle. **-stark,** *a.* moderately strong.

**Mittel-stellung,** *f.* middle or intermediate position, specif. (*Org. Chem.*), meta position. **-strasse,** *f.* middle course. **-stück,** *n.* middle piece central portion. **-stufe,** *f.* middle (or intermediate) stage. **-teil,** *m.* middle or central part, midsection.

**Mittelung,** *f.* approximation to the mean.

**Mittelwand,** *f.* middle wall; (*Paper*) midfeather; (*Anat.*) mediastinum.

**mittelweich,** *a.* medium-soft, moderately soft.

**Mittel-welle,** *f.* (*Mach.*) countershaft; (*Radio*) medium wave. **-wert,** *m.* mean value, average. **-zahl,** *f.* mean. **-zeug,** *n.* (*Paper*) middle stuff, second stuff.

**mitten,** *adv.* in the middle or midst; midway. — *v.t.* center. **-durch,** *adv. & prep.* through the middle, in between. **-richtig,** *a.* centered.

**Mitternacht,** *f.* midnight; north.

**mittig,** *a.* centric; central; concentric.

**mittler,** *a.* middle, central, etc. (see mittel). **-weile,** *adv.* meanwhile.

**mittragen,** *v.t.* carry along; carry jointly.

**Mittwoch,** *m.* Wednesday.

**mitunter,** *adv.* occasionally, now and then.

**Mit-verwendung,** *f.* concomitant use, coincident use. **-welt,** *f.* present age, contemporaries.

**mitwirken,** *v.i.* coöperate, take part, assist.

**Mitwirkung,** *f.* coöperation, assistance.

**mitziehen,** *v.t.* draw along, pull along.

**Mizell,** *n.*, **Mizelle,** *f.* micell(e), micella.

**Mizellenaufbau,** *m.* micellar structure.

**mk.,** *abbrev.* (mikroskopisch) microscopic(al).

**Mk.,** *abbrev.* (Mark, Marken) mark, marks.

**M.K.,** *abbrev.* (Meterkerze) meter candle.

**mkr.,** *abbrev.* (mikroskopisch) microscopic.

**Möbel,** *n.* piece of furniture. **-lack,** *m.* furniture varnish or lacquer, cabinet varnish. **-leder,** *n.* upholstery leather, furniture leather. **-politur,** *f.* furniture polish. **-stoff,** *m.* upholstery fabric.

**mobil,** *a.* mobile; quick, active.

**mobilisieren,** *v.t.* mobilize.

**Mobilität,** *f.* mobility.

**möblieren,** *v.t.* furnish, fit up.

**mochte,** *pret.* (of mögen) might; liked.

**möchte,** *subj.* (of mögen) might; would like.

**Mock, -stahl,** *m.* German steel (made by direct refining of cast iron); semisteel.

**Mode,** *f.* fashion, mode, style.

**Mode-.** fancy, fashionable. **-farbe,** *f.* fashionable color or shade. **-gewürz,** *n.* allspice, pimento.

**Model,** *m.* modulus; mold.

**Modell,** *n.* model; (*Founding*) pattern. **-glasur,** *f.* glaze for molds.

**modellieren,** *v.t.* model, mold.

**Modellier-holz,** *n.* (wooden) modeling tool. **-masse,** *f.* modeling composition (as clay), plastic mass. **-ton,** *m.* modeling clay. **-wachs,** *n.* modeling wax.

**Modell-lack,** *m.* model varnish, pattern varnish.

**modellmässig,** *a.* according to a model, in terms of a model.

**Modell-sand,** *m.* molding sand; facing sand. **-stoff,** *m.* modeling composition, molding material.

**modeln,** *v.t.* model, mold; modulate.

**Modelung,** *f.* modeling, molding; modulation.

**Moder,** *m.* mold; mud, mire; putridity, decay. **-duft,** *m.* musty or moldy smell; smell of de-

cay. **-erde,** *f.* mold, humus. **-fleck,** *m.* mold stain, mildew stain.
**moderfleckig,** *a.* (*Textiles*) mildewed.
**Modergeruch,** *m.* = Moderduft.
**moderhaft,** *a.* moldy, musty, moldering, molded.
**moderieren,** *v.t.* moderate, regulate.
**moderig,** *a.* musty, moldy; decayed.
**modern,** *v.i.* molder, decay, rot.
**modern,** *a.* modern; fashionable.
**Moder-pilz,** *m.* mold fungus, saprophytic fungus. **-stein,** *m.* rottenstone. **-stoff,** *m.* rotted material, specif. humus.
**Mode-ton,** *m.* fashionable shade. **-waren,** *f.pl.* millinery; fancy goods.
**modifizieren,** *v.t.* modify.
**Modul,** *m.* modulus.
**modulieren,** *v.t.* modulate.
**Modus,** *m.* mode; (of verbs) mood.
**mögen,** *v.i.* be able, may; like, choose.
**mögl.,** *abbrev.* of möglich.
**möglich,** *a.* possible; potential; feasible. **-erweise,** *adv.* possibly; as far as possible.
**Möglichkeit,** *f.* possibility; chance; feasibility, practicability. — **nach —,** as far as possible.
**möglichst,** *adv.* (as much) as possible.
**Mohn,** *m.* poppy. **-gewächse,** *n.pl.* (*Bot.*) Papaveraceae. **-kapsel,** *f.*, **-kopf,** *m.* poppy capsule, poppy head. **-öl,** *n.* poppy-seed oil.
**mohnrot,** *a.* poppy-red.
**Mohn-saft,** *m.* poppy juice, opium. **-samen,** *m.* poppy seed. **-säure,** *f.* meconic acid. **-stoff,** *m.* narcotine. **-stroh,** *n. lit.*, poppy straw (residue from extraction of poppy heads and stems).
**Mohr,** *m.* (*Old Chem.*) black, ethiops; watered fabric, moiré; watered effect, moiré; Moor; negro. — **mineralischer —,** = Mineralmohr.
**Möhre,** *f.* carrot.
**möhrenfarbig,** *a.* carrot-colored, carroty.
**Möhrenfarbstoff,** *m.* carotene.
**Mohrenhirse,** *f.* Kafir corn, durra.
**Möhrenöl,** *n.* carrot oil.
**Mohrrübe,** *f.* carrot.
**Mohrrübenfarbstoff,** *m.* carotene.
**Mohrsches Salz.** Mohr's salt (ammonium ferrous sulfate).
**Moiréappretur,** *f.* moiré finish.
**moirieren,** *v.t.* water, cloud (fabrics).
**mol.,** *abbrev.* (molekular) molecular.
**Mol,** *n.* mole, mol.
**Mol-.** molar.
**Molargewicht,** *n.* molar weight.
**Molarität,** *f.* molarity.
**Molar-volumen,** *n.* molar volume. **-wärme,** *f.* molar heat.
**Molch,** *m.* salamander.
**Molekelgewicht,** *n.* molecular weight.
**Molekül, Molekel,** *n.* molecule.
**Molekular-abstossung,** *f.* molecular repulsion. **-anordnung,** *f.* molecular arrangement. **-anziehung,** *f.* molecular attraction. **-bewegung,** *f.* molecular motion or movement. **-brechung,** *f.*, **-brechungsvermögen,** *n.* molecular refraction. **-drehung,** *f.* molecular rotation. **-druck,** *m.* molecular pressure. **-erscheinung,** *f.* molecular phenomenon. **-formel,** *f.* molecular formula. **-gewicht,** *n.* molecular weight.
**Molekulargewichts-bestimmung,** *f.* molecular-weight determination. **-bestimmungsmethode,** *f.* method for determining molecular weights.
**Molekular-grösse,** *f.* molecular magnitude; molecular weight. **-kraft,** *f.* molecular force. **-reibung,** *f.* molecular friction. **-störung,** *f.* molecular disturbance. **-strahl,** *m.* molecular ray. **-verbindung,** *f.* molecular compound. **-wärme,** *f.* molecular heat. **-wirkung,** *f.* molecular action (or effect). **-zustand,** *m.* molecular state or condition, molecularity.
**Molekül-bau,** *m.* molecular structure. **-gitter,** *n.* molecular lattice. **-haufen,** *m.* molecular cluster. **-masse,** *f.* mole, mol. **-schicht,** *f.* layer of molecules. **-sieb,** *n.* microfilter. **-strahl,** *m.* molecular ray. **-teil,** *m.* part of a molecule. **-umlagerung,** *f.* molecular rearrangement. **-verbindung,** *f.* molecular compound.
**molekülzertrümmernd,** *a.* disrupting or disintegrating the molecule.
**Molekülzertrümmerung,** *f.* destruction of the molecule.
**Molen-bruch,** *m.* mole fraction. **-verhältnis,** *n.* mole ratio, molar ratio.
**Mol.-Gew.,** *abbrev.* (Molekulargewicht) molecular weight.
**Mol-gewicht,** *n.* molar weight, gram-molecular weight; inexactly, molecular weight. **-grösse,** *f.* molar magnitude. **-ion,** *n.* mole ion. **-isierung,** *f.* molization (union of ions to form a molecule).
**molk,** *pret.* (of melken) milked.
**Molke,** *f.*, **Molken,** *f.pl.* whey.
**Molken-butter,** *f.* whey butter. **-eiweiss,** *n.* whey protein. **-farbstoff,** *m.* whey pigment. **-käse,** *m.* whey cheese. **-säure,** *f.* lactic acid. **-wesen,** *n.*, **-wirtschaft, Molkerei,** *f.* dairy.
**molkig, molkicht,** *a.* wheyey, wheyish.
**Möller,** *m.* mixture (of ores and fluxes for smelting), charge, burden.
**möllern,** *v.t.* (*Metal.*) mix (the ores and fluxes for the charge).
**Möllerung,** *f.* (*Metal.*) mixture (of ores and fluxes), charge, burden.
**mollig,** *a.* cosy, snug; soft; (of leather) plump.
**Mol.-Refr.,** *abbrev.* of Molekularrefraktion.
**Mol-refraktion,** *f.* molar refraction. **-verhältnis,** *n.* molar ratio. **-volum, -volumen,** *n.* molar volume. **-wärme,** *f.* molar heat.

**Molybdän,** *n.* molybdenum. **-blau,** *n.* molybdenum blue. **-bleispat,** *m.*, **-blei,** *n.* (*Min.*) wulfenite. **-eisen,** *n.* ferromolybdenum. **-erz,** *n.* molybdenum ore. **-glanz,** *m.* molybdenite.

**molybdänhaltig,** *a.* molybdeniferous.

**Molybdänit,** *n.* molybdenite.

**Molybdän-kies,** *m.* molybdenite. **-ocker,** *m.* molybdic ocher, molybdite. **-oxyd,** *n.* molybdenum oxide (specif., one higher than $Mo_2O_3$). **-oxydul,** *n.* molybdous oxide (MoO, also $Mo_2O_3$).

**molybdänsauer,** *a.* of or combined with molybdic acid, molybdate of.

**Molybdän-säure,** *f.* molybdic acid. **-stahl,** *m.* molybdenum steel.

**Mol-zahl,** *f.* molar number. **-zustand,** *m.* molecular condition.

**Moment,** *n.* moment; momentum; reason, motive, impetus.

**momentan,** *a.* momentary; instantaneous.

**Momentanwert,** *m.* instantaneous value; momentary value.

**Moment-aufnahme,** *f.* instantaneous exposure or photograph. **-bild,** *n.* instantaneous photograph, snapshot. **-klemme,** *f.* instantaneous clamp. **-zünder,** *m.* instantaneous fuse, detonator. **-zündpille,** *f.* flash pellet primer. **-zündung,** *f.* instantaneous ignition or firing.

**Mon.,** *abbrev.* (Monographie) monograph; (Monat) month.

**monalkyliert,** *p.a.* having one alkyl group introduced, monoalkylated.

**Monat,** *m.* month.

**monatelang,** *a.* of a month's duration, a month's; for months.

**Monats-bericht,** *m.* monthly report. **-fluss,** *m.* menses, menstruation. **-heft,** *n.* monthly part or number. **-schrift,** *f.* monthly publication.

**Mönch,** *m.* monk; die, punch, stamp; ridge tile.

**Mönchs-kappe,** *f.* monkshood, aconite. **-kolben,** *m.* plunger, ram. **-pfeffer,** *m.* (*Bot.*) agnus castus.

**Mond,** *m.* moon.

**Mondamin,** *n.* a kind of corn starch (maize flour).

**Möndchen,** *n.* meniscus; lune; little moon.

**mondförmig,** *a.* crescent-shaped, lunate.

**Mond-gas,** *n.* Mond gas (named from its inventor). **-gaserzeuger,** *m.* Mond gas producer. **-glas,** *n.* crown glass. **-licht,** *n.* moonlight. **-milch,** *f.* agaric mineral. **-stein,** *m.* moonstone.

**mono-atomar,** *a.* monatomic. **-basisch,** *a.* monobasic.

**Mono-carbonsäure,** *f.* monocarboxylic acid. **-chloressigsäure,** *f.* monochloroacetic acid. **-chlorhydrat,** *n.* monohydrochloride.

**mono-chrom,** *a.* monochromic, monochrome. **-chromatisch,** *a.* monochromatic. **-cyclisch,** *a.* monocyclic.

**Monoderivat,** *n.* mono derivative.

**Monographie,** *f.* monograph.

**mono-heteroatomig,** *a.* monoheteratomic. **-hydratisch,** *a.* monohydric.

**Monokalium-.** monopotassium.

**mono-klin, -klinisch,** *a.* monoclinic.

**Mononatrium-.** monosodium.

**Monooxy-.** (usually) monohydroxy-; monoxy-.

**monophasisch,** *a.* monophase, single-phase.

**Monopol,** *n.* monopoly; Monopol (*T.N.*) **-seife,** *f.* Monopol soap.

**Monosulfosäure,** *f.* monosulfonic acid.

**monoton,** *a.* monotonous.

**Monoxyd,** *n.* monoxide.

**monozyklisch,** *a.* monocyclic.

**Montag,** *m.* Monday.

**Montage,** *f.* mounting, fitting, setting up, erection, assemblage, assembly. **-bahn,** *f.* assembly line.

**Montan-.** mountain; mining; montanic, montan. **-alkohol,** *m.* montanic alcohol. **-industrie,** *f.* mining industry. **-säure,** *f.* montanic acid. **-wachs,** *n.* montan wax.

**Monteur,** *m.* mounter, fitter, erector, assembler.

**montieren,** *v.t.* mount; fit; set up, erect; assemble; adjust.

**Montierung,** *f.* = Montage.

**Montpelliergelb,** *n.* Montpellier yellow (a lead oxychloride).

**Moor-boden,** *m.* marshy soil. **-erde,** *f.* bog earth, peaty soil, muck soil.

**moorig,** *a.* boggy, peaty.

**Moor-kohle,** *f.* moor coal (black subbituminous coal). **-lauge,** *f.* extract from bog earth or peat. **-mergel,** *m.* bog marl. **-salz,** *n.* salt from peaty soil. **-wasser,** *n.* peat water.

**Moos,** *n.* moss. **-achat,** *m.* moss agate.

**moosartig,** *a.* moss-like, mossy.

**Moss-beere,** *f.* cranberry; whortleberry; (**schwarze**) crowberry (*Empetrum nigrum*). **-grün,** *n.* moss green. **-gummi,** *n.* sponge rubber, rubber sponge.

**moosig, moosicht,** *a.* mossy.

**Moos-pflanzen,** *f.pl.* (*Bot.*) Bryophyta. **-pulver,** *n.* lycopodium powder. **-stärke,** *f.* lichen starch, lichenin. **-tierchen,** *n.* (*Zoöl.*) bryozoan, polyzoan. **-torf,** *m.* peat, peat turf, surface peat. **-wuchs,** *m.* mossy growth.

**moralisch,** *a.* moral; ethical.

**Moränenschutt,** *m.* (*Geol.*) moraine deposit.

**Morast,** *m.* bog, marsh, swamp, morass.

**Morasterz,** *n.* bog ore.

**Morbillen,** *f.pl.* (*Med.*) measles.

**Morchel,** *f.* morel.

**Mord,** *m.* murder.

**mordanzieren,** *v.t.* mordant.

**mörderlich,** *a.* horrible, frightful, fearful.
**morgen,** *adv.* tomorrow.
**Morgen,** *m.* morning; East, Orient; morgen (a varying land measure). **-brot,** *n.* breakfast.
**morgend,** *a.* of tomorrow.
**Morgenland,** *n.* East, Orient.
**morgenländisch,** *a.* oriental.
**morgens,** *adv.* in the morning, each morning.
**Moringagerbsäure, Moringerbsäure,** *f.* moringatannic acid (maclurin).
**Morphium,** *n.* morphine.
**morphotropisch,** *a.* morphotropic.
**morsch,** *a.* rotten, decayed; tender, fragile.
**morschen,** *v.i.* rot, decay.
**Morschheit,** *f.* rottenness, decay.
**Morselle,** *f.* lozenge.
**Mörser,** *m.* mortar (the vessel and the cannon). **-keule,** *f.* pestle. **-probe,** *f.* mortar test. **-stössel,** *m.* pestle.
**Mörtel,** *m.* mortar (the material). **-fuge,** *f.* mortar joint. **-schlamm,** *m.* thin mortar, grout. **-struktur,** *f.* (*Petrog.*) brecciated texture. **-wäsche,** *f.* thin mortar, grout.
**mosaikartig,** *a.* mosaic-like, tesselated.
**mosaisch,** *a.* mosaic.
**Moschus,** *m.* musk. **-drüse,** *f.* musk gland. **-korn,** *n.* musk seed (from abelmosk). **-kraut,** *n.* cat thyme. **-wurzel,** *f.* musk root (specif., the root of *Ferula sumbul*).
**Mosel,** *f.* Moselle (the river). — *m.* Moselle (the wine). **-wein,** *m.* Moselle wine, Moselle.
**Moskovade,** *f.* muscovado.
**Most,** *m.* must (fresh fruit juice). **-messer,** *m.* must gage.
**Mostrich,** *m.* mustard.
**Most-sirup,** *m.* arrope (boiled-down must). **-wa(a)ge,** *f.* must hydrometer. **-wein,** *m.* a lightly fermented fruit juice.
**motivieren,** *v.t.* give the reason for; motivate. — **motiviert,** *y.a.* logical, suitable.
**Motor-antrieb,** *m.* motor drive. **-benzin, Motorenbenzin,** *n.* gasoline, petrol.
**Motoren-benzol,** *n.* motor benzol. **-betriebsstoff,** *m.* motor fuel. **-öl,** *n.* motor oil. **-schmieröl,** *n.* motor (lubricating) oil, engine oil.
**motorisch,** *a.* motor, motive.
**motorisieren,** *v.t.* motorize.
**Motor-kanone,** *f.* (*Mil.*) automatic cannon. **-leistung,** *f.* motor output, engine power.
**motorlos,** *a.* motorless, engineless.
**Motor-luftpumpe,** *f.* motor-driven air pump. **-rad,** *n.* motorcycle. **-strom,** *m.* (*Elec.*) motor current. **-treibmittel,** *n.*, **-treibstoff,** *m.* motor propellant, motor fuel. **-wagen,** *m.* motor car, automobile.
**Motte,** *f.* moth.
**mottenecht,** *a.* mothproof.
**Motten-pulver,** *n.* moth powder, insect powder. **-schutz,** *m.* moth prevention, mothproofing. **-schutzmittel,** *n.* moth preventive, mothproofing agent.
**mottensicher,** *a.* mothproof.
**Motze,** *f.* (*Glass*) marver.
**moulinieren,** *v.t.* throw (silk).
**Moulinierseide,** *f.* thrown silk.
**moussieren,** *v.i.* effervesce, froth, sparkle, fizz.
**moussierend,** *p.a.* effervescent, sparkling, frothing.
**Movragen-insäure,** *f.* mowrageninic acid. **-säure,** *f.* mowragenic acid.
**Movrasäure,** *f.* mowric acid.
**Mudargummi,** *n.* mudar rubber.
**Mudde,** *f.* mud.
**müde,** *a.* tired, weary, fatigued.
**Müdigkeit,** *f.* fatigue, weariness.
**Muff,** *m.* muff; (*Tech.*) sleeve, collar, socket, socket joint, clamp, coupling box; musty or moldy smell, mustiness, moldiness.
**Muffe,** *f.* muff; (*Tech.*) sleeve, etc. (see Muff).
**Muffel,** *f.* muffle. **-farbe,** *f.* muffle color. **-ofen,** *m.* muffle furnace. **-röstofen,** *m.* muffle roaster. **-verfahren,** *n.* (*Zinc*) distillation process, retort process.
**Muffen-rohr,** *n.* socket pipe. **-verbindung,** *f.* sleeve joint; socket joint.
**muffig, müffig,** *a.* musty, moldy.
**Mufflerie,** *f.* pottery.
**Mugaseide,** *f.* muga silk, muga.
**Mühe,** *f.* pains, trouble.
**mühelos,** *a.* without trouble, effortless, easy.
**mühen,** *v.r.* trouble, take pains.
**mühevoll,** *a.* troublesome, laborious.
**Mühle,** *f.* mill; crusher, grinder, etc.
**Mühlenstaub,** *m.* mill dust.
**Mühlstein,** *m.* millstone.
**Mühsal,** *n.* difficulty, trouble.
**mühsam,** *a.* troublesome, toilsome, hard.
**Mulde,** *f.* trough; basin, bowl; tray; tub; bucket; mold; (*Metal.*) pig mold, pig.
**muldenartig,** *a.* trough-shaped, basin-shaped, (*Geol.*) synclinal.
**Mulden-blei,** *n.* pig lead. **-heizung,** *f.* (*Rubber*) cure in molds.
**mulinieren,** *v.t.* throw (silk).
**Mulinierseide,** *f.* thrown silk.
**Mull,** *m.* & *n.* mull, (light) muslin; lint; = Müll.
**Müll,** *n.* & *m.* dust, dry mold; refuse.
**Mullbinde,** *f.* lint bandage.
**Müller,** *m.* miller.
**Mullerde,** *f.* humus, mold.
**Müllerei,** *f.* milling, grinding; milling plant.
**Müller-gaze,** *f.* (fine) bolting cloth. **-tuch,** *n.* bolting cloth.
**Müllfeuerung,** *f.* refuse furnace.
**Mullkrapp,** *m.* mull madder.

**Mulm,** *m.* ore dust, earthy ore; mold, humus; decay.
**mulmen,** *v.t.* pulverize. — *v.i.* fall to powder.
**mulmig,** *a.* dusty; earthy; friable; decayed.
**multerig,** *a.* moldy; dusty; decayed.
**multipel,** *a.* multiple.
**Multiplikator,** *m.* multiplier.
**multiplizieren,** *v.t.* multiply.
**Multiplizität,** *f.* multiplicity.
**multrig,** *a.* moldy; dusty; decayed.
**Mumie,** *f.* mummy.
**Mumienbildung,** *f.* mummification.
**mumifizieren,** *v.t.* mummify.
**Mumme,** *f.* mum (a strong beer).
**München,** *n.* Munich.
**Münchener,** *a.* Munich, of Munich.
**Mund,** *m.* mouth; opening, muzzle, vent, orifice, etc. **-art,** *f.* dialect; idiom. **-drüse,** *f.* oral gland, buccal gland.
**munden,** *v.i.* taste good, be palatable.
**münden,** *v.i.* discharge, empty, open.
**Mundhöhle,** *f.* oral cavity.
**mundig,** *a.* palatable, tasty.
**mündig,** *a.* of age.
**Mund-klemme,** *f.* lockjaw. **-leim,** *m.* mouth glue (to be moistened with the mouth).
**mündlich,** *a.* oral, verbal.
**Mund-loch,** *n.* mouth, orifice; (*Expl.*) fuse hole. **-schicht,** *f.* chemical layer (in a gas mask). **-schleim,** *m.* oral mucus. **-schleimhaut,** *f.* mucous membrane of the mouth. **-speichel,** *m.* saliva (of the mouth). **-speicheldrüse,** *f.* salivary gland. **-stück,** *n.* mouthpiece; nozzle.
**Mündung,** *f.* mouth; opening, aperture, orifice, etc.; muzzle (of a gun); terminus (of a railway).
**Mündungs-energie,** *f.* muzzle energy. **-feuer,** *n.* (of a gun) muzzle flash.
**mündungsfeuerfrei,** *a.* (of powder) flashless.
**Mündungsgeschwindigkeit,** *f.* muzzle velocity.
**Mund-verdauung,** *f.* oral digestion. **-wasser,** *n.* gargle, mouth wash.
**Munition,** *f.* ammunition, munition(s).
**munter,** *a.* live, lively, cheerful, vigorous.
**Muntzmetall,** *n.* Muntz metal (copper-zinc alloy).
**Münz-anstalt,** *f.* mint. **-beschickung,** *f.* alloyage.
**Münze,** *f.* coin; money; medal; mint (for coining); mint (the herb).
**münzen,** *v.t.* mint, coin. **-ähnlich, -förmig,** *a.* coin-shaped, nummular, nummiform.
**Münz-erz,** *n.* money ore. **-gehalt,** *m.* fineness (of coins). **-gold,** *n.* mint gold, standard gold. **-kenner,** *m.* numismatist. **-legierung,** *f.* coinage alloy. **-wesen,** *n.* coinage, minting. **-zusatz,** *m.* alloy (in coins).

**mürbe,** *a.* mellow, tender, soft; brittle, friable; (*Metal.*) short.
**Mürbemachemittel,** *n.* softening agent; shortening agent.
**Mürbigkeit,** *f.* mellowness, etc. (see mürbe).
**muriatisch,** *a.* muriatic (hydrochloric).
**murmeln,** *v.i.* murmur.
**Murmeltier,** *n.* marmot.
**Mus,** *n.* pulp; jam, marmalade, (fruit) sauce.
**Musafaser,** *f.* Manila hemp.
**musartig,** *a.* pulpy, thick.
**Muschel,** *f.* (mussel) shell; mussel; cup; external ear.
**muschelförmig,** *a.* shell-shaped.
**Muschelgold,** *n.* ormolu.
**muschelig,** *a.* conchoidal; shelly, shell-like.
**Muschel-kalk,** *m.* shell lime; shell limestone. **-kalkstein,** *m.* shell limestone. **-marmor,** *m.* shell marble, lumachel. **-mergel,** *m.* shell marl. **-sand,** *m.* shell sand. **-schieber,** *m.* (*Mach.*) mushroom valve. **-seide,** *f.* byssus silk. **-tier,** *n.* shellfish, esp. a mollusk.
**Musiker,** *m.* musician.
**Musiv-.** mosaic. **-arbeit,** *f.* mosaic work, mosaic. **-gold,** *n.* mosaic gold. **-silber,** *n.* mosaic silver.
**Muskat-balsam,** *m.* nutmeg butter. **-birne,** *f.* musk pear. **-blüte,** *f.* mace. **-blütöl,** *n.* oil of mace, mace oil. **-butter,** *f.* nutmeg butter.
**Muskate,** *f.* nutmeg.
**Muskateller,** *m.* muscatel.
**Muskatenblüte,** *f.* mace.
**Muskat-fett,** *n.* nutmeg butter. **-nuss,** *f.* nutmeg. **-nussöl, -öl,** *n.* nutmeg oil.
**Muskel,** *m.* muscle.
**Muskel-.** muscular, myo-. **-eiweiss,** *n.* myosin. **-empfindung,** *f.* muscular sensation. **-farbstoff,** *m.* muscle pigment. **-faser,** *f.* muscular fiber. **-fleisch,** *n.* muscular substance. **-gewebe,** *n.* muscular tissue. **-gift,** *n.* muscle poison. **-lehre,** *f.* myology. **-masse,** *f.* muscular substance. **-saft,** *m.* muscle juice. **-stoff,** *m.* sarcosine. **-zucker,** *m.* inositol.
**Muskowit, Muskovit,** *m.* (*Min.*) muscovite.
**muss,** *pr. 1 & 3 sing.* (of müssen) must.
**Muss,** *n.* = Mus; necessity.
**Musse,** *f.* leisure.
**Musselin,** *m.* muslin.
**müssen,** *v.i.* must, be obliged, ought.
**mussieren,** *v.i.* effervesce, sparkle, fizz.
**müssig,** *a.* idle.
**musste,** *pret.* (of müssen) had, was obliged.
**Muster,** *n.* pattern; sample, specimen; model, type; standard; example; design. **-exemplar,** *n.* type specimen. **-flasche,** *f.* sample bottle.
**muster-gültig,** *a.* model, standard, ideal, classic. **-haft,** *a.* standard, typical; exemplary.

**Muster-hahn,** *m.* sampling cock, bleeder. **-karte,** *f.* pattern card, sample card.

**mustermässig,** *a.* standard, typical.

**mustern,** *v.t.* figure (fabrics); emboss (paper); muster; (*Dyeing*) bring to shade; inspect, examine. — **gemustert,** *p.a.* figured, fancy.

**Muster-nehmer,** *m.* sampler. **-probe,** *f.* sample, specimen. **-sammlung,** *f.* specimen collection. **-schutz,** *m.* registered pattern, petty patent. **-stück,** *n.* test specimen, sample.

**mustertreu,** *a.* (*Textiles*) true to shade.

**Muster-vorlage,** *f.* (*Dyeing*) shade to be matched. **-zeichnung,** *f.* design. **-ziehung,** *f.* sampling.

**Mut,** *m.* courage, spirit; humor, mood; anger.

**Muter,** *m.* claimant, petitioner, applicant.

**mutig,** *a.* spirited, courageous.

**mut-massen,** *v.t.* guess, suppose, conjecture. **-masslich,** *a.* supposed, conjectural, apparent.

**Mutmassung,** *f.* conjecture, supposition.

**Mutter,** *f.* mother; matrix; uterus; nut, female screw.

**Mutter-.** mother, maternal; parent; uterine. **-boden,** *m.* (*Biol.*) parent tissue; (*Agric.*) native soil. **-erde,** *f.* garden mold; native soil. **-essig,** *m.* mother of vinegar. **-fass,** *n.* (*Vinegar*) mother vat. **-fieber,** *n.* puerperal fever. **-form,** *f.* (*Ceram.*) master mold; (*Biol.*) parent form. **-gestein,** *n.* (*Mining*) gang(ue), matrix; (*Petroleum*) source rock. **-gewebe,** *n.* mother tissue, matrix; uterine tissue. **-gewinde,** *n.* (*Mach.*) female thread. **-gummi, -harz,** *n.* galbanum. **-hefe,** *f.* mother yeast, parent yeast.

**Mutterkorn,** *n.* ergot. **-pilz,** *m.* ergot fungus. **-säure,** *f.* ergotic acid. **-vergiftung,** *f.* ergotism.

**Mutter-kraut,** *n.* feverfew. **-kuchen,** *m.* placenta. **-kümmel,** *m.* cumin. **-lauge,** *f.* mother liquor. **-leib,** *m.* womb, uterus. **-nelke,** *f.* mother clove. **-pech,** *n.* (*Med.*) meconium. **-pflanze,** *f.* parent plant. **-scheibe,** *f.* (*Mach.*) nut washer. **-schlüssel,** *m.* nut wrench. **-sicherung,** *f.* (*Mach.*) nut lock. **-stoff,** *m.*, **-substanz,** *f.* mother substance, parent substance; matrix. **-verschluss,** *m.* (*Mach.*) nut lock. **-zelle,** *f.* mother cell, parent cell. **-zimt,** *m.* cassia.

**Mutung,** *f.* claim, demand, concession.

**Mütze,** *f.* cap.

**mützenförmig,** *a.* cap-shaped.

**mval.,** *abbrev.* of milliequivalent(s).

**m.W.,** *abbrev.* (meines Wissens) so far as I know.

**Mycelpilze,** *m.pl.* (*Bot.*) Hyphomycetes, Moniliales.

**mydriatisch,** *a.* mydriatic.

**Mykose, Mykosis,** *f.* (*Med.*) mycosis.

**Mykosterin,** *n.* mycosterol.

**mykotisch,** *a.* (*Med.*) mycotic.

**Myrika-fett, -wachs,** *n.* myrtle wax.

**Myristicinsäure,** *f.* myristicic acid.

**Myristinsäure,** *f.* myristic acid.

**Myronsäure,** *f.* myronic acid.

**Myrrhe,** *f.*, **Myrrhenharz,** *n.* myrrh.

**Myrrhenöl,** *n.* oil of myrrh, myrrh oil.

**Myrte,** *f.* myrtle.

**Myrtengewächse,** *n.pl.* (*Bot.*) Myrtaceae.

**myrtengrün,** *a.* myrtle-green.

**Myrten-öl,** *n.* myrtle oil. **-wachs,** *n.* myrtle wax.

**mystifizieren,** *v.t.* mystify.

**mystisch,** *a.* mystic, mystical.

**Myzel,** *n.* mycelium. **-pilze,** *m.pl.* = Mycelpilze.

# N

**n,** *symbol.* (Nutzeffect) efficiency.
**n.,** *abbrev.* normal; neutral; (nördlich) northern; (netto) net; (nach) after.
**N.,** *abbrev.* (nachmittags) afternoon, P.M.; (nachts) at night; (Nord, Norden) north.
**Nabe,** *f.* (*Mach.*) hub, nave, boss.
**Nabel,** *m.* navel; (*Bot.*) hilum.
**Nabel-.** umbilical, navel. **-kraut,** *n.* navelwort.
**nach,** *prep.* (sometimes following its object). to, toward, after, according to, with respect to, (smell, taste) of. — *adv.* behind, after. — **— und —,** little by little, gradually, by degrees.
**Nach-, nach-.** (with nouns) after, post-, subsequent, additional, supplementary, secondary, second, counter-; (with verbs) after, again, re-, post-.
**nachahmen,** *v.t. & i.* imitate, copy, counterfeit, adulterate. — **nachgeahmt,** *p.a.* imitation, counterfeit, fictitious.
**Nach-ahmung,** *f.* imitation; adulteration. **-arbeit,** *f.* subsequent treatment; retouching, etc. (see nacharbeiten).
**nach-arbeiten,** *v.t.* retouch, rework, finish, dress; repair, mend, recondition; copy. **-äschern,** *v.t.* ash (subsequently); (*Leather*) lime (after unhairing).
**Nachavivage,** *f.* (*Textiles*) after-brightening.
**Nachbar,** *m.* neighbor.
**Nachbar-.** neighboring, adjoining, adjacent, vicinal. **-atom,** *n.* neighbor(ing) atom. **-linie,** *f.* adjacent line, neighboring line. **-schaft,** *f.* neighborhood, vicinity. **-stellung,** *f.* neighboring position.
**nach-bearbeiten,** *v.t.* finish, dress; rework. **-behandeln,** *v.t.* treat subsequently, aftertreat.
**Nachbehandlung,** *f.* aftertreatment.
**Nachbehandlungs-bad,** *n.* aftertreating bath. **-farbstoff,** *m.* dye requiring aftertreatment.
**nachbeizen,** *v.t.* (*Dyeing*) redye, also sadden.
**Nachbeschickung,** *f.* (*Metal.*) aftercharging, aftercharge.
**nachbessern,** *v.t.* improve upon, touch up, retouch, strengthen (a solution), repair.
**Nachbesserung,** *f.* improvement, etc. (see nachbessern).
**Nachbild,** *n.* after-image; copy, imitation.
**nachbilden,** *v.t.* copy, reproduce, imitate, counterfeit.
**Nach-bildung,** *f.* copying, etc. (see nachbilden); reproduction; copy, imitation. **-blasen,** *n.* (*Metal.*) afterblow.
**nachbläuen,** *v.i.* turn bluish.
**Nachbleiche,** *f.* (*Textiles*) final bleach.
**nach-bleichen,** *v.t.* bleach again, afterbleach. **-bohren,** *v.t.* rebore.
**Nachbrand,** *m.* second burning, second fire.
**nach-brauen,** *v.t.* brew again. **-brennen,** *v.i.* smolder. — *v.t.* afterburn, burn again, etc. (see brennen).
**Nachbrenner,** *m.* (*Mil.*) hang-fire shell.
**nachchromieren,** *v.t.* (*Dyeing*) afterchrome, back-chrome.
**Nachchromierung,** *f.* afterchroming.
**Nachchromierungsfarbstoff,** *m.* afterchroming (or afterchromed) dye.
**Nachdampf,** *m.* (*Mining*) afterdamp, choke damp.
**nach-dampfen,** *v.t.* resteam. **-decken,** *v.t* (*Dyeing*) fill up, top.
**nachdem,** *adv.* afterward, hereafter. — *conj.* after, according as.
**nachdenken,** *v.i.* meditate, reflect.
**Nachdruck,** *m.* energy, emphasis; reprinting; reprint.
**nachdrücklich,** *a.* energetic; emphatic.
**Nachdruckrecht,** *n.* copyright.
**nach-dunkeln,** *v.t. & i.* darken; (*Dyeing*) sadden. **-eichen,** *v.t.* restandardize, recalibrate; realine.
**Nacheichung,** *f.* restandardization, recalibration; realinement.
**Nacheifer,** *m.* emulation.
**nacheilen,** *v.i.* lag, retard; follow, trail.
**Nacheilwinkel,** *m.* angle of lag.
**nacheinander,** *adv.* one after another, successively.
**Nachen,** *m.* boat.
**nacherhitzen,** *v.t.* reheat; (*Metal.*) temper.
**Nachf.,** *abbrev.* (Nachfolger) successor(s).
**nach-fallen,** *v.i.* fall (after); cave. **-färben,** *v.t.* dye again, redye; counterstain.
**Nachfederung,** *f.* hysteresis.
**Nachfilter,** *m.* second filter.
**nach-filtern,** *v.t.* filter again, refilter. **-fixieren,** *v.t.* afterfix.
**Nachflammer,** *m.* (*Mil.*) flareback.
**nach-fleischen,** *v.t.* (*Leather*) reflesh. **-fliessen,** *v.i.* flow after or again.
**Nachfolge,** *f.* succession; sequence. **-kern,** *m.* product nucleus.
**nachfolgen,** *v.i.* follow, succeed. — **nachfol-**

**gend,** *p.a.* following, subsequent; continuous, consecutive.
**Nachfolger,** *m.* successor; imitator.
**nachforschen,** *v.i.* search, make search, investigate.
**Nach-forschung,** *f.* research, investigation, inquiry, search, scrutiny. **-frage,** *f.* inquiry; (*Com.*) demand.
**Nachfraktionier-turm,** *m.* afterfractionating tower. **-ung,** *f.* afterfractionation.
**nachführen,** *v.t.* carry after, follow up; reset, readjust.
**nachfüllen,** *v.t.* fill up, replenish, add to.
**Nachgare,** *f.* refinished state; refinishing.
**nachgären,** *v.i.* undergo after-fermentation; ferment again.
**Nachgärfass,** *n.* (*Brewing*) cleansing cask.
**Nachgärung,** *f.* after-fermentation, secondary fermentation.
**Nachgärungs-fass,** *n.* (*Brewing*) cleansing vat. **-hefe,** *f.* after-fermentation yeast.
**Nachgasen,** *n.* subsequent gassing.
**nach-geahmt,** *p.a.* see nachahmen. **-geben,** *v.i.* give way, yield.
**Nachgeburt,** *f.* afterbirth.
**Nachgeburts-.** placental.
**nachgehen,** *v.i.* (of timepieces) be slow; (with dative) follow, follow up.
**nach-gemacht,** *p.a.* see nachmachen. **-gerben,** *v.t.* tan again, retan.
**Nach-gerbebrühe,** *f.* retanning liquor. **-gerböl,** *n.* retanning oil.
**Nach-geruch,** *m.* aftersmell. **-geschmack,** *m.* aftertaste.
**nachgiebig,** *a.* flexible, pliable; yielding; compliant.
**Nachgiebigkeit,** *f.* flexibility, pliability.
**nach-giessen,** *v.t.* pour again, add more; refill, replenish. **-gilben,** *v.i.* turn yellowish, yellow. **-glätten,** *v.t.* repolish, etc. (see glätten). **-glühen,** *v.t.* & *i.* glow again; phosphoresce; reanneal. **-grünen,** *v.i.* turn green(ish), green.
**Nach-guss,** *m.* second pouring, refilling; (*Brewing*) after-mash, second wort, also sparging water and sparging. **-hall,** *m.* reverberation; resonance, echo.
**nachhaltig,** *a.* lasting, enduring; persevering.
**Nachhaltigkeit,** *f.* durability; perseverance.
**nachhärten,** *v.t.* harden subsequently or again.
**nachher,** *adv.* afterward, hereafter, later.
**nachherig,** *a.* subsequent.
**Nachhilfe,** *f.* assistance, aid.
**nachhinken,** *v.i.* lag.
**Nachhirn,** *n.* afterbrain, metencephalon.
**nach-hitzen,** *v.t.* reheat; (*Metal.*) temper. **-holen,** *v.t.* recover, make up.
**Nach-hut,** *f.* rear, rear guard. **-impfung,** *f.* reinoculation. **-infektion,** *f.* reinfection. **-klang,** *m.* ring, echo; resonance.
**nachkochen,** *v.t.* continue boiling, boil again.
**Nachkomme,** *m.* descendant, successor.
**nachkommen,** *v.i.* follow; overtake; comply with, perform, fulfill.
**Nachkondensator,** *m.* secondary condenser.
**Nachkriegs-.** postwar.
**nachkrispeln,** *v.t.* regrain (leather).
**nachkühlen,** *v.t.* cool again, recool, aftercool.
**Nach-kühler,** *m.* aftercooler, recooler. **-kühlung,** *f.* aftercooling, recooling.
**nachkupfern,** *v.t.* aftertreat with copper or a copper compound, aftercopper.
**Nach-kupferung,** *f.* aftercoppering. **-kupplung,** *f.* aftercoupling.
**nachladen,** *v.t.* recharge.
**Nach-ladung,** *f.* additional charge, recharge. **-lass,** *m.* relaxation, intermission; diminution; deduction; legacy.
**nachlassen,** *v.t.* temper, anneal (glass or metals); slacken, relax; let loose, let go; allow (gases) to expand; abate, deduct; leave behind, leave. — *v.i.* slacken, subside.
**nachlässig,** *a.* negligent, remiss, careless.
**Nachlauf,** *m.* last runnings, faints; wake.
**nachlaufen,** *v.i.* run after, follow.
**Nachlaufflotte,** *f.* (*Dyeing*) feeding liquor.
**nach-leimen,** *v.t.* resize. **-leuchten,** *v.i.* shine afterward, phosphoresce.
**Nachleuchten,** *n.* afterglow, phosphorescence.
**nachliefern,** *v.t.* furnish subsequently; supplement.
**Nachluft,** *f.* additional air.
**nachm.,** *abbrev.* (nachmittags) P.M.
**nachmachen,** *v.t.* imitate, counterfeit. — **nachgemacht,** *p.a.* imitation, counterfeit, artificial.
**Nachmaische,** *f.* after-mash.
**nachmalig,** *a.* subsequent.
**nach-mattieren,** *v.t.* deluster, deaden (subsequently). **-messen,** *v.t.* remeasure, check, control.
**Nach-mittag,** *m.* afternoon. **-mühlenöl,** *n.* inferior olive oil from the marc. **-musterfärben,** *n.* dyeing to pattern.
**Nachnahme,** *f.* reimbursement. — **unter —,** C.O.D.
**nachnuancieren,** *v.t.* shade, shade off.
**Nach-öl,** *n.* an inferior olive oil. **-oxydation,** *f.* after-oxidation.
**nachpolieren,** *v.t.* repolish.
**Nachpresse,** *f.* re-pressing machine; (*Paper*) press rolls.
**nach-pressen,** *v.t.* re-press. **-prüfen,** *v.t.* reexamine, check.
**Nachprüfung,** *f.* reëxamination, aftertest, checking, check.
**nach-putzen,** *v.t.* repolish, finish off. **-rechnen,** *v.t.* recalculate, check, verify.
**Nachrechnung,** *f.* recalculation, checking.
**nachregeln,** *v.t.* readjust, rearrange.

**Nach-reife,** *f.*, **-reifen,** *n.*, **-reifung,** *f.* subsequent or secondary ripening or maturing. **-reiniger,** *m.* repurifier; cleaner. **-reinigung,** *f.* afterpurification; final cleaning.

**Nachricht,** *f.* news; information; notice, message, communication.

**nach-richten,** *v.t.* adjust, arrange, aline; readjust, reset. **-sacken,** *v.r.* & *i.* sink, settle, sag, drop. **-salzen,** *v.t.* salt again, resalt.

**Nachsatz,** *m.* addition, (of a dye bath) feeding. **-lösung,** *f.* (*Dyeing*) feeding liquor.

**nachschärfen,** *v.t.* resharpen; restrengthen (a solution).

**Nachschlage-buch, -werk,** *n.* reference work.

**nach-schlagen,** *v.t.* look up, refer to, consult. **-schleifen,** *v.t.* regrind, resharpen.

**Nachschlüssel,** *m.* master key; skeleton key.

**nach-schmecken,** *v.i.* leave an aftertaste. **-schmieren,** *v.t.* relubricate.

**Nach-schrift,** *f.* transcript; postscript. **-schub,** *m.* supply, supplies; supplement. **-schuss,** *m.* backshot. **-schwaden,** *m.* afterdamp, choke damp.

**nach-schwärzen,** *v.t.* blacken (as leather by topping with iron salts). **-schwefeln,** *v.t.* (*Textiles*) stove afterward. **-schwelen,** *v.i.* continue to smolder. **-sehen,** *v.i.* look, search, see (to). — *v.t.* look after, look over, inspect, overhaul; overlook, excuse. **-seigern,** *v.t.* (*Metal.*) liquate again. **-setzen,** *v.t.* add; recharge; put after; postpone.

**Nach-setzlöffel,** *m.* spoon or ladle for adding something, as ore. **-sicht,** *f.* inspection; forbearance, indulgence.

**nach-spannen,** *v.t.* retighten. **-speisen,** *v.t.* replenish, feed, feed up. **-spülen,** *v.t.* rinse out (the last parts of), rewash, rerinse.

**nächst,** *adv.* & *prep.* next.

**nächste,** *a.* next, nearest.

**Nachstechbier,** *n.* feed beer.

**nach-stechen,** *v.t.* (*Brewing*) top up. **-stehen,** *v.i.* follow; be inferior. — **-stehend,** *p.a.* following, below. **-stellbar,** *a.* regulable, adjustable.

**Nachstellbarkeit,** *f.* adjustability.

**nachstellen,** *v.t.* regulate, adjust; put back.

**Nachstellvorrichtung,** *f.* adjusting device.

**nächstens,** *adv.* next time, shortly.

**nächst-folgend,** *a.* next following, next in order. **-höher,** *a.* next higher. **-näher,** *a.* next nearest. **-niedrig,** *a.* next lower.

**nachstrahlen,** *v.i.* phosphoresce.

**Nachstrahler, Nachstrahlstoff,** *m.* phosphorescent substance, phosphor.

**Nachstrahlung,** *f.* phosphorescence.

**nachsuchen,** *v.t.* search for; inquire into, investigate; apply for.

**Nachsud,** *m.* second boiling, afterboiling, etc. (see Sud).

**Nacht,** *f.* night.

**nachtannieren,** *v.t.* backtan.

**Nacht-blau,** *n.* night blue. **-blindheit,** *f.* night blindness, nyctalopia.

**Nachteil,** *m.* disadvantage, drawback, difficulty, detriment, damage.

**nachteilig,** *a.* disadvantageous, detrimental.

**Nachtgrün,** *n.* night green.

**Nachtigall,** *f.* nightingale.

**Nachtisch,** *m.* dessert.

**Nachtkerze,** *f.* night light; evening primrose (*Oenothera*).

**nachtleuchtend,** *a.* (*Biol.*) noctilucent, bioluminescent.

**Nachtmahl,** *n.* supper.

**nachtönen,** *v.t.* (*Dyeing*) aftertone, backtone (specif., tone to a tinted white). — *v.i.* echo, ring.

**Nachtrag,** *m.* supplement, addendum.

**nach-tragen,** *v.t.* add, append. **-träglich,** *a.* supplementary, additional; extra; subsequent, later.

**Nach-tragung,** *f.* addition, supplement. **-tripper,** *m.* (*Med.*) gleet.

**nachtrocknen,** *v.t.* dry again, redry.

**nachts,** *adv.* at night, by night.

**Nachtschatten,** *m.* nightshade. **-gewächse,** *n.pl.* (*Bot.*) Solanaceae.

**Nachverbrennung,** *f.* afterburning, aftercombustion.

**nachverdampfen,** *v.t.* evaporate again, re-evaporate.

**Nach-verdampfung,** *f.* re-evaporation. **-vergasung,** *f.* aftergasification. **-verseifung,** *f.* aftersaponification. **-vulkanisation,** *f.* aftervulcanization, aftercure.

**nach-walzen,** *v.t.* reroll. **-wärmen,** *v.t.* reheat, afterheat.

**Nachwärmeofen,** *m.* reheating furnace.

**nach-waschen,** *v.t.* wash (after some operation); rewash. **-weichen,** *v.t.* (*Brewing*) couch.

**Nach-weichen,** *n.*, **-weiche,** *f.* (*Brewing*) couching.

**Nachweis,** *m.* detection; proof; information; index.

**nachweisbar,** *a.* detectable; demonstrable; evident.

**nachweisen,** *v.t.* detect; discover; prove, demonstrate, establish; identify; point out, indicate, refer to.

**nachweislich,** *a.* = nachweisbar.

**Nachweismittel,** *n.* means of detection or proof, agent for detection.

**Nachweisung,** *f.* detection; proof, demonstration; identification; information; indication; reference.

**Nachweisungsmittel,** *n.* = Nachweismittel.

**Nach-welt,** *f.* posterity. **-wert,** *m.* later value, future value.

**nachwiegen,** *v.t.* weigh again, reweigh.
**Nach-wirkung,** *f.* after-effect, secondary effect. **-wirkzeit,** *f.* after-effect period, specif. decay period. **-wuchs,** *m.* second growth, after-growth; new generation. **-würze,** *f.* second wort.
**nach-zählen,** *v.t.* recount, count again. **-ziehen,** *v.t.* (re)tighten; fill up, feed; exhaust; draw after.
**Nachzündung,** *f.* (*Mach.*) retarded ignition.
**Nacken,** *m.* neck, nape.
**Nacken-.** cervical. **-drüse,** *f.* cervical gland.
**nackt,** *a.* naked, bare; plain; open. **-früchtig,** *a.* (*Bot.*) gymnocarpous.
**Nadel,** *f.* needle; pin.
**nadelartig,** *a.* needle-like, acicular.
**Nadel-ausschlag,** *m.* throw (deflection) of the needle. **-baum,** *m.* coniferous tree. **-blatt,** *n.* (*Bot.*) acicular leaf, needle.
**Nädelchen,** *n.* little needle (or pin).
**Nadel-eisenerz,** *n.*, **-eisenstein,** *m.* needle iron ore (göthite in acicular crystals). **-erz,** *n.* needle ore (aikinite in acicular crystals). **-faser,** *f.* acicular fiber.
**nadelförmig,** *a.* needle-shaped, acicular.
**Nadel-holz,** *n.* conifers (collectively), esp. pines and firs; wood of conifers, soft wood. **-hölzer,** *n.pl.* (*Bot.*) Pinales, Coniferae. **-holzkohle,** *f.* soft-wood charcoal. **-holzteer,** *m.* soft-wood tar, (loosely) pine tar. **-holzzellstoff,** *m.* cellulose (or pulp) from conifers.
**nadelig,** *a.* needly, acicular.
**Nadel-punktierung,** *f.* acupuncture. **-spitze,** *f.* pin point, needle point. **-stein,** *m.* needle-stone (natrolite). **-stich,** *m.* needle prick; needle hole. **-ventil,** *n.* needle valve. **-zeolith,** *m.* needle zeolite (natrolite). **-zinnerz,** *n.* acicular cassiterite.
**Nafta,** *f.* naphtha.
**Naftalin,** *n.* naphthalene.
**Nagel,** *m.* nail; spike; peg; claw. **-bohrer,** *m.* gimlet.
**Nägelchen,** *n.* little nail, brad, tack.
**Nägelein,** *n.* little nail; tack; clove; pink. **-öl,** *n.* clove oil. **-pfeffer,** *m.* allspice, pimento. **-rinde,** *f.*, **-zimt,** *m.* clove bark, clove cinnamon.
**Nagel-flue, -fluh,** *f.* (*Geol.*) Nagelfluh (an Alpine conglomerate).
**nagelförmig,** *a.* nail-shaped.
**nageln,** *v.t.* nail; spike, peg, tack, etc
**nagelneu,** *a.* brand-new.
**Nagel-politur,** *f.* nail polish, nail varnish. **-probe,** *f.* nail test.
**nagen,** *v.t.* & *i.* gnaw; eat, corrode.
**Nager,** *m.*, **Nagetier,** *n.* rodent.
**Näglein, Näglein-.** = Nägelein, Nägelein-.
**Näh-.** sewing.
**Nahaufnahme,** *f.* (*Photog.*) close-up view.
**nahe,** *a.* near, adjacent; imminent. — *adv.* near, close. — **— legen,** make plain, bring home.
**Nähe,** *f.* nearness, closeness, proximity; vicinity; presence.
**nahe-liegen,** *v.i.* be near, border (on); be natural, be obvious, suggest itself. **-liegend,** *a.* near-by, adjacent; neighboring; obvious.
**nahen,** *v.i.* approach.
**nähen,** *v.t.* sew; lace (a belt).
**näher,** *a.* nearer, closer.
**Nähere(s),** *n.* particulars, detail(s).
**nähern,** *v.t.* bring near. — *v.r.* draw near, approach.
**Näherung,** *f.* approach; approximation.
**Näherungs-formel,** *f.* approximation formula. **-lösung,** *f.* approximate solution. **-methode,** *f.*, **-verfahren,** *n.* method of approximation. **-wert,** *m.* approximate value.
**nahe-stehend,** *p.a.* closely related or connected; standing near. **-zu,** *adv.* almost, well-nigh.
**Nähfaden,** *m.* sewing thread.
**nahm,** *pret.* (of nehmen) took; received.
**Nähnadel,** *f.* sewing needle.
**Nähr-.** nutritive, nutrient, alimentary. **-agar,** *m.* nutrient agar. **-äquivalent,** *n.* nutritive equivalent or value. **-blatt,** *n.* (*Bot.*) storage leaf. **-boden,** *m.* nutrient medium, nutrient substrate, culture medium. **-bouillon, -brühe,** *f.* nutrient broth.
**nähren,** *v.t.* feed; nourish; support. — **nährend,** *p.a.* nourishing, nutritive, nutritious, nutrient.
**Nähr-flüssigkeit,** *f.* nutrient (or nutritive) liquid or fluid. **-gang,** *m.* alimentary canal; nutrient duct. **-gelatine,** *f.* nutrient gelatin. **-geschäft,** *n.* nutrition. **-gewebe,** *n.* nutrient tissue.
**nahrhaft,** *a.* nutritive, nourishing, nutritious alimentary; productive; lucrative.
**Nahrhaftigkeit,** *f.* nutritiousness; productiveness.
**Nähr-hefe,** *f.* nutrient yeast. **-kraft,** *f.* nutritive power.
**nährkräftig,** *a.* nutritious.
**Nähr-lösung,** *f.* nutrient (or nutritive) solution. **-medium,** *n.* nutrient medium. **-mittel,** *n.* food; nutriment, nutrient. **-plasma,** *f.* (*Biol.*) trophoplasm. **-präparat,** *n.* food preparation. **-saft,** *m.* nutrient juice; chyle; sap. **-salz,** *n.* nutrient salt (salt required for proper nutrition). **-stoff,** *m.* nutritive substance, nutrient; nutritive material, foodstuff, food.
**nährstoffarm,** *a.* poor in food material.
**Nährstoffgehalt,** *m.* nutrient content, food content.
**nährstoffreich,** *a.* rich in nutritive material, (of soil) fertile.
**Nähr-substanz,** *f.* nutrient (or nutritive) sub-

stance. **-substrat,** *n.* nutrient substrate, nutrient base, nutrient medium.

**Nahrung,** *f.* nourishment, nutriment, food; subsistence; (*Leather*) tawing paste.

**Nahrungs-aufnahme,** *f.* reception or absorption of food. **-bedarf,** *m.* food requirement. **-brei,** *m.* chyme. **-dotter,** *m.* (*Biol.*) food yolk, deutoplasm. **-flüssigkeit,** *f.* nutritive liquid; chyle. **-kanal,** *m.* alimentary canal. **-milch,** *f.* (*Physiol.*) chyle.

**Nahrungsmittel,** *n.* food, foodstuff; *pl.* provisions. **-chemie,** *f.* food chemistry. **-chemiker,** *m.* food chemist. **-fälschung,** *f.* food adulteration. **-kunde,** *f.* (science of) nutrition. **-untersuchung,** *f.* examination or investigation of food; food research. **-verfälschung,** *f.* food adulteration.

**Nahrungs-rohr,** *n.*, **-röhre,** *f.* alimentary canal. **-saft,** *m.* nutrient juice; specif., (*Med.*) chyle, (*Bot.*) sap. **-stoff,** *m.* nutritive substance, nourishment, food. **-störung,** *f.* nutritional disturbance. **-teilchen,** *n.* nutritive element. **-vergiftung,** *f.* food poisoning. **-wert,** *m.* nutritive value. **-zufuhr,** *f.* food intake.

**Nähr-vorrat,** *m.* reserve food. **-wasser,** *n.* nutrient solution. **-wert,** *m.* nutritive value, food value.

**Naht,** *f.* seam; joint; weld; suture.

**nahtlos,** *a.* seamless; weldless.

**Nahtschweissung,** *f.* seam welding.

**Nähwachs,** *n.* sewing wax.

**Nahwerfer,** *m.* (*Mil.*) short-range flame thrower.

**Name, Namen,** *f.* name; denomination; title.

**Namen-gebung,** *f.* naming; nomenclature. **-register, -verzeichnis,** *n.* name index, specif. author index; list of names.

**namentlich,** *adv.* by name, namely, especially.

**namhaft,** *a.* named; famous, well-known; considerable.

**nämlich,** *a.* identical. — *adv.* namely, that is.

**Nancysäure,** *f.* (ordinary) lactic acid.

**nannte,** *pret.* (of nennen) named, called.

**Nanziger Säure.** (ordinary) lactic acid.

**Napf,** *m.* bowl, basin, pan; cup; saucer.

**Näpfchen,** *n.* cup; little bowl or basin; blank (for blasting caps); cupule. **-kobalt,** *m.* flaky metallic arsenic.

**napfförmig,** *a.* bowl-shaped, cup-shaped.

**Napht-.** naphth-.

**Naphta,** *f.* naphtha; petroleum.

**Naphtacen,** *n.* naphthacene. **-chinon,** *n.* naphthacenequinone.

**Naphta-chinon,** *n.* naphthoquinone. **-feld,** *n.* oil field.

**Naphtaldehyd,** *n.* naphthaldehyde.

**Naphtalin,** *n.* naphthalene. **-derivat,** *n.* naphthalene derivative. **-farbe,** *f.* naphthalene dye. **-gelb,** *n.* naphthalene yellow. **-reihe,** *f.* naphthalene series. **-rosa,** *n.* naphthalene pink (Magdala red). **-rot,** *n.* naphthalene red (Magdala red). **-säure,** *f.* naphthalenic acid. **-sulfosäure,** *f.* naphthalenesulfonic acid.

**Naphtalsäure,** *f.* naphthalic acid.

**Naphtanthrachinon,** *n.* naphthanthraquinone.

**Naphta-pech,** *n.* naphtha pitch. **-quelle,** *f.* oil well.

**Napht-azarin,** *n.* naphthazarin. **-azen,** *n.* naphthacene. **-azin,** *n.* naphthazine.

**Naphten,** *n.* naphthene.

**Naphtenat,** *n.* naphthenate.

**naphtenisch,** *a.* naphthenic.

**Naphten-kohlenwasserstoff,** *m.* naphthenic hydrocarbon, naphthene. **-säure,** *f.* naphthenic acid. **-seife,** *f.* naphthenic soap. **-trockenstoff,** *m.* (*Paint*) naphthenate drier.

**Naphth-.** see Napht-.

**Naphtidin,** *n.* naphthidine.

**Naphtionat,** *n.* naphthionate.

**Naphtionsäure,** *f.* naphthionic acid.

**Naphto-.** naphtho-. **-brenzcatechin,** *n.* naphthopyrocatechol. **-chinaldin,** *n.* naphthoquinaldine. **-chinhydron,** *n.* naphthoquinhydrone. **-chinolin,** *n.* naphthoquinoline. **-chinon,** *n.* naphthoquinone. **-cumarin,** *n.* naphthocoumarin (or -cumarin).

**Naphtoe-aldehyd,** *n.* naphthaldehyde, naphthoic aldehyde. **-säure,** *f.* naphthoic acid.

**Naphtohydrochinon,** *n.* naphthohydroquinone.

**Naphtol,** *n.* naphthol. **-artikel,** *m.* (*Dyeing*) naphthol style. **-at,** *n.* naphtholate. **-blau,** *n.* naphthol blue. **-gelb,** *n.* naphthol yellow. **-grün,** *n.* naphthol green.

**naphtolieren,** *v.t.* naphtholize, naphtholate.

**Naphtolnatrium,** *n.* sodium naphthoxide.

**naphtolsauer,** *a.* naphtholsulfonate of.

**Naphtolschwarz,** *n.* naphthol black.

**Naphtoyl,** *n.* naphthoyl.

**Napht-sultam,** *n.* naphthosultam, naphsultam. **-sulton,** *n.* naphthosultone, naphsultone.

**Naphtyl,** *n.* naphthyl. **-amin,** *n.* naphthylamine. **-aminsulfosäure,** *f.* naphthylaminesulfonic acid. **-blau,** *n.* naphthyl blue.

**Naphtyridin,** *n.* naphthyridine.

**Nappaleder,** *n.* napa leather.

**Narbe,** *f.* scar; seam; pit, pitting; (of leather and paper) grain; (*Biol.*) mark, spot, stigma.

**narben,** *v.t.* grain (leather, paper, etc.). — *v.i.* scar.

**Narben,** *m.* (*Leather*, etc.) grain. **-bildung,** *f.* scar formation, cicatrization; pitting. **-bindegewebe, -gewebe,** *n.* scar tissue. **-leder,** *n.* grain leather. **-öl,** *n.* (*Leather*) grain oil.

**narbenpressen,** *v.t.* grain.

**Narben-schleim,** *m.* (*Biol.*) stigmatic mucus. **-schmiere,** *f.* (*Leather*) grain dubbing. **-seite,** *f.* grain side.

**narbig,** *a.* scarred, scarry; pitted; grained (leather); grained or embossed (paper).

**Narbung,** *f.* graining, grain (of leather); scarring; pitting.
**Narde,** *f.* spikenard, nard.
**Narden-öl,** *n.* spikenard oil. **-salbe,** *f.* nard (the ointment).
**Narkose,** *f.* narcosis. **-äther,** *m.* ether for anesthesia.
**Narkotin,** *n.* narcotine.
**narkotisch,** *a.* narcotic. — **narkotische Mittel,** narcotic.
**narkotisieren,** *v.t.* narcotize.
**narkotisierung,** *f.* narcotization.
**Narr,** *m.* fool; lunatic.
**narrensicher,** *a.* foolproof.
**närrisch,** *a.* foolish; crazy; odd; merry, funny.
**Narzisse,** *f.* narcissus.
**nascierend,** *p.a.* nascent.
**Nase,** *f.* nose; (projection) beak, cam, tappet, stud, lug, etc.; spout, nozzle.
**näseln,** *v.i.* nasalize; sniff, scent.
**Nasen-.** (*Physiol.*) nasal, naso-. **-bluten,** *n.* nosebleed, epistaxis. **-loch,** *n.*, **-öffnung,** *f.* nostril. **-rachenreizstoff,** *m.* nose and throat irritant, sternutator. **-reizstoff,** *m.* nose irritant, sternutator. **-schlacke,** *f.* (*Metal.*) tuyère (twyer) slag. **-schleim,** *m.* nasal mucus. **-schleimhaut,** *f.* mucous membrane of the nose.
**Nashorn,** *n.* rhinoceros.
**nass,** *a.* wet; moist, humid, damp. — **nasser Weg,** wet way, wet process.
**Nass-behandlung,** *f.* wet treatment. **-beize,** *f.* liquid (or soak) disinfectant or disinfection. **-beizmittel,** *n.* liquid (or soak) disinfectant. **-betrieb,** *m.* wet operation, wet practice. **-binder,** *m.* wet binder, liquid binder. **-bleiche,** *f.* wet bleach. **-dampf,** *m.* wet steam, moist steam; moist vapor. **-dekatur,** *f.* (*Textiles*) wet decatizing.
**Nässe,** *f.* wetness, moisture, humidity.
**Nass-echtheit,** *f.* fastness to wetting or wet processing. **-element,** *n.* (*Elec.*) wet cell, wet battery.
**nässen,** *v.t.* wet, soak, moisten; ooze, discharge. — *v.i.* ooze, discharge, run.
**Nass-entwicklung,** *f.* wet developing. **-fäule,** *f.* wet rot. **-festigkeit,** *f.* strength when wet. **-fettung,** *f.* (*Leather*) wet fatliquoring. **-gas,** *n.* wet gas (specif., wet natural gas).
**Nässgehalt, Nassgehalt,** *m.* moisture content. **-messer,** *m.* hygrometer.
**Nassgussformerei,** *f.* green sand molding.
**nass-kalt,** *a.* wet (or damp) and cold. **-kühl,** *a.* damp and cold, chilly. **-lichtecht,** *a.* fast to light when wet.
**Nassmahlen,** *n.* wet grinding, wet milling.
**nassmechanisch,** *a.* wet mechanical, wet-mill.
**Nass-metallurgie,** *f.* hydrometallurgy. **-mühle,** *f.* wet mill. **-probe,** *f.* wet test.
**Nässprobe,** *f.* moisture test or determination.
**Nass-reinigung,** *f.* wet purification, wet cleaning. **-schlamm,** *m.* (*Sewage*) wet sludge. **-schliff,** *m.* wet grinding. **-verfahren,** *n.* wet process. **-wäsche,** *f.* wet cleaning, washing.
**nasswaschen,** *v.t.* launder.
**Nasswäscherei,** *f.* laundering.
**nasz.,** *abbrev.* (naszierend) nascent.
**naszierend,** *p.a.* nascent.
**nationalsozialistisch,** *a.* National-Socialist, Nazi.
**Nativpräparat,** *n.* (*Micros.*) untreated specimen.
**Natr-acetessigester,** *m.* sodioacetoacetic ester. **-amid,** *n.* sodamide, sodium amide.
**Natrium,** *n.* sodium. **-alaun,** *m.* sodium alum. **-amid,** *n.* sodium amide, sodamide. **-arseniat,** *n.* sodium arsen(i)ate. **-äthylat,** *n.* sodium ethylate. **-azetat,** *n.* sodium acetate. **-benzoat,** *n.* sodium benzoate. **-bisulfat,** *n.* sodium bisulfate, sodium hydrogen sulfate. **-bleichlauge,** *f.* sodium bleach liquor (sodium hypochlorite solution). **-brechweinstein,** *m.* sodium antimonyl tartrate, sodium antimony(III) tartrate. **bromatum.** (*Pharm.*) sodium bromide. **-bromid,** *n.* sodium bromide. **chloratum.** (*Pharm.*) sodium chloride. **chloricum.** (*Pharm.*) sodium chlorate. **-chlorid,** *n.* sodium chloride. **-dampf,** *m.* sodium vapor. **-draht,** *m.* sodium wire. **-flamme,** *f.* sodium flame. **-fluorid,** *n.* sodium fluoride. **-formiat,** *n.* sodium formate. **-gehalt,** *m.* sodium content. **-goldchlorid,** *n.* sodium chloroaurate. **-hydrat,** *n.* sodium hydroxide. **-hydroxyd,** *n.* sodium hydroxide. **-hyperjodat,** *n.* sodium periodate. **-hyperoxyd,** *n.* sodium peroxide **-jodat,** *n.* sodium iodate. **jodatum.** (*Pharm.*) sodium iodide. **-jodid,** *n.* sodium iodide **-kaliumtartrat,** *n.* sodium potassium tartrate **-karbonat,** *n.* sodium carbonate. **-kieselfluorid,** *n.* sodium fluosilicate. **-leuchte,** *f.* sodium light. **-löffel,** *m.* sodium spoon. **-metall,** *n.* sodium metal, metallic sodium. **-nitrat,** *n.* sodium nitrate. **-oxyd,** *n.* sodium oxide. **-oxydhydrat,** *n.* sodium hydroxide. **-phosphat,** *n.* sodium phosphate. **-platinchlorid,** *n.* sodium chloroplatinate. **-presse,** *f.* sodium press. **-rhodanid,** *n.* sodium thiocyanate. **-salz,** *n.* sodium salt. **-seife,** *f.* sodium soap. **-silikofluorid,** *n.* sodium fluosilicate. **-sulfat,** *n.* sodium sulfate. **-sulfhydrat,** *n.* sodium hydrosulfide. **-sulfozyanid,** *n.* sodium thiocyanate. **-superoxyd,** *n.* sodium superoxide (sodium peroxide). **-superoxydbleiche,** *f.* sodium peroxide bleach. **-verbindung,** *f.* sodium compound. **-wasserstoff,** *m.* sodium hydride. **-wolframat,** *n.* sodium tungstate. **-zange,** *f.* sodium tongs.

**-zinnchlorid,** *n.* sodium chlorostannate. **-zyanamid,** *n.* sodium cyanamide. **-zyanid,** *n.* sodium cyanide.

**Natron,** *n.* soda, in the following senses: (1) sodium carbonate, $Na_2CO_3$ ("kohlensaures Natron"); (2) sodium hydrogen carbonate, $NaHCO_3$ ("doppeltkohlensaures Natron"); (3) sodium hydroxide or caustic soda, NaOH, usually called "Ätznatron"; (4) in older names, sodium oxide, $Na_2O$ (as in "schwefelsaures Natron," sodium sulfate). **-alaun,** *m.* soda alum. **-ätzlauge,** *f.* caustic soda solution. **-cellulose,** *f.* sodium (or soda) cellulose; (*Paper*) soda pulp. **-feldspat,** *m.* soda feldspar. **-glas,** *n.* soda glass. **-glimmer,** *m.* (*Min.*) soda mica, paragonite.

**natronhaltig,** *a.* containing soda.

**Natron-hydrat,** *n.* sodium hydroxide. **-hydratlösung,** *f.* sodium hydroxide solution. **-hyperoxyd,** *n.* sodium peroxide. **-kalk,** *m.* soda lime. **-kalkglas,** *n.* soda-lime glass. **-kalkrohr,** *n.*, **-kalkröhre,** *f.* soda-lime tube. **-lauge,** *f.* soda lye, solution of caustic soda.

**natronlauge-echt,** *a.* fast to caustic soda. **-kochecht,** *a.* fast to boiling caustic.

**Natron-metall,** *n.* (metallic) sodium. **-pastille,** *f.* (*Pharm.*) troche of sodium bicarbonate. **-präparat,** *n.* soda preparation. **-reihe,** *f.* (*Petrog.*) soda series. **-salpeter,** *m.* soda saltpeter, Chile saltpeter ($NaNO_3$). **-salz,** *n.* soda salt, sodium salt. **-schwefelleber,** *f.* soda liver of sulfur (essentially $Na_2S$). **-see,** *m.* soda lake. **-seife,** *f.* soda soap. **-stoff,** *m.* (*Paper*) soda pulp. **-Türkischrotöl,** *n.* soda-Turkey-red oil. **-wasserglas,** *n.* soda-water glass, sodium silicate. **-weinstein,** *m.* sodium tartrate, or sodium potassium tartrate. **-zellstoff,** *m.* (*Paper*) soda cellulose, soda pulp. **-zellstof(f)fabrikation,** *f.* soda-pulp manufacture. **-zellulose,** *f.* = Natronzellstoff.

**Natter,** *f.* adder, viper. **-wurz, -wurzel,** *f.* bistort; cuckoopint.

**Natur,** *f.* nature.

**Natur-.** natural.

**naturähnlich,** *a.* like nature, realistic.

**Naturalbleiche,** *f.* sun bleaching, grass bleaching.

**naturbraun,** *a.* natural-brown, nature-brown (said specif. of steamed mechanical wood pulp).

**Natur-erscheinung,** *f.* natural phenomenon. **-erzeugnis,** *f.* natural product. **-farbe,** *f.* natural color.

**naturfarben,** *a.* = naturfarbig.

**Naturfarbfilm,** *m.* natural-color film.

**naturfarbig,** *a.* of natural color, (of leather) fair.

**Natur-farbstoff,** *m.* natural dyestuff. **-fehler,** *m.* natural defect. **-fett,** *n.* natural fat, natural grease, specif. suint.

**naturforschend,** *a.* for the investigation of nature, natural-science.

**Natur-forscher,** *m.* investigator of nature, scientific investigator, (formerly) natural philosopher; naturalist. **-forschung,** *f.* investigation of nature, scientific research; (formerly) natural philosophy. **-gas,** *n.* natural gas. **-gasolin,** *n.* natural gasoline.

**natur-gemäss,** *a.* according to nature, natural. — *adv.* naturally. **-genarbt,** *a.* with natural grain.

**Natur-gerbstoff,** *m.* natural tan. **-geschichte,** *f.* natural history. **-gesetz,** *n.* law of nature, natural law.

**natur-gross,** *a.* natural-size, full-scale. **-grün,** *a.* natural-green.

**Naturgummi,** *n.* natural gum; natural rubber.

**naturhart,** *a.* naturally hard; (of steel) self-hardening.

**Natur-härte,** *f.* natural hardness; (*Metal.*) natural temper. **-harz,** *n.* natural resin. **-heilung,** *f.* spontaneous cure. **-holz,** *n.* natural wood. **-karton,** *m.* unbleached (paper)board. **-kautschuk,** *m.* & *n.* natural rubber (esp., unprocessed). **-körper,** *m.* natural substance, natural body. **-kraft,** *f.* natural force or power. **-lehre,** *f.* natural science, natural philosophy.

**natürlich,** *a.* natural; native; actual, full (size). — *adv.* naturally.

**Natur-papier,** *n.* stuff-colored paper. **-produkt,** *n.* natural product, native substance. **-reich,** *n.* domain or kingdom of nature. **-rostung,** *f.* natural rusting or corrosion. **-schutz,** *m.* nature protection. **-seide,** *f.* natural silk. **-stein,** *m.* (natural) stone, rock. **-stoff,** *m.* natural substance.

**naturtreu,** *a.* true to nature.

**Naturtrieb,** *m.* instinct.

**naturw.,** *abbrev.* (naturwissenschaftlich) of natural science, scientific.

**Natur-wachs,** *n.* natural wax. **-wasser,** *n.* natural water.

**naturwidrig,** *a.* unnatural, abnormal.

**Natur-wissenschaft,** *f.* natural science. **-wissenschaftler,** *m.* natural scientist.

**naturwissenschaftlich,** *a.* of or pertaining to natural science, scientific.

**Natur-zement,** *m.* natural cement. **-zustand,** *m.* natural state.

**nautisch,** *a.* nautical.

**Nd.,** *abbrev.* (Niederschlag) precipitate.

**N.D.,** *abbrev.* (Niederdruck) low pressure.

**Ndd.,** *abbrev.* (Niederschläge) precipitates.

**Ndl.,** *abbrev.* (Nadel) needle; (Niederlage) warehouse.

**N.E.,** *abbrev.* (Nicht-Eisen) nonferrous

**Neapel-gelb,** *n.* Naples yellow. **-rot,** *n.* Naples red.

**Nebel,** *m.* mist, fog, haze; (loosely) smoke. **-apparat,** *m.* atomizer, sprayer; (*Mil.*) smoke generator.

**nebelartig,** *a.* mist-like, fog-like, misty, foggy.

**Nebel-bildung,** *f.* fog (or smoke) formation. **-bombe,** *f.* (*Mil.*) smoke bomb or grenade. **-büchse,** *f.* (*Mil.*) smoke generator. **-decke,** *f.* (*Mil.*) smoke screen, smoke blanket. **-dunst,** *m.* mist, haze. **-düse,** *f.* atomizing nozzle, spray nozzle. **-entwicklung,** *f.* (*Mil.*) generation (or evolution) of smoke. **-fleck,** *m.* nebula. **-gas,** *n.* (*Mil.*) cloud gas, smoke gas. **-gerät,** *n.* (*Mil.*) smoke generator, smoke apparatus. **-geschoss,** *n.* smoke projectile or shell. **-gewehrgranate,** *f.* (*Mil.*) smoke rifle grenade. **-granate,** *f.* (*Mil.*) smoke shell or grenade.

**nebelhaft,** *a.* = nebelig.

**Nebelhandgranate,** *f.* (*Mil.*) smoke hand grenade.

**nebelig,** *a.* misty, foggy, hazy.

**Nebel-kamera, -kammer,** *f.* cloud chamber. **-kasten,** *m.* smoke box, smoke generator. **-kerze,** *f.* (*Mil.*) smoke candle. **-mittel,** *n.* smoke agent; smoke equipment. **-munition,** *f.* (*Mil.*) smoke munitions. **-patrone,** *f.* (*Mil.*) smoke cartridge. **-schiessen,** *n.* (*Mil.*) smoke-shell firing. **-schleier,** *m.* (*Mil.*) smoke screen. **-spur,** *f.* cloud-chamber track; trace of mist or fog. **-spuraufnahme,** *f.* cloud-chamber exposure or photograph. **-stoff,** *m.* (*Mil.*) smoke agent, screening agent. **-topf,** *m.* smoke pot, smoke generator. **-tornister,** *m.* (*Mil.*) pack smoke apparatus. **-trommel,** *f.* smoke drum, smoke generator. **-tröpfchen,** *n.* fog (or mist) droplet. **-wand,** *f.* wall of fog; (*Mil.*) smoke screen. **-werfer,** *m.* (*Mil.*) smoke-shell mortar. **-wolke,** *f.* (*Mil.*) smoke cloud. **-wurfgranate,** *f.* (*Mil.*) mortar smoke shell. **-zerstäuber,** *m.* (*Mil.*) smoke spray(er). **-zerstreuung,** *f.* fog dispersion. **-zone,** *f.* (*Mil.*) smoke-screened zone. **-zündmittel,** *n.* (*Mil.*) firing device for smoke container.

**neben,** *prep.* beside, by, near; besides, in addition to.

**Neben-.** by-, side-, secondary, accessory, subsidiary, subordinate, sub-, auxiliary, supplementary, extra; adjoining; collateral; (*Elec.*) shunt. **-achse,** *f.* secondary axis. **-ader,** *f.* collateral blood vessel. **-anlage,** *f.* secondary plant, branch. **-antrieb,** *m.* (*Mach.*) auxiliary drive. **-apparat,** *m.* accessory apparatus, accessory. **-arbeit,** *f.* by-work, extra work, spare-time work. **-bedingung,** *f.* supplementary condition, subordinate factor. **-bestandteil,** *m.* secondary ingredient or constituent. **-betrieb,** *m.* by-operation, secondary process, "side line." **-beweis,** *m.* accessory proof, additional proof. **-bindung,** *f.* secondary or subsidiary union or bond. **-buhler,** *m.* rival. **-drüse,** *f.* accessory gland. **-eigenschaft,** *f.* secondary property.

**nebeneinander,** *adv.* side by side; together; in juxtaposition; (*Elec.*) in parallel. **-schalten,** *v.t.* (*Elec.*) connect in parallel.

**Neben-einanderschaltung,** *f.* (*Elec.*) connection in parallel. **-einanderstellung,** *f.* juxtaposition; comparison. **-einteilung,** *f.* subdivision. **-ergebnis,** *n.* secondary result, by-result. **-erscheinung,** *f.* attendant phenomenon. **-erzeugnis,** *f.* by-product. **-erzeugnisgewinnung,** *f.* by-product recovery. **-farbe,** *f.* secondary or tertiary color. **-fläche,** *f.* (*Cryst.*) secondary face. **-fluss,** *m.* tributary. **-folge,** *f.* indirect result, secondary effect. **-gang,** *m.* by-way; (*Mining*) lateral vein. **-gärung,** *f.* secondary fermentation. **-gemengteil,** *n.* subsidiary part of a mixture. **-geschmack,** *m.* after-taste, tang. **-gestein,** *n.* (*Mining*) country rock, also gang(ue). **-gewebe,** *n.* accessory tissue. **-gewinnung,** *f.* by-product recovery.

**nebenher,** *adv.* besides, by the way. **-gehend,** *a.* additional, minor.

**Neben-hoden,** *m.* (*Anat.*) epididymis. **-kern,** *m.* (*Biol.*) paranucleus. **-kette,** *f.* side chain, subordinate chain. **-klasse,** *f.* subsidiary class. **-kosten,** *f.pl.* extra costs, extras. **-leiter,** *m.* (*Elec.*) branch conductor. **-leitung,** *f.* bypass; branch line. **-linie,** *f.* secondary line; branch line. **-luft,** *f.* admixed air; secondary air, supplementary air. **-niere,** *f.* suprarenal capsule.

**Nebennieren-.** suprarenal, adrenal. **-rinde,** *f.* suprarenal (or adrenal) cortex.

**Neben-organ,** *n.* (*Anat.*) accessory organ. **-produkt,** *n.* by-product.

**Nebenprodukten-anlage,** *f.* by-product plant. **-kokerei,** *f.* by-product coke plant or coking. **-ofen,** *m.* by-product oven or furnace.

**Neben-quantenzahl,** *f.* secondary (or subsidiary) quantum number. **-raum,** *m.* additional space; anteroom. **-reaktion,** *f.* by-reaction, side reaction, secondary reaction. **-rechnung,** *f.* auxiliary calculation. **-reihe,** *f.* = Nebenserie. **-rohr,** *n.* side tube (or pipe), branch tube (or pipe). **-rolle,** *f.* subordinate rôle. **-sache,** *f.* secondary matter.

**nebensächlich,** *a.* incidental, subsidiary, by-.

**Nebenschilddrüse,** *f.* parathyroid gland.

**nebenschliessen,** *v.t.* (*Elec.*) shunt.

**Neben-schliessung,** *f.*, **-schluss,** *m.* (*Elec.*) shunt, shunting, also shunt circuit. **-schlussschaltung,** *f.* shunt connection. **-schlussstrom,** *m.* (*Elec.*) shunt current. **-serie,** *f.* subsidiary series, secondary series, subordi-

nate series. **-setzung,** *f.* juxtaposition. **-sonne,** *f.* mock sun, parhelion. **-spirale,** *f.* secondary coil.
**neben-ständig,** *a.* collateral, accessory. **-stehend,** *a.* standing beside, annexed.
**Neben-strom,** *m.* (*Elec.*) induction current. **-teil,** *m.* accessory part. **-titel,** *m.* subtitle. **-typus,** *m.* secondary type. **-umstand,** *m.* minor circumstance or detail. **-valenz,** *f.* subsidiary valence, secondary valence. **-widerstand,** *m.* (*Elec.*) shunt resistance. **-winkel,** *n.* adjacent angle. **-wirkung,** *f.* secondary action or effect. **-wort,** *n.* adverb. **-zeit,** *f.* nonproductive time, idle time. **-zelle,** *f.* accessory cell. **-zweig,** *m.* lateral branch.
**neblig,** *a.* misty, foggy, hazy.
**nebst,** *prep.* besides, in addition to.
**negativ-elektrisch,** *a.* negatively electric, electronegative.
**Negativität,** *f.* negativity.
**Negativlack,** *m.* (*Photog.*) varnish for negatives.
**Neger,** *m.* Negro. **-kopf,** *m.* niggerhead; (*Rubber*) negrohead.
**nehmen,** *v.t.* take; receive, get; accept.
**neigbar,** *a.* inclinable.
**Neige,** *f.* inclination; slope, gradient; dregs, sediment; decline, wane.
**neigen,** *v.t.* incline, bend. — *v.r.* incline, bend, lean, slope, dip. decline, bow; tend. — **geneigt,** *p.a.* inclined, etc.; slanting; disposed, favorable.
**Neigung,** *f.* inclination; bending; slope, pitch, dip, gradient; tendency.
**Neigungs-ebene,** *f.* inclined plane. **-messer,** *m.* clinometer; inclinometer. **-winkel,** *m.* angle of inclination.
**nein,** *interj.* no.
**Nekrolog,** *m.* obituary.
**Nekrose,** *f.* necrosis.
**Nelke,** *f.* clove; pink (the flower).
**Nelken-gewächse,** *n.pl.* (*Bot.*) Caryophyllaceae. **-kassie,** *f.* clove cassia. **-öl,** *n.* clove oil, oil of cloves. **-pfeffer,** *m.* allspice, pimento. **-pfefferwasser,** *n.* (*Pharm.*) pimento water. **-rinde,** *f.* clove cassia. **-säure,** *f.* eugenol; caryophyllic acid. **-stein,** *m.* iolite. **-wurzel,** *f.* avens root. **-zim(m)t,** *m.* clove cinnamon, clove cassia.
**Nenn-.** nominal; rated. **-drehzahl,** *f.* rated speed (of a motor). **-druck,** *m.* nominal pressure.
**nennen,** *v.t.* name, call, term; mention.
**nennenswert,** *a.* worth mentioning, noteworthy.
**Nenner,** *m.* denominator.
**Nenn-kraft,** *f.* nominal (horse)power. **-last,** *f.* nominal load, rated load. **-leistung,** *f.* nominal output, rated output. **-strom,** *m.* (*Elec.*) rated current.
**Nennung,** *f.* naming; mention; denomination.
**Nenn-weite,** *f.* nominal width. **-wert,** *m.* nominal value; face value; par value. **-wort,** *n.* noun, substantive.
**Neodym,** *n.* neodymium.
**Neon-glimmlampe,** *f.* neon (glow) lamp. **-licht,** *n.* neon light. **-rohr,** *n.*, **-röhre,** *f.* neon tube.
**neo-plastisch,** *a.* neoplastic. **-zoisch,** *a.* (*Geol.*) Neozoic (Cenozoic).
**Nephelin,** *m.* (*Min.*) nepheline, nephelite.
**Neroliöl,** *n.* neroli (oil of orange flowers).
**Nerv,** *m.* nerve; sinew; fiber; vein (of a leaf).
**Nervatur,** *f.* venation.
**Nerven-.** nerve, neuro-. **-entzündung,** *f.* neuritis. **-faser,** *f.* nerve fiber. **-gewebe,** *n.* nerve tissue. **-kitt,** *m.* (*Anat.*) neuroglia. **-kunde,** **-lehre,** *f.* neurology. **-masse,** *f.* = Nervenstoff. **-reiz,** *m.* nervous stimulus. **-stoff,** *m.* nerve substance, neural substance. **-system,** **-werk,** *n.* nervous system. **-zelle,** *f.* nerve cell.
**nervig,** *a.* nervous; nerved; sinewy; elastic (as silk or rubber), live; vigorous, strong.
**Nervigkeit,** *f.* nervousness, etc. (see nervig).
**nervös,** *a.* nervous; forcible.
**Nerz,** *m.* mink.
**Nessel,** *f.* nettle; unbleached cotton cloth, nettle cloth. **-ausschlag,** *m.* nettle rash. **-gewächse,** *n.pl.* (*Bot.*) Urticaceae.
**Nest,** *n.* nest; (of ore) pocket; (*Textiles*) knot, defect.
**nett,** *a.* neat; pleasant, kind; (*Sugar*) pure white.
**netto,** *adv.* net.
**Netto-ertrag,** *m.* net yield; net proceeds. **-gewicht,** *n.* net weight.
**Netz,** *n.* net, netting, gauze; network, plexus, reticulum; lattice; grid; system (of piping, wiring, etc.); omentum; (of a telescope) reticle.
**Netz-.** wetting, steeping; net, netting, reticular, omental. **-adern,** *f.pl.* netted veins or cracks.
**netz-ähnlich, -artig,** *a.* net-like, reticular, plexiform; grid-like.
**Netz-anschluss,** *m.* (*Elec.*) connection with a distributing system. **-bad,** *n.* (*Dyeing*) wetting-out bath. **-beize,** *f.* (in Turkey-red dyeing) oil mordant. **-bindung,** *f.* covalence; reticular linkage. **-ebene,** *f.* (*Cryst.*) lattice plane. **-elektrode,** *f.* wire-gauze electrode.
**netzen,** *v.t.* wet, moisten, steep, soak.
**Netz-fähigkeit,** *f.* wetting(-out) property. **-fass,** *n.* steeping cask or tub. **-ferment,** *n.* omental enzyme. **-flotte,** *f.* (*Dyeing*) wetting-out liquor.
**netzförmig,** *a.* net-shaped, reticular.
**Netzhaut,** *f.* retina.
**Netzhaut-.** retinal. **-bild,** *n.* retinal image. **-eindruck,** *m.* retinal impression. **-stäbchen,** *n.* retinal rod. **-zäpfchen,** *n.* retinal cone.

**Netz-kasten,** *m.* immersion tank. **-katalysator,** *m.* grid catalyst. **-kessel,** *m.* steeping copper or vat. **-kraft,** *f.* wetting power. **-magen,** *m.* second stomach (of ruminants). **-mittel,** *n.* wetting agent. **-öl,** *n.* wetting(-out) oil. **-polymer,** *n.* net (or netted) polymer, reticular polymer. **-schaltung,** *f.* (*Elec.*) delta connection. **-schutz,** *m.* protecting gauze or grid. **-spannung,** *f.* (*Elec.*) line voltage. **-ständer,** *m.* (*Paper*) steeping tub. **-strom,** *m.* (*Elec.*) current from a distributing system, line current. **-struktur,** *f.* = Netzwerkstruktur.

**netzvermascht,** *a.* interconnected.

**Netz-vermögen,** *n.* wetting(-out) power or property. **-ware,** *f.* netting. **-werk,** *n.* network.

**netzwerkartig,** *a.* network-like, reticular.

**Netz-werkstruktur,** *f.* (*Metal.*, etc.) reticular or cellular structure. **-wirkung,** *f.* wetting(-out) action or effect.

**neu,** *a.* new. — *adv.* newly, lately. — **aufs neue, von neuem,** anew, again.

**Neu, neu-.** new, newly, neo-, again, re-.

**Neuaktivierung,** *f.* reactivation.

**neuartig,** *a.* of a new kind, new, novel.

**Neuaufstellung,** *f.* new setup, reorganization; restatement.

**neubearbeitet,** *a.* reworked, revised.

**Neu-berechnung,** *f.* recalculation. **-bildung,** *f.* new formation; reconstruction; (*Med.*) neoplasm. **-blau,** *n.* new blue. **-braun,** *n.* new brown. **-coccin,** *n.* (*Dyes*) new coccin, neococcin. **-eichung,** *f.* restandardization, recalibration.

**neuentstanden,** *a.* newly formed, newly arisen, recent.

**neuer,** *a.* newer; recent, modern, later. **-dings,** *adv.* newly, recently, lately; again. **-lich,** *adv. & a.* = neulich.

**Neuerung,** *f.* innovation; improvement.

**Neu-erzeugung,** *f.* new production; reproduction. **-fundland,** *n.* Newfoundland.

**neugebildet,** *p.a.* newly formed.

**Neu-gelb,** *n.* new yellow; massicot. **-gestaltung,** *f.* reorganization; modification. **-gewürz,** *n.* allspice, pimento. **-gier, -gierde,** *f.* curiosity.

**neugierig,** *a.* curious. inquisitive.

**Neu-gold,** *n.* Mannheim gold. **-grad,** *m.* (*Math.*) new (or centesimal) degree, 1–400 circle. **-gradteilung,** *f.* centesimal graduation. **-grün,** *n.* new green. **-heit,** *f.* novelty, newness.

**neuheitsschädlich,** *a.* (*Patents*) anticipatory.

**Neu-igkeit,** *f.* news, novelty. **-jahr,** *n.* New Year. **-kristallisation,** *f.* recrystallization.

**neulich,** *adv.* lately, of late. — *a.* late, recent.

**Neu-ling,** *m.* novice; newcomer. **-messing,** *n.* a kind of brass.

**neun,** *a.* nine. **-eckig,** *a.* nine-cornered, nine-sided. **-erlei,** *a.* of nine kinds. **-fach, -fältig,** *a.* ninefold. **-flächig,** *a.* nine-sided (or -faced). **-gliedrig,** *a.* nine-membered. **-mal,** *adv.* nine times.

**neunte,** *a.* ninth.

**Neuntel,** *n.* ninth.

**neunwertig,** *a.* nonavalent.

**neunzehn,** *a.* nineteen.

**neunzig,** *a.* ninety.

**Neu-prüfung,** *f.* new test, reëxamination. **-rot,** *n.* new red. **-rotölung,** *f.* (*Dyeing*) new red oiling. **-rotverfahren,** *n.* new red process. **-schöpfung,** *f.* new creation. **-seeland,** *n.* New Zealand. **-silber,** *n.* nickel silver, German silver. **-steinzeit,** *f.* New Stone Age, Neolithic.

**neutralfärben,** *v.t.* dye neutral, dye sweet.

**Neutral-fett,** *n.* neutral fat. **-grau,** *n.* neutral gray.

**Neutralisations-wärme,** *f.* heat of neutralization. **-zahl,** *f.* neutralization number.

**neutralisieren,** *v.t.* neutralize.

**Neutral-isierung,** *f.* neutralization. **-ität,** *f.* neutrality. **-körper,** *m.* neutral substance or body. **-öl,** *n.* neutral oil. **-punkt,** *m.* neutral point. **-rot,** *n.* neutral red. **-salz,** *n.* neutral salt. **-salzion,** *n.* neutral salt ion. **-salzwirkung,** *f.* neutral salt effect.

**Neutroneneinfang,** *m.* neutron capture.

**Neuweiss,** *n.* permanent white ($BaSO_4$).

**Neuwieder Grün.** Neuwied green (Paris green).

**Neuzeit,** *f.* modern times.

**neuzeitlich,** *a.* modern.

**N.F., n. F.,** *abbrev.* (neue Folge) new series.

**Nichin,** *n.* niquine.

**nicht,** *adv.* not. — **mit nichten,** not at all.

**Nicht-.** non-, not, in-, un-.

**nicht-absetzend,** *a.* nonsettling. **-angreifbar,** *a.* noncorrodible. **-angreifend,** *a.* noncorroding.

**Nicht-arier,** *m.* non-Aryan. **-auflösung,** *f.* nonsolution.

**nicht-aushaltend,** *a.* not lasting; discontinuous. **-backend,** *a.* (*Coal*) noncaking, noncoking.

**Nichtbeobachtung,** *f.* nonobservance.

**nicht-bevorzugt,** *a.* nonpreferential, random. **-bindig,** *a.* nonbinding, noncohesive. **-brennbar,** *a.* noncombustible.

**Nichtchemiker,** *m.* nonchemist, layman.

**nicht-dissoziiert,** *p.a.* undissociated. **-drehend,** *a.* not turning, not rotating.

**Nichte,** *f.* niece.

**Nichteignung,** *f.* unsuitableness, unfitness.

**nichteisenhaltig,** *a.* nonferrous.

**Nicht-eisenmetall,** *n.* nonferrous metal. **-elektrolyt,** *n.* nonelectrolyte.

**nichtentartet,** *a.* nondegenerate.

**Nicht-entartung,** *f.* nondegeneration. **-erz,** *n.* (*Geol.*) a deposit that is not an ore.

**nicht-existenzfähig,** *a.* incapable of existence, **-explosiv,** *a.* nonexplosive. **-faserig,** *a.* nonfibrous. **-flüchtig,** *a.* nonvolatile. **-fortlaufend,** *a.* discontinuous. **-gasförmig,** *a.* nongaseous.

**Nicht-gebrauch,** *m.* disuse, lack of use. **-gerbstoff,** *m.* nontannin, nontan.

**nicht-haltbar,** *a.* unstable, not durable, not fast. **-häufig,** *a.* infrequent.

**nichtig,** *a.* null, void, invalid; futile, idle.

**Nichtigkeit,** *f.* nullity; invalidation, annulment.

**Nichtigkeits-erklärung,** *f.* nullification, annulment. **-klage,** *f.*, **-verfahren,** *n.* (*Patents*) invalidity plea or suit.

**Nichtion,** *n.* non-ion.

**Nichtionen-.** non-ionic.

**nicht-ionisierbar,** *a.* nonionizable. **-ionisiert,** *a.* nonionized, unionized. **-kalkhaltig,** *a.* noncalcareous.

**Nicht-kämpfer,** *m.* noncombatant. **-karbonathärte,** *f.* (*Water*) hardness not due to carbonates, permanent hardness.

**nicht-klebend,** *a.* nonadhesive. **-kohärent,** *a.* noncoherent. **-kondensiert,** *a.* uncondensed. **-kontinuierlich,** *a.* discontinuous. **-kristallisch,** *a.* noncrystalline, amorphous. **-lebend,** *a.* nonliving. **-leitend,** *p.a.* nonconducting.

**Nichtleiter,** *m.* nonconductor.

**nicht-leuchtend,** *a.* nonluminous. **-localisiert,** *a.* unlocalized. **-lohnend,** *a.* unremunerative, unrewarding.

**Nichtlöser,** *m.* nonsolvent.

**nichtlöslich,** *a.* insoluble.

**Nichtmetall,** *n.* nonmetal.

**nicht-metallisch,** *a.* nonmetallic. **-mischbar,** *a.* immiscible.

**Nichtmischbarkeit,** *f.* immiscibility.

**nicht-oxydierbar,** *a.* unoxidizable. **-oxydierend,** *a.* nonoxidizing. **-pathogen,** *a.* nonpathogenic. **-periodisch,** *a.* aperiodic. **-plattiert,** *a.* unplated, unclad. **-reduzierbar,** *a.* not reducible, irreducible. **-reproduzierbar,** *a.* nonreproducible. **-rostend,** *a.* nonrusting, rustproof, (of steel) stainless. **-russend,** *a.* sootless.

**nichts,** *pron.*, **Nichts,** *n.* nothing, none. — **weisses Nichts,** nihil album (sublimed zinc oxide).

**Nichtsättigung,** *f.* nonsaturation, unsaturation.

**nichtschmelzbar,** *a.* nonfusible, infusible.

**nichtsdestoweniger,** *adv.* nevertheless.

**nichtselbständig,** *a.* dependent.

**nichtssagend,** *p.a.* meaningless.

**nichtständig,** *a.* nonpermanent; not fixed.

**nichtswürdig,** *a* worthless; base; futile.

**nicht-symmetrisch,** *a.* unsymmetrical, asymmetric. **-trocknend,** *a.* nondrying. **-tropfend,** *a.* nondripping. **-umkehrbar,** *a.* nonreversible, irreversible; uninvertible. **-umwandelbar,** *a.* inconvertible.

**Nichtumwandelbarkeit,** *f.* inconvertibility.

**nichtvergasbar,** *a.* nongasifiable, nonvolatile.

**Nichtvergrünen,** *n.* ungreenable black.

**nichtverseifbar,** *a.* unsaponifiable.

**Nichtwärmeleiter,** *m.* nonconductor of heat.

**nicht-wässerig,** *a.* nonaqueous. **-zerfallbar,** *a.* nondisintegrable, nonfissionable. **-zerstörend,** *a.* nondestructive.

**Nichtzucker,** *m.* nonsugar.

**Nickelantimonglanz,** *m.* ullmannite.

**nickelarm,** *a.* poor (or low) in nickel.

**Nickel-armierung,** *f.* nickel fitting or mounting. **-arsenik,** *n.* nickel arsenide. **-arsen(ik)glanz, -arsen(ik)kies,** *m.* gersdorffite.

**nickelartig,** *a.* nickel-like.

**Nickel-azetat,** *n.* nickel acetate. **-bad,** *n.* nickel bath. **-beize,** *f.* nickel mordant. **-blech,** *n.* nickel sheet or plate. **-blüte,** *f.* nickel bloom (annabergite). **-bromür,** *n.* nickel(ous) bromide, nickel(II) bromide. **-chlorür,** *n.* nickel(ous) chloride, nickel(II) chloride. **-chromstahl,** *m.* chrome-nickel steel. **-cyanür,** *n.* nickelous cyanide, nickel(II) cyanide. **-draht,** *m.* nickel wire. **-drahtnetz,** *n.* nickel gauze. **-eisen,** *n.* nickel iron, ferronickel. **-erz,** *n.* nickel ore. **-fahlerz,** *n.* (*Min.*) malinowskite. **-flusseisen,** *n.* nickel steel.

**nickelführend,** *a.* nickel-bearing, nickeliferous.

**Nickel-gefäss,** *n.* nickel vessel. **-gehalt,** *m.* nickel content. **-gelb,** *n.* nickel yellow. **-gewinnung,** *f.* nickel recovery. **-glanz,** *m.* nickel glance (gersdorffite). **-granalien,** *f.pl.* granulated nickel; nickel shot.

**nickelhaltig,** *a.* containing nickel, nickeliferous.

**Nickel-hydroxyd,** *n.* nickel hydroxide. **-hydroxydul,** *n.* nickelous hydroxide, nickel(II) hydroxide.

**Nickeli-.** nickelic, nickeli-, nickel(III). **-cyanwasserstoffsäure,** *f.* nickelicyanic acid, cyanonickelic(II) acid.

**Nickelin,** *n.* nickeline (a kind of nickel silver); (*Min.*) niccolite.

**Nickeli-oxyd,** *n.* nickelic oxide, nickel(III) oxide. **-verbindung,** *f.* nickelic compound, nickel(III) compound.

**Nickel-jodid,** *n.* nickel iodide. **-kies,** *m.* millerite. **-kohlenoxyd,** *n.* nickel carbonyl. **-kühler,** *m.* nickel condenser or cooler. **-lauge,** *f.* (*Elec.*) nickel electrolyte. **-legierung,** *f.* nickel alloy. **-metall,** *n.* nickel metal, metallic nickel. **-münze,** *f.* nickel coin. **-niederschlag,** *m.* nickel precipitate; nickel deposit.

**Nickelo-.** nickelous, nickelo-, nickel(II).

**Nickelocker,** *m.* nickel ocher (annabergite).

**Nickelo-cyanwasserstoffsäure,** *f.* nickelocyanic acid, cyanonickelic(I) acid. **-verbindung,** *f.* nickelous compound, nickel(II) compound.

**Nickeloxyd,** *n.* nickel oxide, specif. nickelic oxide, nickel(III) oxide, $Ni_2O_3$ (as contrasted with Nickeloxydul). **-salz,** *n.* nickelic salt, nickel(III) salt.

**Nickeloxydul,** *n.* nickelous oxide, nickel(II) oxide, NiO. **-hydrat,** *n.* nickelous hydroxide, nickel(II) hydroxide. **-salz,** *n.* nickelous salt, nickel(II) salt. **-verbindung,** *f.* nickelous compound, nickel(II) compound.

**Nickelpapier,** *n.* nickel foil.

**nickelplattiert,** *a.* nickel-plated.

**Nickel-salz,** *n.* nickel salt. **-sammler,** *m.* nickel accumulator (storage battery). **-schwamm,** *m.* nickel sponge. **-smaragd,** *m.* emerald nickel (zaratite). **-speise,** *f.* nickel speiss. **-spiessglanz,** *m.*, **-spiessglanzerz,** *n.* ullmannite. **-stahl,** *m.* nickel steel. **-stein,** *m.* (*Metal.*) nickel mat(te). **-sulfür,** *n.* nickelous sulfide, nickel(II) sulfide. **-tiegel,** *m.* nickel crucible. **-überzug,** *m.* nickel plating. **-vitriol,** *m.* nickel sulfate. **-zusatz,** *m.* addition of nickel. **-zyanid,** *n.* nickel cyanide. **-zyanür,** *n.* nickel(ous) cyanide, nickel(II) cyanide.

**nicken,** *v.i. & t.* nod.

**Nicol'sches Prisma.** Nicol prism.

**nie,** *adv.* never.

**nieder,** *a.* low, lower, inferior, secondary, minor. — *adv.* low, down.

**Niederbewegung,** *f.* downward motion.

**nieder-blasen,** *v.t.* blow out (a furnace). **-brechen,** *v.t. & i.* break down.

**Niederdruck,** *m.* low pressure. **-dampf,** *m.* low-pressure steam.

**niederdrücken,** *v.t.* press down, force down; depress.

**Niederdruck-kessel,** *m.* low-pressure boiler. **-schlauch,** *m.* low-pressure tubing or hose.

**niederfallen,** *v.i.* fall down, precipitate, settle.

**Nieder-frequenzstrom,** *m.* low-frequency current. **-gang,** *m.* going down, descent; downstroke (of a piston).

**nieder-gehen,** *v.i.* go down, descend; subside, fall. **-gerissen,** *p.p.* (of niederreissen) carried down, etc. **-geschlagen,** *p.p.* (of niederschlagen) precipitated, etc.

**Nieder-holz,** *n.* undergrowth; coppice. **-lage,** *f.* warehouse; depot; deposit; defeat. **-lande,** *n.pl.* Netherlands.

**nieder-ländisch,** *a.* Dutch. **-legen,** *v.t.* lay down, put down; deposit. **-molekular,** *a.* of low molecular weight. **-reissen,** *v.t.* carry down, drag down; tear down, destroy.

**Niederschlag,** *m.* precipitate, precipitation; deposit, sediment; condensate. **-arbeit,** *f.* = Niederschlagsarbeit.

**niederschlag-arm,** *a.* poor in precipitate. **-bar,** *a.* precipitable.

**Niederschlagbarkeit,** *f.* precipitability.

**niederschlagen,** *v.t.* precipitate; deposit; condense; beat down, quell, refute, depress. — *v.r.* precipitate; settle, deposit. — **niederschlagend,** *p.a.* precipitant; sedative; depressing.

**Niederschlag-gefäss,** *n.* precipitating vessel. **-menge,** *f.* amount of precipitate. **-messung,** *f.* measurement of precipitation or precipitate. **-mittel,** *n.* precipitant. **-raum,** *m.* precipitation space or chamber.

**Niederschlags-apparat,** *m.* precipitation apparatus, precipitator. **-arbeit,** *f.* precipitation process; specif., (*Metal.*) iron reduction process (liberation of metals by means of iron). **-bildung,** *f.* formation of a precipitate. **-kessel,** *m.* precipitation pan. **-mittel,** *n.* precipitant. **-ziffer,** *f.* precipitation number.

**Niederschlagung,** *f.* precipitation, etc. (see niederschlagen).

**Niederschlag-verfahren,** *n.* precipitation process or method. **-vorrichtung,** *f.* precipitation apparatus, precipitator. **-wärme,** *f.* heat of precipitation. **-wasser,** *n.* precipitated water; condensed water. **-zeit,** *f.* time of precipitation.

**nieder-schlesisch,** *a.* Lower Silesian. **-schmelzen,** *v.t.* melt down. **-sinken,** *v.i.* sink down, sink, fall.

**Niederspannung,** *f.* low tension; (of gases) low pressure; (*Elec.*) low voltage.

**niedertransformieren,** *v.t.* (*Elec.*) step down.

**Niederung,** *f.* low ground, lowland, flats.

**niedervoltig,** *a.* low-voltage.

**Niederwald,** *m.* undergrowth; coppice.

**niederwärts,** *adv.* downward.

**niedr.,** *abbrev.* of niedrig.

**niedrig,** *a.* low.

**niedriger,** *a.* lower.

**niedrig-gekohlt,** *a.* (*Metal.*) low-carbon. **-legiert,** *a.* low-alloyed. **-molekular,** *a.* of low molecular weight. **-prozentig,** *a.* low-percentage. **-schmelzend,** *a.* low-melting. **-siedend,** *a.* low-boiling.

**Niedrigsieder,** *m.* low-boiling substance, low boiler.

**niedrigsiliziert,** *a.* (*Metal.*) low-silicon.

**Niedrigst-.** lowest; minimal, minimum. **-gehalt,** *m.* minimum content.

**niedrig-viskos, -viskös,** *a.* of low viscosity.

**niemals,** *adv.* never.

**niemand,** *pron.* nobody, no one.

**Niere,** *f.* kidney; nodule, concretion; (of ore) bunch, pocket.

**Nieren-.** renal, nephro-. **-baum,** *m.* cashew tree, cashew. **-drüse,** *f.* renal gland. **-entzündung,** *f.* nephritis. **-erz,** *n.* kidney ore.

**nierenförmig,** *a.* kidney-shaped, reniform.

**Nieren-gries(s),** *m.* renal gravel. **-haut,** *f.* renal capsule. **-mittel,** *n.* kidney remedy, nephritic. **-stein,** *m.* kidney stone (either spherulite, nephrite, or renal calculus).

**nierig,** *a.* (*Mining*) nodular.
**Niese-fieber,** *n.* hay fever. **-mittel,** *n.* sternutative, sternutator, sneeze-provoking agent.
**niesen,** *v.i.* sneeze.
**Niesenerreger,** *m.* sternutator, (*Mil.*) sneeze gas.
**Nies-gas,** *n.* (*Mil.*) sneeze gas. **-kraut,** *n.* sneezewort (*Achillea ptarmica*). **-wurz, -wurzel,** *f.* hellebore.
**Niet,** *n.*, **Niete,** *f.* rivet, pin.
**Nieteisen,** *n.* rivet iron; rivet steel.
**nieten,** *v.t.* rivet.
**Nietnagel,** *m.* rivet; hangnail.
**Nietung,** *f.* riveting; riveted joint.
**Nietverbindung,** *f.* riveted joint.
**Nigeröl,** *n.* niger(seed) oil.
**Nikol'sches Prisma.** Nicol prism.
**Nikotin,** *n.* nicotine.
**nikotinfrei,** *a.* nicotine-free.
**Nikotin-gehalt,** *m.* nicotine content. **-säure,** *f.* nicotinic (or nicotic) acid. **-vergiftung,** *f.* nicotine poisoning.
**Nilblau,** *n.* Nile blue.
**nilgrün.** *a.* Nile-green.
**nimmer,** *adv.* never. **-satt,** *a.* insatiable.
**nimmt,** *pr. 3 sing.* (of nehmen) takes; gets.
**Nimöl,** *n.* neem oil, margosa oil.
**Niob, Niobium,** *n.* niobium (columbium).
**Niobat,** *n.* niobate (columbate).
**Niob-säure,** *f.* niobic (columbic) acid. **-wasserstoff,** *m.* niobium (columbium) hydride.
**Nippel,** *m.* nipple.
**nippen,** *v.i.* sip.
**nirgend, nirgends,** *adv.* nowhere.
**Nirostastahl,** *m.* a stainless steel. *T.N.*
**-nis.** A noun suffix denoting quality, act, place or concrete effect; -ness, -tion, etc.; as, *Kenntnis*, knowledge, *Ergebnis*, result, *Gefängnis*, prison.
**Nische,** *f.* niche, recess, hole.
**Nitranilin,** *n.* nitroaniline.
**Nitrat,** *n.* nitrate. **-ätze,** *f.* (*Dyeing*) nitrate discharge. **-beize,** *f.* (*Dyeing*) nitrate mordant.
**Nitration,** *f.* nitration. — *n.* nitrate ion.
**Nitrat-kunstseide, -seide,** *f.* nitrocellulose rayon, nitrate rayon.
**nitratreduzierend,** *a.* nitrate-reducing.
**Nitrid,** *n.* nitride (esp., an -ic nitride, as contrasted with Nitrür).
**Nitrierapparat,** *m.* nitrating apparatus.
**nitrierbar,** *a.* nitratable; nitrifiable; nitridable.
**Nitrierbaumwolle,** *f.* nitrating cotton.
**nitrieren,** *v.t.* nitrate; nitrify; (*Iron*) nitride.
**Nitrier-gemisch,** *n.* nitrating mixture. **-härteverfahren,** *n.* nitriding process. **-härtung,** *f.* (*Iron*) hardening by nitridation, nitride hardening, nitriding. **-ofen,** *m.* nitriding furnace or oven. **-säure,** *f.* nitrating acid. **-schleuder,** *f.* acid hydroextractor. **-sonderstahl,** *m.* special steel for nitriding. **-stahl,** *m.* nitriding steel. **-topf,** *m.* nitrating vessel.
**Nitrierung,** *f.* nitration; nitrification; (*Iron*) nitridation.
**Nitrierungs-grad,** *m.* degree of nitration or nitrification or nitridation. **-stufe,** *f.* stage or degree of nitration or nitridation.
**Nitrierwirkung,** *f.* nitrating (or nitriding or nitrifying) action or effect.
**nitrifizieren,** *v.t.* nitrify.
**Nitrilgruppe,** *f.* nitrile group.
**Nitrit,** *n.* nitrite. **-bildner,** *m.* nitrite former, nitrous bacterium.
**nitritfrei,** *a.* free from nitrites, nitrite-free.
**Nitro-bakterien,** *n.pl.* nitrobacteria. **-benzol, -benzin,** *n.* nitrobenzene. **-chinon,** *n.* nitroquinone. **-cocussäure,** *f.* nitrococcic acid. **-derivat,** *n.* nitro derivative. **-farbstoff,** *m.* nitro dye. **-fettkörper,** *m.* aliphatic nitro compound. **-fettsäure,** *f.* nitro fatty acid. **-gruppe,** *f.* nitro group. **-halogenbenzole,** *n.pl.* halonitrobenzenes. **-kohlenstoff,** *m.* tetranitromethane. **-körper,** *m.* nitro substance, nitro compound. **-kupfer,** *n.* nitrocopper. **-lack,** *m.* nitro(cellulose) lacquer. **-lampe,** *f.* (*Elec.*) nitrogen-filled lamp.
**Nitrolsäure,** *f.* nitrolic acid.
**Nitropenta,** *abbrev.* of Nitropentaerythrit.
**Nitropentaerythrit,** *n.* pentaerythritol nitrate, specif. the tetranitrate.
**Nitro-prussidnatrium,** *n.* sodium nitroprusside. **-prussidwasserstoffsäure,** *f.* nitroprussic acid. **-pulver,** *n.* nitro powder.
**nitros,** *a.* nitrous. — **nitrose Säure,** = Nitrose.
**Nitroschwefelsäure,** *f.* nitrosulfuric acid.
**Nitrose,** *f.* (*Sulfuric Acid*) a solution of nitrosylsulfuric acid in sulfuric acid, formed in the lead-chamber process.
**Nitroseide,** *f.* = Nitratkunstseide.
**nitrosieren,** *v.t.* treat with nitrous acid, introduce the nitroso group into.
**Nitrosisulfosäure,** *f.* nitrosisulfonic acid.
**Nitroso-bakterien,** *n.pl.* nitrosobacteria. **-benzol,** *n.* nitrosobenzene. **-blau,** *n.* nitroso blue. **-gruppe,** *f.* nitroso group. **-kobaltwasserstoffsäure,** *f.* cobaltinitrous acid. **-sulfosäure,** *f.* nitrososulfonic acid. **-verbindung,** *f.* nitroso compound.
**Nitro-sprengstoff,** *m.* nitro explosive. **-stärke,** *f.* nitrostarch. **-sulfonsäure,** *f.* nitrosulfonic acid.
**Nitrosyl-säure,** *f.* nitrosylic acid (hyponitrous acid). **-schwefelsäure,** *f.* nitrosylsulfuric acid.
**Nitro-toluol,** *n.* nitrotoluene. **-verbindung,** *f.* nitro compound. **-weinsäure,** *f.* nitrotartaric acid (tartaric acid dinitrate, also the mononitrate). **-zelluloselack,** *m.* nitrocellulose lacquer or dope.

**Nitroxyd,** *n.* nitrogen oxide.
**Nitroxylgruppe,** *f.* nitroxyl group (nitryl group, $NO_2$, nitro group).
**Nitroxylol,** *n.* nitroxylene.
**Nitrür,** *n.* (-ous) nitride. Cf. Chlorür.
**Nitrylsäure,** *f.* nitrylic acid (nitrous acid).
**Niveau,** *n.* level. **-fläche,** *f.* level surface. **-flasche,** *f.* leveling bottle, leveling vessel (as for a gas buret). **-rohr,** *n.*, **-röhre,** *f.* level tube, leveling tube. **-stufe,** *f.* (of electrons) energy level.
**Nivellements-, Nivellier-.** leveling, level.
**nivellieren,** *v.t.* level; grade, smooth.
**Nivellier-schraube,** *f.* leveling screw. **-ung,** *f.* leveling; grading. **-vorrichtung,** *f.* leveling device.
**n.J.,** *abbrev.* (nächstes Jahr) next year.
**Nk., NK.** *abbrev.* (Normalkerze) standard candle.
**nl.,** *abbrev.* (nicht löslich) not soluble.
**nm.,** *abbrev.* (nachmittags) afternoon, P.M.
**n.M.,** *abbrev.* (nächsten Monats) of next month.
**No., N°,** *abbrev.* (Numero) number, no., No.
**noch,** *adv.* still, yet, more, else, however; nor. — **— einmal,** once more. — **— immer,** still. — **— nicht,** not yet.
**noch-malig,** *a.* repeated. **-mals,** *adv.* once more, once again, again.
**Nocken,** *m.*, **Nocke,** *f.* cam; lifter, tappet, stud, lug, etc.; boss, nub. **-welle,** *f.* (*Mach.*) cam shaft.
**Nodus,** *m.* node.
**Nomenklatur,** *f.* nomenclature.
**nominell,** *a.* nominal.
**Nonius,** *m.* (*pl.* **Nonien**) vernier. **-einteilung,** *f.* vernier scale.
**Nonne,** *f.* mold, matrix; nun.
**nonocarbozyklisch,** *a.* nonacarbocyclic.
**Noppe,** *f.* nap; burl; knot, noil.
**Noppenbeize,** *f.* burl dye.
**noppenfärben,** *v.t.* burl-dye, noil-dye.
**Noppen-stift,** *m.* (*Dyeing*) inking pencil. **-tinktur,** *f.* burl dye, burl(ing) ink.
**Nord, Norden,** *m.* north.
**nord-amerikanisch,** *a.* North American. **-deutsch,** *a.* North German.
**Nordhäuser Schwefelsäure, Nordhäuser Vitriolöl.** Nordhausen acid (fuming sulfuric acid).
**nordisch,** *a.* northern, northerly; Nordic.
**nördlich,** *a.* northerly, northern, arctic.
**Nord-licht,** *n.* aurora borealis. **-meer,** *n.* Arctic Ocean. **-ost,** *m.* northeast; northeaster. **-pol,** *m.* north pole. **-see,** *f.* North Sea.
**Norgeraniumsäure,** *f.* norgeranic acid.
**Norgesalpeter,** *m.* Norway saltpeter (calcium nitrate).
**Nor-guajakharzsäure,** *f.* norguaiaretic acid. **-homokamphersäure,** *f.* norhomocamphoric acid. **-kampher,** *m.* norcamphor. **-kamphersäure,** *f.* norcamphoric acid.

**Norm,** *f.* standard, norm; rule.
**Norm-.** standard.
**normal,** *a.* normal; standard.
**Normal-.** normal, standard. **-bedingungen,** *f.pl.* normal conditions; standard specifications. **-benzin,** *n.* a special gasoline free from aromatics. **-druck,** *m.* normal pressure; standard pressure.
**Normale,** *f.* (*Geom.*) normal.
**Normal-Eichungs-Kommission,** *f.* a government bureau corresponding to the Bureau of Standards. **-einheit,** *f.* normal unit, standard unit. **-element,** *n.* (*Elec.*) standard cell.
**normalerweise,** *adv.* normally.
**Normal-essig,** *m.* standard vinegar, proof vinegar. **-fall,** *m.* normal case. **-feuchtigkeit,** *f.* standard moisture. **-flüssigkeit,** *f.* = Normallösung. **-gewicht,** *n.* standard weight. **-glühen,** *n.* controlled tempering or annealing, normalizing. **-grösse,** *f.* normal size; standard size.
**Normalien,** *f.pl.* standards.
**normalisieren,** *v.t.* standardize, normalize.
**Normalisierung,** *f.* standardization.
**Normalität,** *f.* normality.
**Normal-kerze,** *f.* standard candle. **-kupfer,** *n.* (*Elec.*) standard copper. **-leistung,** *f.* normal output, rated output. **-lösung,** *f.* normal solution; standard solution; (*Dyeing*) test liquor. **-null,** *f.* mean sea level. **-probe,** *f.* standard sample. **-säure,** *f.* normal acid; standard acid. **-schliff,** *m.* standard (interchangeable) ground joint. **-seifenlösung,** *f.* standard soap solution. **-spannung,** *f.* (*Elec.*) normal voltage. **-stärke,** *f.* normal strength; standard strength; (of alcohol) proof strength. **-stellung,** *f.* zero position; standard position. **-temperatur,** *f.* standard temperature. **-weingeist,** *m.* proof spirit. **-wert,** *m.* normal value; standard value. **-widerstand,** *m.* normal or standard resistance. **-zeit,** *f.* standard time. **-zusammensetzung,** *f.* standard composition. **-zustand,** *m.* normal or standard state or condition.
**normen,** *v.t.* standardize.
**Normen-aufstellung,** *f.* establishing of standards. **-ausschuss,** *m.* committee on standards. **-sand,** *m.* (*Cement*) standard sand.
**normentsprechend,** *p.a.* normal; standard.
**Normenvorschrift,** *f.* standard specification.
**normgerecht,** *a.* standard.
**normieren,** *v.t.* standardize, gage; regulate.
**Normierung,** *f.* normalization, standardization; gaging.
**normig,** *a.* normal; standard.
**normrecht,** *a.* standard.
**Normteil,** *m.* standard part.
**Normung,** *f.* standardization, normalization.
**normwidrig,** *a.* abnormal.

**Norpinsäure,** *f.* norpinic acid.
**Norwegen,** *n.* Norway.
**Nörz,** *m.* mink.
**Not,** *f.* need; necessity, want; emergency; distress; effort.
**Not-.** emergency, distress; reserve, spare, auxiliary; temporary, provisional. **-absperrhahn,** *m.* emergency stopcock. **-auslass,** *m.* emergency outlet. **-behelf,** *m.* makeshift; last resort.
**notdürftig,** *a.* scanty, needy.
**Notfall,** *m.* emergency, exigency.
**not-gar,** *a.* (*Leather*) undertanned. **-gedrungen,** *p.a.* compulsory. — *adv.* necessarily.
**notieren,** *v.t.* note; quote (prices).
**nötig,** *a.* necessary, needful. — **— haben,** want, need.
**nötigen,** *v.t.* necessitate, force, urge. **-falls,** *adv.* if need be, if necessary.
**Notiz,** *f.* notice, note. **-blatt,** *n.* (*lit.*) notice journal, notice sheet (a name used by periodicals). **-buch,** *n.* note book.
**Not-lage,** *f.* emergency. **-mittel,** *n.* expedient, shift. **-stand,** *m.* urgent state, urgency, emergency, need. **-wehr,** *f.* self-defense.
**notwendig,** *a.* necessary.
**notwendigerweise,** *adv.* necessarily.
**Notwendigkeit,** *f.* necessity.
**Novität,** *f.* novelty.
**Novojodin,** *n.* novoiodin.
**N.P.,** *abbrev.* (norwegisches Patent) Norwegian patent.
**Nr.,** *abbrev.* (Nummer) number.
**Nro.,** *abbrev.* (Numero) number.
**NS.,** *abbrev.* National Socialist.
**N-Substanz,** *f.* nitrogenous substance.
**N.T.,** *abbrev.* (normale Temperatur) normal temperature.
**Ntf.,** *abbrev.* (Naturforscher) scientific investigator.
**Nu,** *m.* moment, trice.
**Nuance, Nüance,** *f.* shade, tint, tone.
**Nuancen-abstufung,** *f.* gradation of shades. **-abweichung,** *f.* deviation in shade. **-unterschied,** *m.* difference in shade.
**Nüancierblau,** *n.* tinting blue.
**nuancieren, nüancieren,** *v.t.* shade, shade off, tint, tone; modulate.
**Nüancierfarbstoff,** *m.* shading dye, toning dye.
**nüchtern,** *a.* empty, fasting; sober, temperate, cool; flat, insipid.
**Nucleinsäure,** *f.* nucleic acid.
**Nudeln,** *f.pl.* noodles; vermicelli; macaroni.
**Nukleinsäure,** *f.* nucleic acid.
**Nukleoproteid,** *n.* nucleoprotein.
**Null,** *f.* zero, naught, nil, cipher. **-ablesung,** *f.* zero reading.
**nullen,** *v.t.* neutralize.
**Null-grad,** *m.* zero. **-lage,** *f.* zero position. **-leiter,** *m.* (*Elec.*) neutral conductor, return wire. **-linie,** *f.* zero line, null line. **-methode,** *f.* zero method. **-niveau,** *n.* zero level. **-punkt,** *m.* zero point, zero; origin. **-punktbestimmung,** *f.* zero point determination. **-setzen,** *n.* setting equal to zero. **-spannung,** *f.* (*Elec.*) zero voltage. **-stelle, -stellung,** *f.* zero position. **-strich,** *m.* zero mark.
**nullt,** *a.* zero. — **nullte Spalte,** zero column.
**Nullung,** *f.* neutralizing.
**Null-vektor,** *m.* zero vector. **-verfahren,** *n.* zero method. **-versuch,** *m.* blank experiment, blank test. **-wert,** *m.* zero value, zero, naught.
**nullwertig,** *a.* nonvalent, avalent.
**Nullzweig,** *m.* zero branch.
**numerieren,** *v.t.* number.
**Numerierung,** *f.* numbering, (e)numeration.
**numerisch,** *a.* numerical.
**Numero,** *m.* (usually abbreviated, Nro.) number.
**Numerus,** *m.* number; antilogarithm.
**Nummer,** *f.* number.
**Nummerierungsart,** *f.* numbering system.
**nummerisch,** *a.* numerical.
**nummern,** *v.t.* number.
**nun,** *adv.* now; well, why; so. — **— einmal,** after all. **-mehr,** *adv.* at present; now, by this time; henceforth; since then; then.
**nunmehrig,** *a.* present.
**nur,** *adv.* only, but, scarcely.
**Nürnberg,** *n.* Nuremberg.
**Nuss,** *f.* nut; specif., walnut. **-baum,** *m.* nut tree, specif. walnut. **-beize,** *f.* (*Paper*) soluble brown.
**nussbraun,** *a.* nut-brown.
**Nuss-griesskohle,** *f.*, **-grus,** *m.* nutty slack. **-kern,** *m.* nut kernel. **-kernmehl,** *n.* nut meal. **-kohle,** *f.* nut coal. **-körnung,** *f.* nut size. **-öl,** *n.* nut oil; specif., walnut oil.
**Nüster,** *f.* nostril.
**Nut, Nute,** *f.* groove, rabbet, slot.
**Nut-.** grooving.
**nuten,** *v.t.* groove, slot.
**Nutrolle,** *f.* grooved pulley.
**Nutschapparat,** *m.* suction filter apparatus.
**Nutsche,** *f.*, **-filter,** *n.* suction filter, esp. a Büchner funnel.
**nutschen,** *v.t.* filter by suction (esp., thru a Büchner funnel).
**Nutschen-becher,** *m.* suction filter cup. **-filter,** *n.* suction filter. **-sieb,** *n.* suction filter sieve. **-trichter,** *m.* suction funnel.
**Nuttharz,** *n.* acaroid resin, acaroid gum.
**Nutz-.** useful, practical, effective, economic, commercial. **-anwendung,** *f.* practical application. **-arbeit,** *f.* useful work.
**nutzbar,** *a.* useful; available; effective; profitable. — **— machen,** utilize.

**Nutzbar-keit,** *f.* usefulness, etc. (see nutzbar). **-machung,** *f.* utilization.

**nutzbringend,** *a.* profitable.

**Nutzdauer,** *f.* useful life, service life.

**nutze, nütze,** *a.* useful, of use, profitable.

**Nutzeffekt,** *m.* useful effect, efficiency, effect.

**nutzen,** *v.t.* use. — *v.i.* be of use.

**Nutzen,** *m.* use, utility, advantage, profit.

**Nutz-gas,** *n.* (*Aero.*) impellent. **-gras,** *n.* grass for feed. **-holz,** *n.* commercial timber, lumber. **-kapazität,** *f.* useful capacity. **-last,** *f.* useful load, pay load. **-leistung,** *f.* useful work, useful effect, effective output.

**nützlich,** *a.* useful, serviceable, profitable, advantageous, expedient.

**Nützlichkeit,** *f.* usefulness, utility, advantage.

**nutzlos,** *a.* useless, unprofitable.

**Nutz-losigkeit,** *f.* uselessness. **-niessung,** *f.* usufruct, use. **-pferdestärke,** *f.* effective horsepower. **-pflanze,** *f.* useful plant, specif. food plant or fodder plant. **-strom,** *m.* (*Elec.*) useful current. **-tier,** *n.* useful animal.

**Nutzung,** *f.* use; revenue; produce, yield.

**Nutzungs-dauer,** *f.* useful life. **-recht,** *n.* right of use.

**Nutz-wert,** *m.* economic value. **-wirkung,** *f.* useful effect, efficiency.

**N.Z.,** *abbrev.* (Normalzeit) standard time; (Neutralisationszahl) neutralization number.

# O

**o.,** *abbrev.* (oder) or; (oben) above; (ohne) without; (ordinär) ordinary.

**O.,** *abbrev.* (Ost) east.

**Oase,** *f.* oasis.

**ob,** *conj.* whether, if; altho. — *prep.* on account of.

**Obacht,** *f.* heed, attention.

**Obdach,** *n.* shelter.

**oben,** *adv.* above; overhead, on top; before. **-an,** *adv.* at the top. **-auf,** *adv.* on (the) top, on the surface. **-aufschwimmend,** *a.* supernatant. **-drein,** *adv.* over and above. **-erwähnt,** *a.* above-mentioned. **-hin,** *adv.* superficially, slightly. **-liegend,** *a.* lying above, overhead.

**Ober-.** upper, chief, high, supreme, head, top, epi-, super-, supra-, superior; gross. **-arm,** *m.* upper arm. **-aufsicht,** *f.* (central) supervision. **-bau,** *m.* superstructure.

**Oberbauch-.** epigastric.

**Ober-bayern,** *n.* Upper Bavaria. **-boden,** *m.* top soil. **-druck,** *m.* pressure from above, downward pressure.

**obere,** *a.* upper; high, higher, superior, chief.

**Oberfläche,** *f.* surface; area.

**oberflächenaktiv,** *a.* surface-active.

**Oberflächenbau,** *m.* surface structure.

**oberflächenbehandelt,** *a.* surface-treated.

**Oberflächen-behandlung,** *f.* surface treatment. **-druck,** *m.* surface pressure. **-einheit,** *f.* unit of area. **-energie,** *f.* surface energy. **-entfaltung,** *f.* surface development. **-erscheinung,** *f.* surface phenomenon. **-farbe,** *f.* surface color. **-färbung,** *f.* surface coloring; surface dyeing or staining. **-fehler,** *m.* surface defect. **-glanz,** *m.* surface luster. **-härte,** *f.* surface hardness. **-härtung,** *f.* surface hardening, (*Metal.*) case-hardening.

**oberflächeninaktiv,** *a.* surface-inactive.

**Oberflächen-kondensator,** *m.* surface condenser. **-kühlung,** *f.* surface cooling. **-kultur,** *f.* (*Agric.*) surface cultivation. **-ladung,** *f.* (*Elec.*) surface charge. **-leimung,** *f.* (*Paper*) surface sizing. **-lösung,** *f.* surface solution. **-niederschlag,** *m.* surface precipitate. **-riss,** *m.* surface crack. **-schicht,** *f.* surface layer. **-schutz,** *m.* surface protection. **-spannung,** *f.* surface tension. **-verbindung,** *f.* surface compound; surface combination. **-wasser,** *n.* surface water. **-wirkung,** *f.* surface action or effect.

**oberflächlich,** *a.* superficial.

**obergärig,** *a.* top-fermenting, top-fermented. — **obergärige Hefe,** top yeast.

**Ober-gärung,** *f.* top fermentation. **-grund,** *m.* surface soil.

**oberhalb,** *prep.* above.

**Ober-hand,** *f.* back of the hand; upper hand advantage. **-haut,** *f.* epidermis.

**Oberhaut-.** epidermic, epidermal.

**Ober-häutchen,** *n.* cuticle. **-hefe,** *f.* top yeast. **-heizwert,** *m.* gross calorific value.

**oberirdisch,** *a.* above-ground, overhead, aerial.

**Ober-kante,** *f.* upper edge, top edge. **-keim,** *m.* (*Zoöl.*) ectoderm. **-kiefer,** *m.* upper jaw. **-licht,** *n.* light from above; skylight. **-niere,** *f.* suprarenal gland. **-realschule,** *f.* technical school equivalent to high school and junior college. **-rinde,** *f.* outer bark. **-schalseife,** *f.* top-layer soap (or one made to resemble it). **-schenkel,** *m.* thigh. **-schicht,** *f.* upper layer, upper stratum.

**oberschlesisch,** *a.* Upper Silesian.

**Ober-schwingung,** *f.* harmonic vibration, overtone. **-seite,** *f.* upper side; right side. **-spannung,** *f.* (*Elec.*) high tension, high-tension voltage.

**oberst,** *a.* uppermost, highest.

**Ober-tasse,** *f.* cup. **-teig,** *m.* (*Brewing*) upper-dough. **-teil,** *m.* upper part, top part. **-ton,** *m.* overtone, upper partial. **-welle,** *f.* (*Physics*) harmonic.

**obgleich,** *conj.* altho.

**Obhut,** *f.* protection, care.

**obig,** *a.* above, above-mentioned, foregoing.

**Objekt-abstand,** *m.* (*Micros.*) working distance. **-glas,** *n.* (*Micros.*) slide, mount. **-halter,** *m.* (*Micros.*) specimen holder.

**Objektiv,** *n.* objective, object glass, lens. **-linse,** *f.* objective lens. **-wechsler,** *m.* (*Micros.*) revolving nosepiece.

**Objekt-sucher,** *m.* (*Optics*) object finder. **-tisch,** *m.* (*Micros.*) stage, stand. **-träger,** *m.* (*Micros.*) slide, mount, also stage, stand.

**Oblate,** *f.* wafer.

**Oblatenpapier,** *n.* wafer paper, rice paper.

**obliegen,** *v.i.* be incumbent (on); attend (to).

**Obliegenheit,** *f.* obligation, duty.

**obligatorisch,** *a.* obligatory.

**Obmann,** *m.* head man (chairman, superintendent, etc.).

**obschon,** *conj.* altho.

**Observatorium,** *n.* observatory.

**Obst,** *n.* fruit. **-art,** *f.* kind of fruit.

**obstartig,** *a.* fruity, fruit-like.

**Obst-bau,** *m.* fruit culture, orcharding. **-baum,** *m.* fruit tree. **-branntwein,** *m.* fruit brandy, fruit spirit. **-essig,** *m.* fruit vinegar. **-garten,** *m.* orchard. **-kern,** *m.* fruit kernel, fruit stone. **-konserve,** *f.* fruit preserve, preserved fruit. **-mark,** *n.* fruit pulp. **-most,** *m.* fruit juice. **-mus,** *n.* fruit sauce, fruit butter, jam, marmalade. **-paprika,** *m.* fruit capsicum. **-saft,** *m.* fruit juice. **-trester,** *m.pl.* marc of fruit. **-wein,** *m.* fruit wine, cider, perry, etc. **-weinbereitung,** *f.* fruit wine manufacture. **-zucker,** *m.* fruit sugar (levulose).

**obwalten,** *v.i.* exist; prevail, predominate.

**obwohl, obzwar,** *conj.* altho, tho.

**Ocher-, ocher-.** see Ocker-, ocker-.

**ocherig,** *a.* ocherous, ochery.

**Ochras,** *m.* black salt (crude potash or soda from ashes).

**Ochs, Ochse,** *m.* ox.

**Ochsenblut,** *n.* oxblood.

**ochsenblutfarbig,** *a.* oxblood(-colored).

**Ochsen-fleisch,** *n.* beef. **-galle,** *f.* ox gall, ox bile. **-klauenfett, -klauenöl,** *n.* neat's-foot oil. **-leder,** *n.* neat's leather. **-zunge,** *f.* bugloss (*Anchusa*); borage; (**farbende**) alkanet.

**Ocker,** *m.* ocher.

**ocker-artig, -ähnlich,** *a.* like ocher, ocherous.

**Ockerfarbe,** *f.* ocher (as a pigment).

**ocker-farbig,** *a.* ocher-colored, ocherous. **-gelb,** *a.* ocher-yellow. **-haltig,** *a.* containing ocher, ocherous.

**ockerig,** *a.* ocherous, ochery.

**Oct-.** see Okt-.

**od.,** *abbrev.* (oder) or.

**O.D.,** *abbrev.* (optisches Drehungsvermögen) optical rotatory power.

**od. dgl.,** *abbrev.* (oder dergleichen) or the like.

**öde,** *a.* waste, deserted.

**Ödem,** *n.* edema.

**oder,** *conj.* or.

**Odermennig,** *m.* (*Bot.*) agrimony.

**o. dgl., o. drgl.,** *abbrev.* (oder dergleichen) or the like.

**Ödland,** *n.* waste land.

**Oel, Oel-.** see Öl, Öl-.

**Oe.P.,** *abbrev.* (oesterreichisches Patent) Austrian patent.

**oest-.** see öst-.

**Öfchen,** *n.* little furnace, oven or stove.

**Ofen,** *m.* furnace; oven; kiln; stove; heater. **-auskleidung,** *f.* furnace (or oven or kiln) lining. **-bruch,** *m.* (*Zinc*) tutty. **-einsatz,** *m.* furnace (or oven) charge. **-emaille,** *f.* stove (or stoving) enamel. **-farbe,** *f.* graphite, black lead. **-futter,** *n.* furnace lining. **-galmei,** *m.* furnace cadmia, tutty. **-gang,** *m.* working or working order of a furnace, oven, or kiln. **-gewölbe,** *n.* (arched) furnace roof. **-gut,** *n.* material to be treated in a furnace or oven or kiln. **-kachel,** *f.* stove tile. **-lack,** *m.* stove (or stoving) lacquer or varnish. **-lackfarbe,** *f.* stove lacquer pigment. **-putzmittel,** *n.* stove polish. **-russ,** *m.* furnace soot; oven soot. **-sau,** *f.* (*Metal.*) furnace sow. **-schlacke,** *f.* furnace slag. **-schwamm,** *m.* (*Zinc*) tutty. **-schwarz,** *n.* graphite, black lead.

**ofen-trocken,** *a.* kiln-dried; oven-dried. **-trocknend,** *a.* kiln-drying; oven-drying; stove-drying, stoving.

**Ofen-trocknung,** *f.* kiln (or oven or stove) drying. **-tür, -türe,** *f.* door (esp., the fire door) of a furnace, oven, kiln or stove; (*Ceram.*) wicket. **-verkokung,** *f.* coking in ovens. **-ziegel,** *m.* fire brick; stove tile. **-zug,** *m.* furnace (or oven or kiln) draft.

**offen,** *a.* open; (of sound) hollow; clear, clever, frank. — **offener Dampf,** direct steam, live steam.

**offen-bar,** *a.* manifest, obvious, plain. **-baren,** *v.t.* disclose, reveal.

**Offenbarung,** *f.* disclosure, revelation.

**offen-kundig,** *a.* well-known, notorious; evident. **-sichtlich,** *a.* evident, obvious.

**öffentlich,** *a.* public; open.

**Öffentlichkeit,** *f.* publicity.

**Offerte,** *f.* offer, proffer.

**offiziell, officiell,** *a.* official.

**Offizier,** *m.* officer.

**Offizin,** *f.* (*Pharm.*) laboratory, dispensary, apothecary's shop; workshop, specif. printing shop.

**offizinell,** *a.* officinal.

**öffnen,** *v.t* open; disclose. — **öffnend,** *p.a.* (*Med*) aperient.

**Öffner,** *m.* opener; (*Paper*) pulper, kneader.

**Öffnung,** *f.* opening; aperture, orifice, mouth; hole, gap; dissection; evacuation.

**Öffnungs-mittel,** *n.* (*Med.*) aperient. **-weite,** *f.* width of opening. **-winkel,** *m.* angle of aperture.

**Offsetdruck-erei,** *f.* offset printing. **-farbe,** *f.* offset-printing ink.

**oft,** *adv.* often.

**öfter,** *adv.* oftener; (also **öfters**) often.

**oft-malig,** *a.* frequent, repeated. **-mals,** *adv.* frequently, often.

**ohne,** *prep.* without. — *conj.* but that. — **— weiteres,** without further ado, forthwith.

**ohne-dem, -dies,** *adv.* apart from that, besides. **-hin,** *adv.* besides.

**ohngefähr,** *adv.* approximately. — *a.* approximate.

**Ohnmacht,** *f.* weakness; fainting, syncope.

**ohnmächtig,** *a.* weak, faint, unconscious.

**Ohr,** *n.* ear.

**Ohr-.** aural, auricular.

**Öhr,** *n.* (*Tech.*) ear, lug, handle, eye, loop, catch; bog iron ore.
**Öhrchen,** *n.* auricle; little ear; eyelet.
**Ohren-schmalz,** *n.* ear wax, cerumen. **-stein,** *m.*, **-steinchen,** *n.* otolith.
**Ohrfinger,** *m.* little finger.
**ohrförmig,** *a.* auriform.
**Ohr-speicheldrüse,** *f.* parotid gland. **-stein,** *m.* otolith. **-trommel,** *f.* eardrum. **-trompete,** *f.* (*Anat.*) Eustachian tube. **-wachs,** *n.* ear wax, cerumen. **-wasser,** *n.* endolymph.
**Oker,** *m.* ocher. See ocker-, Ocker-.
**okkludieren,** *v.t.* occlude.
**ökologisch,** *a.* ecologic.
**ökonomisch,** *a.* economic, economical; agricultural.
**Oktaeder,** *n.* octahedron. **-gitter,** *n.* (*Cryst.*) octahedral lattice.
**oktaedrisch,** *a.* octahedral.
**Oktan-wert,** *m.* octane value or rating. **-zahl,** *f.* octane number or rating.
**Oktettregel,** *f.* octet rule.
**Okto-.** octa- (preferably), octo-.
**oktocarbocyclisch,** *a.* octacarbocyclic.
**Oktonaphten,** *n.* octanaphthene.
**Okular,** *n.* (*Optics*) eyepiece, ocular. **-muschel,** *f.* (*Micros.*) eyepiece cup.
**okulieren,** *v.t.* bud, graft (by budding).
**-ol.** (1) In names of alcohols or phenols (*i.e.*, when the ending signifies hydroxyl), -ol. (2) In names of a few hydrocarbons, -ene; as, *Benzol*, benzene (but the commercial product is called benzol or benzole). (3) In the case of other compounds, -ole; as, *Pyrrol*, pyrrole.
**Öl,** *n.* oil. **-abdichtung,** *f.* oil seal. **-ablass,** *m.* oil draining; oil drain. **-abscheider,** *m.* oil separator; (*Brewing*) oil trap. **-abscheidung,** *f.* oil separation. **-anstrich,** *m.* painting in oil; coat of oil or oil paint. **-anstrichfarbe,** *f.* oil-painting color; oil paint.
**öl-arm,** *a.* poor in oil. **-artig,** *a.* oily, oleaginous.
**Öl-aufnahme,** *f.* oil absorption. **-ausscheider,** *m.* oil separator. **-avivage,** *f.* (*Dyeing*) brightening with oil. **-bad,** *n.* oil bath; (in Turkey-red dyeing) green liquor. **-basis,** *f.* oil base; (*Dyeing*) fatty base.
**Ölbaum,** *m.* olive tree. — **falscher —,** oleaster.
**Öl-baumgummi, -baumharz,** *n.* elemi. **-beere,** *f.* olive. **-behälter,** *m.* oil container, oil tank. **-beize,** *f.* oil mordant; (in Turkey-red dyeing) oiling; (for wood) oil stain.
**ölbeständig,** *a.* oil-resistant, oilproof.
**ölbildend,** *p.a.* oil-forming, olefiant. — **ölbildendes Gas,** olefiant gas (ethylene).
**Öl-bindevermögen,** *n.* oil-binding property. **-blau,** *n.* smalt. **-bleiche,** *f.* oil bleaching. **-bodensatz,** *m.* oil sediment, oil foot. **-bohnermasse,** *f.* oil floor polish. **-bohrung,** *f.* oil well. **-bombe,** *f.* oil bomb. **-brenner,** *m.* oil burner. **-brunnen,** *m.* oil well. **-büchse,** *f.* (*Mach.*) oil cup, also oil can. **-buntlack,** *m.* colored oil enamel. **-creme,** *f.* oil cream, oil preparation. **-dampf,** *m.* oil vapor, oil smoke. **-dämpfung,** *f.* oil damping.
**öldicht,** *a.* oil-tight, impermeable to oil.
**Öl-drass,** *m.* oil dregs, oil foots. **-druck,** *m.* oil pressure; oleography; oleograph. **-druckmesser,** *m.* oil-pressure gage. **-drucktapete,** *f.* sanitary wallpaper. **-dunst,** *m.* oil vapor, oil fume.
**öldurchtränkt,** *a.* saturated with oil.
**Oleat,** *n.* oleate.
**ölecht,** *a.* fast to oil, oil-insoluble.
**Ölechtheit,** *f.* fastness to oil.
**Olefin,** *n.* olefin, olefine. **-alkohol,** *m.* olefinic alcohol, olefin alcohol. **-haloid,** *n.* olefin halide.
**olefinisch,** *a.* olefinic.
**Olefinketon,** *n.* olefinic ketone, olefin ketone.
**Olein-säure,** *f.* oleic acid. **-säureseife, -seife,** *f.* olein soap, red-oil soap. **-schmälze,** *f.* (*Textiles*) olein softener, olein emulsion.
**ölen,** *v.t.* oil; lubricate, grease.
**Oleokreosot,** *n.* (*Pharm.*) creosote oleate.
**Öler,** *m.* oiler; oil cup. **-glas,** *n.* glass oil cup.
**Ölersatz,** *m.* oil substitute.
**Oleum,** *n.* oleum, fuming sulfuric acid; (in Latin *Pharm.* names) oil.
**Öl-fabrik,** *f.* oil factory. **-fänger,** *m.* oil catcher, oil collector. **-farbe,** *f.* oil color; oil paint. **-farbenanstrich,** *m.* painting in oil colors; coat of oil paint. **-farbendruck,** *m.* oleography; oleograph. **-fass,** *n.* oil drum; oil barrel. **-feld,** *n.* oil field.
**ölfest,** *a.* oilproof, oil-insoluble.
**Öl-feuerung,** *f.* oil burning or heating; oil furnace. **-film,** *m.* oil film. **-firnis,** *m.* oil varnish. **-fläschchen,** *n.* (*Micros.*) immersion oil bottle. **-fleck,** *m.* oil spot, oil stain.
**öl-frei,** *a.* free from oil, oil-free. **-führend,** *a.* oil-bearing, oleiferous, petroliferous.
**Ölfüllung,** *f.* oil filling.
**ölgar,** *a.* oiled (leather); chamois.
**Öl-gas,** *n.* oil gas. **-gasteer,** *m.* oil-gas tar. **-gefäss,** *m.* oil vessel, oil tank.
**öl-gefeuert, -geheizt,** *a.* oil-fired, oil-heated.
**Öl-gehalt,** *n.* oil content. **-geläger,** *n.* oil dregs, oil foots. **-geschmack,** *m.* oily taste.
**ölgetränkt,** *a.* impregnated with oil, oiled.
**Ölgewinnung,** *f.* oil extraction, oil production.
**ölglanzend,** *a.* shining with, or as with, oil, having an oily luster.
**Öl-glanzlack,** *m.* oil gloss paint. **-grün,** *n.* oil green. **-grundierung,** *f.* oil priming or primer, oil bottom. **-hahn,** *m.* oil cock.
**ölhaltig,** *a.* containing oil, oleiferous.
**Öl-handel,** *m.* oil trade. **-härten,** *n.*, **-härtung,** *f.* oil hardening. **-härtungsanlage,** *f.* oil-hardening plant. **-härtungsstahl,** *m.* oil-

hardening steel. **-harz,** *n.* oleoresin. **-haut,** *f.* oil skin; (*Textiles*) oilskin. **-häutchen,** *n.* oil pellicle; oil film. **-hefen,** *f.pl.* oil dregs, oil lees.

**Oliban,** *n.* olibanum, frankincense.

**ölig, ölicht,** *a.* oily, oleaginous.

**Öligkeit,** *f.* oiliness.

**Oligoklas,** *m.* oligoclase.

**Oligozän,** *n.* (*Geol.*) Oligocene.

**ölimprägniert,** *a.* oil-impregnated.

**Öl-industrie,** *f.* oil industry. **-isolation,** *f.* oil insulation.

**Olive,** *f.* olive; enlargement on a tube for rubber connection.

**olivenartig,** *a.* (*Anat.*) olivary.

**Olivenbaum,** *m.* olive tree.

**olivenbraun,** *a.* olive-brown.

**Olivenfarbe,** *f.* olive color.

**oliven-farben, -farbig,** *a.* olive-colored. **-förmig,** *a.* (*Anat.*) olivary.

**Oliven-gelb,** *n.* olive yellow. **-grün,** *n.* olive green. **-kern,** *m.* olive kernel; (*Anat.*) olivary nucleus. **-kernasche,** *f.* olive-kernel ashes, pepperet(te). **-kernöl,** *n.* olive kernel oil. **-nachöl,** *n.* an inferior olive oil. **-öl,** *n.* olive oil. **-ölfettsäure,** *f.* fatty acid of olive oil. **-ölschmierseife,** *f.* olive-oil soft soap. **-ölseife,** *f.* olive-oil soap, (genuine) Castile soap.

**olivgrau,** *n.* olive gray; olive drab.

**Öl-kalk,** *m.* oil-bearing limestone. **-kammer,** *f.* oil chamber. **-kännchen,** *n.*, **-kanne,** *f.* oil can. **-karburierung,** *f.* oil carburizing. **-kautschuk,** *m.* factice. **-kitt,** *m.* putty. **-kohle,** *f.* oil carbon (formed from oil on heating). **-körper,** *n.* (*Biol.*) oil body. **-kreidestift,** *m.* oil crayon. **-krem,** *m.* oil cream. **-kruste,** *f.* oil crust. **-kuchen,** *n.* oil cake. **-kugel,** *m.* oil globule, oil drop. **-lack,** *m.* oil varnish. **-lackfarbe,** *f.* oil varnish paint. **-leder,** *n.* chamois. **-leinen,** *n.* oiled linen. **-leitung,** *f.* oil line, pipe line. **-lösevermögen,** *n.* oil-dissolving power.

**öllöslich,** *a.* oil-soluble.

**Öl-malerei,** *f.* oil painting. **-menge,** *f.* amount of oil. **-messer,** *m.* eleometer, oleometer, oilometer. **-milch,** *f.* oil emulsion. **-mischung,** *f.* oil mixture. **-mühle,** *f.* oil mill. **-nuss,** *f.* oil nut, oleiferous nut. **-nussbaum,** *m.* butternut tree; horse-radish tree (*Moringa*). **-packpapier,** *n.* oiled wrapping paper. **-papier,** *n.* oil paper, oiled paper. **-pauspapier,** *n.* oiled tracing paper. **-präparat,** *n.* oil preparation; specif., oil polish. **-probe,** *f.* sample of oil; test of oil. **-prüfer,** *m.* oil tester. **-pumpe,** *f.* oil pump. **-raffinerie,** *f.* oil refinery. **-rauch, -qualm,** *m.* oil smoke, oil vapor.

**ölreich, -haltig,** *a.* rich in oil.

**Öl-reinigung,** *f.* purification of oil. **-rückstand,** *m.* oil residue. **-russ,** *m.* lampblack. **-saat,** *f.* oil seed, oleiferous seed. **-same(n),** *m.* oil seed, esp. rapeseed or linseed. **-satz,** *m.* oil sediment, oil foots.

**ölsauer,** *a.* of or combined with oleic acid, oleate of.

**Ölsäure,** *f.* oleic acid. **-reihe,** *f.* oleic-acid series. **-seife,** *f.* oleic-acid soap, olein soap.

**Öl-schicht,** *f.* layer of oil; oil film; oil-bearing bed. **-schiefer,** *m.* oil shale. **-schlagen,** *n.* oil pressing. **-schlamm,** *m.* oil sludge, oil sediment. **-schmierung,** *f.* oil lubrication. **-schuhcreme,** *f.* oil shoe polish. **-schwarz,** *n.* oil black; = Mineralschwarz. **-schwemmverfahren,** *n.* oil flotation. **-seide,** *f.* oiled silk. **-seife,** *f.* oil soap, soap made from oil; specif., olive-oil soap, Castile soap, Venetian soap. **-sieb,** *n.* oil screen, oil strainer. **-siederei,** *f.* oil refinery. **-sodaseife,** *f.* soda soap made from oil, specif. Castile soap. **-sorte,** *f.* kind, quality or brand of oil. **-spachtel,** *f.* oil filler. **-spur,** *f.* trace of oil. **-staub,** *m.* oil spray. **-stein,** *m.* oilstone; stinkstone. **-stoff,** *m.* olein; oiled cloth. **-sud,** *m.* oil boiling. **-süss,** *n.* glycerol, glycerin. **-sylvinsäure,** *f.* oleosylvic acid. **-trester,** *m.pl.* oil marc (residue left after expressing oil from olives, etc.). **-tropfen,** *m.* drop of oil, oil drop. **-tubenfarbe,** *f.* oil color in tube. **-tuch,** *n.* oilcloth. **-überzug,** *m.* oil coating, oil film. **-umlauf,** *m.* oil circulation.

**Ölung,** *f.* oiling.

**Öl-verbrauch,** *m.* oil consumption. **-vergüten,** *n.*, **-vergütung,** *f.* (*Metal.*) heat treatment using oil. **-wa(a)ge,** *f.* oil hydrometer, eleometer. **-wachsbeize,** *f.* oil-wax stain. **-wasser,** *n.* oily water. **-werk,** *n.* oil works, oil mill, oil factory. **-zelle,** *f.* oil cell. **-zelluloselack,** *m.* oil cellulose lacquer. **-zeug,** *m. & n.* oilskin. **-zucker,** *m.* (*Pharm.*) elaeosaccharum, oleosaccharum; (formerly) glycerin. **-zufluss,** *m.* oil inflow, oil feed. **-zusatz,** *m.* addition of oil.

**Ombréfärbung,** *f.* ombré dyeing, shaded dyeing.

**-on.** (as a chemical ending denoting the ketonic group) -one.

**Önanth-.** enanth-, oenanth-. **-äther,** *m.* enanthic (or oenanthic) ether. **-säure,** *f.* enanthic (or oenanthic) acid. **-ylsäure,** *f.* enanthylic (or oenanthylic) acid.

**Önidin,** *n.* enidin, oenidin.

**Önin,** *n.* enin, oenin.

**Oolith,** *m.* oölite.

**oolithisch, oolitisch,** *a.* oölitic.

**O.P.,** *abbrev.* (österreichisches Patent) Austrian patent.

**opak,** *a.* opaque.

**opalartig,** *a.* opal-like, opaline.

**Opal-ausrüstung,** *f.* (*Textiles*) opal finish. **-blau,** *n.* opal blue. **-druck,** *m.* (*Calico*) opal(ine) print.
**opalescieren, opaleszieren,** *v.i.* opalesce. — **opalescierend, opaleszierend,** *p.a.* opalescent.
**Opaleszenz,** *f.* opalescence.
**Opal-farbe,** *f.* opal color. **-firnis,** *m.* opal varnish. **-glanz,** *m.* opaline luster, opalescence.
**opalglänzend,** *a.* opalescent.
**opalisieren,** *v.i.* opalesce. — *v.t.* render opalescent, opalize. — **opalisierend,** *p.a.* opalescent.
**Opalmutter,** *f.* opal matrix.
**opalschillernd,** *a.* opalescent.
**Opazität,** *f.* opacity.
**Oper,** *f.* opera.
**operieren,** *v.i.* & *t.* operate.
**Operment,** *n.* orpiment.
**Opfer,** *n.* offering, sacrifice, victim.
**opfern,** *v.t.* sacrifice.
**Opheliasäure,** *f.* ophelic acid.
**ophitisch,** *a.* (*Petrog.*) ophitic.
**Opiansäure,** *f.* opianic acid.
**Opiumsäure,** *f.* meconic acid.
**opsonisch,** *a.* opsonic.
**opt.-akt.,** *abbrev.* (optisch-aktiv) optically active.
**optieren,** *v.t.* focus.
**Optierung,** *f.* focusing.
**Optik,** *f.* optics; optical equipment.
**optimistisch,** *a.* optimistic.
**optisch,** *a.* optic, optical.
**Orangefarbe,** *f.* orange color or dye.
**orange-farben, -farbig,** *a.* orange-colored.
**Orange-gelb,** *n.* orange yellow. **-lack,** *m.* orange lac; orange lake. **-mennig,** *m.*, **-mennige,** *f.* orange minium, orange lead.
**Orangen-blüte,** *f.* orange blossom. **-essenz,** *f.* orange (peel) oil. **-essig,** *m.* orange vinegar. **-farbe,** *f.* orange color. **-frucht,** *f.* orange; (*Bot.*) citrus fruit, hesperidium. **-gelb,** *n.* orange yellow. **-öl,** *n.* orange (peel) oil. **-samenöl,** *n.* orange seed oil. **-schale,** *f.* orange peel. **-schalenöl,** *n.* orange peel oil.
**orangerot,** *a.* orange-red.
**Orangesamenöl,** *n.* orange-seed oil.
**orangieren,** *v.t.* (*Calico*) treat with milk of lime.
**Ord.,** *abbrev.* of Ordnung.
**Orden,** *m.* order; badge, decoration.
**ordentlich,** *a.* ordinary; regular; orderly; exact; steady; downright.
**ordinär,** *a.* ordinary, regular; common, inferior.
**Ordinatenachse,** *f.* axis of ordinates.
**Ordinatestrecke,** *f.* distance on the ordinate.
**Ordinierung,** *f.* (*Med.*) prescription.
**ordnen,** *v.t.* order, arrange, organize, regulate, classify, settle.
**Ordnung,** *f.* order; arrangement, regulation, classification; class; succession, series; system.
**ordnungs-gemäss, -mässig,** *a.* orderly, methodical. — *adv.* duly, well. **-widrig,** *a.* irregular, disorderly.
**Ordnungszahl,** *f.* number in a series, serial number, specif. atomic number; ordinal number.
**org.,** *abbrev.* (organisch) organic.
**Organ-brei,** *f.* (*Biol.*) organ (tissue) pulp. **-eiweiss,** *n.* organ protein.
**Organiker,** *m.* organic chemist.
**organisatorisch,** *a.* organizing; organizational.
**organisch,** *a.* organic. **-chemisch,** *a.* pertaining to organic chemistry, organic chemical.
**organisieren,** *v.t.* organize.
**Organismus,** *m.* organism.
**Organometall,** *n.* organometallic compound.
**organometallisch,** *a.* organometallic.
**Organteil,** *m.* part of an organ.
**Orgel,** *f.* organ. **-metall,** *n.* organ-pipe metal.
**orientalisch,** *a.* Oriental.
**orientieren,** *v.t.* orient.
**Orientierung,** *f.* orientation.
**Originalgrösse,** *f.* original size.
**Originalität,** *f.* originality.
**Orkan,** *m.* hurricane.
**Orlean,** *m.* (*Dyes*) orlean, annatto.
**orogenetisch,** *a.* (*Geol.*) orogenetic, orogenic.
**Orseille,** *f.* archil (the dyestuff). **-flechte,** *f.* archil (*Roccella tinctoria*).
**Orsell-insäure,** *f.* orsellinic acid. **-säure,** *f.* orsellic (diorsellinic, lecanoric) acid.
**Ort,** *m.* place; locus; region, locality, spot.
**orten,** *v.t.* locate, spot, detect; orient.
**Ortho-achse,** *f.* (*Cryst.*) ortho axis. **-ameisensäure,** *f.* orthoformic acid. **-antimonigsäure,** *f.* orthoantimonious acid. **-antimonsäure,** *f.* orthoantimonic acid. **-arsenigsäure,** *f.* orthoarsenious acid. **-arsensäure,** *f.* orthoarsenic acid. **-borsäure,** *f.* orthoboric acid. **-chinon,** *n.* orthoquinone, *o*-quinone.
**orthochromatisch,** *a.* orthochromatic.
**Ortho-chromatisierung,** *f.* orthochromatic processing. **-cymol,** *n.* orthocymene, *o*-cymene. **-essigsäure,** *f.* orthoacetic acid.
**orthogonalisieren,** *v.t.* orthogonalize.
**Orthogonalität,** *f.* orthogonality.
**Ortho-kieselsäure,** *f.* orthosilicic acid. **-klas,** *m.* orthoclase. **-kohlensäure,** *f.* orthocarbonic acid. **-phosphorsäure,** *f.* orthophosphoric acid. **-phtalsäure,** *f.* orthophthalic acid.
**orthorhombisch,** *a.* orthorhombic.
**Orthosalpetersäure,** *f.* orthonitric acid.
**orthosalpetrig,** *a.* orthonitrous.
**Orthosäure,** *f.* ortho acid.
**orthoständig,** *a.* in the ortho position.
**Orthostellung,** *f.* ortho position.
**orthotomisch,** *a.* (*Geom.*) orthotomic.
**Ortho-verbindung,** *f.* ortho compound. **-xylol,** *n.* orthoxylene, *o*-xylene. **-zimtsäure,** *f.* orthocinnamic acid.

**-ortig.** -place. (Proposed as a substitute for -wertig for coördination numbers; as, *drei-ortig*, three-place, 3-place.)
**Ortisomerie,** *f.* position isomerism.
**örtlich,** *a.* local; topical; endemic.
**Orts-.** local. **-bestimmung,** *f.* determination of position, orientation.
**ortsbeweglich,** *a.* movable, portable.
**Ortschaft,** *f.* place, village.
**ortsfest,** *a.* stationary, fixed.
**Orts-funktion,** *f.* position function. **-isomerie,** *f.* place isomerism, position isomerism.
**Ortstein,** *m.* (*Min.*) bog iron ore; hardpan.
**ortsveränderlich,** *a.* movable, portable.
**Orts-veränderung,** *f.* change of position. **-wechsel,** *m.* change of position or location. **-zahl,** *f.* position number, index number.
**Ortung,** *f.* location; orientation.
**-ös.** -ous.
**Oschakkpflanze,** *f.* oshac, ammoniac plant.
**Öse,** *f.* loop, ring, eye, eyelet, lug, ear; specif., platinum-wire loop.
**Ösen-blatt,** *n.* (*Tech.*) tongue, lip, flange. **-schraube,** *f.* eye screw, screw eye.
**osmig,** *a.* osmious.
**Osmiumchlorwasserstoffsäure,** *f.* chloroösmic(III) acid ($H_3OsCl_6$); chloroösmic(IV) acid ($H_2OsCl_6$).
**osmiumhaltig,** *a.* containing osmium.
**Osmium-legierung,** *f.* osmium alloy. **-oxyd,** *n.* osmium oxide; specif., osmium dioxide, osmium(IV) oxide, $OsO_2$. **-oxydul,** *n.* osmious oxide. **-salmiak,** *m.* ammonium chloroösmate. **-säure,** *f.* osmic acid. **-verbindung,** *f.* osmium compound.
**Osmose,** *f.* osmosis, osmose.
**osmosieren,** *v.t.* osmose.
**osmotisch,** *a.* osmotic.
**Ost, Osten,** *m.* east; East, Orient.
**ostdeutsch,** *a.* East German.
**Osterluzei,** *n.* birthwort (*Aristolochia*, esp. *A clematitis* or *A. longa*).
**Ostern,** *n.* Easter.
**Österreich,** *n.* Austria.
**österreichisch,** *a.* Austrian. **-ungarisch,** *a.* Austro-Hungarian.
**Österreich-Ungarn,** *n.* Austria-Hungary.
**osteuropäisch,** *a.* East European.
**Ostindien,** *n.* (East) India.
**ostindisch,** *a.* East Indian.
**östlich,** *a.* eastern, oriental, easterly.
**Ost-mark,** *f.* Austria. **-preussen,** *n.* East Prussia.
**Östreich,** *n.* Austria.
**Ostritzwurzel,** *f.* masterwort (*Imperatoria ostruthium*), or its rhizome.
**Ostsee,** *f.* Baltic (Sea).
**Oszillationsquantumzahl,** *f.* vibrational quantum number.
**oszillieren,** *v.i.* oscillate.
**Otter,** *m* otter. — *f.* adder.
**Otto,** *m.* gasoline, petrol.
**Ö.U.P., O.U.P.,** *abbrev.* (österreich-ungarisches Patent) Austro-Hungarian patent.
**o.V.,** *abbrev.* (ohne Verzögerung) without delay, instantaneous(ly).
**ovalförmig,** *a.* oval-shaped, oval.
**Oxalat,** *n.* oxalate.
**Oxal-äther,** *m.* oxalic ether (ethyl oxalate). **-essigester,** *m.* oxalacetic ester. **-essigsäure,** *f.* oxalacetic acid. **-ester,** *m.* oxalic ester (specif., ethyl oxalate).
**Oxalkyl-.** hydroxyalkyl-.
**Oxalsalz,** *n.* oxalate.
**oxalsauer,** *a.* of or combined with oxalic acid, oxalate of.
**Oxalsäure,** *f.* oxalic acid. **-äthylester,** *m.* ethyl oxalate. **-lösung,** *f.* oxalic acid solution. **-salz,** *n.* oxalate.
**Oxalursäure,** *f.* oxaluric acid.
**Oxamidsäure, Oxaminsäure,** *f.* oxamic acid.
**Oxäthyl-.** hydroxyethyl-.
**Oxhämoglobin,** *n.* oxyhemoglobin.
**Oxhoft,** *n.* hogshead.
**Oxim,** *n.* oxime.
**Oxo-.** (*Org. Chem.*) oxo- (denoting replacement of $H_2$ by O and often equivalent to keto-). **-säure,** *f.* oxo acid (keto or aldehydo acid).
**Oxy-.** oxy-, hydroxy-. (In organic names this indicates, in the great majority of cases, the hydroxyl group and should then be translated hydroxy- to conform to the best usage in English; *e.g.*, *Oxyäpfelsäure*, hydroxymalic acid. If the group is known to be ketonic, the translation keto- or oxo- is preferable; if Oxy- denotes ring oxygen, the preferable translation is oxa-.)
**Oxy-aldehyd,** *n.* hydroxy aldehyde. **-ammoniak,** *n.* oxyammonia (hydroxylamine). **-azoverbindung,** *f.* hydroxyazo compound. **-benzol,** *n.* hydroxybenzene (phenol). **-bernsteinsäure,** *f.* hydroxysuccinic acid (malic acid). **-biazol,** *n.* oxadiazole, oxdiazole. **-bitumen,** *n.* oxidized bitumen. **-carbonsäure,** *f.* hydroxycarboxylic acid. **-chinolin,** *n.* hydroxyquinoline. **-chinon,** *n.* hydroxyquinone. **-chlorid,** *n.* oxychloride. **-chlorkupfer,** *n.* copper oxychloride. **-cyan,** *n.* oxycyanogen.
**Oxyd,** *n.* oxide (specif., a higher or -ic oxide, as contrasted with Oxydul).
**oxyd-abel,** *a.* oxidizable. **-artig,** *a.* of the nature of, or like, an oxide.
**Oxydase,** *f.* oxidase.
**Oxydations-artikel,** *m.* (*Calico*) oxidation style. **-ätze,** *f.* (*Calico*) oxidation discharge. **-bad,** *n.* oxidizing bath. **-beständigkeit,** *f.* resistance to oxidation. **-bestreben,** *n.* tendency to

oxidize. **-bleiche,** *f.* oxidizing bleach; specif., peroxide bleach. **-braun,** *n.* oxidation brown.
**oxydations-empfindlich,** *a.* sensitive to oxidation. **-fähig,** *a.* capable of oxidation, oxidizable.
**Oxydations-farbe,** *f.* (*Dyeing*) oxidation color (produced on the fiber by oxidation). **-flamme,** *f.* oxidizing flame. **-geschwindigkeit,** *f.* rate of oxidation. **-grad,** *m.* degree of oxidation. **-mittel,** *n.* oxidizing agent. **-ofen,** *m.* oxidizing furnace or oven. **-schlacke,** *f.* (*Metal.*) oxidizing slag. **-schutz,** *m.* protection against oxidation. **-schwarz,** *n.* oxidation black, specif. aniline black. **-stoffwechsel,** *m.* oxidation metabolism. **-stufe,** *f.* stage or degree of oxidation.
**oxydationsverzögernd,** *a.* antioxidant.
**Oxydations-vorgang,** *m.* oxidation process. **-wärme,** *f.* heat of oxidation. **-wirkung,** *f.* oxidizing action or effect. **-ziffer,** *f.* oxidation number or index.
**Oxydbeschlag,** *m.* coating of oxide.
**oxydbildend,** *a.* oxide-forming.
**Oxyd-chlorid,** *n.* oxychloride. **-einschluss,** *m.* oxide inclusion. **-faden,** *m.* (*Elec.*) oxide-coated filament. **-firnis,** *m.* oxide varnish (thickened drying oil).
**oxydhaltig,** *a.* containing oxide or oxides, oxidic.
**Oxyd-haut,** *f.*, **-häutchen,** *n.* film of oxide. **-hydrat,** *n.* hydrated oxide (hydroxide), esp. one from a higher oxide (-ic hydroxide), as contrasted with *Oxydulhydrat.*
**oxydierbar,** *a.* oxidizable.
**Oxydierbarkeit,** *f.* oxidizability.
**oxydieren,** *v.t.* & *i.* oxidize.
**Oxydier-mittel,** *n.* oxidizing agent. **-stoff,** *m.* oxidizing substance.
**Oxydierung,** *f.* oxidation.
**oxydisch,** *a.* oxidic, oxygenic; of higher valence, -ic.
**Oxydoxydul,** *n.* = Oxyduloxyd.
**oxydreich,** *a.* rich in oxide.
**Oxyd-rot,** *n.* a kind of iron red; Turkey red. **-schicht,** *f.* layer or film of oxide. **-überzug,** *m.* coating of oxide.
**Oxydul,** *n.* (lower or -ous) oxide, (formerly) protoxide. **-eisen,** *n.* ferrous iron. **-hydrat,** *n.* hydrated -ous oxide (-ous hydroxide).
**oxydulisch,** *a.* of lower valence, -ous.
**Oxydul-oxyd,** *n.* an oxide in which the metal has a lower and a higher valence, oso-ic oxide, mixed oxide. **-salz,** *n.* lower or -ous salt.
**Oxyessigsäure,** *f.* hydroxyacetic acid.
**Oxyfettsäure,** *f.* hydroxy fatty acid.
**oxygenieren,** *v.t.* oxygenate, oxygenize.
**Oxygenierung,** *f.* oxygenation.
**Oxyketon,** *n.* hydroxy ketone, ketol. **-carbonsäure,** *f.* hydroxyketocarboxylic acid.
**Oxymethyl-.** hydroxymethyl-; (incorrectly) methoxy-. **-gruppe,** *f.* hydroxymethyl group.
**Oxy-salz,** *n.* oxysalt. **-säure,** *f.* oxyacid (either oxacid — an acid containing oxygen — or hydroxy acid). **-schwefelsäure,** *f.* oxysulfuric acid. **-toluol,** *n.* hydroxytoluene. **-verbindung,** *f.* oxy compound; hydroxy compound. **-zellulose,** *f.* oxycellulose. **-zyanid,** *n.* oxycyanide.
**Ozäna,** *f.* (*Med.*) ozena.
**Ozean,** *m.* ocean.
**ozeanisch,** *a.* oceanic, marine.
**o.Zers.,** *abbrev.* (ohne Zersetzung) without decomposition.
**Ozobenzol,** *n.* ozobenzene.
**Ozokerit,** *m.* ozocerite.
**Ozon,** *n.* ozone. **-bildung,** *f.* ozone formation. **-bleiche,** *f.* ozone bleach(ing).
**ozonerzeugend,** *p.a.* producing ozone, ozoniferous.
**Ozongehalt,** *m.* ozone content.
**ozonhaltig,** *a.* containing ozone, ozoniferous.
**Ozonisator, Ozoniseur,** *m.* ozonizer.
**ozonisieren,** *v.t.* ozonize.
**Ozon-isierung,** *f.* ozonization. **-messer,** *m.* ozonometer. **-messung,** *f.* ozonometry. **-papier, -reagenspapier,** *n.* ozone paper, ozone test paper.
**ozonreich,** *a.* rich in ozone.
**ozonsauer,** *a.* ozonate of.
**Ozonsauerstoff,** *m.* ozonized oxygen, oxygen in the form of ozone.

# P

**p.**, *abbrev.* (pro) per.
**p.a.**, *abbrev.* (pro anno) per year.
**paar,** *a.* even; (a) pair (of).
**Paar,** *n.* pair, couple; few; (*Mech.*) couple.
**paaren,** *v.t.* conjugate; pair, couple, mate. — **gepaart,** *p.a.* conjugated, etc., conjugate. — **gepaarte Verbindung,** conjugated compound; (*Old Chem.*) copulated compound.
**paarig,** *a.* in pairs, paired; even.
**Paarling,** *n.* conjugated substance; (*Old Chem.*) copula; (*Biol.*) allelomorph.
**Paarung,** *f.* pairing, coupling, conjugation.
**paarweise,** *adv.* in pairs, in couples.
**Pacht,** *f.* lease, tenure.
**Pachter, Pächter,** *m.* tenant.
**Pack,** *m.* pack, packet, bale, bundle.
**Päckchen,** *n.* packet, (little) parcel. **-farben,** *f.pl.* packet dyes.
**packen,** *v.t.* pack; seize.
**packetieren,** *v.t.* = paketieren.
**Pack-hahn,** *m.* gland cock, packed cock. **-haus,** *n.*, **-hof,** *m.* warehouse; custom house. **-lack,** *m.* sealing wax for packing. **-leinen,** *n.*, **-leinwand,** *f.* packing cloth, pack cloth. **-papier,** *n.* wrapping paper, packing paper. **-pappe,** *f.* packing board, pasteboard for packing. **-schnur,** *f.* packing twine. **-seidenpapier,** *n.* tissue wrapping paper. **-stoff,** *m.* packing material, packing. **-tuch,** *n.* packing cloth.
**Packung,** *f.* packing; seizing, seizure.
**Packungs-art,** *f.* kind of packing; (*Cryst.*) structure. **-erscheinung,** *f.* packing phenomenon.
**Packzeug,** *n.* packing material, packing; packing tools.
**PAe.,** *abbrev.* (Petroleumäther) petroleum ether.
**paginieren,** *v.t.* page, paginate.
**Paket,** *n.* packet, parcel, bundle.
**paketieren,** *v.t.* briquet(te); make into a packet; (*Iron*) pile.
**Paketierschweissstahl, Paketstahl,** *m.* refined iron, merchant bar.
**Paketierung,** *f.* briquetting, etc. (see paketieren).
**Paläozoikum,** *n.* (*Geol.*) Paleozoic.
**Palisanderholz,** *n.* rosewood.
**Palladgold,** *n.* palladium-gold (alloy).
**Palladi-.** palladic. **-chlorwasserstoffsäure,** *f.* chloropalladic acid, chloropalladic(IV) acid.
**Palladium-asbest,** *m.* palladium asbestos, palladized asbestos. **-bromür,** *n.* palladous bromide, palladium(II) bromide. **-chlorid,** *n.* palladium chloride, specif. palladic chloride. **-chlorür,** *n.* palladous chloride, palladium(II) chloride. **-chlorwasserstoff,** *m.* chloropalladic acid. **-erz,** *n.* palladium ore. **-gehalt,** *m.* palladium content. **-jodür,** *n.* palladous iodide, palladium(II) iodide. **-legierung,** *f.* palladium alloy. **-mohr,** *m.* palladium black. **-oxyd,** *n.* palladium oxide, specif. palladium(IV) oxide.
**Palladiumoxydul,** *n.* palladous oxide, palladium(II) oxide. **-nitrat,** *n.* palladous nitrate, palladium(II) nitrate. **-salz,** *n.* palladous salt, palladium(II) salt.
**Palladium-reihe,** *f.* palladium series. **-salz,** *n.* palladium salt. **-schwamm,** *m.* palladium sponge. **-schwarz,** *n.* palladium black. **-wasserstoff,** *m.* palladium hydride.
**Pallado-.** palladous, palladium(II). **-chlorid,** *n.* palladous chloride, palladium(II) chloride. **-chlorwasserstoffsäure,** *f.* chloropalladous acid, chloropalladic(II) acid. **-hydroxyd,** *n.* palladous hydroxide, palladium(II) hydroxide.
**Palmarosaöl,** *n.* palmarosa oil.
**Palmatinseife,** *f.* palmatin soap.
**Palme,** *f.* palm.
**Palmen-öl,** *n.* palm oil. **-stärke,** *f.* palm starch, sago. **-wachs,** *n.* palm wax.
**Palm-fett,** *n.* palm oil, palm butter. **-honig,** *m.* palm honey.
**Palmin,** *n.* palmitin.
**Palminsäure,** *f.* palmitic acid.
**Palmitin-säure,** *f.* palmitic acid. **-seife,** *f.* palmitin soap.
**Palm-kernöl,** *n.* palm-kernel oil. **-kernölseife, -kernseife,** *f.* palm(-kernel) oil soap. **-lilie,** *f.* yucca. **-nuss,** *f.* palm nut, palm kernel; coconut. **-nussöl,** *n.* palm-kernel oil; coconut oil. **-öl,** *n.* palm oil. **-ölseife,** *f.* palm oil soap. **-seife,** *f.* palm (oil) soap. **-sekt,** *m.* palm wine, palm toddy. **-stärke,** *f.* palm starch, sago. **-wachs,** *n.* palm wax. **-zucker,** *m.* palm sugar, jaggery.
**palpieren,** *v.t.* palpate.
**Panamarinde,** *f.* Panama bark, quillai bark.
**Panaschierung,** *f.* variegation.
**Panazee,** *f.* panacea.
**panchromatisch,** *a.* (*Photog.*) panchromatic.
**Paneel,** *f.* panel; wainscot(ing).
**Pankreas,** *n.*, **-drüse,** *f.* pancreas. **-saft,** *m.* pancreatic juice.

**pankreatisch,** *a.* pancreatic.
**Panne,** *f.* breakdown, failure, trouble; (*Textiles*) panne.
**Panzer,** *m.* armor; armor plate; metal casing or lining; shield. **-blech,** *n.* armor plate. **-bombe,** *f.* armor-piercing bomb. **-brandgranate,** *f.* armor-piercing incendiary shell.
**panzerbrechend,** *a.* armor-piercing.
**Panzerdraht,** *m.* armored wire.
**panzerdurchschlagend,** *a.* armor-piercing.
**Panzer-geschoss,** *n.* armor-piercing shell. **-glas,** *n.* bulletproof glass. **-granate,** *f.* armor-piercing shell or grenade. **-holz,** *n.* metal-clad wood. **-kampfwagen,** *m.* (*Mil.*) tank. **-kopfgranate,** *f.* armor-piercing shell. **-kraftwagen,** *m.* (*Mil.*) armored car. **-mine,** *f.* (*Mil.*) antitank mine.
**panzern,** *v.t.* armor, armor-plate.
**Panzer-platte,** *f.* armor plate. **-schlauch,** *m.* armored hose. **-sprenggeschoss,** *n.* armor-piercing projectile. **-sprenggranate,** *f.* armor-piercing shell. **-stahl,** *m.* armor plate.
**Panzerung,** *f.* armor plating, armor; metal casing or lining; shielding, screening.
**Panzerwagen,** *m.* (*Mil.*) tank, also armored car.
**Päon-.** peon-, paeon-.
**Päonie,** *f.* peony.
**Papagei,** *m.* parrot.
**papageigrün,** *a.* parrot-green.
**Papel,** *f.* papule, pimple.
**Papier,** *n.* paper. **-abfall, -abgang,** *m.* paper waste.
**papierartig,** *a.* paper-like, papery.
**Papier-band,** *n.* paper tape; web of paper. **-blatt,** *n.* sheet (or leaf) of paper. **-bogen,** *m.* sheet of paper. **-brei,** *m.* paper pulp.
**papieren,** *a.* paper; papery.
**Papier-fabrik,** *f.* paper factory, paper mill. **-fabrikant,** *m.* paper maker. **-fabrikation,** *f.* paper making. **-farbe,** *f.* paper color. **-filter,** *n.* paper filter. **-fläche,** *f.* paper surface, surface of the paper. **-garn,** *n.* paper yarn, paper twine. **-handel,** *m.* paper trade; stationery. **-handlung,** *f.* stationer's shop. **-holz,** *n.* pulpwood. **-jod,** *n.* a solution of iodine and potassium iodide for test paper.
**papierkaschiert,** *a.* paper-covered, paper-backed (as metal foil).
**Papier-kohle,** *f.* paper coal (variety of lignite). **-leim,** *m.* paper size. **-macher,** *m.* paper maker. **-masse,** *f.* paper pulp; papier-mâché. **-mühle,** *f.* paper mill. **-pappe,** *f.* paper board. **-pergament,** *n.* parchment paper. **-prüfung,** *f.* paper testing. **-sack,** *m.* paper bag, paper sack. **-scheibe,** *f.* paper disk. **-sorte,** *f.* sort or quality of paper. **-stoff,** *m.* paper pulp. **-stoffbrei,** *m.* paper pulp (in water). **-streifen,** *m.* paper strip; paper web. **-teig,** *m.* papier-mâché. **-trommel,** *f.* paper drum. **-überseite,** *f.* (*Paper*) felt side. **-wolle,** *f.* shredded paper. **-zeichen,** *n.* watermark. **-zeug,** *n.* paper pulp, "stuff."
**Papille,** *f.* papilla; nipple.
**Papillen-.** papillary.
**papinianischer Topf, Papin'scher Topf.** Papin's digester (autoclave).
**Papp,** *m.* paste; pap.
**Papp-.** paperboard, pasteboard, cardboard. **-band,** *m.* board binding; volume bound in boards. **-bogen,** *m.* sheet of pasteboard (or cardboard). **-deckel,** *m.* pasteboard, paperboard. **-druck,** *m.* paste resist printing. **-düte,** *f.* heavy-paper bag.
**Pappe,** *f.* (paper)board, pasteboard, cardboard, pulp sheet; pap; paste. — **geformte —,** millboard.
**Pappel,** *f.* poplar; mallow. **-art,** *f.* (variety of) poplar; (variety of) mallow. **-holz,** *n.* poplar (wood). **-kraut,** *n.* mallow.
**pappen,** *v.t. & i.* paste; work in paperboard.
**Pappen-art,** *f.* (paper)board. **-deckel,** *m.* = Pappdeckel. **-fabrik,** *f.* (paper)board mill. **-guss,** *m.* cast paperboard, pressboard, millboard. **-leim,** *m.* pasteboard glue. **-stiel,** *m.* trifle.
**Papphülse,** *f.* paperboard case.
**pappig,** *a.* pasty, doughy; sticky.
**Papp-karton,** *m.* paperboard box, carton. **-masse,** *f.* papier-mâché. **-reserve,** *f.* (*Calico*) paste resist. **-schachtel,** *f.* paperboard box. **-schirm,** *m.* paperboard screen. **-tüte,** *f.* heavy-paper bag. **-weiss,** *n.* (*Calico*) pigment white.
**Parabansäure,** *f.* parabanic acid.
**Parabel,** *f.* parabola; parable.
**parabelförmig,** *a.* parabolic.
**parabolisch,** *a.* parabolic.
**Para-chinon,** *n.* paraquinone, *p*-quinone. **-consäure,** *f.* paraconic acid. **-cyan,** *n.* paracyanogen. **-cymol,** *n.* paracymene, *p*-cymene.
**Paradies,** *n.* paradise. **-apfel,** *m.* tomato. **-feige,** *f.* banana. **-holz,** *n.* agalloch, aloes wood. **-körner,** *n.pl.* grains of paradise.
**paradox,** *a.* paradoxical.
**Paraffin-anstrich,** *m.* paraffin coat(ing). **-bad,** *n.* paraffin bath. **-durchtränkung,** *f.* impregnation with paraffin. **-einbettung,** *f.* imbedding in paraffin.
**paraffinhaltig,** *a.* containing paraffin(s), paraffinic.
**paraffinieren,** *v.t.* paraffin.
**paraffinisch,** *a.* paraffinic, paraffin.
**Paraffin-kerze,** *f.* paraffin candle. **-kohlenwasserstoff,** *m.* paraffin hydrocarbon, paraffin, alkane. **-lack,** *m.* paraffin varnish. **-leimung,** *f.* (*Paper*) paraffin sizing. **-öl,** *n.* paraffin oil. **-öldestillat,** *n.* paraffin distillate. **-reihe,** *f.* paraffin series, alkane series. **-salbe,** *f.*

petrolatum; paraffin ointment. **-säure,** *f.* paraffinic acid (saturated aliphatic acid). **-schuppen,** *f.pl.* paraffin scale. **-tränkung,** *f.* impregnation with paraffin. **-wachs,** *n.* paraffin wax, solid paraffin.

**Para-gummi,** *n.* Pará rubber. **-gummischlauch,** *m.* Pará rubber tubing. **-kamphersäure,** *f.* paracamphoric acid. **-kautschuk,** *m.* Pará rubber. **-klasen,** *pl.* chinks, fissures, cleavages. **-kresol,** *n.* paracresol, *p*-cresol.

**Parallel-ismus,** *m.* parallelism. **-ität,** *f.* parallelism. **-probe,** *f.* parallel sample or test. **-schaltung,** *f.* (*Elec.*) connection in parallel.

**parallelsteng(e)lig,** *a.* (*Cryst.*) parallel-columnar.

**Parallelversuch,** *m.* parallel experiment, duplicate determination.

**parallelwandig,** *a.* parallel-walled, parallel-sided.

**Paralysator,** *m.* anticatalyst.

**Paralyse,** *f.* paralysis.

**paralysieren,** *v.t.* paralyze.

**paramagnetisch,** *a.* paramagnetic.

**Paramidophenol,** *n.* *p*-aminophenol.

**Paramilchsäure,** *f.* paralactic acid (*dextro*-lactic acid).

**paramorph,** *a.* (*Min.*) paramorphic, paramorphous.

**Para-nuss,** *f.* Brazil nut. **-nussöl,** *n.* Brazil-nut oil. **-phtalsäure,** *f.* paraphthalic acid. **-rot,** *n.* para red.

**parasitär,** *a.* parasitic.

**Parasitenkunde,** *f.* parasitology.

**parasitentötend,** *a.* parasiticidal, -cide.

**parasitisch,** *a.* parasitic.

**paraständig,** *a.* in the para position.

**Parastellung,** *f.* para position.

**parat,** *a.* prepared, ready.

**Para-verbindung,** *f.* para compound. **-weinsäure,** *f.* paratartaric acid (racemic acid). **-xylol,** *n.* paraxylene, *p*-xylene.

**parazentrisch,** *a.* paracentric.

**Parellinsäure,** *f.* parellinic acid.

**Parellsäure,** *f.* parellic acid.

**parenchymatisch,** *a.* parenchymatous.

**Parenthese,** *f.* parentheses; brackets.

**Parfüm,** *n.* perfume.

**Parfümerie,** *f.* perfumery. **-seife,** *f.* perfumed soap.

**Parfümeur,** *m.* perfumer.

**Parfümgrundstoff,** *m.* perfume base.

**parfümieren,** *v.t.* perfume, scent.

**Parfümör,** *m.* perfumer.

**Pari,** *n.* par. — **auf pari,** at par.

**Parierschwerung,** *f.* (*Silk*) par weighting.

**Parininsäure,** *f.* parininic acid.

**Parinsäure,** *f.* parinic acid.

**Pariser,** *a.* Paris. — **— Blau,** Paris blue; **— Grün,** Paris green.

**Pariser-rot,** *n.* colcothar, Paris red. **-weiss,** *n.* Paris white (a good grade of whiting).

**Pariwert,** *m.* par value.

**parkerisieren,** *v.t.* parkerize, subject to the Parker process.

**Parkerverfahren,** *n.* (*Metal.*) Parker process.

**parkesieren,** *v.t.* (*Metal.*) subject to the Parkes process.

**Parkesieren,** *n.* Parkes process.

**Parkettwachs,** *n.* floor wax.

**Parrotkohle,** *f.* parrot coal, cannel coal.

**Partei,** *f.* part; party.

**parteiisch,** *a.* partial, prejudiced.

**Partial-bruch,** *m.* (*Math.*) partial fraction. **-druck,** *m.* partial pressure.

**partiär,** *a.* partial. — *adv.* partially; by parts.

**Partie,** *f.* parcel, lot; batch; section; company; party, picnic; game; match.

**partiell,** *a.* partial.

**partienweise,** *adv.* in lots, in batches.

**Partikel,** *f.* particle. **-chen,** *n.* small particle.

**parzellieren,** *v.t.* parcel out.

**Passagier,** *m.* passenger.

**passen,** *v.i.* fit, be fit, suit, be suited; match; wait. — **passend,** *p.a.* fit, suitable, appropriate.

**Pass-farbe,** *f.* (*Dyeing*) illuminating color. **-glas,** *n.* graduated glass.

**passieren,** *v.t.* pass; (*Dyeing*) liquor. — *v.i.* pass, happen, occur.

**Passiermaschine,** *f.* sieving or straining machine, liquoring machine; meat grinder.

**passiv,** *a.* passive; inactive, inert.

**passivieren,** *v.t.* passivate, render passive.

**Passivierung,** *f.* passivation.

**Passivität,** *f.* passivity.

**Pass-rohr,** *n.* pipe fitting. **-sitz,** *m.* snug fit. **-stück,** *n.* adjusting piece, adapter, fitting.

**Passung,** *f.* fitting, etc. (see passen); fit.

**Paste, Pasta,** *f.* paste; pulp.

**Pastekathode,** *f.* pasted cathode.

**Pastell-blau,** *n.* pastel blue. **-farbe,** *f.* pastel color.

**pastellfarbig,** *a.* pastel-colored.

**Pastell-papier,** *n.* pastel paper. **-stift,** *m.* pastel crayon.

**pastenartig,** *a.* pasty.

**Pastenfarbe,** *f.* (*Paint*) paste color.

**pastenförmig,** *a.* pasty.

**Pastenkonsistenz,** *f.* pasty consistency.

**Pastete,** *f.* pie, pastry.

**pasteurisieren,** *v.t.* pasteurize.

**Pastezementieren,** *n.* (*Metal.*) cementation using a paste.

**pastieren,** *v.t.* paste.

**pastig,** *a.* pasty.

**Pastille,** *f.* pastille, pastil, tablet, lozenge; button, bead.

**Pastillenpresse,** *f.* tablet press.

**Pastinake,** *f.* parsnip.
**Pastinakwurzel,** *f.* parsnip (root).
**pastös,** *a.* pasty.
**Patent,** *n.* patent (in the proper sense; cf. Gebrauchsmuster). **-amt,** *n.* patent office. **-anmeldung,** *f.* application for a patent. **-anspruch,** *m.* patent claim. **-anwalt,** *m.* patent attorney. **-beschreibung,** *f.* patent description or specification. **-blatt,** *n.* patent gazette. **-dauer,** *f.* life of a patent. **-einspruch,** *m.* patent interference.
**patentfähig,** *a.* patentable.
**Patent-frage,** *f.* patent question or problem. **-gelb,** *n.* patent yellow. **-gesetz,** *n.* patent law. **-grün,** *n.* patent green. **-gummi,** *n.* (*Rubber*) cut sheet.
**patentierbar,** *a.* patentable.
**patentieren,** *v.t.* patent.
**Patent-inhaber,** *m.* patentee. **-klage,** *f.* patent suit. **-kohle,** *f.* briquet(te). **-recht,** *n.* patent right; patent law. **-rot,** *n.* patent red (mercuric sulfide). **-salz,** *n.* ammonium antimony fluoride. **-schrift,** *f.* patent (the document), patent specification. **-schutz,** *m.* protection by patent. **-streit,** *m.* patent contest. **-träger,** *m.* patentee. **-verletzung,** *f.* patent infringement. **-zement,** *m.* Roman cement.
**pathogen,** *a.* pathogenic.
**pathologisch,** *a.* pathological.
**patinieren,** *v.t.* patinate.
**Patrize,** *f.* patrix, male mold.
**Patrone,** *f.* thimble, shell (for extractions); cartridge; pattern; stencil; mandrel; die; collet.
**Patronen-hülse,** *f.*, **-zylinder,** *m.* cartridge case. **-papier,** *n.* cartridge paper.
**Patsche,** *f.* fix, mess; slush, mud.
**patschen,** *v.i.* splash; clap, slap.
**Patschulen,** *n.* patchoulene.
**Patschuli,** *n.* patchouli.
**pattinsonieren,** *v.t.* pattinsonize.
**Pauke,** *f.* (kettle) drum; (*Anat.*) tympanum; harangue.
**Pauken-.** drum; (*Anat.*) tympanic. **-fell,** *n.* (kettle) drumhead; (*Anat.*) membrana tympani.
**Paulyseide,** *f.* Pauly silk (a cuprammonium rayon).
**Pauschal-.** total, lump (sum, etc.).
**pauschen,** *v.t.* swell; (*Metal.*) refine.
**Pauscht,** *m.* & *n.* (*Paper*) post.
**Pause,** *f.* tracing; copy; blueprint; pause.
**pausen,** *v.t.* trace, calk.
**Paus-leinwand,** *f.*, **-leinen,** *n.* tracing cloth. **-papier,** *n.* tracing paper. **-zeichnung,** *f.* tracing.
**-pctig.,** *abbrev.* (procentig) per cent.
**Pe-Ce-Faser.** PeCe fiber (a polyvinyl chloride). *T.N.*
**Pech,** *n.* pitch; asphalt. **-art,** *f.* kind or variety of pitch or asphalt.
**pechartig,** *a.* pitchy, bituminous.
**Pech-blende,** *f.* pitchblende. **-draht,** *m.* pitched thread, shoemaker's thread. **-eisenerz,** *n.* pitchy iron ore (applied to pitticite, triplite, and a compact variety of limonite).
**pecheln,** *v.i.* smell pitchy; extract pitch. — *v.t.* extract pitch from; pitch, coat with pitch.
**pechen,** *v.t.* pitch, coat with pitch.
**Pech-erde,** *f.* bituminous earth. **-erz,** *n.* = Pechblende; = Pecheisenerz.
**pechfinster,** *a.* pitch-dark.
**Pech-gang,** *m.* asphalt rock. **-geschmack,** *n.* pitchy taste. **-glanz,** *m.* pitchy luster. **-granat,** *m.* colophonite (a variety of andradite of pitchy appearance).
**pechhaltig,** *a.* containing pitch or asphalt, bituminous, asphaltic.
**Pechharz,** *n.* pitch resin.
**pechig,** *a.* pitchy.
**Pech-kiefer,** *f.* pitch pine. **-kohle,** *f.* pitch coal; jet. **-koks,** *m.* coke from pitch or tar. **-öl,** *n.* tar oil, oil of tar. **-pflaster,** *n.* asphalt paving. **-rückstand,** *m.* pitch residue.
**pechschwarz,** *a.* pitch-black.
**Pech-stein,** *m.* pitchstone. **-steinkohle,** *f.* pitch coal. **-tanne,** *f.* pitch pine. **-torf,** *m.* pitch peat, black peat. **-uran,** *n.* pitchblende.
**Pegel,** *n.* level; water gage.
**pegmatitisch,** *a.* (*Petrog.*) pegmatitic.
**Peil-.** sounding, bearing, directional. **-bombe,** *f.* pilot bomb.
**peilen,** *v.t.* sound, gage; take bearings of.
**Pein,** *f.* pain, trouble, torture.
**peinigen,** *v.t.* torment, trouble.
**peinlich,** *a.* painful; precise, painstaking, careful; penal.
**Peitsche,** *f.* whip.
**peitschen,** *v.t.* whip, beat, lash. **-förmig,** *a.* whip-shaped, flagelliform.
**Pekannuss,** *f.* pecan nut, pecan.
**pektin-artig,** *a.* pectin-like. **-ig,** *a.* pectinous.
**Pektin-körper,** *m.* pectic substance. **-säure,** *f.* pectic acid. **-stoff,** *m.*, **-substanz,** *f.* pectic substance. **-zucker,** *m.* arabinose.
**pelagisch,** *a.* pelagic.
**Pelargonsäure,** *f.* pelargonic acid.
**Péligot-rohr,** *n.*, **-röhre,** *f.* Péligot tube.
**Pelle,** *f.* peel, skin, husk.
**Peloteur,** *m.*, **Peloteuse,** *f.* (*Soap*) plodder, plotter.
**Pelz,** *m.* pelt, skin; fur; (of textiles) fleece, nap.
**pelz-artig, -ig,** *a.* furry; cottony; nappy.
**Pelz-gerbung,** *f.* fur-skin tanning. **-lustrierung,** *f.* fur lustering. **-werk,** *n.* peltry, peltries.
**Pendel,** *n.* pendulum. **-lager,** *n.* (*Mach.*) swing bearing.

**pendeln,** *v.i.* oscillate, vibrate, undulate, swing.
**Pendelung,** *f.* oscillation, etc. (see pendeln).
**Penetrationsmesser,** *m.* penetrometer.
**penetrieren,** *v.t.* penetrate.
**Pensee,** *n.* pansy.
**penseefarbig,** *a.* pansy-colored.
**Pension,** *f.* pension; board; boarding house; boarding school.
**Pentabromphosphor,** *n.* phosphorus pentabromide, phosphorus(V) bromide.
**pentacarbocyclisch,** *a.* pentacarbocyclic.
**Pentathionsäure,** *f.* pentathionic acid.
**pentazyklisch,** *a.* pentacyclic.
**Pentinsäure,** *f.* pentinoic (pentynoic) acid.
**Pentosurie,** *f.* pentosuria.
**Pentoxyd,** *n.* pentoxide.
**Pepsindrüse,** *f.* peptic gland.
**pepsinhaltig,** *a.* containing pepsin.
**Peptisator,** *m.* peptizer, peptizing agent.
**peptisch,** *a.* peptic.
**peptisieren,** *v.t.* peptize.
**Peptisierung,** *f.* peptization.
**peptolytisch,** *a.* peptolytic.
**peptonerzeugend,** *a.* peptogenous, -genic.
**Peptonfleischbrühe,** *f.* peptone-beef broth.
**peptonisieren,** *v.t.* peptonize.
**Per-acidität,** *f.* superacidity. **-ameisensäure,** *f.* performic (peroxyformic) acid. **-benzoesäure,** *f.* perbenzoic (peroxybenzoic) acid. **-borsäure,** *f.* perboric acid. **-bromsäure,** *f.* perbromic acid. **-buttersäure,** *f.* perbutyric (peroxybutyric) acid.
**Percha,** *f.*, **-gummi,** *m.* n. gutta-percha.
**Perchlor-äthan,** *n.* perchloroethane, hexachloroethane. **-äthylen,** *n.* perchloroethylene, tetrachloroethylene. **-methan,** *n.* perchloromethane (carbon tetrachloride).
**Per-chloron,** *n.* Perchloron (calcium hypochlorite). *T.N.* **-chlorsäure,** *f.* perchloric acid. **-chromsäure,** *f.* perchromic acid.
**Pereirarinde,** *f.* pereira bark, pereira.
**perennierend,** *p.a.* perennial.
**Per-essigsäure,** *f.* peracetic acid, peroxyacetic acid. **-ferricyanwasserstoffsäure,** *f.* perferricyanic acid, hexacyanoferric(IV) acid, $H_2Fe(CN)_6$.
**perforieren,** *v.t.* perforate.
**Pergament,** *n.* parchment.
**pergament-ähnlich,** *a.* parchment-like. **-ieren,** *v.t.* parchmentize.
**Pergamentierung,** *f.* parchmentization.
**Pergament-leder,** *n.* vellum. **-papier,** *n.* parchment paper. **-schlauch,** *m.* parchment-paper tubing.
**Pergamyn,** *n.* a kind of parchment paper. *T.N.*
**perhydrieren,** *v.t.* perhydrogenate.
**Perihel,** *n.* perihelion.
**Perikard,** *n.* (*Anat.*) pericardium.
**Periklas,** *m.* periclase, periclasite.
**Perilla-aldehyd,** *n.* perillaldehyde. **-alkohol,** *m.* perillic alcohol. **-säure,** *f.* perillic acid.
**Periode,** *f.* period; (*Elec.*) cycle.
**Periodenzahl,** *f.* number of periods or cycles, frequency.
**periodisch,** *a.* periodic, periodical.
**Periodizität,** *f.* periodicity.
**peripher, peripherisch,** *a.* peripheral.
**Per-jodat,** *n.* periodate. **-jodsäure,** *f.* periodic acid. **-kohlensäure,** *f.* percarbonic acid.
**Perkussions-ladung,** *f.* detonator charge. **-zünder,** *m.* percussion fuse. **-zündhütchen,** *n.* percussion cap. **-zündung,** *f.* percussion priming.
**perlartig,** *a.* pearly, nacreous; bead-like.
**Perlasche,** *f.* pearlash.
**Perle,** *f.* pearl; bead.
**perlen,** *v.i.* form bubbles, bubble, sparkle; form drops; glisten like pearls. **-artig,** *a.* = perlartig.
**Perlen-glanz,** *m.* pearly (or nacreous) luster. **-probe,** *f.* bead test. **-schnur,** *f.* string of beads or pearls.
**Perlerz,** *n.* pearl ore.
**perlfarben,** *a.* pearl-colored.
**Perlglanz,** *m.* = Perlenglanz.
**Perlglimmer,** *m.* (*Min.*) margarite.
**perlgrau,** *a.* pearl-gray.
**Perlgraupen,** *f.pl.* pearl barley.
**Perlhuhn,** *n.* guinea fowl, guinea hen.
**perlig,** *a.* pearly.
**Perlit,** *m.* (*Petrog.*) perlite; (*Metal.*) pearlite.
**perlitähnlich,** *a.* (*Metal.*) pearlitoid, pearloid.
**Perlitinsel,** *f.* (*Metal.*) pearlite area.
**perlit-isch,** *a.* (*Min.*) perlitic; (*Metal.*) pearlitic. **-isieren,** *v.t.* (*Metal.*) pearlitize, render pearlitic.
**Perl-kohle,** *f.* pea coal. **-koks,** *m.* coke breeze. **-leim,** *m.* pearl glue. **-moos,** *n.* pearl moss, carrageen. **-mutter,** *f.* mother-of-pearl, nacre.
**perlmutterartig,** *a.* like mother-of-pearl, nacreous.
**Perlmutter-blech,** *n.* crystallized tinplate, moiré métallique. **-glanz,** *m.* mother-of-pearl luster, nacreous luster.
**perlmutterglänzend,** *p.a.* having a mother-of-pearl luster, pearly.
**Perl-mutterpapier,** *n.* nacreous paper. **-rohr,** *n.*, **-röhre,** *f.* bead tube (tube filled with glass beads). **-sago,** *m.* pearl sago. **-salz,** *n.* microcosmic salt. **-samen,** *m.* seed pearl. **-schicht,** *f.* nacreous layer. **-schnur,** *f.* string of beads or pearls; row of droplets. **-seide,** *f.* embroidery silk; ardassine. **-spat,** *m.* pearl spar (pearly dolomite). **-stein,** *m.* perlite; adularia. **-sucht,** *f.* bovine tuberculosis. **-weiss,** *n.* pearl white.

**Permanent-gelb,** *n.* permanent yellow. **-rot,** *n.* permanent red, red toner. **-weiss,** *n.* permanent white.
**Permanenzsatz,** *m.* permanence principle.
**Permanganatlösung,** *f.* permanganate solution.
**Permangansäure,** *f.* permanganic acid.
**permeabel,** *a.* permeable.
**Permeabilität,** *f.* permeability.
**Permeabilitätsmesser,** *m.* permeameter.
**permisch,** *a.* (*Geol.*) Permian.
**permutieren,** *v.t.* (*Math.*) permute; treat with permutite.
**Permutitverfahren,** *n.* permutite process.
**Perna.** perchloronaphthalene. *T.N.*
**Pernambuk-holz,** *n.* Pernambuco wood. **-kautschuk,** *m.* & *n.* Pernambuco rubber, mangabeira.
**perniciös,** *a.* pernicious.
**Perowskit,** *n.* (*Min.*) perovskite.
**Peroxyd,** *n.* peroxide.
**peroxydieren,** *v.t.* peroxidize.
**Perpendikel,** *n.* perpendicular; pendulum.
**Persalz,** *n.* per salt, (if containing the -O-O-group) peroxy salt.
**Persanerstahl,** *m.* Brescian steel.
**Per-saüre,** *f.* per acid, (if containing the -O-O-group) peroxy acid. **-schwefelsäure,** *f.* persulfuric acid (peroxydisulfuric acid, $H_2S_2O_8$).
**Perseit,** *n.* perseitol, perseite.
**Persien,** *n.* Persia.
**Persio,** *m.* cudbear, archil.
**persisch,** *a.* Persian. — **persische Erde, persisches Rot,** Persian red.
**Persischrot,** *n.* Persian red.
**Personal,** *n.* personnel, staff.
**Personen-.** of or for persons, passenger.
**persönlich,** *a.* personal; subjective.
**Perstoff,** *m.* (*Mil.*) diphosgene, superpalite ($ClCO_2CCl_3$).
**Persulfo-cyansäure,** *f.* perthiocyanic acid, persulfocyanic acid. **-molybdänsäure,** *f.* perthiomolybdic acid, thiopermolybdic acid. **-zyansäure,** *f.* perthiocyanic acid.
**Perthiokohlensäure,** *f.* perthiocarbonic acid.
**peruanisch,** *a.* Peru, Peruvian.
**Peru-gummi,** *n.* Peruvian gum. **-rinde,** *f.* Peruvian bark. **-salpeter,** *m.* Peruvian saltpeter ($NaNO_3$). **-silber,** *n.* a kind of nickel silver.
**peruvianisch,** *a.* Peruvian, of Peru.
**Perverbindung,** *f.* per compound, specif. peroxy compound.
**Perylenchinon,** *n.* perylenequinone.
**perzentig,** *a.* per cent, percental, percentual.
**Pest,** *f.* plague, pest; pestilence.
**pestähnlich,** *a.* pestilential, infectious, contagious.
**Pestilenzkraut,** *n.* = Geissraute.
**Petersilie,** *f.* parsley.
**petersilienähnlich,** *a.* parsley-like.
**Petersilien-öl,** *n.* parsley oil. **-samen,** *m.* parsley seed.
**Peterskraut,** *n.* (*Bot.*) wall pellitory.
**petiotisieren,** *v.t.* (*Wines*) petiotize.
**Petri'sches Schälchen, Petri-Schale,** *f.* Petri dish.
**petrographisch,** *a.* petrographic.
**Petrol,** *n.* petroleum.
**Petrol-äther,** *m.* petroleum ether. **-benzin,** *n.* = Petroleumbenzin.
**Petrolen,** *n.* petrolene.
**Petroleum-äther,** *m.* petroleum ether. **-behälter,** *m.* petroleum container, petroleum tank. **-benzin,** *n.* petroleum spirit; gasoline, petrol. **-brunnen,** *m.* oil well. **-dampf,** *m.* petroleum vapor. **-destillationsgefäss,** *n.* petroleum still. **-essenz,** *f.* petroleum spirit. **-geruch,** *m.* petroleum odor.
**petroleumhaltig,** *a.* containing petroleum, oil-bearing.
**Petroleum-handel,** *m.* petroleum trade. **-heizung,** *f.* heating with petroleum. **-pech,** *n.* petroleum pitch. **-prober, -prüfer,** *m.* petroleum tester. **-quelle,** *f.* oil well. **-seifenbrühe,** *f.* (*Agric.*) kerosene emulsion.
**Petrol-koks,** *m.* petroleum coke, oil coke. **-pech,** *n.* petroleum pitch. **-säure,** *f.* petrolic acid.
**Petschaft,** *n.* seal, signet; impression die.
**Petsche,** *f.* drying room; drying frame.
**Pf.,** *abbrev.* (Pfund) pound; pfennig; (Pferd, Pferde) horse, horsepower, H.P.
**Pfad,** *m.* path; trail.
**Pfaff,** *m.* rivet stamp; nut driver; (*Brewing*) underlet.
**Pfaffe,** *m.* priest.
**Pfaffenhütchen,** *n.* wahoo (*Evonymus atropurpureus*).
**Pfahl,** *m.* stake, pile, stick, pole, post, prop.
**pfählen,** *v.t.* pale; prop; empale.
**Pfahlgründung,** *f.* pile foundation.
**Pfahlwurzel,** *f.* taproot.
**Pfalz,** *f.* Palatinate.
**Pfand,** *n.* pledge, security, forfeit.
**Pfännchen,** *n.* little pan.
**Pfanne,** *f.* pan; copper, boiler; ladle; knife-edge bearing; pantile; (*Mach.*) bearing, bush; cup; socket; (*Anat.*) acetabulum.
**Pfannen-probe,** *f.* (*Metal.*) ladle test. **-stein,** *m.* pan scale; boiler scale. **-werk,** *m.* salt works. **-ziegel,** *m.* pantile.
**Pfänner,** *m.* salt manufacturer.
**Pfau,** *m.* peacock, peafowl.
**pfaublau, pfauenblau,** *a.* peacock-blue.
**Pfeffer,** *m.* pepper.
**pfefferartig,** *a.* like pepper, peppery.
**Pfeffer-kraut,** *n.* savory (*Satureia hortensis*); peppergrass (*Lepidium*); stonecrop (*Sedum*).

-**kuchen,** *m.* gingerbread. -**minze,** *f.* peppermint.
**Pfefferminz-geruch,** *m.* peppermint odor. -**kampher,** *m.* menthol. -**öl,** *n.* peppermint oil.
**Pfeffer-münze,** *f.* = Pfefferminze. -**öl,** *n.* pepper oil. -**stein,** *m.* peperino.
**Pfeife,** *f.* pipe; whistle; fife; (in blasting) blown-out shot; (*Metal.*) pipe, also blowhole.
**pfeifen,** *v.t.* & *i.* pipe, whistle, squeal.
**Pfeifen-erde,** *f.* pipe clay. -**rohr,** *n.* pipestem. -**stein,** *m.* pipestone. -**ton,** *m.* pipe clay.
**Pfeifpatrone,** *f.* (*Mil.*) whistling cartridge.
**Pfeil,** *m.* arrow; dart; convexity, camber.
**Pfeiler,** *m.* pillar; pier; post; column.
**pfeilförmig,** *a.* arrow-shaped, sagittate.
**Pfeil-gift,** *n.* arrow poison. -**höhe,** *f.* height (of a meniscus, arch, etc.). -**rad,** *n.*, -**räder,** *n.pl.* (*Mach.*) herringbone gear. -**wurz,** -**wurzel,** *f.* arrowroot. -**wurzelmehl,** *n.* arrowroot (starch). -**zeichen,** *n.* arrow.
**Pfennig,** *m.* penny, pfennig ($\frac{1}{100}$ mark).
**Pferd,** *n.* horse.
**Pferde-bohne,** *f.* horse bean. -**dung,** -**dünger,** *m.* horse manure. -**fett,** *n.* horse fat, horse grease. -**fleisch,** *n.* horse flesh, horse meat. -**fussöl,** *n.* horse's-foot oil. -**haar,** *n.* horsehair. -**harnsäure,** *f.* hippuric acid. -**kammfett,** *n.* horse grease. -**kraft,** *f.* horsepower. -**kraftstunde,** *f.* horsepower hour. -**milch,** *f.* mare's milk. -**minze,** *f.* horsemint. -**mist,** *m.* horse manure. -**serum,** *n.* horse serum. -**stärke,** *f.* horsepower.
-**pferdig.** (so many) horsepower.
**Pfg.,** *abbrev.* pfennig, pfennigs.
**pfiff,** *pret.* (of pfeifen) whistled, piped.
**Pfiff,** *m.* whistle; trick, knack.
**Pfingstrose,** *f.* peony.
**Pfirsich,** *m.*, **Pfirsche,** *f.* peach.
**Pfirsich-blüte,** *f.* peach blossom. -**branntwein,** *m.* peach brandy.
**Pfirsiche,** *f.* peach.
**Pfirsichfarbe,** *f.* peach color.
**pfirsichfarbig,** *a.* peach-colored.
**Pfirsich-holz,** *n.* peachwood. -**kern,** *m.* peach kernel. -**kernöl,** *n.* peach-kernel oil. -**kernschwarz,** *n.* peach black.
**Pfl.,** *abbrev.* (Pflanze) plant.
**pflag,** *pret.* (of pflegen) was accustomed, etc.
**Pflänzchen,** *n.* little plant, seedling.
**Pflanze,** *f.* plant.
**pflanzen,** *v.t.* plant.
**Pflanzen-.** plant, vegetable. -**abfälle,** *m.pl.* plant (or vegetable) remains. -**alkali,** *n.* vegetable alkali (old name for potash, also for plant alkaloids). -**alkaloid,** *n.* plant alkaloid, vegetable alkaloid. -**art,** *f.* kind or species of plant.
**pflanzenartig,** *a.* plant-like; vegetable.
**Pflanzen-asche,** *f.* plant ashes. -**aufguss,** *m.* plant infusion. -**auszug,** *m.* plant (or vegetable) extract. -**base,** *f.* vegetable base, (plant) alkaloid. -**beschreibung,** *f.* description of plants, phytography. -**bestandteil,** *m.* plant (or vegetable) constituent. -**butter,** *f.* vegetable butter. -**chemie,** *f.* plant chemistry, phytochemistry.
**pflanzenchemisch,** *a.* phytochemical.
**Pflanzen-dekokt,** *n.* plant decoction. -**eiweiss,** *n.* vegetable albumin (or albumen); vegetable protein. -**erde,** *f.* vegetable mold, humus. -**ernährung,** *f.* plant nutrition. -**erzeugnis,** *n.* plant product, vegetable product. -**farbe,** *f.* vegetable color. -**farbstoff,** *m.* plant pigment; vegetable dye. -**faser,** *f.* vegetable fiber, plant fiber. -**faserstoff,** *m.* vegetable fibrin (gluten; cellulose). -**fett,** *n.* vegetable fat. -**fettseife,** *f.* soap made from vegetable oils. -**fibrin,** *n.* = Pflanzenfaserstoff. -**forscher,** *m.* botanist.
**pflanzenfressend,** *p.a.* herbivorous.
**Pflanzen-gallert,** *n.* vegetable gelatin, pectin. -**gattung,** *f.* genus of plants. -**gift,** *n.* plant poison. -**grün,** *n.* chlorophyll. -**gummi,** *n.* plant gum; plant (or natural) rubber; natural resin. -**haar,** *n.* vegetable horsehair (palm fiber). -**harz,** *n.* vegetable resin. -**kasein,** *n.*, -**käsestoff,** *m.* vegetable casein, legumin. -**kleber,** *m.* gluten. -**kohle,** *f.* vegetable charcoal. -**krankheit,** *f.* plant disease. -**kunde,** *f.* botany. -**laugensalz,** *n.* (*Old Chem.*) potash. -**laus,** *f.* plant louse, aphis. -**leben,** *n.* plant life. -**lehre,** *f.* botany. -**leim,** *m.* vegetable glue, gliadin, gluten; vegetable size; tree glue. -**nahrung,** *f.* plant food. -**nucleinsäure,** *f.* vegetable nucleic acid. -**öl,** *n.* vegetable oil. -**pech,** *n.* vegetable pitch. -**reich,** *n.* vegetable kingdom. -**rest,** *m.* plant remains, vegetable residue. -**rot,** *n.* carthamin. -**saft,** *m.* vegetable juice, plant juice, sap. -**salz,** *n.* vegetable salt. -**säure,** *f.* vegetable acid. -**schädling,** *m.* plant pest. -**schleim,** *m.* mucilage. -**schutzmittel,** *n.* plant protective (agent). -**schwarz,** *n.* vegetable black. -**seide,** *f.* vegetable silk. -**stoff,** *m.* vegetable matter, plant substance. -**talg,** *m.* vegetable tallow. -**wachs,** *n.* vegetable wax. -**wachstum,** *m.* & *n.*, -**wuchs,** *m.* plant growth, vegetation. -**wolle,** *f.* vegetable wool. -**zelle,** *f.* plant cell, vegetable cell. -**zellenstoff,** *m.* cellulose. -**zucht,** *f.* plant breeding.
**Pflanzerde,** *f.* compost.
**pflanzlich,** *a.* plant, vegetable.
**Pflaster,** *n.* (medical) plaster; pavement, paving; patch. -**käfer,** *m.* Spanish fly, blister beetle.
**pflastern,** *v.t.* plaster; pave.

**Pflasterstein,** *m.* paving stone; paving brick.
**Pflasterung,** *f.* paving; pavement.
**Pflaster-werkstoff,** *m.* paving material. **-ziegel,** *m.* paving brick, paving tile.
**pflatschen,** *v.t.* (*Calico*) pad.
**Pflatsch-druck,** *m.* (*Calico*) slop padding. **-farbe,** *f.* (*Calico*) padding color or liquor. **-färbung,** *f.* (*Calico*) slop pad.
**Pflaume,** *f.* plum; prune.
**Pflaumenbaum,** *m.* plum tree.
**pflaumenblau,** *a.* plum-blue.
**Pflaumenbranntwein,** *m.* plum brandy.
**pflaumen-farben, -farbig,** *a.* plum-colored.
**Pflaumen-gummi,** *n.* plum gum. **-sieder,** *m.* plum distiller.
**Pflege,** *f.* care; nursing, rearing, education, superintendence; upkeep.
**pflegen,** *v.i.* be accustomed, be wont; indulge. — *v.t.* attend to, care for, tend, cultivate, nurse; carry on, manage.
**pfleglich,** *a.* careful; prudent; economical.
**Pflicht,** *f.* duty; obligation.
**pflicht-mässig,** *a.* obligatory. **-schuldig,** *a.* in duty bound; obligatory.
**Pflock,** *m.* peg, pin; stake; plug, tampon; (*Med.*) embolus.
**pflog,** *pret.* (of pflegen) carried on, managed.
**pflücken,** *v.t.* pluck, pick, gather.
**Pflug,** *m.* plow.
**pflügen,** *v.t.* plow.
**Pflugschar,** *f.* plowshare; (*Anat.*) vomer.
**Pfortader,** *f.* portal vein.
**Pforte,** *f.* gate, door, entrance; orifice.
**Pförtner,** *m.* porter, doorkeeper; (*Anat.*) pylorus.
**Pfoste,** *f.* plank; post.
**Pfosten,** *m.* post; column, pillar.
**Pfriem, Pfriemen,** *m.*, **Pfrieme,** *f.* punch, awl.
**Pfriemen-gras,** *n.* esparto; matgrass, matweed (*Nardus stricta*). **-kraut,** *n.* = Besenginster.
**Pfropf, Pfropfen,** *m.* stopper, plug, wad, cork; tampon; graft; (*Med.*) thrombus, embolus, clot.
**pfropfen,** *v.t.* stopper, cork; plug; cram; graft.
**Pfropfenzieher,** *m.* corkscrew.
**Pfropfwachs,** *n.* grafting wax.
**Pfuhl,** *m.* pool, puddle, slough.
**Pfühl,** *m.* & *n.* pillow, bolster.
**Pfund,** *n.* pound. **-leder,** *n.* sole leather.
**pfuschen,** *v.i.* blunder, bungle; meddle.
**Pfütze,** *f.* pool, puddle, wallow.
**pH,** *abbrev.* pH, pH (symbol for hydrogen-ion concentration); (pro Hundert) per cent.
**phagedänisches Wasser.** (*Pharm.*) yellow mercurial lotion.
**Phagozyt,** *m.* phagocyte.
**phagozytär, phagozytisch,** *a.* phagocytic.
**Phänomen,** *n.* phenomenon.
**Phantasie,** *f.* imagination, fancy. **-artikel,** *m.* (*Calico*) fancy style. **-leder,** *n.* fancy leather. **-papier,** *n.* fancy paper.
**phantasieren,** *v.i.* imagine, muse, dream; be delirious, wander.
**phantasievoll,** *a.* fanciful.
**Phantast,** *m.* dreamer, visionary.
**Phäo-.** pheo-, phaeo-.
**Pharaoschlange,** *f.* Pharaoh's serpent.
**Pharmako-log,** *m.* pharmacologist. **-logie,** *f.* pharmacology.
**pharmakologisch,** *a.* pharmacological.
**Pharmakopöe,** *f.* pharmacopeia.
**Pharmazeut,** *m.* pharmaceutist, pharmacist.
**Pharmazeutik,** *f.* pharmaceutics.
**pharmazeutisch,** *a.* pharmaceutical.
**Pharmazie,** *f.* pharmacy.
**Phasen-änderung,** *f.* phase change. **-gesetz,** *n.* phase law.
**phasengleich,** *a.* of like phase. — *adv.* in the same phase, in phase.
**Phasen-gleichgewicht,** *n.* equilibrium between (or among) phases, phase-rule equilibrium. **-gleichheit,** *f.* phase coincidence. **-grenze,** *f.* phase boundary. **-lehre,** *f.* phase theory. **-mass,** *n.* phase constant. **-messer,** *m.* (*Elec.*) phasemeter. **-regel,** *f.* phase rule. **-spannung,** *f.* (*Elec.*) phase voltage. **-unterschied,** *m.* difference of phase. **-welle,** *f.* phase wave. **-zahl,** *f.* number of phases.
**Phaseomannit,** *n.* phaseomannitol, phaseomannite.
**-phasig.** -phased.
**phasisch,** *a.* phasic, phase.
**Phasotropie,** *f.* phasotropy, phasotropism.
**Phenant(h)ren,** *n.* phenanthrene. **-chinon,** *n.* phenanthrenequinone.
**Phenochinon,** *n.* phenoquinone.
**Phenol-.** phenol, phenol-, phenolic; (in combination with the name of a metal) phenoxide (or phenolate) of, as *Phenolaluminium,* aluminum phenoxide, aluminum phenolate.
**phenolartig,** *a.* of the nature of or like a phenol, phenoloid.
**Phenolat,** *n.* phenoxide, phenolate.
**Phenol-äther,** *m.* phenol ether. **-carbonsäure,** *f.* phenolcarboxylic acid. **-gruppe,** *f.* phenol group.
**phenolhaltig,** *a.* containing phenol, phenolic.
**Phenol-harz,** *n.* phenol(ic) resin. **-kalium,** *n.* potassium phenoxide (or phenolate). **-kalzium,** *n.* calcium phenoxide (or phenolate).
**phenollöslich,** *a.* phenol-soluble.
**Phenol-lösung,** *f.* phenol solution. **-natrium,** *n.* sodium phenoxide (or phenolate). **-phtalein,** *n.* phenolphthalein. **-quecksilber,** *n.* mercury phenoxide (or phenolate). **-rot,** *n.* phenol red. **-säure,** *f.* phenol acid. **-schwefelsäure,** *f.* phenolsulfuric acid (general term, $ROSO_3H$, where R is an aromatic radical), specif. phen-

ylsulfuric acid. **-sulfo(n)säure,** *f.* phenolsulfonic acid. **-verbindung,** *f.* phenol(ic) compound. **-wismut,** *m. & n.* bismuth phenoxide (or phenolate).

**Phensäure,** *f.* phenic acid (phenol, $C_6H_5OH$).

**Phenyl-arsenchlorür,** *n.* dichlorophenylarsine, $C_6H_5AsCl_2$. **-äther,** *m.* phenyl ether. **-borchlorid,** *n.* dichlorophenylborine, $C_6H_5BCl_2$. **-braun,** *n.* phenyl brown.

**Phenylenblau,** *n.* phenylene blue.

**Phenyl-essigäther,** *m.* phenyl acetate. **-essigsäure,** *f.* phenylacetic acid. **-fettsäure,** *f.* phenylated fatty acid.

**phenylieren,** *v.t.* phenylate.

**Phenyl-jodidchlorid,** *n.* phenyl iodochloride. **-milchsäure,** *f.* phenyllactic acid. **-säure,** *f.* phenylic acid (phenol, $C_6H_5OH$). **-schwefelsäure,** *f.* phenylsulfuric acid. **-senföl,** *n.* phenyl mustard oil. **-siliciumchlorid,** *n.* trichlorophenylsilane, $C_6H_5SiCl_3$. **-verbindung,** *f.* phenyl compound. **-wasserstoff,** *m.* phenyl hydride, benzene.

**Ph.g., Ph.G.,** *abbrev.* (Pharmakopoeia germanica) German pharmacopeia.

**philan-ieren, -isieren,** *v.t.* philanize (mercerize by a special process).

**Philosoph,** *m.* philosopher.

**Philosophenwolle,** *f.* philosopher's wool (sublimed zinc oxide).

**philosophisch,** *a.* philosophical.

**Phiole,** *f.* vial, phial.

**Phlegma,** *n.* phlegm.

**phlegmatisieren,** *v.t.* (*Expl.*) desensitize.

**phlobaphenlösend,** *a.* dissolving phlobaphenes.

**phlogistisch,** *a.* phlogistic.

**Phlorchinyl,** *n.* phloroquinyl.

**Phloro-glucid, -gluzid,** *n.* phloroglucidol, phloroglucide. **-gluzin,** *n.* phloroglucinol.

**Phokänsäure,** *f.* phocenic acid (valeric acid).

**Phön-.** phen-, phoen-.

**Phönicin, Phönizin,** *n.* phenicin, phoenicin.

**Phoresezelle,** *f.* electrophoresis cell.

**Phosgen,** *n.* phosgene, carbonyl chloride.

**Phosphat,** *n.* phosphate. **-dünger,** *m.* phosphate fertilizer.

**phosphatführend,** *a.* phosphate-bearing.

**phosphatieren,** *v.t.* phosphatize, phosphate.

**phosphatisch,** *a.* phosphatic.

**Phosphatpuffer,** *m.* phosphate buffer.

**phosphenylig,** *a.* phosphenylous.

**Phosphenylsäure,** *f.* phosphenylic acid.

**phosphinig,** *a.* phosphinous.

**Phosphinigsäure,** *f.* phosphinous acid.

**Phosphinsäure,** *f.* phosphinic acid.

**Phosphor,** *m.* phosphorus; phosphor, phosphorescent substance.

**Phosphor-.** phosphorus, phospho-, phosphide of.

**phosphor-arm,** *a.* poor in phosphorus, low-phosphorus. **-artig,** *a.* like phosphorus, phosphorous.

**Phosphor-äther,** *m.* phosphoric ether (ester of phosphoric acid, specif. ethyl phosphate). **-basis,** phosphorus base. **-bestimmung,** *f.* determination of phosphorus. **-blei,** *n.* lead phosphide; (*Min.*) pyromorphite. **-bombe,** *f.* phosphorus bomb. **-brandgranate,** *f.* phosphorus incendiary shell. **-brei,** *m.* phosphorus paste. **-bromid,** *n.* phosphorus bromide, specif. phosphorus pentabromide, phosphorus(V) bromide. **-bromür,** *n.* phosphorus tribromide, phosphorus(III) bromide. **-bronze,** *f.* phosphor bronze. **-calcium,** *n.* calcium phosphide. **-chlorid,** *n.* phosphorus chloride, specif. phosphorus pentachloride, phosphorus(V) chloride. **-chlorür,** *n.* phosphorous chloride (phosphorus trichloride, phosphorus(III) chloride). **-dampf,** *m.* phosphorus vapor or fume. **-eisen,** *n.* ferrophosphorus; iron phosphide. **-eisensinter,** *m.* diadochite.

**phosphoren,** *v.t.* phosphorize, phosphorate.

**Phosphoreszenz,** *f.* phosphorescence.

**phosphoreszenzerzeugend,** *a.* phosphorogenic.

**phosphoreszieren,** *v.i.* phosphoresce. — **phosphoreszierend,** *p.a.* phosphorescent.

**Phosphor-eszierung,** *f.* phosphorescence. **-fleischsäure,** *f.* phosphocarnic acid.

**phosphorfrei,** *a.* free from phosphorus.

**Phosphor-gehalt,** *m.* phosphorus content. **-geruch,** *m.* phosphorus odor. **-geschoss,** *n.* phosphorus bullet, incendiary bullet. **-gruppe,** *f.* phosphorus group. **-guano,** *m.* phosphatic guano.

**phosphorhaltig,** *a.* containing phosphorus, phosphatic, phosphorated.

**Phosphorhandgranate,** *f.* phosphorus grenade.

**phosphorig,** *a.* phosphorous. **-sauer,** *a.* of or combined with phosphorous acid, phosphite of.

**Phosphorigsäureanhydrid,** *n.* phosphorous anhydride (phosphorus trioxide, phosphorus(III) oxide).

**phosphorisch,** *a.* phosphoric.

**phosphorisieren,** *v.t.* phosphorize, phosphorate.

**Phosphor-jodid,** *n.* phosphorus iodide, specif. a higher iodide ($PI_3$, sometimes $PI_5$). **-jodür,** *n.* phosphorus diiodide ($P_2I_4$); sometimes, phosphorus triiodide, phosphorus(III) iodide ($PI_3$). **-kalzium,** *n.* calcium phosphide. **-kanister,** *m.* phosphorus bomb. **-kerzchen,** *n.* wax match, vesta. **-kupfer,** *n.* copper phosphide; (*Min.*) libethenite. **-kupfererz,** *n.* libethenite. **-löffel,** *m.* phosphorus spoon (deflagrating spoon). **-mangan,** *n.* phosphormanganese. **-masse,** *f.* phosphorus paste or composition. **-metall,** *n.* phosphide (of a metal). **-molybdänsäure,** *f.* phosphomolybdic acid. **-natrium,** *n.* sodium phosphide. **-nebelgranate,** *f.* phosphorus smoke shell. **-öl,** *n.* (*Pharm.*) phosphorated oil. **-oxyd,** *n.* (any) phosphorus oxide, specif. the pentoxide, phosphorus(V) oxide. **-oxydul,** *n.* phosphorus trioxide, phosphorus(III) oxide. **-proteid,** *n.* phosphoprotein. **-roheisen,** *n.* phosphoric pig iron. **-salz,** *n.* microcosmic salt ($HNaNH_4PO_4 \cdot 4H_2O$).

**phosphorsauer,** *a.* of or combined with phosphoric acid, phosphate of.

**Phosphorsäure,** *f.* phosphoric acid. **-anhydrid,** *n.* phosphoric anhydride (phosphorus pentoxide). **-lösung,** *f.* phosphoric acid solution. **-salz,** *n.* phosphate.

**Phosphor-stahl,** *m.* phosphorus steel. **-stange,** *f.* stick of phosphorus. **-sulfid,** *n.* (any) phosphorus sulfide.

**Phosphorung,** *f.* phosphor(iz)ation.

**Phosphor-verbindung,** *f.* phosphorus compound. **-vergiftung,** *f.* phosphorus poisoning. **-wasserstoff,** *m.* hydrogen phosphide, phosphorus hydride (**gasförmiger,** $PH_3$; **flüssiger,** $P_2H_4$; **fester,** $P_{12}H_6$). **-wasserstoffgas,** *n.* phosphoretted hydrogen gas (phosphine, $PH_3$). **-weinsäure,** *f.* phosphovinic acid (*Obs.*). **-wolframsäure,** *f.* phosphotungstic acid. **-zink,** *n.* zinc phosphide. **-zinn,** *n.* tin phosphide. **-zündhölzchen,** *n.* phosphorus match.

**Phosphosäure,** *f.* phosphonic acid ($RPO_3H_2$).

**Photo-.** photo-; photographic. **-bakterien,** *n.pl.* photobacteria. **-chemie,** *f.* photochemistry.

**photo-chemisch,** *a.* photochemical. **-elektrisch,** *a.* photo-electric.

**Photoelektrizität,** *f.* photo-electricity.

**photogen,** *a.* photogenic.

**Photo-gramm,** *n.* photograph. **-graph,** *m.* photographer. **-graphie,** *f.* photography; photograph.

**photo-graphieren,** *v.t.* photograph. **-graphisch,** *a.* photographic.

**Photo-klebstoff,** *m.* photographic paste. **-kopie,** *f.* photographic copy, photocopy, photoprint.

**photokopieren,** *v.t.* copy by photography, photocopy.

**Photo-lyse,** *f.* photolysis. **-metrierung,** *f.* photometric evaluation or recording.

**photometrisch,** *a.* photometric.

**Photo-physik,** *f.* photophysics. **-platte,** *f.* photographic plate. **-präparat,** *n.* photographic preparation. **-sphäre,** *f.* photosphere. **-strom,** *m.* photoelectric current. **-tropie,** *f.* phototropism, phototropy.

**phototropisch,** *a.* phototropic.

**Photozelle,** *f.* photocell, photoelectric cell.

**Phtal-.** phthal-, phthalo-, phthalic. **-amidsäure, -aminsäure,** *f.* phthalamic acid. **-azin,** *n.* phthalazine. **-ein,** *n* phthalein. **-einfarbstoff,** *m.* phthalein dye. **-id,** *n.* phthalide. **-monopersäure,** *f.* monoper(oxy)phthalic acid. **-onsäure,** *f.* phthalonic acid. **-säure,** *f.* phthalic acid. **-säureanhydrid,** *n.* phthalic anhydride. **-säureharzlack,** *m.* phthalic acid resin varnish.

**Phthal-.** see Phtal-.

**pH-Wert,** *m.* *p*H value.

**Phyko-cyan, -zyan,** *n.* phycocyanin. **-phäin,** *n.* phycophein, phycophaein.

**Phyllohämin,** *n.* phyllohemin, phyllohaemin.

**phys.,** *abbrev.* (physikalisch) physical.

**Physciasäure,** *f.* physcic acid (physcione).

**Physik,** *f.* physics; (*Dyeing*) tin composition (solution of tin in aqua regia).

**physikalisch,** *a.* physical. **-chemisch,** *a.* physical-chemical, physicochemical. **-metallurgisch,** *a.* physicometallurgical.

**Physikbad,** *n.* (*Dyeing*) tin composition.

**Physiker,** *m.* physicist.

**physiko-chemisch,** *a.* physicochemical.

**Physiksalz,** *n.* (*Dyeing*) red spirit.

**Physiolog,** *m.* physiologist.

**physiologisch,** *a.* physiological.

**physisch,** *a.* physical.

**Phytochemie,** *f.* phytochemistry.

**phytochemisch,** *a.* phytochemical.

**Phytosterin,** *n.* phytosterol.

**Picenchinon,** *n.* picenequinone.

**Pichapparat,** *m.* (*Brewing*) pitching machine.

**pichen,** *v.t.* pitch.

**Pich-pech,** *n.* common pitch. **-wachs,** *n.* propolis.

**Picke,** *f.* pickax, pick.

**Pickel,** *m.* pimple; pickax, pick; pickle, brine (see also Pökel). **-bad,** *n.* pickle bath, pickle. **-bildung,** *f.* (*Metal.*) pitting. **-brühe,** *f.* pickle.

**pickeln,** *v.t.* pickle, soak in a pickle.

**Pickelsäure,** *f.* pickling acid.

**picken,** *v.i.* peck, pick.

**Pickharz,** *n.* galipot.

**Picolinsäure,** *f.* picolinic acid.

**Piezochemie,** *f.* piezochemistry.

**piezoelektrisch,** *a.* piezoelectric.

**Piezoelektrizität,** *f.* piezoelectricity.

**Piezokristall,** *m.* piezoelectric crystal.

**pigmentarisch,** *a.* pigmentary.

**Pigment-bakterien,** *n.pl.* chromogenic bacteria. **-bildung,** *f.* (*Biol.*) pigment formation, chromogenesis. **-druck,** *m.* pigment printing. **-farbe,** *f.* pigment color. **-farbstoff,** *m.* pigment dye.

**pigment-frei,** *a.* free from pigment, nonpigmented. **-haltig,** *a.* containing pigment, pigmented.

**pigmentieren,** *v.t.* pigment. — *v.i.* become pigmented.

**pigment-los,** *a.* without pigment, nonpigmented.

**-mattiert,** *a.* dulled by addition of a pigment.
**Pigmentpapier,** *n.* carbon paper.
**Pik,** *m.* peak; pique; (at cards) spades.
**pikant,** *a.* piquant, pungent.
**Piknometer,** *n.* pycnometer.
**Pikraminsäure,** *f.* picramic acid.
**Pikrin-pulver,** *n.* picric powder. **-säure,** *f.* picric acid.
**Pikro-.** picro-. **-toxininsäure,** *f.* picrotoxininic acid. **-toxinsäure,** *f.* picrotoxinic acid.
**Pikryl,** *n.* picryl.
**Pilee,** *f.*, **-zucker,** *m.* crushed sugar.
**Pilieranlage,** *f.* (*Soap*) milling plant.
**pilieren,** *v.t.* grind, mill (as soap).
**Piliermaschine,** *f.* (*Soap*) milling machine, soap mill.
**Pille,** *f.* pill; pellet; primer.
**Pillen-farn,** *m.* pillwort (*Pilularia*). **-glas,** *n.* pill bottle, pill vial. **-schachtel,** *f.* pill box.
**Pilz,** *m.* fungus; mushroom; (*Mil.*) small pillbox.
**pilz-ähnlich, -artig,** *a.* like a mushroom or fungus, fungoid.
**Pilz-art,** *f.* species of fungus or mushroom. **-bildung,** *f.* fungus (or fungoid) growth.
**Pilzenentwickelung,** *f.* fungus development.
**pilzförmig,** *a.* fungiform; mushroom-shaped.
**pilzig, pilzicht,** *a.* fungous, fungoid, spongy.
**Pilz-isolator,** *m.* (*Elec.*) petticoat insulator. **-krankheit,** *f.* fungus disease. **-kunde,** *f.* mycology. **-maischverfahren,** *n.* = Amyloverfahren. **-samen,** *m.* spawn (of fungi), mycelium. **-stoff,** *m.* fungin.
**pilztötend,** *p.a.* fungicidal.
**Pilzwucherung,** *f.* fungus (or fungoid) growth.
**Pimarsäure,** *f.* pimaric acid.
**Pimelin-keton,** *n.* pimelic ketone (cyclohexanone). **-säure,** *f.* pimelic acid.
**Piment,** *n.* pimento, allspice. **-öl,** *n.* pimento oil, allspice oil. **-pfeffer,** *m.* pimento, allspice. **-rum,** *m.* bay rum.
**Pimpelstein,** *m.* (*Copper*) pimple metal.
**Pimpernuss,** *f.* bladder nut.
**Pimpinelle,** *f.* burnet saxifrage (*Pimpinella saxifraga*).
**Pimstein,** *m.* pumice stone.
**Pinafaser,** *f.* piña fiber.
**Pinakon,** *n.* pinacol, (less correctly) pinacone. **-bildung,** *f.* pinacol formation.
**Pinaldrüse,** *f.* pineal gland.
**Pincette,** *f.* = Pinzette.
**Pinealdrüse,** *f.* pineal gland.
**Pineytalg,** *m.* piney tallow.
**Pinie,** *f.* pine (esp., *Pinus pinea*); pine kernel, piñon.
**Pinien-kern,** *m.* pine kernel, piñon. **-kiefer,** *f.* white pine (*Pinus strobus*): **-talg,** *m.* piney tallow.
**Pininsäure,** *f.* pininic acid.
**Pinit,** *n.* pinitol, (less correctly) pinite.
**pinkeln,** *v.i.* piddle, putter.
**pinken,** *v.t.* treat with pink salt; hammer, forge.
**Pinksalz,** *n.* pink salt (ammonium chlorostannate, $(NH_4)_2SnCl_6$; less commonly, potassium sodium tartrate). **-bad,** *n.* pink-salt bath.
**Pinne,** *f.* (*Tech.*) pin, peg, tack; (of a hammer) peen; quill feather.
**Pinokamphersäure,** *f.* pinocamphoric acid.
**Pinsäure,** *f.* pinic acid.
**Pinsel,** *m.* (painter's) brush, pencil.
**pinselförmig,** *a.* brush-shaped, pencil-shaped.
**pinseln,** *v.t.* pencil, paint.
**Pinselschimmel,** *m.* any species of *Penicillium.*
**Pinusharz,** *n.* pine resin.
**Pinzette,** *f.* forceps, tweezers, nippers, pincers.
**Pionier,** *m.* pioneer; (*Mil.*) engineer. **-sprengmittel,** *n.* engineer explosive.
**Piperinsäure,** *f.* piperic acid.
**Pipette,** *f.* pipet, pipette.
**Pipetten-etagere,** *f.* pipet rack, pipet stand. **-flasche,** *f.*, **-fläschchen,** *n.* pipet bottle (dropping bottle with pipet). **-gestell,** *n.*, **-ständer,** *m.* pipet stand.
**pipettieren,** *v.t.* transfer or measure with a pipet, pipet(te).
**Pisangwachs,** *n.* pisang wax.
**Pistazie,** *f.* pistachio (nut).
**Pistazien-grün,** *n.* pistachio green. **-öl,** *n.* pistachio oil.
**Pistill,** *n.* pestle; (*Bot.*) pistil.
**Pistole,** *f.* pistol; gun; torpedo fuse.
**Pistolengebläse,** *n.* hand-operated blast.
**Pitehanf, Pitahanf,** *m.* pita hemp, pita.
**Pitot-rohr,** *n.*, **-röhre,** *f.*, **Pitotsches Rohr.** Pitot tube.
**P.K.,** *abbrev.* (Pferdekraft) horsepower, H.P
**Pkt.,** *abbrev.* (Punkt) point.
**placentar,** *a.* placental.
**placken,** *v.t.* flatten; ram; pester.
**Plackerei,** *f.* drudgery.
**Plage,** *f.* trouble, bother, plague, drudgery.
**plagen,** *v.t.* plague, trouble, bother, worry.
**Plagge,** *f.* sod.
**plagiedrisch,** *a.* (*Cryst.*) plagihedral.
**Plagioklas,** *m.* plagioclase.
**Plakat,** *n.* placard, poster. **-farbe,** *f.* poster color, lithographic color. **-papier,** *n.* poster paper.
**Plan,** *m.* plane, plain; plan; (*Painting*) ground.
**planen,** *v.t.* plan, design, project; plane.
**Planenstoff,** *m.* awning cloth; tarpaulin.
**planetarisch,** *a.* planetary.
**Planeten-bahn,** *f.* planetary orbit. **-getriebe,** *n.* planetary gear(ing).
**Planfläche,** *f.* plane surface.
**Plangitter,** *n.* (*Optics*) plane grating.

**planieren,** *v.t* plane, planish, smooth; level, grade; size (paper).
**Planier-löffel,** *m.* skimmer. **-masse,** *f.* (*Paper*) size. **-ung,** *f.* planing, etc. (see planieren). **-wasser,** *n.* glue water, size.
**Planke,** *f.* plank, (thick) board.
**plan-konkav,** *a.* plano-concave. **-konvex,** *a.* plano-convex. **-mässig,** *a.* systematic, methodical.
**planschen,** *v.i.* splash.
**Planspiegel,** *m.* plane mirror.
**plansymmetrisch,** *a.* planisymmetric(al).
**Plantage,** *f.* plantation.
**Plantagenkautschuk,** *m. & n.* plantation rubber.
**Planung,** *f.* planning; plan, design; planing.
**planzeichnen,** *v.t.* plot.
**Plasmolyse,** *f.* plasmolysis.
**plasmolytisch,** *a.* plasmolytic.
**plastifizieren,** *v.t.* plasticize, plastify.
**Plastifiziermittel,** *n.* plasticizer.
**Plastik,** *f.* stereoscopic effect; plastic art.
**plastisch,** *a.* plastic; stereoscopic.
**plastizieren,** *v.t.* plasticize.
**Plastizierer,** *m.* plasticizer.
**Plastizierung,** *f.* plasticizing, plasticization.
**Plastizität,** *f.* plasticity.
**Plastizitätsmesser,** *m.* plastometer.
**Platane,** *f.* plane, plane tree.
**platieren,** *v.t.* plate.
**Platin,** *n.* platinum. **-abfall,** *m.* platinum waste. **-ammonchlorid,** *n* platinum ammonium chloride, ammonium chloroplatinate.
**platinartig,** *a.* like platinum, platinoid.
**Platin-asbest,** *m.* platinized asbestos. **-bad,** *n.* platinum bath. **-baryumzyanür,** *n.* barium cyanoplatinite, barium cyanoplatinate(II). **-blase,** *f.* platinum still. **-blech,** *n.* platinum foil or sheet. **-chlorid,** *n.* platinum chloride, specif. platinic chloride, platinum(IV) chloride. **-chlorür,** *n.* platinous chloride, platinum(II) chloride. **-chlorwasserstoff,** *m.*, **-chlorwasserstoffsäure,** *f.* chloroplatinic acid, chloroplatinic(IV) acid. **-cyanür,** *n.* platinous cyanide, platinum(II) cyanide; cyanoplatinite, cyanoplatinate(II), platinocyanide. **-cyanürwasserstoff,** *m.*, **-cyanürwasserstoffsäure,** *f.* cyanoplatinous acid, cyanoplatinic(II) acid, platinocyanic acid. **-draht,** *m.* platinum wire. **-drahtöse,** *f.* platinum-wire loop. **-dreieck,** *n.* platinum triangle.
**Platine,** *f.* plate bar, sheet bar; platen.
**Platin-element,** *n.* platinum thermocouple. **-ersatz,** *m.* platinum substitute. **-erz,** *n.* platinum ore. **-folie,** *f.* platinum foil. **-gefäss,** *n.* platinum vessel. **-gehalt,** *m.* platinum content. **-gerät,** *n.*, **-gerätschaft,** *f.* platinum apparatus, platinum ware.
**platinhaltig,** *a.* containing platinum, platiniferous.
**Platin-hydroxyd,** *n.* platinum hydroxide, specif. platinic hydroxide, platinum(IV) hydroxide. **-hydroxydul,** *n.* platinous hydroxide, platinum(II) hydroxide.
**Platini-.** platinic, platini-, platinum(IV). **-chlorid,** *n.* platinic chloride, platinum(IV) chloride. **-chlorwasserstoff,** *m.*, **-chlorwasserstoffsäure,** *f.* chloroplatinic acid, chloroplatinic(IV) acid. **-cyanwasserstoffsäure,** *f.* cyanoplatinic acid, cyanoplatinic(IV) acid, platinicyanic acid.
**platinieren,** *v.t.* platinize.
**Platinierung,** *f.* platinization.
**Platini-rhodanwasserstoffsäure,** *f.* thiocyanoplatinic acid, thiocyanoplatinic(IV) acid. **-salz,** *n.* platinic salt, specif. platinum(IV) salt. **-selencyanwasserstoffsäure,** *f.* selenocyanoplatinic acid, selenocyanoplatinic(IV) acid. **-verbindung,** *f.* platinic compound, specif. platinum(IV) compound.
**Platin-kegel,** *m.* platinum cone. **-kohle,** *f.* platinized charcoal. **-konus,** *m.* platinum cone. **-legierung,** *f.* platinum alloy. **-löffel,** *m.* platinum spoon. **-magnesiumzyanür,** *n.* magnesium cyanoplatinite, magnesium cyanoplatinate(II). **-metall,** *n.* platinum metal, metal of the platinum group. **-mohr,** *m.* platinum black. **-nadel,** *f.* platinum needle, platinum wire. **-natriumchlorür,** *n.* sodium chloroplatinite, sodium chloroplatinate(II).
**Platino-.** platinous, platino-, platinum(II). **-chlorid,** *n.* platinous chloride, platinum(II) chloride. **-chlorwasserstoff,** *m.*, **-chlorwasserstoffsäure,** *f.* chloroplatinous acid, chloroplatinic(II) acid. **-cyanwasserstoff,** *m.*, **-cyanwasserstoffsäure,** *f.* cyanoplatinous acid, cyanoplatinic(II) acid, platinocyanic acid. **-rhodanwasserstoffsäure,** *f.* thiocyanoplatinous acid, thiocyanoplatinic(II) acid.
**Platinöse,** *f.* platinum-wire loop.
**Platinoverbindung,** *f.* platinous compound, platinum(II) compound.
**Platin-oxyd,** *n.* platinum oxide, specif. platinic oxide, platinum(IV) oxide. **-oxydul,** *n.* platinous oxide, platinum(II) oxide. **-oxydulverbindung,** *f.* platinous compound, platinum(II) compound. **-oxydverbindung,** *f.* platinic compound, specif. platinum(IV) compound.
**Platinozyan-.** see Platinocyan-.
**platinplattiert,** *a.* platinum-plated.
**Platin-plattierung,** *f.* platinum plating. **-reihe,** *f.* platinum series. **-rhodium,** *n.* platinum-rhodium. **-rohr,** *n.*, **-röhre,** *f.* platinum tube. **-rückstand,** *m.* platinum residue. **-salmiak,** *m.* ammonium chloroplatinate. **-salz,** *n.* platinum salt. **-sand,** *m.* sand for cleaning platinum. **-säure,** *f.* platinic acid. **-schale,**

*f.* platinum dish. **-schiffchen,** *n.* platinum boat. **-schwamm,** *m.* platinum sponge. **-schwarz,** *n.* platinum black. **-spatel,** *m.* platinum spatula. **-spirale,** *f.* platinum coil. **-spitze,** *f.* platinum point. **-stern,** *m.* platinum star. **-sulfür,** *n.* platinous sulfide, platinum(II) sulfide. **-tiegel,** *m.* platinum crucible. **-tonbad,** *n.* (*Photog.*) platinum toning bath. **-verbindung,** *f.* platinum compound.

**Platinzyan-.** see Platincyan-.

**plätschern,** *v.i.* splash, plash, ripple.

**platt,** *a.* flat; plain; level; low.

**Plättchen,** *n.* platelet, lamella, scale.

**Platte,** *f.* plate; slab; sheet; board; flat tile; (phonographic) disk, (flat) record; lamina; planchet; tray; leaf (of a table); flagstone; plateau; (*Bact.*) plate culture.

**Plätte,** *f.* flat wire; flatiron; ironing.

**platten,** *v.t.* flatten; laminate; iron; flag.

**Platten-dekatur,** *f.* hydraulic press-finish. **-druck,** *m.* printing from plates. **-flasche,** *f.*, **-fläschchen,** *n.* (*Bact.*) flat culture flask.

**plattenförmig,** *a.* plate-like, lamellar, lamelliform, laminated.

**Platten-gewebe,** *n.* lamellar tissue. **-glimmer,** *m.* sheet mica. **-gummi,** *n.* plate rubber; sheet rubber. **-kalk,** *m.* slab limestone. **-kautschuk,** *n.* plate rubber; sheet rubber. **-kondensator,** *m.* (*Elec.*) plate condenser. **-kultur,** *f.* plate culture. **-kupfer,** *n.* sheet copper. **-pulver,** *n.* (*Expl.*) rolled powder, flake powder. **-schale,** *f.* flat dish, specif. Petri dish. **-turm,** *m.* plate column, plate tower. **-zink,** *n.* slab zinc.

**plattgedrückt,** *a.* flat-pressed, flattened.

**plattieren,** *v.t.* plate; clad.

**Plattierung,** *f.* plating, plate; cladding.

**Plattier-verfahren,** *n.* plating or cladding process. **-werkstoff,** *m.* plating or cladding material.

**plattig,** *a.* (*Cryst.*) platelike, bladed, lath-shaped.

**Plattine,** *f.* (*Tech.*) plate; (*Metal.*) mill bar.

**Plattwurm,** *m.* flatworm.

**Platz,** *m.* place; room, spot, seat, square, etc.

**Plätzchen,** *n.* little cake, lozenge, troche, tablet.

**platzen,** *v.i.* burst; explode; crack, split.

**plätzen,** *v. t. & i.* bang, pop, smack.

**Platz-mangel,** *m.* lack of space. **-nummer,** *f.* position number, serial number; specif., atomic number. **-patrone,** *f.* blank cartridge. **-quecksilber,** *n.* = Knallquecksilber. **-wechsel,** *m.* exchange of places (of electrons or atoms); change of place, displacement, transposition; migration.

**plausibel,** *a.* plausible.

**Pleistozän,** *n.* (*Geol.*) Pleistocene.

**Plejade,** *f.* pleiad.

**Pleochroismus,** *m.* pleochroism.

**pleochroitisch,** *a.* pleochroic, pleochroitic.

**pleomorph,** *a.* pleomorphic.

**Pleuelstange,** *f.* connecting rod.

**pleuritisch,** *a.* pleuritic.

**Plombe,** *f.* filling, plug (for teeth); lead seal.

**plombieren,** *v.t.* plug, fill; lead.

**Plombiergold,** *n.* dental gold.

**Plombierung,** *f.* plumbing; filling; leading.

**Plotz,** *m.* explosion.

**plotzen,** *v.i.* explode.

**plötzlich,** *a.* sudden. — *adv.* suddenly.

**Plumbi-.** plumbic, plumbi-, lead(IV). **-oxyd,** *n.* plumbic oxide, lead dioxide, lead(IV) oxide. **-salz,** *n.* plumbic salt, lead(IV) salt. **-verbindung,** *f.* plumbic compound, lead(IV) compound.

**Plumbo-.** plumbous, plumbo-, lead(II). **-salz,** *n.* plumbous salt, lead(II) salt. **-verbindung,** *f.* plumbous compound, lead(II) compound.

**plump,** *a.* bulky, clumsy, gross.

**Plunscher,** *m.* plunger.

**Plüsch,** *m.* plush. **-leder,** *n.* ooze leather, velvet leather.

**Plus-platte,** *f.* (*Elec.*) positive plate. **-pol,** *m.* positive pole. **-zeichen,** *n.* plus sign. **-zucker,** *m.* plus sugar, dextrorotatory sugar.

**plutonisch,** *a.* (*Geol.*) plutonic.

**p.m.,** *abbrev.* (pro mille) per mill, per thousand; (pro mense) per month; (pro minute) per minute; (post meridiem) after noon, P.M.

**Pneu,** *m.*, **Pneumatik,** *f.* pneumatic tire.

**pneumatisch,** *a.* pneumatic.

**pneumatolytisch,** *a.* (*Petrog.*) pneumatolytic.

**pneumonisch,** *a.* pneumonic.

**pochen,** *v.t.* pound, stamp, crush. — *v.i.* beat, knock, pound, stamp; brag.

**Poch-erz,** *n.* stamping ore, milling ore. **-gänge,** *m.pl.* poor ore, halvans. **-gestein,** *m.* (*Mining*) stamp rock. **-mehl,** *n.* pulverized ore. **-mühle,** *f.* stamp mill. **-satz, -schlamm, -schlich,** *m.* ore slime. **-stempelreihe,** *f.* stamp battery. **-trübe,** *f.* (*Metal.*) stamp pulp. **-werk,** *n.* stamp mill.

**Pocke,** *f.* pock; (*pl.*) smallpox.

**Pocken-gift,** *n.* smallpox virus. **-holz,** *n.* = Pockholz. **-impfung,** *f.* vaccination. **-lymphe,** *f.* vaccine lymph. **-narbe,** *f.* pit. **-wurzel,** *f.* chinaroot.

**Pockholz,** *n.* lignum vitae, guaiacum wood, pockwood.

**Pokal,** *m.* goblet, cup.

**Pökel,** *m.* pickle (the liquid). See also Pickel.

**Pökelei,** *f.* salting house (for meat).

**Pökel-fass,** *n.* pickling tub or vat. **-fleisch,** *n.* pickled meat, salt meat. **-kufe,** *f.* pickling vat or tub.

**pökeln,** *v.t.* pickle.

**Pökeltrog,** *m.* pickling trough.

**Pol,** *m.* pole; (of fabrics) pile, nap. **-achse,** *f.* polar axis. **-anziehung,** *f.* polar attraction.

**Polargegend,** *f.* polar region.
**Polarisations-apparat,** *m.* polarizing apparatus. **-ebene,** *f.* plane of polarization. **-einrichtung,** *f.* (*Micros.*) polarizing attachment. **-erscheinung,** *f.* polarization phenomenon. **-farbe,** *f.* polarization color. **-prisma,** *n.* polarizer. **-rohr,** *n.*, **-röhre,** *f.* polarization tube. **-spannung,** *f.* (*Elec.*) polarization voltage. **-strom,** *m.* polarization current. **-vorrichtung,** *f.* (*Micros.*) polarizing attachment. **-winkel,** *m.* angle of polarization.
**Polarisator,** *m.* polarizer.
**polarisch,** *a.* polar.
**polarisierbar,** *a.* polarizable.
**Polarisierbarkeit,** *f.* polarizability.
**polarisieren,** *v.t.* polarize.
**Polarisierung,** *f.* polarization.
**Polarität,** *f.* polarity.
**Polar-licht,** *n.* aurora polaris. **-röhre,** *f.* electrode tube. **-stern,** *m.* polestar. **-winkel,** *m.* polar angle.
**Pol-bildung,** *f.* pole formation, polarization. **-dreck,** *m.* (*Metal.*) skimmings, dross.
**Pole,** *f.* (*Textiles*) pile, nap.
**Pol-eck,** *n.*, **-ecke,** *f.* (*Cryst.*) summit.
**Polei,** *m.* pennyroyal. **-öl,** *n.* pennyroyal oil.
**Polemik,** *f.* polemic, controversy; polemics.
**polen,** *v.t.* render polar; (*Metal.*) pole.
**Polen,** *n.* (*Metal.*) poling; Poland.
**pölen,** *v.t.* (*Leather*) unhair.
**Polhöhe,** *f.* altitude of the pole, latitude.
**Police,** *f.* (insurance) policy.
**Polier-.** polishing, burnishing.
**polierbar,** *a.* capable of being polished.
**polieren,** *v.t.* polish, burnish.
**polierfähig,** *a.* capable of being polished.
**Polier-flüssigkeit,** *f.* polishing liquid, liquid polish. **-grün,** *n.* green rouge, chrome green. **-kalk,** *m.* polishing chalk. **-lack,** *m.* polishing lacquer. **-masse,** *f.* polishing paste or composition. **-mittel,** *n.* polishing agent. **-öl,** *n.* polishing oil. **-papier,** *n.* polishing paper, sandpaper. **-paste,** *f.* polishing paste. **-pulver,** *n.* polishing powder. **-rot,** *n.* polishing red, colcothar, crocus, rouge. **-scheibe,** *f.* polishing wheel. **-schiefer,** *m.* polishing earth, tripoli. **-schleifen,** *n.* fine grinding (of surfaces). **-staub,** *m.* polishing dust. **-tinte,** *f.* polishing ink. **-trommel,** *f.* polishing drum. **-wachs,** *n.* polishing wax.
**polig,** *a.* polar.
**politisch,** *a.* political.
**Politur,** *f.* polish, gloss; polishing; shellac varnish, French polish.
**politurfähig,** *a.* polishable.
**Politur-lack,** *m.* polishing varnish. **-masse,** *f.* polishing paste. **-messer,** *m.* glossmeter. **-öl,** *n.* polishing oil.
**Polizei,** *f.* police; police station.
**Pol-klemme,** *f.* (*Elec.*) pole terminal, pole clamp. **-körper,** *m.*, **-körperchen,** *n.* (*Biol.*) polar body, polar cell.
**Pollen-korn,** *n.* pollen grain. **-überträgung,** *f.* pollen transfer, pollination.
**pollos,** *a.* poleless, without poles.
**polnisch,** *a.* Polish.
**Pol-papier, -reagenzpapier,** *n.* (*Elec.*) pole paper. **-platte,** *f.* (*Elec.*) pole plate, pole piece. **-stärke,** *f.* pole strength.
**Polster,** *n.* cushion; padding; pad; compress.
**Polsterung,** *f.* upholstery; padding.
**Pol-strahl,** *m.* (*Math.*) radius vector. **-strahlung,** *f.* polar radiation. **-suchpapier,** *n.* (*Elec.*) pole(-finding) paper. **-ung,** *f.* making polar; polarity; (*Metal.*) poling.
**polwärts,** *adv.* toward the pole, poleward.
**Polwechsel,** *m.* change or reversal of poles; (*Elec.*) alternation of polarity.
**Polychroismus,** *m.* polychroism, pleochroism.
**polychromatisch,** *a.* polychromatic, polychrome.
**Polychromsäure,** *f.* polychromic acid.
**polycyclisch,** *a.* polycyclic.
**Polyeder,** *n.* polyhedron.
**poly-edrisch,** *a.* polyhedral. **-gonisch,** *a.* polygonal. **-heteroatomig,** *a.* polyheteratomic.
**Poly-hyperjodat,** *n.* polyperiodate. **-kieselsäure,** *f.* polysilicic acid.
**polymer,** *a.* polymeric.
**polymereinheitlich,** *a.* of uniform degree of polymerization.
**Polymerie,** *f.* polymerism.
**Polymerisat,** *n.* polymerizate.
**poly-merisch,** *a.* polymeric. **-merisierbar,** *a.* polymerizable.
**Polymerisierbarkeit,** *f.* polymerizability.
**polymerisieren,** *v.t.* & *i.* polymerize.
**Polymerisierung,** *f.* polymerization.
**Polymolybdansäure,** *f.* polymolybdic acid.
**polymorph, polymorphisch,** *a.* polymorphous, polymorphic.
**Poly-morphie,** *f.* polymorphism, polymorphy. **-nom,** *n.* polynomial. **-säure,** *f.* poly acid. **-schwefelwasserstoff,** *m.* hydrogen persulfide (either $H_2S_2$ or $H_2S_3$). **-siliciumsäure,** *f.* polysilicic acid. **-styrol,** *n.* polystyrene. **-thionsäure,** *f.* polythionic acid. **-zimtsäure,** *f.* polycinnamic acid.
**polyzyklisch,** *a.* polycyclic.
**Polzelle,** *f.* polar cell.
**Pomeranze,** *f.* orange, esp. bitter orange.
**pomeranzenartig,** *a.* orange-like.
**Pomeranzen-bitter,** *n.* hesperidin. **-blütenöl,** *n.* orange-flower oil, neroli. **-branntwein,** *m.* orange brandy.
**pomeranzengelb,** *a.* orange-yellow, orange.
**Pomeranzen-liqueur, -likör,** *m.* curaçao. **-öl,** *n.* orange (peel) oil. **-schalenöl,** *n.* orange-peel oil, orange oil.

**pompejanisch**, *a.* Pompeian.
**Pompejanischrot**, *n.* Pompeian red.
**Pompelmuse**, *f.* (*Bot.*) shaddock.
**ponderabel**, *a.* ponderable, weighable.
**ponderomotorisch**, *a.* (*Physics*) ponderomotive.
**Popanz**, *m.* bugbear, bogy.
**populär**, *a.* popular. — *adv.* popularly.
**Porcellan**, *n.* = Porzellan.
**Pore**, *f.* pore; interstice, void.
**Porenanteil**, *m.* proportion of voids.
**poren-frei**, *a.* free from pores. **-füllend**, *a.* pore-filling.
**Poren-füller**, *m.* pore filler, primer. **-gehalt**, *m.* content of pores or voids. **-grösse**, *f.* size of pore(s) or voids. **-raum**, *m.* pore space. **-volumen**, *n.* volume of pores or voids. **-weg**, *n.* pore passage. **-weite**, *f.* pore width, pore diameter.
**Porigkeit**, *f.* porosity.
**porös, porig**, *a.* porous.
**Porosität**, *f.* porosity.
**Porositätsgrad**, *m.* degree of porosity.
**Porphyr**, *m.* porphyry.
**porphyr-artig, -ähnlich**, *a.* porphyritic.
**Porphyr-felsen**, *m.*, **-gestein**, *n.* porphyritic rock.
**porphyrisch**, *a.* porphyritic.
**Porrissäure**, *f.* purreic acid (euxanthic acid).
**Porsch, Porst**, *m.* marsh tea (*Ledum palustre*).
**Porterwürze**, *f.* (*Brewing*) porter wort.
**Portier**, *m.* porter, doorkeeper.
**portionsweise**, *adv.* in portions.
**Portlandkalk**, *m.* Portland (lime)stone.
**Porto**, *n.* postage.
**portofrei**, *a.* post-free, postpaid.
**Portugalöl, Portugalloöl**, *n.* Portugal (or portugallo) oil, orange-peel oil.
**Portugalwasser**, *n.* laurel water.
**Porzellan**, *n.* porcelain, china.
**porzellanartig**, *a.* porcelaneous.
**Porzellan-becher**, *m.* porcelain beaker. **-brei**, *m.* porcelain slip. **-brennofen**, *m.* porcelain kiln. **-dampfschale**, *f.* porcelain evaporating dish or basin. **-einsatz**, *m.* porcelain insert, (in a desiccator) porcelain support. **-erde**, *f.* porcelain clay, china clay, kaolin. **-fabrikation**, *f.* porcelain manufacture. **-gefäss**, *n.* porcelain vessel. **-glasur**, *f.* porcelain glaze. **-griff**, *m.* porcelain handle. **-isolator**, *m.* porcelain insulator. **-jaspis**, *m.* porcelain jasper (variety of porcelanite). **-kachel**, *f.* porcelain tile. **-kitt**, *m.* porcelain cement. **-kugel**, *f.* porcelain ball. **-kugelmühle**, *f.* porcelain ball mill. **-löffel**, *m.* porcelain spoon. **-malerei**, *f.* china painting. **-masse**, *f.* porcelain body or paste. **-mörser**, *m.* porcelain mortar. **-mörtel**, *m.* pozzuolana mortar. **-platte**, *f.* porcelain plate. **-rohr**, *n.*, **-röhre**, *f.* porcelain tube. **-schale**, *f.* porcelain dish. **-schiffchen**, *n.* porcelain boat. **-spat**, *m.* scapolite. **-spatel**, *m.* porcelain spatula. **-stab**, *m.* porcelain rod or bar. **-tiegel**, *m.* porcelain crucible. **-ton**, *m.* porcelain clay, kaolin. **-tonumschlag**, *m.* (*Pharm.*) cataplasm of kaolin. **-trichter**, *m.* porcelain funnel. **-wanne**, *f.* porcelain trough. **-waren**, *f.pl.* porcelain ware, china(ware).
**Posaune**, *f.* trombone.
**Pose**, *f.* quill; pose.
**positiv-elektrisch**, *a.* positively electric, electropositive.
**Positivpause**, *f.* (*Photog.*) positive print.
**Post**, *f.* post, mail; news. — *m.* = Porsch.
**Postament**, *n.* stand, base, pedestal.
**Post-amt**, *n.*, **-anstalt**, *f.* postoffice.
**Posten**, *m.* post, place; item; sum; lot, parcel; (*Metal.*) batch; (*Glass*) piece, lump; (*Math.*) term.
**postfrei**, *a.* post-free, postpaid.
**Postkarte**, *f.* postcard, postal card; post map.
**postlagernd**, *p.a.* general delivery.
**Post-papier**, *n.* letter paper, note paper. **-stempel**, *m.* postmark. **-verein**, *m.* postal union. **-zeichen**, *n.* postmark.
**Potasche**, *f.* = Pottasche.
**Potential-abfall**, *m.* fall of potential. **-gefäll(e)**, *n.* drop in potential; potential gradient. **-sprung**, *m.* (*Elec.*) jump in potential. **-unterschied**, *m.* difference in potential.
**potentiell**, *a.* potential.
**potentiieren**, *v.t.* render potent, potentize.
**potentiometrisch**, *a.* potentiometric.
**Potenz**, *f.* power. **-gefäll(e)**, *n.* = Potentialgefäll(e). **-gesetz**, *n.* (*Math.*) law of exponents.
**potenzieren**, *v.t.* (*Math.*) raise to a higher power.
**Potenzreihe**, *f.* (*Math.*) exponential series; power series.
**Poterieguss**, *m.* heavy earthenware.
**Pottasche**, *f.* potash (potassium carbonate). **-lauge**, *f.* potash lye. **-lösung**, *f.* potash solution. **-(n)fluss**, *m.* crude potash (from ashes). **-(n)siederei**, *f.* potash factory.
**pottecht**, *a.* (*Dyeing*) fast to potting.
**Pottfisch**, *m.* sperm whale. **-öl**, *n.*, **-tran**, *m.* sperm oil.
**pottingecht**, *a.* (*Textiles*) fast to potting.
**Pottlot**, *n.* graphite, black lead.
**Poussiere**, *f.* (*Zinc*) blue powder.
**poussieren**, *v.t.* push, promote; court.
**Pozzolan**, *n.*, **Pozzolanerde**, *f.* pozzuolana.
**Pracht**, *f.* pomp, splendor, magnificence, display. **-ausgabe**, *f.* edition de luxe.
**prächtig, prachtvoll**, *a.* splendid, magnificent, sumptuous.
**Präci-**. see Präzi-.
**pract-**. see prakt-.
**prädisponieren**, *v.t.* predispose.

**Prädissoziation,** *f.* predissociation.
**Präexistenz,** *f.* preëxistence.
**prägbar,** *a.* capable of being stamped.
**Präge-anstalt,** *f.* mint. **-form,** *f.* (stamping) mold, matrix.
**prägen,** *v.t.* stamp, coin, imprint, emboss.
**Prägepapier,** *n.* embossing (or embossed) paper.
**Präglobulin,** *n.* preglobulin.
**prägnant,** *a.* pregnant, significant.
**Prägung,** *f.* stamping; coinage, coinage.
**prähistorisch,** *a.* prehistoric.
**prahlen,** *v.i.* boast; (of colors) be loud.
**Präjudiz,** *f.* prejudice; (legal) precedent.
**präjudizieren,** *v.i.* prejudge.
**präkambrisch,** *a.* (*Geol.*) Pre-Cambrian.
**prakt.,** *abbrev.* (praktisch) practical.
**Praktikant,** *m.* laboratory worker, laboratory student, assistant; practitioner.
**Praktiker,** *m.* practician, experienced person, expert.
**Praktikum,** *n.* practice; practical course, laboratory course; laboratory manual.
**praktisch,** *a.* practical; applied; practised.
**praktizieren,** *v.t.* practice.
**prall,** *a.* tight, taut, stretched, tense; plump.
**Prall,** *m.* shock; rebound; reflection. **-blech,** *n.* deflecting plate, baffle. **-elektrode,** *f.* reflecting electrode.
**prallen,** *v.i.* bounce, bound, rebound; be reflected.
**Prall-heit,** *f.* tightness, tenseness, tension; plumpness. **-kraft,** *f.* resiliency; elasticity. **-wand,** *f.* baffle. **-winkel,** *m.* angle of reflection.
**Prämie,** *f.* premium, prize; bonus.
**prangen,** *v.i.* make a show, be resplendent, shine.
**Pranke,** *f.* clutch; claw; paw.
**Präparat,** *n.* preparation.
**Präparaten-glas,** *n.* preparation glass. **-kunde,** *f.* knowledge relating to preparations. **-röhrchen,** *n.* preparation tube, specimen tube. **-schachtel,** *f.* (*Micros.*) slide box.
**präparativ,** *a.* relating to preparation(s), preparative.
**Präparier-.** preparing; dissecting. **-arbeit,** *f.* (*Micros.*) dissecting work.
**präparieren,** *v.t.* prepare; dissect. — **präpariertes Papier,** (*Photog.*) sensitized paper.
**Präparier-lupe,** *f.* (*Biol.*) dissecting lens or magnifier. **-nadel,** *f.* (*Biol.*) dissecting needle. **-salz,** *n.* preparing salt (sodium stannate).
**Prasenstein, Prasem,** *m.* prase (green variety of quartz).
**präsentieren,** *v.t.* present.
**Praseodym,** *n.* praseodymium.
**Praseokobaltsalz,** *n.* praseocobaltic salt.
**Präservativ,** *n.* preservative.
**Präserven,** *n.pl.* preserves.
**präservieren,** *v.t.* preserve.
**Präservierung,** *f.* preservation, preserving.
**Präservierungsmittel,** *n.* preservative.
**prasseln,** *v.i.* crackle, rustle, rattle.
**Pratze,** *f.* claw; arm, lug, bracket.
**Präventivimpfung,** *f.* preventive inoculation.
**praxi, in.** in practice.
**Praxis,** *f.* practice. **-versuch,** *m.* experiment in practice.
**präzessieren, präzedieren,** *v.i.* precess.
**Präzession,** *f.* precession.
**Präzipitat,** *n.& m.* precipitate.
**Präzipitation,** *f.* precipitation.
**Präzipitationswärme,** *f.* heat of precipitation.
**Präzipitierbottich,** *m.* precipitating vat.
**präzipitieren,** *v.t.* precipitate.
**Präzipitier-fass,** *n.* precipitating cask or vat. **-gefäss,** *n.* precipitating vessel. **-mittel,** *n.* precipitant. **-zylinder,** *m.* precipitating jar.
**Präzipitin,** *n.* precipitin.
**präzis,** *a.* precise.
**präzisieren,** *v.t.* render precise, define.
**Präzision,** *f.* precision.
**Präzisions-arbeit,** *f.* precision work. **-gewicht,** *n.* precision weight. **-messung,** *f.* precision measurement. **-wa(a)ge,** *f.* balance of precision, precision balance.
**Preis,** *m.* price; value; rate; prize; praise.
**Preiselbeere,** *f.* mountain cranberry.
**preisen,** *v.t.* praise, commend.
**preisgeben,** *v.t.* give over, give up, expose.
**Preisselbeere,** *f.* mountain cranberry.
**preiswert,** *a.* praiseworthy; worth the price.
**prekär,** *a.* precarious.
**Prellblock,** *m.* stop block, stop.
**prellen,** *v.t.* make to rebound; cushion, buffer; toss; cheat. — *v.i.* bounce; rebound.
**Prell-kraft,** *f.* resiliency. **-platte,** *f.* baffle plate, baffle. **-stein,** *m.* curbstone. **-stoss,** *m.* rebound; bump.
**Press-.** pressed, compressed, expressed, pressing, press; glazed. **-artikel,** *m.* (*Rubber*) press-cured article(s).
**pressbar,** *a.* pressable.
**Press-bernstein,** *m.* amberoid, ambroid. **-beutel,** *m.* pressing bag, press bag, filter bag (for presses). **-blei,** *n.* (*Metal.*) inferior lead obtained in the Carinthian process after the addition of charcoal. **-druck,** *m.* pressing pressure, press power.
**Presse,** *f.* press; gloss.
**pressen,** *v.t.* press, compress; stamp; force; squeeze, pinch, cram.
**Presser,** *m.* presser; compressor; pressman.
**Press-erzeugnis,** *n.* pressings. **-fehler,** *m.* molding defect. **-filter,** *n.* pressure filter, press filter. **-flüssigkeit,** *f.* pressure fluid. **-form,** *f.* press(ure) mold, compression mold. **-gas,** *n.* compressed gas. **-glanz,** *m.* gloss from

pressing. **-glas,** *n.* pressed glass. **-glimmer,** *m.* pressed mica. **-guss,** *m.* pressure casting. **-hefe,** *f.* pressed yeast, compressed yeast. **-holz,** *n.* laminated wood.

**Pression,** *f.* pressure.

**Press-kohle,** *f.* pressed charcoal; pressed coal, briquet(te). **-körper,** *m.* pressed object or article. **-kuchen,** *m.* press cake; briquet(te). **-lauge,** *f.* expressed liquor. **-ling,** *m.* something pressed, pressed article, as a briquet(te) or molding; (*pl.*, *Sugar*) expressed beet pulp. **-luft,** *f.* compressed air. **-luftleitung,** *f.* compressed-air line. **-luftmaschine,** *f.* air compressor. **-luftschlauch,** *m.* compressed-air hose. **-luftzerstäuber,** *m.* compressed-air atomizer. **-masse,** *f.* molded mass or article; molding composition, plastic mass. **-mischung,** *f.* molding mixture. **-most,** *m.* expressed fruit juice, must. **-mühle,** *f.* pressing mill. **-naht,** *f.* burr (on molded articles). **-öl,** *n.* oil obtained by pressure, (often) fixed oil; oil under pressure, forced-feed oil, hydraulic oil. **-ölschmierung,** *f.* forced oil lubrication. **-platte,** *f.* pressed plate, specif. phonograph record.

**presspolieren,** *v.t.* burnish.

**Press-pulver,** *n.* molding powder. **-rückstand,** *m.* expressed residue. **-sack,** *m.* = Pressbeutel. **-saft,** *m.* expressed juice, press juice. **-schmierung,** *f.* forced-feed lubrication. **-schraube,** *f.* pressure screw, thrust screw. **-sitz,** *m.* forced fit, driving fit. **-span,** *m.* pressboard. **-stahl,** *m.* pressed steel. **-stein,** *m.* briquet(te). **-stoff,** *m.* pressed material, molding composition, plastic. **-stück,** *m.* pressed piece, molded piece. **-talg,** *m.* pressed tallow. **-teil,** *m.* pressed part, molded part. **-torf,** *m.* pressed peat. **-tuch,** *n.* filter cloth (for presses).

**Pressung,** *f.* pressure, pressing, compression.

**Press-verfahren,** *n.* pressing process; molding technic. **-vulkanisation,** *f.* (*Rubber*) press cure. **-walze,** *f.* press roll. **-ziegel,** *m.* pressed brick. **-zucker,** *m.* compressed sugar.

**Preussen,** *n.* Prussia.

**preussisch,** *a.* Prussian.

**Preussisch-blau,** *n.* Prussian blue. **-braun,** *n.* Prussian brown.

**prickeln,** *v.t.* prickle, prick, sting. — **prickelnd,** *p.a.* sharp, pungent.

**Priemtabak,** *m.* chewing tobacco.

**pries,** *pret.* (of preisen) praised.

**prim.,** *abbrev.* (primär) primary.

**Prima-.** of first, prime, or best quality.

**primär,** *a.* primary.

**Primär-akt,** *m.* primary act. **-element,** *n.* (*Elec.*) primary cell. **-fleck,** *m.* primary spot. **-gefüge,** *n.* primary structure or texture. **-kreis,** *m.* primary circuit. **-linie,** *f.* primary line. **-spannung,** *f.* (*Elec.*) primary voltage. **-strahl,** *m.* (*Optics*) primary ray. **-strahlung,** *f.* primary radiation. **-strom,** *m.* primary current.

**Prima-soda,** *f.* refined soda. **-sprit,** *m.* refined spirit. **-ware,** *f.* prime or superior article or goods.

**Primel,** *f.* primrose. **-kratzstoff,** *m.* an unpleasant-tasting substance in primrose root.

**Primzahl,** *f.* prime number.

**Princip,** *n.* principle.

**Prinz,** *m.* prince.

**Prinzip,** *n.* principle.

**prinzipiell,** *a.* on principle, in principle.

**Prinzipium,** *n.* principle.

**Prinzipskizze,** *f.* diagrammatic sketch.

**Prinzmetall,** *n.* Prince's metal, Prince Rupert's metal.

**Priorität,** *f.* priority.

**Prioritäts-beleg,** *n.* certificate of priority. **-recht,** *n.* priority right.

**Prise,** *f.* prize; pinch.

**Prisma,** *n.* prism.

**prisma-ähnlich, -artig,** *a.* prism-like, prismoidal. **-förmig,** *a.* prism-shaped, prismatic.

**prismatisch,** *a.* prismatic.

**prismatoidförmig,** *a.* prismatoidal.

**Prismenfläche,** *f.* prismatic face.

**prismenförmig,** *a.* prism-shaped, prismatic.

**Prismen-glas,** *n.* prism glass. **-kante,** *f.* prismatic edge. **-spektrum,** *n.* prismatic spectrum.

**Pritsche,** *f.* bat; bed, platform; (*Alum*) washing floor; (*Dyeing*) stillage (to support goods while drying).

**Privatdozent,** *m.* a licensed university lecturer receiving student fees but no salary.

**pro,** *prep.* pro, per.

**pro anal.,** *abbrev.* (pro analyse) for analysis.

**probat,** *a.* proved, tried.

**Probe,** *f.* test; assay; sample, specimen; pattern; proof; trial, probation; rehearsal.

**Probe-.** testing, trial, probationary; sampling. **-abdruck,** *m.* proof, proof print. **-bogen,** *m.* proof sheet, proof. **-brand,** *m.* fire test. **-brühe,** *f.* (*Dyeing*) test bath, dye test. **-druck,** *m.* (printer's) proof. **-entnahme,** *f.* sample taking, sampling. **-essig,** *m.* proof vinegar. **-färbung,** *f.* test dyeing. **-fläche,** *f.* sample area, test area. **-fläschchen,** *n.* sampling bottle. **-flasche,** *f.* sample bottle, specimen bottle. **-flüssigkeit,** *f.* test liquid, test liquor.

**probegemäss,** *a.* according to sample or pattern.

**Probe-gewicht,** *n.* test weight, standard weight. **-glas,** *n.* sample glass, sample tube, specimen tube; test glass; test tube. **-gold,** *n.* standard gold. **-gut,** *n.* sample material, sample. **-hahn,** *m.* try cock, gage cock, bleeder.

**probehaltig,** *a.* proof, standard.

**Probe-kolben,** *m.* test flask; sample flask. **-korn,** *n.* assay button. **-körper,** *m.* test body, test specimen; sample. **-löffel,** *m.* assay spoon. **-machen,** *n.* testing, assaying. **-mass,** *n.* standard measure.

**probemässig,** *a.* according to sample.

**Probe-münze,** *f.* proof coin. **-muster,** *n.* sample for testing.

**proben,** *v.t.* test; assay; try; prove.

**Probe-nadel,** *f.* touch needle. **-nahme,** *f.* sampling; sample. **-nehmen,** *n.* sampling. **-nehmer,** *m.* sampler.

**Proben-glas,** *n.* specimen glass, specimen tube. **-stecher,** *m.* = Probestecher.

**Probe-objekt,** *n.* specimen; test piece. **-papier,** *n.* test paper.

**Prober,** *m.* tester, specif. assayer.

**Probe-rohr, -röhrchen,** *n.*, **-röhre,** *f.* test tube; (*Mach.*) trial pipe. **-säure,** *f.* test acid, standard acid. **-schachtel,** *f.* sample box. **-scherbe,** *f.*, **-scherben,** *m.* cupel; (*Ceram.*) trial piece. **-silber,** *n.* standard silver. **-spiritus,** *m.* proof spirit. **-stab,** *m.* test rod or bar, trial rod. **-stange,** *f.* test rod, test stick, test bar. **-stecher,** *m.* sampler (inserted into the material to be sampled); (for liquids) thief tube; (*Sugar*) proof stick. **-stein,** *m.* touchstone; sample stone. **-stoff,** *m.* sample material. **-stück,** *n.* specimen, sample; test piece. **-tiegel,** *m.* assay crucible (see Tüte); cupel. **-wa(a)ge,** *f.* assay balance. **-weingeist,** *m.* proof spirit.

**probeweise,** *adv.* by way of testing, on trial, on approval.

**Probe-ziehen,** *n.* sampling. **-zieher,** *m.* sampler. **-zinn,** *n.* standard tin. **-zylinder,** *m.* trial jar; test tube.

**Probhahn,** *m.* try cock, gage cock.

**Probier-.** testing, test; assaying, assay. **-blei,** *n.* test lead, assay lead.

**probieren,** *v.t.* test; assay; try; prove.

**Probierer,** *m.* tester, assayer, analyst.

**Probier-gefäss,** *n.* testing (or assaying) vessel. **-geräte,** *n.pl.*, **-gerätschaften,** *f.pl.* assaying apparatus. **-gewicht,** *n.* assay weight. **-glas,** *n.* test tube. **-glätte,** *f.* test litharge. **-gold,** *n.* standard gold. **-hahn,** *m.* try cock, gage cock, bleeder. **-kluft,** *f.* assayer's tongs. **-korn,** *n.* assay button. **-kunst,** *f.* assaying. **-laboratorium,** *n.* assay laboratory. **-löffel,** *m.* assay spoon. **-metall,** *n.* test metal. **-methode,** *f.* method of trial or experiment. **-nadel,** *f.* touch needle. **-ofen,** *m.* assay furnace. **-papier,** *n.* test paper. **-röhre,** *f.* test tube. **-röhrengestell,** *n.* test-tube rack. **-scherben,** *m.* = Probescherben. **-stein,** *m.* touchstone. **-tiegel,** *m.* = Probetiegel. **-tüte, -tute, -tutte,** *f.* assay crucible. See Tüte. **-ventil,** *n.* gage valve, test valve. **-verfahren,** *n.* testing (or assaying) process or method. **-wa(a)ge,** *f.* assay balance. **-zange,** *f.* assayer's tongs.

**proc.,** *abbrev.* (procentig) per cent.

**Proc.,** *abbrev.* (Procent) per cent.

**Procent,** *n.* per cent. See Prozent-.

**procentig,** *a.* per cent, percentage.

**Prod.,** *abbrev.* (Produkt) product.

**Produkt,** *n.* product; produce.

**Produktions-fähigkeit,** *f.* productiveness, productivity. **-leistung,** *f.* productive capacity.

**Produktivität,** *f.* productivity.

**Produzent,** *m.* producer, grower.

**produzieren,** *v.t.* produce.

**Professorat,** *n.* professorship.

**professor-haft, -isch,** *a.* professorial.

**Professorschaft, Professur,** *f.* professorship.

**Profileisen,** *n.* sectional iron or steel.

**profilieren,** *v.t.* profile, form, shape; streamline.

**Profilprüfer,** *m.* profilometer.

**projektieren,** *v.t.* project; plan, design; purpose.

**projizieren,** *v.t.* project.

**promillig,** *a.* per mille, by the thousand (often expressed 0/00).

**promovieren,** *v.t. & i.* graduate (as a doctor).

**prononcieren,** *v.t.* pronounce.

**Propansäure,** *f.* propanoic (propionic) acid.

**prophylaktisch,** *a.* prophylactic.

**Prophylaxe,** *f.* prophylaxis.

**Propiolsäure,** *f.* propiolic acid.

**propionsauer,** *a.* of propionic acid, propionate of.

**Propionsäure,** *f.* propionic acid.

**Propiopersäure,** *f.* per(oxy)propionic acid.

**Proportionalität,** *f.* proportionality.

**proportionieren,** *v.t.* proportionate, proportion.

**Propyl-itisierung,** *f.* (*Petrog.*) propylitization. **-wasserstoff,** *m.* propyl hydride, propane.

**Prospekt,** *m.* prospectus; prospect.

**prosthetisch,** *a.* prosthetic.

**proteinhaltig,** *a.* containing protein.

**Protein-körper,** *m.* protein substance, protein. **-säure,** *f.* proteic acid. **-silber,** *n.* silver proteinate. **-stoff,** *m.* protein substance, protein. **-urie,** *f.* albuminuria. **-verbindung,** *f.* protein compound.

**Proteolyse,** *f.* proteolysis.

**proteolytisch,** *a.* proteolytic.

**Proto-cocasäure,** *f.* protococaic acid. **-katechusäure,** *f.* protocatechuic acid.

**Protokoll,** *n.* minutes, record; protocol.

**Protonen-beschleunigung,** *f.* acceleration of protons. **-geschoss,** *n.* proton projectile. **-wanderung,** *f.* traveling of protons.

**Protoplasma-bewegung,** *f.* protoplasmic motion. **-körper,** *m.* protoplasmic body. **-strahl,** *m.* protoplasmic ray.

**Protoxyd,** *n.* protoxide.

**Protozoen,** *n.pl.* (*Zoöl.*) Protozoa.
**protozoisch,** *a.* protozoan, protozoic.
**Provence(r)öl,** *n.* olive oil.
**Provenienz,** *f.* provenience, source, origin.
**Proviant,** *m.* provisions, victuals.
**Provision,** *f.* provision; commission.
**Provisor,** *m.* pharmacist's assistant, dispenser.
**provisorisch,** *a.* provisional.
**proz.,** *abbrev.* (prozentig) per cent.
**Proz.,** *abbrev.* (Prozent) per cent.
**Prozedur,** *f.* procedure.
**Prozent,** *n.* per cent. **-gehalt,** *m.* per cent content, percentage.
**prozentig, prozentisch,** *a.* per cent, percentage.
**Prozent-satz,** *m.* percentage. **-teilung,** *f.* percentage scale.
**prozentual,** *a.* per cent, percentage.
**Prozess,** *m.* process.
**prozessieren,** *v.i.* litigate.
**Prüf-anstalt,** *f.* testing laboratory. **-apparat,** *m.* testing apparatus, tester. **-arbeit,** *f.* testing, assaying, checking; experimenting.
**prüfbar,** *a.* capable of being tested, assayed, tried or examined.
**Prüfdruck,** *m.* test pressure.
**prüfen,** *v.t.* test; assay; try; prove; taste (wine, etc.); examine, check, control, inspect.
**Prüfer,** *m.* tester; meter; assayer; examiner.
**Prüf-ergebnis,** *n.* test result. **-feld,** *n.* proving ground; test floor. **-gerät,** *n.* testing apparatus or instrument, tester. **-glas,** *n.* test glass; test tube. **-hahn,** *m.* try cock, gage cock, test cock. **-kelch,** *m.* test glass, reaction glass. **-ling,** *m.* test sample, test piece, test specimen; examinee. **-mittel,** *n.* testing agent. **-nadel,** *f.* testing needle. **-rohr,** *n.*, **-röhre,** *f.* testing tube. **-scheibe,** *f.* test disk. **-stein,** *m.* touchstone. **-stöpsel,** *m.* test plug. **-stück,** *n.* test piece, test specimen.
**Prüfung,** *f.* test, testing, assay, trial, examination, proof, control, inspection.
**Prüfungs-ergebnis,** *n.* test result. **-methode,** *f.* method of testing. **-mittel,** *n.* testing agent, means for testing or examining. **-schein,** *m.* certificate (that a thing has been tested). **-schrift,** *f.* (university) thesis. **-stein,** *m.* touchstone.
**Prüf-verfahren,** *n.* testing method or process. **-zeichen,** *n.* test mark.
**Prügel,** *m.* cudgel, club; blow; drubbing.
**Prunellensalz, Prunellsalz,** *n.* sal prunelle (fused potassium nitrate).
**Prunk,** *m.* pomp, state, show.
**PS, P.S.,** *abbrev.* (Pferdestärke) horsepower, H.P.
**Pseudo-harnsäure,** *f.* pseudouric acid. **-harnstoff,** *m.* pseudourea. **-katalysator,** *m.* pseudocatalyst. **-katalyse,** *f.* pseudocatalysis.
**pseudokatalytisch,** *a.* pseudocatalytic.
**Pseudo-lösung,** *f.* pseudo solution. **-merie,** *f* pseudomerism.
**pseudomorph,** *a.* pseudomorphous.
**Pseudo-morphose,** *f.* pseudomorphosis; pseudomorph. **-säure,** *f.* pseudo acid. **-schwefelzyan,** *n.* pseudothiocyanogen.
**Pst.,** *abbrev.* (Pferdestärke) horsepower.
**Psylla-alkohol,** *m.* psyllic alcohol. **-säure,** *f.* psyllic acid.
**publizieren,** *v.t.* publish.
**Puddel-arbeiter,** *m.* puddler. **-bett,** *n.* = Puddelsohle. **-eisen,** *n.* puddled iron. **-luppe,** *f.* puddle-ball.
**puddeln,** *v.t.* puddle.
**Puddel-ofen,** *m.* puddling furnace. **-prozess,** *m.* puddling process. **-roheisen,** *n.* forge pig (iron). **-schlacke,** *f.* puddling slag, puddle cinder. **-sohle,** *f.* puddling-furnace bed. **-spiegel,** *m.* specular forge pig (iron). **-spitze,** *f.* puddler's paddle. **-stab,** *m.* puddle-bar. **-stahl,** *m.* puddled steel. **-verfahren,** *n.* puddling process, puddling. **-walze,** *f.* puddle roll. **-werk,** *n.* puddling works.
**Puddingstein,** *m.* pudding stone, conglomerate.
**Pudel,** *m.* poodle; blunder, miss.
**Puder,** *m.* powder.
**puderig,** *a.* powdery.
**pudern,** *v.t.* powder.
**Puderzucker,** *m.* powdered sugar.
**pudrig,** *a.* powdery.
**Puff,** *m.* blow, thump; pop, bang; puff.
**puffen,** *v.i.* puff (up), swell (up); pop.
**Puffer,** *m.* buffer; cushion, pad; bumper. **-lösung,** *f.* buffer solution.
**puffern,** *v.t.* buffer; cushion.
**Puffer-salz,** *n.* buffer salt. **-säure,** *f.* buffer acid. **-system,** *n.* buffer system.
**Pufferung,** *f.* buffering; cushioning.
**Puffer-wert,** *m.* buffer value. **-wirkung,** *f.* buffer action or effect.
**Pukallmasse,** *n.*, **Pukallsche Masse.** Pukall mass or composition (a porous porcelain for cells).
**Pulpe,** *f.* pulp.
**Puls,** *m.* pulse. **-ader,** *f.* artery. **-aderblut,** *n.* arterial blood. **-glas,** *n.*, **-hammer,** *m.* cryophorus.
**pulsieren, pulsen,** *v.i.* pulsate. — **pulsierend,** *p.a.* pulsating; intermittent.
**Pulsschlag,** *m.* pulse beat, pulsation, pulse.
**Pulsung,** *f.* pulsation, pulsing.
**Pulszahl,** *f.* pulse rate.
**Pult,** *n.* desk. **-feuerung,** *f.* firing on stepped grate bars. **-ofen,** *m.* (*Metal.*) back-flame hearth.
**Pulver,** *n.* powder. **-alitieren,** *n.* aluminizing (calorizing) with a powder.
**pulverartig,** *a.* powdery, pulverulent.

**Pulver-band,** *m.* (*Expl.*) powder strand. **-blättchen,** *n.* (*Expl.*) powder flake, powder grain. **-brennzündung,** *f.* powder-train ignition. **-dampf,** *m.* powder smoke. **-diagramm,** *n.* powder pattern. **-fabrik,** *f.* powder factory. **-fabrikation,** *f.* powder manufacture. **-fass,** *n.* powder cask, powder keg. **-flasche,** *f.* powder bottle (wide-mouthed bottle).

**pulverförmig,** *a.* in the form of powder, powdery, pulverulent.

**Pulver-förmigkeit,** *f.* powderiness, pulverulence. **-gas,** *n.* gas from burned powder. **-glas,** *n.* = Pulverflasche. **-holz,** *n.* wood for gunpowder.

**pulverig,** *a.* powdery, pulverulent.

**pulverisierbar,** *a.* pulverable, pulverizable.

**pulverisieren,** *v.t.* powder, pulverize.

**Pulver-isiermühle,** *f.* pulverizing mill, pulverizer. **-isierung,** *f.* pulverization. **-kapsel,** *f.* powder capsule; small powder scoop. **-korn,** *n.* grain of powder. **-kuchen,** *m.* (*Gunpowder*) press cake. **-ladung,** *f.* powder charge. **-masse,** *f.* powder composition. **-mehl,** *n.* mealed powder. **-mörser,** *m.* powder mortar, mortar for powdering. **-mühle,** *f.* powder mill.

**pulvern,** *v.t.* powder, pulverize.

**Pulver-presskuchen,** *m.* = Pulverkuchen. **-pressling,** *m.* (piece of) compressed powder. **-probe,** *f.* powder test; powder sample. **-probiermörser,** *m.* small powder mortar. **-rakete,** *f.* powder rocket. **-rauch,** *m.* powder smoke. **-satz,** *m.* powder composition; powder train; powder pellet. **-schlag,** *m.* (*Pyro.*) cracker, petard. **-seele,** *f.* (*Expl.*) powder core. **-sprengstoff,** *m.* powder explosive, low explosive. **-staub,** *m.* powder dust. **-streifen,** *m.* (*Expl.*) powder strand. **-tonne,** *f.* powder cask, powder keg. **-trichter,** *m.* powder funnel.

**pulvertrocken,** *a.* dry as powder.

**Pulverung,** *f.* powdering, pulverization.

**Pulver-vertreibladung,** *f.* propellent powder charge. **-zementieren,** *n.* (*Metal.*) cementation using a powder. **-zerstäuber,** *m.* dusting apparatus. **-zucker,** *m.* powdered sugar.

**Pumpe,** *f.* pump.

**pumpen,** *v.t.* pump.

**Pumpen-benzin,** *n.* pump gasoline, pump petrol. **-kolben,** *m.* pump piston. **-kühlung,** *f.* forced-circulation cooling.

**punkt,** *adv.* punctually; exactly, just.

**Punkt,** *m.* point; dot; spot, speck; period.

**Pünktchen,** *n.* dot, speck.

**punkten,** *v.t.* dot; spot-weld.

**punkt-förmig,** *a.* in the form of points or a point, point-like, punctiform. **-frei,** *a.* (*Dyeing*) free from spots or specks.

**punktieren,** *v.t.* point; dot; punctuate; speckle, spot, stipple.

**Punktion,** *f.* puncturing, puncture.

**Punktionsflüssigkeit,** *f.* puncture exudate.

**Punktkathode,** *f.* point source cathode, crater cathode.

**pünktlich,** *a.* punctual; exact.

**Punktmechanik,** *f.* point mechanics, mechanics of particles.

**punktmechanisch,** *a.* pertaining to the mechanics of particles, point-mechanical.

**Punkt-reihe,** *f.* series of points or dots. **-schweissung,** *f.* spot welding. **-strich,** *m.* semicolon.

**punktsymmetrisch,** *a.* of or pertaining to point symmetry, point-symmetrical.

**punktuell,** *a.* (*Optics*) point-focal.

**Punktum,** *n.* period.

**Punktur,** *f.* puncture.

**punktursicher,** *a.* puncture-resisting, puncture-proof.

**punktweise,** *adv.* point by point.

**Punsch,** *m.* punch (the drink).

**Punzen,** *m.* punch (the tool).

**Pupille,** *f.* pupil.

**Pupillenerweiterung,** *f.* dilation of the pupil.

**Puppe,** *f.* pupa; cocoon; doll; puppet; dummy.

**Puppenkokon,** *n.* cocoon.

**Purganz,** *f.* purgative.

**purgieren,** *v.t.* & *i.* purge; boil off (silk) with soap.

**Purgier-harz,** *n.* scammony. **-kassie, -kassia,** *f.* purging cassia. **-korn,** *n.* purging grain or seed; **(grosses)** castor bean; **(kleines)** croton seed. **-kraut,** *n.* purgative herb, specif. hedge hyssop. **-lein,** *n.* purging flax. **-mittel,** *n.* purgative. **-nuss,** *f.* purging nut, physic nut. **-paradiesapfel,** *m.* colocynth. **-salz,** *n.* purgative salt.

**purifizieren,** *v.t.* purify.

**Purin-basen,** *f.pl.* purine bases. **-gruppe,** *f.* purine group.

**Purpur,** *m.* purple.

**purpurblau,** *a.* purple-blue.

**Purpureo-kobaltverbindung,** *f.* purpureocobaltic compound, chloropentamminecobalt(III) compound. **-verbindung,** *f.* purpureo compound.

**Purpur-erz,** *n.* purple ore, blue billy. **-farbe,** *f.* purple color, purple.

**purpur-farben, -farbig,** *a.* purple-colored.

**Purpur-färbung,** *f.* purple coloring. **-holz,** *n.* violet wood. **-karmin,** *m.* purple carmine, murexide. **-lack,** *m.* purple lake, specif. madder purple. **-muschel,** *f.* purple shell.

**purpurn,** *a.* purple.

**purpurrot,** *a.* purple-red, crimson.

**purpursauer,** *a.* purpurate of.

**Purpur-säure,** *f.* purpuric acid. **-schwefelsäure,** *f.* sulfopurpuric acid.

**purzeln,** *v.i.* tumble.

**Pustel,** *f.* pustule, pimple; blotch.
**pustel-ähnlich, -artig,** *a.* pustular.
**pusten,** *v.i.* blow; pant. — *v.t.* blow.
**Pust-lampe,** *f.* blowlamp, blowtorch. **-probe,** *f.* blow test, bubble test. **-rohr,** *n.* blowpipe; blowgun. **-span,** *m.* skimmer.
**Puter,** *m.* turkey.
**Putz,** *m.* plaster, plastering; dress, ornament. **-baumwolle,** *f.* cotton waste (for cleaning).
**putzen,** *v.t.* clean, cleanse, scour, polish, trim, dress; plaster.
**Putzerei,** *f.* dressing; cleaning.
**Putz-kalk,** *m.* plastering lime; stucco; polishing chalk. **-lage,** *f.* coat of plaster. **-lappen,** *m.* cleaning (or polishing) rag. **-leder,** *n.* chamois (leather). **-macherei,** *f.* millinery. **-maschine,** *f.* cleaning machine. **-mittel,** *n.* cleaning or polishing agent or material. **-öl,** *n.* polishing oil, cleaning oil. **-präparat,** *n.* polishing preparation, polish. **-pulver,** *n.* cleaning powder, polishing powder. **-sand,** *m.* cleaning sand, abrasive sand. **-schicht,** *f.* coat of plaster. **-stein,** *m.* cleaning or polishing stone or brick. **-tisch,** *m.* dressing table; (*Ceram.*) cleaning table. **-trommel,** *f.* tumbling barrel. **-tuch,** *n.* cloth for cleaning or polishing, sponge cloth. **-wasser,** *n.* dilute acid for scouring. **-wirkung,** *f.* cleaning action or effect. **-wolle,** *f.* (*Mach.*) waste.
**Puzzolane, Puzzolanerde,** *f.* pozzuolana.
**Puzzolanzement,** *m.* pozzuolana cement.
**Puzzuolanerde,** *f.* pozzuolana.
**Pyämie,** *f.* pyemia.
**pyämisch,** *a.* pyemic.
**pyogen,** *a.* pyogenic.
**Pyorrhöe,** *f.* pyorrhea.
**pyramidenförmig,** *a.* pyramidal.
**Pyramiden-oktaeder,** *n.* (*Cryst.*) trisoctahedron. **-stumpf,** *m.* frustum of a pyramid. **-würfel,** *m.* tetrahexahedron.
**Pyrenchinon,** *n.* pyrenequinone.
**Pyritabbrände,** *m.pl.* pyrites cinders.
**pyritartig,** *a.* pyritic.
**Pyriterz,** *n.* pyritic ore.
**pyrithaltig,** *a.* pyritiferous.
**pyritisch,** *a.* pyritic.
**pyritisieren,** *v.t.* pyritize.
**Pyritisierung,** *f.* pyritization.
**Pyritofen,** *m.* pyrites oven, pyrites burner.
**Pyritschwefel,** *m.* pyritic sulfur.
**Pyro-antimonsäure,** *f.* pyroantimonic acid. **-arsensäure,** *f.* pyroarsenic acid.
**pyrochemisch,** *a.* pyrochemical.
**Pyrochinin,** *n.* pyroquinine.
**pyroelektrisch,** *a.* pyroelectric.
**Pyro-elektrizität,** *f.* pyroelectricity. **-gallolgerbstoff,** *m.* pyrogallol tannin. **-gallussäure,** *f.* pyrogallic acid (pyrogallol).
**pyrogen,** *a.* pyrogenic.
**Pyrokatechin,** *n.* pyrocatechol. **-gerbstoff,** *m.* pyrocatechol tannin.
**pyroklastisch,** *a.* pyroclastic.
**Pyrolösung,** *f.* (*Photog.*) pyro(gallol) solution.
**Pyrolyse,** *f.* pyrolysis.
**pyrolytisch,** *a.* pyrolytic.
**pyrometrisch,** *a.* pyrometric.
**Pyroperjodsäure,** *f.* pyroperiodic acid, dimesoperiodic acid ($H_4I_2O_9$).
**Pyrophor,** *n.* pyrophorus.
**pyro-phor, -phorisch,** *a.* pyrophoric. **-phosphorig,** *a.* pyrophosphorous. **-phosphorsauer,** *a.* of or combined with pyrophosphoric acid, pyrophosphate of.
**Pyro-phosphorsäure,** *f.* pyrophosphoric acid. **-säure,** *f.* pyro acid. **-schleimsäure,** *f.* pyromucic acid, furoic acid. **-schwefelsäure,** *f.* pyrosulfuric acid, disulfuric acid ($H_2S_2O_7$).
**pyroschweflig,** *a.* pyrosulfurous.
**Pyrotechnik,** *f.* pyrotechnics, pyrotechny.
**pyrotechnisch,** *a.* pyrotechnic. — **pyrotechnische Waren,** fireworks.
**Pyro-traubensäure,** *f.* pyroracemic acid, pyruvic acid. **-weinsäure,** *f.* pyrotartaric acid.
**Pyrrol,** *n.* pyrrole. **-blau,** *n.* pyrrole blue.

# Q

**q.,** *abbrev.* (quadrat) square (esp., in qcm., etc.).
**qcm.,** *abbrev.* square centimeter(s), sq. cm.
**qdm.,** *abbrev.* square decimeter(s), sq. dm.
**qkm.,** *abbrev.* square kilometer(s), sq. km.
**qm.,** *abbrev.* square meter(s), sq. m.
**qmm.,** *abbrev.* square millimeter(s), sq. mm.
**Q.S., Q.-S.,** *abbrev.* (Quecksilbersäule) mercury column; (Quecksilberstand) mercury level.
**quabbeln,** *v.i.* shake, quiver; be flabby.
**Quacksalber,** *m.* quack, charlatan.
**Quader,** *m.* parallelepiped; ashlar; freestone. **-stein,** *m.* ashlar; freestone.
**Quadrat,** *n.* square.
**quadratförmig,** *a.* square; quadratic.
**Quadratfuss,** *m.* square foot.
**quadratisch,** *a.* square; quadratic; (*Cryst.*) tetragonal.
**Quadrat-meter,** *m.* square meter. **-pyramide,** *f.* square pyramid. **-wurzel,** *f.* square root. **-zahl,** *f.* square number, square. **-zentimeter,** *m.* square centimeter. **-zoll,** *m.* square inch.
**quadrieren,** *v.t.* square.
**Quadroxyd,** *n.* quadroxide (tetroxide).
**Quadrupolkraft,** *f.* quadrupole force.
**quälen,** *v.t.* mill, crush, disaggregate; torment, worry, afflict, distress.
**qualifizieren,** *v.t. & r.* qualify.
**Qualifizierung,** *f.* qualification.
**Qualität,** *f.* quality.
**Qualitäts-abweichung,** *f.* deviation in quality. **-guss,** *m.* high-grade cast iron. **-leder,** *n.* high-grade leather. **-stahl,** *m.* high-grade steel.
**Qualle,** *f.* jellyfish.
**Qualm,** *m.* dense smoke, vapor.
**qualmen,** *v.i.* emit dense smoke or vapor.
**Quant,** *n.* quantum.
**quanteln,** *v.t.* quantize.
**Quantelung,** *f.* quantizing, quantization.
**Quanten,** *n.pl.* quanta, quantums. **-ausbeute,** *f.* quantum yield. **-bahn,** *f.* quantum orbit. **-bedingung,** *f.* quantum condition. **-empfindlichkeit,** *f.* quantum sensitivity.
**quantenhaft,** *a.* of or pertaining to quanta, in the form of quanta.
**Quantenhypothese,** *f.* quantum hypothesis.
**quantenmässig,** *a.* pertaining to quanta, in relation to quanta.
**Quantenmechanik,** *f.* quantum mechanics.
**quantenmechanisch,** *a.* quantum-mechanical.
**Quantensprung,** *f.* quantum transition, quantum leap or jump.
**quantentheoretisch,** *a.* of or according to the quantum theory.
**Quanten-theorie,** *f.* quantum theory. **-zahl,** *f.* quantum number. **-zustand,** *m.* quantum state.
**-quantig.** -quantum.
**quantisieren,** *v.t.* quantize.
**Quantisierung,** *f.* quantizing, quantization.
**Quantität,** *f.* quantity.
**Quantitätsbestimmung,** *f.* quantitative determination.
**Quantum,** *n.* quantum; quantity, portion, quota. **-ausbeute,** *f.* quantum yield. **-gewicht,** *n.* quantum weight. **-übergang,** *m.* quantum transition, quantum jump. **-zustand,** *m.* quantum state.
**Quarantäne,** *f.* quarantine.
**Quark,** *m.* curd, curds; trash.
**quarkartig, quarkig,** *a.* curd-like, curdy.
**Quart,** *n.* quarto; quart.
**Quartal,** *n.* quarter (of a year).
**quartär,** *a.* quaternary.
**Quartband,** *m.* quarto volume.
**Quarte,** *f.* quarter, fourth.
**Quartier,** *n.* quarter, quarters.
**Quartierung,** *f.* quartation, quartering.
**quartmässig,** *a.* by quartation.
**Quartscheidung,** *f.* separation by quartation.
**Quarz,** *m.* quartz.
**quarz-ähnlich, -artig,** *a.* quartzose, quartzous.
**Quarz-balken,** *m.* quartz beam. **-dreieck,** *n.* quartz triangle. **-druse,** *f.* (*Min.*) quartz druse.
**quarzelektrisch,** *a.* piezoelectric.
**Quarz-faden,** *m.* quartz thread, quartz filament. **-fels,** *m.* quartz rock, quartzite. **-fenster,** *n.* quartz window.
**quarzfrei,** *a.* free from quartz.
**Quarz-gang,** *m.* quartz vein. **-gefäss,** *n.* quartz vessel. **-gerät,** *n.* quartz apparatus, quartz ware. **-glas,** *n.* quartz glass. **-gut,** *n.* quartz ware.
**quarzhaltig,** *a.* quartziferous, quartz-bearing.
**quarzig,** *a.* quartzy, quartzose.
**Quarzit,** *m.* quartzite. **-gestein,** *n.* quartzite rock.
**Quarz-keil,** *m.* (*Optics*) quartz wedge. **-kiesel,** *m.* quartz gravel. **-kristall,** *m.* quartz crystal, rock crystal. **-lager,** *n.* quartz deposit. **-linse,** *f.* quartz lens. **-mehl, -pulver,** *n.* quartz powder. **-rohr,** *n.*, **-röhre,** *f.* quartz tube. **-sand,** *m.* quartz sand. **-scheibe,** *f.*

quartz plate, crystal plate. **-schiefer,** *m.* quartz schist. **-sinter,** *m.* siliceous sinter. **-ziegel,** *m.* quartz brick, Dinas brick.

**quasielastisch,** *a.* quasi-elastic.

**quasiunendlich,** *a.* quasi-infinite.

**Quassiaholz, Quassienholz,** *n.* quassia wood, quassia.

**Quast,** *m.*, **Quaste,** *f.* tassel, tuft; brush.

**quaternär,** *a.* quaternary.

**Quaternärstahl,** *m.* quaternary steel.

**Quebrachit,** *n.* quebrachitol, quebrachite.

**Quebracho-gerbsäure,** *f.* quebracho tannic acid. **-rinde,** *f.* quebracho bark.

**Quecke,** *f.* couch grass; (**rote**) (*Pharm.*) carex root.

**Quecksilber,** *n.* mercury, quicksilver.

**quecksilber-ähnlich, -artig,** *a.* mercury-like, mercurial.

**Quecksilber-arsenitoxyd,** *n.* mercuric arsenite, mercury(II) arsenite. **-azetatoxydul,** *n.* mercurous acetate, mercury(I) acetate. **-bad,** *n.* mercury bath. **-beize,** *f.* mercury mordant; mercury disinfectant. **-beizmittel,** *n.* (*Med.*) mercurial disinfectant. **-bogen,** *m.* mercury arc. **-branderz,** *n.* idrialite. **-bromid,** *n.* mercury bromide, specif. mercuric bromide, mercury(II) bromide. **-chlorid,** *n.* mercury chloride, specif. mercuric chloride, mercury(II) chloride. **-chlorür,** *n.* mercurous chloride, mercury(I) chloride. **-chromatoxyd,** *n.* mercuric chromate, mercury(II) chromate. **-cyanid,** *n.* mercury cyanide, specif. mercuric cyanide, mercury(II) cyanide. **-cyanür,** *n.* mercurous cyanide, mercury(I) cyanide. **-cyanwasserstoffsäure,** *f.* cyanomercuric acid. **-dampf,** *m.* mercury vapor. **-dampfgleichrichter,** *m.* (*Elec.*) mercury (vapor) rectifier. **-dampflampe,** *f.* mercury vapor lamp. **-druck,** *m.* mercury pressure. **-erz,** *n.* mercury ore. **-faden,** *m.* mercury thread. **-fahlerz,** *n.* tetrahedrite containing mercury. **-falle,** *f.* mercury trap. **-füllung,** *f.* mercury filling. **-gefäss,** *n.* mercury vessel. **-gehalt,** *m.* mercury content. **-halogen,** *n.* mercury halide.

**quecksilberhaltig,** *a.* containing mercury, mercurial.

**Quecksilber-hornerz,** *n.* horn quicksilver (native calomel). **-hüttenwesen,** *n.* metallurgy of mercury. **-jodid,** *n.* mercury iodide, specif. mercuric iodide, mercury(II) iodide. **-jodür,** *n.* mercurous iodide, mercury(I) iodide. **-kuppe,** *f.* mercury meniscus. **-lampe,** *f.* mercury lamp. **-lebererz,** *n.* hepatic cinnabar. **-legierung,** *f.* mercury alloy, amalgam. **-licht,** *n.* mercury light. **-luftdruckmesser,** *m.* mercury barometer. **-luftpumpe,** *f.* mercury (air) pump. **-masse,** *f.* mercury pool. **-mittel,** *n.* (*Pharm.*) mercurial. **-mohr,** *m.* ethiops mineral (black mercuric sulfide).

**quecksilbern,** *a.* mercury, mercurial.

**Quecksilber-nitratoxyd,** *n.* mercuric nitrate, mercury(II) nitrate. **-nitratoxydul,** *n.* mercurous nitrate, mercury(I) nitrate. **-ofen,** *m.* mercury furnace. **-oxyd,** *n.* mercury oxide, specif. mercuric oxide, mercury(II) oxide. **-oxydnitrat,** *n.* mercuric nitrate, mercury(II) nitrate. **-oxydsalbe,** *f.* mercury oxide ointment. **-oxydsalz,** *n.* mercuric salt, mercury(II) salt. **-oxydul,** *n.* mercurous oxide, mercury(I) oxide. **-oxydulsalz,** *n.* mercurous salt, mercury(I) salt. **-pflaster,** *n.* (*Pharm.*) mercurial plaster. **-pille,** *f.* blue pill. **-präparat,** *n.* mercurial preparation. **-präzipitat,** *n.* (*Pharm.*) (mercury) precipitate (**rotes,** red precipitate; **gelbes,** yellow precipitate). **-rhodanid,** *n.* mercury thiocyanate, specif. mercuric thiocyanate, mercury(II) thiocyanate. **-rhodanür,** *n.* mercurous thiocyanate, mercury(I) thiocyanate. **-russ,** *m.* mercurial soot, stupp. **-salbe,** *f.* mercurial ointment. **-salpeter,** *m.* mercury nitrate. **-salz,** *n.* mercury salt. **-säule,** *f.* column of mercury. **-schalter,** *m.* (*Elec.*) mercury switch. **-schliff,** *m.* mercury ground-glass joint. **-spat,** *m.* horn quicksilver. **-spiegel,** *m.* mercury mirror; mercury surface. **-stand,** *m.* mercury level. **-sublimat,** *n.* corrosive sublimate. **-sulfatoxydul,** *n.* mercurous sulfate, mercury(I) sulfate. **-sulfid,** *n.* mercury sulfide, specif. mercuric sulfide, mercury(II) sulfide. **-sulfozyanid,** *n.* mercury (specif., mercuric) thiocyanate. **-sulfür,** *n.* mercurous sulfide, mercury(I) sulfide. **-tropfelektrode,** *f.* dropping-mercury electrode. **-verbindung,** *f.* mercury compound. **-verfahren,** *n.* mercury process. **-vergiftung,** *f.* mercury poisoning. **-vitriol,** *m.* mercuric sulfate, mercury(II) sulfate. **-wa(a)ge,** *f.* mercury level. **-wanne,** *f.* mercury trough. **-zyanid,** *n.* mercury (specif., mercuric) cyanide. **-zyanür,** *n.* mercurous cyanide, mercury(I) cyanide.

**Quell,** *m.* = Quelle.

**quellbar,** *a.* capable of swelling.

**Quell-barkeit,** *f.* capability of swelling. **-bottich,** *m.* steeping vat, steeping tub.

**Quelle,** *f.* source; spring, well.

**quellen,** *v.i.* swell, expand; spring, well, flow. — *v.t.* soak, steep. **-frei,** *a.* free from swelling; (*Math.*) solenoidal.

**Quellennachweis,** *m.* indication of sources.

**quellfähig,** *a.* capable of swelling.

**Quell-gas,** *n.* gas from springs. **-grad,** *m.* degree of swelling. **-kuppe,** *f.* (*Geol.*) volcanic plug.

**quellreif,** *a.* sufficiently steeped or soaked.

**Quell-reife,** *f.* sufficient steeping. **-salz,** *n.* spring salt, well salt. **-satzsäure,** *f.* apocrenic acid. **-säure,** *f.* crenic acid. **-schicht,** *f.* swelling layer. **-sole,** *f.* spring brine, well brine. **-stock,** *m.* steep tank, steeping cistern. **-substanz,** *f.* substance that swells.

**Quellung,** *f.* swelling, tumefaction; welling; soaking.

**quellungsfördernd,** *a.* promoting swelling.

**Quellungs-kolloid,** *n.* swelling colloid. **-vermögen,** *n.* swelling power. **-wärme,** *f.* heat of swelling, heat of tumefaction. **-zustand,** *m.* swelling state.

**Quell-vermögen,** *n.* swelling power. **-wasser,** *n.* spring water, well water. **-widerstand,** *m.* resistance to swelling.

**Quendel,** *m.* wild thyme.

**quer,** *a.* cross, transverse, diagonal, oblique.

**Quer-achse,** *f.* transverse axis. **-arm,** *m.* cross arm, cross bar. **-balken,** *m.* cross beam, cross bar. **-bewegung,** *f.* transverse motion.

**Quercit,** *n.* quercitol, quercite.

**Quercitronrinde,** *f.* quercitron bark.

**Quer-durchmesser,** *m.* transverse diameter. **-durchschnitt,** *m.* = Querschnitt.

**Quere,** *f.* cross direction, transverse direction; breadth.

**Quer-ebene,** *f.* lateral plane. **-effekt,** *m.* transverse effect. **-faser,** *f.* transverse fiber; cross grain. **-feld,** *n.* transverse field, cross field.

**quer-gestreift,** *a.* cross-striped, transversely striated. **-gewellt,** *a.* transversely corrugated.

**Querkraft,** *f.* transverse force, shearing force, shear.

**querlaufend,** *p.a.* transversal, transverse.

**Quer-profil,** *n.* cross section. **-richtung,** *f.* transverse direction. **-riss,** *m.* transverse crack, cross crack; cross section; (*Min.*) fracture. **-schlag,** *m.* (*Mining*) crosscut.

**querschleifen,** *v.t.* grind (wood) across the grain.

**Quer-schnitt,** *m.* cross section, transverse section, crosscut; cross-sectional area.

**Querschnitts-ebene,** *f.* cross-sectional plane. **-fläche,** *f.* cross-sectional area. **-serie,** *f.* series of cross sections. **-zeichnung,** *f.* sectional drawing.

**Quer-schwingung,** *f.* transverse vibration. **-spalte,** *f.* transverse split or fissure. **-spiessglanz,** *m.* jamesonite. **-streifung,** *f.* cross striping or striation. **-strom,** *m.* cross current; (*Elec.*) wattless current. **-stück,** *n.* crosspiece. **-teilung,** *f.* crosswise division. **-verbindung,** *f.* cross connection.

**querverlaufend,** *a.* running transversely.

**Quer-wand,** *f.* diaphragm; partition; transverse wall. **-welle,** *f.* transverse wave.

**Querzit,** *n.* quercitol, quercite.

**Querzitronrinde,** *f.* quercitron bark.

**Querzusammenziehung,** *f.* lateral contraction.

**Quetsche,** *f.* squeezer, wringer, presser, crusher; plum.

**quetschen,** *v.t.* pinch, squeeze; crush, mash; bruise, contuse.

**Quetscher,** *m.* pincher, etc. (see quetschen); (*Dyeing*) squeezer.

**Quetsch-fuss,** *m.* (*Elec.*) pinched base (of a lamp). **-grenze,** *f.* compression limit, compressive yield point. **-hahn,** *m.*, **-klemme,** *f.* pinchcock, pinch clamp. **-mühle,** *f.* bruising mill, crushing mill.

**Quetschung,** *f.* pinching, etc. (see quetschen); bruise, contusion.

**Quetsch-walze,** *f.* crushing roll. **-werk,** *n.* crushing mill, crusher; squeezing apparatus. **-wirkung,** *f.* squeezing action or effect. **-wunde,** *f.* bruise, contusion.

**Quick-.** amalgamating. **-arbeit,** *f.* amalgamation. **-beutel,** *m.* amalgamating skin. **-brei,** *m.* amalgam.

**quicken,** *v.t* amalgamate.

**Quick-erz,** *n.* mercury ore. **-gold,** *n.* gold amalgam. **-metall,** *n.* amalgamated metal. **-mühle,** *f.* amalgamating mill. **-wasser,** *n.* (*Plating*) quickening liquid (solution of a mercuric salt).

**quieken, quietschen,** *v.i.* squeak, squeal, creak.

**Quillaja-rinde,** *f.* quillai bark, quillaia bark. **-säure,** *f.* quillaic acid.

**quillt,** *pr. 3 sing.* (of quellen) swells, etc.

**Quirl,** *m.* twirling device, twirler, twirl, whirl; stirrer; (*Bot.*) whorl; restless person.

**quirlen,** *v.t.*, twirl; stir with a whirling motion. — *v.i.* twirl, turn.

**quitt,** *a.* even, quits, rid.

**Quitte,** *f.* quince.

**Quitten-äther,** *m.*, **-essenz,** *f.* quince essence. **-kern, -samen,** *m.* quince seed. **-öl,** *n.* (*lit.*, quince oil), amyl acetate, "banana oil." **-schleim,** *m.* quince mucilage.

**quittieren,** *v.t.* quit, leave; receipt.

**Quittung,** *f.* receipt.

**quoll,** *pret.* (of quellen) swelled, etc.

**Quote,** *f.* quota.

# R

**r.,** *abbrev.* (rechtsdrehend) dextrorotatory; (rund) roundly, in round numbers.
**R.,** *abbrev.* (Referat) abstract, review; Réaumur; ring (cyclic); (Radikal) radical.
**Rabatt,** *m.* deduction, discount; rebate.
**Rabe,** *m.* raven; crow.
**rabenschwarz,** *a.* jet black.
**Rabenstein,** *m.* gallows.
**rac.,** *abbrev.* of racemisch.
**Racemie,** *f.* racemism.
**racemisch,** *a.* racemic.
**racemisieren,** *v.t.* racemize.
**Racemisierung,** *f.* racemization.
**Racem-körper,** *m.* racemic substance (or compound). **-verbindung,** *f.* racemic compound.
**Rache,** *f.* revenge, vengeance.
**Rachen,** *m.* throat; mouth; jaws; (*Med.*) pharynx, fauces.
**Rachen-.** throat; pharyngeal; jaw.
**rächen,** *v.t.* revenge, avenge.
**Rachen-lehre,** *f.* calipers. **-reizstoff,** *m.* throat irritant.
**Rad,** *n.* wheel. **-achse,** *f.* axle or shaft of a wheel. **-arm,** *m.* spoke (of a wheel). **-bewegung,** *f.* rotary motion, rotation. **-drehung,** *f.* rotation; torsion.
**Rädelerz,** *n.* wheel ore (bournonite).
**Rädelsführer,** *m.* ringleader.
**Räder-antrieb,** *m.* gear drive. **-fahrzeug,** *n.* wheeled vehicle.
**rädern,** *v.t.* sift, screen; furnish with wheels.
**Räder-tierchen, -tier,** *n.* rotifer. **-werk,** *n.* wheelwork, gearing; sifting apparatus.
**radförmig,** *a.* wheel-shaped, rotate.
**Radialschnitt,** *m.* radial section.
**radial-strahlig,** *a.* (*Cryst.*) radiating. **-symmetrisch,** *a.* radially symmetric.
**Radien,** *m.pl.* radii.
**radieren,** *v.t.* etch; erase.
**Radier-firnis,** *m.* etching varnish. **-grund,** *m.* etching ground. **-gummi,** *m.* (rubber) eraser. **-kunst,** *f.* (art of) etching. **-messer,** *n.* erasing knife.
**Radierung,** *f.* etching; erasure.
**Radieschen,** *n.* radish. **-bombe,** *f.* (*Mil.*) smoke grenade.
**radiieren,** *v.i.* radiate.
**Radikalessig,** *m.* radical vinegar (old name for acetic acid, esp. glacial acetic acid).
**Radio-aktivität,** *f.* radioactivity. **-blei,** *n.* radiolead. **-chemie,** *f.* radiochemistry. **-tellur,** *n.* radiotellurium (polonium). **-thor,** *n.* radiothorium.
**Radium-behälter,** *m.* radium container, radiode. **-belag,** *m.* radium coating. **-erz,** *n.* radium ore. **-jodid,** *n.* radium iodide. **-salz,** *n.* radium salt. **-strahlen,** *m.pl.* radium rays.
**radizieren,** *v.t.* (*Math.*) extract the root of.
**Radizierung,** *f.* (*Math.*) root extraction.
**Rad-kranz,** *m.* (wheel) rim, tire. **-linie,** *f.* cycloid. **-reif, -reifen,** *m.* tire; rim. **-schlauch,** *m.* inner tube (of a tire). **-schuh,** *m.* brake. **-speiche,** *f.* spoke. **-welle,** *f.* axle; wheel and axle. **-zahn,** *m.* tooth, cog (of a wheel).
**raff.,** *abbrev.* (raffiniert) refined.
**raffen,** *v.t.* snatch up, snatch away.
**Raffinade,** *f.*, **-zucker,** *m.* refined sugar. **-zink,** *n.* refined spelter.
**Raffinat,** *n.* (*Petroleum*) raffinate. **-blei,** *n.* refined lead.
**Raffination,** *f.* refining.
**Raffinations-abfall,** *m.* refinery waste. **-anlage,** *f.* refining plant, refinery. **-ertrag,** *m.* (*Sugar*) rendement. **-ofen,** *m.* refining furnace. **-verfahren,** *n.*, **-vorgang,** *m.* refining process. **-wert,** *m.* (*Sugar*) rendement.
**Raffinat-kupfer,** *n.* refined copper. **-silber,** *n.* refined silver.
**Raffinerie,** *f.* refinery; finesse.
**Raffineur,** *m.* refiner; refining mill. **-stein,** *m.* (*Paper*) refining stone.
**Raffinier-anlage,** *f.* refining plant, refinery. **-arbeit,** *f.* refining operation.
**raffinieren,** *v.t.* refine.
**Raffinier-feuer,** *n.*, **-herd, -ofen,** *m.* refining furnace, refinery. **-gesellschaft,** *f.* refining company. **-schlacke,** *f.* refinery slag. **-stahl,** *m.* refined steel, refined iron.
**Raffinierung,** *f.* refining; refinery.
**Raffinierungsabfall,** *m.* refinery waste.
**Raffinierverfahren,** *n.* refining process.
**ragen,** *v.i.* project, tower.
**Rahm,** *m.* cream; crust (forming on the top of something); frame; soot.
**rahm-ähnlich, -artig,** *a.* cream-like, creamy.
**Rahmeis,** *n.* ice cream.
**rahmen,** *v.t.* skim, take the cream from; frame. — *v.i.* form a cream.
**Rahmen,** *m.* frame, framing; stator; rack; border, gasket; compass, bounds, scope. **-filterpresse,** *f.* frame filter press. **-leder,** *n.* welting leather.

**Rahm-erz,** *n.* (*Min.*) a foamy variety of wad. **-farbe,** *f.* cream color, cream.

**rahm-farbig, -farben,** *a.* cream-colored. **-ig,** *a.* sooty; creamy.

**Rahm-käse,** *m.* cream cheese. **-messer,** *m.* creamometer.

**Rain,** *m.* ridge, bank, border, hillock.

**Rainfarn,** *m.*, **-kraut,** *n.* tansy. **-öl,** *n.* tansy oil.

**Rainweide,** *f.* privet.

**Rakel,** *m.* & *f.* (*Calico,* etc.) doctor, wiper. **-appretur,** *f.* doctor finish. **-lineal,** *n.* doctor rule. **-messer,** *n.* doctor blade, doctor. **-stärkemaschine,** *f.* starching machine with doctor. **-streifen,** *m.* doctor streak.

**Rakete,** *f.* rocket; (less often) firecracker.

**Raketen-antrieb,** *m.* rocket propulsion. **-bombe,** *f.* rocket bomb. **-leuchtgeschoss,** *n.* rocket flare fire. **-satz,** *m.* rocket composition; rocket attachment. **-verfahren,** *n.*, **-vortrieb,** *m.* rocket propulsion. **-wurfmaschine,** *f.* rocket launcher, rocket projector. **-zeichen,** *n.* rocket signal.

**Ramiefaser,** *f.* ramie fiber.

**ramifizieren,** *v.t.* & *r.* ramify.

**Ramifizierung,** *f.* ramification.

**Ramm-bär, -block, -bock,** *m.* ram, rammer, pile driver.

**Ramme,** *f.* ram, rammer.

**rammen,** *v.t.* ram, beat down, drive (piles).

**Rammvorrichtung,** *f.* ramming apparatus.

**Rampe,** *f.* ramp; slope; platform; footlights.

**ramponieren,** *v.t.* damage, injure.

**Ramsayfett,** *n.* Ramsay grease or lubricant.

**Ramsch,** *m.* lot, bulk; cheap stuff. **-ware,** *f.* job goods.

**Rand,** *m.* edge; border, rim, margin, brim; periphery; boundary; flange, lip.

**Rand-.** marginal, boundary, border, peripheral. **-anmerkung,** *f.* marginal note. **-bedingung,** *f.* boundary condition, marginal condition. **-bemerkung,** *f.* marginal note.

**rändeln, rändern,** *v.t.* edge, border, rim; knurl, mill.

**Randentkohlung,** *f.* marginal decarbonization.

**Ränderscheibe,** *f.* edge cutter.

**Rand-fassung,** *f.* rim. **-feuerpatrone,** *f.* rimfire cartridge. **-fläche,** *f.* margin; (*Cryst.*) lateral face. **-gärung,** *f.* (*Brewing*) rim fermentation. **-gebiet,** *n.* border region. **-kante,** *f.* (*Cryst.*) lateral edge.

**rand-lich,** *a.* marginal, peripheral. **-los,** *a.* rimless, marginless, borderless.

**Rand-schärfe,** *f.* sharpness of edge or border. **-schicht,** *f.* marginal or surface layer or zone

**randständig,** *a.* marginal, peripheral.

**Randstrahl,** *m.* marginal ray, peripheral ray.

**Randung,** *f.* edging, edge, border(ing).

**randwärts,** *adv.* toward the edge or margin.

**Rand-wert,** *m.* boundary value. **-winkel,** *m.* angle of contact.

**rang,** *pret.* (of ringen) struggled, etc.

**Rang,** *m.* rank; position; quality; row, tier. **-folge,** *f.* ordered series, order (of precedence).

**rangieren,** *v.t.* arrange, classify; switch (cars).

**Rangordnung,** *f.* ranking, gradation; order (of precedence).

**Ranke,** *f.* tendril, runner, shoot.

**ranken,** *v.i.* (of plants) creep, climb, run.

**rann,** *pret.* (of rinnen) ran, flowed.

**rannte,** *pret.* (of rennen) ran.

**Ränzel,** *n.*, **Ranzen,** *m.* wallet, knapsack, satchel.

**Ranzidität,** *f.* rancidity.

**ranzig,** *a.* rancid.

**ranzigen,** *v.i.* become rancid.

**Ranzig-keit,** *f.* rancidity, rancidness. **-werden,** *n.* becoming rancid; tendency to rancidity.

**Raphia,** *f.* raffia.

**Rapidstahl,** *m.* high-speed steel.

**Rapp,** *m.*, **Rappe,** *f.* rape, grape pomace.

**Rappel,** *m.* rage, madness; staggers.

**Rapport,** *m.* report; relation; repetition.

**Rapputz,** *m.* rough coat (of plaster).

**Raps,** *m.* rape; (**rotblühender**) garden rocket. **-kuchen,** *m.* rape(seed) cake. **-mehl,** *n.* rape(seed) meal. **-öl,** *n.* rape oil, rapeseed oil, colza oil. **-saat,** *f.*, **-same(n),** *m.* rapeseed, colza.

**Rasanz,** *f.* flatness (as of a trajectory).

**rasch,** *a.* quick, brisk, swift, rapid, prompt. — **rascher Satz,** (*Pyro.*) meal-powder composition.

**rascheln,** *v.i.* rustle.

**Raschkochverfahren,** *n.* quick-cook process.

**raschtrocknend,** *a.* quick-drying.

**Rasen,** *m.* turf, sod, lawn; furry coating, fur. **-asche,** *f.* turf ashes. **-bleiche,** *f.* grass bleaching, sun bleaching. **-eisenerz,** *n.*, **-eisenstein,** *m.*, **-erz,** *n.* bog iron ore.

**rasieren,** *v.t.* shave; raze.

**Rasier-klinge,** *f.* razor blade. **-messer,** *n.* razor. **-pulver,** *n.* shaving powder. **-seife,** *f.* shaving soap. **-stein,** *m.* styptic stick.

**Raspel, Raspe,** *f.* rasp; grater.

**raspeln,** *v.t.* rasp, grate, scrape.

**Rasse,** *f.* race, breed, strain, type, stock.

**rasseln,** *v.i.* rattle, clatter, clank.

**Rast,** *f.* rest; groove, notch; catch, detent; (of a furnace) boshes.

**Raste,** *f.* notch, indentation; detent.

**rasten,** *v.i.* rest; halt. — *v.t.* (*Radio*) tune.

**Raster,** *m.* screen; grating; graph paper. **-druck,** *m.* screen printing.

**Rast-gärung,** *f.* (*Brewing*) arrested fermentation. **-klinke,** *f.* catch, detent, pawl, latch.

**rastlos,** *a.* restless.

**Rastmälzerei,** *f.* arrest malting.
**Rasur,** *f.* erasure.
**rät,** *pr. 3 sing.* (of raten) advises, etc.
**Rat,** *m.* counsel, advice; consultation; means; council, board; councilor.
**Rata,** *f.* rate; installment.
**Ratanhia,** *f.* rhatany. **-wurzel,** *f.* rhatany root, rhatany.
**Rate,** *f.* rate; installment.
**raten,** *v.t. & i.* advise, counsel; guess, solve. — **geraten,** *p.a.* advisable.
**Rat-geber,** *m.* counselor, adviser; manual, guide. **-haus,** *n.* town hall.
**rationell,** *a.* rational, reasonable; economical.
**rätlich,** *a.* advisable, expedient, wholesome.
**rat-los,** *a.* helpless, perplexed. **-sam,** *a.* advisable, expedient, fit.
**Ratsche,** *f.* ratchet.
**Ratschlag,** *m.* advice, counsel.
**ratschlagen,** *v.i.* consult, deliberate.
**Ratschluss,** *m.* resolution, decision, decree.
**Rätsel,** *n.* riddle, puzzle, enigma.
**rätselhaft,** *a.* enigmatical, mysterious.
**Ratte,** *f.* rat.
**rätten,** *v.t.* screen, sieve, riddle.
**Ratten-gift,** *n.* rat poison, specif. white arsenic. **-pulver,** *n.* rat powder, rat poison. **-schwanz,** *m.* rat-tail file. **-tod,** *m.* rat poison. **-vertilgungsmittel,** *n.* rat killer, vermicide.
**Rätter,** *m.* grating, grate, screen, riddle.
**rauben,** *v.t.* rob.
**räuber-isch, -haft,** *a.* predatory; rapacious.
**Raubtier,** *n.* beast of prey, carnivorous animal.
**rauch.,** *abbrev.* (rauchend) fuming.
**Rauch,** *m.* smoke; fume; vapor. **-achat,** *m.* smoky agate.
**rauchartig,** *a.* smoky.
**Rauch-bahngeschoss,** *n.* (*Mil.*) tracer projectile. **-bahngranate,** *f.* (*Mil.*) tracer shell. **-ball,** *m.* (*Mil.*) smoke bomb, also float light. **-behälter,** *m.* (*Mil.*) smoke box. **-belästigung,** *f.* smoke nuisance. **-bildung,** *f.* formation of smoke. **-bombe,** *f.* smoke bomb; float light.
**rauchdicht,** *a.* smoke-tight, smokeproof.
**Rauch-dichte, -dichtigkeit,** *f.* density of smoke. **-dose,** *f.* (*Mil.*) smoke float. **-düse,** *f.* smoke nozzle.
**rauchen,** *v.i.* fume; smoke; reek. — *v.t.* smoke. — **rauchend,** *p.a.* fuming; smoking.
**Rauch-entwickler,** *m.* smoke generator. **-entwicklung,** *f.* smoke generation.
**Räucher-.** fumigating; smoking (as of meat); perfuming; aromatic.
**Räucherer,** *m.* fumigator.
**Räucher-essenz,** *f.* aromatic essence, fragrant essence. **-essig,** *m.* aromatic vinegar.
**räucherig,** *a.* smoky; dingy.
**Räucher-igkeit,** *f.* smokiness; dinginess. **-kerze,** *f.*, **-kerzchen,** *n.* fumigating candle. **-lachs,** *m.* smoked salmon. **-mittel,** *n.* fumigant.
**räuchern,** *v.t.* fumigate; smoke; perfume.
**Räucher-papier,** *n.* fumigating paper. **-pulver,** *n.* fumigating powder.
**Räucherung,** *f.* fumigation; smoking (of meat); incense burning.
**Räucherwerk,** *n.* perfume, perfumes; incense.
**Rauch-erzeuger,** *m.* smoke generator or producer. **-erzeugung,** *f.* smoke production; (*Agric.*) smudging. **-fahne,** *f.* smoke streamer. **-fang,** *m.* chimney, flue.
**rauch-farben, -farbig,** *a.* smoke-colored.
**Rauch-färbung,** *f.* smoke coloring. **-fleisch,** *n.* smoked meat.
**rauchfrei,** *a.* free from smoke, smokeless.
**rauchgar,** *a.* smoke-cured.
**Rauchgas,** *n.* smoke gas, flue gas, chimney gas, burned gas. **-analyse,** *f.* flue-gas analysis. **-vorwärmer,** *m.* flue-gas preheater, economizer.
**Rauch-gehalt,** *m.* smoke content. **-gerät,** *n.* smoke apparatus. **-gerbung,** *f.* smoke tanning. **-geschmack,** *m.* taste of smoke, fire flavor.
**rauchgeschwärzt,** *a.* blackened by smoke, smoke-stained.
**Rauch-glas,** *n.* tinted glass, smoked glass. **-granate,** *f.* smoke shell.
**rauchgrau,** *a.* smoke-gray.
**Rauchhelm,** *m.* smoke helmet.
**rauchig,** *a.* smoky; fumy.
**Rauch-kalk,** *m.* magnesian limestone. **-kammer,** *f.* smoke box; combustion chamber. **-kanal,** *m.* (smoke) flue. **-kasten,** *m.* smoke box. **-kern,** *m.* smoke nucleus. **-kerze,** *f.* smoke candle. **-körper,** *m.* (*Mil.*) smoke filler, smoke charge. **-ladung,** *f.* (*Mil.*) smoke charge.
**rauchlos,** *a.* smokeless.
**Rauch-losigkeit,** *f.* smokelessness. **-malz,** *n.* smoke-dried malt. **-meldebüchse,** *f.* (*Mil.*) smoke signal cartridge. **-meldepatrone,** *f.* (*Mil.*) smoke signal cartridge (or shell or bomb). **-ofen,** *m.* smudge pot, smoke generator. **-patrone,** *f.* (*Mil.*) smoke signal cartridge. **-pulver,** *n.* fumigating powder. **-quarz,** *m.* smoky quartz. **-rohr,** *n.* smoke flue; fire tube. **-rohrkessel,** *m.* fire-tube boiler. **-satz,** *m.* (*Mil.*) smoke composition or mixture. **-schaden,** *m.* damage by fumes or smoke. **-schieber,** *m.* smoke damper. **-schirm, -schleier,** *m.* smoke screen. **-schriftmasse,** *f.* (*Aero.*) smoke-writing (or sky-writing) composition.
**rauch-schwach,** *a.* giving little smoke, "smokeless." **-schwarz,** *a.* smoky black, sooty.
**Rauch-schwimmer,** *m.* (*Mil.*) floating smoke pot. **-signalgerät,** *n.* smoke-signal apparatus.

-**spurgeschoss,** *n.* tracer projectile or bullet. **-stärke,** *f.* density of smoke. **-tabak,** *m.* smoking tobacco. **-topas,** *m.* smoky topaz, smoky quartz. **-verbrennung,** *f.* smoke combustion; smoke consumption. **-verbrennungseinrichtung,** *f.* smoke consumer. **-verdünnung,** *f.* smoke dilution. **-verhütung,** *f.* smoke prevention. **-verminderung,** *f.* smoke reduction. **-verzehrung,** *f.* smoke consumption. **-vorhang,** *m.* smoke curtain, smoke screen. **-wand,** *f.* wall of smoke, smoke screen. **-waren,** *f.pl.* furs, peltry. **-wolke,** *f.* smoke cloud. **-zeichen,** *n.* smoke signal. **-zug,** *m.* smoke flue.

**Raude,** *f.* scab, scurf.

**Räude,** *f.* mange; scab, scurf.

**räudig,** *a.* scabbed, scabby, mangy.

**Raufe,** *f.* hackle; rack.

**raufen,** *v.t.* pull, pluck. — *v.r. & i.* scuffle.

**Raufwolle,** *f.* plucked wool.

**rauh,** *a.* rough (specif., unglazed); harsh (to touch); raw; coarse, rude; hoarse; rugged.

**Rauhartikel,** *m.* (*Calico*) raised style.

**Rauheit,** *f.* roughness, etc. (see rauh).

**Rauheitsbeiwert,** *m.* coefficient of roughness.

**rauhen,** *v.t.* roughen; (*Textiles*) raise, nap.

**rauhgar,** *a.* (*Leather*) dressed with the hair on.

**Rauhigkeit,** *f.* roughness, etc. (see rauh).

**rauhnarbig,** *a.* (*Leather*) harsh-grained.

**Rauh-reif,** *m.* hoarfrost. **-reserve,** *f.* (*Textiles*) resist against raising.

**Raum,** *m.* space; volume; room, scope; place; chamber; hold (of a ship); opportunity, occasion. **-analyse,** *f.* volumetric analysis (of gases).

**Räumasche,** *f.* (*Zinc*) retort residue.

**Raumbeanspruchung,** *f.* space requirement.

**raumbeständig,** *a.* constant-volume.

**Raum-beständigkeit,** *f.* constancy of volume. **-bestimmung,** *f.* determination of volume. **-bewetterung,** *f.* ventilation; air conditioning. **-bild,** *n.* space diagram; stereoscopic image. **-chemie,** *f.* stereochemistry.

**raumchemisch,** *a.* stereochemical.

**Raum-dichte,** *f.* density by volume. **-einheit,** *f.* unit of space or volume. **-element,** *n.* spatial unit.

**räumen,** *v.t.* clear away, remove; clear; ream; evacuate, leave.

**Räumer,** *m.* (*Mach.*) reamer.

**Raumersparnis,** *f.* space saving, space economy.

**raumfest,** *a.* fixed in space, stationary.

**Raum-formel,** *f.* spatial formula. **-fuss,** *m.* cubic foot. **-gebild(e),** *n.* space diagram; three-dimensional structure. **-gehalt,** *m.* content by volume, spatial content. **-geometrie,** *f.* solid geometry. **-gewicht,** *n.* weight per unit volume, bulk density. **-gitter,** *n.* (*Cryst.*) space lattice, "raumgitter." **-glas,** *n.* stereoscope. **-grösse,** *f.* amount or size of space. **-hundertel,** *n.* per cent by volume.

**räumig,** *a.* roomy, spacious, ample.

**Räumigkeit,** *f.* specific volume; roominess.

**Rauminhalt,** *m.* volume, content, capacity.

**raumisomer,** *a.* stereoisomeric.

**Raum-isomerie,** *f.* spatial isomerism, stereoisomerism. **-kurve,** *f.* solid curve. **-lehre,** *f.* geometry.

**räumlich,** *a.* relating to or occupying space, spatial, steric, three-dimensional; relating to volume. — **räumliche Behinderung, raümliche Hinderung,** steric hindrance.

**Räumlichkeit,** *f.* quality of occupying space, extension; specific volume; spatiality, space; room, part (of a house).

**Raum-mass,** *n.* measure of capacity or volume, cubic measure. **-menge,** *f.* amount of space, volume. **-meter,** *m.* cubic meter. **-modell,** *n.* space model. **-orientierung,** *f.* orientation in space. **-quantelung,** *f.* spatial quantization. **-richtung,** *f.* direction in space. **-strahl,** *m.* cosmic ray. **-strahlenstoss,** *m.* burst of cosmic rays. **-strahlung,** *f.* cosmic radiation. **-teil,** *m.* part by volume, volume.

**Räumung,** *f.* clearance, removal; reaming; evacuation.

**Raum-veränderung,** *f.* change in volume. **-verhältnis,** *f.* volume relation, proportion by volume. **-verminderung,** *f.* decrease in volume. **-verteilung,** *f.* spatial distribution. **-wärme,** *f.* room temperature. **-welle,** *f.* space wave, sky wave. **-winkel,** *m.* solid angle.

**raumzentriert,** *a.* (*Cryst.*) body-centered.

**raunen,** *v.t. & i.* whisper.

**Raupe,** *f.* caterpillar; worm; whim, fancy.

**Raupen-antrieb,** *m.* (*Mach.*) caterpillar drive. **-leim,** *m.* Raupenleim (a petroleum product used for protecting trees against caterpillars, etc.). *T.N.* **-schlepper,** *m.* caterpillar tractor.

**Rausch,** *m.* drunkenness, intoxication; rushing, rush, roar; murmur; rustle; noise; (*Mining*) pounded ore.

**rauschen,** *v.i.* rush, gurgle, murmur, rustle, whistle, roar.

**Rausch-gelb,** *n.* orpiment. **-gift,** *n.* narcotic poison or drug. **-gold,** *n.* Dutch gold, tinsel. **-leder,** *n.* chamois (leather). **-mittel,** *n.* intoxicant. **-rot,** *n.* realgar. **-silber,** *n.* imitation silver foil.

**Raute,** *f.* rue; rhombus, diamond.

**rautenähnlich,** *a.* like rue; rhomboid.

**Rauten-flach,** *n.*, **-flächner,** *m.* rhombohedron. **-fläche,** *f.* rhombus.

**rautenförmig,** *a.* rhombic, diamond-shaped.

**Rauten-gewächse,** *n.pl.* (*Bot.*) Rutaceae. **-öl,** *n.* oil of rue. **-spat,** *m.* rhomb spar (dolomite).

**razem-.** see racem-.

**rd.**, *abbrev.* (rund) round, approximately.

**Reagens, Reagenz,** *n.* reagent. **-farbe,** *f.* test color. **-flasche,** *f.* reagent bottle. **-glas,** *n.* test tube. **-glasbürste,** *f.* test-tube brush. **-glasgestell,** *n.* test-tube rack or stand. **-glashalter,** *m.* test-tube holder. **-glasstichkultur,** *f.* (*Bact.*) test-tube stab culture. **-kelch,** *m.* test glass, test cup. **-lösung,** *f.* test solution. **-mittel,** *n.* reagent. **-papier,** *n.* test paper. **-röhre,** *f.*, **-röhrchen,** *n.* test tube.

**Reagenzien, Reagentien,** *n.pl.* reagents. **-flasche,** *f.* reagent bottle. **-kasten,** *m.* reagent box or case. **-raum,** *m.* reagent space or room.

**reagieren,** *v.i.* react. — **reagierend,** *p.a.* reactive.

**Reagierglas,** *n.* test tube. **-bürste,** *f.* test-tube brush. **-gestell,** *n.* test-tube stand. **-halter,** *m.* test-tube holder.

**Reagier-kelch,** *m.* test glass, test cup. **-zylinder,** *m.* test tube.

**Reaktanz,** *f.* reactance.

**Reaktions-bahn,** *f.* path of a reaction. **-bereitschaft,** *f.* readiness to react, reactivity. **-druck,** *m.* reaction pressure.

**reaktionsfähig,** *a.* capable of reacting, reactive.

**Reaktions-fähigkeit,** *f.* capability of reacting, reactivity. **-flüssigkeit,** *f.* reaction liquid. **-formel,** *f.* reaction formula. **-fortgang,** *m.* progress of a reaction. **-gemisch,** *n.* reaction mixture. **-geschehen,** *n.* occurrence of a reaction. **-geschwindigkeit,** *f.* reaction velocity. **-gleichung,** *f.* equation (of a reaction). **-hemmung,** *f.* inhibition of reaction. **-kammer,** *f.* reaction chamber. **-kern,** *m.* nucleus of reaction. **-kette,** *f.* chain or series of reactions, reaction chain. **-kurve,** *f.* reaction curve.

**reaktionslos,** *a.* reactionless.

**Reaktions-losigkeit,** *f.* absence of reaction, nonreaction. **-masse,** *f.* reaction mass, mass resulting from a reaction. **-mischung,** *f.* reaction mixture. **-mittel,** *n.* reagent. **-ordnung,** *f.* order of a reaction. **-ort,** *m.* field or sphere of reaction. **-papier,** *n.* test paper. **-rohr,** *n.*, **-röhre,** *f.* reaction tube. **-stufe,** *f.* step or stage of a reaction. **-teilnehmer,** *m.* participant in a reaction, reactant.

**reaktionsträge,** *a.* slow to react.

**Reaktions-trägheit,** *f.* slowness in reaction. **-turm,** *m.* reaction tower. **-verhältnis,** *n.* reaction proportion or ratio. **-verlauf,** *m.* course of a reaction. **-versuch,** *m.* reaction test. **-wärme,** *f.* heat of reaction. **-zeit,** *f.* reaction time.

**Reaktiv,** *n.* reagent.

**reaktivieren,** *v.t.* reactivate.

**Reaktivierung,** *f.* reactivation.

**Reaktivität,** *f.* reactivity.

**realisierbar,** *a.* realizable.

**realisieren,** *v.t.* realize.

**Realität,** *f.* reality.

**Real-schule,** *f.* industrial school, scientific school (for teaching science, modern languages, etc.). **-wissenschaft,** *f.* practical science.

**Rebe,** *f.* vine, esp. grapevine; tendril.

**Reben-russ,** *m.* = Rebenschwarz. **-saft,** *m.* juice of the grape, wine. **-schwarz,** *n.* vine black, vegetable black, Frankfort black.

**Reb-huhn,** *n.* partridge. **-laus,** *f.* vine louse, phylloxera.

**Rebromierung,** *f.* rebromination.

**Rebschwarz,** *n.* = Rebenschwarz.

**Recept,** etc. = Rezept, etc.

**Rechen,** *m.* rake; rack; screen, grating.

**Rechen-.** calculating, counting, reckoning; rake, raking. **-beispiel,** *n.* example (in calculation). **-bild,** *n.* nomogram. **-fehler,** *m.* error in calculation. **-hilfsmittel,** *n.* aid to calculation. **-kunst,** *f.* arithmetic. **-maschine,** *f.* calculating machine, calculator.

**Rechenschaft,** *f.* account. — **— geben,** give account, answer.

**Rechen-schieber, -stab,** *m.* slide rule. **-stift,** *m.* slate pencil. **-tafel,** *f.* reckoning table; multiplication table; nomograph, nomogram; slate; blackboard; counting board. **-verfahren,** *n.* method or process of calculation.

**rechnen,** *v.t. & i.* calculate, reckon, count, compute, estimate.

**rechnerisch,** *a.* computational, mathematical.

**Rechnung,** *f.* calculation, etc. (see rechnen); arithmetic; calculus; account; bill.

**Rechnungs-art,** *f.* mode of calculation. **-betrag,** *m.* amount or total of an account. **-führer,** *m.* bookkeeper, accountant. **-jahr,** *n.* fiscal year, financial year.

**rechnungsmässig,** *a.* in accordance with calculation.

**Rechnungstafel,** *f.* reckoning table.

**recht,** *a.* right; correct, true, genuine, legitimate, own; fitting, agreeable. — *adv.* right, rightly, very.

**Recht,** *n.* right; justice; law. — **mit —,** rightly, with reason.

**Recht-.** right, ortho-, rect-, legal. **-bild,** *n.* (*Photog.*) positive.

**Rechte,** *f.* right (side, hand, party).

**Rechteck,** *n.* rectangle.

**rechteckig,** *a.* rectangular.

**rechten,** *v.i.* litigate; dispute; remonstrate.

**rechterhand,** *adv.* on the right-hand side.

**Rechtfertigung,** *f.* justification.

**recht-gläubig,** *a.* orthodox. **-haberisch,** *a.* dogmatic. **-läufig,** *a.* running to the right; clockwise. **-lich,** *a.* just, honest; legal, judicial.

-**los,** *a.* illegal; lawless. -**mässig,** *a.* legal, rightful.
**rechts,** *adv.* to the right, on the right, right-hand, dextro-, clockwise.
**Rechts-.** to the right, dextro-; of the law, legal. -**anwalt,** *m.* attorney, solicitor. -**beistand,** *m.* (legal) counsel.
**rechtsbeständig,** *a.* valid, legal.
**rechtschaffen,** *a.* just, honest, upright.
**Rechtschreibung,** *f.* orthography, spelling.
**rechtsdrehend,** *p.a.* dextrorotatory.
**Rechtsdrehung,** *f.* dextrorotation, right-handed polarization.
**rechtsgängig,** *a.* right-hand, clockwise.
**Rechts-gelehrte,** *m.* lawyer; jurist. -**gewinde,** *n.* right-handed (screw) thread.
**rechtsgültig,** *a.* valid (in law), legal.
**Rechts-gültigkeit,** *f.* validity, legality. -**handel,** *m.* law case, lawsuit.
**rechtskräftig,** *a.* valid, legal, effective.
**Rechtslauf,** *m.* motion, to the right, clockwise motion.
**rechts-laufend,** -**läufig,** *a.* to the right, clockwise.
**Rechts-milchsäure,** *f.* dextrolactic acid. -**mittel,** *n.* legal remedy. -**pflege,** *f.* administration of justice. -**polarisation,** *f.* = Rechtsdrehung. -**quarz,** *m.* right-handed quartz. -**säure,** *f.* dextro acid. -**schraube,** *f.* right-handed screw. -**schutz,** *m.* legal protection (as by patents). -**weinsäure,** *f.* dextrotartaric acid.
**recht-winklig,** *a.* right-angled, rectangular. -**zeitig,** *a.* timely, opportune, seasonable, prompt.
**Recipient,** *m.* receiver; (of persons) recipient.
**reciprok,** *a.* reciprocal.
**Reck,** *n.,* **Recke,** *f.* rack, stretcher, horizontal pole or bar.
**recken,** *v.t.* stretch, extend, elongate, rack; (*Metal.*) shingle, tilt.
**Reck-probe,** *f.* elongation (or stretching) test. -**spannung,** *f.* tensile stress; tensile strain.
**Reckung,** *f.* stretching, etc. (see recken).
**Reck-walzen,** *f.pl.,* -**werk,** *n.* (*Metal.*) finishing rolls.
**Redakteur,** *m.* editor.
**Redaktion,** *f.* editing, editorship, editorial staff, editorial office.
**Rede,** *f.* speech, language, talk, discourse; rumor; account.
**reden,** *v.t.* & *i.* speak, talk, discourse.
**Redensart,** *f.* phrase, expression, term.
**redestillieren,** *v.t.* redistil.
**Redeweise,** *f.* way of speaking, style, language.
**redigieren,** *v.t.* edit.
**redlich,** *a.* upright, honest, fair, candid.
**Redner,** *m.* orator, speaker. -**bühne,** *f.* (public) platform.
**redselig,** *a.* talkative.
**reducier-.** see reduzier-.
**Reduktions-arbeit,** *f.* reduction process, reduction. -**ätze,** *f.* (*Calico*) reduction discharge. -**bad,** *n.* reducing bath.
**reduktions-beständig,** *a.* resistant to reduction. -**fähig,** *a.* capable of reduction.
**Reduktions-fähigkeit,** *f.* reducibility. -**ferment,** *n.* reducing ferment, reductase. -**flamme,** *f.* reducing flame. -**geschwindigkeit,** *f.* rate of reduction. -**hütte,** *f.* (*Metal.*) reduction works. -**kraft,** *f.* reducing power. -**mittel,** *n.* reducing agent. -**ofen,** *m.* reduction furnace. -**ort,** *m.* reduction region. -**röhre,** *f.* reduction tube. -**schlacke,** *f.* reducing slag. -**tiegel,** *m.* reduction crucible. -**ventil,** *n.* reducing valve. -**verhältnis,** *n.* reduction ratio. -**vermögen,** *n.* reducing power. -**vorgang,** *m.* reduction process. -**wärme,** *f.* heat of reduction. -**wirkung,** *f.* reducing action or effect.
**reduktiv,** *a.* reductive, by reduction.
**reduzierbar,** *a.* reducible.
**Reduzierbarkeit,** *f.* reducibility.
**reduzieren,** *v.t.* reduce.
**reduzierfähig,** *a.* capable of reduction.
**Reduzier-salz,** *n.* reducing salt. -**stück,** *n.* reducing piece, reducer.
**Reduzierung,** *f.* reduction.
**Reduzierventil,** *n.* reducing valve.
**reell,** *a.* real, sound, honest.
**Reep,** *n.* rope.
**Referat,** *n.* abstract; review; report.
**Referent,** *m.* abstractor; reviewer; reporter.
**Referierdienst,** *m.* abstracting service; reporting service.
**referieren,** *v.t.* & *i.* report; abstract.
**reflektieren,** *v.t.* reflect. — *v.i.* reflect, consider.
**Reflektierstrahl,** *m.* reflected ray.
**Reflektions-.** see Reflexions-.
**Reflexbewegung,** *f.* reflex movement.
**Reflexionsebene,** *f.* plane of reflection.
**reflexionsfrei,** *a.* nonreflecting.
**Reflexions-goniometer,** *n.* reflecting goniometer. -**vermögen,** *n.* reflecting power. -**winkel,** *m.* angle of reflection.
**Reflexwirkung,** *f.* reflex action or effect.
**reformieren,** *v.t.* reform.
**Refr.,** *abbrev.* (Refraktion) refraction.
**refraktär,** *a.* refractory.
**Refraktions-winkel,** *m.* angle of refraction. -**zahl,** *f.* refractive index.
**refrigerieren,** *v.t.* refrigerate. — *v.i.* freeze.
**Regal,** *n.* shelves, case with shelves.
**rege,** *a.* moving, movable, quick, active, lively, industrious.
**Regel,** *f.* rule; principle, standard; (*Med.*) menstruation.
**regelbar,** *a.* regulable, adjustable.

**Regel-barkeit,** *f.* regulability, adjustability. **-einrichtung,** *f.* regulating or controlling device.
**regelfähig,** *a.* regulable, adjustable.
**Regel-grösse,** *f.* regular size, standard size. **-hahn,** *m* regulating cock. **-leistung,** *f.* normal output, normal load.
**regel-los,** *a.* anomalous, irregular; random. **-mässig,** *a.* regular; ordinary; normal. — *adv.* regularly.
**Regel-mässigkeit,** *f.* regularity; uniformity; normality. **-metall,** *n.* standard metal.
**regeln,** *v.t.* regulate, order, arrange, adjust, control, govern.
**Regelorgan,** *n.* regulating or adjusting or controlling device.
**regelrecht,** *a.* regular, normal, correct.
**Regelschraube,** *f.* regulating or adjusting screw.
**Regelung,** *f.* regulation, adjustment, control.
**regelwidrig,** *a.* irregular, abnormal.
**regen,** *v.t.* move, rouse. — *v.r.* stir, be active.
**Regen,** *m.* rain.
**regenarm,** *a.* having little rain, dry.
**Regenbogen,** *m.* rainbow.
**regenbogenfarbig,** *a.* rainbow-colored, iridescent.
**Regenbogenhaut,** *f.* iris.
**regendicht,** *a.* rainproof, showerproof.
**Regenerat,** *n.* reclaimed product (rubber, oil or the like), reclaim. **-gummi,** *m.* reclaimed rubber.
**Regenerativ-feuerung,** *f.* regenerative firing or heating. **-ofen,** *m.* regenerative furnace.
**Regeneratmischung,** *f.* (*Rubber*) reclaim mix.
**regenerieren,** *v.t.* regenerate; reclaim.
**Regenerierung,** *f.* regeneration; reclaiming.
**Regeneriervorrichtung,** *f.* regenerative device.
**Regenfang,** *m.* cistern.
**regenlos,** *a.* rainless, dry.
**Regen-mass,** *n.*, **-messer,** *m.* rain gage. **-menge,** *f.* amount of rain. **-schirm,** *m.* umbrella. **-schutz,** *m.* protection against rain. **-tropfen,** *m.* raindrop. **-wasser,** *n.* rain water. **-wurm,** *m.* earthworm. **-zeit,** *f.* rainy season.
**Regie,** *f.* administration; management.
**regieren,** *v.t.* rule, govern, regulate, manage. — *v.i.* rule, reign.
**Regierung,** *f.* government, administration; direction; rule, reign; steerage.
**Regieverschluss,** *m.* bond. — **unter —,** in bond, bonded.
**Register,** *n.* index; (table of) contents; register; record. **-band,** *n.* index volume. **-karte,** *f.* index card.
**Registratur,** *f.* registry; registry book.
**Registrier-.** recording; indexing. **-apparat,** *m.* recording (or indexing) apparatus.
**registrieren,** *v.t.* register, record; file; index.
**Registrier-ung,** *f.* registration; recording; filing; indexing. **-vorrichtung,** *f.* recording device.
**Regler,** *m.* regulator, governor, controller.
**Reglisse,** *f.* licorice (juice or drops); marshmallow paste.
**Reglung,** *f.* regulation, etc. (see regeln).
**regnen,** *v.i.* rain.
**regnerisch,** *a.* rainy.
**regsam,** *a.* active, quick, agile.
**Regstoff,** *m.* ferment.
**regulär,** *a.* regular.
**Regularität,** *f.* regularity.
**Regulationsvorgang,** *m.* regulatory process.
**regulierbar,** *a.* regulable, adjustable.
**regulieren,** *v.t.* regulate; adjust, control.
**regulierfähig,** *a.* regulable, adjustable.
**Regulier-hahn,** *m.* regulating cock. **-schraube,** *f.* adjusting screw.
**Regulierung,** *f.* regulation.
**Regulierungsvorrichtung,** *f.* regulating or adjusting device.
**Regulierwiderstand,** *m.* adjustable resistance.
**regulinisch,** *a.* reguline.
**Regulusofen,** *m.* regulus furnace; reduction crucible (for antimony).
**Regung,** *f.* motion, moving; emotion.
**Reh,** *n.* roe (deer), doe, buck. **-braun,** *n.* velvet brown (an iron pigment); fawn color.
**reh-braun, -farben, -farbig,** *a.* fawn-colored.
**Reh-leder,** *n.* doeskin; buckskin; chamois. **-posten,** *m.pl.* buckshot.
**Reibe,** *f.* grater, rasp.
**reibecht,** *a.* fast to rubbing.
**Reibechtheit,** *f.* fastness to rubbing, resistance to abrasion.
**Reibeisen,** *n.* rasp; grater.
**Reibemühle,** *f.* grinding mill, grinder.
**reiben,** *v.t.* rub; grind, triturate (colors, etc.); rasp, grate; scour; chafe; erase; abrade.
**Reibepulver,** *n.* abrasive powder.
**Reiber,** *m.* rubber, brayer, pestle; grater.
**Reib-festigkeit,** *f.* resistance to abrasion. **-fläche,** *f.* rubbing surface; rubbed surface. **-gut,** *n.* material to be ground. **-kasten,** *m.* grinding mill, grinder. **-keule,** *f.* pestle. **-mühle,** *f.* grinding mill. **-oxydation,** *f.* frictional oxidation. **-probe,** *f.* rubbing or grinding test or sample. **-satz,** *m.* friction composition; specif., fulminate. **-schale,** *f.* mortar.
**Reibsel,** *n.* grindings, raspings.
**Reib-stein,** *m.* grinding stone. **-stelle,** *f.* rubbed place, friction mark.
**reibunecht,** *a.* not fast to rubbing.
**Reibung,** *f.* friction; rubbing, etc. (see reiben); rub, difficulty.
**Reibungs-antrieb,** *m.* (*Mach.*) friction drive. **-beiwert,** *m.* coefficient of friction. **-elektrizität,** *f.* frictional electricity. **-festigkeit,**

*f.* resistance to rubbing or abrasion. **-fläche,** *f.* friction surface.

**reibungsfrei,** *a.* frictionless.

**Reibungskoefficient,** *m.* coefficient of friction.

**reibungslos,** *a.* frictionless.

**Reibungs-messer,** *m.* friction meter, tribometer. **-messung,** *f.* measurement of friction. **-probe,** *f.* friction test, rubbing test. **-wärme,** *f.* frictional heat. **-wert,** *m.* coefficient of friction. **-widerstand,** *m.* frictional resistance. **-zahl, -ziffer,** *f.* coefficient of friction.

**Reibzünd-hölzchen,** *n.* friction match. **-schraube,** *f.* (*Expl.*) friction primer.

**reich,** *a.* rich; abundant.

**Reich,** *n.* state, body politic; empire, kingdom, etc.

**-reich.** rich (in), abounding (in).

**Reichblei,** *n.* rich lead (argentiferous).

**reichen,** *v.t.* reach, pass, give. — *v.i.* reach, extend, suffice, last.

**Reich-frischen,** *n.* (*Copper*) enriching. **-gas,** *n.* rich gas.

**reich-haltig,** *a.* plentiful, abundant. **-lich,** *a.* abundant, copious, rich, full.

**Reichs-.** State, Government, National; (formerly, under the Kaiser) Imperial. **-amt,** *n.* Government (or National) Office or Bureau. **-anstalt,** *f.* Government Institute. **-bahn,** *f.* National Railway.

**Reich-schaum,** *m.* (*Metal.*) the zinc crust, rich in silver, etc., formed in the Parkes process. **-schlacke,** *f.* rich slag. **-schmelzen,** *n.* smelting of precious metals.

**Reichs-gesundheitsamt,** *n.* Government Board of Health. **-kraftstoff,** *m.* a motor fuel containing benzol, alcohol and tetralin. **-mark,** *f.* reichsmark (the German monetary unit). **-patent,** *n.* German patent.

**Reich-tum,** *m.* wealth, richness, abundance. **-weite,** *f.* range, reach, scope.

**reif,** *a.* ripe; mature.

**Reif,** *m.* ring, hoop; tire; collar; **hoarfrost.**

**Reife,** *f.* ripeness; maturity; (of beer, etc.) age; puberty. **-grad,** *m.* degree of ripeness.

**reifeln,** *v.t.* channel, groove; rifle.

**reifen,** *v.t. & i.* ripen, mature.

**Reifen,** *m.* ring, hoop; tire; collar.

**reifenartig,** *a.* ring-like, hoop-like.

**Reifen-mischung,** *f.* (*Rubber*) tire stock. **-regenerat,** *n.* (*Rubber*) tire reclaim. **-schlauch,** *m.* inner tube (of a tire).

**Reife-stadium,** *n.* stage of maturity. **-vorgang,** *m.* ripening or maturing process. **-zustand,** *m.* ripe state, ripeness.

**Reifholz,** *n.* heartwood; hoop wood.

**reiflich,** *a.* mature, thorough.

**Reifpunkt,** *m.* frost point.

**Reifung,** *f.* ripening, maturing.

**Reifungskörper,** *m.* ripening substance, accelerator, (*Photog.*) sensitizer.

**Reihe,** *f.* series; row, succession; order; course; range; suite, train; rank, file; turn; column, line. — **der — nach,** in succession.

**reihen,** *v.t.* arrange in a series or row; (*Elec.*) connect in series; string (beads); baste.

**Reihen-anordnung,** *f.* (*Elec.*) series connection. **-bilder,** *n.pl.* pictures in a series, specif. motion pictures. **-fertigung,** *f.* assembly-line production. **-folge,** *f.* sequence, order, succession. **-formel,** *f.* series formula. **-nummer,** *f.* serial number. **-schaltung,** *f.* (*Elec.*) connection in series.

**Reihenschluss-.** (*Elec.*) series-wound.

**reihenweise,** *adv.* in a series.

**Reiher,** *m.* heron.

**Reihung,** *f.* arranging in series, etc. (see reihen).

**rein,** *a.* pure; undiluted; clean, clear, tidy; sheer. — *adv.* purely, clean, absolutely.

**Reinbenzol,** *n.* (pure) benzene.

**reinblau,** *a.* pure blue; sky-blue.

**Rein-blauton,** *m.* (*Dyeing*) sky-blue shade. **-darstellung,** *f.* preparation in a pure condition, purification. **-element,** *n.* pure element (consisting of but one isotope). **-ertrag,** *m.* net yield; net profit.

**reingelb,** *a.* pure yellow.

**Rein-gewicht,** *n.* net weight. **-gewinn,** *m.* net yield; net profit. **-gewinnung,** *f.* purification.

**Reinheit,** *f.* purity, pureness, etc. (see rein).

**Reinheits-grad,** *m.* degree of purity. **-probe,** *f.* test for purity.

**reinigen,** *v.t.* purify; refine (metals, etc.); rectify (spirits); clarify (liquids); clean, cleanse, scrub, strain, scour (silk), purge; disinfect.

**Reiniger,** *m.* purifier, etc. (see reinigen).

**Reinigerei,** *f.* purifying; cleaning; purifying or cleaning plant.

**Reiniger-masse,** *f.* purifier mass; cleansing material. **-wasser,** *n.* cleansing water.

**Reinigung,** *f.* purification, etc. (see reinigen); menstruation.

**Reinigungs-anlage,** *f.* purification plant. **-apparat,** *m.* purifying apparatus, purifier, etc. (see reinigen). **-bad,** *n.* purifying bath, cleaning bath, clearing bath. **-bassin,** *n.* purifying tank or basin. **-behälter,** *m.* filtering basin or tank. **-benzin,** *n.* gasoline (or petroleum naphtha) for cleaning. **-feuer,** *n.* refining fire. **-flasche,** *f.* (for gases) washing bottle, wash bottle. **-kraft,** *f.* purifying or cleaning power. **-masse,** *f.* purifying mass, cleansing material. **-mittel,** *n.* purifying agent, purifier; cleansing agent, detergent; purgative. **-möller,** *m.* (*Metal.*) purifying charge. **-verfahren,** *n.* purifying (or refining or cleansing) process. **-vermögen,** *n.* detergent power,

cleansing power, etc. (see reinigen). **-wirkung,** *f.* purifying or cleansing action or effect.
**Rein-kohle,** *f.* pure coal, clean(ed) coal; solid carbon. **-koks,** *m.* pure coke, clean coke. **-kultur, -kultivierung,** *f.* (*Bact.*) pure culture, pure cultivation.
**reinlich,** *a.* neat, trim, tidy, smart.
**Rein-öl,** *n.* pure oil, clean oil. **-schrift,** *f.* fair copy, final copy. **-seide,** *f.* pure silk, all-silk.
**reinst,** *a.* purest, etc. (see rein).
**Rein-toluol,** *n.* pure toluene. **-wasser,** *n.* pure water. **-weiss,** *n.* pure white, clear white.
**reinwollen,** *a.* (*Textiles*) all-wool.
**Rein-wismut,** *n.* pure bismuth. **-xylol,** *n.* (*Com.*) a mixture of the three xylenes (*m*-xylene predominating). **-zellulose,** *f.* pure cellulose. **-zucht,** *f.* (*Bact.*) pure culture. **-zuchthefe,** *f.* pure-culture yeast. **-züchtung,** *f.* obtaining a pure culture.
**Reis,** *m.* rice. — *n.* twig, sprig; shoot, scion. **-branntwein,** *m.* rice spirit.
**Reise,** *f.* journey, trip, travel, voyage; (*Tech.*) campaign.
**reisen,** *v.i.* travel, go, set out, leave.
**Reis-faser,** *f.* rice fiber. **-futtermehl,** *n.* rice flour, ground rice.
**Reisig, Reisicht,** *n.* brushwood, twigs, prunings.
**Reis-kleie,** *f.* rice bran. **-körper,** *m.* (*Med.*) rice body. **-mehl,** *n.* rice flour. **-papier,** *n.* rice paper. **-puder,** *m.* rice powder.
**Reissbelastung,** *f.* breaking load.
**Reissblei,** *n.* graphite. **-tiegel,** *m.* graphite crucible.
**Reissbrett,** *n.* drawing board.
**Reisschleim,** *m.* rice water.
**Reissebene,** *f.* fracture plane.
**reissen,** *v.t.* tear, pull, drag; split, rend, rupture; trace, draw; bruise, crush (malt); rough-grind (glass). — *v.i.* burst, split, crack, break; tear along. — *v.r.* scratch oneself, tear one's clothes; scramble (for). — **reissend,** *p.a.* tearing, etc. (see reissen); rapacious; rapid.
**Reiss-feder,** *f.* drawing pen, ruling pen. **-festigkeit,** *f.* resistance to tearing or breaking, tenacity, tensile strength. **-gelb,** *n.* orpiment. **-kohle,** *f.* charcoal crayon. **-korn,** *n.* (*Leather*) artificial grain. **-lack,** *m.* crackle lacquer. **-länge,** *f.* breaking length (of fibers). **-last,** *f.* breaking load. **-nagel,** *m.* thumbtack. **-schiene,** *f.* T-square.
**Reisstärke,** *f.* rice starch.
**Reiss-verschluss,** *m.* slide fastener, zipper. **-wolf,** *m.* breaker, teaser, willow **-wolle,** *f.* reclaimed wool (from old fabrics). **-zeug,** *n.* drawing instruments. **-zwecke,** *f.* thumbtack.
**Reit-.** riding.
**reiten,** *v.t.* & *i.* ride (horseback).
**Reiter,** *m.* rider; slider; horseman. **-gewicht,** *n.* rider (the weight).
**Reiz,** *m.* irritation; excitation; irritant; stimulus; excitement; charm, attraction, grace.
**reizbar,** *a.* irritable, sensitive.
**Reizbeantwortung,** *f.* response to stimulus.
**reizen,** *v.t.* irritate, stimulate, excite; charm, attract, allure.
**Reiz-gas,** *n.* irritant gas, (*Mil.*) tear gas or sneeze gas. **-geschoss,** *n.* irritant gas projectile. **-gift,** *n.* irritant poison. **-kerze,** *f.* (*Mil.*) irritant candle. **-körper,** *m.* irritant substance, (*Mil.*) lacrimator.
**reizlos,** *a.* nonirritant, nonstimulating; unattractive, insipid.
**Reiz-losigkeit,** *f.* nonirritance, etc. (see reizlos). **-mittel,** *n.* irritant, stimulant, incitement, inducement. **-stoff,** *m.* irritating or stimulating substance; (*Med.*) adjuvant; (*Mil.*) irritant or harassing agent. **-topf,** *m.* (*Mil.*) irritant candle.
**Reizung,** *f.* irritation, etc. (see reizen).
**Reiz-wirkung,** *f.* irritating effect; stimulating effect. **-würfel,** *m.* (*Mil.*) irritant capsule.
**rekapitulieren,** *v.t.* recapitulate.
**Reklamation,** *f.* complaint; objection; claim.
**Reklame,** *f.* advertisement, advertising; puffery.
**reklamieren,** *v.t.* claim, reclaim. — *v.i.* object.
**rekombinieren,** *v.t.* & *i.* recombine.
**rekristallisieren,** *v.t.* recrystallize.
**Rekteseite,** *f.* right-hand page, odd page.
**Rektifikations-apparat,** *m.* rectifying apparatus, rectifier. **-becken,** *n.* rectifying vessel. **-kolonne,** *f.* rectifying column.
**Rektifizierapparat,** *m.* rectifying apparatus.
**rektifizieren,** *v.t.* rectify.
**Rektifizier-kolonne, -säule,** *f.* rectifying column.
**Rektifizierung,** *f.* rectification.
**Relais,** *n.* relay.
**relationieren,** *v.t.* relate, correlate.
**relativistisch,** *a.* relativistic.
**Relativität,** *f.* relativity.
**relaxieren,** *v.t.* & *i.* relax.
**Relevanz,** *f.* relevance, relevancy.
**Reliefdruck,** *m.* relief printing.
**remittieren,** *v.t.* & *i.* remit.
**Renchgneis,** *m.* (*Petrog.*) paragneiss.
**Rendement,** *m.* yield, rendement.
**Rendita,** *f.* extent of weighting (fabrics).
**renken,** *v.t.* bend, turn; wrench, sprain.
**Renn-arbeit,** *f.* (*Iron*) direct process. **-eisen,** *n.* malleable iron extracted by the direct process.
**rennen,** *v.i.* run; race. — *v.t.* run; (*Metal.*) extract (malleable iron) directly from the ore.
**Renn-feuer,** *n.* bloomery hearth (where malleable iron is extracted by the direct process). **-feuereisen,** *n.* = Renneisen. **-feuerschlacke,**

*f.* (*Iron*) direct-process slag. **-herd,** *m.* = Rennfeuer. **-schlacke,** *f.* = Rennfeuerschlacke. **-stahl,** *m.* steel made directly from the ore, natural steel, bloomery iron. **-tier,** *n.* reindeer. **-verfahren,** *n.* (*Iron*) direct process.

**Renommee,** *n.* renown.

**renommieren,** *v.i.* boast, brag. — **renommiert,** *p.a.* renowned, well-known.

**renovieren,** *v.t.* renovate, renew.

**rentabel,** *a.* profitable.

**Rentabilität,** *f.* profitableness.

**Rente,** *f.* rent, revenue, income.

**Rentenmark,** *f.* a monetary unit based on securities and normally equivalent in value to the reichsmark.

**rentieren,** *v.i. & r.* be profitable, pay.

**Reparatur,** *f.* repair.

**reparieren,** *v.t.* repair.

**Repassierbad,** *n.* (*Silk*) second boiling-off bath.

**repassieren,** *v.t.* boil off (silk) a second time; trim, mend (cloth).

**repastieren,** *v.t.* repaste.

**Repertorium,** *n.* index, compendium (as in titles of periodicals); repertoire.

**repetieren,** *v.t. & i.* repeat.

**Repetition,** *f.* repetition; recapitulation.

**Repetitorium,** *n.* (as book title) compendium, summary; (in schools) review course.

**Repräsentant,** *m.* representative.

**Reprise,** *f.* normal or allowable moisture.

**Reproduktionskraft,** *f.* reproductive power.

**reproduzierbar,** *a.* reproducible.

**reproduzieren,** *v.t.* reproduce.

**Reps,** *m.* rape. **-öl,** *n.* rape oil, rapeseed oil.

**Reptilleder,** *n.* reptile leather.

**requirieren,** *v.t.* request; requisition.

**Reseda,** *f.* mignonette. — **gelbe —,** dyer's rocket.

**Resedagrün,** *n.* a kind of chrome green.

**Reservage,** *f.* (*Calico*) resist, reserve. **-artikel,** *m.* (*Calico*) resist style. **-druck,** *m.* resist printing, resist style. **-papp,** *m.* resist paste.

**Reserve,** *f.* reserve; (*Calico*) reserve, resist, also resist paste. **-artikel,** *m.* = Reservageartikel. **-druck,** *m.* = Reservagedruck. **-druckfarbe,** *f.* resist printing paste. **-mittel,** *n.* reserve, resist. **-muster,** *n.* reference pattern. **-papp,** *m.* (*Calico*) resist paste. **-stärke,** *f.* reserve starch; reserve strength. **-stoff,** *m.* reserve material. **-teil,** *m.* spare part.

**reservierbar,** *a.* reservable; (*Calico*) resistible.

**Reservierbarkeit,** *f.* reservability; (*Calico*) resistibility.

**reservieren,** *v.t.* reserve; (*Calico*) subject to the action of a reserve or resist. — **reserviert,** *p.a.* reserved; (*Calico*) resist-printed, resist.

**Reservierungs-artikel,** *m.* (*Calico*) resist-printed goods, also resist style. **-mittel,** *n.* (*Calico*) resist, reserve. **-wirkung,** *f.* (*Calico*) resist effect.

**residuell,** *a.* residual.

**Residuum,** *n.* residuum, residue.

**Resinat,** *n.* resinate; rosinate. **-firnis,** *m.* resinate varnish, resinate boiled oil.

**resinogen,** *a.* resinogenous, resiniferous.

**Resonanz-schwingung,** *f.* resonance vibration, covibration. **-spannung,** *f.* resonance potential. **-zustand,** *m.* state of resonance.

**resorbieren,** *v.t.* resorb, reabsorb.

**Resorbierung,** *f.* resorption, reabsorption.

**Resorcin,** *n.* resorcinol, resorcin. **-blau,** *n.* resorcin blue. **-gelb,** *n.* resorcin yellow.

**Resorzin,** *n.* resorcinol, resorcin.

**resp.,** *abbrev.* of respektive.

**respektive,** *adv.* respectively, or rather, or.

**Respirationsnahrungsmittel,** *n.* respiratory food.

**Rest,** *m.* residue; part (of a molecule), radical; remainder, rest, remains, remnant.

**Rest-.** residual. **-affinität,** *f.* residual affinity. **-bier,** *n.* (*Brewing*) waste beer. **-block,** *m.* (*Metal.*) ingot butt. **-feuchtigkeit,** *f.* residual moisture. **-flüssigkeit,** *f.* residual liquid. **-gas,** *n.* residual gas. **-glied,** *n.* residual term or member; (*Math.*) remainder in an infinite series. **-härte,** *f.* residual hardness, (of water) permanent hardness.

**restieren,** *v.i.* remain, be left.

**Rest-ion,** *m.* residual ion. **-keim,** *m.* residual nucleus. **-kohle,** *f.* residual coal or carbon; carbonized residue. **-kraft,** *f.* residual force or power; (*Magnetism*) remanence. **-lauge,** *f.* residual liquor or liquid.

**restlich,** *a.* residual, remaining.

**restlos,** *a.* without residue (or remainder), total.

**Rest-lösung,** *f.* residual solution. **-luft,** *f.* residual air. **-magnetismus,** *m.* residual magnetism, remanence. **-plasma,** *m.* residual plasma, specif. residual electrons. **-schmelze,** *f.* (*Metal.*) residual melt or heat; (*Petrog.*) residual magma. **-stickstoff,** *m.* residual nitrogen. **-stickstoffkörper,** *m.* residual nitrogenous substance. **-strahl,** *m.* residual ray. **-strom,** *m.* residual current. **-valenz,** *f.* residual valence.

**resublimieren,** *v.t.* resublime.

**Resultat,** *n.* result.

**resultieren,** *v.i.* result. — **resultierend,** *p.a.* resulting, resultant.

**Resultierende,** *f.* resultant.

**retardieren,** *v.t.* retard.

**Retenchinon,** *n.* retenequinone.

**Retorte,** *f.* retort.

**Retorten-bauch,** *m.* belly or bulb of a retort. **-gestell,** *n.* retort stand. **-hals,** *m.* neck of a retort. **-halter,** *m.* retort holder, retort stand. **-haus,** *n.* retort house. **-helm,** *m.* retort head, retort helm. **-kammer,** *f.* retort chamber. **-kitt,** *m.* retort cement, retort lute. **-kohle,** *f.* retort carbon. **-mündung,** *f.* mouth of a retort. **-ofen,** *m.* retort furnace. **-paraffin,** *n.* (*Petroleum*) still wax. **-reihe,** *f.* series or bank of retorts. **-rückstand,** *m.* retort residue. **-vergasung,** *f.* gasification in retorts. **-verkokung,** *f.* retort coking. **-vorstoss,** *m.* adapter; (*Zinc*) condenser (of clay or iron).

**Retouchier-.** see Retuschier-.

**retouchieren,** *v.t.* retouch.

**Retour-.** return, returning.

**Retournöl,** *n.* recovered oil.

**Retourschlacke,** *f.* (*Metal.*) return slag.

**retten,** *v.t.* save, rescue, recover.

**Rettich, Rettig,** *m.* black radish.

**Rettung,** *f.* rescue, recovery, saving, salvage.

**rettungslos,** *a.* irrecoverable, irretrievable.

**Rettungsmittel,** *n.* remedy, resource.

**Retusche,** *f.* (*Photog.*) retouching.

**retuschieren,** *v.t.* retouch.

**Retuschier-essenz,** *f.* retouching varnish. **-farbe,** *f.* retouching color. **-lack,** *m.* retouching varnish. **-mittel,** *n.* retouching agent.

**reuen,** *v.t.* repent of, regret.

**Reugeld,** *n.* forfeit.

**Reuse,** *f.* cage, cage grid; bow net.

**Reusse,** *m.* Russian.

**reverberieren,** *v.t.* reverberate.

**Reverberier-ofen,** *m.*, **-feuer,** *n.* reverberatory furnace, reverberatory.

**reversibel,** *a.* reversible.

**Reversibilität,** *f.* reversibility.

**Reversier-.** reversing, reversible.

**reversierbar,** *a.* reversible.

**reversieren,** *v.t. & i.* reverse.

**Revertex,** *n.* Revertex (a concentrated latex). *T.N.*

**revidieren,** *v.t.* revise; check, examine.

**Revier,** *n.* district, region; field; range; precinct; (*Mining*) country.

**Revision,** *f.* revision; review, checking.

**Revisionsspachtel,** *f.* glazing putty.

**Revolver-.** revolving.

**rez.,** *abbrev.* of reziprok.

**Rezension,** *f.* review, criticism.

**rezent,** *a.* recent.

**Rezept,** *n.* recipe, formula, prescription. **-buch,** *n.* receipt book.

**Rezeptor,** *m.* receptor, receiver.

**Rezeptorenseitenkette,** *f.* receptor sidechain.

**Rezeptur,** *f.* dispensing (of medicines); recipe; receivership.

**rezessiv,** *a.* recessive.

**Rezipient,** *m.* receiver; (of persons) recipient.

**reziprok,** *a.* reciprocal. — *adv.* reciprocally, conversely.

**Reziproke,** *f.* reciprocal.

**RGT-Regel,** *abbrev.* (*R*eaktions*g*eschwindigkeit-*T*emperatur-Regel). reaction-velocity-temperature rule.

**Rhabarber,** *m.* rhubarb. — **falscher—,** (*Pharm.*) the root of European rhubarb.

**Rhabarber-gelb,** *n.* chrysophanic acid. **-gerbsäure,** *f.* rheotannic acid. **-säure,** *f.* chrysophanic acid.

**Rhachitis,** *f.* rachitis, rickets.

**rhachitisch,** *a.* rachitic.

**rheinisch, rheinländisch,** *a.* Rhenish.

**Rheinsäure,** *f.* rheic acid (chrysophanic acid).

**Rheinwein,** *m.* Rhine wine, Rhenish wine.

**Rhigolen,** *n.* rhigolene (a very volatile petroleum distillate).

**Rhizocarpinsäure,** *f.* rhizocarpinic acid.

**Rhizocarpsäure,** *f.* rhizocarpic acid.

**Rhizoninsäure,** *f.* rhizoninic acid.

**Rhizonsäure,** *f.* rhizonic acid.

**Rhld.,** *abbrev.* (Rheinland) Rhineland.

**Rhöadin,** *n.* rheadine, rhoeadine.

**Rhodan,** *n.* thiocyanogen, (formerly) sulfocyanogen.

**Rhodan-.** thiocyanogen, thiocyanate of, thiocyano-. **-aluminium,** *n.* aluminum thiocyanate. **-ammonium,** *n.* ammonium thiocyanate. **-ammonlösung,** *f.* ammonium thiocyanate solution.

**Rhodanat,** *n.* thiocyanate, (formerly) sulfocyanate. **-lösung,** *f.* thiocyanate solution.

**Rhodan-baryum,** *n.* barium thiocyanate. **-eisen,** *n.* iron thiocyanate, esp. ferric thiocyanate, iron(III) thiocyanate. **-eisenrot,** *n.* ferric thiocyanate, iron(III) thiocyanate.

**Rhodanid,** *n.* thiocyanate, (formerly) sulfocyanate( esp. an -ic salt; cf. Rhodanür).

**Rhodanierung,** *f.* introduction of thiocyanogen, thiocyanation.

**Rhodan-ion,** *n.* thiocyanogen ion, $CNS^-$. **-kali, -kalium,** *n.* potassium thiocyanate. **-kalzium,** *n.* calcium thiocyanate. **-kupfer,** *n.* cupric thiocyanate, copper(II) thiocyanate. **-lösung,** *f.* thiocyanate solution. **-metall,** *n.* (metallic) thiocyanate. **-methyl,** *n.* methyl thiocyanate. **-natrium,** *n.* sodium thiocyanate. **-nickel,** *m.* nickel thiocyanate. **-quecksilber,** *n.* mercury thiocyanate. **-salz,** *n.* thiocyanate. **-säure,** *f.* (*Org. Chem.*) thiocyan(at)o acid. **-tonerde,** *f.* aluminum thiocyanate.

**Rhodanür,** *n.* (-ous) thiocyanate.

**Rhodan-verbindung,** *f.* thiocyanogen compound. **-wasserstoff,** *m.* hydrogen thiocyanate, thiocyanic acid. **-wasserstoffsäure,** *f.* thiocyanic acid, (formerly) sulfocyanic acid. **-zinn, -zinnoxyd,** *n.* stannic thiocyanate, tin(IV) thiocyanate. **-zinnoxydul,** *n.* stannous thiocyanate, tin(II) thiocyanate.

**Rhodinasäure,** *f.* rhodinic acid.

**Rhodium-chlorwasserstoffsäure,** *f.* chlororhodic

acid. **-metall,** *n.* rhodium metal, metallic rhodium. **-salz,** *n.* rhodium salt. **-überzug,** *m.* rhodium coating or plating. **-verbindung,** *f.* rhodium compound.

**Rhombendodekaeder,** *n.* rhombic dodecahedron.

**rhombenförmig,** *a.* rhomb-shaped, rhombic.

**rhombisch,** *a.* rhombic.

**Rhomboeder,** *n.* rhombohedron.

**rhomboedrisch,** *a.* rhombohedral.

**rhomboidisch,** *a.* rhomboid, rhomboidal.

**Rhuslack,** *m.* rhus varnish (from the Japanese varnish tree, *Rhus vernicifera*).

**rhythmisch,** *a.* rhythmic.

**Rhythmus,** *m.* rhythm.

**Richt-analyse,** *f.* guide analysis, approximate analysis. **-blei,** *n.* plumb line, plummet.

**richten,** *v.t.* direct, turn; arrange, adjust, align, set, straighten; orient; dress; raise, erect; judge. — *v.r.* turn, rise, conform.

**Richter,** *m.* judge; justice.

**richtig,** *a.* right, correct, accurate, exact, just, fair, true.

**Richtigkeit,** *f.* rightness, etc. (see richtig).

**richtigphasig,** *a.* of the right phase.

**Richtigstellung,** *f.* rectification, correction.

**Richt-kraft,** *f.* directive force. **-lineal,** *n.* straightedge. **-linie,** *f.* guide line, guiding line; guiding principle; direction, instruction. **-mass,** *n.* standard, gage. **-platte,** *f.* adjusting plate, adjusting table. **-scheit,** *n.* rule, straightedge. **-schnur,** *f.* chalk line; plumb line; guide, pattern. **-schraube,** *f.* adjusting screw. **-strom,** *m.* (*Elec.*) rectified current.

**Richtung,** *f.* direction, bearing; directing, etc. (see richten); trend.

**Richtungsänderung,** *f.* change of direction.

**richtungslos,** *a.* directionless.

**Richtungsquantelung,** *f.* directional quantization.

**richtungsweisend,** *a.* directing, guiding.

**Richtwert,** *m.* coefficient; datum; approximate value.

**Ricinölsäure,** *f.* ricinoleic acid.

**Ricinus,** *m.* castor-oil plant. **-öl,** *n.* castor oil. **-ölsäure,** *f.* ricinoleic acid. **-ölseife,** *f.* castor-oil soap. **-ölsulfosäure,** *f.* castor-oil sulfonic acid. **-samen,** *m.* castor bean. **-säure,** *f.* ricinic (ricinoleic) acid. **-seife,** *f.* castor-oil soap.

**rieb,** *pret.* (of reiben) rubbed, etc.

**Riech-.** smelling, scented, odoriferous; olfactory. **-bein,** *n.* (*Anat.*) ethmoid.

**riechen,** *v.i. & t.* smell. — **— nach,** smell of. — **riechend,** *p.a.* smelling, redolent, strong, fragrant.

**Riech-essig,** *m.* aromatic vinegar. **-fläschchen,** *n.* smelling bottle. **-mittel,** *n.* scent, perfume. **-nerv,** *m.* olfactory nerve. **-probe,** *f.* smelling test or sample. **-rohr,** *n.* volatilizing tube. **-salz,** *n.* smelling salts. **-spur,** *f.* scent. **-stoff,** *m.* odoriferous substance, perfume. **-topf,** *m.* (*Mil.*) irritant gas generator. **-wasser,** *n.* scented water. **-würfel,** *m.* (*Mil.*) chemical capsule.

**Ried,** *n.* reed; moor; fagot.

**rief,** *pret.* (of rufen) called.

**Riefe,** *f.* groove, channel; striation.

**riefeln, riefen,** *v.t.* channel, groove; knurl, mill; rifle.

**riefig,** *a.* grooved, channeled; striated.

**Riegel,** *m.* rail; bar; bolt. **-schneiden,** *n.* (*Soap*) barring.

**Riemen,** *m.* belt, band, strap, thong; oar. **-antrieb,** *m.* (*Mach.*) belt drive. **-fett,** *n.* belt dressing. **-kitt,** *m.* belt (or strap) cement. **-leder,** *n.* belt leather, belting; strap leather. **-scheibe,** *f.* belt pulley. **-schmiere,** *f.*, **-schmiermittel,** *n.* belt lubricant. **-trieb,** *m.* belt drive, belt transmission.

**Ries,** *n.* (*Paper*) ream.

**Riese,** *m.* giant.

**Riesel-feld,** *n.* field irrigated with sewage. **-höhe,** *f.* packing depth (of a tower). **-jauche,** *f.* sewage (as a fertilizer). **-kolonne,** *f.* trickling column. **-kühler,** *m.* spray cooler, trickling cooler.

**rieseln,** *v.i.* trickle, drip, ripple, gush. — *v.t.* sprinkle; spray; irrigate.

**Riesel-turm,** *m.* trickling tower, spray tower, washing tower. **-wasser,** *n.* trickling water; irrigation water.

**Riesen-.** gigantic, colossal. **-schlange,** *f.* python, boa constrictor, anaconda. **-zelle,** *f.* giant cell.

**riesig,** *a.* gigantic, huge.

**riet,** *pret.* (of raten) advised, etc.

**Riet,** *n.* (*Weaving*) reed.

**Riff,** *n.* reef, ridge, shelf, ledge.

**Riffel-.** grooved, channeled, fluted; ribbed; corrugated. **-blech,** *n.* corrugated plate or sheet. **-glas,** *n.* ribbed (channeled, corrugated) glass.

**riffeln,** *v.t.* channel, groove, corrugate, rib; riffle (flax).

**Riffeltrichter,** *m.* ribbed funnel.

**rigorös,** *a.* rigorous.

**Rille,** *f.* furrow, groove, channel.

**Rillenscheibe,** *f.* grooved pulley, sheave.

**Rind,** *n.* bovine animal, neat, (*pl.*) cattle.

**Rinde,** *f.* rind; bark, cortex; crust.

**Rinden-.** cortical, bark. **-auszug,** *m.* bark extract. **-borke,** *f.* outer bark. **-farbstoff,** *m.* phlobaphene.

**rindenförmig,** *a.* like bark, corticiform.

**Rinden-gerbstoff,** *m.* bark tannin. **-gewebe,** *n.* cortical tissue. **-grau,** *n.* (*Anat.*) gray matter of the cortex. **-haut,** *f.* (*Bot.*) periderm. **-mühle,** *f.* bark(-grinding) mill. **-schicht,** *f.* cortical layer. **-span,** *m.* bark paring, bark chip. **-substanz,** *f.* cortical substance.

**Rinder-.** beef, cattle, bovine. **-blut,** *n.* oxblood. **-bouillon,** *f.* beef broth. **-braten,** *m.* roast beef. **-fett,** *n.* beef suet, beef fat. **-galle,** *f.* ox gall. **-klauenöl,** *n.* neat's-foot oil. **-markfett,** *n.* beef marrow fat. **-talg,** *m.* beef tallow. **-tuberkulose,** *f.* bovine tuberculosis.

**Rind-fleisch,** *n.* beef. **-fleischbrühe,** *f.* beef broth, beef tea. **-leder,** *n.* neat's leather, cowhide.

**Rinds-galle,** *f.* ox gall. **-klauenfett,** *n.* neat's-foot oil. **-leder,** *n.* neat's leather, cowhide.

**Rindspalte,** *f.* split cowhide.

**Rindstalg,** *m.* beef tallow, beef fat.

**Rind-vachette,** *f.* light cowhide. **-vieh,** *n.* cattle.

**Ring,** *m.* ring; cycle; link; coil; collar, band, hoop, loop.

**Ring-.** (*Org. Chem.*) cyclic, ring.

**ringähnlich,** *a.* ring-like, circular, cyclic, annular, areolar.

**Ring-alkohol,** *m.* cyclic alcohol. **-amin,** *n.* cyclic amine.

**ringartig,** *a.* = ringähnlich.

**Ring-aufspaltung,** *f.* ring cleavage. **-bildung,** *f.* ring formation. **-brenner,** *m.* ring burner. **-düse,** *f.* ring nozzle.

**Ringel,** *m.* & *n.* little ring or circle, ringlet, circlet, loop. **-blume,** *f.* marigold (*Calendula*). **-erz,** *n.* ring ore.

**ringelig,** *a.* ring-like, annular.

**ringeln,** *v.t.* ring; curl; girdle (trees). — *v.r.* curl.

**ringen,** *v.i.* struggle, wrestle. — *v.t.* wring; ring; curl.

**Ringerlösung,** *f.* (*Physiol.*) Ringer's solution.

**Ring-erweiterung,** *f.* ring extension. **-faser,** *f.* annular fiber.

**ringförmig,** *a.* cyclic; ring-shaped, annular.

**Ring-gasbrenner,** *m.* ring (gas) burner. **-gefüge,** *n.* ring structure. **-geschoss,** *n.* (*Mil.*) laminated shell. **-glied,** *n.* ring member. **-granate,** *f.* (*Mil.*) laminated shell. **-keton,** *n.* cyclic ketone. **-ofen,** *m.* (*Ceram.*) annular kiln, Hofmann kiln. **-öffnung,** *f.* ring opening. **-platte,** *f.* ring plate, annular plate. **-pulver,** *n.* (*Expl.*) ring-shaped powder, annular powder.

**rings,** *adv.* around.

**Ringschicht,** *f.* annular layer.

**ringschliessen,** *v.r.* form a ring.

**Ring-schliessung,** *f.*, **-schluss,** *m.* ring closure, cyclization.

**ringsher(um),** *adv.* round about, all around.

**Ring-spaltung,** *f.* ring cleavage. **-spannung,** *f.* ring tension. **-sprengung,** *f.* ring cleavage.

**ringsum,** *adv.* around, all around.

**ringungesättigt,** *p.a.* cyclically unsaturated, containing an unsaturated ring.

**Ring-verbindung,** *f.* cyclic compound, ring compound; ring(-type) joint; ring fastening. **-verkleinerung,** *f.* reduction of a ring to smaller size. **-wulst,** *n.* (*Geom.*) tore, torus, anchor ring. **-zahl,** *f.* number of rings.

**Rinne,** *f.* channel, groove, furrow, gutter.

**rinnen,** *v.i.* run, flow; drip, trickle; leak.

**Rinnenschlacke,** *f.* (*Metal.*) spout slag.

**Rinnstein,** *m.* sink; gutter; gutter stone.

**Rippe,** *f.* rib; fin, vane, flange.

**rippen,** *v.t.* rib. — **gerippt,** *p.a.* ribbed, fluted, corded, laid (paper).

**Rippen-.** ribbed; costal. **-fell,** *n.*, **-haut,** *f.* (costal) pleura. **-glas,** *n.* ribbed glass. **-heizkörper,** *m.* ribbed (or finned) radiator. **-rohr,** *n.* ribbed or finned pipe or tube. **-trichter,** *m.* ribbed funnel.

**rippenversehen,** *a.* (*Mach.*) ribbed, finned.

**Risigallum,** *n.* realgar.

**Risiko,** *n.* risk.

**riskieren,** *v.t.* risk.

**Rispe,** *f.* panicle; wild oat (*Avena fatua*).

**riss,** *pret.* (of reissen) tore, pulled, etc.

**Riss,** *m.* fissure, crack, flaw; rent, tear, gap; draft, sketch, design, plan.

**Riss(e)bildung,** *f.* formation of cracks, fissuring.

**rissempfindlich,** *a.* liable to crack or tear.

**Rissfestigkeit,** *f.* resistance to cracking or fissuring or tearing.

**rissfrei,** *a.* free from cracks, etc., flawless.

**rissig,** *a.* fissured, cracked, flawy, torn.

**Rissigkeit,** *f.* cracked or torn state.

**ritt,** *pret.* (of reiten) rode.

**Ritter,** *m.* knight. **-sporn,** *m.* larkspur.

**Ritz,** *m.*, **Ritze,** *f.* rift, cleft, fissure, crack, chink; slit; scratch.

**ritzbar,** *a.* capable of being cracked, scratched, etc. (see ritzen).

**Ritzel,** *n.* (*Mach.*) pinion.

**ritzen,** *v.t.* crack; slit; scratch; etch; cut.

**Ritzhärte,** *f.* hardness to scratching. **-probe,** *f.* abrasive hardness test, scratch test. **-prüfer,** *m.* abrasive hardness tester, sclerometer. **-verfahren,** *n.* = Ritzhärteprobe. **-zahl,** *f.* (scratch) hardness number.

**Ritz-probe,** *f.* scratch test or sample. **-versuch,** *m.* scratch test.

**Rizin,** *n.* ricin.

**Rizin-.** see Ricin-.

**Rk.,** *abbrev.* (Reaktion) reaction.

**Rkk.,** *abbrev.* (Reaktionen) reactions.

**rm.,** *abbrev.* (Raummeter) cubic meter, cu.m.

**Rm., RM.,** *abbrev.* Reichsmark; Rentenmark.

**Robbe,** *f.* (*Zoöl.*) seal.

**Robbentran,** *m.* seal oil.

**roch,** *pret.* (of riechen) smelled.

**Rochellesalz,** *n.* Rochelle salt, sodium potassium tartrate.

**röcheln,** *v.i.* rattle.

**Rock,** *m.* coat; gown, robe; skirt; frock.

**roden,** *v.t.* root out, grub, clear.

**Rogen,** *m.* roe, spawn. **-stein,** *m.* oölite.

**rogensteinartig,** *a.* oölitic.

**Roggen,** *m.* rye. **-brot,** *n.* rye bread. **-kleber,** *m.* rye gluten. **-kleie,** *f.* rye bran. **-mehl,** *n.* rye flour. **-mutter,** *f.* ergot. **-stärke,** *f.* rye starch. **-stroh,** *n.* rye straw.

**roh,** *a.* raw, crude; unrefined; blank; rough, coarse; gross.

**Roh-alkohol,** *m.* crude (or raw) alcohol. **-analyse,** *f.* rough or approximate analysis. **-antimon,** *n.* crude antimony. **-arbeit,** *f.* (*Metal.*) ore smelting. **-asbest,** *m.* crude asbestos. **-aufbereitung,** *f.* preliminary preparation. **-benzol,** *n.* crude benzene, benzol (or benzole). **-blei,** *n.* crude lead. **-blende,** *f.* (*Mining*) crude blende. **-block,** *m.* (*Metal.*) (raw) ingot. **-boden,** *m.* (*Agric.*) virgin soil. **-braunkohle,** *f.* crude lignite. **-brom,** *n.* crude bromine.

**Roheisen,** *n.* crude iron, pig iron. **-gans,** *f.* (iron) pig. **-guss,** *m.* pig-iron casting. **-mischer,** *m.* (*Iron*) hot-metal mixer. **-verfahren,** *n.* (*Iron*) pig process.

**Roh-ertrag,** *m.* gross yield; gross returns. **-erz,** *n.* raw ore. **-erzeugnis,** *f.* raw product. **-faser,** *f.* crude fiber. **-faserbestimmung,** *f.* determination of crude fiber. **-fett,** *n.* crude fat; raw fat. **-film,** *m.* (*Photog.*) blank film, raw stock, also negative film. **-filter,** *n.* coarse filter. **-formel,** *f.* empirical formula. **-frischen,** *n.* (*Metal.*) first refining. **-frischperiode,** *f.* (*Iron*) boiling stage, boil. **-frucht,** *f.* raw produce; (*Brewing*) unmalted grain. **-gang,** *m.* (*Metal.*) irregular working, abnormal driving.

**rohgar,** *a.* (*Metal.*) partly refined.

**Rohgas,** *n.* crude gas.

**rohgegossen,** *a.* crude-cast.

**Roh-geschmack,** *m.* raw taste. **-gewebe,** *n.* unbleached fabric. **-gewicht,** *n.* gross weight. **-gift,** *n.* crude poison; crude toxin. **-glas,** *n.* crude glass; rough glass. **-gold,** *n.* gold bullion. **-gummi,** *n.* crude rubber; unvulcanized rubber; crude gum. **-gummimilch,** *f.* (*Rubber*) latex. **-haut,** *f.* rawhide. **-humus,** *m.* virgin humus. **-kautschuk,** *m.* crude rubber; raw (unvulcanized) rubber. **-kohle,** *f.* rough coal, run of mine. **-koks,** *m.* crude coke, impure coke. **-kost,** *f.* raw food, uncooked food. **-kresol,** *n.* crude cresol. **-kultur,** *f.* (*Bact.*) impure culture; (*Agric.*) culture of new land. **-kupfer,** *n.* crude copper. **-leinöl,** *n.* raw linseed oil. **-ling,** *m.* unfinished or unworked piece or product, blank, slug. **-mass,** *n.* rough size. **-material,** *n.* raw material. **-messing,** *n.* crude brass. **-metall,** *n.* crude metal. **-naphta,** *f.* crude naphtha; crude petroleum. **-ofen,** *m.* ore furnace. **-öl,** *n.* crude oil. **-pappe,** *f.* raw (paper)board. **-paraffin,** *n.* crude paraffin, crude scale. **-petroleum,** *n.* crude petroleum. **-phosphat,** *m.* (*Agric.*) rock phosphate. **-probe,** *f.* crude sample. **-produkt,** *n.* raw product, crude product. **-protein,** *n.* crude protein; raw protein.

**Rohr,** *n.* tube; pipe; canal; reed, cane; flue; barrel (of a gun). **-ansatz,** *m.* tube (or pipe) attachment.

**rohrartig,** *a.* tube-like; reed-like, reedy.

**Rohr-bogen,** *m.* bend (in a tube or pipe); elbow. **-brunnen,** *m.* fountain; cased well. **-bürste,** *f.* tube brush; flue brush.

**Röhrchen,** *n.* little tube or pipe; tubule; cane; reed (in an organ).

**Röhre,** *f.* tube; pipe; nozzle, spout; channel, duct; conduit; shaft, tunnel.

**röhrenartig,** *a.* tubular; fistular.

**Röhren-bürste,** *f.* tube brush. **-destillationsofen,** *m.* pipe still.

**röhrenförmig,** *a.* tubular; fistular.

**Röhren-halter,** *m.* tube (or pipe) holder, tube (or pipe) clamp. **-kassie,** *f.* purging cassia. **-klemme,** *f.* tube clamp. **-kühler,** *m.* tubular condenser, tube condenser; tubular cooler. **-libelle,** *f.* spirit level, air level. **-lot,** *n.* pipe solder. **-manna,** *f.* flake manna. **-nudeln,** *f.pl.* macaroni. **-ofen,** *m.* tube furnace (for heating tubes liable to explosion); pipe still. **-pulver,** *n.* (*Expl.*) perforated powder. **-struktur,** *f.* tubular structure. **-substanz,** *f.* (*Anat.*) medullary substance. **-träger,** *m.* tube (or pipe) support. **-wachs,** *n.* petroleum ceresin. **-werk,** *n.* tubing; piping; tube mill. **-wischer,** *m.* tube brush. **-wulst,** *n.* tubular tore, "doughnut". **-zelle,** *f.* tubular cell, specif. (*Bot.*) tracheid.

**rohrförmig,** *a.* tubular.

**röhrig,** *a.* tubular; fistular.

**Rohrkessel,** *m.* tubular boiler.

**Rohrkopf,** *m.* (*Petroleum*) casing head. **-benzin, -gasolin,** *n.* casing-head gasoline.

**Rohr-krümmung,** *f.* tube or pipe bend(ing). **-leitung,** *f.* tubing, piping, pipe line. **-muffe,** *f.* pipe sleeve, pipe joint. **-mühle,** *f.* tube mill. **-pulver,** *n.* tubular powder. **-schelle,** *f.* pipe clamp; sleeve. **-schellenverbindung,** *f.* sleeve connection. **-schlange,** *f.* coil (of pipe), worm, spiral tube. **-seele,** *f.* bore of a tube or pipe. **-stutzen,** *m.* = Stutzen. **-verbindung,** *f.* tube (or pipe) connection. **-wand, -wandung,** *f.* tube (or pipe) wall. **-weite,** *f.* bore of a tube or pipe. **-werk,** *n.*

tubing; piping; tube mill. **-zange,** *f.* pipe wrench.

**Rohrzucker,** *m.* cane sugar, sucrose. **-saft,** *m.* cane juice. **-verbindung,** *f.* cane-sugar compound, sucrate.

**Roh-saft,** *m.* crude juice; crude sap. **-salpeter,** *m.* crude saltpeter. **-säure,** *f.* crude acid. **-schlacke,** *f.* raw slag, ore slag. **-schliff,** *m.* (*Paper*) semipulp. **-schmelzen,** *n.* raw smelting, ore smelting. **-schwefel,** *m.* crude sulfur. **-seide,** *f.* raw silk. **-sieb,** *n.* coarse screen, coarse filter. **-silber,** *n.* crude silver; silver bullion. **-soda,** *f.* crude soda, (in the Leblanc process) black ash. **-sole,** *f.* raw brine, crude brine. **-spaltbenzin,** *n.* cracked gasoline. **-spiessglanzerz,** *n.* kermesite. **-spiritus,** *m.* raw spirit, crude spirit. **-stahl,** *m.* raw steel; natural steel. **-stahleisen,** *n.* pig iron for steel making, steel pig. **-stein,** *m.* (*Copper*) coarse metal. **-steinschlacke,** *f.* coarse-metal slag. **-stoff,** *m.* raw material, raw stock; crude substance. **-stück,** *n.* blank (as of metal). **-sulfat,** *n.* crude sulfate, raw sulfate. **-teer,** *m.* crude tar, raw tar. **-ton,** *m.* unburned clay; beige, ecru. **-wachs,** *n.* crude wax. **-wasser,** *n.* raw water, untreated water.

**rohweiss,** *a.* (*Textiles*) raw, gray, unbleached.

**Roh-wismut(h),** *n.& m.* crude bismuth. **-wolle,** *f.* raw wool. **-zink,** *n.* crude zinc, spelter. **-zucker,** *m.* raw sugar, unrefined sugar. **-zustand,** *m.* raw or crude or unrefined state.

**Roll-.** rolling, roller; rolled, coiled.

**Rolle,** *f.* roll; roller; caster; pulley; calender; reel, spool; record, file; rôle.

**rollen,** *v.t. & i.* roll; rotate; curl; calender. **-artig, -förmig,** *a.* cylindrical.

**Rollen-lager,** *n.* roller bearing. **-zug,** *m.* block and tackle.

**Roll-fass,** *n.* tumbling barrel, tumbler. **-flasche,** *f.* narrow-necked cylindrical bottle.

**rollig,** *a.* loose, crumbly, rubbly, shingly.

**Roll-kalander,** *m.* roller calender; (*Paper*) supercalender. **-mass,** *n.* (coiled) tape measure. **-reibung,** *f.* rolling friction. **-schicht,** *f.* upright course (bricks set on end). **-stein,** *m.* boulder. **-wagen,** *m.* truck, lorry. **-widerstand,** *m.* resistance to rolling; rolling friction.

**Roman,** *m.* novel, romance.

**Römerkerze,** *f.* (*Pyro.*) Roman candle.

**römisch,** *a.* Roman. — **römische Bertramwurzel** = Bertramwurzel. — **römische Kamille,** Roman camomile (*Anthemis nobilis*). — **römische Kerze,** Roman candle. — **römischer Kümmel,** cumin. — **römische Minze,** spearmint.

**Römisch-kamillenöl,** *n.* Roman-camomile oil. **-kümmelöl,** *n.* cumin oil.

**rommeln,** *v.t.* tumble.

**Ronde,** *f.* round blank; round; (*Type*) ronde.

**Rongalitätze,** *f.* (*Dyeing*) rongalite discharge.

**rönne,** *pret. subj.* (of rinnen) would run, etc.

**Röntgen-.** X-ray, Roentgen. **-analyse,** *f.* X-ray analysis. **-anlage,** *f.* X-ray laboratory. **-aufnahme,** *f.* X-ray photograph. **-beugung,** *f.* X-ray diffraction. **-bild,** *n.* X-ray image or photograph. **-bremsstrahlung,** *f.* X-radiation due to checking or impact. **-durchleuchtung,** *f.* radioscopy (with X-rays). **-einheit,** *f.* X-ray unit (specif., roentgen). **-einrichtung,** *f.* X-ray equipment.

**röntgenisieren,** *v.t.* subject to X-rays, X-ray.

**Röntgen-kunde, -lehre,** *f.* roentgenology. **-licht,** *n.* X-ray radiation, X rays. **-messer,** *m.* roentgenometer.

**röntgenographisch,** *a.* roentgenographic, X-ray-photographic.

**Röntgen-prüfung,** *f.* X-ray testing or examination. **-röhre,** *f.* Röntgen tube, X-ray tube. **-spektralanalyse,** *f.* X-ray spectrum analysis. **-spektrum,** *n.* X-ray spectrum. **-strahlen,** *m.pl.* Röntgen rays, X rays.

**röntgenstrahlenundurchlässig,** *a.* impervious to X rays, radiopaque.

**Röntgen-strahlung,** *f.* X radiation. **-untersuchung,** *f.* X-ray investigation or examination.

**Rosa,** *n.* pink, rose (color).

**rosa, -farben, -farbig,** *a.* rose-colored, rose, pink, rosy.

**Rosa-färbung,** *f.* rose coloration, pink color. **-rot,** *n.* pink.

**rösch,** *a.* brittle; coarse; (of paper pulp) free; hard baked or roasted.

**röschen,** *v.t.* age or cure; dig (a trench or tunnel).

**Rösch-erz, -gewächs,** *n.* brittle silver ore, stephanite. **-heit,** *f.* brittleness, etc. (see rösch).

**Rose,** *f.* rose; roset(te); erysipelas.

**Rosen-essenz,** *f.* attar of roses. **-farbe,** *f.* rose color.

**rosen-farben, -farbig,** *a.* rose-colored, rosy.

**Rosen-geruch,** *m.* rose odor. **-gewächse,** *n.pl.* (*Bot.*) Rosaceae. **-holz,** *n.* rosewood. **-honig,** *m.* (*Pharm.*) honey of rose. **-kohl,** *m.* Brussels sprouts. **-konserve,** *f.* (*Pharm.*) confection of rose. **-kranz,** *m.* rosary; rose garland.

**rosenkranzförmig,** *a.* like a rosary or string of beads, moniliform.

**Rosen-kupfer,** *n.* rose copper. **-lack,** *m.* rose lake. **-lorbeer,** *m.* oleander; mountain rose (*Rosa*). **-öl,** *n.* rose oil, attar of roses. **-quarz,** *m.* rose quartz.

**rosenrot,** *a.* rose-red.

**Rosen-schwamm,** *m.* bedeguar, bedegar. **-spat,**

*m.* rhodochrosite. **-stahl,** *m.* rose steel. **-stock,** *m.* rosebush. **-wasser,** *n.* rose water.
**Roseokobaltsalz,** *n.* roseocobaltic salt, penta-ammineaquocobalt(III) salt.
**rosettenartig,** *a.* like a roset(te).
**Rosetten-bahn,** *f.* roset(te) orbit or path. **-herd,** *m.* (*Copper*) refining hearth. **-kupfer,** *n.* roset(te) copper.
**rosettieren,** *v.i.* make roset(te) copper.
**rosieren,** *v.t.* dye pink or rose.
**Rosiersalz,** *n.* (*Dyeing*) rose salt, tin composition (solution of tin in aqua regia).
**rosig,** *a.* rosy; rosacic (uric; *Obs.*).
**Rosigsäure,** *f.* rosacic (uric) acid. *Obs.*
**Rosine,** *f.* raisin.
**Rosmarin,** *m.* rosemary. **-öl,** *n.* rosemary oil.
**Rosolsäure,** *f.* rosolic acid.
**Ross,** *n.* horse, steed. **-fenchel,** *m.* (*Pharm.*) water fennel, horsebane (*Oenanthe phellandrium*). **-haar,** *n.* horsehair. **-huf,** *m.* coltsfoot (*Tussilago farfara*). **-kastanie,** *f.* horsechestnut. **-leder,** *n.* horsehide leather. **-schwefel,** *m.* horse brimstone (impure grayish sulfur). **-wurzel,** *f.* carline thistle; carline root.
**Rost,** *m.* rust; mildew; roasting charge; grate, grating; screen, grid, grill; gridiron.
**Röstabgang,** *m.* loss of weight on roasting.
**Rost-anfressung,** *f.* corrosion (of metals). **-angriff,** *m.* corrosive action (on metals).
**Röst-anlage,** *f.* roasting plant. **-arbeit,** *f.* roasting process, roasting.
**Rostbehandlung,** *f.* rust treatment, rustproofing.
**rostbeständig,** *a.* rust-resistant, corrosion-resistant.
**Rostbeständigkeit,** *f.* resistance to rusting or corrosion.
**Röst-betriebsdauer,** *f.* roasting time, duration of roasting. **-bett,** *n.* roasting bed.
**Rost-bildner,** *m.* rusting or corroding agent. **-bildung,** *f.* rust formation.
**Röst-bitter,** *n.* assamar. **-blende,** *f.* roasting blende.
**Rostbrand,** *m.* rust, mildew, smut.
**rostbraun,** *a.* rust-brown, rusty brown.
**Röste,** *f.* roasting; roasting place; roasting charge; retting, steeping; rettery.
**rostempfindlich,** *a.* liable to rust, corrodible.
**Rostempfindlichkeit,** *f.* sensitiveness to rusting or corrosion.
**rosten,** *v.i.* rust.
**rösten,** *v.t.* roast; calcine; torrefy; ret, steep (flax or hemp); broil, grill; toast.
**Rostentfernung,** *f.* rust removal.
**Röster,** *m.* roaster, calciner.
**Röst-erz,** *n.* roasted ore, calcined ore. **-erzeugnis,** *n.* product of roasting, of calcining, etc. (see rösten).
**Rostfarbe,** *f.* rust color.
**rost-farben, -farbig,** *a.* rust-colored. **-fest,** *a.* rustproof, rust-resisting.
**Rost-feuer,** *n.* grate fire. **-fläche,** *f.* grate surface. **-fleck,** *m.* rust spot, iron spot. **-fleckenwasser,** *n.* rust stain remover.
**rostfleckig,** *a.* rust-spotted, rust-stained.
**Rostfrass,** *m.* corrosion (of metals).
**rostfrei,** *a.* rust-free; stainless.
**Rostfreiheit,** *f.* freedom from (or immunity to) rust or corrosion.
**Röstgas,** *n.* gas from roasting.
**rostgelb,** *a.* rust-yellow, rusty yellow.
**Rostgelb,** *n.* iron buff (hydrous iron oxide).
**Röst-gummi,** *n.* dextrin. **-gut,** *n.* material to be roasted; roasted material.
**rosthindernd,** *a.* rust-preventing, anticorrosive.
**Rösthütte,** *f.* (*Metal.*) roasting plant.
**rostig,** *a.* rusty; (of water) chalybeate.
**Rostig-keit,** *f.*, **-sein,** *n.* rustiness. **-werden,** *n.* rusting; (*Bot.*) russeting.
**Rostkitt,** *m.* iron-rust cement.
**Röst-kufe,** *f.* retting vat. **-malz,** *n.* roasted malt, black malt.
**Rost-mittel,** *n.* rust preventive, antirust agent; rusting or corroding agent. **-neigung,** *f.* rusting tendency.
**Röstofen,** *m.* roasting furnace, roasting kiln, calciner, roaster.
**Rost-öl,** *n.* slushing oil. **-pilz,** *m.* (*Bot.*) rust fungus, rust.
**Röst-posten,** *m.* roasting charge. **-probe,** *f.* calcination assay or test. **-produkt,** *n.* = Rösterzeugnis. **-prozess,** *m.* roasting process, calcination process. **-reduktionsarbeit,** *f.* (*Metal.*) roast reduction process.
**rostrein,** *a.* rust-free.
**Röstrohr,** *n.* roasting tube, open tube (for qualitative tests).
**rostrot,** *a.* rust-red, brown-red.
**Röst-rückstand,** *m.* residue from roasting. **-scherben,** *m.* roasting dish, scorifier.
**Rostschicht,** *f.* layer of rust; (*Metal.*) layer of raw mat(te).
**Röst-schlacke,** *f.* slag from roasting. **-schmelzen,** *n.* (*Metal.*) roasting and smelting.
**Rostschutz,** *m.* protection against rust, rust prevention.
**rostschützend,** *a.* rust-preventing.
**Rostschutz-farbe,** *f.* antirust paint. **-grund,** *m.* antirust primer. **-lack,** *m.* antirust lacquer or varnish. **-mittel,** *n.* antirust agent, rust preventive. **-öl,** *n.* slushing oil. **-verfahren,** *n.* rustproofing process. **-wirkung,** *f.* rust-preventive action or effect.
**rostsicher,** *a.* rustproof; stainless.
**Rostsicherheit,** *f.* rustproofness, stainless property.
**Röststaub,** *m.* dust of roasted ore.

**Rostung,** *f.* rusting.
**Röstung,** *f.* roasting, etc. (see rösten).
**Rostungsversuch,** *m.* rusting test, corrosion test.
**Röstverfahren,** *n.* roasting process.
**rostverhütend,** *a.* rust-preventing, antirust, anticorrosive.
**Röst-verlust,** *m.* loss from roasting. **-vorrichtung,** *f.* roasting apparatus or contrivance. **-wasser,** *n.* steeping water.
**Rostwiderstand,** *m.* resistance to rusting.
**Röstzuschlag,** *m.* flux for roasting.
**rot,** *a.* red. — **roter Präzipitat,** red precipitate (red mercuric oxide).
**Rot,** *n.* red; rouge.
**Rotamesser,** *m.* a kind of meter for gases.
**Rotang,** *m.* rattan. **-palme,** *f.* rattan palm, rotang.
**Rotations-achse,** *f.* axis of rotation. **-bewegung,** *f.* rotational motion, rotary motion. **-druck,** *m.* rotary printing. **-filter,** *n.* rotary drum filter.
**rotationsfrei,** *a.* rotation-free, irrotational.
**Rotations-körper,** *m.* body (or solid) of rotation. **-mischmaschine,** *f.* rotary mixer. **-pumpe,** *f.* rotary pump. **-quantenzahl,** *f.* rotational quantum number. **-schwingung,** *f.* rotation vibration. **-sinn,** *m.* direction of rotation.
**rotationssymmetrisch,** *a.* axially symmetric.
**Rotationszähler,** *m.* revolution counter.
**Rot-auszug,** *m.* (*Color Photog.*) red record. **-beize,** *f.* (*Dyeing*) red mordant, red liquor.
**rotblau,** *a.* reddish-blue.
**Rotblei-erz,** *n.*, **-spat,** *m.* red lead ore (crocoite).
**rotbraun,** *a.* red-brown.
**Rot-braunstein,** *m.*, **-braunsteinerz,** *n.* rhodonite. **-bruch,** *m.* red-shortness.
**rotbrüchig,** *a.* red-short; (of wood) rotten.
**Rotbuche,** *f.* red beech.
**rotbunt,** *a.* red and white.
**Röte,** *f.* redness, red; madder; blush.
**Roteiche,** *f.* red oak.
**Roteisen-erz,** *n.* red iron ore (hematite). **-ocker,** *m.* red iron ocher (earthy hematite). **-stein,** *m.* = Roteisenerz.
**Rötel,** *m.*, **Rötelerde,** *f.* ruddle, red ocher.
**Röteln,** *f.pl.* German measles, rubella.
**Rötelton,** *m.* brownish-red tone.
**rotempfindlich,** *a.* (*Photog.*) red-sensitive.
**röten,** *v.t.* redden. — **rötend,** *p.a.* rubefacient.
**Rot-erde,** *f.* red earth. **-erle,** *f.* red alder. **-esche,** *f.* red ash.
**rot-färben,** *v.t.* color red. **-farbig,** *a.* red-colored.
**Rot-färbung,** *f.* red coloration, red color. **-fäule,** *f.* red rot, heart rot. **-feuer,** *n.* red fire.
**rot-gar,** *a.* tanned (to a russet color). **-gebrannt,** *a.* roasted red, red-burned. **-gelb,** *a.* reddish-yellow, orange. **-gerben,** *v.t.* tan.
**Rot-gerber,** *m.* bark tanner. **-giesser,** *m.* brazier. **-giesserei,** *f.* braziery. **-gilderz, -giltigerz,** *n.* = Rotgültigerz.
**rot-glühen,** *v.t.* heat to redness. **-glühend,** *p.a.* glowing red, red-hot.
**Rot-glühhärte,** *f.* (*Metal.*) red-hardness. **-glühhitze, -glut,** *f.* red heat. **-gluthärte,** *f.* (*Metal.*) red-hardness. **-gold,** *n.* red gold (gold-copper alloy). **-gültig, -gültigerz, -gulden,** *n.* red silver ore (**dunkles,** pyrargyrite; **lichtes,** proustite). **-guss,** *m.* red brass or bronze; gun metal; braziery.
**roth, Röthe,** etc. See rot, Röte, etc.
**Rot-heizen,** *n.* heating to redness. **-hitze,** *f.* red heat. **-holz,** *n.* redwood.
**rotieren,** *v.i.* rotate. — **rotierend,** *p.a.* rotating, rotary.
**Rotierofen,** *m.* rotating furnace or kiln.
**Rot-kali,** *n.* red prussiate of potash (potassium ferricyanide). **-kiefer,** *f.* red pine. **-klee,** *m.* red clover. **-kohl,** *m.* red cabbage. **-kohle,** *f.* red charcoal. **-kupfer, -kupfererz,** *n.* red copper, red copper ore (cuprite). **-lauf,** *m.* erysipelas.
**rötlich,** *a.* reddish. **-braun,** *a.* reddish-brown. **-gelb,** *a.* reddish-yellow.
**Rotliegendes,** *n.* (*Geol.*) a system of sandstones, shales and conglomerates of the lower Permian of Germany.
**rotmachend,** *p.a.* rubefacient.
**Rot-messig,** *n.* red brass. **-nickelkies,** *m.* niccolite, kupfernickel. **-ocker,** *m.* red ocher. **-öl,** *n.* red oil. **-rauschgelb,** *n.* realgar. **-reserve,** *f.* (*Dyeing*) red resist. **-salz,** *n.* crude sodium acetate (from pyroligneous acid). **-säure,** *f.* erythric acid (erythrin). **-schönung,** *f.* (*Wine*) red-clearing (treatment with iron oxide to remove arsenic). **-silber, -silbererz,** *n.* = Rotgültig. **-spat,** *m.* rhodonite. **-spiessglanz,** *m.*, **-spiessglanzerz,** *n.* kermesite. **-stein,** *m.* red ocher, ruddle; rhodonite; red brick. **-stich,** *m.* red cast, red tinge.
**rotstichig,** *a.* reddish.
**Rot-stift,** *m.* red pencil, red crayon. **-tanne,** *f.* Norway spruce (*Picea abies*).
**Rotte,** *f.* retting (of flax); troop, band, set, gang.
**rotten,** *v.t.* ret, steep (flax, etc.).
**Rottombak,** *m.* red tombac.
**Rötung,** *f.* reddening; red tint, redness.
**Rotverschiebung,** *f.* displacement toward the red.
**rot-verschoben,** *p.p.* displaced toward the red. **-warm,** *a.* red-hot.
**Rot-warmhärte,** *f.* (*Metal.*) red-hardness. **-warmhitze,** *f.* red heat. **-wein,** *m.* red wine. **-weinfarbe,** *f.* color of red wine, claret.
**Rotz,** *m.* glanders; nasal mucus.
**Rotzinkerz,** *n.* red zinc ore (zincite).

**Rotz-krankheit,** *f.* glanders. **-nase,** *f.* (*Paint*) run.

**Roulette,** *f.* (*Mach.*) horizontal ball mill, ball-and-race mill. **-küpe,** *f.* continuous dyeing vat.

**routiniert,** *a.* experienced, practiced.

**R-P.,** *abbrev.* (Reichs-Patent) Government patent.

**R-Säure,** *f.* R-acid (2-naphthol-3, 6-disulfonic acid).

**R.-T.,** *abbrev.* (Raumteil) part by volume.

**Rübe,** *f.* (**rote**) beet, beetroot; (**gelbe**) carrot; (**weisse**) turnip; rape.

**Rubeanwasserstoff,** *m.* old name for dithiooxamide, $H_2NCSCSNH_2$.

**Rüben-asche,** *f.* beet ashes (usually; see Rübe). **-beizung,** *f.* beet-seed disinfection. **-brei,** *m.* beet(root) pulp. **-breiapparat,** *m.* (*Sugar*) root pulper. **-brennerei,** *f.* beet (molasses) distillery. **-essig,** *m.* beet vinegar, beetroot vinegar.

**rübenförmig,** *a.* turnip-shaped, napiform.

**Rüben-harzsäure,** *f.* resin acid of beets. **-melasse,** *f.* beet molasses, beetroot molasses. **-pottasche,** *f.* potash from beet molasses. **-pulpe,** *f.* beet pulp. **-rohzucker,** *m.* raw beet sugar. **-saft,** *m.* beet(root) juice. **-samen,** *m.* turnip, rape-, beet, or carrot seed. **-schlempe,** *f.* beet vinasse. **-schnitzel,** *m.* beet chip, beet slice. **-sirup,** *m.* beet sirup, beetroot sirup. **-spiritus,** *m.* beet spirit (from beet molasses). **-stecher,** *m.* beet sampler.

**Rübenzucker,** *m.* beet sugar, beetroot sugar. **-fabrik,** *f.* beet-sugar factory. **-industrie,** *f.* beet-sugar industry.

**Rubidium-alaun,** *m.* rubidium alum. **-chlorid,** *n.* rubidium chloride. **-jodid,** *n.* rubidium iodide. **-oxydhydrat,** *n.* rubidium hydroxide. **-platinchlorid,** *n.* rubidium chloroplatinate.

**Rubin,** *m.* ruby. **-balas,** *m.* balas ruby (ruby spinel). **-blende,** *f.* pyrargyrite. **-farbe,** *f.* ruby color, ruby.

**rubin-farben, -farbig,** *a.* ruby-colored, ruby.

**Rubin-glas,** *n.*, **-fluss,** *m.* ruby glass. **-glimmer,** *m.* a variety of göthite. **-granat,** *m.* rock ruby (variety of garnet).

**rubinrot,** *a.* ruby-red, ruby.

**Rubin-schwefel,** *m.* ruby sulfur (realgar). **-spinell,** *m.* ruby spinel.

**Rüböl,** *n.* rape oil, rapeseed oil, colza oil. **-faktis,** *n.* rape oil factice. **-kuchen,** *m.* rapeseed cake.

**Rubrik,** *f.* heading; column; paragraph.

**Rübsamen,** *m.* = Rübensamen.

**Rübsen,** *m.* rapeseed. **-öl,** *n.* rape oil, rapeseed oil, colza oil.

**ruchlos,** *a.* scentless; vicious, wicked.

**Ruck,** *m.* jerk, jolt, tug, shock.

**rück,** *adv.* back, backward, behind.

**Rück-.** back, rear, retro-, re-, counter-. **-ansicht,** *f.* rear view, back view.

**ruckartig,** *a.* jerky, jolting.

**Rück-bau,** *m.* reconstruction; dismantling. **-bewegung,** *f.* back(ward) motion.

**rückbilden,** *v.t.* form again, re-form; retrograde.

**Rückbildung,** *f.* re-formation; retrogression, involution.

**Rück-blick,** *m.* backward look; retrospect. **-destillation,** *f.* redistillation. **-druck,** *m.* back pressure, reaction pressure.

**rücken,** *v.t.* & *i.* move, push, pull, shove, shift.

**Rücken,** *m.* back; ridge; rear.

**Rücken-.** back, dorsal, spinal. **-ansicht,** *f.* rear view. **-bein,** *n.* backbone, spine. **-mark,** *n.* spinal cord. **-säule,** *f.* vertebral column. **-seite,** *f.* back side, back, rear. **-weh,** *n.* lumbago. **-wirbel,** *m.* dorsal vertebra.

**Rück-erinnerung,** *f.* reminiscence. **-fahrt,** *f.* return. **-fall,** *m.* relapse; reversion; (*pl.*, **Rückfälle**) matter fallen back, returns. **-feinerung,** *f.* recovery; regeneration.

**rückfliessend,** *a.* flowing back, reflux.

**Rückfluss,** *m.* reflux. **-kühler,** *m.* reflux condenser, return condenser. **-luftkühler,** *m.* reflux air condenser.

**Rück-führung,** *f.* reconduction; return(ing); restoration. **-gang,** *m.* return; retrogression; relapse; decline; backward motion; (*Mach.*) back stroke.

**rückgängig,** *a.* backward; retrograde, retrogressive; of no effect, null.

**Rück-gewinnung,** *f.* recovery; reclaiming; regeneration. **-glühung,** *f.* (*Metal.*) drawing, tempering. **-grat,** *m.* vertebral column, spine.

**Rückgrats-.** vertebral, spinal.

**Rückhalt,** *m.* support, stay; reserve, restraint.

**rückhaltlos,** *a.* unreserved.

**Rück-infektion,** *f.* reinfection. **-kehr,** *f.* return. **-kohlung,** *f.* recarbonization, recarburization; recharring. **-kopplung,** *f.* (*Elec.*) feedback, regenerative circuit. **-kristallisation,** *f.* recrystallization. **-kühlanlage,** *f.* recooling plant. **-kühlturm,** *m.* cooling tower. **-kühlwasser,** *n.* condensing water. **-kunft,** *f.* return. **-lauf,** *m.* return motion, back motion, retrogression, (of guns) recoil; return; recurrence.

**rück-laufend, -läufig,** *a.* recurrent; retrogressive, retrograde; return(ing).

**Rücklauf-kondensator, -verdichter,** *m.* reflux condenser.

**Rück-leiter,** *m.* (*Elec.*) return conductor, return wire. **-leitung,** *f.* return line.

**rücklings,** *adv.* backward; from behind.

**Rück-oxydation,** *f.* reoxidation. **-phosphorung,** *f.* rephosphorization. **-prall,** *m.* rebound, recoil. **-reaktion,** *f.* back reaction, reverse reaction. **-saugung,** *f.* sucking back.

**Rückschlag,** *m.* striking back; back stroke, rebound, recoil, return; backlash; reaction; reverberation; setback. **-hemmung,** *f.* prevention of, or device to prevent, "striking back." **-ventil,** *n.* check valve.

**Rückschluss,** *m.* inference, conclusion; (*Elec.*) ground.

**rückschreitend,** *a.* retrogressive, retrograde.

**Rück-schritt,** *m.* backward motion, recession, retrogression; relapse. **-schwefelung,** *f.* resulfurization. **-seite,** *f.* back side, back; wrong side, reverse.

**Rücksicht,** *f.* regard, respect, attention, consideration; motive. — **mit — auf,** with regard to, with respect to, in consideration of.

**rücksichtlich,** *adv.* with regard (to), in consideration (of).

**Rücksichtnahme,** *f.* allowance, consideration.

**Rücksprache,** *f.* consultation, conference.

**Rückstand,** *m.* residue, residuum; (often *pl.*) refuse, leavings, remains, dregs, etc.; (*pl.*) arrears. **-brenner,** *m.* burner for residues.

**rückständig,** *a.* residual, residuary; in arrears, overdue, outstanding; backward, back.

**Rück-standserzeugnis,** *n.* residual product. **-standsgewicht,** *n.* weight of residue. **-stein,** *m.* (*Metal.*) back stone; crucible bottom. **-stellkraft,** *f.* restoring force; resiliency. **-stoss,** *m.* back stroke, recoil; repulsion; jet propulsion. **-stossatom,** *n.* recoil atom. **-stossbahn,** *f.* recoil path or track. **-stosselektron,** *n.* recoil electron. **-strahl,** *m.* reflected ray.

**rückstrahlen,** *v.t.* reflect.

**Rück-strahler,** *m.* reflector. **-strahlung,** *f.* reflection. **-strahlungsmesser,** *m.* reflectometer. **-strahlverfahren,** *n.* reflection method. **-streuung,** *f.* scattering (of rays). **-strom,** *m.* back flow; (*Elec.*) reverse current, return current. **-strömung,** *f.* backflow, reflux. **-titrieren,** *n.* back titration.

**rücktreiben,** *v.t.* drive back; repel.

**Rück-tritt,** *m.* stepping back, retreat, withdrawal, retrogression. **-umwandlung, -verwandlung,** *f.* reconversion, retransformation. **-wand,** *f.* back wall, rear wall.

**rück-wärtig,** *a.* backward, back. **-wärts,** *adv.* backward, back.

**Rückwärtsbewegung,** *f.* retrograde motion.

**Rückweg,** *m.* return path.

**ruckweise,** *adv.* by jerks; intermittently.

**rückwerfen,** *v.t.* throw back; reflect.

**rückwirken,** *v.i.* react.

**Rück-wirkung,** *f.* reaction; reactance; retroaction. **-wurf,** *m.* throwing back; reflection. **-zug,** *m.* retreat; return. **-zündung,** *f.* backfiring.

**Rudel,** *n.* flock, herd; stirring pole.

**Ruder,** *n.* oar; rudder, helm; (*Aero.*) control(s).

**rudern,** *v.t. & i.* row, paddle.

**Ruf,** *m.* call; calling; report; reputation.

**rufen,** *v.t. & i.* call.

**Ruffrequenz,** *f.* audiofrequency.

**Rufigallussäure,** *f.* rufigallic acid.

**Ruhbütte,** *f.* (*Brewing*) storage vat, stock tub.

**Ruhe,** *f.* rest; quiescence; repose, quiet, peace. **-lage,** *f.* position of rest. **-masse,** *f.* rest mass.

**ruhen,** *v.i.* rest, repose; sleep. — **ruhend,** *p.a.* resting, etc.; stationary, motionless, still; latent; stagnant; (*Elec.*) static.

**Ruhe-pulver,** *n.* sedative powder. **-punkt,** *m.* point of rest; fulcrum; pause. **-spannung,** *f.* (*Elec.*) steady potential. **-stadium,** *n.* resting stage. **-stand,** *m.* state of rest; retirement. **-stellung,** *f.* position of rest. **-stoffwechsel,** *m.* resting metabolism. **-strom,** *m.* (*Elec.*) steady current, closed-circuit current (cf. Arbeitsstrom). **-system,** *n.* static system. **-umsatz,** *m.* (*Physiol.*) resting metabolism. **-winkel,** *m.* angle of repose. **-zustand,** *m.* state of rest.

**ruhig,** *a.* at rest, quiet, still, stationary, stagnant, calm; (of molten metal) dead, killed. — *adv.* quietly, smoothly. — **ruhige Färbung,** solid dyeing. — **ruhiger Glanz,** smooth luster.

**Ruhm,** *m.* fame, reputation, glory, praise.

**Ruhmasse,** *f.* rest mass, static mass.

**rühmen,** *v.t.* commend, praise, extol. — *v.r.* boast, pride oneself.

**Ruhr,** *f.* dysentery; diarrhea; stirring.

**Rühr-apparat,** *m.* stirring apparatus, stirrer, agitator, (*Ceram.*) blunger. **-arm,** *m.* stirrer, agitator. **-äscher,** *m.* (*Leather*) lime pit with agitator. **-aufsatz,** *m.* stirring attachment.

**Ruhrbazillen,** *m.pl.* dysentery bacilli.

**Rühr-blei,** *n.* (*Metal.*) the first lead removed in the Carinthian process. **-eisen,** *n.* poker, iron stirrer. **-einrichtung,** *f.* stirring or agitating arrangement.

**rühren,** *v.t.* stir; agitate, beat; crutch (soap); play (an instrument); strike; move, touch (one's feelings).

**Rührer,** *m.* stirrer, etc. (see rühren).

**Rühr-fass,** *n.* churn; (*Metal.*) dolly tub. **-form,** *f.* form or shape of stirrer. **-frischen,** *n.* (*Metal.*) puddling. **-geschwindigkeit,** *f.* velocity of stirring. **-häkchen,** *n.* small stirring hook. **-haken,** *m.* stirring implement, rake, rabble, poker. **-holz,** *n.* wooden stirrer, stirring stick, paddle.

**rührig,** *a.* stirring, busy, active, nimble.

**Rühr-kessel,** *m.* vessel with stirrer, (*Soap*) crutching pan. **-krücke,** *f.* stirring crutch, rake. **-kühler,** *m.* condenser with stirrer. **-laugung,** *f.* leaching (or bucking) with agitation. **-maschine,** *f.* stirring machine, agitator.

**Ruhrmittel,** *n.* remedy for dysentery.
**Rührofen,** *m.* (*Metal.*) rabble furnace.
**Ruhrrinde,** *f.* Simarouba bark.
**Rühr-schaufel,** *f.* stirring paddle. **-scheit,** *n.* paddle, rake, stirrer; spatula. **-spatel,** *m.* stirring spatula. **-stab,** *m.* stirring rod, stirring pole, paddle, rabble. **-stativ,** *n.* stirring stand. **-tank,** *m.* agitating tank.
**Rührung,** *f.* stirring, etc. (see rühren); emotion, feeling.
**Rühr-vorrichtung,** *f.* stirring or agitating contrivance. **-wärme,** *f.* heat of stirring or agitation. **-werk,** *n.* = Rührapparat.
**Ruhrwurzel,** *f.* tormentil root; ipecac; calumba.
**Rührzeit,** *f.* time of stirring or agitation.
**Ruinenmarmor,** *m.* ruin marble.
**Rujaholz,** *n.* Venetian sumac wood, young fustic.
**Rüllöl,** *n.* cameline oil.
**Rumänien,** *n.* Romania, Rumania.
**Rum-äther,** *m.* rum ether (ethyl butyrate or formate). **-brennerei,** *f.* rum distillery. **-essenz,** *f.* rum essence (ethyl butyrate or formate). **-fabrik,** *f.* rum distillery.
**Rumpelfass,** *n.* tumbling barrel.
**rumpeln,** *v.i.* rumble, rattle.
**Rumpf,** *m.* body (of an engine, etc.); core (of an atom or ion); trunk, torso; hull (of a ship); (*Aero.*) fuselage. **-elektron,** *n.* inner electron (as distinguished from an optical or valence electron). **-fläche,** *f.* (*Geol.*) peneplain. **-wirkung,** *f.* (atomic) core effect.
**Rumsprit,** *m.* double rum.
**rund,** *a.* round; circular; spherical. — *adv.* around; roundly, in round numbers.
**Rund-blick,** *m.* all-round view, panorama. **-brecher,** *m.* rotary crusher. **-brenner,** *m.* ring burner. **-eisen,** *n.* round iron, rod iron.
**runderhaben,** *a.* convex.
**Rund-faser,** *f.* round fiber. **-feile,** *f.* round file. **-filter,** *m.* round or circular filter. **-flasche,** *f.* round flask, Florence flask. **-funk,** *m.* (radio) broadcasting.
**rundhohl,** *a.* concave.
**Rund-holz,** *n.* round wood, logs. **-kolben,** *m.* round-bottomed flask.
**rundkörnig,** *a.* round-grained, globular.
**Rundkupfer,** *n.* copper billets.
**rundlaufen,** *v.i.* run around, revolve, circulate.
**Rund-reise,** *f.* round trip; circuit. **-schreiben,** *n.* circular. **-stahl,** *m.* round steel bar or rod.
**Rundung,** *f.* rounding; roundness; curve, arc.
**rundweg,** *adv.* plainly, bluntly.
**Runkel,** *f.*, **-rübe,** *f.* beet, beetroot. **-rübenmelasse,** *f.* beet(root) molasses. **-rübenzucker,** *m.* beet sugar, beetroot sugar.
**Runzel,** *f.* wrinkle; fold, crease, rumple. **bildung,** *f.* wrinkling, creasing.
**runzelig, runzlig,** *a.* wrinkled, puckered, shriveled, rugose, corrugated.
**Runzellack,** *m.* wrinkle varnish, wrinkle finish.
**Rupertsmetall,** *n.* Prince Rupert's metal.
**rupfen,** *v.t.* pluck, pick, pull.
**Rupffestigkeit,** *f.* resistance to picking or plucking.
**Ruprechtskraut,** *n.* herb Robert (*Geranium robertianum*).
**Rusaöl,** *n.* ginger-grass oil.
**Russ,** *m.* soot; lampblack, carbon black; (*Agric.*) rust. **-abscheidung,** *f.* deposition of soot. **-ansatz,** *m.* deposit of soot.
**russartig,** *a.* soot-like, fuliginous.
**Russ-bildung,** *f.* soot formation. **-braun,** *n.* bister. **-brennerei,** *f.* manufacture of lampblack. **-dampf,** *m.* sooty vapor.
**Rüssel,** *m.* nose, snout, nozzle; proboscis.
**russen,** *v.t. & i.* soot, smoke, blacken.
**russend,** *a.* sooty, smoky.
**Russ-farbe,** *f.* bister. **-flocke,** *f.* flake of soot. **-hütte,** *f.* lampblack works.
**russig,** *a.* sooty, fuliginous.
**russisch,** *a.* Russian. — **russisches Glas,** Muscovy glass, mica.
**Russisch Grün.** Russian green.
**Russ-kobalt,** *m.* asbolite. **-kohle,** *f.* sooty coal. **-kreide,** *f.* black chalk.
**Russland,** *n.* Russia.
**russschwarz,** *a.* soot-black.
**Russ-schwarz,** *n.* lampblack, carbon black. **-vorlage,** *f.* soot collector.
**rüsten,** *v.t.* prepare, equip, furnish.
**Rüster,** *f.* elm. **-rinde,** *f.* elm bark.
**rüstig,** *a.* vigorous, robust, active.
**Rüstung,** *f.* preparation, equipment, armament; scaffolding; (*Elec.*) armature.
**Rüstzeug,** *n.* set of tools; crane; scaffolding.
**Rute,** *f.* rod, wand; yard, rod (measures); (*Med.*) penis.
**rutenförmig,** *a.* rod-shaped, wand-shaped, virgate.
**Ruthenium-oxyd,** *n.* (any) ruthenium oxide, esp. the sesquioxide, ruthenium(III) oxide. **-oxydul,** *n.* ruthenium monoxide, ruthenium(II) oxide. **-säure,** *f.* ruthenic acid. **-verbindung,** *f.* ruthenium compound.
**Rutsche,** *f.* shoot, chute, slide.
**rutschen,** *v.i.* slide, slip, glide, skid.
**Rutschfläche,** *f.* (*Geol.*) slickenside.
**rutschlos,** *a.* free from slip.
**Rutschpulver,** *n.* talc powder.
**rutschsicher,** *a.* nonslipping, (of tires) nonskid.
**Rutschung,** *f.* sliding, slipping, slide, slip.
**Rüttelbewegung,** *f.* shaking motion.
**rütteln,** *v.t. & i.* shake, jolt, jar, rattle, vibrate.
**Rüttel-sieb,** *n.* vibrating (or shaking) screen. **-stoss,** *m.* jolt, jar.
**Rütt(e)lung,** *f.* shaking, jolting, vibration.
**ryt(h)misch,** *a.* rhythmic.

# S

**s.,** *abbrev.* (siehe) see; (symmetrisch) symmetric(al); (schwer) difficultly; (sehr) very; (Sekunde) second.
**S.,** *abbrev.* (Seite) page; (Säure) acid; (Sankt) Saint, St.; (Sekunde) second.
**s.a.,** *abbrev.* (siehe auch) see also.
**S.-A.,** *abbrev.* (Sonder-Abdruck) separate, reprint.
**Sa.,** *abbrev.* (Summa) sum.
**Saal,** *m.* hall, assembly room.
**Saat,** *f.* seed; sowing; young crops. **-beizmittel,** *n.* seed disinfectant. **-gut,** *n.* seed grain, seed. **-gutbeize,** *f.* seed disinfection; seed steep. **-gutkrankheit,** *f.* seed-borne disease. **-zeit,** *f.* sowing time, sowing season.
**Sabadillsamen,** *m.pl.* sabadilla seeds.
**Säbel,** *m.* saber, sword.
**säbelförmig,** *a.* saber-shaped, ensiform.
**Säbelkolben,** *m.* = Schwertkolben.
**Sabinerbaum,** *m.* savin.
**saccharimetrisch,** *a.* saccharimetric.
**saccharinhaltig,** *a.* containing saccharin.
**Saccharinsäure,** *f.* saccharinic acid.
**saccharoidisch,** *a.* saccharoid, saccharoidal.
**Sache,** *f.* affair, matter, subject, thing, object, topic, cause, case.
**sachgemäss,** *a.* appropriate, pertinent, relevant, suitable, proper.
**Sach-index,** *m.* subject index. **-kenner,** *m.* expert. **-kenntnis, -kunde,** *f.* expert or special knowledge; experience.
**sachkundig,** *a.* experienced, expert.
**Sachkundiger,** *m.* expert, specialist.
**Sachlage,** *f.* state of affairs.
**sachlich,** *a.* real, objective, material. — *adv.* objectively; positively; by subjects.
**Sachlichkeit,** *f.* reality, actuality.
**Sachregister,** *n.* subject index; table of contents.
**Sachsen,** *n.* Saxony.
**sächsisch,** *a.* Saxon. — **sächsisches Blau,** = Sächsischblau.
**Sächsischblau,** *n.* Saxon blue, smalt; (sometimes) indigo; a kind of Prussian blue.
**sacht, sachte,** *a.* soft, gentle, light, smooth, easy; (of silk) scoured. — *adv.* softly, gently, gradually.
**Sach-verhalt,** *m.*, **-verhältnis,** *n.* state of affairs.
**sachverständig,** *a.* experienced, expert.
**Sach-verständiger,** *m.* expert, authority. **-verzeichnis,** *n.* subject index. **-walter,** *m.* lawyer, attorney. **-wörterbuch,** *n.* encyclopedia.
**Sack,** *m.* bag, sack; pocket, pouch; sac, cyst. **-band,** *n.* bag string, sack tie.
**Säckel,** *m.* purse; little bag.
**sacken,** *v.t.* sack; pack. — *v.r. & i.* bag, bulge; sink, sag, settle, fall.
**Sackfilter,** *n.* bag filter, sack filter.
**sackförmig,** *a.* sack-like, bag-like, pouch-like.
**Sack-gerbung,** *f.* (*Leather*) bag tannage. **-leinwand,** *f.*, **-leinen,** *n.* sackcloth, sacking, bagging.
**Sackung,** *f.* sacking, etc. (see sacken).
**Sadebaum,** *m.* savin. **-öl,** *n.* savin oil.
**säen,** *v.t.* sow, seed.
**Saffian,** *m.*, **-leder,** *n.* morocco (leather).
**Safflor,** *m.* safflower. **-blüte,** *f.* safflower blossom. **-gelb,** *n.* safflower (the dye). **-öl,** *n.* safflower oil. **-rot,** *n.* safflower red, carthamin.
**Safran,** *m.* saffron.
**safranähnlich,** *a.* saffron-like, saffrony.
**Safranfarbe,** *f.* saffron color.
**safran-farben, -farbig,** *a.* saffron-colored. **-gelb,** *a.* saffron-yellow, saffron. **-haltig,** *a.* containing saffron.
**Safranöl,** *n.* saffron oil.
**Saft,** *m.* juice; sap; lymph; fluid, liquid, liquor, sirup, gravy. **-blau,** *n.* sap blue. **-braun,** *n.* sap brown. **-fluss,** *m.* flow of sap or juice or liquor.
**saftfrisch,** *a.* (of wood) green.
**Saftgrün,** *n.* sap green.
**saftig,** *a.* juicy, succulent; sappy; (*Metal.*) wet.
**Saftigkeit,** *f.* juiciness; sappiness.
**Saftpflanze,** *f.* succulent plant.
**saftreich,** *a.* rich in juice or sap, succulent.
**Saftzelle,** *f.* lymph cell.
**Sagapengummi,** *n.* sagapenum.
**Sage,** *f.* saying; rumor; tradition, legend.
**Säge,** *f.* saw.
**säge-artig,** *a.* saw-like, serrated. **-gezähnt,** *a.* sawtoothed, serrate, dentate.
**Sägemehl,** *n.* sawdust.
**sägemehlartig,** *a.* like sawdust.
**sagen,** *v.t.* say, tell, speak.
**sägen,** *v.t.* saw.
**sagenhaft,** *a.* legendary, traditionary.
**Sägenmehl,** *n.* sawdust.
**Säge-späne,** *m.pl.*, **-staub,** *m.* sawdust. **-zahn,** *m.* saw tooth; (*pl.*) indentations.
**Sago-mehl,** *n.* sago flour. **-stärke,** *f.* sago starch, sago.

**Sagradarinde,** *f.* cascara sagrada.
**sah,** *pret.* (of sehen) saw.
**Sahlband,** *n.* selvage; wall (of a lode).
**Sahne,** *f.* cream.
**sahnen,** *v.t.* skim (milk).
**Sahnenkäse,** *m.* cream cheese.
**sahnig,** *a.* creamy.
**Saidschützer Salz.** Epsom salt ($MgSO_4.7H_2O$).
**saiger,** *a.* perpendicular, vertical.
**Saiger-.** see Seiger-.
**saigern,** *v.t.* (*Metal.*) liquate. — *v.i.* segregate.
**Saisonfarbe,** *f.* season color, fashion shade.
**Saite,** *f.* catgut; string (of an instrument); cord; chord.
**Saiten-draht,** *m.* music wire. **-galvanometer,** *n.* string galvanometer.
**säkulär,** *a.* secular, of long duration.
**Salat,** *m.* salad; lettuce. **-machen,** *n.* (*Brewing*) doughing in and keeping the mash very cold. **-öl,** *n.* salad oil, specif. olive oil.
**Salband,** *n.* selvage; wall (of a lode).
**Salbe,** *f.* salve, ointment, pomade.
**Salbei,** *f.* sage.
**salbeigrün,** *a.* sage-green.
**Salbeiöl,** *n.* sage oil, oil of sage.
**salben,** *v.t.* salve; anoint. **-artig,** *a.* salve-like, salvy, unctuous.
**Salben-grundlage,** *f.* ointment base. **-spatel,** *m.* salve spatula, slice.
**salbig,** *a.* salvy, unctuous.
**Saldo,** *m.* balance (of an account).
**Salep,** *m.*, **-wurzel,** *f.* salep. **-schleim,** *m.* salep mucilage.
**Salicoylsäure,** *f.* salicylic acid.
**Salicyl-.** salicyl; salicylic.
**salicyliert,** *p.a.* salicylated.
**salicylig,** *a.* salicylous.
**salicylsauer,** *a.* of or combined with salicylic acid, salicylate of.
**Salicyl-säure,** *f.* salicylic acid. **-streupulver,** *n.* salicylated talc. **-sulfonsäure,** *f.* sulfosalicylic acid. **-talg,** *m.* salicylated tallow. **-ursäure,** *f.* salicyluric acid. **-watte,** *f.* salicylic cotton.
**Saline,** *f.* salt works, saline, saltern.
**Salinenwasser,** *n.* saline water.
**salinisch,** *a.* saline.
**salisch,** *a.* (*Petrog.*) salic.
**salivieren,** *v.t.* salivate.
**Salizin,** *n.* salicin.
**Salizyl-,** etc. = Salicyl-, etc.
**Salm,** *m.* salmon; psalm.
**Salmiak,** *m.* sal ammoniac (ammonium chloride). **-element,** *n.* (*Elec.*) sal ammoniac cell, Leclanché cell. **-geist,** *m.* aqueous ammonia. **-kristall,** *m.* (crystallized) sal ammoniac. **-lakritze,** *f.* sal ammoniac-licorice pastilles. **-lösung,** *f.* ammonium chloride solution. **-salz,** *n.* sal volatile (ammonium carbonate); sal ammoniac. **-spiritus,** *m.* aqueous ammonia.
**Salmrot,** *n.* salmon red.
**Salniter,** *m.* saltpeter, potassium nitrate.
**Salomonssiegel,** *n.* Solomon's seal.
**Salpeter,** *m.* saltpeter, niter.
**salpeterartig,** *a.* like saltpeter or niter.
**Salpeter-äther,** *m.* nitric ether (ethyl nitrate). **-bakterien,** *n.pl.* nitrifying bacteria. **-bildung,** *f.* nitrification. **-blumen,** *f.pl.* niter efflorescence. **-dampf, -dunst,** *m.* nitrous fumes. **-erde,** *f.* nitrous earth. **-erzeugung,** *f.* niter production; nitrification.
**salpeteressigsauer,** *a.* nitrate and acetate of.
**Salpeter-frass,** *m.* corrosion by niter. **-gas,** *n.* nitrous oxide; nitric oxide.
**Salpetergeist,** *m.* spirit of niter (old name for nitric acid). — **versüsster —,** see versüssen.
**Salpeter-grube,** *f.* saltpeter mine. **-gütemesser,** *m.* nitrometer. **-hafen,** *m.* niter pot.
**salpeterhaltig,** *a.* containing saltpeter, nitrous. — **salpeterhaltiger Höllenstein,** (*Pharm.*) mitigated silver nitrate.
**Salpeterhütte,** *f.* niter works.
**salpeterig,** *a.* = salpetrig.
**Salpeter-luft,** *f.* nitrogen (old name). **-messer,** *m.* nitrometer. **-milchsäure,** *f.* lactic acid nitrate. **-papier,** *n.* niter paper, nitrous paper. **-plantage,** *f.* saltpeter plantation. **-probe,** *f.* saltpeter test, nitrate test; saltpeter sample.
**salpetersalzsauer,** *a.* nitromuriate of.
**Salpetersalzsäure,** *f.* nitrohydrochloric acid, nitromuriatic acid, aqua regia.
**salpetersauer,** *a.* of or combined with nitric acid, nitrate of. — **salpetersaures Natron,** sodium nitrate. — **salpetersaures Zinnoxyd,** stannic nitrate, tin(IV) nitrate. — **salpetersaures Zinnoxydul,** stannous nitrate, tin(II) nitrate.
**Salpetersäure,** *f.* nitric acid. **-anhydrid,** *n.* nitric anhydride, (di)nitrogen pentoxide, nitrogen(V) oxide. **-äther,** *m.* nitric ether (ethyl nitrate). **-bad,** *n.* nitric acid bath. **-dampf,** *m.* nitric acid vapor or fume.
**salpetersäurehaltig,** *a.* containing nitric acid.
**Salpeter-säuresalz,** *n.* salt of nitric acid, nitrate. **-schaum,** *m.* wall saltpeter (calcium nitrate efflorescence).
**salpeterschwefelsauer,** *a.* of or combined with nitrosulfuric acid, nitrosulfate of.
**Salpeter-schwefelsäure,** *f.* nitrosulfuric acid (a mixture); nitrosylsulfuric acid. **-siederei,** *f.* saltpeter works. **-stärkemehl,** *n.* nitrated starch. **-stoff,** *m.* nitrogen. **-strauch,** *m.* niter bush (*Nitraria*). **-ung,** *f.* nitrification. **-verbindung,** *f.* nitrate. **-wa(a)ge,** *f.* nitrometer.
**salpetrig,** *a.* nitrous. — **salpetrige Säure,** ni-

trous acid. — **salpetrige Schwefelsäure,** nitrosylsulfuric acid.
**Salpetrigäther,** *m.* ethyl nitrite.
**salpetrigsauer,** *a.* of or combined with nitrous acid, nitrite of.
**Salpetrigsäure,** *f.* nitrous acid. **-anhydrid,** *n.* nitrous anhydride, dinitrogen trioxide. **-äther,** *m.* nitrous ether (ethyl nitrite).
**salpetrisch,** *a.* nitrous.
**Salve,** *f.* volley; salute.
**Salvei,** *f.* sage.
**Salz,** *n.* salt. — **schwefelsaures —,** sulfate; **palmitinsaures —,** palmitate; etc.
**Salz-ablagerung,** *f.* salt deposit. **-ader,** *f.* salt vein.
**salz-ähnlich,** *a.* salt-like. **-artig,** *a.* of the nature of or like (a) salt, saline.
**Salz-äther,** *m.* muriatic ether (old name for ethyl chloride). **-ausblühung,** *f.* efflorescence of salt. **-bad,** *n.* salt bath. **-base,** *f.* salifiable base (old term). **-bedarf,** *m.* salt requirement. **-beize,** *f.* (*Leather*) salt dressing. **-bergwerk,** *n.* salt mine.
**salzbildend,** *p.a.* salt-forming.
**Salz-bilder, -bildner,** *m.* salt former, halogen. **-bildung,** *f.* salt formation, salification.
**salzbildungs-fähig,** *a.* salifiable. **-unfähig,** *a.* nonsalifiable.
**Salz-blumen,** *f.pl.* efflorescence of salt. **-boden,** *m.* saline soil. **-brühe,** *f.* brine, pickle. **-brunnen,** *m.* salt spring, saline spring. **-chemie,** *f.* chemistry of salts, halochemistry. **-decke,** *f.* a quilted cover impregnated with salts to absorb toxic gases. **-drüse,** *f.* salt-secreting gland.
**salzen,** *v.t.* salt; season.
**salzerzeugend,** *a.* salt-producing.
**Salzerzeugung,** *f.* salt production; salification.
**salzfähig,** *a.* salifiable.
**Salz-farbe,** *f.* metallic dye, dye salt. **-fehler,** *m.* salt error. **-fleisch,** *n.* salt meat. **-fluss,** *m.* saline flux; salt rheum, eczema.
**salz-förmig,** *a.* saliniform. **-frei,** *a.* free from salt, salt-free.
**Salz-garten,** *m.* salt garden. **-gehalt,** *m.* salt content.
**Salzgeist,** *m.* (*Old Chem.*) spirit of salt (hydrochloric acid). — **leichter —,** light spirit of salt (ethyl chloride). — **schwerer —, versüsster —,** heavy spirit of salt, sweet spirit of salt. — **Libavius' rauchender —,** fuming liquor of Libavius (stannic chloride).
**Salz-gemisch,** *n.* salt mixture, mixture of salts. **-geschmack,** *m.* salty taste. **-gestein,** *n.* rock salt; saliferous rock.
**salzgetränkt,** *a.* impregnated with salt; (of coal) mineralized.
**Salz-glasur,** *f.* salt glaze. **-grube,** *f.* salt pit, salt mine.
**salzhaltig,** *a.* containing salt, salt-bearing, saliferous.
**Salzhaut,** *f.* salted hide; film or crust of salt.
**salzig,** *a.* salty, saline, briny.
**Salz-igkeit,** *f.* saltiness, salineness, salinity. **-ion,** *n.* salt ion. **-korn,** *n.* grain of salt. **-kraut,** *n.* saltwort. **-krücke,** *f.* salt crutch, salt stirrer. **-kuchen,** *m.* salt cake. **-kupfererz,** *n.* atacamite. **-lager,** *n.*, **-lagerstätte,** *f.* salt bed, salt layer, salt deposit. **-lake, -lauge,** *f.* brine, pickle. **-laugung,** *f.* brine leaching. **-löser,** *m.* salt dissolver, brine mixer. **-lösung,** *f.* salt solution; brine. **-messer,** *m.* salinometer, salimeter. **-messung,** *f.* salinometry, salimetry. **-mutterlauge,** *f.* (*Salt*) bittern. **-niederschlag,** *m.* deposit of salt, saline deposit. **-paar,** *n.* pair of salts, salt pair. **-pfanne,** *f.* salt pan, brine pan. **-pfannenstein,** *m.* (*Salt*) pan scale. **-pflanze,** *f.* (*Bot.*) halophyte. **-probe,** *f.* salt test; salt sample. **-quelle,** *f.* salt spring, saline spring; salt well.
**salzreich,** *a.* rich in salt.
**Salz-rinde,** *f.* salt crust. **-rückstand,** *m.* salt residue. **-salpetersäure,** *f.* nitrohydrochloric acid, aqua regia.
**salzsauer,** *a.* of or combined with hydrochloric acid, chloride of (metals, etc.), hydrochloride of (aniline and similar bases).
**Salzsäure,** *f.* hydrochloric acid, muriatic acid.
**salzsäurebindend,** *a.* fixing hydrochloric acid.
**Salzsäure-gas,** *n.* hydrochloric acid gas. **-lösung,** *f.* hydrochloric acid solution.
**Salz-schicht,** *f.* layer of salt. **-schmelze,** *f.* salt melt, fused salt. **-see,** *f.* salt lake. **-siedepfanne,** *f.* salt pan. **-sieder,** *m.* salt boiler, salt maker. **-siederei,** *f.* salt making; salt works. **-sole, -soole,** *f.* brine, salt water; salt spring. **-speck,** *m.* bacon. **-stein,** *m.* boiler scale; rock salt. **-stoffwechsel,** *m.* salt metabolism. **-ton,** *m.* salt clay, saliferous clay. **-wa(a)ge,** *f.* brine gage, salinometer.
**Salzwasser,** *n.* salt water, brine.
**salzwasserecht,** *a.* fast to salt water.
**Salz-wasserkühlung,** *f.* brine cooling. **-werk,** *n.* salt works, saline, saltern. **-wirkung,** *f.* effect (or action) of salt. **-zusatz,** *m.* addition of salt.
**-sam.** An adjective suffix attached to nouns, adjectives and verb roots; -some, -ble, -ive, etc.; as, *heilsam,* wholesome; *biegsam,* flexible.
**Same, Samen,** *m.* seed; semen, sperm.
**Samen-.** seed; seminal, spermatic. **-behandlung,** *f.* seed treatment. **-beizung,** *f.* seed disinfection. **-blättchen,** *n.* cotyledon. **-drüse,** *f.* testicle. **-eiweiss,** *n.* (*Bot.*) endosperm. **-faden,** *m.* spermatozoön. **-flüssigkeit,** *f.* seminal fluid.

**samenführend,** *p.a.* seminiferous.

**Samen-haar,** *n.* (*Bot.*) seed hair, coma. **-hefe,** *f.* seed yeast. **-keim,** *m.* germ, embryo. **-kern,** *m.* seed kernel; (*Bot.*) endosperm; (*Physiol.*) spermatic nucleus. **-lappen,** *m.* seed lobe, cotyledon. **-öl,** *n.* seed oil. **-pflanzen,** *f.pl.* seed plants, Spermatophyta. **-probe,** *f.* seed test or sample. **-saft,** *m.* seminal fluid. **-staub,** *m.* pollen. **-tierchen,** *n.* spermatozoön. **-zelle,** *f.* seminal cell, spermatozoön. **-zucker,** *m.* quercitol, quercite.

**sämig,** *a.* creamy.

**samisch,** *a.* Samian.

**sämisch,** *a.* **-gar,** oil-tanned, chamois.

**Sämisch-gerben,** *n.* chamoising. **-leder,** *n.* chamois leather, chamois.

**Sammel-.** collecting, collective. **-batterie,** *f.* storage battery, accumulator. **-becken,** *n.* collecting tank or vessel, cistern, reservoir. **-behälter,** *m.* collector, reservoir, storage tank. **-bottich,** *m.* (*Brewing*) collecting vat, starting tub. **-faktor,** *m.* collective factor. **-flasche,** *f.* collecting flask, receiver. **-gefäss,** *n.* collecting vessel, receiver, receptacle, reservoir. **-glas,** *n.* preparation tube, specimen tube; converging lens. **-leitung,** *f* (*Mach.*) manifold. **-linse,** *f.* converging lens. **-literatur,** *f.* reference literature.

**sammeln,** *v.t.* collect, gather, assemble, accumulate; harvest; focus.

**Sammel-raum,** *m.* receiver, receptacle. **-referat,** *n.* collective review. **-rohr,** *n.* collecting tube or pipe; collecting main. **-schiene,** *f.* (*Elec.*) bus bar. **-sirup,** *m.* sirup from spilt sugar. **-spiegel,** *m.* concave mirror. **-stelle,** *f.* collecting point, converging point. **-trichter,** *m.* collecting funnel. **-vorrichtung,** *f.* collecting apparatus, collector.

**Sammet,** *m.* velvet.

**sammetartig,** *a.* velvet-like, velvety.

**Sammet-blende,** *f.* göthite. **-braun,** *n.* velvet brown (an iron pigment). **-eisenerz,** *n.* göthite.

**sammeten,** *a.* velvet, velvety.

**Sammet-erz,** *n.* cyanotrichite. **-schwarz,** *n.* ivory black.

**Sammler,** *m.* accumulator, storage battery; gatherer, collector. **-säure,** *f.* accumulator acid.

**Sammlung,** *f.* collection, gathering, assembly.

**Sammlungsglas,** *n.* specimen glass, display glass; converging lens.

**samt,** *prep.* together with.

**Samt,** *m.* velvet.

**Samt-.** see Sammet-.

**samt-artig,** *a.* velvet-like, velvety. **-glänzend,** *a.* velvety.

**sämtlich,** *a.* all together, all. — *adv.* jointly, collectively.

**Sandarak, Sandarach,** *m.* realgar; sandarac.

**Sandarak-gummi, -harz,** *n.* sandarac resin, sandarac.

**sandartig,** *a.* sand-like, sandy.

**Sand-bad,** *n.* sand bath. **-badschale,** *f.* sand-bath dish. **-beerbaum,** *m.* arbutus (the tree). **-beere,** *f.* bearberry; arbutus. **-bestrahlung,** *f.* sandblasting. **-boden,** *m.* sandy soil. **-büchsenbaum,** *m.* sand-box tree (*Hura crepitans*). **-dornbeere,** *f.* sea buckthorn berry.

**Sandel,** *m.*, **-holz,** *n.* sandalwood. **-holzöl, -öl,** *n.* sandalwood oil, santal oil. **-rot,** *n.* santalin.

**Sandfarbe,** *f.* sand color.

**sandfarben,** *a.* sand-colored.

**Sandform,** *f.* (*Founding*) sand mold.

**sandführend,** *a.* sand-bearing; sand-conveying.

**Sand-gieserei,** *f.* sand casting. **-glimmer,** *m.* mica. **-gries,** *m.* coarse sand, fine gravel. **-gummi,** *n.* sandarac resin, sandarac. **-guss,** *m.* sand casting.

**sandhaltig,** *a.* containing sand, arenaceous.

**sandig,** *a.* sandy, arenaceous.

**Sand-kohle,** *f.* coal forming a powdery coke, sand coal. **-korn,** *n.* sand grain. **-mergel,** *m.* sandy marl. **-papier,** *n.* sandpaper.

**sandreich,** *a.* rich in sand, sandy.

**Sand-riedgras,** *n.* sea sedge, carex. **-schicht,** *f.* layer of sand. **-schiefer,** *m.* schistous sandstone, sandy shale. **-segge,** *f.* sea sedge, carex. **-stein,** *m.* sandstone. **-strahl,** *m.* sand blast, sand jet. **-strahlgebläse,** *n.* sandblast machine.

**sandte,** *pret.* (of senden) sent.

**Sand-ton,** *m.* sandy clay. **-traube,** *f.* bearberry. **-uhr,** *f.* sandglass, hourglass. **-wüste,** *f.* sandy desert. **-zucker,** *m.* raw ground sugar, brown sugar.

**sanforisieren,** *v.t.* sanforize.

**sanft,** *a.* soft, mild, gentle, smooth.

**sang,** *pret.* (of singen) sang.

**Sang,** *m.* song.

**Sangajol,** *n.* (*Paint*) mineral spirits. *T.N.*

**sanieren,** *v.t.* cure, restore; reorganize.

**Sanierung,** *f.* curing; sanitation; restoration; reorganization.

**Sanierungsmittel,** *n.* curative agent; restorative; prophylactic.

**Sanikel,** *m.* sanicle.

**sanitär, sanitärisch,** *a.* sanitary.

**Sanität,** *f.* health, hygiene, sanity.

**Sanitäts-.** sanitary, hygienic, health, medical. **-anstalt,** *f.* health institute. **-geschirr,** *n.* sanitary ware. **-kollegium,** *n.* board of health. **-pflege,** *f.* sanitation. **-polizei,** *f.* sanitary police.

**sanitätspolizeilich,** *a.* of or pertaining to the sanitary police.
**Sanitätswesen,** *n.* sanitary affairs.
**sank,** *pret.* (of sinken) sank, fell.
**sann,** *pret.* (of sinnen) thought, etc.
**Santel, Santel-.** = Sandel, Sandel-.
**santonig,** *a.* santonous.
**Santoninsäure,** *f.* santoninic acid.
**Santonsäure,** *f.* santonic acid.
**Sapanholz,** *n.* sapanwood.
**Saphir,** *m.* sapphire. **-blau,** *n.* sapphire blue.
**saphiren,** *a.* sapphire, sapphirine.
**Saphirspat,** *m.* cyanite.
**Saponifikatglyzerin,** *n.* glycerin from saponification of fats.
**Saprämie,** *f.* (*Med.*) sapremia.
**saprogen,** *a.* saprogenic, putrefactive.
**saprophytisch,** *a.* saprophytic.
**Sardelle,** *f.* anchovy; sardine.
**Sardinenöl,** *n.* sardine oil.
**Sarg,** *m.* coffin.
**Sark-.** sarc-.
**Sarkin,** *n.* sarcine (hypoxanthine).
**Sarkom,** *n.* sarcoma.
**sarkomatös,** *a.* sarcomatous.
**Sarsa,** *f.* sarsaparilla.
**Sasapalme,** *f.* nipa palm.
**sass,** *pret.* (of sitzen) sat, stayed, etc.
**Sassafrasöl,** *n.* sassafras oil.
**Sassaparille,** *f.* sarsaparilla.
**Satinage,** *f.* glazing, finish.
**Satinappretur,** *f.* satin finish, glazed finish.
**satinieren,** *v.t.* satin, glaze, gloss; calender or supercalender (paper).
**Satin-papier,** *n.* glazed paper. **-weiss,** *n.* satin white.
**satt,** *a.* satisfied; satiated; (of colors) saturated, deep, full. **-blau,** *a.* deep blue.
**Sattdampf,** *m.* saturated steam or vapor.
**Satte,** *f.* bowl, dish, pan.
**Sattel,** *m.* saddle; bridge. **-fass,** *n.* (*Brewing*) rider cask.
**sattelförmig,** *a.* saddle-shaped.
**Sattel-gang,** *m.* (*Mining*) saddle reef. **-schlange,** *f.* saddle(shaped) coil.
**sattgelb,** *a.* deep-yellow.
**sättigen,** *v.t.* saturate; impregnate; satisfy; satiate, sate.
**Sättiger,** *m.* saturator.
**Sättigung,** *f.* saturation; satisfaction; satiety.
**Sättigungs-apparat,** *m.* saturating apparatus, saturator. **-druck,** *m.* saturation pressure.
**sättigungsfähig,** *a.* capable of saturation.
**Sättigungs-fähigkeit,** *f.* capability of saturation. **-gefäss,** *n.* saturating vessel. **-grad,** *m.* degree of saturation. **-grenze,** *f.* saturation limit. **-kapazität,** *f.* saturation capacity. **-mittel,** *n.* saturating agent, saturant. **-punkt,** *m.* saturation point. **-strom,** *m.* (*Elec.*) saturation current. **-verhältnis,** *n.* (of air) relative humidity. **-wert,** *m.* saturation value; valence, valency.
**Sattler,** *m.* saddler. **-leder,** *n.* saddler's leather. **-pech,** *n.* saddler's pitch, saddler's wax.
**sattsam,** *a.* sufficient. — *adv.* sufficiently.
**Saturateur,** *m.* saturator.
**Saturations-gefäss,** *n.* saturation vessel, saturator. **-scheidung,** *f.* (*Sugar*) purification by carbonation (separation of impurities with the lime when the juice is saturated with carbon dioxide). **-schlamm,** *m.* (*Sugar*) sediment from carbonation.
**Saturei,** *f.*, **-kraut,** *n.* savory. **-öl,** *n.* savory oil.
**saturieren,** *v.t.* saturate; (*Sugar*) carbonate.
**Saturnrot,** *n.* Saturn red, minium.
**Satz,** *m.* deposit, sediment, settlings; composition; set (of weights, beakers, etc.); charge, batch; principle, proposition; leap, jump; young (of fish), fry; price, rate; pool, stake; sentence; (*Brewing*) yeast, sediment. **-betrieb,** *m.* batch operation.
**satzbildend,** *a.* deposit-forming, sediment-forming.
**Satzbrauen,** *n.* brewing with cold malt extract.
**satzfrei,** *a.* deposit-free, sediment-free.
**Satz-krücke,** *f.* (*Brewing*) yeast rouser. **-mehl,** *n.* fecula, starch flour. **-schale,** *f.* settling dish.
**Satzung,** *f.* statute, ordinance, law.
**satzweise,** *adv.* intermittently.
**Sau,** *f.* sow (also *Metal.*); drying kiln; blot.
**sauber,** *a.* clean; neat; pretty.
**Sauberkeit,** *f.* cleanness, cleanliness, neatness.
**säubern,** *v.t.* clean, cleanse, purify.
**Saubohne,** *f.* fodder bean, specif. (1) vetch, (2) soybean.
**Saubohnen-fett, -öl,** *n.* soybean oil.
**sauer,** *a.* acid; sour, tart; troublesome, hard. — **— machen,** acidify.
**Sauer-ampfer,** *m.* sorrel, sour dock (*Rumex*). **-bad,** *n.* (*Bleaching*) sour bath, sour.
**säuer-bar,** *a.* acidifiable. **-beständig,** *a.* = säurebeständig.
**Sauer-blei,** *n.* lead chromate. **-bleiche,** *f.* sour bleaching. **-brühe,** *f.* (*Tech.*) sour liquor, acid liquor. **-brunnen,** *m.* acidulous spring water.
**sauerchromsauer,** *a.* dichromate of.
**Sauer-dorn,** *m.* barberry. **-dornbitter,** *n.* berberine (old name). **-eisen,** *n.* (*Metal.*) iron oxide. **-futter,** *n.* ensilage.
**sauerhaltig,** *a.* acidiferous.
**Sauerhonig,** *m.* oxymel.
**Säuerkasten,** *m.* (*Textiles*) souring tank.
**Sauerkeit,** *f.* acidity, sourness.
**Sauerklee,** *m.* clover sorrel, wood sorrel. **-salz,** *n.* salt of sorrel (potassium hydrogen oxalate). **-säure,** *f.* oxalic acid.

**säuerlich,** *a.* sourish, acidulous, subacid.
**Säuerlichkeit,** *f.* (slight) acidity, subacidity.
**säuerlichstechend,** *a.* turning sourish.
**säuerlichsüss,** *a.* sourish-sweet.
**Säuerling,** *m.* acidulous mineral water, sparkling mineral water; sparkling mineral spring; sour wine; cheese from sour milk; clover sorrel, wood sorrel.
**Sauermachen,** *n.* acidification.
**sauermachend,** *p.a.* acidifying.
**säuern,** *v.t.* acidify; acidulate; sour; leaven (bread). — *v.i.* sour.
**sauerphosphorsauer,** *a.* acid phosphate of.
**Sauerquelle,** *f.* carbonated (or aerated) spring.
**sauerreagierend,** *a.* of acid reaction.
**Sauersalz,** *n.* acid salt.
**sauerschwefligsauer,** *a.* acid sulfite of.
**Sauerstoff,** *m.* oxygen. **-abgabe,** *f.* evolution of oxygen. **-alterung,** *f.* aging with oxygen.
**sauerstoffarm,** *a.* poor in oxygen.
**Sauerstoff-äther,** *m.* acetaldehyde. **-atmung,** *f.* breathing of oxygen; (*Biol.*) aerobic respiration. **-atom,** *n.* oxygen atom. **-aufnahme,** *f.* oxygen absorption. **-bedürfnis,** *n.* oxygen requirement. **-bildung,** *f.* formation of oxygen. **-bleiche,** *f.* oxidation bleaching. **-bombe,** *f.* oxygen cylinder. **-brücke,** *f.* oxygen bridge. **-druck,** *m.* oxygen pressure. **-entwickelung,** *f.* evolution of oxygen.
**sauerstoffentziehend,** *a.* removing oxygen, deoxidizing.
**Sauerstoff-entzug,** *m.* removal of oxygen. **-erzeuger,** *m.* oxygen producer or generator. **-fänger,** *m.* a substance that absorbs oxygen, as barium oxide. **-flasche,** *f.* oxygen cylinder.
**sauerstof(f)frei,** *a.* free from oxygen.
**Sauerstoff-gas,** *n.* oxygen gas. **-gehalt,** *m.* oxygen content. **-gerät,** *n.* oxygen apparatus.
**sauerstoffhaltig,** *a.* containing oxygen.
**Sauerstoff-ion,** *n.* anion. **-mangel,** *m.* lack of oxygen, oxygen deficiency. **-menge,** *f.* amount of oxygen. **-messer,** *m.* eudiometer. **-ort,** *m.* oxidation region. **-pol,** *m.* oxygen pole, anode.
**sauerstoffreich,** *a.* rich in oxygen.
**Sauerstoff-salz,** *n.* oxysalt, salt of an oxyacid. **-sättigung,** *f.* saturation with oxygen. **-säure,** *f.* oxygen acid, oxyacid. **-schlauch,** *m.* oxygen tubing. **-strom,** *m.* current of oxygen. **-träger, -überträger,** *m.* oxygen carrier. **-überschuss,** *m.* excess of oxygen. **-verbindung,** *f.* oxygen compound. **-verwandtschaft,** *f.* affinity for oxygen. **-zufuhr,** *f.* supply(ing) of oxygen.
**sauersüss,** *a.* sour-sweet.
**Sauerteig,** *m.* leaven.
**Säuerung,** *f.* acidification; souring; leavening.
**säuerungsfahig,** *a.* acidifiable; capable of souring.
**Säuerungs-grad,** *m.* degree of acidity. **-mittel,** *n.* acidifying agent.
**Sauer-wasser,** *n.* sour water, sour (any of various dilute acid solutions used in the arts); acidulous (sparkling) water. **-wein,** *m.* sour wine; verjuice.
**sauerwein-sauer, -steinsauer,** *a.* acid tartrate of, bitartrate of.
**Sauerwerden,** *n.* souring; (of liquors) acetification.
**sauerwerdend,** *a.* souring, acescent.
**sauerzugestellt,** *a.* (*Metal.*) acid-lined.
**Saug-.** suction, sucking, absorbing, absorbent, aspirating. **-ader,** *f.* (*Anat.*) absorbing vessel, lymphatic vessel. **-aderdrüse,** *f.* lymphatic gland. **-apparat,** *m.* suction apparatus; aspirator. **-druck,** *m.* suction pressure. **-düse,** *f.* suction nozzle; Venturi tube.
**Sauge-.** = Saug-.
**saugen,** *v.t. & i.* suck; suck up, absorb.
**Saugen,** *n.* sucking, suction.
**säugen,** *v.t.* suckle, nurse.
**Sauger,** *m.* sucker; suction apparatus; aspirator; exhauster.
**Säugetier,** *n.* mammal.
**saugfähig,** *a.* absorptive, absorbent; hygroscopic.
**Saug-fähigkeit,** *f.* absorptive capacity, absorptivity. **-festigkeit,** *f.* resistance to suction, suction strength. **-filter,** *n.* suction filter. **-flasche,** *f.* suction bottle; filter flask. **-gas,** *n.* suction producer gas; aspirated gas. **-gefäss,** *n.* suction vessel; absorbent vessel. **-geschwindigkeit,** *f.* velocity of suction. **-glas,** *n.* suction bottle; breast pump. **-haar,** *n.* absorbent hair. **-hahn,** *m.* suction cock. **-heber,** *m.* siphon. **-höhe,** *f.* suction head, suction height, absorption height. **-kasten,** *m.* suction box, vacuum box. **-kolben,** *m.* suction flask. **-korb,** *m.* suction strainer. **-leitung,** *f.* suction pipe (or piping), suction line. **-ling,** *m.* (*Plastics*) pulp product.
**Säugling,** *m.* suckling, infant.
**Saug-luft,** *f.* vacuum, suction; inlet air. **-luftanlage,** *f.* vacuum equipment or plant. **-lüfter,** *m.* exhauster. **-luftkessel,** *m.* vacuum vessel. **-maschine,** *f.* exhauster; aspirator. **-messer,** *m.* vacuometer. **-näpfchen,** *n.* suction cup. **-papier,** *n.* absorbent paper. **-pipette,** *f.* suction pipet(te). **-pumpe,** *f.* suction pump. **-raum,** *m.* suction chamber. **-rohr,** *n.*, **-röhre,** *f.* suction tube or pipe, sucking pipe; siphon; Venturi tube. **-röhrchen,** *n.* pipet(te). **-schiefer,** *m.* absorbent shale. **-schlauch,** *m.* suction tubing or hose. **-stäbchen,** *n.* micro immersion filter, filterstick. **-strahlpumpe,** *f.* jet suction pump. **-stutzen,** *m.* suction cylinder (on which is fitted a filtering vessel with perforated bottom); vacuum

pump intake; exhaust connection. **-tiegel,** *m.* suction crucible. **-trichter,** *m.* pipe (in a casting). **-trockner,** *m.* suction drier.

**Saugung,** *f.* suction, sucking.

**Saug-ventil,** *n.* suction valve. **-vorrichtung,** *f.* suction arrangement. **-widerstand,** *m.* resistance to suction. **-wirkung,** *f.* suction effect, sucking action. **-zone,** *f.* suction zone; absorption zone. **-zug,** *m.* suction draft, induced draft. **-zuglüfter,** *m.* exhaust fan.

**Säulchen,** *n.* little column, etc. (see Säule).

**Säule,** *f.* column; pillar; post; (*Cryst.*) prism; (*Elec.*) pile.

**Sauleder,** *n.* hogskin, pigskin.

**Säulen-.** columnar; (*Cryst.*) prismatic. **-achse,** *f.* prismatic axis.

**säulen-artig, -förmig,** *a.* columnar; prismatic.

**Säulenzelle,** *f.* columnar cell.

**säulig,** *a.* columnar; columned.

**Saum,** *m.* seam, hem, edge, fringe, selvage; border, margin; (*Tin Plate*) list.

**säumen,** *v.t.* hem, edge, border; square (planks). — *v.i.* tarry, stay.

**Saum-pfanne,** *f.* (*Tin Plate*) list pot. **-riff,** *n.* fringing reef. **-spiegel,** *m.* gray spiegeleisen. **-topf,** *m.* = Saumpfanne.

**Säure,** *f.* acid; sourness, acidity. **-abfall,** *m.* acid sludge. **-amid,** *n.* acid amide. **-angriff,** *m.* attack by acid, acid corrosion. **-anhydrid,** *n.* acid anhydride. **-anzug,** *m.* acid-proof clothing.

**säureartig,** *a.* acid-like, of acid nature.

**Säure-äther,** *m.* ester. **-avivage,** *f.* (*Dyeing*) brightening with acid. **-bad,** *n.* acid bath. **-ballon,** *m.* acid carboy. **-basengleichgewicht,** *n.* acid-base equilibrium. **-behälter,** *m.* acid container. **-behandlung,** *f.* acid treatment. **-beize,** *f.* (*Leather*) sour.

**säurebeständig,** *a.* stable toward acids, acid-proof, acid-resisting, (of colors) fast to acid.

**Säure-beständigkeit,** *f.* resistance to acid. **-bestimmung,** *f.* determination of acid.

**säurebildend,** *p.a.* acid-forming.

**Säure-bildner,** *m.* acid former, acidifier. **-bildung,** *f.* acid formation, acidification.

**säurebindend,** *a.* acid-binding, combining with acids.

**Säure-bindungsvermögen,** *n.* power to combine with acids, acid capacity. **-bottich,** *m.* acid vat. **-braun,** *n.* acid brown. **-bromid,** *n.* acid bromide. **-chlorid,** *n.* acid chloride. **-dampf,** *m.* acid vapor. acid fume. **-dichte,** *f.* acid density. **-dichtemesser,** *m.* hydrometer. **-druckbehälter,** *m.* acid egg. acid blow case. **-dunst,** *m.* acid fume, acid vapor

**säureecht,** *a.* fast to acid.

**Säure-echtheit,** *f.* fastness to acid. **-eiweiss,** *n.* acid protein.

**säureempfindlich,** *a.* sensitive to acids.

**Säure-empfindlichkeit,** *f.* sensitiveness to acids. **-ester,** *m.* ester of an acid, ester.

**säurefähig,** *a.* acidifiable.

**Säurefarbstoff,** *m.* acid dye.

**säurefest,** *a.* acid-proof, acid-fast.

**Säure-flasche,** *f.* acid bottle. **-flotte,** *f.* acid bath, acid liquor. **-fluorid,** *n.* acid fluoride.

**säurefrei,** *a.* free from acid, nonacid.

**Säure-gehalt,** *m.* acid content, acidity. **-gelb,** *n.* acid yellow. **-grad,** *m.* (degree of) acidity. **-grün,** *n.* acid green. **-grundlage,** *f.* acidifiable base. **-haloid,** *n.* acid halide.

**säurehaltig,** *a.* containing acid, acidiferous.

**Säure-harz,** *n.* (*Petroleum*) acid sludge. **-heber,** *m.* acid siphon. **-herstellung,** *f.* acid manufacture. **-hydrat,** *n.* acid hydrate. **-imid,** *n.* acid imide.

**säurekochecht,** *a.* fast to boiling acid.

**Säurekochechtheit,** *f.* fastness to boiling acid.

**säurelöslich,** *a.* acid-soluble.

**Säure-lösung,** *f.* solution of an acid. **-maschine,** *f.* souring machine. **-menge,** *f.* amount of acid. **-messer,** *m.* acidimeter; hydrometer. **-messkunst,** *f.* acidimetry. **-messung,** *f.* acidimetry. **-probe,** *f.* acid test; acid sample. **-pumpe,** *f.* acid pump. **-radikal,** *n.* acid radical. **-regenerat,** *n.* (*Rubber*) acid reclaim.

**säurereich,** *a.* rich in acid.

**Säure-rest,** *m.* acid residue. **-schlamm,** *m.* acid sludge. **-schlauch,** *m.* acid hose. **-schleuder,** *f.* acid hydro-extractor. **-schwarz,** *n.* acid black. **-schwellung,** *f.* (*Leather*) acid plumping. **-schwemmverfahren,** *n.* acid flotation process. **-spaltung,** *f.* acid cleavage. **-ständer,** *m.* acid cistern. **-titer,** *m.* acid titer. **-trog,** *m.* acid trough. **-turm,** *m.* acid tower. **-überschuss,** *m.* excess of acid.

**säureunlöslich,** *a.* insoluble in acid, acid-insoluble.

**Säure-ventil,** *n.* acid valve. **-verteiler,** *m.* acid distributor.

**säurewalkecht,** *a.* fast to acid milling.

**Säure-wechsel,** *m.* change in acidity. **-widerstandsfähigkeit,** *f.* resistance to acid.

**säure-widerstehend,** *p.a.* resistant (or fast) to acid. **-widrig,** *a.* antacid.

**Säure-wirkung,** *f.* action of acids. **-zahl,** *f.* acid number. **-zufuhr,** *f.* addition of acid.

**Säurung,** *f.* = Säuerung.

**säuseln,** *v.i.* rustle; murmur; lisp; hum.

**sausen,** *v.i.* rush, whiz, whistle, hum.

**Sca-.** see Ska-.

**Schaar,** *f.* = Schar.

**Schabe,** *f.* scraper; grater; scab, itch; cockroach; moth.

**Schäbe,** *f.* awn, chaff (of flax or hemp); scab, itch.

**schabecht,** *a.* fast to scraping.

**Schabeisen,** *n.* scraper; shaver.
**Schabemesser,** *n.* scraping or paring knife.
**schaben,** *v.t.* scrape; shave, pare; grate, rub.
**Schabenpulver,** *n.* roach powder, specif. white arsenic.
**Schaber,** *m.* scraper, etc. (see schaben); doctor blade, doctor. **-messer,** *n.* doctor blade, doctor.
**schäbig,** *a.* shabby; mean.
**Schabin,** *n.*, **Schabine,** *f.* parings (of gold, etc.).
**Schablone,** *f.* model, pattern, template; mold, form; stencil; screen.
**schablonenartig,** *a.* according to pattern, mechanical, automatic.
**Schablonen-blech,** *n.* sheet metal for stencils. **-lack,** *m.* screen varnish.
**schablonenmässig,** *a.* = schablonenartig.
**Schablonenpapier,** *n.* stencil paper.
**schablonieren,** *v.t.* stencil; trace (a pattern).
**Schabsel,** *n.* scrapings, parings, shavings.
**Schabstoff,** *m.* (*Paper*) scraped pulp.
**Schach,** *n.* chess; check. **-brett,** *n.* chessboard, checkerboard.
**schachbrettartig,** *a.* checkered.
**Schacht,** *m.* shaft; tunnel; pit; gorge. **-deckel,** *m.* manhole cover.
**Schachtel,** *f.* box, case. **-halm,** *m.*, **-kraut,** *n.* horsetail (*Equisetum*). **-halmsäure,** *f.* equisetic acid.
**schachteln,** *v.t.* put in a box, box, pack.
**Schacht-ofen,** *m.* shaft furnace; blast furnace; shaft kiln. **-speicher,** *m.* (*Metal.*) storage bin; (*Agric.*) silo. **-trockner,** *m.* tunnel drier.
**schade,** *a.* unfortunate, a pity.
**Schade,** *m.* damage, injury, loss, detriment.
**Schädel,** *m.* skull, cranium.
**Schädel-.** cranial.
**schaden,** *v.i.* do injury, damage, hurt, harm.
**Schaden,** *m.* = Schade. **-ersatz,** *m.* compensation, damages.
**schadhaft,** *a.* damaged, defective, spoiled.
**schädigen,** *v.t.* harm, injure, damage.
**Schädigung,** *f.* injury, damage, harm.
**schädlich,** *a.* noxious, injurious, harmful, deleterious, detrimental; (*Mach.*, of space) dead.
**Schädlich-keit,** *f.* injuriousness, harmfulness. **-keitsgrad,** *m.* degree of injuriousness. **-machung,** *f.* rendering noxious, vitiation, contamination.
**Schädling,** *m.* pest.
**Schädlings-bekämpfung,** *f.* pest control. **-bekämpfungsmittel,** *n.* pest-controlling agent, pesticide, insecticide, etc.
**schadlos,** *a.* harmless; compensated. — **— halten,** compensate, indemnify.
**Schaf,** *n.* sheep; ewe. **-bein,** *n.* bone ash; sheep bone; sheep's leg. **-bock,** *m.* ram. **-darmsaite,** *f.* catgut. **-fell,** *n.* sheepskin.
**schaffen,** *v.t.* make, produce, create, do; get, provide; take, bring. — *v.i.* work, be busy.
**Schaffleisch,** *n.* mutton.
**Schaffner,** *m.* manager, conductor, guard.
**Schaffnerin,** *f.* housekeeper, stewardess, manageress.
**Schaffung,** *f.* making, etc. (see schaffen); production, creation.
**Schaf-garbe,** *f.* yarrow, milfoil. **-haut,** *f.* sheepskin; amnion. **-häutchen,** *n.* amnion. **-käse,** *m.* cheese from ewe's milk. **-leder,** *n.* sheepskin (leather), sheep. **-milch,** *f.* ewe's milk.
**Schafott,** *n.* scaffold.
**Schaf-schmiere,** *f.* sheep dip. **-schweiss,** *m.* suint, yolk.
**Schafsklauenöl,** *n.* sheep's-foot oil.
**Schaft,** *m.* shaft, shank, stock, handle, stalk, trunk.
**-schaft.** A noun suffix used to form abstract and collective nouns, cognate with the English -ship; as, *Freundschaft*, friendship.
**Schaf-talg,** *m.* mutton tallow. **-waschmittel,** *n.* sheep dip. **-wasser,** *n.* amniotic fluid. **-wolle,** *f.* sheep's wool.
**Schagrin,** *n.* shagreen.
**schal,** *a.* stale, flat, insipid.
**Schälchen,** *n.* little dish or cup, capsule; cupel.
**Schale,** *f.* dish, basin, bowl; pan; tray; cup; (dished) cover; pan, scale (of a balance); shell; husk, skin, peel, rind, bark; cover (of a book); (*Founding*) chill.
**schälen,** *v.t.* shell, husk, peel, pare, bark. — *v.r.* peel off, scale off.
**Schalen-bau,** *m.* shell structure. **-blende,** *f.* fibrous sphalerite. **-entwickelung,** *f.* (*Photog.*) tray (or dish) development.
**schalenförmig,** *a.* bowl-shaped, dish-shaped, cup-shaped; shell-like.
**Schalen-frucht,** *f.* dry fruit, specif. caryopsis. **-guss,** *m.* chill casting. **-gussform,** *f.* chill. **-gusskern,** *m.* (*Founding*) chilled core.
**schalenhart,** *a.* chilled.
**Schalen-haut,** *f.* (*Anat.*) chorion. **-lack,** *m.* shellac. **-lederhaut,** *f.* chorion. **-obst,** *n.* (*Bot.*) = Schalenfrucht. **-träger,** *m.* dish support, tripod.
**schalig,** *a.* scaly, foliated; crusted; shelled; shelly; shaly.
**Schall,** *m.* sound; ring, peal; resonance; noise.
**Schall-.** sound, acoustic. **-abwehr,** *f.* noise abatement.
**schalldämpfend,** *a.* sound-absorbing, sound-deadening.
**Schalldämpfer,** *m.* sound absorber, silencer, muffler.
**schalldicht,** *a.* soundproof.
**schallen,** *v.i.* sound, resound, ring.
**Schall-färbung,** *f.* tone color, timbre. **-ge-**

schwindigkeit, *f.* velocity of sound; sonic speed. **-lehre,** *f.* acoustics. **-platte,** *f.* phonograph disk, record. **-schutz,** *m.* soundproofing, sound insulation. **-schwingung,** *f.* sound vibration.
**schallsicher,** *a.* soundproof.
**Schallstärke,** *f.* intensity of sound.
**schalltot,** *a.* acoustically dead, nonresonant.
**Schallverstärkung,** *f.* sound amplification.
**schallweich,** *a.* sound-absorbent.
**Schallwelle,** *f.* sound wave.
**schallzuleitend,** *a.* sound-conducting.
**Schalt-.** inserted, interposed, intercalary; (*Elec.*) switch. **-brett,** switchboard.
**schalten,** *v.t.* insert; (*Elec.*) connect, switch; shift (gears); control. — *v.i.* rule, have one's way.
**Schalter,** *m.* wicket, window; ruler, manager; (*Elec.*) switch. **-öl,** *n.* switch oil.
**Schaltier,** *n.* crustacean.
**Schalt-jahr,** *n.* leap year. **-plan,** *m.*, **-skizze,** *f.* (*Elec.*) wiring diagram. **-stück,** *n.* insert piece, insert; (*Elec.*) contact part, contact. **-tafel,** *f.* switchboard; instrument board.
**Schaltung,** *f.* disposal; (*Elec.*) connection, hookup, wiring, also switching; gear shift; control.
**Schalung,** *f.* casing, sheathing, form.
**Schälung,** *f.* shelling, etc. (see schälen); excoriation, desquamation.
**Scham,** *f.* shame; modesty, chastity; pudenda.
**Scham-.** pudic. **-bein,** *n.* pubis.
**schämen,** *v.r.* be ashamed.
**Schamgang,** *m.* vagina.
**Schamotte,** *f.* (*Ceram.*) chamotte (dead-burned fireclay grog with plastic fire clay as binder). **-retorte,** *f.* fireclay retort. **-stein,** *m.* firebrick. **-tiegel,** *m.* chamotte crucible. **-ton,** *m.* fireclay. **-ziegel,** *m.* chamotte brick.
**Schande,** *f.* shame, dishonor, disgrace.
**Schankbier, Schänkbier,** *n.* schenk beer, draft beer.
**Schanze,** *f.* trench, intrenchment; chance.
**Schar,** *f.* troop, band, host, crowd, herd, flock; (*fig.*) group, family; (plow) share.
**Scharbock,** *m.* scurvy.
**scharbockheilend,** *p.a.* antiscorbutic.
**Scharbockmittel,** *n.* antiscorbutic.
**scharen,** *v.r.* flock together, assemble.
**scharf,** *a.* sharp; acrid, pungent, strong, corrosive; acute; keen; precise; severe, rigorous. **— trocknen,** dry at a high temperature.
**Schärfe,** *f.* sharpness, etc. (see scharf); edge.
**scharfeckig,** *a.* sharp-cornered.
**Scharfeinstellung,** *f.* sharp adjustment or focusing.
**schärfen,** *v.t.* sharpen; strengthen (a solution).
**Schärfen-fläche,** *f.* (*Optics*) surface of distinct vision. **-tiefe,** *f.* (*Opt.*) depth of focus.
**Scharffeuer,** *n.* (*Ceram.*) hard fire, sharp fire. **-farbe,** *f.* hard-fire color.
**scharf-getrocknet,** *a.* dried at a high temperature. **-kantig,** *a.* acute-angled; sharp-edged. **-konturig,** *a.* of sharp outline. **-körnig,** *a.* sharp-grained.
**Scharfmanganerz,** *n.* hausmannite.
**scharf-salzig,** *a.* very salty. **-sauer,** *a.* strongly acid, very sour. **-schmeckend,** *p.a.* of a sharp taste, acrid, pungent, tart. **-schweflig,** *a.* strongly sulfurous.
**Scharfsinn,** *m.* acuteness, acumen.
**scharf-sinnig,** *a.* clever, sagacious, shrewd. **-winklig,** *a.* acute-angled.
**Scharlach,** *m.* scarlet; scarlet fever; scarlet runner. **-beeren,** *f.pl.* kermes berries, kermes.
**scharlachen, scharlachfarben,** *a.* scarlet.
**Scharlach-farbe,** *f.* scarlet color or dye. **-fieber,** *n.* scarlet fever, scarlatina.
**scharlachrot,** *a.* scarlet, bright red.
**Scharlach-rot,** *n.* scarlet; cochineal. **-wurm,** *m.* cochineal insect.
**Scharnier,** *n.* hinge, (hinged) joint. **-ventil,** *n.* clack valve, flap valve.
**Schärpe,** *f.* scarf, sash; (*Med.*) sling.
**Scharpie,** *f.* charpie, lint.
**Scharre,** *f.* rake, raker, scraper.
**scharren,** *v.t.* scrape, scratch.
**Scharrharz,** *n.* scraped resin or rosin.
**Scharrwerk,** *n.* scraping mechanism, scraper.
**Scharte,** *f.* notch, nick, fissure; sawwort.
**schartig,** *a.* notchy, nicked, jagged.
**Scharung,** *f.* assembling, grouping.
**schatten,** *v.t.* shade.
**Schatten,** *m.* shade, shadow. **-färbung,** *f.* shadow dyeing. **-riss,** *m.* silhouet(te).
**schattentrocken,** *a.* dried in the shade.
**schattieren,** *v.t.* shade.
**Schattierung,** *f.* shading; shade, tint.
**Schattung,** *f.* shading; shade.
**Schatz,** *m.* treasure; stock; wealth. **-amt,** *n.* (public) treasury.
**schätzbar,** *a.* capable of valuation or estimation; valuable, esteemed.
**schatzen,** *v.t.* assess, tax.
**schätzen,** *v.t.* value; estimate; evaluate; appraise; appreciate, esteem.
**Schatzkammer,** *f.* treasury; storehouse.
**Schätzung,** *f.* valuation, etc. (see schätzen); estimate.
**Schätzungswert,** *m.* estimated value.
**Schau,** *f.* view, review; show. **-bild,** *n.* diagram; graph; (picture for) exhibit.
**schaubildlich,** *a.* diagrammatic, graphic.
**schaudern,** *v.t.* cause to shudder. — *v.i.* shudder.
**schauen,** *v.t.* look at, behold, examine. — *v.i.* look, gaze.
**Schauer,** *m.* shudder, thrill, fit; shower; spectator; inspector; shed.

**Schaufel,** *f.* shovel, scoop; paddle; blade; (of a turbine) bucket.
**schaufeln,** *v.t.* shovel, scoop.
**Schau-fenster,** *n.* show window. **-glas,** *n.* display glass, specimen glass, sample glass; sight glass; (*Optics*) eyepiece, ocular; (*Mech.*) oil gage.
**schaukeln,** *v.t. & i.* swing, rock.
**Schau-linie,** *f.* line, curve (in a graph). **-loch,** *n.* peephole, inspection window.
**schaulustig,** *a.* curious.
**Schaum,** *m.* foam, froth; scum; lather; (*Brewing*) head.
**schaum-ähnlich,** *a.* foam-like, foamy. **-artig,** *a.* foamy, frothy.
**Schaum-beständigkeit,** *f.* foam-holding capacity. **-bier,** *n.* foaming beer. **-bildner,** *m.* frothing agent, foamer. **-bildung,** *f.* formation of foam or froth. **-blase,** *f.* bubble. **-brecher,** *m.* foam breaker, froth killer.
**schäumen,** *v.i.* froth, foam; (of wine, etc.) sparkle, fizz; (of soap) lather. — *v.t.* skim, scum.
**Schaum-erde,** *f.* aphrite (variety of calcite). **-erz,** *n.* (soft or foamy) wad.
**schaumfähig, schäumfähig,** *a.* (capable of) foaming; (of soap) lathering.
**Schaum-feuerlöscher,** *m.* foam extinguisher. **-fleck,** *m.* froth spot, froth stain. **-gärung,** *f.* frothy fermentation. **-gemisch,** *n.* foam mixture. **-gips,** *m.* foliated gypsum. **-gold,** *n.* Dutch metal, imitation gold. **-gummi,** *n.* sponge rubber; crêpe rubber.
**schaumhaft,** *a.* foamy, frothy.
**Schaum-hahn,** *m.* scum cock. **-haken,** *m.* skimmer. **-haube,** *f.* (*Brewing*) head.
**schaumig, schäumig,** *a.* foamy, frothy; (of soap) lathering; porous.
**Schäumigkeit,** *f.* foaminess, frothiness.
**Schaum-kalk,** *n.* sparry aphrite (form of aragonite). **-kelle,** *f.* skimming ladle, skimmer. **-korb,** *m.* (*Sugar*) scum basket. **-kraft,** *f.* foaming (or lathering) power. **-löffel,** *m.* skimming spoon, skimmer.
**schaumlos,** *a.* foamless, frothless.
**Schaum-löschmittel,** *n.* foam fire-extinguishing agent. **-mittel,** *n.* foaming agent. **-rohr,** *n.*, **-röhre,** *f.* foam tube; scum pipe. **-schlacke,** *f.* slag pumice. **-schwärze,** *f.* finely powdered animal charcoal. **-schwimmaufbereitung,** *f.* (*Ores*) flotation. **-seife,** *f.* lathering soap. **-spat,** *m.* a hard, foliated variety of calcite; laumontite. **-stand.** *m.* (*Brewing*) head. **-stoff,** *m.* a cellular or spongy plastic. **-ton,** *m.* fuller's earth. **-verhinderung,** *f.* foam prevention. **-verhinderungsöl,** *n.* antifroth oil. **-wein,** *m.* sparkling wine.
**Schau-öffnung,** *f.* peephole, inspection hole. **-platz,** *m.* scene, stage, theater. **-sammlung,** *f.* display collection. **-spiel,** *n.* spectacle, sight; play, drama. **-stellung,** *f.* exhibition. **-tafel,** *f.* diagram. **-versuch,** *m.* lecture (or demonstration) experiment. **-zeichen,** *n.* visual signal or sign.
**Scheabutter,** *f.* shea butter.
**Scheck,** *m.* check; ticket.
**schecken,** *v.t.* dapple, spot.
**scheckig,** *a.* dappled, spotted, mottled.
**Scheel-bleierz,** *n.*, **-bleispat,** *m.* scheeletite. **-erz,** *m.* scheelite.
**Scheele'sches Grün.** Scheele's green.
**Scheele'sches Süss.** glycerol, glycerin.
**scheelisieren,** *v.t.* (*Wine*) scheelize (treat with glycerin).
**Scheel-säure,** *f.* tungstic acid. **-spat,** *m.* scheelite.
**Scheere,** *f.* = Schere.
**Scheffel,** *m.* bushel.
**Scheibchen,** *n.* little disk; little slice.
**Scheibe,** *f.* disk; slice; plate; cake (of wax, etc.); pane (of glass); (honey)comb; washer; pulley, wheel, target, dial, etc.
**scheiben-ähnlich, -artig,** *a.* disk-like, discoid, discoidal.
**Scheiben-blei,** *n.* window lead. **-eisen,** *n.* pig iron in disks. **-filter,** *n.* disk filter.
**scheibenförmig,** *a.* disk-shaped, discoid.
**Scheiben-glas,** *n.* window glass. **-holländer,** *m.* (*Paper*) disk beater. **-honig,** *m.* comb honey. **-kupfer,** *n.* rose copper, rosette copper. **-lack,** *m.* shellac. **-reissen,** *n.* (*Metal.*) conversion into disks or rosettes. **-wachs,** *n.* cake wax. **-zelle,** *f.* discoid cell.
**scheidbar,** *a.* separable; analyzable.
**Scheidbarkeit,** *f.* separability; analyzability.
**Scheide,** *f.* sheath; vagina; boundary, border.
**Scheide-.** separating, parting; separated. **-anstalt,** *f.* refinery. **-bad,** *n.* separating bath. **-bank,** *f.* sorting table. **-bock,** *m.* retort stand. **-bürette,** *f.* separating buret(te). **-erz,** *n.* picked ore; screened ore.
**scheidefähig,** *a.* separable, etc. (see scheiden).
**Scheide-flüssigkeit,** *f.* separating (or parting) liquid. **-gang,** *m.* poor ore (separated from good). **-gefäss,** *n.* separating or parting vessel. **-gold,** *n.* gold purified by parting. **-gut,** *n.* material to be separated. **-kalk,** *m.* (*Sugar*) defecation lime. **-kapelle,** *f.* cupel. **-kolben,** *m.* separating flask; (*Old Chem.*) alembic. **-kuchen,** *m.* (*Metal.*) liquation disk. **-kunst,** *f.* (analytical) chemistry. **-künstler,** *m.* (analytical) chemist.
**scheidekünstlerisch,** *a.* chemical.
**Scheide-linie,** *f.* boundary line. **-mauer,** *f.* partition wall. **-mehl,** *n.* dust of picked ore. **-mittel,** *n.* separating agent, parting agent. **-münze,** *f.* billon; small coin.
**scheiden,** *v.t.* separate; part; analyze, decom-

pose; pick, sort (ore); clear, clarify (a liquid); (*Sugar*) defecate; divide, sever, divorce. — *v.r.* separate; (of milk) turn; divide. — *v.i.* separate, part, depart.

**Scheiden-.** sheath; (*Physiol.*) vaginal. **-schleim,** *m.* vaginal mucus.

**Scheide-ofen,** *m.* parting furnace, almond furnace. **-pfanne,** *f.* (*Sugar*) defecating pan, clarifier. **-punkt,** *m.* separation point.

**Scheider,** *m.* separator, etc. (see scheiden).

**Scheiderz,** *n.* separated ore.

**Scheide-schlamm,** *m.* (*Sugar*) defecation slime. **-sieb,** *n.* separating sieve. **-silber,** *n.* parting silver. **-trichter,** *m.* separating funnel, separatory funnel. **-verfahren,** *n.*, **-vorgang,** *m.* separating or refining process. **-vorrichtung,** *f.* separating (or parting) apparatus; screening or sorting device. **-wand,** *f.* partition wall, partition, midfeather, septum, diaphragm. **-wasser,** *n.* nitric acid (for parting); aqua regia. **-weg,** *m.* forked way, crossroads.

**Scheidung,** *f.* separation, etc. (see scheiden).

**Scheidungsmittel,** *n.* = Scheidemittel.

**Schein,** *m.* appearance; luster, light, shine, sheen; cast, tinge; (of oils, etc.) bloom; document, paper, bill, certificate.

**Schein-.** apparent, mock, false, pseudo-.

**scheinbar,** *a.* apparent, seeming, plausible; showy.

**scheinen,** *v.i.* shine; appear, seem.

**Schein-farbe,** *f.* accidental color. **-fuss,** *m.* pseudopodium. **-gold,** *n.* imitation gold. **-grund,** *m.* apparent reason, pretext, fallacy. **-leistung,** *f.* apparent output. **-mine,** *f.* (*Mil.*) dummy mine.

**scheintot,** *a.* apparently dead.

**Schein-vergiftung,** *f.* (*Mil.*) fake contamination. **-vernebelung,** *f.* (*Mil.*) dummy smoke screening. **-werfer,** *m.* projector; reflector; headlight; searchlight; flashlight; floodlight. **-widerstand,** *m.* (*Elec.*) apparent resistance, impedance.

**Scheit,** *n.* log, billet, block.

**Scheitel,** *m.* vertex, apex, summit, crown, crest, top.

**Scheitel-.** vertical; peak, maximum; (*Anat.*) parietal. **-ausschlag,** *m.* amplitude. **-linie,** *f.* vertical line. **-punkt,** *m.* vertex; zenith.

**scheitelrecht,** *a.* vertical.

**Scheitelwert,** *m.* peak value, maximum value.

**scheitern,** *v.i.* suffer wreck, be wrecked.

**Schelfe,** *f.* husk, shell, pod.

**Schellack-bindung,** *f.* shellac bond(ing). **-firnis,** *m.* shellac varnish.

**schellackieren,** *v.t.* shellac.

**Schellack-lösung,** *f.* shellac solution. **-politur,** *f.* shellac polish. **-steife,** *f.* shellac stiffening. **-wachs,** *n.* shellac wax.

**Schellan,** *n.* shellan ($C_{13}H_{22}$); schellan (a synthetic resin).

**Schelle,** *f.* (*Mach.*) clamp, clip, sleeve, collar; little bell.

**schellen,** *v.t.* ring.

**Schell-fisch,** *m.* cod; haddock. **-harz,** *n.* white rosin. **-olsäure,** *f.* shellolic acid.

**Schema,** *n.* model, pattern; blank, form; schedule; scheme; diagram. **-bild,** *n.* diagram; flow sheet.

**schematisch,** *a.* schematic, diagrammatic.

**schematisieren,** *v.t. & i.* sketch; schematize.

**Schemel,** *m.* (low) stool, seat; trestle.

**Schemen,** *m.* shadow, phantom.

**Schenkbier,** *n.* draft beer, schenk beer (contrasted with Lagerbier).

**Schenke,** *f.* public house, tavern.

**Schenkel,** *m.* leg; shank; thigh; limb; branch; side, side piece.

**Schenkel-.** femoral, crural. **-bein,** *n.* thigh bone, femur. **-rohr,** *n.*, **-röhre,** *f.* bent tube, V-tube, elbow tube, elbow pipe.

**schenken,** *v.t.* pour out; give, present; retail (liquors); suckle.

**Scherbe,** *f.* potsherd, shard; fragment, piece; crock, pot (esp. flowerpot); cupel; scorifier; (*Ceram.*) body.

**Scherbel,** *m.* = Scherbe; = Schirbel. **-krautwurzel,** *f.* asarum, asarabacca.

**Scherben,** *m.* = Scherbe.

**Scherben-kobalt, -stein,** *m.* native arsenic.

**Schere,** *f.* scissors, shears; cutter; notch, nick; groove; shafts; claw, chela.

**scheren,** *v.t.* shear, clip, cut; plague, vex. — *v.r.* go, be off; care.

**Scheren-bindung,** *f.* chelate linkage, chelation. **-spreizen,** *f. pl.* lazy tongs. **-stahl,** *m.* shear steel. **-zange,** *f.* cutting forceps; wire cutter; (*Metal.*) shingling tongs.

**Scherfestigkeit,** *f.* shearing strength.

**Scherflein,** *n.* mite.

**Scher-kraft,** *f.* shearing force or stress. **-spannung,** *f.* shearing stress.

**Scherung,** *f.* shearing, etc. (see scheren); shear.

**Scherungs-festigkeit,** *f.* shearing strength. **-winkel,** *m.* angle of shear.

**Scher-versuch,** *m.* shearing test. **-wirkung,** *f.* shearing action or effect.

**Scherz,** *m.* joke, jest, fun, sport.

**scherzen,** *v.i.* joke, jest.

**scherzhaft,** *a.* playful, jocular, humorous.

**scheu,** *a.* shy, timid, timorous.

**scheuen,** *v.t.* shun, avoid, dread, grudge. — *v.i.* shy.

**Scheuer,** *f.* barn, granary.

**scheuerfest,** *a.* resistant to scouring or rubbing.

**Scheuermittel,** *n.* scouring agent.

**scheuern,** *v.t.* scour, scrub, wash, clean; rub, chafe.

**Scheuer-pulver,** *n.* scouring powder. **-trommel,** *f.* scouring barrel, tumbling barrel. **-wirkung,** *f.* scouring action or effect.

**Scheune,** *f.* barn, granary.

**Schicht,** *f.* layer; ply; stratum, bed, course; (when thin) film, coat; lamina; (*Photog.*) emulsion; charge (of a furnace); batch; shift, turn (of work). **-boden,** *m.* (*Metal.*) mixing place. **-dicke,** *f.* thickness of a layer or stratum. **-ebene,** *f.* bedding plane.

**schichten,** *v.t.* arrange in layers or beds, stratify, bed, laminate; pile, stack; charge.

**Schichten-aufbau, -bau,** *m.* layered or stratified structure, stratification. **-folge,** *f.* series of strata or layers. **-fuge,** *f.* bedding plane; stratum joint. **-gitter,** *n.* layer lattice, stratified lattice. **-glas,** *n.* laminated glass, shatterproof glass. **-gruppe,** *f.* (*Geol.*) group of strata, formation. **-kohle,** *f.* foliated coal.

**schichtenweise,** *a.* & *adv.* in layers or strata, stratified.

**Schicht-fläche,** *f.* surface of a layer or stratum; bedding plane. **-folge,** *f.* = Schichtenfolge. **-folie,** *f.* laminating sheet. **-fuge,** *f.* bedding plane; stratum joint. **-gefüge,** *n.* layered or stratified structure. **-gestein,** *n.* stratified rock. **-holz,** *n.* plywood; stacked wood, cordwood.

**schichtig,** *a.* layered, bedded, stratified; laminated; foliated.

**Schicht-pressen,** *n.* laminate molding. **-pres(s)-stoff,** *m.* laminated plastic, molded laminate. **-seite,** *f.* (*Photog.*) emulsion side. **-spaltung,** *f.* delamination. **-stoff,** *m.* laminated material. **-textur,** *f.* stratified structure.

**Schichtung,** *f.* stratification, bedding; lamination; arranging in layers; piling; charging.

**Schichtungsebene,** *f.* plane of stratification, bedding plane.

**Schicht-verband,** *m.* laminar bonding. **-wasser,** *n.* ground water.

**schichtweise,** *adv.* in layers or laminas.

**Schick,** *m.* skill; tact; order; fitness; style.

**schicken,** *v.t.* send; cause to happen. — *v.r.* happen; suit, fit; conform, accommodate oneself; prepare. — **geschickt,** *p.a.* sent, etc.; skilled, qualified, clever; suitable, fit.

**schicklich,** *a.* becoming, proper, fit, suitable.

**Schickprobe,** *f.* (*Med.*) Schick test.

**Schicksal,** *n.* fate, destiny, lot.

**Schickung,** *f.* dispensation, fate, lot.

**Schieb-.** sliding, slide.

**Schiebehülse,** *f.* sliding sleeve.

**schieben,** *v.t.* shove, push, thrust, slide, slip, shift.

**Schieber,** *m.* slide, slider, slide bar, slide valve, carriage; shovel; pusher, shover; damper. **-kasten,** *m.* (*Mach.*) slide box, valve chest.

**Schieberohr,** *n.* sliding tube or sleeve.

**Schieberventil,** *n.* slide valve.

**schiebfest,** *a.* nonslip.

**Schieb-karren,** *m.* wheelbarrow. **-kraft,** *f.* thrust(ing) power, thrust, shear. **-lehre,** *f.* slide gage.

**Schiebung,** *f.* shoving, etc. (see schieben); glide (of metals); maneuver.

**Schiebungsfläche,** *f.* (*Geol.*) shear(ing) plane; (*Cryst.*) slip plane.

**schied,** *pret.* (of scheiden) separated, etc.

**Schieds-analyse,** *f.* umpire analysis. **-mann, -richter,** *m.* umpire, arbiter, referee. **-spruch,** *m.* award, decision. **-versuch,** *m.* referee test.

**schief,** *a.* inclined, oblique; skew, crooked. — *adv.* obliquely; askew, awry, amiss.

**schiefachsig,** *a.* oblique-axial.

**Schiefagarkultur,** *f.* sloped-agar culture.

**Schiefe,** *f.* inclination, slope; inclined plane; obliqueness; crookedness, skew.

**Schiefeinfall,** *m.* (*Physics*) oblique incidence.

**Schiefer,** *m.* slate; schist; shale; flaw (in iron).

**schiefer-ähnlich, -artig,** *a.* slate-like, slaty, schistous. **-blau,** *a.* slate-blue.

**Schiefer-boden,** *m.* slaty or schistous soil. **-bruch,** *m.* slaty or shaly fracture. **-farbe,** *f.* slate color.

**schiefer-farben, -farbig,** *a.* slate-colored.

**Schiefergips,** *m.* foliated gypsum.

**schiefer-grau,** *a.* slate-gray. **-haltig,** *a.* containing slate or shale, slaty, schistous.

**schieferig,** *a.* slaty, slate-like; schistous, schistose; scaly, flaky, foliated, foliaceous.

**Schiefer-kohle,** *f.* slaty coal; splint coal. **-letten,** *m.* clay shale. **-mehl,** *n.* ground shale. **-mergel,** *m.* slaty marl.

**schiefern,** *v. i.* & *r.* scale off, exfoliate.

**Schiefer-öl,** *n.* shale oil. **-paraffin,** *n.* (*Petroleum*) shale wax. **-platte,** *f.* slab or plate of slate.

**schieferschwarz,** *a.* slate-black.

**Schiefer-spat,** *m.* slate spar (lamellar variety of calcite). **-stein,** *n.* slate. **-talk,** *m.* talc slate. indurated talc. **-teer,** *m.* shale tar. **-teeröl,** *n.* shale tar oil. **-ton,** *m.* slate clay, clay slate, shale.

**Schieferung,** *f.* scaling off, exfoliation; schistosity, foliated structure.

**Schieferweiss,** *n.* flake white.

**Schiefheit,** *f.* = Schiefe.

**schiefliegend,** *p.a.* inclined, sloping, oblique.

**schiefrig,** *a.* = schieferig.

**schiefwinklig,** *a.* oblique-angled.

**schien,** *pret.* (of scheinen) seemed; shone.

**Schienbein,** *n.* shin bone, tibia.

**Schiene,** *f.* rail; skid; slat, strip, bar; beam; tube support; rim, tire (of a wheel); (*Med.*) splint.

**Schienen-weg,** *m.* railway; tramway. **-weite,** *f.* railway gage.

**schier,** *a.* sheer, pure. — *adv.* simply; nearly.

**Schierling,** *m.* hemlock (the herb). **-saft,** *m.* hemlock juice, juice of conium.

**Schierlings-kraut,** *n.* hemlock (the herb). **-tanne,** *f.* hemlock spruce, hemlock.

**schiert,** *pr. 3 sing.* (of scheren) shears, etc.

**Schiess-arbeit,** *f.* shooting, blasting. **-baumwolle,** *f.* guncotton.

**schiessen,** *v. t. & i.* shoot; fire; dart, emit, dash; launch; (of dyes) flush on; sprout.

**Schiess-ofen,** *m.* bomb oven, tube furnace, Carius oven. **-pulver,** *n.* gunpowder. **-rohr,** *n.*, **-röhre,** *f.* a sealed tube in which substances are heated under pressure, bomb tube. **-stoff,** *m.* powder (for shooting). **-stoffwesen,** *n.* powder business. **-wolle,** *f.* guncotton. **-wollpulver,** *n.* guncotton powder.

**Schiff,** *n.* ship, vessel; shuttle; nave.

**schiffbar,** *a.* navigable.

**Schiff-bruch,** *m.* shipwreck. **-chen,** *n.* boat; little ship; shuttle; (*Bot.*) keel.

**schiffen,** *v.t. & i.* navigate, sail.

**Schifffahrt,** *f.* navigation.

**Schiffsbedürfnisse,** *n.pl.* naval stores.

**Schiff'sche Base.** Schiff base.

**Schiffs-leim,** *m.* marine glue. **-pech,** *n.* common black pitch. **-teer,** *m.* ship's tar, wood tar.

**Schild,** *n.* label; sign, signboard; badge; (of hides) butt; (turtle) shell. — *m.* shield; escutcheon. **-chen,** *n.* little label, little shield, etc. (see Schild). **-drüse,** *f.* thyroid gland.

**Schilddrüsen-.** thyroid. **-essenz,** *f.*, **-extrakt,** *n.* (*Pharm.*) thyroid solution.

**Schilderblau,** *n.* (*Dyeing*) pencil blue.

**schildern,** *v.t.* depict, portray, draw, sketch.

**Schilderung,** *f.* depiction, portrayal.

**schildförmig,** *a.* shield-shaped, scutiform; (*Anat.*) thyroid.

**Schild-knorpel,** *m.* thyroid cartilage. **-kraut,** *n.* skullcap (*Scutellaria*). **-kröte,** *f.* turtle, tortoise. **-laus,** *f.* cochineal insect. **-patt,** *n.* tortoise shell.

**schildpatten,** *a.* tortoise-shell.

**Schildwache,** *f.* sentinel.

**Schilf,** *n.* reed, rush.

**schilferig,** *a.* scaly.

**schilfern,** *v.i.* scale off, exfoliate.

**Schilf-glaserz,** *n.* freieslebenite. **-rohr,** *n.* reed.

**Schiller,** *m.* play of colors, iridescence; surface color, metallic color, schiller. **-farbe,** *f.* changeable color; schiller color, surface color, metallic color.

**schillerfarbig,** *a.* showing a play of colors, iridescent; exhibiting schiller or metallic color.

**Schillerglanz,** *m.* iridescent luster; colored metallic luster, schiller.

**schillerig,** *a.* iridescent, chatoyant.

**schillern,** *v.i.* exhibit a play of colors, iridesce, opalesce; exhibit surface color or schiller. — **schillernd,** *p.a.* iridescent, opalescent, chatoyant; possessing schiller.

**Schiller-quarz,** *m.* (*Min.*) cat's-eye. **-seide,** *f.* shot silk, changeable silk. **-spat,** *m.* schiller spar (altered enstatite); diallage. **-stein,** *m.* schiller spar. **-stoff,** *m.* iridescent substance. **-wein,** *m.* wine from red and white grapes mixed.

**Schimmel,** *m.* mold; mildew; gray or white horse.

**schimmelartig,** *a.* mold-like, moldy.

**Schimmel-bildung,** *f.* mold formation, molding. **-farbe,** *f.* mold color. **-fleck,** *m.* mold (or mildew) stain.

**schimmelfleckig,** *a.* spotted with mold.

**Schimmelgeruch,** *m.* moldy smell.

**schimmelgrau,** *a.* moldy gray.

**schimmelig, schimmelicht,** *a.* moldy, musty.

**schimmeln,** *v.i.* mold.

**Schimmel-pilz,** *m.* mold fungus, mold. **-rasen,** *m.* coating of mold.

**Schimmer,** *m.* glimmer, shimmer, glitter; luster; (of oil) bloom.

**schimmern,** *v.i.* glisten, glitter, gleam, shine.

**Schindel,** *f.* shingle; (*Med.*) splint.

**schinden,** *v.t.* skin, flay.

**Schinken,** *m.*, **-fleisch,** *n.* ham.

**Schippe,** *f.* shovel, scoop; (*Cards*) spade.

**schipperig,** *a.* (*Dyeing*) mixtury, skittery, not solid.

**Schiras,** *m.* (*Wines*) Shiraz.

**Schirbel,** *m.* (*Metal.*) bloom; piece of a bloom, stamp.

**Schirm,** *m.* screen; shelter, shade; umbrella; parachute; visor (of a cap); (*Bot.*) umbel. **-bild,** *n.* screen image.

**schirmen,** *v.t.* screen; shelter; protect.

**Schirm-gitter,** *n.* (*Radio*) screen grid. **-gitterröhre,** *f.* screen-grid tube. **-pflanze,** *f.* umbelliferous plant. **-wirkung,** *f.* screening or shielding effect.

**schlabbern,** *v.i.* slobber; overflow; gossip.

**Schlabber-rohr,** *n.* overflow pipe or tube **-ventil,** *n.* overflow valve, check valve.

**Schlacht,** *f.* battle.

**schlachten,** *v.t.* kill, slaughter.

**Schlacht-feld,** *n.* battlefield. **-fett,** *n.* (butcher's) fat. **-haus,** *n.*, **-hof,** *m.* slaughterhouse, abattoir. **-haustalg,** *m.* packinghouse tallow. **-schiff,** *n.* battleship.

**Schlack,** *m.* niter deposit.

**Schlacke,** *f.* slag; cinder, scoria, dross; (in coal) clinker; undigested residue.

**schlackebildend,** *a.* slag-forming.

**schlacken,** *v.i.* slag, form slag, clinker.

**Schlacken-abscheider,** *m.* slag separator, slag

skimmer. **-absonderung,** *f.* slag separation.

**schlacken-ähnlich, -artig,** *a.* slag-like, scoriaceous, slaggy, drossy.

**Schlacken-auge,** *n.* = Schlackenloch. **-beton,** *m.* slag concrete.

**schlackenbildend,** *a.* slag-forming.

**Schlacken-bildner,** *m.* slag former. **-bildung,** *f.* formation of slag, scorification. **-blei,** *n.* slaggy lead. **-einschluss,** *m.* slag inclusion. **-eisen,** *n.* cinder iron. **-form,** *f.* cinder block; cinder notch.

**schlackenfrei,** *a.* slag-free, clinkerless.

**Schlacken-frischen,** *n.* (*Metal.*) pig boiling. **-gang,** *m.* slag duct, cinder fall. **-grube,** *f.* slag pit. **-halde,** *f.* slag dump, cinder tip.

**schlackenhaltig,** *a.* containing slag or clinker.

**Schlacken-herd,** *m.* slag hearth, slag furnace. **-klotz, -klumpen,** *m.* lump of slag, clinker. **-kobalt,** *m.* safflorite. **-kost,** *f.* diet containing unassimilable material. **-kuchen,** *m.* cake of slag or clinker. **-lava,** *f.* scoriaceous lava. **-loch,** *n.* cinder notch, slag hole, cinder tap. **-mehl,** *n.* ground slag, Thomas meal. **-ofen,** *m.* slag furnace. **-puddeln,** *n.* pig boiling.

**schlacken-reich,** *a.* rich in slag or clinker, slaggy, scoriaceous. **-rein,** *a.* free from slag or clinker.

**Schlacken-rösten,** *n.* roasting of slag; scorification roasting. **-scherbe,** *f.*, **-scherben,** *m.* scorifier. **-spiess,** *m.* cinder iron, slag iron. **-spur,** *f.* = Schlackenloch. **-staub,** *m.* coal dust. **-stein,** *m.* slag block, slag brick. **-stich,** *m.*, **-stichloch,** *n.* cinder notch, slag hole. **-wolle,** *f.* slag wool, mineral wool. **-zacken,** *m.* cinder plate, front plate. **-ziegel, -ziegelstein,** *m.* slag brick. **-zinn,** *n.* tin extracted from slag, prillion.

**schlackig,** *a.* slaggy, drossy, cindery, scoriaceous; (of coal) clinkering.

**Schlaf,** *m.* sleep; temple (of the head). **-arznei,** *f.* soporific, hypnotic, narcotic.

**schlafbefördernd,** *p.a.* soporific.

**Schläfe,** *f.* temple (of the head).

**schlafen,** *v.i.* sleep; lie dormant.

**Schläfen-.** (*Anat.*) temporal.

**schläferig,** *a.* sleepy, drowsy.

**schlaff,** *a.* slack, loose, limp, flabby, soft.

**Schlaffheit,** *f.* slackness, limpness, softness.

**Schlaf-krankheit,** *f.* sleeping sickness. **-losigkeit,** *f.* sleeplessness, insomnia. **-mittel,** *n.* soporofic, narcotic. **-mohn,** *m.* opium poppy.

**schläfrig,** *a.* sleepy, drowsy.

**schläft,** *pr. 3 sing.* (of schlafen) sleeps.

**Schlaf-trank,** *m.* sleeping draft. **-wagen,** *m.* sleeping car. **-zimmer,** *n.* bedroom.

**Schlag,** *m.* stroke, blow, percussion, knock, shock, impact, jar, kick, beat; apoplexy; coinage, stamp, sort; cutting (of wood or in the woods); field; song (of birds). **-ader,** *f.* artery. **-aluminium,** *n.* hammered aluminum. **-arbeit,** *f.* work resulting from a blow, impact energy.

**schlagartig,** *a.* shock-like, sudden; apoplectoid.

**Schlag-biegefestigkeit,** *f.* impact bending strength. **-druck,** *m.* impact compression.

**Schlägel,** *m.* = Schlegel.

**Schlagelot,** *n.* hard solder.

**Schlagempfindlichkeit,** *f.* sensitiveness to percussion.

**schlagen,** *v.t.* strike, beat, hit, knock; fell (trees); churn (butter); press (oil); drive (nails, etc.); put (into barrels); etc., etc. — *v.r.* strike, beat, knock, kick; warble; belong, concern. — **schlagend,** *p.a.* striking, impressive. — **schlagende Wetter,** fire damp.

**Schläger,** *m.* beater, etc. (see schlagen); fighter; batter; rapier.

**Schlag-festigkeit,** *f.* resistance to shock, impact strength. **-figur,** *f.* percussion figure. **-fläche,** *f.* striking surface, surface of impact. **-gold,** *n.* leaf gold. **-härte,** *f.* impact hardness. **-kraft,** *f.* striking force, impact force. **-kreuzmühle,** *f.* cross-beater mill, disintegrator. **-ladung,** *f.* (*Expl.*) booster charge. **-licht,** *n.* strong light, glare. **-lot,** *n.* hard solder. **-mühle,** *f.* hammer mill; beetling mill, beetle. **-patrone,** *f.* (*Expl.*) priming cartridge. **-probe,** *f.* percussion test, impact test. **-pulver,** *n.* fulminating powder; (*Pharm.*) antapoplectic powder. **-saat,** *f.* hempseed. **-sahne,** *f.* whipped cream. **-sieb,** *n.* vibrating screen. **-siebprobe,** *f.* shatter test.

**schlägt,** *pr. 3 sing.* (of schlagen) strikes, etc.

**Schlag-versuch,** *m.* impact test, percussion test. **-wasser,** *n.* bilge water. **-weite,** *f.* striking distance (of an electric spark), spark distance. **-werk,** *n.* striking appparatus, specif. rammer; signal bell. **-wetter,** *n. pl.* fire damp.

**schlagwetter-frei,** *a.* free from fire damp, nongassy. **-geschützt,** *a.* (*Mining*) flameproof.

**Schlagwettergrube,** *f.* gassy mine, fire mine.

**schlagwetter-sicher,** *a.* proof against fire damp, flameproof. **-zündfähig,** *a.* ignitable by fire damp.

**Schlag-widerstand,** *m.* impact resistance. **-wort,** *n.* catchword, slogan; cue. **-zünder,** *m.* percussion fuse.

**Schlamm,** *m.* mud, sludge, slime; slurry; sediment; silt; ooze; (*Ceram.*) slip.

**Schlämm-.** elutriating, washing, elutriated, washed. **-analyse,** *f.* analysis by elutriation; sedimentation analysis. **-apparat,** *m.* elutriating apparatus. **-arbeit,** *f.* elutriation, washing.

**schlammartig,** *a.* in the form of mud or slime.

**schlämmbar,** *a.* washable (by elutriation).

**Schlammeindicker,** *m.* (*Ores*) pulp thickener; (*Sewage*) sludge densifier.

**schlämmen,** *v.t.* elutriate, wash (powdered substances); levigate; (*Mining*) buddle.

**Schlämm-fass,** *n.* washing tub or tank (for precipitates, etc.); (*Mining*) dolly tub. **-flasche,** *f.* elutriating flask.

**Schlammflüssigkeit,** *f.* mud-laden liquid.

**Schlämm-gefäss,** *n.* elutriating vessel or reservoir. **-glas,** *n.* elutriating glass.

**Schlammgrube,** *f.* mud pit, slime pit.

**schlammhaltig,** *a.* containing mud or sludge, muddy.

**Schlämmherd,** *m.* (*Metal.*) slime pit, also slime table.

**schlammig,** *a.* muddy, sludgy, slimy, oozy.

**Schlamm-kalk,** *m.* sludge lime. **-kohle,** *f.* coal slime, mud coal.

**Schlämm-kohle,** *f.* washed coal. **-kreide,** *f.* prepared chalk; whiting.

**Schlamm-mischapparat,** *m.* mud mixer, slime mixer. **-pfännchen,** *n.* (*Salt*) scum pan. **-scheider,** *m.* slime separator.

**Schlammschlich, Schlämmschlich,** *m.* washed ore slime.

**Schlämmtrichter,** *m.* elutriating funnel.

**Schlammtrübe,** *f.* (*Metal.*) slime pulp.

**Schlämmung,** *f.* elutriating, etc. (see schlämmen).

**Schlämm-verfahren,** *n.* elutriating or washing process. **-vorrichtung,** *f.* elutriating apparatus, washing apparatus.

**Schlamm-vulkan,** *m.* mud "volcano", mud spring. **-wasser,** *n.* water charged with sludge or slime, (*Sewage*) sludge liquor.

**Schlämmwerk,** *n.* washing mill.

**Schlämmzylinder,** *m.* elutriating cylinder.

**schlang,** *pret.* (of schlingen) wound, etc.

**Schlange,** *f.* snake, serpent; (*Tech.*) worm, coil; hose (flexible tube).

**schlängeln,** *v.r.* wind, meander. — **schlängelnd,** *p.a.* sinuous, winding, serpentine.

**schlangenartig,** *a.* snake-like, serpentine.

**Schlangen-gift,** *n.* snake venom. **-holz,** *n.* snakewood. **-kühler,** *m.* spiral (or coil) condenser; tubular cooler. **-rohr,** *n.*, **-röhre,** *f.* worm, spiral pipe (or tube), coil. **-stein,** *m.* ophite; serpentine. **-wurzel,** *f.* snakeroot.

**schlank,** *a.* slender, slim, thin, fine.

**Schlappermilch,** *f.* curdled milk.

**Schlauch,** *m.* tube, tubing, pipe (of flexible material), hose; skin (for holding something); (*Mining*) ore pipe, ore chimney; drunkard; glutton.

**schlauchen,** *v.t.* (*Brewing*) hose, transfer (beer) or fill (casks) by means of hose or pipes.

**Schlauch-filter,** *n.* tube filter. **-klemme,** *f.* tube clamp. **-leitung,** *f.* hose line. **-pilz,** *m.* ascomycete. **-sicherung,** *f.* hose protection (as spiral wire rings). **-stück,** *n.* tubing attachment (part to which tubing may be attached), hose coupling. **-verbindung,** *f.* rubber-tube connection; hose connection.

**Schlaufe,** *f.* loop.

**schlecht,** *a.* bad, ill, poor. — *adv.* badly, ill. **-erdings,** *adv.* utterly, absolutely. **-hin, -weg,** *adv.* merely, plainly.

**schlecken, schleckern,** *v.t.* lick, lap. — *v.i.* be dainty.

**Schlegel,** *m.* mallet, beater, beetle, (wooden) hammer; drumstick.

**Schlehdorn,** *m.* blackthorn, sloe tree.

**Schlehe,** *f.* sloe.

**schleichen,** *v.i.* slink, sneak; creep. — **schleichend,** *p.a.* slow, creeping.

**Schleich-gut,** *n.* smuggled goods, contraband. **-handel,** *m.* illicit trade, black market, smuggling.

**Schleier,** *m.* veil; haze; screen, curtain (as of smoke); lawn (the fabric); (*Photog.*) fog; cloudiness, turbidity. **-bildung,** *f.* haze formation, fogging.

**schleierfrei,** *a.* free from haze or fog.

**schleierig,** *a.* hazy, foggy, clouded.

**schleiern,** *v.t.* veil; cloud; (*Photog.*) fog.

**Schleifapparat,** *m.* grinding apparatus, grinder.

**schleifbar,** *a.* capable of being ground, sharpened, etc. (see schleifen).

**Schleife,** *f.* loop; noose, knot; slide; sled.

**schleifecht,** *a.* (*Leather*) fast to buffing.

**Schleifemaillelack,** *m.* (*Varnish*) dull finish.

**schleifen,** *v.t.* grind; sharpen; polish; buff (leather); rub; cut (gems); abrade; drag, trail. — *v.i.* slip, slide.

**Schleiferei,** *f.* grindery; grinder's trade; (*Paper*) pulp mill.

**schleiffähig,** *a.* capable of being ground, sharpened, etc. (see schleifen).

**Schleif-fläche,** *f.* wearing surface. **-flüssigkeit,** *f.* (*Varnish*) rubbing-down liquid. **-güte,** *f.* abrasive temper. **-härte,** *f.* resistance to abrasion. **-holz,** *n.* pulpwood. **-kontakt,** *m.* sliding contact. **-korn,** *n.* abrasive grain. **körper,** *m.* abrasive object, specif. grinding wheel. **-lack,** *m.* rubbing varnish, body varnish. **-lackwaren,** *f.pl.* polished lacquer goods. **-leinen,** *n.* abrasive cloth. **-material, -mittel,** *n.* abrasive. **-öl,** *n.* grinding oil. **-papier,** *n.* abrasive paper. **-paste,** *f.* abrasive paste (e.g., emery paste), (*Varnish*) flatting paste. **-polieren,** *n.* fine grinding (of surfaces). **-pulver,** *n.* grinding powder, polishing powder. **-rad,** *n.* grinding wheel, polishing wheel. **-rohstoff,** *m.* abrasive raw material. **-sel,** *n.*, **-staub,** *m.* grindings, swarf. **-stein,** *m.* grinding stone, grindstone, whetstone. **-stoff,** *m.* grinding material, abrasive; (*Paper*) ground pulp.

**Schleifung,** *f.* grinding, etc. (see schleifen).

**Schleif-wachs,** *n.* (*Varnish*) flatting paste. **-wirkung,** *f.* abrasive action, abrasion, attrition.

**Schleim,** *m.* slime; mucilage; mucus. **-absonderung,** *f.* secretion of mucus.

**schleimartig,** *a.* slimy, glutinous; mucoid.

**Schleimbakterien,** *n.pl.* slime bacteria, Myxobacteriaceae.

**schleimbildend,** *p.a.* slime-forming; (*Physiol.*) muciparous.

**Schleim-bildung,** *f.* slime (or mucilage or mucus) formation. **-drüse,** *f.* mucous gland. **-gärung,** *f.* viscous fermentation.

**schleimgebend,** *a.* glutinous, mucilaginous.

**Schleim-harz,** *n.* gum resin. **-haut,** *f.* mucous membrane, mucosa.

**schleimig,** *a.* slimy, mucilaginous; mucous. — **schleimige Gärung,** mucous, or viscous, fermentation.

**Schleim-igkeit,** *f.* sliminess, mucosity. **-membran,** *f.* mucous membrane. **-pilz,** *m.* slime fungus, slime mold (*Myxomycetes*).

**schleimsauer,** *a.* of or combined with mucic acid, mucate of.

**Schleim-säure,** *f.* mucic acid. **-schicht,** *f.* layer of slime or mucilage or mucus; specif., mucous layer, Malpighian layer (of the epidermis). **-stoff,** *m.* slimy substance; mucin.

**schleimstoffartig,** *a.* mucin-like, mucoid.

**Schleim-tier,** *n.* mollusk. **-zellulose,** *f.* mucocellulose. **-zucker,** *m.* levulose.

**Schleisse,** *f.* splint, splinter.

**schleissen,** *v.t.* slit; split; strip; wear, wear out.

**Schleisswirkung,** *f.* abrasive action.

**Schlemm-.** = Schlämm-.

**schlemmen,** *v.t.* = schlämmen. — *v.i.* eat greedily; carouse.

**Schlempe,** *f.* residual liquid from distillation of alcoholic liquors, vinasse, slops, spent wash. **-kohle, -asche,** *f.* crude potash from beet vinasse, saline. **-ofen,** *m.* spent-wash furnace. **-verdampfer,** *m.* vinasse (or slops) evaporator.

**schlenkern,** *v.t.* swing, sling, fling.

**Schleppe,** *f.* train, trail; (*Paper*) felt board; (*Founding*) truck.

**schleppen,** *v.t. & i.* drag, trail, haul, tow; lag.

**Schlepper,** *m.* tractor; hauler; pusher; tug.

**Schlepp-kraft,** *f.* tractive force. **-mühle,** *f.* drag mill, drag-stone mill.

**Schleppung,** *f.* dragging, etc. (see schleppen); time lag.

**Schlesien,** *n.* Silesia.

**schlesisch,** *a.* Silesian.

**Schleuder,** *f.* centrifuge; sling. **-gebläse,** *n.* centrifugal blower. **-guss,** *m.* centrifugal casting. **-honig,** *m.* extracted honey. **-korb,** *m.* centrifuge (or hydro-extractor) basket. **-kraft,** *f.* centrifugal force. **-maschine,** *f.* centrifugal machine, centrifugal (specif., hydro-extractor); catapult. **-mühle,** *f.* centrifugal mill.

**schleudern,** *v.t.* centrifuge, hydro-extract; sling, fling, hurl. — *v.i.* swing, roll; cut prices.

**Schleuder-sortierer,** *m.* centrifugal sorter. **-trommel,** *f.* centrifugal drum. **-wirkung,** *f.* centrifugal or slinging action or effect.

**schleunig,** *a.* speedy, hasty, quick, immediate. — *adv.* speedily, etc.

**Schleuse,** *f.* sluice; sewer; air lock.

**Schleusengas,** *n.* sewer gas.

**schlich,** *pret.* (of schleichen) slunk, crept.

**Schlich,** *m.* byway; trick; (*Metal.*) slimes, schlich. **-arbeit,** *f.* smelting of slimes.

**schlicht,** *a.* smooth, even, plane; sleek; (of files) fine; (of fabrics) plain; simple, homely.

**Schlichtarbeit,** *f.* smooth-finishing work.

**Schlichte,** *f.* dressing; size (for fabrics); (*Founding*) black wash, facing; (*Plastering*) skim coat, white coat.

**schlichtecht,** *a.* fast to sizing.

**schlichtehaltig,** *a.* (*Textiles*) containing size.

**Schlichtemittel,** *n.* (*Textiles*) sizing agent, size.

**Schlichtemulsion,** *f.* sizing emulsion.

**schlichten,** *v.t.* smooth, plane, dress; finish; sleek (leather, etc.); planish (metals); size (fabrics); blackwash (molds); adjust, settle.

**Schlicht-flüssigkeit,** *f.* (*Textiles*) size. **-leim,** *m.* sizing, size. **-masse,** *f.* (*Textiles*) sizing paste. **-mittel,** *n.* = Schlichtemittel. **-öl,** *n.* sizing oil. **-walze,** *f.* finishing roll.

**Schlick,** *m.* slime, mud, ooze, silt; (*Metal.*) schlich (ore slimes).

**Schlicker,** *m.* (*Ceramics*) slip, slop; (*Metal.*) dross.

**schlickern,** *v.t.* (*Metal.*) dross.

**Schliech,** *m.* (*Metal.*) slimes, schlich.

**schlief,** *pret.* (of schlafen) slept.

**schliefen,** *v.i.* slip, creep.

**Schlieren,** *f.pl.* schlieren (regions of varying refraction, as in liquids); streaks, striae, schlieren (as in glass and igneous rocks). **-verfahren,** *n.* (*Photog.*) schlieren process.

**schlierig,** *a.* streaked, striated, banded.

**Schliesse,** *f.* pin, peg, catch, anchor, clasp.

**schliessen,** *v.t.* close; shut, lock; seal (tubes); bind; embrace; contract; conclude. — *v.r.* close; be related, be apropos. — *v.i.* close. — **geschlossene Kette,** closed chain; (*Mech.*) endless chain.

**schliesslich,** *a.* final, ultimate. — *adv.* finally.

**Schliess-rohr,** *n.*, **-röhre,** *f.* sealed tube.

**schliff,** *pret.* (of schleifen) ground, etc.

**Schliff,** *m.* grinding, sharpening; smoothness, polish; grindings; ground pulp; powder; cut (of a gem); ground section or specimen (as of metals for etching); ground joint. **-ap-**

parat, *m.* apparatus with ground joints. **-bild,** *n.* photomicrograph. **-kolben,** *m.* flask with ground top or ground stopper. **-rohr,** *n.*, **-röhre,** *f.* tube with ground joint. **-stelle,** *f.* ground place, grinding. **-stopfen,** *m.* ground-in stopper. **-stück,** *n.* ground piece. **-verbindung,** *f.* ground joint.

**schlimm,** *a.* bad; sad, severe, sore, ill. — *adv.* badly, ill.

**Schling-.** winding, twisting, (of plants) climbing; pertaining to swallowing or deglutition.

**Schlinge,** *f.* loop, noose, sling; snarl; snare.

**schlingen,** *v.t.* wind, twine, twist; swallow, gulp.

**Schlippe'sches Salz.** Schlippe's salt.

**schliss,** *pret.* (of schleissen) slit, split, etc.

**Schlitten,** *m.* sledge, sled, sleigh; truck; sliding carriage; slide; slide rail.

**Schlittschuh,** *m.* skate.

**Schlitz,** *m.* slit, slot, groove, fissure, cleft, slash. **-aufsatz,** *m.* wing top (of a burner). **-brenner,** *m.* batswing burner.

**schlitzen,** *v.t.* slit, slot, slash, split, cleave, rip.

**schlitzförmig,** *a.* slit-shaped, slit-like.

**schloff,** *pret.* (of schliefen) slipped, crept.

**schloss,** *pret.* (of schliessen) closed, shut, etc.

**Schloss,** *n.* lock; snap, clasp; castle, palace.

**Schlosse,** *f.* hailstone.

**Schlosser,** *m.* locksmith, fitter, mechanic.

**Schlot,** *m.*, **Schlotte,** *f.* flue, smokestack, stack; vent; soil pipe.

**Schlotter,** *m.* (*Salt*) sediment from boiling.

**schlottern,** *v.i.* dangle, flap, hang loose, shake, wabble.

**Schlucht,** *f.* ravine, gorge.

**schluchzen,** *v.i.* sob; hiccup.

**Schluckbeiwert,** *m.* coefficient of absorption, absorptivity.

**schlucken,** *v.t.* & *i.* absorb; swallow, gulp. — **schluckend,** *p.a.* absorbent.

**Schluckerzahl,** *f.* absorption coefficient.

**Schluckstoff,** *m.* absorbent material.

**Schluckung,** *f.* absorption; swallowing.

**Schluff,** *m.* silt; (*Ceram.*) poor clay.

**schlug,** *pret.* (of schlagen) struck, beat, etc.

**Schlummer,** *m.* slumber.

**schlummern,** *v.i.* slumber. — **schlummernd,** *p.a.* dormant.

**Schlund,** *m.* throat, pharynx; gulf, chasm.

**Schlund-.** pharyngeal. **-kopf,** *m.* upper pharynx. **-rohr,** *n.*, **-röhre,** *f.* esophagus.

**Schlupf,** *m.* slipping, slippage, slip, sliding.

**schlupfen, schlüpfen,** *v.i.* slip, slide.

**schlupffrei,** *a.* free from slipping, nonslip.

**Schlupfloch,** *n.* loophole.

**schlüpfrig,** *a.* slippery; lascivious. — **— machen,** lubricate.

**Schlüpfrigkeit,** *f.* slipperiness, lubricity, (of lubricants) oiliness.

**Schlupfung, Schlüpfung,** *f.* slipping, slip, sliding.

**Schlupfwinkel,** *m.* lurking place, haunt.

**schlürfen,** *v.t.* sip, lap. — *v.i.* (of pumps) suck air.

**Schluss,** *m.* closing; close; seal; conclusion; end; (*Elec.*) connection, contact, also circuit; (*Textiles*) closeness, body. **-deckel,** *m.* cover.

**Schlüssel,** *m.* key; code; screw driver or wrench; (*Elec.*) key, switch. **-bein,** *n.* collar bone, clavicle. **-blume,** *f.* primrose. **-formel,** *f.* key formula. **-nummer,** *f.* key number.

**Schlüsselung,** *f.* coding.

**Schluss-ergebnis,** *n.* final result. **-folge, -folgerung,** *f.* conclusion, inference. **-härten,** *n.*, **-härtung,** *f.* final hardening. **-prüfer,** *m.* (*Elec.*) short-circuit tester. **-punkt,** *m.* full point. **-stein,** *m.* keystone. **-weise,** *f.* manner of reasoning.

**Schlutte,** *f.* alkekengi.

**schm.,** *abbrev.* (schmelzend) melting; (schmilzt) melts.

**Schmack,** *m.* sumac.

**schmacken,** *v.t.* treat with sumac, sumac.

**schmack-gar,** *a.* dressed with sumac. **-haft,** *a.* palatable, savory. **-ieren,** *v.t.* treat with sumac, sumac.

**schmal,** *a.* narrow; slender; scanty.

**schmälern,** *v.t.* narrow, reduce, abridge.

**Schmal-film,** *m.* narrow film, substandard film. **-leder,** *n.* small tanned hides, tanned skins. **-seite,** *f.* narrow side, edge.

**Schmalt,** *m.* (proposed term for) enamel. **-blau,** *n.* smalt.

**Schmalte,** *f.* smalt.

**schmalten,** *v.t.* (proposed term for) enamel.

**Schmalz,** *n.* lard; melted fat, drippings.

**schmalzartig,** *a.* lardaceous, lardy.

**Schmalzbutter,** *f.* melted butter.

**Schmälze,** *f.* (*Textiles*) oil, softener, lubricant.

**schmalzen, schmälzen,** *v.t.* grease, lard; (*Textiles*) oil.

**schmalzig,** *a.* lardy, lardaceous.

**Schmälz-masse,** *f.* (*Textiles*) softening material, softener. **-mittel,** *n.* lubricant.

**Schmalzöl,** *n.* lard oil; oleo oil; wool oil.

**Schmälzvorgang,** *m.* (*Textiles*) oiling process.

**Schmand, Schmant,** *m.* slime, sludge, mud, ooze; cream.

**Schmarotzer,** *m.* parasite.

**schmarotzerisch,** *a.* parasitic.

**Schmauch,** *m.* smoke.

**schmauchen,** *v.t.* & *i.* smoke.

**schmecken,** *v.t.* & *i.* taste; relish, like.

**Schmeckzelle,** *f.* taste cell.

**Schmeer,** *m.* fat, grease; suet.

**schmeichelhaft,** *a.* flattering, complimentary

**schmeicheln,** *v.i.* flatter, compliment; coax.

**schmeissen,** *v.t.* throw, fling, hurl, dash; deposit (insect eggs).

**Schmeissen,** *n.* warping, distortion; throwing, etc. (see schmeissen).

**Schmelz,** *m.* enamel, glaze; fusion, melting, melt; (*Zinc*) blue powder.

**Schmelz-.** melting; smelting; fusible; cast. **-anlage,** *f.* smeltery; melting plant; foundry. **-arbeit,** *f.* smelting, smelting process; enameling, enameled work. **-arbeiter,** *m.* smelter; founder; enameler.

**schmelzartig,** *a.* enamel-like.

**Schmelz-ausdehnung,** *f.* expansion on melting. **-bad,** *n.* molten bath.

**schmelzbar,** *a.* fusible, meltable.

**Schmelz-barkeit,** *f.* fusibility. **-basalt,** *m.* cast basalt. **-behälter,** *m.* melting pot. **-blau,** *n.* smalt. **-butter,** *f.* melted butter. **-diagramm,** *n.* melting-point diagram. **-draht,** *m.* (*Elec.*) fuse wire. **-druckkurve,** *f.* melting-point-pressure curve.

**Schmelze,** *f.* melting, fusion; smelting; smeltery; fused mass, melt, heat; (*Glass*) batch; (*Soda*) ball; (*Spinning*) mill oil; (*Petrog.*) magma.

**Schmelzeinsatz,** *m.* (*Elec.*) fuse.

**schmelzen,** *v.t.* melt, fuse; smelt; (**teilweise**) frit. — *v.i.* melt, fuse; smelt; deliquesce. — **geschmolzen,** *p.a.* melted, fused, molten; smelted.

**Schmelzen,** *n.* melting, fusion; smelting.

**Schmelzer,** *m.* melter; founder; smelter.

**Schmelzerde,** *f.* fusible earth.

**Schmelzerei,** *f.* smeltery; foundry.

**Schmelz-erz,** *n.* smelting ore. **-farbe,** *f.* enamel color, vitrifiable pigment, majolica color. **-feuer,** *n.* (*Iron*) refinery. **-fluss,** *m.* fused mass, melt; fusion; flux; enamel.

**schmelzflüssig,** *a.* fusible; molten.

**Schmelz-gang,** *m.* (*Metal.*) heat. **-gefäss,** *n.* melting pot, melting hearth. **-glas,** *n.* fusible glass; enamel. **-glasur,** *f.* enamel. **-grad,** *m.* melting point. **-gut,** *n.* material suitable for smelting (or melting), material to be smelted (or melted), charge. **-hafen,** *m.* melting pot. **-herd,** *m.* smelting hearth; smelting furnace; (*Soda*) front hearth of a black-ash furnace. **-hitze,** *f.* melting heat. **-hütte,** *f.* smelting house or works, smeltery; foundry.

**schmelzig,** *a.* fusible.

**Schmelz-käse,** *m.* processed cheese. **-kegel,** *m.* (*Ceram.*) fusible cone. **-kessel,** *m.* melting pot or vessel; smelting crucible; (*Soda*) caustic pan. **-kirsche,** *f.* igniting pellet. **-kitt,** *m.* fusible cement. **-koks,** *m.* smelting coke, smelter coke. **-küche,** *f.* laboratory. **-kunst,** *f.* (art of) enameling; smelting. **-kurve,** *f.* melting-point curve, fusion curve. **-lampe,** *f.* glass-blower's lamp; enameler's lamp. **-legierung,** *f.* fusible alloy. **-linie,** *f.* line of fusion, fusion curve. **-löffel,** *m.* melting ladle.

**schmelzlos,** *a.* without enamel or glaze.

**Schmelz-lösung,** *f.* molten solution, melt. **-malerei,** *f.* enamel painting. **-mittel,** *n.* flux. **-ofen,** *m.* melting furnace; smelting furnace. **-öl,** *n.* = Schmälzöl.

**Schmelzp.,** *abbrev.* (Schmelzpunkt) melting point.

**Schmelz-patrone,** *f.* (*Elec.*) fuse cartridge. **-perle,** *f.* blowpipe bead; enamel bead, bugle. **-pfanne,** *f.* melting pan. **-pfropfen,** *m.* fusible plug. **-post,** *f.* smelting charge, post. **-prozess,** *m.* melting or smelting process. **-pulpe,** *f.* (*Anat.*) enamel pulp. **-pulver,** *n.* (powdered) flux.

**Schmelzpunkt,** *m.* melting point, fusing point. **-bestimmung,** *f.* melting-point determination. **-bestimmungsrohr,** *n.* (or **-röhre,** *f.*), melting-point tube.

**Schmelz-raum,** *m.* (*Metal.*) hearth. **-raupe,** *f.* fused-quartz spiral. **-röhrchen,** *n.* melting tube. **-schleuder,** *m.* melting centrifuge. **-schweissung,** *f.* fusion welding. **-sicherung,** *f.* (*Elec.*) fuse. **-soda,** *f.* a crude recovered sodium carbonate. **-stahl,** *m.* German steel, natural steel. **-stein,** *m.* (*Min.*) mizzonite. **-stopfen,** *n.*, **-stöpsel,** *m.* fusible plug, fuse plug. **-temperatur,** *f.* fusing temperature.

**Schmelztiegel,** *m.* crucible, melting pot. **-deckel,** *m.* crucible cover; (*Metal.*) tile. **-halter,** *m.* crucible holder, crucible support. **-zange,** *f.* crucible tongs.

**Schmelztopf,** *m.* melting pot, crucible.

**Schmelztröpfchen,** *n.* blowpipe bead.

**Schmelzung,** *f.* melting, fusion; smelting.

**Schmelzungspunkt,** *m.* melting point.

**Schmelz-verfahren,** *n.* melting process, fusion process; smelting process. **-wärme,** *f* heat of fusion. **-wasser,** *n.* water from melting ice or snow. **-werk,** *n.* smeltery; foundry; enameled work.

**schmelzwürdig,** *a.* suitable for smelting, workable.

**Schmelz-zeit,** *f.* time of melting or fusion; (*Glass*) journey. **-zement,** *m.* alumina cement. **-zeug,** *n.* smelting tools. **-zone,** *f.* zone of fusion; smelting zone.

**Schmer,** *m.* & *n.* fat, grease; suet.

**Schmergel,** *m.* emery. See Schmirgel-.

**Schmerz,** *m.* pain; grief, sorrow. **-anfall,** *m.* attack of pain.

**schmerz-betäubend,** *a.* pain-deadening. **-empfindlich,** *a.* sensitive to pain.

**schmerzen,** *v.t.* pain; grieve. — *v.i.* & *r.* hurt, ache.

**schmerz-erregend,** *a.* pain-producing. **-frei,** *a.* free from pain, painless.
**Schmerzgefühl,** *n.* sensation of pain.
**schmerz-haft,** *a.* painful; distressing. **-los,** *a.* painless.
**Schmerzlosigkeit,** *f.* painlessness.
**schmerzstillend,** *a.* stilling pain, anodyne.
**Schmetterling,** *m.* butterfly; lint.
**Schmetterlings-blütler,** *m.* papilionaceous plant, fabaceous plant (such as the bean, pea, etc.; not so wide a term as "leguminous plant"). **-brenner,** *m.* wing burner. **-ventil,** *n.* butterfly valve.
**schmettern,** *v.t.* dash, smash. — *v.i.* clang, ring, crash, blare.
**Schmied,** *m.* smith; blacksmith.
**schmiedbar,** *a.* malleable, forgeable.
**Schmiedbarkeit,** *f.* malleability.
**Schmiede,** *f.* forge, smithy. **-arbeit,** *f.* forging, smithing.
**schmiedebar,** *a.* capable of being wrought, forgeable.
**Schmiedeeisen,** *n.* wrought iron; forging steel, mild steel.
**schmiedeeisern,** *a.* wrought-iron.
**Schmiede-feuer,** *n.* smith's hearth, forge. **-herd,** *m.* forge; forge hearth.
**Schmiedeisen,** *n.* = Schmiedeeisen.
**schmiedeisern,** *a.* wrought-iron.
**Schmiede-kohle,** *f.* forge coal. **-legierung,** *f.* wrought alloy. **-metall,** *n.* malleable metal.
**schmieden,** *v.t.* forge, smith; devise, concoct. — **geschmiedetes Eisen,** wrought iron.
**Schmiede-schlacke,** *f.* forge cinder. **-sinter,** *m.* forge scale. **-stahl,** *m.* wrought steel.
**schmiegen,** *v.t.* bevel; wind. — *v.r.* bend, bow; press close, cling; (*Geom.*) osculate.
**schmiegsam,** *a.* flexible, pliant.
**Schmiegsamkeit,** *f.* flexibility, pliancy.
**Schmiegungsebene,** *f.* (*Geom.*) osculating plane.
**Schmier-apparat,** *m.* lubricator. **-büchse,** *f.* grease cup, oil cup, lubricator.
**Schmiere,** *f.* grease (for smearing or lubricating), smear; ointment; (for animals) dip.
**schmieren,** *v.t.* lubricate, oil; grease, smear, anoint; spread (butter); butter (bread); scrawl; thrash. — **schmierend,** *p.a.* greasy.
**schmierfähig,** *a.* capable of acting as a lubricant.
**Schmier-fähigkeit,** *f.* lubricating property, lubricity. **-fett,** *n.* = Schmiere. **-film,** *m.* lubricating film. **-fleck,** *m.* grease spot. **-flüssigkeit,** *f.* lubricating fluid. **-hahn,** *m.* lubricating cock, grease cock.
**schmierig,** *a.* greasy, smeary, oily; glutinous, viscous; dirty.
**Schmierigkeit,** *f.* greasiness, etc. (see schmierig).
**Schmier-kalk,** *m.* fat lime. **-kanne,** *f.* oil can. **-käse,** *m.* cottage cheese, smearcase. **-leder,** *n.* leather dressed with oil. **-masse,** *f.* (*Mach.*) lubricating paste. **-mittel, -material,** *n.* lubricant; ointment, salve, liniment. **-mittelindustrie,** *f.* lubricant industry. **-öl,** *n.* lubricating oil, lube. **-öldestillat,** *n.* (*Petroleum*) lube distillate. **-seife,** *f.* soft soap. **-stoff,** *m.* lubricant; ointment.
**Schmierung,** *f.* lubrication, etc. (see schmieren).
**Schmier-vorrichtung,** *f.* lubricating device, lubricator. **-wert,** *m.* lubricating value. **-wirkung,** *f.* lubricating effect. **-wolle,** *f.* greasy wool. **-zapfenöl,** *n.* journal oil.
**schmilzt,** *pr. 3 sing.* (of schmelzen) melts, etc.
**Schminkbohne,** *f.* kidney bean.
**Schminke,** *f.* (face) paint, make-up.
**Schmink-mittel,** *n.* cosmetic. **-rot,** *n.* rouge (the cosmetic). **-weiss,** *n.* flake white, pearl white (basic nitrate or oxychloride of bismuth).
**Schmirgel,** *m.* emery. **-leinen,** *n.*, **-leinwand,** *f.* emery cloth.
**schmirgeln,** *v.t.* rub with emery, emery.
**Schmirgel-papier,** *n.* emery paper. **-paste,** *f.* emery paste. **-pulver,** *n.* emery powder. **-scheibe,** *f.* emery wheel. **-staub,** *m.* emery dust.
**schmiss,** *pret.* (of schmeissen) threw, etc.
**schmitzen,** *v.t.* splash; blur; dye (leather); dress (cloth); lash.
**schmolz,** *pret.* (of schmelzen) melted; smelted.
**schmoren,** *v.t.* stew. — *v.i.* stew; (*Elec.*) arc; (*Radio*) fry.
**Schmorstelle,** *f.* (*Elec.*) point of arcing.
**Schmp., Schmpt.,** *abbrev.* (Schmelzpunkt) melting point.
**schmuck,** *a.* neat, trim, pretty.
**Schmuck,** *m.* ornament; jewelry; finery.
**schmücken,** *v.t.* adorn, decorate, dress.
**Schmuck-stein,** *m.* gem, gem stone. **-waren,** *f.pl.* jewelry, jewels.
**Schmutz,** *m.* dirt, mud, smut, filth. **-decke,** *f.* a thin upper layer of sand in a filter bed. **-farbe,** *f.* dingy (or dirty) color.
**schmutzig,** *a.* dirty; soiled, dingy; smutty; filthy. **-rot,** *a.* dull red, dingy red.
**schmutzlösend,** *a.* dirt-dissolving.
**Schmutz-lösungsmittel,** *n.* dirt solvent. **-papier,** *n.* waste paper. **-ventil,** *n.* mud valve. **-wasser,** *n.* dirty water, waste water; sewage. **-wolle,** *f.* wool in the yolk.
**Schnabel,** *m.* beak, bill; nozzle, nose; jaw.
**schnabelförmig,** *a.* beak-shaped.
**Schnalle,** *f.* buckle, clasp.
**schnallen,** *v.t.* buckle.
**schnalzen,** *v.i.* smack, cluck, snap.
**Schnappdecke,** *f.* snap cover; extension (to the drum of a German mask).
**schnappen,** *v.i.* snap; gasp.
**Schnappschuss,** *m.* snapshot.
**Schnaps,** *m.* spirits; dram. **-brenner,** *m.* distiller (of spirits).

**schnarchen,** *v.i.* snore.
**Schnarre,** *f.* (*Elec.*) buzzer.
**schnarren,** *v.i.* rattle, jar, buzz, vibrate.
**schnattern,** *v.i.* cackle; chatter.
**Schnatterrohr,** *n.* direct steam pipe.
**Schnauze,** *f.* snout, mouth; (*Tech.*) nose, nozzle, spout.
**Schnecke,** *f.* snail; slug; worm (of a still); (*Geom.*) helix; (*Mach.*) worm, endless screw; volute; spiral stairway; (*Anat.*) cochlea.
**Schneckel,** *f.* conical spiral.
**Schneckenantrieb,** *m.* (*Mach.*) worm drive.
**schneckenartig,** *a.* snail-like, spiral, helical.
**Schneckenfeder,** *f.* coil spring.
**schneckenförmig,** *a.* spiral, helical.
**Schnecken-gang,** *m.* auger; spiral walk; snail's pace. **-getriebe,** *n.* worm gear. **-gewinde,** *n.* helix; worm thread; endless screw. **-klee,** *m.* snail clover (*Medicago* species). **-linie,** *f.* spiral, helical line. **-presse,** *f.* screw press. **-rad,** *n.* worm wheel, worm gear.
**Schnee,** *m.* snow.
**schneeartig,** *a.* snow-like.
**Schnee-flocke,** *f.* snowflake. **-gips,** *m.* snowy (foliated) gypsum. **-glöckchen,** *n.* snowdrop. **-grenze,** *f.* snow line. **-wehe,** *f.* snowdrift.
**schneeweiss,** *a.* snow-white.
**Schneeweiss,** *n.* snow white (zinc white).
**schneidbar,** *a.* capable of being cut, sectile, scissile.
**Schneidbrenner,** *m.* cutting torch.
**Schneide,** *f.* knife edge; edge; keenness. **-brenner,** *m.* cutting torch. **-kante,** *f.* cutting edge. **-kessel,** *m.* (*Cellulose*) masticator. **-maschine,** *f.* cutting machine.
**schneiden,** *v.t.* cut; intersect; saw; prune; adulterate; gripe. — *v.i.* cut, carve.
**Schneiden-berührung,** *f.* knife-edge contact. **-lager,** *n.* knife-edge bearing.
**Schneider,** *m.* cutter; tailor.
**Schneid-fähigkeit,** *f.* cutting quality. **-flamme,** *f.* cutting flame. **-geschwindigkeit,** *f.* cutting speed.
**schneidhaltig,** *a.* (of tools) holding an edge.
**Schneidhärte,** *f.* cutting hardness.
**schneidig,** *a.* sharp, keen; (of rock) soft; plucky.
**Schneid-kante,** *f.* cutting edge. **-legierung,** *f.* alloy for cutting tools. **-maschine,** *f.* cutting machine, cutter, slicer. **-metall,** *n.* cutting metal, cutting alloy. **-öl,** *n.* cutting oil. **-vermögen,** *n.* cutting power.
**schneien,** *v.i.* snow.
**Schneise,** *f.* path, lane, track, course.
**schnell,** *a.* fast, rapid, quick, sudden. — *adv.* quickly, rapidly. **-abbindend,** *a.* quick-setting.
**Schnell-analyse,** *f.* rapid analysis. **-arbeitsstahl,** *m.* high-speed steel. **-auflöser,** *m.* rapid dissolver. **-bad,** *n.* quick bath. **-beizverfahren,** *n.* quick disinfection process (for seeds). **-binder,** *m.* quick-setting cement. **-bleiche,** *f.* quick bleaching, chemical bleaching. **-dämpfer,** *m.* (*Printing*) rapid ager. **-drehmessing,** *n.* high-speed brass. **-drehstahl,** *m.* high-speed steel.
**schnellen,** *v.i.* spring, snap, jerk. — *v.t.* let fly, fling; jerk; cheat.
**Schnell-entladung,** *f.* rapid discharge. **-essig,** *m.* quick vinegar. **-essigbereitung,** *f.*, **-essigverfahren,** *n.* quick vinegar process. **-färbung,** *f.* (*Micros.*) quick staining. **-feuer-,** (*Mil.*) rapid-fire. **-filter,** *n.* rapid filter. **-filtrieren,** *n.* rapid filtration.
**schnellfliegend,** *a.* fast (flying), of high velocity.
**Schnellfluss,** *m.* quick flux.
**schnellflüssig,** *a.* easily fusible.
**Schnell-gang,** *m.* rapid motion, high speed. **-gärung,** *f.* quick (or accelerated) fermentation.
**schnellgehend,** *a.* fast-running, fast.
**Schnellgerben,** *n.* rapid tanning.
**schnellhärtend,** *a.* quick-hardening.
**Schnell-igkeit,** *f.* rapidity, quickness, speed, velocity. **-kochtopf,** *m.* autoclave, pressure cooker. **-kraft,** *f.* elasticity.
**schnell-kräftig,** *a.* elastic. **-laufend,** *a.* high-speed, rapid.
**Schnell-läufer,** *m.* high-speed mill or machine. **-laufstahl,** *m.* high-speed steel. **-lot,** *n.* soft solder; fusible metal. **-methode,** *f.* rapid method, quick method. **-photographie,** *f.* instantaneous photography or photograph. **-probe,** *f.* rapid test. **-röste,** *f.* quick retting, chemical retting. **-säurer,** *m.* acetifier (in the quick vinegar process). **-schnittstahl,** *m.* high-speed steel. **-schrift,** *f.* shorthand, stenography. **-stahl,** *m.* high-speed steel. **-trockenfarbe,** *f.* quick-drying color or ink.
**schnelltrocknend,** *p.a.* quick-drying, siccative.
**Schnell-verfahren,** *n.* rapid or quick process. **-wa(a)ge,** *f.* steelyard. **-zug,** *m.* fast train, express train. **-zünder,** *m.* instantaneous fuse; quick match.
**Schneppe,** *f.* spout, snout, nozzle, lip.
**Schnipsel,** *n.* chip, scrap, bit.
**schnitt,** *pret.* (of schneiden) cut, intersected, etc.
**Schnitt,** *m.* cut; cutting, incision; section; intersection; slice; die; edge (of a book); (surgical) operation; crop. **-band,** *n.* (*Micros.*) serial section, ribbon.
**schnittbearbeitbar,** *a.* machinable.
**Schnitt-brenner,** *m.* slit burner, batswing burner. **-dicke,** *f.* thickness of a slice or section.
**Schnitte,** *f.* cut, slice; sulfur match (for casks); chop; steak.

**Schnitt-ebene,** *f.* cutting (or intersecting) plane. **-fänger,** *m.* (*Micros.*) section lifter. **-färbung,** *f.* (*Micros.*) section staining. **-fläche,** *f.* surface of a cut or section, sectional plane, section. **-geschwindigkeit,** *f.* cutting speed. **-holz,** *n.* sawed timber.

**schnittig,** *a.* streamlined.

**Schnitt-kante,** *f.* cutting edge. **-länge,** *f.* length of cut or section. **-lauch,** *m.* chive. **-linie,** *f.* line of section or intersection. **-präparat,** *n.* section preparation. **-punkt,** *m.*, **-stelle,** *f.* point or place of intersection. **-wachs,** *n.* cobbler's wax. **-waren,** *f.pl.* draper's goods, dry goods; sawed timber, lumber. **-zeichnung,** *f.* sectional drawing, cross section.

**Schnitz,** *m.* cut, slice, chip; cutlet.

**Schnitzel,** *n.* slice, chip, clipping, snipping, paring, (of sugar beets) cossette, shred, scrap; cutlet. **-maschine,** *f.* slicing machine, slicer (as for sugar beets), shredding machine. **-masse,** *f.* diced plastic, molded macerate. **-messer,** *n.* slicing knife, chip cutter.

**schnitzeln, schnitzen,** *v.t. & i.* cut, carve, chip, slice, shred, whittle.

**Schnitzelpres(s)stoff,** *m.* = Schnitzelmasse.

**Schnitzer,** *m.* cutter, carver; blunder.

**Schnupfen,** *m.* cold, catarrh, coryza.

**Schnupftabak,** *m.* snuff.

**Schnur,** *f.* string, cord, line, twine, tape, band.

**schnüren,** *v.t.* tie up, string, lace, strap, constrict.

**Schnürkolben,** *m.* a flask with neck constricted at the top.

**Schnurre,** *f.* rattle; joke, story.

**schnurren,** *v.i.* buzz, hum, whir, whiz, purr.

**Schnurscheibe,** *f.* pulley, pulley wheel.

**schob,** *pret.* (of schieben) shoved, pushed, etc.

**schobern,** *v.t.* pile, stack.

**Schock,** *n.* sixty; mass, lot.

**Schofel,** *m.* trash, refuse.

**Schokolade,** *f.* chocolate.

**schokoladen-braun, -farbig,** *a.* chocolate-brown, chocolate-colored.

**Schokoladentafel,** *f.* cake of chocolate.

**Scholle,** *f.* clod; soil; lump; flounder.

**Schöllkraut,** *n.* celandine.

**schon,** *adv.* already; yet, since, ever, now, duly; indeed, surely, no doubt, to be sure; merely, alone; even.

**schön,** *a.* beautiful, handsome, fine, lovely.

**Schöne,** *f.* fining, isinglass; fair one.

**schonen,** *v.t. & i.* spare, save, protect, preserve, care for. — **schonend,** *p.a.* careful; considerate; sparing.

**schönen,** *v.t.* fine, clarify, clear; gloss; brighten, tone up (colors); beautify.

**Schön-färber,** *m.* garment dyer, dyer in fine colors. **-färberei,** *f.* garment dyeing, job dyeing. **-grün,** *n.* Paris green. **-heit,** *f.* beauty; fineness.

**Schönheits-mittel,** *n.* cosmetic. **-wasser,** *n.* beauty wash, liquid cosmetic.

**schonlich,** *a.* careful.

**Schönseite,** *f.* right side (of fabrics).

**Schonung,** *f.* sparing, etc. (see schonen).

**Schönung,** *f.* fining, etc. (see schönen).

**Schönungsfarbstoff,** *m.* brightening dye.

**schonungslos,** *a.* unsparing, pitiless.

**Schönungsmittel,** *n.* fining agent, fining; (for colors) brightening agent.

**Schopf,** *m.* tuft; (head of) hair; (tree) top.

**Schöpf-bütte,** *f.* (*Paper*) pulp vat, stuff vat. **-eimer,** *m.* (dipping) bucket.

**schopfen,** *v.t.* top, crop.

**schöpfen,** *v.t.* draw (liquids, air, containers); scoop, dip, bail, ladle.

**Schöpfer,** *m.* drawer (of water, etc.) dipper, scoop, ladle, bucket; creator, maker, author, originator.

**Schöpf-gefäss,** *n.* scoop, dipper, ladle, bucket. **-herd,** *m.* casting crucible (of a furnace). **-kelle,** *f.*, **-löffel,** *m.* scoop, ladle. **-papier,** *n.* handmade paper. **-probe,** *f.* drawn (dipped, ladled) sample; ladle test, cup test. **-rad,** *n.* bucket wheel. **-rahmen,** *m.* (*Paper*) deckle.

**Schöpfung,** *f.* creation.

**Schöpfwerk,** *n.* bucket elevator.

**Schöps,** *m.* wether; mutton; simpleton.

**Schöpsen-fleisch,** *n.* mutton. **-talg,** *m.* mutton tallow, (*Pharm.*) prepared suet.

**schor,** *pret.* (of scheren) sheared, etc.

**Schorf,** *m.* scurf, scab, crust, eschar.

**Schörl,** *m.* schorl.

**Schörlit,** *m.* pycnite (variety of topaz).

**Schornstein,** *m.* chimney, stack, flue. **-gas,** *n.* stack gas, flue gas.

**schoss,** *pret.* (of schiessen) shot, fired, etc.

**Schoss,** *m.* lap; womb; (coat) tails; shoot, sprig. **-gerinne,** *n.* channel, trough.

**Schössling,** *m.* shoot, sprout, sucker.

**Schote,** *f.* pod, shell, husk.

**Schoten-dorn,** *m.* acacia; black locust. **-gewächse,** *n.pl.* leguminous plants. **-pfeffer,** *m.* red pepper, capsicum. **-pflanze,** *f.* leguminous plant.

**Schott,** *n.* partition; bulkhead; flood gate.

**Schotter,** *m.* broken stone, macadam; gravel. **-boden,** *m.* gravelly soil.

**schottisch,** *a.* Scotch.

**Schottkolben,** *m.* Schott flask.

**Schottland,** *n.* Scotland.

**Sch. P.,** *abbrev.* (Schmelzpunkt) melting point, m. p.

**Sch.-R.,** *abbrev.* (*Paper*) Schopper-Riegler degree of freeness (of pulp).

**schr.,** *abbrev.* (schriftlich) in writing.

**schraffieren, schraffen,** *v.t.* (in drawings, etc.) shade, hatch, line.
**Schraffur,** *f.* shaded or hatched part.
**schräg,** *a.* oblique, sloping, slanting, inclined, bevel, diagonal.
**Schräg-agar,** *m.* (*Bact.*) agar slant. **-druck,** *m.* italics.
**Schräge,** *f.* slant, slope, bevel; diagonal.
**schrägen,** *v.t.* slope, slant, bevel.
**schrägliegend,** *a.* slanting, inclined.
**Schräg-linie,** *f.* slanting line; diagonal. **-retortenofen,** *m.* oven or furnace with inclined retort. **-rohr,** *n.*, **-röhre,** *f.* slanting tube.
**schrägschichtig,** *a.* obliquely bedded.
**Schrägschnitt,** *m.* oblique cut or section.
**schräg-stellbar,** *a.* inclinable. **-stellen,** *v.t.* incline, tilt.
**Schrägstrahlen,** *m.pl.* (*Physics*) skew rays.
**Schrägung,** *f.* slope, slant, inclination, bevel, chamfer.
**schrägwink(e)lig,** *a.* oblique, bevel.
**schrak,** *pret.* (of schrecken) was alarmed.
**Schram,** *m.* trench, channel, furrow; kerf.
**schrämen,** *v.t.* cut, carve, kerve.
**Schramme,** *f.* scratch, slash; scar, cicatrix.
**schrammen,** *v.t.* scratch, score, slash, scar.
**Schrank,** *m.* cabinet, case, press, cupboard, closet, safe.
**Schranke,** *f.* bar, barrier; bound, limit. — **in die Schranken treten,** enter the lists.
**schränken,** *v.t.* put across, cross; set (a saw).
**schränkweise,** *adv.* crosswise.
**Schraper, Schrapper,** *m.*, **Schrape,** *f.* scraper; tracer.
**Schräubchen,** *n.* small screw.
**Schraubdeckel,** *m.* screw cap, screw cover.
**Schraube,** *f.* screw; (screw) bolt; propeller.
**schrauben,** *v.t.* screw; banter, mock. **-artig,** *a.* screw-shaped, spiral, helical.
**Schrauben-bakterie,** *f.* spirillum. **-bohrer,** *m.* screw tap; screw auger; twist drill. **-bolzen,** *m.* screw bolt, bolt. **-dreher,** *m.* screw driver; wrench. **-feder,** *f.* helical spring, coil spring.
**schraubenförmig,** *a.* screw-shaped, spiral, helical.
**Schrauben-gang,** *m.* thread or pitch of a screw. **-gewinde,** *n.* screw thread. **-kappe,** *f.* screw cap. **-klammer, -klemme,** *f.* screw clamp, screw clip. **-kühler,** *m.* helical condenser or cooler. **-lehre,** *f.* screw-thread caliper, micrometric gage. **-linie,** *f.* helical line, helix. **-mutter,** *f.* nut, female screw. **-presse,** *f.* screw press, fly press. **-quetschhahn,** *m.* screw pinchcock. **-rohr,** *n.*, **-röhre,** *f.* spiral (helical) tube. **-rührwerk,** *n.* screw stirrer. **-schlüssel,** *m.* screw wrench, nut wrench. **-stock,** *m.* vise. **-zieher,** *m.* screw driver.
**Schraubglas,** *n.* screw-top glass bottle or tube or jar.
**schraubig,** *a.* screwed, screwy.
**Schraub-lehre,** *f.* = Schraubenlehre. **-stock,** *m.* vise.
**Schraubung,** *f.* screwing, screw motion.
**Schraub-verschluss,** *m.* screw cap; screw plug. **-zwinge,** *f.* screw clamp.
**Schreck,** *m.* fright, terror.
**schrecken,** *v.t.* chill; frighten. — *v.i.* be alarmed.
**Schreckladung,** *f.* (*Mil.*) booby trap.
**schrecklich,** *a.* frightful, terrible, awful.
**Schreck-mine,** *f.* (*Mil.*) booby mine. **-wirkung,** *f.* chilling action or effect.
**Schrei,** *m.* cry, shriek, shout; (*Metal.*) bloom, ball, lump.
**Schreib-anzeiger,** *m.* recording indicator. **-art,** *f.* mode of writing; style; spelling. **-barometer,** *n.* barograph. **-blatt,** *n.* record sheet.
**schreiben,** *v.t. & i.* write; (of instruments) record, trace.
**Schreiber,** *m.* writer; recorder, recording instrument.
**Schreib-feder,** *f.* (writing or recording) pen, stylus, style. **-fehler,** *m.* error in writing, clerical error. **-fläche,** *f.* record surface or sheet. **-gerät,** *n.* recording instrument or apparatus. **-kies,** *m.* marcasite. **-kreide,** *f.* writing chalk. **-maschine,** *f.* typewriter. **-maschinenband,** *n.* typewriter ribbon. **-materialien,** *f.* writing materials, stationery. **-papier,** *n.* writing paper. **-röhrchen,** *n.* recording siphon. **-stift,** *m.* pencil; crayon. **-tinte,** *f.* writing ink. **-trommel,** *f.* recording drum. **-waren,** *f.pl.* writing materials, stationery. **-weise,** *f.* manner of writing, spelling, style. **-werk,** *n.* recording mechanism.
**schreien,** *v.i.* cry, shout, scream, shriek, bray. — **schreiend,** *p.a.* (of colors) loud.
**Schreien,** *n.* crying, etc. (see schreien); (of tin) cry.
**Schrein,** *m.* case, cabinet, chest, casket, press.
**Schreiner,** *m.* cabinet maker, carpenter.
**schreinern,** *v.t.* (*Textiles*) schreiner(ize).
**schreiten,** *v.i.* step, stride; proceed, advance.
**Schrenz,** *m.*, **-packpapier, -papier,** *n.* common wrapping paper, screenings. **-pappe,** *f.* straw board.
**schrie,** *pret.* (of schreien) cried, shouted, etc.
**schrieb,** *pret.* (of schreiben) wrote.
**Schrift,** *f.* writing; record; characters; type; paper, publication, work; pitch (of a screw). **-absatz,** *m.* paragraph. **-erz,** *n.* sylvanite. **-flasche,** *f.* bottle with permanent label, labeled reagent bottle. **-führer,** *m.* secretary. **-giesser,** *m.* type founder. **-giessermetall,** *n.* type metal. **-gold,** *n.* sylvanite. **-granit,** *m.* graphic granite.
**schriftgranitisch,** *a.* graphic, granophyric.

**Schrift-guss,** *m.* type founding. **-jaspis,** *m.* jasper opal. **-leiter,** *m.* editor.

**schriftlich,** *a.* written, in writing.

**Schrift-malen,** *n.*, **-malerei,** *f.* sign painting; lettering. **-material,** *n.* written or recorded material, literature, documentation; bibliography. **-metall,** *n.* type metal. **-mutter,** *f.* type mold, matrix. **-setzer,** *m.* typesetter, compositor. **-stein,** *m.* graphic granite. **-steller,** *m.* writer, author. **-stück,** *n.* piece of writing, document. **-tellur,** *n.* graphic tellurium (sylvanite). **-tum,** *n.* literature; literature references, bibliography. **-tumverzeichnis,** *n.* list of literature references. **-wechsel,** *m.* correspondence. **-zeichen,** *n.* character, letter. **-zeug,** *n.* type metal. **-zug,** *m.* (written) character; stroke; handwriting.

**schritt,** *pret.* (of schreiten) stepped, etc.

**Schritt,** *m.* step; stride; pace.

**schrittweise,** *adv.* step by step, gradually.

**Schrittweite,** *f.* interval (as between spectral lines).

**schrob,** *pret.* (of schrauben) screwed.

**schroff,** *a.* rough, harsh; steep, abrupt; gruff.

**schröpfen,** *v.t.* cup; scarify.

**Schrot,** *n. & m.* cut, piece, block, clipping; small shot; groats; selvage; due weight (of a coin); plumb bob; (*Brewing*) grist. **-effekt,** *m.* (*Physics*) (small) shot effect.

**schroten,** *v.t.* cut in pieces, chip, clip; bruise, crush, rough-grind; shoot (casks); gobble (food).

**Schröter,** *m.* handler of barrels; woodcutter; stag beetle.

**Schrot-fabrik,** *f.* shot factory. **-gewehr,** *n.* shotgun. **-korn,** *n.*, **-kugel,** *f.* grain of shot, (single) shot.

**Schrötling,** *m.* piece, cutting; (*Minting*) blank, planchet.

**Schrot-mehl,** *n.* coarse meal. **-metall,** *n.* shot metal. **-mühle,** *f.* grist mill, bruising mill; malt mill.

**Schrott,** *m.* scrap (metal), esp. scrap iron. **-martinieren,** *n.*, **-roheisenverfahren,** *n.* (*Iron*) pig-and-scrap process. **-schmelze,** *f.* (*Metal.*) scrap heat. **-verfahren,** *n.* (*Iron*) pig-and-scrap process. **-wert,** *m.* scrap value.

**schrubben,** *v.t.* scrub, scour.

**Schrubber,** *m.* scrubber.

**schrüen,** *v.t.* give the biscuit baking to (porcelain).

**Schrulle,** *f.* whim, crotchet.

**schrumpfen,** *v.t. & i.* shrink, contract, shrivel. — **schrumpfend,** *p.a.* shrinking; astringent.

**Schrumpfgrenze,** *f.* shrinkage limit.

**schrumpfig,** *a.* shriveled, wrinkled, crumpled.

**Schrumpf-mass,** *n.* (amount of) shrinkage, contraction. **-niere,** *f.* shrunken kidney, atrophic cirrhosis. **-riss,** *m.* shrinkage crack. **-sitz,** *m.* shrink fit.

**Schrumpfung,** *f.* shrinking, shrinkage, contraction, shriveling.

**Schrumpfungsgeschwindigkeit,** *f.* rate of shrinkage.

**schruppen,** *v.t.* rough.

**Schub,** *m.* shove, push; thrust; shear; throw; outburst; batch, lot. **-fach,** *n.* drawer. **-fenster,** *n.* sash window, sash. **-festigkeit,** *f.* shearing strength. **-kraft,** *f.* shearing force or strain; pushing force, thrust. **-kurbel,** *f.* (*Mach.*) crank. **-lade,** *f.* drawer. **-lehre,** **-leere,** *f.* sliding gage, slide gage. **-spannung,** *f.* shearing stress. **-vektor,** *m.* thrust vector.

**schubweise,** *adv.* by shoves, by thrusts; in batches; gradually.

**schuf,** *pret.* (of schaffen) made, created, etc.

**schuften,** *v.i.* drudge, toil.

**Schuh,** *m.* shoe. **-band,** *n.* shoestring, shoelace. **-krem,** **-kreme,** *f.* shoe cream, shoe polish. **-leder,** *n.* shoe leather. **-macherwachs,** **-pech,** *n.* cobbler's wax. **-putzmittel,** *n.* shoe polish. **-riemen,** *m.* shoestring, shoe lace. **-schmiere,** *f.* dubbing. **-schwärze,** *f.* shoe blacking. **-wachs,** *n.*, **-wichse,** *f.* shoe polish.

**Schulbombe,** *f.* (*Mil.*) training bomb.

**Schuld,** *f.* debt; fault, blame; guilt; crime. **-buch,** *n.* ledger, account book.

**schulden,** *v.t.* owe.

**schuldig,** *a.* guilty, at fault; indebted, owing; due.

**Schuldigkeit,** *f.* duty, obligation, debt.

**Schuldner,** *m.* debtor.

**Schule,** *f.* school.

**Schüler,** *m.* scholar, pupil.

**Schulpe, Schülpe,** *f.* shell; barnacle.

**Schulter,** *f.* shoulder. **-blatt,** *n.* shoulder blade, scapula.

**Schumanngebiet,** *n.* Schumann region.

**schund,** *pret.* (of schinden) skinned.

**Schund,** *m.* refuse, offal, rubbish, trash.

**Schüppchen,** *n.* little scale, flake.

**Schuppe,** *f.* scale; flake.

**Schüppe,** *f.* shovel, scoop.

**schuppen,** *v.t. & r.* scale, scale off, desquamate.

**Schuppen,** *m.* shed, barn, garage, hangar.

**schuppenartig,** *a.* scaly, squamous.

**Schuppenbildung,** *f.* scaling, flaking.

**schuppenförmig,** *a.* scale-like, scaly, flaky.

**Schuppen-glätte,** *f.* flake litharge. **-graphit,** *m.* flaky graphite. **-paraffin,** *n.* (*Petroleum*) scale wax. **-stein,** *m.* lepidolite.

**schüpperig,** *a.* (*Dyeing*) skittery.

**schuppig,** *a.* scaly, flaky, squamous.

**Schuppigkeit,** *f.* scaliness.

**schüpprig,** *a.* (*Dyeing*) skittery.

**Schur,** *f.* shearing; mowing; fleece; annoyance;

**Schürbel,** *m.* = Schirbel.
**Schüreisen,** *n.* poker, fire hook, fire iron.
**schüren,** *v.t.* stir, poke, stoke (fire).
**Schurf,** *n.* scratch, abrasion; hole, pit; prospecting.
**schürfen,** *v. t.* scratch, scrape; open (a mine). — *v.i.* prospect.
**Schür-haken,** *m.* = Schüreisen. **-loch,** *n.* stoke hole, fire hole.
**Schurre,** *f.* slide, chute.
**Schurz,** *m.*, **Schürze,** *f.* apron.
**schürzen,** *v.t.* tie; tuck up, gird up.
**Schuss,** *m.* shot; blast; charge; shoot, shooting; weft (of fabrics); ring, collar; (*Baking*) batch.
**Schüssel,** *f.* dish; bowl; pan.
**schüsselförmig,** *a.* dish-shaped, bowl-shaped.
**Schüsselzinn,** *n.* pewter.
**schussfest,** *a.* bulletproof.
**Schus(s)schweissung,** *f.* shot welding.
**schus(s)sicher,** *a.* bulletproof, shellproof.
**Schussweite,** *f.* range.
**Schuster,** *m.* shoemaker; cobbler. **-pech,** *n.* shoemaker's wax.
**Schutt,** *m.* rubbish, refuse, debris, (*Geol.*) scree; ruins; batch.
**Schüttbeton,** *m.* poured concrete.
**Schuttbreccie,** *f.* debris breccia, scree breccia.
**Schüttdichte,** *f.* apparent density, bulk density.
**Schüttel-apparat,** *m.* shaking apparatus. **-bewegung,** *f.* shaking motion. **-fass,** *n.* shaking drum. **-glas,** *n.* shaking glass, shaking bottle, shaking tube. **-maschine,** *f.* shaking machine.
**schütteln,** *v.t.* shake, agitate, churn.
**Schüttel-sieb,** *n.* shaking screen, riddler. **-sortierer,** *m.* oscillating separator. **-trichter,** *m.* separatory funnel. **-werk,** *n.* shaking mechanism or apparatus. **-zahl,** *f.* shaking number. **-zylinder,** *m.* shaking cylinder (stoppered cylinder).
**schütten,** *v.t.* pour, pour out; discharge; shed; heap up; charge; yield.
**Schüttergebiet,** *n.* (*Geol.*) region of disturbance.
**schüttern,** *v.i.* shake, tremble, vibrate. — *v.t.* shake.
**Schütt-gelb,** *n.* Dutch pink. **-gewicht,** *n.* bulk weight; loose weight; bulk density, apparent density. **-gut,** *n.* bulk goods; loose material.
**Schutthalde,** *f.* (*Geol.*) rock debris, talus.
**Schütt-loch,** *n.* feed hole. **-röstofen,** *m.* continuous roasting furnace. **-trichter,** *m.* feed hopper; discharge hopper.
**Schüttung,** *f.* pouring, etc. (see schütten); ballasting; (*Brewing*) extract-yielding materials.
**Schütt-volumen,** *n.* (*Plastics*) pourability, also bulk factor. **-winkel,** *m.* angle of repose.
**Schütz,** *m.* relay; shuttle; sluice.
**Schutz,** *m.* protection, defense, shelter, screen, safeguard.
**Schutz-.** protecting, protective, guard, preserving. **-anstrich,** *m.* protective coating. **-anwendung,** *f.* protective use. **-anzug,** *m.* protective clothing. **-beize,** *f.* (*Calico*) resist, reserve. **-beizendruck,** *m.* resist style. **-brille,** *f.* protecting spectacles, goggles. **-decke,** *f.* protective cover or coating.
**schützen,** *v.t.* protect, guard, defend, shelter.
**Schützengrabenkrieg,** *m.* trench warfare.
**Schutz-farbe,** *f.* protective (esp., anticorrosion) paint; protective color. **-färbung,** *f.* protective coloration; protective paint. **-firnis,** *m.* protective varnish. **-gas,** *n.* protective gas, safety gas. **-glas,** *n.* protecting glass. **-glocke,** *f.* bell jar, bell glass (for covering). **-handschuh,** *m.* protective glove. **-hülle,** *f.* protective covering or casing. **-impfung,** *f.* protective inoculation, vaccination. **-kappe,** *f.* protecting cap. **-kleidung,** *f.* protective clothing. **-kolloid,** *n.* protective colloid.
**schutzkolloidal,** *a.* protective-colloid.
**Schutz-kraft,** *f.* protective power. **-lack,** *m.* protective varnish.
**Schützling,** *m.* protégé, charge.
**schutzlos,** *a.* unprotected.
**Schutz-mann,** *m.* policeman. **-mantel,** *m.* protecting jacket (or case); windbreak. **-marke,** *f.* trademark. **-maske,** *f.* protecting mask, gas mask, face guard. **-masse,** *f.* (*Calico*) resist. **-massnahme, -massregel,** *f.* protective measure. **-mittel,** *n.* preservative; preventive, prophylactic; (*Calico*) resist. **-muffe,** *f.* protecting sleeve, protector. **-papp,** *m.* (*Calico*) resist paste, reserve. **-pockengift,** *n.* vaccine virus. **-raum,** *m.* protective space, specif. air-raid shelter. **-recht,** *n.* patent right. **-ring,** *m.* guard ring. **-rohr,** *n.* protecting tube or pipe. **-salbe,** *f.* protective ointment. **-salzlösung,** *f.* protective salt solution (as for gas masks). **-schicht,** *f.* protective layer or coat or film. **-stoff,** *m.* protective substance or material; specif., alexin. **-trichter,** *m.* protecting funnel (see Ablauftrichter). **-überzug,** *m.* protective coating or covering. **-ummantelung,** *f.* protective sheathing or casing. **-vorrichtung,** *f.* protecting device, protective contrivance. **-wand,** *f.* protecting screen or partition; safety wall. **-wert,** *m.* protective value. **-widerstand,** *m.* (*Elec.*) protective resistance. **-wirkung,** *f.* protective effect. **-zoll,** *m.* protective duty.
**Schw.,** *abbrev.* (Schweizerisch) Swiss.
**Schwabbel,** *m.* swab; mop. **-lack,** *m.* swab varnish; swab lacquer.
**schwabbeln,** *v.t.* buff, polish (by buffing).

**Schwabber,** *m.* = Schwabbel.
**schwach,** *a.* weak; feeble, faint, low, dim, thin, poor, slight, light. — **swach färben,** color faintly, tint, tinge. — **schwach kochen,** boil gently, simmer.
**Schwachammoniakwasser,** *n.* weak ammonia water.
**Schwäche,** *f.* weakness, etc. (see schwach).
**schwächen,** *v.t.* weaken; enfeeble, impair; diminish; tender (fibers); seduce.
**schwach-erhitzt,** *a.* gently heated. **-färben,** *v.t.* tint, tone, tinge.
**Schwachgas,** *n.* poor gas, lean gas.
**schwachlegiert,** *a.* (*Metal.*) low-alloy.
**schwächlich,** *a.* weak, feeble, frail.
**schwach-sauer, -säuerlich,** *a.* weakly acid. **-siedend,** *p.a.* gently boiling, simmering.
**Schwachstrom,** *m.* (*Elec.*) weak current.
**Schwächung,** *f.* weakening, etc. (see schwächen).
**Schwächungsmittel,** *n.* depressant.
**schwach-wandig,** *a.* thin-walled. **-wirksam,** *a.* feebly active.
**Schwaden,** *m.* noxious vapor or exhalation, damp; specif., choke damp; gas cloud; smoke cloud; swath. — **feuriger —,** fire damp.
**Schwadenfang,** *m.* hood; ventilator.
**Schwahl, Schwal,** *m.* (*Iron*) rich finery cinder, slag. **-arbeit,** *f.* (*Iron*) single refining, slag washing. **-boden,** *m.* slag bed, slag bottom.
**Schwalbe,** *f.* swallow.
**Schwalben-nest,** *n.* swallow's nest; (of slag) honeycomb. **-schwanz,** *m.* swallowtail; dovetail. **-wurz, -wurzel,** *f.* swallowwort; (*Pharm.*) vincetoxicum.
**Schwall,** *m.* swell, flood, throng; = Schwahl. **-wasser,** *n.* splash(ed) water.
**schwamm,** *pret.* (of schwimmen) swam.
**Schwamm,** *m.* sponge; mushroom; fungus; tinder; spongy growth; (*Zinc*) tutty; mass, lot.
**schwammartig,** *a.* sponge-like, spongy; fungous.
**Schwammfilter,** *n.* sponge filter.
**schwammförmig,** *a.* spongy, porous.
**Schwamm-gewebe,** *n.* spongy tissue. **-gift,** *n.* mushroom poison, muscarine. **-gummi,** *n.* sponge rubber, rubber sponge. **-holz,** *n.* spongy wood, decayed wood.
**schwammig,** *a.* spongy, porous; (of paper) bibulous; fungous, fungoid.
**Schwamm-igkeit,** *f.* sponginess. **-kupfer,** *n.* spongy copper, copper sponge. **-säure,** *f.* boletic acid (fumaric acid); fungic acid (a mixture). **-stoff,** *m.* fungin. **-tod,** *m.* fungicide. **-zucker,** *m.* mannitol.
**Schwan,** *m.* swan.
**schwand,** *pret.* (of schwinden) shrank, etc.
**Schwand,** *m.* shrinkage, contraction; wasting; disappearance.
**Schwanenhals,** *m.* gooseneck; swan neck. **-rohr,** *n.* gooseneck.
**schwang,** *pret.* (of schwingen) vibrated, etc.
**Schwang,** *m.* swing; vogue.
**schwanger,** *a.* pregnant.
**schwängern,** *v.t.* impregnate, saturate.
**Schwangerschaft,** *f.* pregnancy.
**Schwängerung,** *f.* impregnation, saturation.
**schwank,** *a.* flexible, pliant; slender; wavering.
**schwanken,** *v.i.* fluctuate, oscillate; vary; shake, rock, reel; hesitate, waver. — **schwankend,** *p.a.* unsettled, unsteady, uncertain, fluctuating, variable.
**Schwankung,** *f.* fluctuation, etc. (see schwanken).
**Schwankungsgrenze,** *f.* limit of variation.
**Schwanz,** *m.* tail; train. **-hahn,** *m.* stopcock with an outlet thru the end of the key. **-kügelchen,** *n.* bulb drawn out to a narrow opening. **-pfeffer,** *m.* cubebs. **-stern,** *m.* comet.
**schwären,** *v.i.* fester, suppurate.
**Schwarm,** *m.* swarm, crowd, throng; cluster; (*Bact.*) colony. **-bildung,** *f.* formation of clusters or swarms or (*Bact.*) colonies.
**schwärmen,** *v.i.* swarm; wander, migrate; revel; daydream; rave.
**Schwärmer,** *m.* rover; reveler; visionary; enthusiast; (*Zoöl.*) sphinx; firecracker, serpent.
**Schwarmion,** *n.* exchangeable ion.
**Schwarte,** *f.* rind, skin, crust, covering; scalp.
**schwarz,** *a.* black; dark, swarthy. — **— liegen,** (of beer, etc.) be settled, be clear. — **schwarzes Öl,** (*Petroleum*) blackstrap, also black oil. — **schwarzes Wasser,** (*Pharm.*) black mercurial lotion.
**Schwarz,** *n.* black; blackness. **-beere,** *f.* bilberry; elder(berry); melastoma. **-beize,** *f.* (*Dyeing*) black liquor, iron liquor.
**schwarzblau,** *a.* very dark blue.
**Schwarz-blech,** *n.* black plate (untinned iron plate). **-blei,** *n.* black lead (graphite). **-bleierz,** *n.* black lead spar (carboniferous cerussite).
**schwarzbraun,** *a.* very dark brown.
**Schwarz-braunstein,** *m.* psilomelane. **-brot,** *n.* black bread.
**schwarzbrüchig,** *a.* (*Metal.*) black-short.
**Schwarzdruck,** *m.* printing in black.
**Schwärze,** *f.* black; blacking; printer's ink; (*Founding*) black wash; blackness; swarthiness; smut.
**Schwarzeisen,** *n.* high-silicon pig iron.
**schwärzen,** *v.t.* blacken, black; darken.
**Schwarz-erde,** *f.* black earth, black soil. **-erz,**

*n.* tetrahedrite; stephanite. **-farbe,** *f.* black color. **-färber,** *m.* dyer in black.

**schwarzfarbig,** *a.* black-colored, black.

**Schwarz-färbung,** *f.* black coloration, blackening; dyeing black. **-fäule,** *f.* black rot.

**schwarz-gar,** *a.* black-tanned. **-gebrannt,** *p.a.* (*Metal.*) kishy. **-gelb,** *a.* very dark yellow, tawny. **-grau,** *a.* very dark gray. **-grün,** *a.* very dark green.

**Schwarz-gültigerz,** *n.* stephanite; polybasite. **-guss,** *m.* black malleable cast iron.

**schwarzheiss,** *a.* black-hot.

**Schwarz-kerntemperguss,** *m.* blackheart malleable cast iron. **-kohle,** *f.* black charcoal; black coal. **-kreide,** *f.* black chalk. **-kümmel,** *m.* nutmeg flower (*Nigella sativa*). **-kupfer,** *n.* black copper, coarse copper. **-kupfererz,** *m.* melaconite. **-lack,** *m.* black varnish. **-lauge,** *f.* black liquor.

**schwärzlich,** *a.* blackish.

**Schwarz-manganerz,** *n.* hausmannite. **-meer,** *n.* Black Sea. **-mehl,** *n.* dark-colored flour, esp. rye flour. **-öl,** *n.* black oil, specif. a dark, pasty, boiled linseed oil. **-pech,** *n.* black pitch, common pitch. **-pulver,** *n.* black powder.

**schwarzrot,** *a.* very dark red.

**Schwarz-schmelz,** *m.* black enamel. **-seher,** *m.* pessimist. **-senföl,** *n.* black-mustard oil. **-silbererz,** *n.*, **-silberglanz,** *m.* black silver (stephanite). **-spiessglanzerz,** *n.* bournonite. **-strahlen,** *m.pl.* black radiation.

**Schwärzung,** *f.* blackening; density.

**Schwarz-vitriol,** *m.* black vitriol (impure ferrous sulfate). **-werden,** *n.* blackening. **-wurz, -wurzel,** *f.* (*Pharm.*) symphytum; (**amerikanische**) baneberry root. **-zinkerz,** *n.* franklinite.

**Schwebe,** *f.* suspension; suspense; sling; suspender. **-fähigkeit,** *f.* floating power, buoyancy; suspension property. **-flora,** *f.* (*Biol.*) phytoplankton. **-körper,** *m.* suspended substance; floating body. **-methode,** *f.* suspension method.

**schweben,** *v.i.* hang, hover, float, be suspended, be pending. — **schwebend,** *p.a.* suspended, in suspension, hanging, floating; pending.

**Schwebe-stoff,** *m.* suspended substance (or matter). **-teilchen,** *n.* suspended particle. **-zustand,** *m.* state of suspension.

**Schwebstoff,** *m.* = Schwebestoff; (*Mil.*) nonpersistent chemical agent. **-filter,** *n.* filter for suspended material.

**Schwebung,** *f.* hanging, etc. (see schweben); (*Physics*) beat; surge.

**Schwebungstheorie,** *f.* beat theory.

**Schweden,** *n.* Sweden.

**Schweden-.** Swedish.

**schwedisch,** *a.* Swedish. — **schwedisches Grün,** Swedish green (Scheele's green). — **schwedisches Hölzchen,** *n.* safety match.

**Schwedisch, Schwedische,** *n.* Swedish (language).

**Schwed.P.,** *abbrev.* (schwedisches Patent) Swedish patent.

**schweel-.** see schwel-.

**Schwefel,** *m.* sulfur.

**Schwefel-.** of sulfur, sulfur, sulfuric, sulfide of, thio-, sulfo-. **-abdruck,** *m.* sulfur print. **-alkali,** *n.* alkali sulfide. **-alkohol,** *m.* sulfur alcohol, thiol; carbon disulfide (old name). **-ammonium, -ammon,** *n.* ammonium sulfide. **-antimon,** *n.* antimony sulfide. **-antimonblei,** *n.* antimony lead sulfide; (*Min.*) boulangerite.

**schwefel-antimonig,** *a.* thioantimonious. **-antimonsauer,** *a.* of or combined with thioantimonic acid, thioantimonate of.

**Schwefelantimonsäure,** *f.* thioantimonic acid.

**schwefelarm,** *a.* poor (or low) in sulfur.

**Schwefelarsen,** *n.* (any) arsenic sulfide.

**schwefelarsenig,** *a.* thioarsenious.

**Schwefelarsenik,** *n.* = Schwefelarsen. **-säure,** *f.* = Schwefelarsensäure. **-verbindung,** *f.* arsenic sulfide; sulfarsenide.

**Schwefel-arsensäure,** *f.* thioarsenic acid. **-art,** *f.* kind or variety of sulfur.

**schwefelartig,** *a.* sulfurous, sulfureous.

**Schwefel-äther,** *m.* sulfuric ether (ethyl ether). **-ausscheidung,** *f.* separation of sulfur. **-ausschlag,** *m.* sulfur bloom. **-bad,** *n.* sulfur bath. **-bakterien,** *f.pl.* sulfur bacteria.

**schwefelbar,** *a.* sulfurizable.

**Schwefel-baryum,** *n.* barium sulfide. **-bestimmung,** *f.* sulfur determination. **-blau,** *n.* sulfur blue. **-blausäure,** *f.* thiocyanic acid. **-blei,** *n.* lead sulfide. **-bleiche,** *f.* sulfur bleach. **-blumen, -blüten,** *f.pl.* flowers of sulfur. **-brennofen,** *m.* sulfur kiln. **-bromid,** *n.* sulfur bromide, specif. sulfur dibromide, $SBr_2$. **-bromür,** *n.* sulfur monobromide. **-brot,** *n.* loaf of sulfur. **-cadmium,** *n.* cadmium sulfide. **-calcium,** *n.* calcium sulfide. **-chlorid,** *n.* sulfur chloride, specif. sulfur dichloride, $SCl_2$. **-chlorür,** *n.* sulfur monochloride ($S_2Cl_2$). **-chrom,** *n.* chromium sulfide. **-cyan,** *n.* thiocyanogen; cyanogen sulfide.

**Schwefelcyan-.** thiocyanate of. **-ammonium,** *n.* ammonium thiocyanate. **-kali, -kalium,** *n.* potassium thiocyanate. **-metall,** *n.* metallic thiocyanate. **-säure,** *f.* thiocyanic acid.

**schwefelcyanwasserstoffsauer,** *a.* thiocyanate of.

**Schwefel-cyanwasserstoffsäure,** *f.* thiocyanic acid. **-dampf,** *m.* sulfur vapor. **-dioxyd,** *n.* sulfur dioxide. **-dunst,** *m.* sulfurous vapor.

**schwefelecht,** *a.* (*Dyeing*) fast to stoving, fast to sulfurous acid.

**Schwefel-einschlag,** *m.* sulfur match (for casks); sulfuring (of casks). **-eisen,** *n.* iron sulfide (usually ferrous sulfide, iron(II) sulfide). **-entfernung,** *f.* removal of sulfur, desulfurization. **-erz,** *n.* sulfur ore. **-faden,** *m.* sulfured wick, sulfur match. **-farbe,** *f.* sulfur color; sulfur dye; (of wool) stoved shade.

**schwefel-farben, -farbig,** *a.* sulfur-colored.

**Schwefel-farbstoff,** *m.* sulfur dye. **-form,** *f.* mold for sulfur, brimstone mold.

**schwefelfrei,** *a.* free from sulfur.

**Schwefel-gallium,** *n.* gallium sulfide. **-gehalt,** *m.* sulfur content.

**schwefelgelb,** *a.* sulfur-yellow, brimstone-yellow.

**Schwefel-gerbung,** *f.* sulfur tannage. **-germanium,** *n.* germanium sulfide. **-geruch,** *m.* sulfur odor.

**schwefelgesäuert,** *a.* treated with sulfuric acid, sulfated.

**Schwefel-gold,** *n.* gold sulfide. **-grube,** *f.* sulfur pit, sulfur mine. **-halogen,** *n.* sulfur halide.

**schwefelhaltig,** *a.* containing sulfur, sulfurous.

**Schwefel-harnstoff,** *m.* thiourea. **-hölzchen, -holz,** *n.* sulfur match. **-hütte,** *f.* sulfur refinery.

**schwefelig,** *a.* sulfurous.

**Schwefel-indium,** *n.* indium sulfide. **-jodür,** *n.* sulfur monoiodide. **-kadmium,** *n.* cadmium sulfide. **-kalium,** *n.* potassium sulfide. **-kalk,** *m.* lime-sulfur. **-kalkbrühe,** *f.* lime-sulfur mixture (for spraying). **-kalzium,** *n.* calcium sulfide. **-kammer,** *f.* sulfur chamber, sulfuring room, sulfur stove. **-karbolsäure,** *f.* sulfocarbolic acid. **-kastenbleiche,** *f.* (*Dyeing*) stoving.

**Schwefelkies,** *m.* iron pyrites. — **gemeiner —,** pyrite. — **prismatischer —,** marcasite.

**Schwefel-kobalt,** *m.* cobalt sulfide. **-kohle,** *f.* sulfurous coal, high-sulfur coal. **-kohlensäure,** *f.* sulfocarbonic acid (trithiocarbonic acid, $H_2CS_3$). **-kohlenstoff,** *m.* carbon disulfide. **-kolben,** *m.* retort for distilling sulfur. **-korn, -körnchen,** *n.* sulfur granule. **-kuchen,** *m.* cake of sulfur. **-kupfer,** *n.* copper sulfide. **-kupferoxydul,** *n.* cuprous sulfide, copper(I) sulfide. **-latwerge,** *f.* (*Pharm.*) confection of sulfur. **-läuterofen,** *m.* sulfur refining furnace. **-leber,** *f.* liver of sulfur, hepar. **-leinöl,** *n.* (*Pharm.*) balsam of sulfur. **-magnesium,** *n.* magnesium sulfide. **-mangan,** *n.* manganese sulfide. **-metall,** *n.* metallic sulfide. **-milch,** *f.* milk of sulfur. **-molybdän,** *n.* molybdenum sulfide.

**schwefein,** *v.t.* sulfurize, sulfurate, sulfur; vulcanize; (*Textiles*) stove; cure (hops). — **geschwefelter Alkohol,** thiol, thio alcohol, mercaptan. — **geschwefelter Äther,** thio ether, (organic) sulfide.

**Schwefel-natrium, -natron,** *n.* sodium sulfide. **-nickel,** *m.* nickel sulfide. **-niederschlag,** *m.* precipitate of sulfur, precipitated sulfur. **-ofen,** *m.* sulfur burner. **-oxyd,** *n.* (any) sulfur oxide. **-phosphor,** *m.* (any) phosphorus sulfide. **-probe,** *f.* sulfur sample or test. **-pulver,** *n.* powdered sulfur. **-quecksilber,** *n.* mercury sulfide. **-quelle,** *f.* sulfur spring. **-räucherung,** *f.* sulfur fumigation. **-rubin,** *m.* ruby sulfur, realgar. **-salz,** *n.* sulfur salt, thio salt, sulfo salt; sulfate.

**schwefelsauer,** *a.* of or combined with sulfuric acid, sulfate of. — **schwefelsaures Natrium,** sodium sulfate.

**Schwefelsäure,** *f.* sulfuric acid. **-anhydrid,** *n.* sulfuric anhydride, sulfur trioxide. **-ballon,** *m.* sulfuric acid carboy. **-bestimmung,** *f.* determination of sulfuric acid. **-chlorhydrin,** *n.* chlorosulfonic acid. **-fabrik,** *f.* sulfuric acid works. **-fabrikation,** *f.* manufacture of sulfuric acid. **-kammer,** *f.* sulfuric acid chamber. **-salz,** *n.* salt of sulfuric acid, sulfate.

**Schwefel-schlacke,** *f.* sulfur dross. **-schwarz,** *n.* sulfur black. **-seife,** *f.* sulfur soap. **-selen,** *n.* selenium sulfide; (*Min.*) selensulfur. **-silber,** *n.* silver sulfide. **-spiessglanz,** *m.*, **-spiessglanzerz,** *n.* stibnite. **-stange,** *f.* roll of sulfur. **-stickstoff,** *m.* nitrogen sulfide. **-stück,** *n.* piece of sulfur. **-thallium,** *n.* thallium sulfide. **-tonerde,** *f.* aluminum sulfide. **-tonung,** *f.* (*Photog.*) sulfide toning.

**Schwefelung,** *f.* sulfurization, sulfuring.

**Schwefelungsmittel,** *n.* sulfur(iz)ing agent.

**Schwefel-verbindung,** *f.* sulfur compound. **-wasser,** *n.* sulfur water.

**Schwefelwasserstoff,** *m.* hydrogen sulfide. **-rest,** *m.* mercapto group, sulfhydryl, SH. **-säure,** *f.* hydrosulfuric acid ($H_2S$). **-strom,** *m.* current of hydrogen sulfide. **-verbindung,** *f.* hydrosulfide.

**Schwefel-weinsäure,** *f.* sulphovinic acid (old name for ethylsulfuric acid). **-werk,** *n.* sulfur refinery. **-wismut,** *n.* bismuth sulfide. **-wurz,** *f.* brimstonewort. **-wurzel,** *f.* (*Pharm.*) peucedanum root, brimstonewort root. **-zink,** *m.* & *n.* zinc sulfide. **-zinkweiss,** *n.* a pigment containing chiefly zinc sulfide (lithopone, zincolith). **-zinn,** *n.* tin sulfide.

**Schwefelzyan-.** see Schwefelcyan-.

**schweflig,** *a.* sulfurous. — **schweflige Säure,** sulfurous acid.

**schwefligsauer,** *a.* of or combined with sulfurous acid, sulfite of.

**Schwefligsäure,** *f.* sulfurous acid. **-anhydrid,** *n.* sulfurous anhydride, sulfur dioxide. **-gas,** *n.* sulfur dioxide. **-wasser,** *n.* aqueous sulfurous acid.

**Schweif,** *m.* tail; train; warp (of fabrics).

**schweifen,** *v.t.* curve; chamfer; rinse; tail. — *v.i.* stray, ramble.
**Schweifstern,** *m.* comet.
**Schweifung,** *f.* curve, rounding, swell; slant.
**schweigen,** *v.i.* be silent, hush.
**Schweigen,** *n.* silence.
**schweigsam,** *a.* silent; taciturn, reserved.
**Schwein,** *n.* hog, pig, swine. **-brot,** *n.* sow bread (*Cyclamen europaeum*); = Erdbrot. **-chen,** *n.* weighing bottle with feet; little pig.
**Schweine-eisen,** *n.* pig iron. **-fett,** *n.* hog fat, lard. **-fleisch,** *n.* pork. **-pest,** *f.* hog cholera. **-schmalz, -schmer,** *n.* lard.
**Schweinfurtergrün,** *n.* Schweinfurt green, Paris green.
**Schweins-gummi,** *n.* hog gum. **-haut,** *f.* hogskin, pigskin. **-leder,** *n.* hogskin, pigskin (leather).
**Schweiss,** *m.* sweat, perspiration; suint, yolk (of wool).
**Schweiss-.** welding, weld; sweat, sweaty, sudorific. **-abgabe,** *f.* perspiration. **-apparat,** *m.* welding set. **-arbeit,** *f.* welding. **-asche,** *f.* suint ash (a source of potash). **-bad,** *n.* (*Wool*) degreasing bath.
**schweissbar,** *a.* weldable, welding.
**Schweissbarkeit,** *f.* weldability.
**schweissbefördernd,** *p.a.* sudorific, diaphoretic.
**Schweiss-bogen,** *m.* welding arc. **-brenner,** *m.* welding torch. **-drüse,** *f.* sweat gland.
**schweissecht,** *a.* fast to perspiration.
**Schweisseisen,** *n.* weld iron; wrought iron.
**schweissen,** *v.t.* weld; heat-seal, bond by heating. — *v.i.* begin to melt; (of liquids) leak.
**Schweissen,** *n.* welding.
**Schweisser,** *m.* welder.
**schweisserregend,** *p.a.* sudorific, diaphoretic.
**Schweiss-fehler,** *m.* defect in welding. **-flüssigkeit,** *f.* sweat. **-gang,** *m.* sweat duct. **-gehalt,** *m.* (*Wool*) suint content.
**schweiss-gewaschen,** *p.a.* (of wool) washed in the grease. **-härten,** *v.t.* (*Metal.*) weld-harden.
**Schweiss-hitze,** *f.* welding heat. **-loch,** *n.* sweat pore. **-metall,** *m.* welding metal; wrought iron. **-mittel,** *n.* sudorific, diaphoretic; welding agent, flux. **-naht,** *f.* weld seam. **-ofen,** *m.* welding furnace, reheating furnace. **-paste,** *f.* welding paste, flux. **-prozess,** *m.* welding process. **-pulver,** *n.* welding powder; diaphoretic powder. **-schlacke,** *f.* welding cinder. **-schmiedeeisen,** *n.* weld iron (as distinguished from weld steel). **-stahl,** *m.* weld steel. **-stelle,** *f.* place where metal is welded, shut.
**schweisstreibend,** *p.a.* sudorific, diaphoretic.
**Schweissung,** *f.* welding, weld.
**Schweiss-verfahren,** *n.* welding process. **-wachs,** *m.* wax from suint, yolk wax. **-walzen,** *f.pl.* roughing rolls.
**schweisswarm,** *a.* welding-hot.
**Schweiss-wärme,** *f.* welding heat. **-wasser,** *n.* water condensed on a surface. **-wolle,** *f.* wool containing suint, wool in the yolk.
**Schweiz,** *f.* Switzerland.
**Schweizer,** *m.* Swiss.
**schweizerisch,** *a.* Swiss.
**Schweizerkäse,** *m.* Swiss cheese, Gruyère cheese.
**Schwel-.** relating to low-temperature carbonization; smoldering. **-anlage,** *f.* low-temperature carbonizing plant.
**schwelbar,** *a.* suitable for low-temperature carbonization.
**schwelchen,** *v.t.* (Brewing) wither, air-dry.
**Schwelchmalz,** *n.* withered (air-dried) malt.
**schwelen,** *v. t. & i.* burn slowly, smolder, distil (or carbonize) at low temperature.
**Schweler,** *m.* low-temperature carbonizer.
**Schwelerei,** *f.* low-temperature carbonization process or plant.
**Schwelgas,** *n.* gas from low-temperature carbonization; producer gas; partially burned gas.
**schwelken,** *v.t.* = schwelchen.
**Schwelkerze,** *f.* (*Mil.*) smoke candle.
**Schwelkmalz,** *n.* = Swelchmalz.
**Schwel-kohle,** *f.* a kind of lignite rich in volatile matter (and hence suitable for carbonization). **-koks,** *m.* low-temperature coke.
**Schwell-.** swelling; (*Anat.*) erectile. **-äscher,** *m.* (*Leather*) fresh lime, white lime.
**schwellbar,** *a.* capable of swelling; (*Anat.*) erectile.
**Schwellbeize,** *f.* (*Leather*) swelling liquor.
**Schwelle,** *f.* sill, threshold; beam, sleeper, (railroad) tie; cross bar; swell; (*Geol.*) uplift.
**schwellen,** *v.t. & i.* swell, distend; (*Leather*) plump; increase.
**Schwellenwert,** *m.* threshold value, threshold; (*Photog.*) exposure factor.
**Schwell-farbe,** *f.* (*Leather*) plumping liquor. **-gewebe,** *n.* (*Anat.*) erectile tissue.
**schwellig,** *a.* threshold, liminal.
**Schwell-körper,** *m.* (*Anat.*) corpus cavernosum. **-kraft,** *f.* (*Leather*) plumping power. **-mittel,** *n.* (*Leather*) plumping agent.
**Schwellung,** *f.* swelling, tumefaction; (*Leather*) plumping.
**Schwellwert,** *m.* threshold value, threshold.
**Schwel-ofen,** *m.* low-temperature carbonizing furnace. **-raum,** *m.* carbonizing space or chamber. **-retorte,** *f.* retort for low-temperature distillation. **-teer,** *m.* tar from low-temperature carbonization. **-teeröl,** *n.* carbonization tar oil, esp. from lignite.

**Schwelung,** *f.* low-temperature carbonization; slow burning, smoldering.

**Schwel-vorgang,** *m.* low-temperature process of carbonization. **-wasser,** *n.* an aqueous liquid from the low-temperature carbonizing process, containing ammonia, phenols, etc.; foul water. **-werk,** *n.* low-temperature carbonization plant.

**Schwemmboden,** *m.* alluvial soil.

**Schwemme,** *f.* watering; watering place.

**schwemmen,** *v.t.* water; wash; flush; irrigate; float; deposit.

**Schwemm-land,** *n.* alluvial land. **-stein,** *m.* a kind of porous brick made from clay and gravel, porous concrete block; pumice stone. **-verfahren,** *n.* flotation process. **-wasser,** *n.* wash water; flushing water.

**Schwendung,** *f.* = Schwinden.

**Schwengel,** *m.* handle, bar, lever.

**schwenk-bar,** *a.* (*Mach.*) swinging, turning, swiveling, tilting. **-echt,** *a.* fast to rinsing or clearing.

**schwenken,** *v.t.* swing, wave; rinse; clear. — *v.i.* turn about, swing, swivel.

**Schwenkrohr,** *n.* swing pipe.

**Schwenkung,** *f.* swinging, etc. (see schwenken); deviation.

**schwer,** *a.* heavy; difficult, hard, severe, serious. — *adv.* heavily, difficultly, etc. — **schweres Weinöl,** heavy oil of wine.

**Schwer-benzin,** *n.* heavy gasoline (boiling over 100–120° C.), heavy petrol. **-benzol,** *n.* heavy benzol (boiling at about 160–200° C.). **-betrieb,** *m.* heavy operation, heavy duty. **-bleierz,** *n.* plattnerite.

**schwerbrennbar,** *a.* difficultly combustible, slow-burning.

**Schwerbrennbarkeit,** *f.* difficult combustibility.

**schwerdurchlässig,** *a.* difficultly permeable.

**Schwere,** *f.* heaviness, weight; gravity; difficulty, hardness. **-feld,** *n.* gravitational field. **-messer,** *m.* barometer.

**Schwererde,** *f.* heavy earth, baryta (BaO).

**schwererlöslich,** *a.* more difficultly soluble.

**schwer-fällig,** *a.* clumsy, heavy, dull, slack. **-flüchtig,** *a.* difficultly volatile.

**Schwerflüchtigkeit,** *f.* difficult volatility.

**schwerflüssig,** *a.* difficultly fusible, refractory; viscous.

**Schwer-flüssigkeit,** *f.* difficult fusibility, refractoriness. **-frucht,** *f.* heavy grain (as wheat, rye).

**schwergefrierbar,** *a.* difficultly freezable, low-freezing.

**Schwer-hörigkeit,** *f.* difficulty of hearing. **-industrie,** *f.* heavy industry. **-kraft,** *f.* force of gravity. **-kraftbeschleunigung,** *f.* acceleration of gravity. **-kraftfeld,** *n.* gravitational field. **-kraftstoff,** *m.* heavy fuel, specif. Diesel fuel. **-kraftwirkung,** *f.* action or effect of gravity.

**schwerl.,** *abbrev.* (schwerlöslich) difficultly soluble.

**Schwerleder,** *n.* sole leather.

**schwer-lich,** *adv.* hardly, scarcely, difficultly. **-löslich,** *a.* difficultly soluble.

**Schwer-löslichkeit,** *f.* difficult solubility. **-metall,** *n.* heavy metal. **-metallsalz,** *n.* salt of a heavy metal. **-mut,** *f.* melancholy. **-naphta,** *f.* heavy naphtha. **-öl,** *n.* heavy oil. **-petroleum,** *n.* heavy oil. **-punkt,** *m.* center of gravity, center of mass. **-punktssatz,** *m.* principle of the center of gravity.

**schwer-rostend,** *a.* rusting with difficulty, "rustproof." **-schmelzbar,** *a.* difficultly fusible. **-schmelzend,** *a.* fusing with difficulty.

**Schwerschwarz,** *n.* (*Dyeing*) weighted black.

**schwersiedend,** *a.* high-boiling.

**Schwer-spat,** *m.* heavy spar, barite. **-stein,** *m.* scheelite.

**Schwert,** *n.* sword.

**Schwertantalerz,** *n.* (*Min.*) tantalite.

**Schwert-kolben,** *m.* sausage flask (Anschütz distillation flask). **-lilie,** *f.* iris, fleur-de-lis.

**Schweruranerz,** *n.* (*Min.*) uraninite.

**schwerwiegend,** *p.a.* weighty, serious.

**Schwester,** *f.* sister; nurse.

**schwieg,** *pret.* (of schweigen) was silent.

**Schwiele,** *f.* callosity, callus; wale, welt.

**schwielig,** *a.* callous, horny; waled.

**schwierig,** *a.* hard, difficult; fastidious.

**Schwierigkeit,** *f.* difficulty, obstacle.

**schwiert,** *pr. 3 sing.* (of schwären) festers.

**schwillt,** *pr. 3 sing.* (of schwellen) swells, etc.

**Schwimm-äscher,** *m.* floating lime. **-aufbereitung,** *f.* (*Ores*) flotation. **-auftrieb,** *m.* buoyancy. **-badeseife,** *f.* floating bath soap. **-blase,** *f.* air bladder, sound. **-decke,** *f.* surface scum.

**schwimmen,** *v.i.* swim; float. — **schwimmend,** *p.a.* swimming, floating, supernatant.

**Schwimmer,** *m.* float; swimmer; pontoon. **-probe,** *f.* float test. **-ventil,** *n.* float valve.

**schwimmfähig,** *a.* buoyant; floatable.

**Schwimm-fähigkeit,** *f.* buoyancy; floatability. **-gerät,** *n.* (*Ores*) flotation apparatus. **-gerste,** *f.* (*Brewing*) float barley, skimmings. **-kiesel,** *m.* floatstone. **-körper,** *m.* swimming or floating body, float. **-kraft,** *f.* buoyancy. **-methode,** *f.* flotation method. **-sand,** *m.* quicksand. **-schlamm,** *m.* scum. **-stein,** *m.* floatstone. **-stoff,** *m.* floating material. **-verfahren,** *n.* (*Ores*) flotation process. **-vermögen,** *n.* floating power, buoyancy. **-ziegel,** *m.* floating brick.

**Schwindel,** *m.* vertigo; sell, swindle; kit, lot.

**schwindelhaft,** *a.* fraudulent, bogus; dizzy.

**Schwindelkorn,** *n.* cubeb; coriander seed.

**schwinden,** *v.i.* shrink, contract; dwindle, waste; atrophy; disappear, vanish.
**Schwinden,** *n.* shrinking, shrinkage, etc. (see schwinden).
**Schwind-mass,** *n.* amount of shrinkage, shrinkage; shrinkage gage. **-sucht,** *f.* consumption, phthisis.
**Schwindung,** *f.* = Schwinden.
**Schwindungs-fähigkeit,** *f.* tendency to shrink, property of shrinking. **-loch,** *n.* shrinkage cavity. **-riss,** *m.* shrinkage crack.
**Schwinge,** *f.* link; rocker arm; wing; swingle.
**Schwingelgras,** *n.* fescue grass, fescue.
**schwingen,** *v.i.* vibrate; swing, oscillate. — *v.t.* swing, wave; centrifuge; winnow; swingle. — **schwingend,** *p.a.* vibrating, vibratory, oscillating, oscillatory, swinging.
**Schwinger,** *m.* vibrator, oscillator.
**schwingfähig,** *a.* capable of vibrating, vibratory, oscillatory.
**Schwing-kreis,** *m.* oscillating circuit; circuit. **-kristall,** *m.* crystal oscillator. **-neigung,** *f.* oscillating tendency. **-rohr,** *n.* swing pipe. **-röhre,** *f.* oscillatory valve.
**Schwingung,** *f.* vibration; swinging, swing, oscillation.
**Schwingungs-bewegung,** *f.* vibratory (or oscillatory) motion. **-bogen,** *m.* arc of oscillation. **-dauer,** *f.* time of vibration. **-ebene,** *f.* plane of vibration. **-energie,** *f.* vibrational energy.
**schwingungsfähig,** *a.* capable of vibrating or oscillating.
**Schwingungsfestigkeit,** *f.* vibration strength, fatigue strength.
**schwingungsfrei,** *a.* vibrationless.
**Schwingungs-gleichung,** *f.* vibration equation. **-kreis,** *m.* (*Elec.*) oscillatory circuit. **-methode,** *f.* swing method. **-quantenzahl,** *f.* vibrational quantum number. **-schreiber,** *m.* oscillograph. **-weite,** *f.* amplitude of vibration. **-welle,** *f.* undulation, vibrational wave. **-zahl,** *f.* vibration number, vibration frequency. **-zeit,** *f.* time of vibration. **-zustand,** *m.* state of vibration or oscillation.
**Schwingweite,** *f.* amplitude of vibration.
**Schwingzahl,** *f.* = Schwingungszahl.
**schwirren,** *v.i.* whiz, whir, buzz, hum; whirl, swirl. — *v.t.* whiz, centrifuge.
**Schwitze,** *f.* sweat, sweating; (*Leather*) sweating room.
**schwitzen,** *v.i. & t.* sweat; leak.
**Schwitz-kammer,** *f.* sweating room, sweating stove. **-mittel,** *n.* sudorific, diaphoretic. **-öl,** *n.* (*Petroleum*) foots oil. **-pulver,** *n.* diaphoretic powder. **-röste,** *f.* steam retting. **-verfahren,** *n.* sweating process. **-wasser,** *n.* condensed moisture, sweat.
**Schwöde,** *f.* place where hides are limed; state of being limed. **-blei,** *m.* (*Leather*) lime cream. **-fass,** *n.* (*Leather*) lime vat, lime. **-grube,** *f.* (*Leather*) lime pit, lime. **-masse,** *f.* (*Leather*) lime cream.
**schwöden,** *v.t.* lime (hides).
**Schwodwasser,** *n.* lime water.
**schwoll,** *pret.* (of schwellen) swelled, etc.
**schwomm,** *pret.* (of schwimmen) swam, floated.
**schwor,** *pret.* (of schwären) festered; (of schwören) swore.
**schwören,** *v.t. & i.* swear.
**schwül,** *a.* sultry, close.
**Schwül,** *m.* concretion.
**Schwüle,** *f.* sultriness.
**Schwulst,** *m.* swelling, tumor.
**Schwund,** *m.* atrophy, withering, disappearance; shrinkage, contraction; (*Radio*) fading; wastage, leakage.
**Schwung,** *m.* vibration, oscillation, swing; soaring, flight; activity; momentum. **-bewegung,** *f.* vibratory motion. **-gewicht,** *n.* pendulum.
**schwunghaft,** *a.* swinging, soaring, lively.
**Schwung-kraft,** *f.* centrifugal force; vibrating power; liveliness. **-maschine,** *f.* centrifugal whirler. **-rad,** *n.* flywheel; balance wheel.
**schwur,** *pret.* = schwor.
**Schwur,** *m.* oath.
**schwürig,** *a.* suppurating.
**Schwz.P.,** *abbrev.* (schweizerisches Patent) Swiss patent.
**sd.,** *abbrev.* (siedend) boiling; (siedet) boils.
**Sd.,** *abbrev.* (Siedepunkt) boiling point.
**s.d.,** *abbrev.* (siehe dies) see this, which see, *q.v.;* (siehe dort) see there; (siehe den, siehe die, siehe das) see the.
**Sdp.,** *abbrev.* (Siedepunkt) boiling point.
**SE,** *abbrev.* (Siemens-Einheit) Siemens unit.
**Sebacinsäure, Sebazinsäure,** *f.* sebacic acid.
**secernieren,** *v.t.* secrete.
**sechs,** *a.* six.
**sechs-, Sechs-.** six-, hexa-, sex-, sexi-, sextuple.
**sechsatomig,** *a.* hexatomic.
**Sechseck,** *n.* hexagon.
**sechseckig,** *a.* hexagonal.
**Sechsergruppe,** *f.* group of six, 6-group.
**sechs-fach, -fältig,** *a.* sixfold, sextuple.
**Sechs-flach,** *n.*, **-flächner,** *m.* hexahedron.
**sechs-flächig,** *a.* hexahedral. **-gliedrig,** *a.* six-membered.
**Sechskant-.** hexagonal.
**sechskantig,** *a.* six-angled, hexagonal; six-edged.
**sechsmonatlich,** *a.* half-yearly, semi-annual.
**Sechsring,** *m.* six-membered ring.
**sechs-säurig,** *a.* hexacid. **-seitig,** *a.* six-sided, hexagonal.
**sechste,** *a.* sixth.
**Sechstel,** *n.* sixth.
**sechswertig,** *a.* sexivalent, hexavalent.

**Sechswertigkeit,** *f.* sexivalence.
**sechs-winklig,** *a.* six-angled, hexangular, hexagonal. **-zählig,** *a.* sixfold.
**sechzehn,** *a.* sixteen.
**Sechzehntel,** *n.* sixteenth.
**sechzig,** *a.* sixty.
**Sedanschwarz,** *n.* Sedan black.
**Sedativsalz,** *n.* sedative salt (old name for boric acid).
**sedimentär,** *a.* sedimentary.
**Sedimentgestein,** *n.* sedimentary rock.
**sedimentieren,** *v.i.* deposit sediment; settle out.
**Sediment-ieren,** *n.*, **-ierung,** *f.* sedimentation.
**See,** *f.* sea; lake. **-ablagerung,** *f.* sea (or lake) deposit. **-algen,** *f.pl.* marine algae. **-asphalt,** *m.* lake asphalt. **-bad,** *n.* seaside resort; sea bath. **-erz,** *m.* lake (iron) ore. **-flugzeug,** *n.* seaplane. **-gewächs,** *n.* sea plant, marine plant, seaweed.
**seegrün,** *a.* sea-green.
**See-höhe,** *f.* height above sea level. **-hund,** *m.* seal. **-hundsöl,** *n.*, **-hundstran,** *m.* seal oil. **-kabel,** *n.* submarine cable. **-kohl,** *m.* sea kale. **-krebs,** *m.* lobster.
**Seele,** *f.* soul; shaft (of a blast furnace); core (as of a rope or cable); bore (of a tube).
**Seelenruhe,** *f.* tranquillity; mental rest.
**See-licht,** *n.* marine phosphorescence. **-luft,** *f.* sea air. **-moos,** *n.* sea moss, carrageen. **-pflanze,** *f.* marine plant, sea plant. **-rose,** *f.* water lily (esp., *Nymphaea*). **-salz,** *n.* sea salt. **-sand,** *m.* sea sand. **-schlick,** *m.* sea ooze. **-seide,** *f.* sea silk (from algae); byssus silk. **-tang,** *m.* seaweed (esp., *Fucus*), sea tang. **-tier,** *n.* marine animal. **-wasser,** *n.* sea water.
**seewasserecht,** *a.* fast to sea water.
**Segel,** *n.* sail; fin; (*Anat.*) velum. **-flieger,** *m.* (*Aero.*) glider, sailplane. **-flug,** *m.* (*Aero.*) gliding. **-flugzeug,** *n.* (*Aero.*) glider, sailplane. **-tuch,** *n.* sailcloth, canvas, duck.
**Segen,** *m.* blessing, benediction; abundance, yield.
**Segerkegel,** *m.*, **Seger'scher Kegel.** Seger cone.
**Segge,** *f.* sedge (*Carex*).
**segmentförmig,** *a.* segmental.
**Segmentierung,** *f.* segmentation.
**segnen,** *v.t.* bless; cross.
**Seh-.** of sight, visual, optic, opto-.
**Sehe,** *f.* pupil (of the eye).
**sehen,** *v.t.* see. — *v.i.* see, look.
**Sehen,** *n.* seeing, sight, vision.
**Sehenswürdigkeit,** *f.* sight, spectacle, curiosity.
**Seher,** *m.* seer.
**Seh-feld,** *n.* field of vision, field of view. **-lehre,** *f.* optics. **-linse,** *f.* (*Anat.*) crystalline lens.
**Sehne,** *f.* sinew, tendon; string, cord; (*Metal.*) fiber; (*Geom.*) chord.
**Sehneisen,** *n.* fibrous iron.
**sehnen,** *v.r.* long, yearn.
**Sehnen-.** of a tendon, tendinous. **-schmiere,** *f.* (*Physiol.*) synovial fluid.
**Sehnepuddeln,** *n.* puddling of fibrous iron.
**Sehnerv,** *m.* optic nerve.
**sehnig,** *a.* tendinous, sinewy; (*Metal.*, etc.) fibrous.
**Sehnsucht,** *f.* longing, yearning, desire.
**Sehpurpur,** *m.* visual purple.
**sehr,** *adv.* very, very much, very well.
**Seh-rohr,** *n.* periscope; telescope; viewing tube. **-schärfe,** *f.* sharpness of vision. **-weite,** *f.* visual range or distance. **-zelle,** *f.* visual cell.
**sei,** *pr. subj.* (of sein) may be, let be.
**seicht,** *a.* shallow; low, flat.
**Seide,** *f.* silk.
**Seidel,** *n.* pint, half-liter; tankard (for beer). **-bast,** *m.* mezereon (*Daphne mezereum*).
**seiden,** *a.* silk, silken.
**Seidenabfall,** *m.* silk waste, waste silk.
**seiden-ähnlich,** *a.* silk-like, silky. **-artig,** *a.* silky.
**Seiden-asbest,** *m.* silky asbestos. **-bast,** *m.* tussah silk; sericin. **-bau,** *m.* silk culture, sericulture. **-beschwerung, -erschwerung,** *f.* silk weighting. **-fabrik,** *f.* silk mill. **-faden,** *m.* silk thread; silk fiber, silk filament. **-faserstoff,** *m.*, **-fibrin,** *n.* fibroin. **-flor,** *m.* silk gauze. **-florsieb.** *n.* sieve of silk gauze. **-garn,** *n.* silk yarn, spun silk. **-glanz,** *m.* silky luster.
**seidenglänzend,** *a.* of silky luster, silky.
**Seiden-grün,** *n.* silk green. **-holz,** *n.* satinwood. **-krep(p)papier,** *n.* creped tissue paper. **-leim,** *m.* silk glue, sericin. **-papier,** *n.* tissue paper. **-raupe,** *f.* silkworm. **-raupenzucht,** *f.* sericulture. **-schrei,** *m.* scroop of silk. **-stoff,** *m.* silk cloth. **-substanz,** *f.* fibroin.
**seidig,** *a.* silky.
**Seidlitz-pulver,** *n.* Seidlitz powder. **-salz,** *n.* Epsom salt.
**seiend,** *p.pr.* (of sein) being.
**Seife,** *f.* soap; alluvial ore, placer.
**seifecht,** *a.* fast to soaping.
**seifen,** *v.t.* soap, lather; wash, scour; (*Mining*) wash.
**Seifen-abfälle,** *m.pl.* soap scraps, soap waste. **-ansatz,** *m.* soap stock.
**seifenartig,** *a.* soapy, saponaceous.
**Seifen-asche,** *f.* soap ashes. **-bad,** *n.* soap bath. **-balsam,** *m.* soap liniment, opodeldoc. **-baum,** *m.* soapbark tree, quillai. **-baumrinde,** *f.* soapbark, quillai bark. **-bereitung,** *f.* soap making. **-bildung,** *f.* formation of soap, saponification. **-blase,** *f.* soap bubble. **-brühe,** *f.* soap suds.
**seifenecht,** *a.* fast to soaping.
**Seifen-erde,** *f.* fuller's earth; marl; sapona-

ceous clay. **-ersatz,** *m.*, **-ersatzmittel,** *n.* soap substitute. **-erz,** *n.* alluvial ore. **-fabrik,** *f.* soap factory, soap works. **-fabrikant,** *m.* soap maker. **-fabrikation,** *f.* soap making or manufacture. **-farbe,** *f.* soap color, soap dye. **-flocken,** *f.pl.* soap flakes. **-form,** *f.* soap frame. **-füllung,** *f.* soap filling. **-gold,** *n.* placer gold.

**seifenhaltig,** *a.* containing soap, saponaceous.

**Seifen-industrie,** *f.* soap industry. **-kessel,** *m.* soap boiler.

**seifenkochecht,** *a.* fast to boiling with soap.

**Seifen-kocher,** *m.* soap boiler. **-kraut,** *n.* soap plant, soap weed. **-krem,** *m.* soap cream. **-lauge,** *f.* soap solution, soap suds. **-leim,** *m.* soap glue, soap paste; (*Paper*) soap size. **-lösung,** *f.* soap solution. **-pflaster,** *n.* soap plaster. **-platte,** *f.* soap slab. **-probe,** *f.* soap test; sample of soap. **-pulver,** *n.* soap powder. **-riegel,** *m.* bar of soap, soap bar. **-rinde,** *f.* soapbark. **-rückstand,** *m.* soap residue. **-schabsel,** *n.* soap scraps. **-schaum,** *m.* lather. **-schmiere,** *f.* (*Leather*) soap stuffing. **-sieder,** *m.* soap boiler. **-siederasche,** *f.* soap ashes. **-siederei,** *f.* soap works. **-siederlauge,** *f.* soap boiler's lye. **-späne,** *m.pl.* soap chips. **-spiritus,** *m.* spirit of soap (alcoholic soap solution). **-stein,** *m.* soapstone, steatite; caustic soda. **-stoff,** *m.* saponin. **-tafel,** *f.* slab of soap. **-täfelchen,** *n.* cake or tablet of soap. **-teig,** *m.* soap paste. **-ton,** *m.* fuller's earth; saponaceous clay. **-wäsche,** *f.* (*Textiles*) soap wash. **-wasser,** *n.* soap suds, soap water. **-wurzel,** *f.* soapwort; soaproot. **-zinn,** *n.* stream tin.

**seifig,** *a.* soapy, saponaceous.

**seiger,** *a.* perpendicular, vertical.

**Seiger-arbeit,** *f.* (*Metal.*) liquation, liquation process. **-blei,** *n.* liquation lead. **-dörner,** *m.pl.* liquation dross.

**seigergerade,** *a.* perpendicular.

**Seiger-herd,** *m.* liquation hearth. **-hütte,** *f.* liquation works.

**seigern,** *v.t.* (*Metal.*) liquate. — *v.i.* segregate.

**Seiger-ofen,** *m.* liquation furnace. **-pfanne,** *f.* liquation pan. **-riss,** *m.* vertical section. **-rückstand,** *m.* liquation residue. **-schlacke,** *f.* liquation slag. **-stück,** *n.* liquation cake.

**Seigerung,** *f.* liquation; segregation.

**Seigerwerk,** *n.* liquation works.

**Seignettesalz,** *n.* Seignette salt (Rochelle salt, sodium potassium tartrate).

**Seihe,** *f.* strainer, filter; (*Brewing*) spent malt. **-beutel,** *m.* filtering bag. **-boden,** *m.* strainer bottom, perforated bottom. **-fass,** *n.* filtering cask or tub. **-gefäss,** *n.* straining vessel, filtering vessel. **-löffel,** *m.* straining ladle, strainer.

**seihen,** *v.t.* strain, filter, sieve, percolate.

**Seihepapier,** *n.* filter paper.

**Seiher,** *m.* strainer, filter, screen.

**Seihe-rahmen,** *m.* filtering frame. **-sack,** *m.* filtering bag. **-stein,** *m.* filtering stone. **-trichter,** *m.* straining funnel, strainer. **-tuch,** *n.* straining cloth, filtering cloth. **-vermögen,** *n.* straining power, filtering power.

**Seihgefäss,** etc. = Seihegefäss, etc.

**Seil,** *n.* rope, cable, cord, line.

**Seiler,** *m.* rope maker. **-waren,** *f.pl.* cordage.

**Seil-faser,** *n.* rope fiber, cordage fiber. **-öl,** *n.* cordage oil. **-schmiere,** *f.* rope lubricant, rope grease.

**Seim,** *m.* glutinous liquid; strained honey.

**seimen,** *v.i.* yield a glutinous liquid. — *v.t.* strain (as barley water).

**seimig,** *a.* glutinous, mucilaginous.

**sein,** *v.i.* be. — *pron.* his, its.

**Sein,** *n.* being, existence.

**seiner,** *pron.* of him, of it, his, its. **-seits,** *adv.* for his part. **-zeit,** *adv.* in his or its time, at that time.

**seinige,** *pron.* his, his own.

**seismisch,** *a.* seismic.

**seit,** *prep. & conj.* since. — **— kurzem,** recently, lately. — **— langem,** this long time, for a long time.

**seitdem,** *adv.* since then, ever since. — *conj.* since.

**Seite,** *f.* side; face (of a solid); page (of a book).

**Seiten-.** side, lateral. **-achse,** *f.* lateral axis. **-anmerkung,** *f.* marginal note. **-ansatz,** *m.* side attachment, side arm, side tube, etc. **-ansicht,** *f.* side view, profile. **-arm,** *m.* side arm; side tube; side branch. **-bewegung,** *f.* lateral motion. **-destillat,** *n.* side stream, side cut. **-druck,** *m.* lateral pressure. **-eck,** *n.*, **-ecke,** *f.* lateral summit. **-fläche,** *f.* lateral face; flat side, facet.

**seitengleich,** *a.* alike on both sides, reversible.

**Seiten-gummi,** *n.* side wall (of a rubber tire). **-isomerie,** *f.* chain isomerism. **-kante,** *f.* lateral edge. **-kette,** *f.* side chain. **-kettenisomerie,** *f.* side-chain isomerism. **-kraft,** *f.* component force, component. **-lage,** *f.* lateral position. **-länge,** *f.* length of a side, lateral length. **-riss,** *m.* side elevation. **-rohr,** *n.*, **-röhre,** *f.* side tube, branch tube, branch pipe.

**seitens,** *adv.* on behalf (of), on the part (of).

**seitenständig,** *a.* lateral.

**Seiten-strahlung,** *f.* secondary (or lateral) radiation. **-stück,** *n.* sidepiece; counterpart. **-wand,** *f.* side wall; side plate. **-zahl,** *f.* page number; number of pages; folio.

**seither,** *adv.* since then; till now.

**-seitig.** -sided, -lateral.

**seit-lich,** *a.* side, lateral; collateral. — *adv.* at the side, laterally. **-wärts,** *adv.* sideways; laterally; aside.
**Sekante,** *f.* secant.
**Sekret,** *n.* secretion; privy.
**sekretionshemmend,** *a.* checking secretion.
**sekretorisch,** *a.* secretory.
**Sekret-präparat,** *n.* preparation from a secretion. **-stoff,** *m.* secreted substance.
**Sekt,** *m.* champagne; dry wine.
**Sektion,** *f.* section; (*Med.*) dissection.
**Sektwein,** *m.* dry wine.
**sekundär,** *a.* secondary.
**Sekundär-farbe,** *f.* secondary color. **-kreis,** *m.* (*Elec.*) secondary circuit. **-strahlung,** *f.* secondary radiation. **-strom,** *m.* secondary current.
**Sekunde,** *f.* second.
**Sekundenuhr,** *f.* watch (or clock) with a seconds hand.
**sekundlich,** *a.* per second.
**selb,** *a.* same.
**selber,** *pron.* self.
**selbgleich,** *a.* identical.
**selbst,** *pron.* self, myself, himself, etc. — *adv.* even.
**Selbst-.** self-, automatic, spontaneous, auto-.
**selbstabdichtend,** *a.* self-sealing.
**Selbstachtung,** *f.* self-respect, self-esteem.
**selbständig,** *a.* independent, self-dependent; spontaneous.
**Selbständigkeit,** *f.* independence, self-reliance.
**Selbst-ansteckung,** *f.* self-infection. **-befruchtung,** *f.* self-fertilization. **-beherrschung,** *f.* self-control. **-bestäubung,** *f.* (*Bot.*) self-pollination.
**selbstbewusst,** *p.a.* self-conscious; conceited.
**Selbst-binder,** *m.* (*Varnish*) self-binder. **-biographie,** *f.* autobiography.
**selbstdichtend,** *a.* self-sealing.
**Selbstdiffusion,** *f.* self-diffusion, autodiffusion.
**selbstemulgierend,** *a.* self-emulsifying.
**selbstentzünd-bar, -lich,** *a.* spontaneously (in)-flammable.
**Selbst-entzündlichkeit,** *f.* spontaneous (in)-flammability. **-entzündung,** *f.* spontaneous ignition. **-erhitzung,** *f.* self-heating.
**selbsterregend,** *p.a.* self-exciting.
**Selbst-erwärmung,** *f.* spontaneous heating. **-erzeugung,** *f.* spontaneous generation, autogenesis. **-farbe,** *f.* self color, solid color.
**selbstfarbig,** *a.* self-colored, of a single color.
**Selbst-gang,** *m.* automatic action. **-gärung,** *f.* spontaneous fermentation. **-gefühl,** *n.* self-consciousness; self-confidence.
**selbst-gehend,** *a.* automatic; (of ore) self-fluxing. **-gemacht,** *p.a.* self-made; homemade.
**Selbstgift,** *n.* autotoxin.
**selbsthärtend,** *a.* self-hardening.
**Selbsthärter,** *m.* self-hardener, specif. self-hardening steel.
**selbsthemmend,** *a.* irreversible; self-stopping; self-locking.
**Selbst-induktivität,** *f.* self-inductance. **-kante,** *f.* selvage, list.
**selbstklebend,** *a.* self-adhesive.
**Selbst-kosten,** *f.pl.* cost of production, prime cost. **-kühlung,** *f.* self-cooling, natural cooling. **-laut, -lauter,** *m.* vowel.
**selbstleuchtend,** *a.* self-luminous.
**Selbstleuchter,** *m.* phosphorescent substance, phosphor.
**selbstlos,** *a.* unselfish, selfless.
**Selbst-löschung,** *f.* (of lime) spontaneous slaking. **-lötung,** *f.* autogenic soldering. **-oxydation,** *f.* autoxidation, self-oxidation.
**selbstpolymerisieren,** *v.t.* & *i.* autopolymerize.
**Selbstpolymerisierung,** *f.* autopolymerization.
**selbst-redend,** *p.a.* self-evident. **-registrierend,** *a.* self-recording. **-reglend,** *a.* self-regulating; automatic.
**Selbstreinigung,** *f.* self-purification, autopurification.
**selbstschmierend,** *a.* self-lubricating.
**Selbstschmierung,** *f.* self-lubrication.
**selbstschreibend,** *a.* self-registering, recording.
**Selbst-schreiber,** *m.* recording instrument or device. **-schrift,** *f.* autograph. **-schutzmittel,** *n.* prophylactic.
**selbstständig,** *a.* = selbständig.
**Selbststrahlung,** *f.* self-emission (of rays), spontaneous radiation.
**selbsttätig,** *a.* self-acting, automatic; (of flour) self-rising.
**Selbstteilung,** *f.* spontaneous division.
**selbsttonend,** *a.* (*Photog.*) self-toning.
**Selbst-umkehr,** *f.* self-reversal (as of a spectral line). **-unterbrecher,** *m.* (*Elec.*) automatic interrupter. **-verbrennung,** *f.* spontaneous combustion. **-verdauung,** *f.* autodigestion; autolysis. **-vergiftung,** *f.* autointoxication.
**selbst-verständlich,** *a.* self-evident. — *adv.* of course. **-vulkanisierend,** *a.* self-vulcanizing. **-wirkend,** *p.a.* self-acting, automatic.
**Selbst-zersetzung,** *f.* spontaneous decomposition; autolysis. **-zerstörung,** *f.* self-destruction. **-zeugung,** *f.* spontaneous generation, abiogenesis.
**selbstzündend,** *a.* self-igniting, pyrophoric.
**Selbst-zünder,** *m.* pyrophorus; self-igniter, automatic lighter. **-zündung,** *f.* spontaneous ignition.
**Selbung,** *f.* automatization.
**Selektivität,** *f.* selectivity.
**Selen,** *n.* selenium.
**Selen-.** selenium, selenic, selenide of, seleno-. **-ammonium,** *n.* ammonium selenide. **-äthyl,** *n.* ethyl selenide. **-blei,** *n.* lead selenide.

**-bleisilber,** *n.* (*Min.*) naumannite. **-bleiwismutglanz,** *m.* galenobismuthite. **-brücke,** *f.* selenium bridge. **-chlorid,** *n.* selenium chloride, specif. selenium tetrachloride. **-chlorür,** *n.* selenium monochloride ($Se_2Cl_2$). **-cyanid,** *n.* selenium cyanide; selenocyanate. **-cyankalium,** *n.* potassium selenocyanate. **-cyansäure,** *f.* selenocyanic acid. **-eisen,** *n.* ferrous selenide, iron(II) selenide (FeSe). **-erz,** *n.* selenium ore. **-halogen,** *n.* selenium halide.

**selenhaltig,** *a.* containing selenium, seleniferous.

**Selen-harnstoff,** *m.* selenourea. **-hydrat,** *n.* hydroselenide.

**Selenid,** *n.* selenide, specif. -ic selenide (cf. Selenür).

**selenig,** *a.* selenious. — **selenige Säure,** selenious acid.

**selenigsauer,** *a.* of or combined with selenious acid, selenite of.

**Selenigsäure,** *f.* selenious acid. **-anhydrid,** *n.* selenious anhydride ($SeO_2$).

**Selen-kupfer,** *n.* copper selenide. **-kupfersilber,** *n.* copper silver selenide; (*Min.*) eucairite. **-metall,** *n.* metallic selenide.

**Selenocyan,** *n.* selenocyanogen.

**Selen-oxyd,** *n.* selenium oxide. **-quecksilber,** *n.* mercury selenide. **-quecksilberblei,** *n.* (*Min.*) lehrbachite. **-salz,** *n.* selenide.

**selensauer,** *a.* of or combined with selenic acid, selenate of.

**Selen-säure,** *f.* selenic acid. **-säureanhydrid,** *n.* selenic anhydride ($SeO_3$). **-schlamm,** *m.* selenium mud, selenium slime (seleniferous deposit in sulfuric acid works). **-schwefel,** *m.* (*Min.*) selensulfur. **-schwefelkohlenstoff,** *m.* carbon sulfide selenide, CSSe. **-silber,** *n.* silver selenide. **-silberglanz,** *m.* naumannite.

**Selenür,** *n.* (lower or -ous) selenide.

**Selen-verbindung,** *f.* selenium compound. **-wasserstoff,** *m.* hydrogen selenide. **-wasserstoffsäure,** *f.* hydroselenic acid. **-wismutglanz,** *m.* guanajuatite. **-zelle,** *f.* selenium cell. **-zyanid,** *n.* selenium cyanide; selenocyanate. **-zyankalium,** *n.* potassium selenocyanate.

**Seifbogen,** *m.* (*Elec.*) flashover.

**selig,** *a.* blessed; happy; late, deceased.

**seligieren,** *v.t.* select.

**Sellerie,** *m.& f.* celery.

**selten,** *a.* rare, scarce, unusual. — *adv.* seldom, rarely. — **seltene Erde,** rare earth.

**Seltenheit,** *f.* rareness, rarity, scarcity.

**Selterswasser,** *n.* Seltzer water, seltzer.

**seltsam,** *a.* singular, strange, curious, odd.

**Selzerbrunnen,** *m.* Seltzer water.

**Semichrom-gerbung,** *f.* semichrome tanning. **-leder,** *n.* semichrome leather.

**semicyclisch,** *a.* semicyclic.

**Semidinumlagerung,** *f.* semidine rearrangement.

**semimer,** *a.* semimeric.

**Semmel,** *f.* roll (the bread). **-mehl,** *n.* flour for rolls; ground rolls.

**senden,** *v.t. & i.* send.

**Sendung,** *f.* sending; shipment; parcel; mission.

**Senegalgummi,** *n.* Senegal gum.

**Senegawurzel,** *f.* senega root.

**Senf,** *m.* mustard. **-gas,** *n.* mustard gas. **-geist,** *m.* (volatile) oil of mustard. **-korn,** *n.* mustard seed. **-mehl,** *n.* ground mustard. **-öl,** *n.* mustard oil; isothiocyanate, specif. allyl isothiocyanate. **-ölessigsäure,** *f.* (*lit.*, mustard-oil-acetic-acid) 2, 4-thiazoledione. **-pulver,** *n.* ground mustard. **-same,** *m.* mustard seed.

**sengen,** *v.t.* singe; flame; scorch, parch.

**senkbar,** *a.* sinkable; depressable.

**Senk-blei,** *n.* plumb bob; plumb line; sounding lead. **-boden,** *m.* (*Brewing*) false bottom, strainer. **-bombe,** *f.* depth bomb, depth charge.

**Senke,** *f.* depression; declivity.

**Senkel,** *m.* plummet; (shoe) lace.

**senken,** *v.t.* sink, submerge; lower, depress. — *v.r.* sink, subside, settle; sag, slope.

**Senk-grube,** *f.* cesspool; sump; catch basin. **-körper,** *m.* sinker, bob. **-küpe,** *f.* (*Textiles*) dipping frame. **-loch,** *n.* sink hole; catch basin; drain. **-lot,** *n.* plumb bob, plummet.

**senkrecht,** *a.* perpendicular, vertical, normal.

**Senkrechte,** *f.* perpendicular, normal.

**Senkspindel,** *f.* specific-gravity spindle, hydrometer.

**Senkung,** *f.* sinking, lowering, subsiding; inclination, incline, dip; hollow, depression.

**Senk-wa(a)ge,** *f.* = Senkspindel; plumb rule. **-zylinder,** *m.* separating cylinder.

**Sennes-blätter,** *n.pl.* senna leaves, senna. **-strauch,** *m.* senna (the herb).

**Sense,** *f.* scythe.

**sensibel,** *a.* sensitive, sensible; sensory.

**Sensibilisator,** *m.* sensitizer.

**sensibilisieren,** *v.t.* sensitize.

**Sensibilisierung,** *f.* sensitization.

**Sensibilisierungs-farbstoff,** *m.* sensitizing dye. **-mittel,** *n.* sensitizing agent.

**Sensibilität,** *f.* sensibility, sensitiveness.

**separat,** *a.* separate, detached.

**Separat-abdruck, -druck,** *m.* separate impression, reprint, preprint.

**separieren,** *v.t. & r.* separate.

**Separiertrichter,** *m.* separatory funnel.

**sepiabraun,** *a.* sepia-brown.

**Septikämie,** *f.* septicemia.

**Septikopyämie,** *f.* septicopyemia.

**septisch,** *a.* septic.

**Seren,** *n.pl.* serums, sera.

**Serie,** *f.* series.
**Serien-bad,** *n.* series bath; series tank. **-fabrikation,** *f.* mass production.
**serienfremd,** *a.* of another series, of different series.
**Seriengrenze,** *f.* series limit.
**serienmässig,** *a. & adv.* in a series, in series; (of production) mass, quantity.
**Serien-nummer,** *f.* serial number. **-schaltung,** *f.* (*Elec.*) series connection. **-schnitt,** *m.* serial section. **-spektrum,** *n.* series spectrum. **-versuch,** *m.* serial experiment or test.
**Serizin,** *n.* sericin.
**Serizitisierung,** *f.* (*Petrog.*) sericitization.
**serologisch,** *a.* serological.
**serös,** *a.* serous.
**serpentinieren,** *v.i.* wind, meander.
**Serum-eiweiss,** *n.* serum albumin; serum protein. **-krankheit,** *f.* serum sickness.
**Serviette,** *f.* napkin.
**Sesam-.** sesame; (*Anat.*) sesamoid.
**Sesam,** *m.* sesame. **-knorpel,** *m.* sesamoid cartilage. **-kuchen,** *m.* sesame (oil) cake. **-öl,** *n.* sesame oil. **-saat,** *f.* sesame seed.
**Sesquioxyd,** *n.* sesquioxide.
**Sessel,** *m.* easy chair, stool, seat.
**sesshaft,** *a.* resident, settled; stationary; persistent (as a war gas); sedentary.
**Sesshaftigkeit,** *f.* (of war gases) persistency.
**Setz-arbeit,** *f.* settling; (of ore) jigging. **-bottich,** *m.* settling vat or tank.
**setzen,** *v.t.* set, put, place; apply; plant; jig, sieve (ore); wager. — *v.r.* settle, precipitate, be deposited; sink, subside; sit down. — *v.i* run, leap, cross. — **gesetzt,** *p.a.* set, etc.; settled, steady, serious; supposing, assuming.
**Setzenlassen,** *n.* settling, allowing to settle.
**Setzer,** *m.* compositor; setter; tamper. **-fehler,** *m.* compositor's error.
**Setz-fehler,** *m.* compositor's error. **-kasten,** *m.* settling tank; type case. **-phiole,** *f.* (flat-bottomed) vial. **-sieb,** *n.* jig(ging) screen, jig(ging) sieve. **-zapfen,** *m.* suppository.
**Seuche,** *f.* contagious or infectious disease, pestilence, epidemic.
**seuchen-artig,** *a.* contagious, infectious, epidemic. **-fest,** *a.* immune. **-haft,** *a.* = seuchenartig.
**Seven-baum,** *m.*, **-kraut,** *n.* savin. **-krautöl,** *n.* savin oil.
**Sexualzelle,** *f.* (*Biol.*) germ cell.
**sexuell,** *a.* sexual.
**sezernieren,** *v.t.* secrete.
**sezieren,** *v.t.* dissect.
**S-förmig,** *a.* S-shaped.
**s.g.,** *abbrev.* (sogenannt) so-called.
**Sg.,** *abbrev.* (Streckung) stretching, spread.
**s.G.,** *abbrev.* (spezifisches Gewicht) specific gravity, sp. gr.
**sherardisieren,** *v.t.* (*Metal.*) sherardize.
**Shikimisäure,** *f.* shikimic acid.
**Shorehärte,** *f.* Shore hardness.
**siamesisch,** *a.* Siamese, Siam.
**sibirisch,** *a.* Siberian.
**Siccativ,** *n.* siccative, drier. (For compounds see Sikkativ-.)
**sich,** *pron.* oneself, himself, herself, itself, themselves; each other, one another.
**Sichel,** *f.* sickle; crescent.
**sichelförmig,** *a.* crescent-shaped.
**sicher,** *a.* safe, secure, certain, sure, reliable. — **— stellen,** make safe, secure, ensure, guarantee.
**Sicherheit,** *f.* safety, security, certainty.
**Sicherheits-brennstoff,** *m.* safety fuel. **-farbe,** *f.* (*Mil.*) safety paint. **-flasche,** *f.* safety bottle or flask. **-glas,** *n.* safety glass. **-grad,** *m.* degree of safety; safety factor. **-koeffizient,** *m.* factor of safety. **-kraftstoff,** *m.* safety fuel. **-lampe,** *f.* safety lamp. **-massregel,** *f.* safety measure, precaution. **-nadel,** *f.* safety pin. **-papier,** *n.* safety paper. **-rohr,** *n.*, **-röhre,** *f.* safety tube. **-sprengstoff,** *m.* safety explosive. **-trichterrohr,** *n.* safety tube. **-ventil,** *n.* safety valve. **-vorrichtung,** *f.* safety device. **-waschflasche,** *f.* safety wash bottle. **-wasserbad,** *n.* safety water bath. **-wert,** *m.*, **-zahl,** *f.* factor of safety. **-zünder,** *m.* safety fuse. **-zündhölzchen,** *n.* safety match.
**sichern,** *v.t.* secure, ensure, guarantee, check, block. — **gesichert,** *p.a.* secured; guaranteed; safe, certain.
**Sicherstellung,** *f.* securing, security, guarantee warrant.
**Sicherung,** *f.* securing, security; security (or securing) device, safety device, as an electric fuse or cut-out.
**Sicherungs-.** safety, security; (*Elec.*) fuse. **-körper,** *m.* (*Elec.*) fuse holder. **-patrone,** *f.* (*Elec.*) fuse cartridge. **-stöpsel,** *m.* safety plug, fuse plug.
**Sicht,** *f.* sight; visibility.
**sichtbar,** *a.* visible; evident.
**Sichtbar-keit,** *f.* visibility; obviousness. **-machung,** *f.* rendering visible, visualizing; revealing; (*Photog.*) developing. **-werden,** *n.* becoming visible.
**sichten,** *v.t.* sift, screen; sort, classify; bolt (flour).
**Sichter,** *m.* sifter, sorter, separator.
**sichtlich,** *a.* visible; evident.
**Sichtschmierapparat,** *m.* sight-feed lubricator.
**Sichtung,** *f.* sifting, etc. (see sichten).
**sicilianisch,** *a.* Sicilian.
**Sicke,** *f.* seam, edge, crease, corrugation.
**Sicker-kühlung,** *f.* trickle cooling. **-laugung,** *f.* leaching, lixiviation.
**sickern,** *v.i.* trickle, ooze, percolate.

**Sicker-tank,** *m.* percolating tank. **-wasser,** *n.* ground water; infiltrated water, percolating water.
**Sideringelb,** *n.* siderin yellow.
**siderophil,** *a.* (*Petrog.*) siderophilic.
**sie,** *pron.* she, her, it, they, them.
**Sie,** *pron.* you.
**Sieb,** *n.* sieve; screen, riddle, bolter, strainer; (for rays) filter; mesh. **-analyse,** *f.* screen analysis.
**siebartig,** *a.* sieve-like, full of holes.
**Sieb-aufsatz,** *m.* (on a burner) gauze top. **-boden,** *m.* bottom of a sieve; perforated bottom. **-brille,** *f.* goggles with gauze frame. **-draht,** *m.* sieve wire, screen wire. **-durchfall, -durchgang,** *m.* material that has passed thru a sieve or screen. **-einsatz,** *m.* strainer.
**sieben,** *a.* seven. — *v.t.* sift, sieve; riddle, screen, bolt; filter (rays). **-atomig,** *a.* heptatomic. **-eckig,** *a.* heptagonal. **-fach,** *a.* seven times, sevenfold. **-flächig,** *a.* heptahedral. **-gliedrig,** *a.* seven-membered.
**Siebenring,** *m.* seven-membered ring.
**siebent,** *a.* seventh.
**siebenwertig,** *a.* septivalent, heptavalent.
**Siebenwertigkeit,** *f.* septivalence.
**Sieberei,** *f.* sifting, screening; sifting or screening plant.
**Sieb-feines,** *n.* siftings, screenings. **-feinheit,** *f.* fineness of sieve or screen, mesh. **-fläche,** *f.* screen area.
**siebförmig,** *a.* sieve-shaped, sieve-like.
**Sieb-klassierung,** *f.* screen sizing or classifying. **-koks,** *m.* screened coke. **-korb,** *m.* wire basket, wire strainer. **-kurve,** *f.* screen-analysis curve. **-leistung,** *f.* screen output, screening capacity. **-maschine,** *f.* sifting machine, screening machine. **-mehl,** *n.* coarse flour; siftings. **-mittel,** *n.* filtering medium or material. **-platte,** *f.* sieve plate; filter plate. **-probe,** *f.* screening test, sieve test. **-rost,** *m.* sieve grating, mesh grating. **-rückstand,** *m.* screenings. **-satz,** *m.* set of sieves. **-schale,** *f.* dish with perforated bottom. **-schleuder,** *f.* centrifugal sifter. **-sel,** *n.* siftings. **-skala,** *f.* mesh gage. **-staub,** *m.* siftings. **-struktur,** *f.* (*Petrog.*) sieve texture. **-trichter,** *m.* strainer funnel, filter funnel. **-trommel,** *f.* screening drum, revolving screen. **-tuch,** *n.* bolting cloth.
**Siebung,** *f.* sifting, etc. (see sieben, *v.t.*).
**Sieb-walze,** *f.* (*Paper*) dandy roll. **-wasser,** *n.* (*Paper*) back water. **-weite,** *f.* mesh size (width); width of sieve or screen.
**siebzehn,** *a.* seventeen.
**siebzehnt,** *a.* seventeenth.
**siebzig,** *a.* seventy.
**Siebzylinder,** *n.* cylindrical sieve, sieve drum.
**siech,** *a.* sick, sickly, infirm.
**Siechheit,** *f.*, **Siechtum,** *n.* sickliness, (chronic) ill health.
**sied.,** *abbrev.* (siedend) boiling.
**Siede,** *f.* chopped straw; chaff; mash.
**Siede-.** boiling; distilling, distillation. **-abfälle,** *m.pl.* scum or sediment from boiling. **-analyse,** *f.* analysis by fractional distillation. **-apparat,** *m.* boiling (or boiling-point) apparatus. **-beginn,** *m.* beginning of boiling; initial boiling point. **-bereich,** *m.* boiling range. **-blech,** *n.* boiling plate. **-erleichterer,** *m.* aid to boiling (promoter of bubble formation). **-flüssigkeit,** *f.* boiling liquid; (*Metal.*) blanching liquid. **-gefäss,** *n.* boiling vessel, boiler; distillation flask. **-grad,** *m.* boiling point. **-grenze,** *f.* boiling limit, boiling range. **-haus,** *n.* boiling house, boilery. **-hitze,** *f.* boiling heat. **-kessel,** *m.* boiling vessel, boiling pan, boiler. **-kolben,** *m.* boiling flask; distillation flask. **-kühlung,** *f.* vapor cooling. **-kurve,** *f.* boiling-point curve. **-lauge,** *f.* boiling lye, boiling liquor. **-linie,** *f.* boiling-point curve. **-messer,** *m.* boiling-point instrument.
**sieden,** *v.t.* & *i.* boil; brew (beer); distil.
**Sieden,** *n.* boiling, ebullition. **-lassen,** *n.* allowing to boil.
**Siedeofen,** *m.* (*Metal.*) blanching furnace.
**Siedep.,** *abbrev.* (Siedepunkt) boiling point.
**Siedepfanne,** *f.* boiling pan, evaporating pan.
**Siedepunkt,** *m.* boiling point. **-bestimmung,** *f.* boiling-point determination. **-(s)erhöhung,** *f.* boiling-point elevation.
**Sieder,** *m.* boiler.
**Siederei,** *f.* boilery, boiling room or house; (*Sugar*) refinery.
**Siede-rohr,** *n.*, **-röhre,** *f.* boiling tube, distilling tube; boiler tube. **-röhrchen,** *n.* small boiling (or distilling) tube. **-salz,** *n.* common salt. **-sole,** *f.* brine. **-stein,** *m.*, **-steinchen,** *n.* boiling stone (or other object to facilitate boiling). **-temperatur,** *f.* boiling temperature. **-trennung,** *f.* distillation; fractionation (by distillation). **-verzug,** *m.* delay in boiling. **-zeit,** *f.* boiling period or time.
**Sied-kessel,** *m.* = Siedekessel. **-kolben,** *m.* boiling flask.
**Sieg,** *m.* victory.
**Siegel,** *n.* seal. **-erde,** *f.* terra sigillata (Lemnian earth). **-lack,** *m.* & *n.* sealing wax. **-wachs,** *n.* soft sealing wax.
**siegen,** *v.i.* be victorious, triumph, conquer.
**sieht,** *pr. 3 sing.* (of sehen) sees; looks.
**Sieke,** *f.* seam, edge, crease, corrugation.
**sieken,** *v.t.* crease, seam.
**Siel,** *m.* & *n.* sluice; sewer, drain. **-wasser,** *n.* effluent; sewage.
**Sienaerde,** *f.* sienna.
**Sigel, -zeichen,** *n.* sign, symbol.

**Signal-bombe,** *f.* (*Mil.*) signal flare. **-emaille-lack,** *m.* signal enamel. **-farbe,** *f.* signal color; signal paint. **-geschoss,** *n.*, **-granate,** *f.* (*Mil.*) star shell. **-lampenöl,** *n.* signal oil. **-mittel,** *n.* signaling device or material. **-patrone,** *f.* signal cartridge. **-rakete,** *f.* signal rocket.

**signalrot,** *a.* bright red, vermilion.

**Signatur,** *f.* signature; mark, stamp, brand.

**signieren,** *v.t.* sign; mark, brand.

**Signier-farbe,** *f.* marking color, marking ink. **-tinte,** *f.* marking ink.

**Signum,** *n.* sign, mark, brand.

**Sikkativ,** *n.* siccative, drier. **-firnis,** *m.* siccative varnish. **-mittel,** *n.* siccative, drier. **-pulver,** *n.* drying powder, specif. manganese borate.

**Silbe,** *f.* syllable.

**Silber,** *n.* silver.

**silber-arm,** *a.* poor (or low) in silver. **-artig,** *a.* silvery, argentine.

**Silber-ätzstein,** *m.* lunar caustic (silver nitrate). **-azetat,** *n.* silver acetate. **-bad,** *n.* silver bath. **-baum,** *m.* silver tree, arbor Dianae. **-belag,** *m.*, **-belegung,** *f.* silver coating. **-blatt,** *n.* silver leaf, silver foil. **-blech,** *n.* silver foil, (thin) silver plate. **-blei,** *n.* crude lead (containing silver). **-blende,** *f.* pyrargyrite; proustite. **-blick,** *m.* brightening or fulguration of silver, silver "blick." **-brennen,** *n.* silver refining. **-brennherd,** *m.* silver-refining hearth. **-bromid,** *n.* silver bromide. **-bromür,** *n.* silver subbromide. **-chlorid,** *n.* silver chloride. **-chlorür,** *n.* silver subchloride. **-draht,** *m.* silver wire, silver thread. **-erz,** *n.* silver ore. **-essigsalz,** *n.* silver acetate. **-fahlerz,** *n.* argentiferous tetrahedrite. **-fällung,** *f.* precipitation of silver. **-farbe,** *f.* silver color, silver.

**silber-farben, -farbig,** *a.* silver-colored, silvery.

**Silber-fluorür,** *n.* silver subfluoride. **-folie,** *f.* silver foil.

**silberführend,** *a.* silver-bearing, argentiferous.

**Silber-gare,** *f.* silver refining. **-gehalt,** *m.* silver content. **-gewinnung,** *f.* extraction of silver. **-glanz,** *m.* silvery luster; silver glance, argentite.

**silberglänzend,** *p.a.* silvery.

**Silber-glas, -glaserz,** *n.* argentite. **-glätte,** *f.* litharge. **-glimmer,** *m.* common mica, muscovite. **-gold,** *n.* argentiferous gold, electrum.

**silbergrau,** *a.* silver-gray.

**Silber-grube,** *f.* silver mine. **-halogen,** *n.* silver halide.

**silber-haltig,** *a.* containing silver, argentiferous. **-hell,** *a.* silver-bright; silvery.

**Silber-hornerz,** *n.* horn silver, cerargyrite. **-hütte,** *f.* silver foundry, silver works.

**silberig,** *a.* silvery.

**Silber-jodid,** *n.* silver iodide. **-jodür,** *n.* silver subiodide. **-kies,** *m.* sternbergite. **-korn,** *n.* silver grain, silver bead. **-körper,** *m.* (*Colloids*) "silver body" (silver ion). **-kupferglanz,** *m.* stromeyerite. **-lack,** *m.* silver enamel, silver varnish. **-lauge,** *f.* silver solution. **-laugerei,** *f.* silver-leaching plant. **-legierung,** *f.* silver alloy. **-lösung,** *f.* silver solution. **-lot,** *n.* silver solder. **-metall,** *n.* silver metal, metallic silver. **-münze,** *f.* silver coin.

**silbern,** *a.* silver.

**Silber-niederschlag,** *m.* silver precipitate. **-nitrat,** *n.* silver nitrate.

**Silberoxyd,** *n.* silver oxide. **-ammoniak,** *n.* fulminating silver. **-salz,** *n.* silver oxysalt.

**Silber-oxydul,** *n.* silver suboxide. **-oxydverbindung,** *f.* compound of silver oxide; specif., argentate. **-papier,** *n.* silver paper, silvered paper.

**silberplattiert,** *p.a.* silver-plated.

**Silber-plattierung,** *f.* silver plating. **-probe,** *f.* test for silver, silver assay. **-protein,** *n.* (*Pharm.*) silver protein.

**silberreich,** *a.* rich in silver.

**Silber-rhodanid,** *n.* silver thiocyanate. **-salbe,** *f.* (*Pharm.*) colloid silver ointment. **-salpeter,** *m.* silver nitrate. **-salz,** *n.* silver salt. **-sau,** *f.* silver ingot. **-schaum,** *m.* silver in thin leaves, or an imitation of it. **-scheidung,** *f.* separation of silver; silver refining. **-schein,** *m.* silvery luster. **-schicht,** *f.* layer of silver; silver film or coating. **-schlaglot,** *n.* silver solder. **-schwärze,** *f.* earthy argentite.

**silberschweflig,** *a.* argentosulfurous.

**Silber-spat,** *m.* cerargyrite. **-spiegel,** *m.* silver mirror. **-spiessglanz,** *m.* antimonial silver, dyscrasite. **-stahl,** *m.* silver steel. **-tanne,** *f.* silver fir. **-tiegel,** *m.* silver crucible. **-überzug,** *m.* silver coating. **-vitriol,** *m.* silver sulfate. **-waren,** *f.pl.* silverware. **-wasser,** *n.* nitric acid (for dissolving silver).

**silberweiss,** *a.* silver-white.

**Silber-weiss,** *n.* silver white. **-wismutglanz,** *m.* matildite. **-zyanid,** *n.* silver cyanide.

**Silicierung,** *f.* silication; silicification.

**Silicium,** *n.* silicon.

**Silicium-.** silicon, silico-, silicide of. **-ameisensäure,** *f.* silicoformic acid (HSiOOH, existence unconfirmed).

**siliciumarm,** *a.* poor (or low) in silicon.

**Silicium-äthan,** *n.* silicoethane (methylsilane, $CH_3SiH_3$, or disilane, $SiH_3SiH_3$). **-bromid,** *n.* silicon bromide. **-chlorid,** *n.* silicon chloride. **-chloroform,** *n.* silicochloroform (trichlorosilane). **-eisen,** *n.* iron silicide; (*Metal.*) ferrosilicon. **-fluorid,** *n.* silicofluoride (fluosilicate); silicon fluoride. **-fluorverbindung,** *f.* fluosilicate.

**Siliciumfluorwasserstoff,** *m.*, **-säure,** *f.* fluosilicic acid. **-salz,** *n.* fluosilicate.
**siliciumfrei,** *a.* silicon-free.
**Siliciumgehalt,** *m.* silicon content.
**siliciumhaltig,** *a.* containing silicon, siliceous.
**Silicium-jodid,** *n.* silicon iodide. **-karbid,** *n.*, **-kohlenstoff,** *m.* silicon carbide. **-kupfer,** *n.* copper silicide; (*Metal.*) cuprosilicon. **-legierung,** *f.* silicon alloy. **-magnesium,** *n.* magnesium silicide. **-metall,** *n.* metallic silicide. **-methan,** *n.* silicomethane (silicon tetrahydride, silane). **-oxalsäure,** *f.* silicoöxalic acid. **-oxyd,** *n.* silicon dioxide. **-oxydhydrat,** *n.* hydrated oxide of silicon (silicic acid).
**siliciumreich,** *a.* rich (or high) in silicon.
**Silicium-spiegel,** *m.* siliceous ferromanganese, ferrosilicomanganese, silicospiegel. **-stahl,** *m.* silicon steel. **-tetrahydrür,** *n.* silicon tetrahydride, silane. **-verbindung,** *f.* silicon compound. **-wasserstoff,** *m.* hydrogen silicide, silicon hydride.
**Silicon,** *n.* silicone.
**silifiziert,** *a.* silicified, siliceous.
**Silika-gel,** *n.* silica gel. **-stein,** *m.* silica brick.
**Silikat,** *n.* silicate. **-emaille,** *f.* silicate enamel. **-gestein,** *m.* silicate rock.
**silikat-haltig,** *a.* containing silicate. **-isch,** *a.* of silicate nature.
**Silikat-schmelzfluss,** *m.* silicate melt. **-schmelzlösung,** *f.* silicate-melt solution. **-stein,** *m.* silica brick.
**Silikaziegel,** *m.* silica brick.
**Siliko-ameisensäure,** *f.* = Siliciumameisensäure. **-äthan,** *n.* = Siliciumäthan. **-essigsäure,** *f.* silicoacetic acid (methanesiliconic acid).
**Silikon,** *n.* silicone.
**Silikose,** *f.* silicosis.
**Silikospiegel,** *m.* = Siliciumspiegel.
**Silizid,** *n.* silicide.
**silizieren,** *v.t.* siliconize.
**Silizierung,** *f.* siliconizing.
**Silizium,** *n.* silicon (for compounds see Silicium-).
**Silkin,** *n.* nitrate rayon. *T.N.*
**Silo,** *n.* silo; bin, bunker.
**Simmerring,** *m.* sealing ring; oil seal. *T.N.*
**simpel,** *a.* simple.
**Sims,** *m.* molding; shelf; ledge; cornice.
**simulieren,** *v.t. & i.* simulate, sham, feign.
**simultan,** *a.* simultaneous.
**Sinapinsäure,** *f.* sinapic acid.
**sind,** *pr. 1 & 3 pl.* (of sein) are; have.
**singen,** *v. t. & i.* sing.
**Singrün,** *n.* periwinkle, myrtle (*Vinca*).
**singulär,** *a.* singular.
**Singularität** *f.* singularity.
**Singulett,** *n.* singlet.
**Singulosilikat,** *n.* monosilicate.
**sinken,** *v.i.* sink, fall, subside, drop.
**Sink-körper,** *m.* sinker. **-stoff,** *m.* deposited substance or matter, sediment, settlings; suspended matter.
**Sinn,** *m.* sense; direction; mind; inclination, feeling; taste. **-bild,** *n.* symbol, emblem.
**sinnen,** *v.i.* meditate, speculate, think. — **gesinnt,** *p.a.* minded, disposed. — **gesonnen sein,** be inclined, intend.
**Sinnen-.** of the senses, sensory, sensual. **-welt,** *f.* external world.
**Sinnes-.** of sense, sensory; of mind, mental. **-werkzeug,** *n.* organ of sense.
**sinnfällig,** *a.* obvious.
**Sinngedicht,** *n.* epigram.
**sinn-gemäss,** *a.* corresponding, analogous; rational, logical. — *adv.* accordingly. **-getreu,** *a.* faithful (translation). **-gleich,** *a.* synonymous.
**Sinngrün,** *n.* periwinkle, myrtle (*Vinca*).
**sinn-ig,** *a.* sensible; thoughtful; ingenious; pretty. **-lich,** *a.* sentient, sensitive, sensuous, sensual. **-los,** *a.* senseless.
**Sinnpflanze,** *f.* sensitive plant.
**sinnreich,** *a.* ingenious; witty.
**Sinnspruch,** *m.* maxim, motto, sentiment.
**sinn-verwandt,** *p.a* synonymous. **-voll,** *a.* meaningful, significant. **-widrig,** *a.* unmeaning, illogical, absurd.
**sinopische Erde.** (*Min.*) sinopite.
**Sinter,** *m.* iron dross, cinder; sinter. **-erzeugnis,** *n.* sintered product, agglomerate. **-gut,** *n.* sintered material. **-kohle,** *f.* sintering coal, sinter coal. **-kuchen,** *m.* sinter cake, agglomerate. **-metallurgie,** *f.* powder metallurgy.
**sintern,** *v.i.* sinter; trickle, drip, drop; form sinter; form clinker or slag; (*Ceram.*) vitrify. — *v.t.* sinter, frit.
**Sinter-ofen,** *m.* sintering furnace. **-prozess,** *m.* (*Metal.*) slag process. **-quarz,** *m.* siliceous sinter. **-röstung,** *f.* sinter roasting. **-schlacke,** *f.* clinker. **-stein,** *m.* sinter brick.
**Sinterung,** *f.* sintering, etc. (see sintern).
**Sinterungshitze,** *f.* sintering heat.
**Sinter-vorgang,** *m.* sintering process; (*Metal.*) slag process. **-wasser,** *n.* (*Min.*) water impregnated with mineral matter so as to be capable of forming sinter.
**Sinus,** *m.* (*Math.*) sine; (*Anat.*) sinus.
**sinus-ähnlich,** *a.* sinus-like, sinusoidal. **-förmig,** *a.* sinus-shaped, sinusoidal.
**Sinus-kurve, -linie,** *f.* sine curve.
**sinuskurvenartig,** *a.* sinusoidal.
**siphonieren,** *v.t.* siphon.
**Sippe,** *f.* kin, kindred; sib; set, lot; (*Biol.*) tribe.
**Sippschaft,** *f.* kinship; kindred; set, lot.
**sirupartig,** *a.* sirupy.

**Sirup-dichte, -dicke,** *f.* sirupy consistency.
**sirup-dick,** *a.* thick like sirup, sirupy. **-haltig,** *a.* containing sirup, sirupy. **-ös,** *a.* sirupy.
**Siruppfanne,** *f.* sirup pan.
**Sisalhanf,** *m.* sisal hemp, sisal.
**sistieren,** *v.i.* end, finish, stop.
**Sitte,** *f.* habit, custom, usage, practice; (*pl.*) manners, morals.
**Sittenlehre,** *f.* ethics.
**sittlich,** *a.* moral.
**Sittlichkeit,** *f.* morality, morals.
**Sitz,** *m.* seat; fit; site.
**Sitz., Sitzber.,** *abbrev.* (Sitzungsberichte) proceedings.
**sitzen,** *v.i.* sit; stay; rest; dwell; (of clothes) fit. — **— bleiben,** remain in the same place or status; stick fast. — **sitzend,** *p.a.* sitting; fixed; sedentary; (*Bot.*) sessile.
**Sitzfläche,** *f.* (*Mach.*) seating.
**Sitzung,** *f.* sitting, session, meeting.
**Sitzungsberichte,** *m.pl.* reports of sessions, proceedings (of a society).
**sizilianisch,** *a.* Sicilian.
**S.K.,** *abbrev.* (Seger-Kegel) Seger cone.
**Skala,** *f.* scale; dial. **-lineal,** *n.* graduated rule, lineal scale. **-scheibe,** *f.* graduated disk or dial.
**Skale,** *f.* scale.
**Skalen-ablesung,** *f.* scale reading. **-aräometer,** *n.* graduated hydrometer. **-einteilung,** *f.* scale graduation. **-intervall,** *n.* scale interval, scale division.
**Skalenoeder,** *n.* scalenohedron.
**skalenoedrisch,** *a.* scalenohedral.
**Skalen-rohr,** *n.* scale tube (as of a spectroscope). **-scheibe,** *f.* dial face, dial. **-teil,** *m.*, **-teilung,** *f.* scale division or graduation.
**Skammoniaharz, Skammonienharz, Skammonium,** *n.* scammony resin, scammony.
**skandinavisch,** *a.* Scandinavian.
**Skapolith,** *m.* scapolite.
**Skarifikator,** *m.* scarifier.
**Skelett,** *n.* skeleton.
**Skizze,** *f.* sketch, draft.
**skizzieren,** *v.t.* sketch, draft.
**Sklave,** *m.* slave.
**sklavisch,** *a.* slavish.
**Sklerenchym,** *n.* (*Biol.*) sclerenchyma.
**sklerosieren,** *v.i.* become indurated, harden.
**Skleroskophärte,** *f.* scleroscope hardness.
**Skonto,** *m.* discount.
**Skorbut,** *m.* scurvy.
**Skorie,** *f.* scoria, dross, slag, cinder.
**Skrofel,** *f.* scrofula.
**skrofulös,** *a.* scrofulous.
**Sliwowitz, Slibowitz,** *m.* a kind of spirit made from plums.
**sll.,** *abbrev.* (sehr leicht löslich) very readily soluble.
**Slowakei,** *f.* Slovakia.
**Sm.,** *abbrev.* (Schmelzpunkt) melting point.
**S.M.,** *abbrev.* (Seine Majestät) His Majesty.
**Smalte,** *f.* smalt.
**Smaragd,** *m.* emerald.
**smaragd-farben,** *a.* emerald. **-grün,** *a.* emerald-green, emerald.
**Smaragd-grün,** *n.* Guignet's green. **-malachit,** *m.* euchroite. **-spat,** *m.* green feldspar, amazonite.
**Smekalsprung,** *m.* Smekal transition.
**Smirgel,** *m.* emery. See Schmirgel-.
**SMK,** *abbrev.* (Sekunden-Meter-Kerze) meter-candle-second.
**SM-Stahl,** *m.* Siemens-Martin steel, open-hearth steel.
**so,** *adv.* so, thus. — *conj.* so, then. — **— ein guter,** such a good; **— etwas,** such a thing; **— . . . wie,** as . . . as; **— viel,** so far as; **— . . . auch,** however.
**s.o.,** *abbrev.* (siehe oben) see above, *vide supra.*
**sobald,** *conj.* as soon as.
**Societät,** *f.* society, company, partnership.
**Sockel,** *m.* base; pedestal; socket.
**socken,** *v.i.* crystallize out; (of metals) contract.
**Sod,** *m.* boiling; bubbling up; brew; broth.
**Soda,** *f.* soda (usually, neutral sodium carbonate; cf. Natron). — **kaustische —,** caustic soda.
**sodaalkalisch,** *a.* alkaline with soda.
**Soda-asche,** *f.* soda ash. **-auszug,** *m.* soda extraction or extract. **-bad,** *n.* soda bath. **-blau,** *n.* ultramarine (made with soda). **-fabrik,** *f.* soda factory, alkali works. **-fabrikation,** *f.* manufacture of soda.
**sodafest,** *a.* fast to soda, sodaproof.
**Sodagehalt,** *m.* soda content.
**sodahaltig,** *a.* containing soda.
**Sodakochchlorbleiche,** *f.* boiling soda-chlorine bleach.
**sodakochecht,** *a.* fast to boiling soda.
**Soda-kristalle,** *m.pl.* soda crystals, sal soda. **-küpe,** *f.* soda vat. **-lauge,** *f.* soda lye.
**sodalkalisch,** *a.* alkaline with soda.
**Soda-lösung,** *f.* soda solution. **-mehl,** *n.* (*Soda*) sodium carbonate monohydrate in the form of powder. **-menge,** *f.* amount of soda.
**sodann,** *adv.* then.
**Soda-ofen,** *m.* soda furnace, black-ash furnace. **-rückstände,** *m.pl.* soda residues, tank waste (in the Leblanc process). **-salz,** *n.* soda salt (sodium salt), specif. sodium carbonate. **-schmelze,** *f.* black ash. **-see,** *m.* soda lake. **-seife,** *f.* soda soap. **-stein,** *m.* caustic soda. **-wasser,** *n.* soda water. **-zahl,** *f.* soda number.
**Sodbrennen,** *n.* heartburn.
**Sode,** *f.* salt works; salt making; sod.

**Sodenbrot,** *n.* carob bean, St.-John's-bread.
**sodieren,** *v.t.* treat or wash with soda.
**soeben,** *adv.* just, just now.
**sof.,** *abbrev.* (sofort) immediately; (sofortig) immediate; (sofern) so far as.
**sofern,** *conj.* so far as, inasmuch as.
**sofort,** *adv.* immediately, at once.
**sofortig,** *a.* immediate, instantaneous.
**sog,** *pret.* (of saugen) sucked, sucked up.
**Sog,** *m.* suction; wake (of a boat, etc.).
**sog.,** *abbrev.* (sogenannt) so-called.
**sogar,** *adv.* even.
**sogen.,** *abbrev.* of sogenannt.
**sogenannt,** *p.a.* so-called.
**soggen,** *v.i.* crystallize out. — *v.t.* precipitate in the form of crystals, salt down.
**Soggenpfanne,** *f.* crystallizing pan.
**Sogge-pfanne,** *f.* crystallizing pan. **-salz,** *n.* common salt.
**sogleich,** *adv.* at once.
**Sohlband,** *n.* (*Mining*) matrix, gang(ue).
**Sohle,** *f.* sole, bottom, floor, bed, base.
**Sohlenleder,** *n.* sole leather.
**Sohlfläche,** *f.* bottom surface.
**söhlig,** *a.* horizontal.
**Sohl-leder,** *n.* sole leather. **-platte,** *f.* base plate, bottom plate.
**Sohn,** *m.* son.
**Soja,** *f.* soy (the sauce); soybean. **-bohne,** *f.* soybean, soja bean. **-bohnenöl,** *n.* soy(bean) oil. **-kuchen,** *m.* soy(bean) cake. **-öl,** *n.* soy(bean) oil.
**Sol-.** brine, salt-water.
**solange,** *conj.* as long as.
**Solaröl,** *n.* solar oil.
**Sol-bad,** *n.* brine bath, salt-water bath. **-behälter,** *m.* brine cistern. **-bohrloch,** *n.*, **-brunnen,** *m.* salt well.
**solch, solcher,** *pron.* such, such a. — **solche die,** such as.
**Sold,** *m.* pay.
**Soldat,** *m.* soldier; (temporary) prop.
**Sole,** *f.* brine, salt water; salt spring. **-bereiter,** *m.* brine mixer. **-eindampfer,** *m.* brine concentrator. **-erzeuger,** *m.* brine mixer.
**Solenhofener,** *a.* of Solenhofen, hence, lithographic. — **— Platte (Schiefer, Stein),** lithographic stone.
**Solfass,** *n.* brine tub.
**sölig,** *a.* level, horizontal.
**Solinglas,** *n.* crown glass.
**Soll,** *n.* debit.
**Soll-.** (what should be), calculated, estimated, theoretical, ideal, standard, rated, correct, predetermined, prescribed, desired.
**sollen,** *v.i.* shall; be, be destined, be supposed; should, ought.
**Soll-gewicht,** *n.* standard weight; theoretical weight. **-mass,** *n.* theoretical dimension. **-wert,** *m.* theoretical value, rated value.
**Solorinsäure,** *f.* solorinic acid.
**Solorsäure,** *f.* soloric acid.
**Sol-pfanne,** *f.* brine pan. **-quelle,** *f.* brine spring, salt well. **-salz,** *n.* spring salt, well salt; brine salt.
**Solubilisator,** *m.* solubilizer.
**Solvayverfahren,** *n.* Solvay process.
**Solvens,** *n.* solvent.
**Solventnaphta,** *f.* solvent naphtha.
**Solvenzien,** *n.pl.* solvents.
**solvieren,** *v.t.* dissolve. — **solvierend,** *p.a.* solvent, dissolving.
**Sol-wa(a)ge,** *f.* brine gage, salimeter. **-wasser,** *n.* brine, salt water.
**somit,** *adv.* therefore, consequently, so.
**Sommer,** *m.* summer. **-benzin,** *n.* summer gasoline or petrol. **-flecken,** *m.* freckle. **-getreide,** *n.* summer cereals.
**sommergrün,** *a.* deciduous.
**Sommerweizen,** *m.* spring wheat.
**sonach,** *adv.* accordingly, so.
**Sonde,** *f.* sound, probe; sonde; (*Med.*) bougie; plummet; riser (vertical pipe); boring, well, pit.
**Sonder-.** separate, special, peculiar, exclusive, exceptional. **-abdruck,** *m.* separate impression, reprint, separate. **-ausgabe,** *f.* separate edition.
**sonderbar,** *a.* strange, singular.
**Sonder-blatt,** *n.* extra leaf, extra page. **-fall,** *m.* special case; exceptional case.
**sondergleichen,** *a.* unequaled.
**Sondergusseisen,** *n.* special cast iron.
**sonderlich,** *a.* special, particular.
**Sondermethode,** *f.* special method.
**sondern,** *v.t.* separate; sever; segregate; sort (ore, etc.). — *conj.* but.
**sonders,** *adv.* separately.
**Sonder-schrift,** *f.* separate or special work or treatise. **-stahl,** *m.* special steel. **-stellung,** *f.* separate or special position.
**Sonderung,** *f.* separation, etc. (see sondern).
**Sonder-verfahren,** *n.* special process. **-werk,** *n* special work, special treatise. **-zweck,** *m.* special purpose, special object.
**sondieren,** *v.t.* probe; sound; try.
**Sonne,** *f.* sun.
**Sonnen-.** of the sun, sun, solar, helio-. **-auge,** *n.* adularia. **-bahn,** *f.* ecliptic. **-belichtung,** *f.* exposure to sunlight, solar irradiation, insolation.
**sonnenbeständig,** *a.* fast to sunlight.
**Sonnen-bestrahlung,** *f.* = Sonnenbelichtung. **-bleiche,** *f.* sun bleach. **-blume,** *f.* sunflower; heliotrope. **-blumenöl,** *n.* sunflower oil. **-brand,** *m.* sunburn; sunscald. **-brenner,** *m.* floodlight; lamp cluster. **-distel,** *f.* carline

thistle (*Carlina*). **-finsternis,** *f.* solar eclipse. **-fleck,** *m.* sun spot. **-gas,** *n.* helium. **-geflecht,** *n.* solar plexus. **-gelb,** *n.* sun yellow.

**sonnen-getrocknet,** *a.* sun-dried. **-haft,** *a.* sunny, radiant.

**Sonnen-hitze,** *f.* solar heat. **-licht,** *n.* sunlight. **-schein,** *m.* sunshine. **-schirm,** *m.* sunshade, parasol. **-spektrum,** *n.* solar spectrum. **-stein,** *m.* sunstone (aventurine feldspar). **-strahl,** *m.* solar ray, sunbeam. **-strahlung,** *f.* solar radiation. **-system,** *n.* solar system. **-tau,** *m.* sundew (*Drosera*).

**sonnentrocken,** *a.* sun-dried.

**Sonnen-uhr,** *f.* sundial. **-wärme,** *f.* sun's heat, solar heat. **-wende,** *f.* solstice; heliotrope.

**sonnig,** *a.* sunny.

**Sonntag,** *m.* Sunday.

**sonntrocken,** *a.* sun-dried.

**sonst,** *adv.* else; otherwise, besides, in other respects, usually, formerly.

**sonstig,** *a.* other, remaining; former.

**sonstwie,** *adv.* in some other way.

**Soole,** *f.* = Sole.

**Sorbett,** *n.* sherbet.

**sorbieren,** *v.t.* sorb. — **sorbierend,** *p.a.* sorbent, sorptive.

**Sorbinsäure,** *f.* sorbic acid.

**Sorbit,** *n.* (*Org. Chem.*) sorbitol; (*Metal.*) sorbite.

**sorbitisch,** *a.* sorbitic.

**Sorge,** *f.* care; concern, anxiety; sorrow.

**sorgen,** *v.i.* care, provide; be anxious, worry.

**Sorgfalt,** *f.* carefulness, care.

**sorg-fältig,** *a.* careful, meticulous. — *adv.* carefully. **-lich,** *a.* anxious, solicitous. **-los,** *a.* careless, unconcerned, reckless. **-sam,** *a.* careful, painstaking.

**Sorrelsalz,** *n.* salt of sorrel (potassium hydrogen oxalate).

**Sorte,** *f.* sort, kind, variety, quality, brand, grade.

**Sortierapparat,** *m.* sorting or grading apparatus.

**sortieren, sorten,** *v.t.* sort, assort, size, grade.

**Sortierer,** *m.* sorter.

**Sortier-maschine,** *f.* sorting machine, sorter. **-sieb,** *n.* sorting sieve. **-trommel,** *f.* sorting drum.

**Sortierung,** *f.* sorting, etc. (see sortieren).

**Sortiment,** *n.* assortment; sorting.

**sott,** *pret.* (of sieden) boiled.

**Souple-schwarz,** *n.* (*Dyeing*) souple black. **-seide,** *f.* souple silk.

**souplieren,** *v.t.* souple (silk).

**soviel,** *a.* & *adv.* so much. — *conj.* as much as, so far as.

**soweit,** *adv.* so far. — *conj.* as far as.

**sowie,** *adv.* as, as well as, as also. **-so,** *adv.* in any case, anyhow.

**Sowjet-.** Soviet.

**sowohl,** *conj.* as well. — — . . . **als,** both . . . and.

**Soya, -bohne,** *f.* soybean, soya bean. **-bohnenöl,** *n.* soybean oil.

**So.Z.,** *abbrev.* (Sodazahl) soda number or value.

**sozial,** *a.* social.

**Sozolsäure,** *f.* sozolic acid (*o*-phenolsulfonic acid).

**sozusagen,** *adv.* so to speak, as it were.

**Spachtel,** *f.* spatula; smoother; filler; putty. **-grund,** *m.*, **-masse,** *f.* (*Paint*) foundation surfacer, filler. **-kitt,** *m.* filler; putty. **-material,** *n.* filler. **-messer,** *n.* putty knife, filler knife.

**spachteln,** *v.t.* smooth (by filling up depressions, as with a spatula); fill; putty.

**spagirisch,** *a.* spagyric, spagyrical.

**spakig,** *a.* moldy; rotten.

**Spalt,** *m.* split, rent, fissure, slit, crack, cleft, gap. **-ausleuchtung,** *f.* slit illumination.

**spaltbar,** *a.* cleavable; fissionable; fissile, scissile.

**Spalt-barkeit,** *f.* cleavability, cleavage; fissionability. **-barkeitsrichtung,** *f.* (*Min.*) direction of cleavage. **-benzin,** *n.* cracked gasoline or petrol. **-bild,** *n.* (*Optics*) slit image. **-bildung,** *f.* splitting, fissuring. **-breite,** *f.* width of slit (of a spectroscope or the like).

**spaltbrüchig,** *a.* (*Min.*) cleaving easily.

**Spalt-brüchigkeit,** *f.* cleavage brittleness. **-destillation,** *f.* cracking distillation, cracking.

**Spalte,** *f.* split, etc. (see Spalt); column (of printed matter).

**Spaltebene,** *f.* (*Cryst.*) cleavage plane, also cleavage face.

**spalten,** *v.t.* cleave, split, slit, rend, fissure; dissociate; crack (as petroleum). — *v.i.* cleave, split, chink.

**Spaltengang,** *m.* (*Geol.*) fissure vein.

**Spalt-festigkeit,** *f.* resistance to splitting; (*Plastics*) interlaminar strength. **-fläche,** *f.* cleavage surface. **-funkenzünder,** *m.* (*Expl.*) jump-spark cap. **-glimmer,** *m.* sheet mica. **-glühzünder,** *m.* (*Expl.*) high-tension cap.

**spaltig,** *a.* split, fissured, cracked; (*Printing*) -columned.

**Spalt-körper,** *m.* cleavage substance, cleavage product. **-lampe,** *f.* (*Optics*) slit lamp. **-mündung, -öffnung,** *f.* (*Bot.*) stoma. **-pflanze,** *f.* schizophytum. **-pilz,** *m.* fission fungus, schizomycete; splitting mold. **-pilzgärung,** *f.* schizomycetous (or bacterial) fermentation. **-produkt,** *n.* cleavage product; fission product. **-riss,** *m.* cleavage crack (or fissure). **-rohr,** *n.* slit tube, collimator (of a spectroscope). **-stück,** *n.* detached portion, segment, fragment; cleavage product; fission fragment.

**Spaltung,** *f.* cleaving, etc. (see spalten), cleavage, scission, fission, division.

**Spaltungs-energie,** *f.* energy of splitting or fission. **-fläche,** *f.* cleavage plane, cleavage face. **-gärung,** *f.* cleavage fermentation. **-gestein,** *n.* differentiated dike rock. **-kristall,** *m.* cleavage crystal. **-probe,** *f.* (*Min.*) cleavage test; (of rock) spalling test; (of wood) splitting test. **-produkt,** *n.* cleavage product; fission product. **-prozess,** *m.* cleavage (fission, scission) process. **-richtung,** *f.* direction of cleavage, cleavage. **-stück,** *n.* = Spaltstück. **-vorgang,** *m.* = Spaltungsprozess. **-wärme,** *f.* heat of dissociation or decomposition or fission.

**Spalt-versuch,** *m.* (*Min.*) cleavage test. **-winkel,** *m.* (*Cryst.*) cleavage angle. **-zünder,** *m.* high-tension detonator.

**Span,** *m.* chip, splint, splinter, shaving, boring, turning, filing, paring, shred.

**Spänfass,** *n.* (*Brewing*) chip cask.

**Spange,** *f.* clasp, buckle; stay bolt; bracelet; spangle.

**Spangeleisen,** *n.* crystalline pig iron.

**spangelig, spanglig, spanglich,** *a.* spangled, glistening, (hence) crystalline.

**Spangrün,** *n.* verdigris.

**Spanien,** *n.* Spain.

**spanisch,** *a.* Spanish. — **spanische Fliegen,** Spanish flies, cantharides. — **spanischer Pfeffer,** red pepper, capsicum. — **spanisches Rohr,** Spanish (or Italian) reed (*Arundo donax*); rattan.

**Spanischbraun,** *n.* Spanish brown.

**Spanischfliegen-.** cantharides.

**spann,** *pret.* (of spinnen) spun.

**Spann,** *m.* instep.

**Spann-.** tension, stretching; coupling; tensor.

**spannbar,** *a.* tensile, extensible, ductile.

**Spannbarkeit,** *f.* tensibility, extensibility, ductility.

**Spanne,** *f.* span; interval.

**spannen,** *v.t.* stretch, strain; tighten; grip, clamp; (of steam) increase the tension of, superheat; span; cock (a gun). — *v.i.* pinch; be exciting. — **gespannt,** *p.a.* stretched, superheated, etc.; tight; intense.

**Spann-knorpel,** *m.* thyroid cartilage. **-kraft,** *f.* tension; extensibility, expansibility, elasticity, tonicity.

**spannkräftig,** *a.* elastic.

**Spann-lack,** *m.* (*Aero.*) stiffening dope or varnish. **-muskel,** *m.* tensor muscle.

**Spannung,** *f.* tension; (gaseous) pressure; (*Mech.*) stress; stretching, etc. (see spannen); (*Elec.*) potential, voltage; tenseness, strain; width.

**spannungführend,** *a.* (*Elec.*) charged, live, hot.

**Spannungs-abfall,** *m.* (*Elec.*) voltage drop. **-festigkeit,** *f.* (*Elec.*) dielectric strength.

**spannungsfrei,** *a.* free from tension or strain, strainless.

**Spannungs-freiglühen,** *n.* (*Metal.*) stress-relief anneal. **-grad,** *m.* degree of tension.

**spannungslos,** *a.* without tension or strain; (*Elec.*) dead.

**Spannungs-messer,** *m.* strain gage; tensiometer; (*Elec.*) voltmeter. **-optik,** *f.* photoelasticity.

**spannungsoptisch,** *a.* photoelastic.

**Spannungs-regler,** *m.* (*Elec.*) voltage regulator. **-reihe,** *f.* electromotive (or electrochemical) series. **-theorie,** *f.* (*Org. Chem.*) strain theory, tension theory. **-unterschied,** *m.* difference in tension; (*Elec.*) potential difference. **-verlust,** *m.* loss of tension, specif. (*Elec.*) loss of voltage. **-zeiger,** *m.* tension indicator; (*Elec.*) voltmeter.

**Spannweite,** *f.* span, width, distance.

**Spanversuch,** *m.* glowing-splint test.

**Spar-beize,** *f.* (*Metal.*) inhibitor, restrainer. **-beton,** *m.* lean concrete. **-brenner,** *m.* economical burner; pilot burner.

**sparen,** *v.t.* spare, save.

**Spar-flämmchen,** *n.*, **-flamme,** *f.* pilot flame.

**Spargel,** *m.* asparagus. **-stein,** *m.* asparagus stone (variety of apatite). **-stoff,** *m.* asparagine.

**Spar-gemisch,** *n.* (of fuel) lean mixture. **-kalk,** *m.* = Estrichgips. **-kapsel,** *f.* (*Ceram.*) space-saving sagger, economy sagger. **-lampe,** *f.* economy lamp, small lamp.

**spärlich,** *a.* sparse, scarce, scanty.

**Spar-metall,** *n.* scarce metal. **-mittel,** *n.* (*Biol. Chem.*) sparing substance, protein sparer.

**Sparren,** *m.* rafter; spar.

**sparsam,** *a.* sparing, economical, close.

**Sparsamkeit,** *f.* economy; parsimony.

**Sparstoff,** *m.* scarce (or rationed) material.

**sparstoffarm,** *a.* low in scarce materials.

**Sparte,** *f.* subject, branch.

**Spartgras,** *n.* esparto grass, esparto.

**Spartopapier,** *n.* esparto paper.

**Spar-vorrichtung,** *f.* economizing device. **-werkstoff,** *m.* scarce (or critical) material.

**spasmodisch,** *a.* spasmodic.

**spastisch,** *a.* spastic, spasmodic.

**Spat,** *m.* spar; parallelepiped; spavin.

**spät,** *a.* & *adv.* late.

**spatartig,** *a.* sparry, spathic.

**Spat-eisen,** *n.*, **-eisenstein,** *m.* spathic iron ore, sparry iron, siderite.

**Spatel,** *m.* spatula; trowel; surfacer.

**spatelförmig,** *a.* spatula-shaped, spatulate.

**Spatelmesser,** *n.* steel spatula (shaped like a knife).

**spateln,** *v.t.* smooth (as with a spatula).

**Spaten,** *m.* spade.
**später,** *a. & adv.* later. **-hin,** *adv.* later on.
**Spaterz,** *n.* spathic ore.
**spätestens,** *adv.* at the latest.
**Spatfluss,** *m.* fluor spar, fluorite.
**spat-förmig,** *a.* spathic, spathose. **-ig,** *a.* sparry, spathic; spavined.
**Spat-lack,** *m.* barytes lake. **-sand,** *m.* silica sand. **-säure,** *f.* hydrofluoric acid. **-stein,** *m.* selenite (the mineral).
**Spät-wirkung,** *f.* tardy action; after-effect. **-zündung,** *f.* retarded ignition.
**spazieren,** *v.i.* walk, stroll, ride, drive.
**spec.,** *abbrev.* (specifisch) specific.
**speci-, Speci-.** see spezi-, Spezi-.
**Speck,** *m.* lard; fat; bacon; blubber.
**Speck-.** fatty, lardaceous, amyloid.
**speck-ähnlich, -artig,** *a.* fatty, lardaceous.
**Speck-glanz,** *m.* greasy luster. **-haut,** *f.* (*Physiol.*) buffy coat.
**speckig,** *a.* lardy, lardaceous, very fat; amyloid; greasy; heavy (bread); flinty (barley).
**Speck-kienholz,** *n.* resinous pine wood. **-öl,** *n.* lard oil. **-stein,** *m.* soapstone, steatite, talc.
**specksteinartig,** *a.* steatitic.
**Speck-steinbrenner,** *m.* steatite burner. **-stoff,** *m.*, **-substanz,** *f.* lardaceous substance, amyloid substance. **-torf,** *m.* pitch peat. **-tran,** *m.* train oil.
**spedieren,** *v.t.* forward, dispatch.
**Speer,** *m.* spear. **-kies,** *m.* spear pyrites (variety of marcasite).
**Speiche,** *f.* spoke; (*Anat.*) radius.
**Speichel,** *m.* saliva, spittle.
**Speichel-.** salivary. **-absonderung,** *f.* secretion of saliva.
**speichelbefördernd,** *p.a.* promoting the flow of saliva, sialagog.
**Speicheldrüse,** *f.* salivary gland.
**speichelecht,** *a.* fast to saliva.
**Speichel-fluss,** *m.* flow of saliva; salivation. **-flüssigkeit,** *f.* saliva. **-kasten,** *m.* saliva chamber (as in a blowpipe); moisture chamber. **-mittel,** *n.* sialagog. **-saft,** *m.* saliva. **-stoff,** *m.* ptyalin.
**Speicher,** *m.* loft, granary, warehouse, storehouse, elevator; reservoir; storer, accumulator. **-batterie,** *f.* storage battery. **-gestein,** *n.* (*Petroleum*) reservoir rock. **-gewebe,** *n.* storage tissue.
**speichern,** *v t.* store, store up, accumulate.
**Speicherung,** *f.* storage; accumulation.
**speien,** *v.i. & t.* spit; vomit.
**Speiköl,** *n.* oil of Celtic nard.
**Speise,** *f.* food, nourishment; material (for a process); (*Metal.*) speiss; bell metal; gun metal; mortar.
**Speise-.** feed, feeding, food, nutrient, edible. **-apparat,** *m.* (*Mech.*) feed apparatus. **-bestandteil,** *m.* constituent of food. **-brei,** *m.* chyme. **-eis,** *n.* ice cream; sherbet. **-fett,** *n.* edible fat; nutrient fat. **-flotte,** *f.* replenishing liquor. **-gang,** *m.* alimentary canal. **-gefäss,** *n.* feed vessel, feed tank.
**speisegelb,** *a.* pale bronze-yellow, like speiss.
**Speise-hahn,** *m.* feed cock. **-kanal,** *m.* alimentary canal. **-karte,** *f.* bill of fare, menu. **-kartoffel,** *f.* food potato. **-kobalt,** *m.* smaltite. **-leitung,** *f.* feed pipe, feed wire, feed line. **-masse,** *f.* ration.
**speisen,** *v.t.* feed; supply; charge (as a battery); eat. — *v.i.* eat, take food, board.
**Speisenträger,** *m.* food carrier, specif. a vacuum vessel.
**Speise-öl,** *n.* edible oil; specif., olive oil. **-ordnung,** *f.* diet, regimen. **-pilz,** *m.* edible fungus. **-pumpe,** *f.* feed pump. **-quark,** *m.* cottage cheese.
**Speiser,** *m.* feeder.
**Speise-rest,** *m.* food residue. **-rohr,** *n.* feed pipe or tube, supply pipe or tube. **-röhre,** *f.* = Speiserohr; (*Anat.*) esophagus. **-rübe,** *f.* garden turnip. **-saft,** *m.* chyle. **-salz,** *n.* common salt. **-schnecke,** *f.* feed screw. **-trichter,** *m.* supply funnel, hopper. **-vorrichtung,** *f.* feeding contrivance, feeder. **-walze,** *f.* feed roll. **-wasser,** *n.* feed water. **-zucker,** *m.* table sugar.
**Speisezwiebel,** *f.* onion.
**speisig,** *a.* cobaltiferous.
**Speiskobalt,** *m.* smaltite.
**Speisung,** *f.* feeding, etc. (see speisen); feed, supply, input.
**Spektralanalyse,** *f.* spectrum analysis.
**spektralanalytisch,** *a.* spectroscopic, spectrometric. — *adv.* by spectrum analysis.
**Spektral-apparat,** *m.* spectroscopic apparatus. **-beobachtung,** *f.* spectroscopic observation. **-bereich, -bezirk,** *m.* spectral region. **-farbe,** *f.* spectral color, spectrum color. **-gegend,** *f.* spectral region. **-lampe,** *f.* spectrum lamp. **-linie,** *f.* spectrum line, spectral line. **-probe,** *f.* spectrum test. **-rohr,** *n.*, **-röhre,** *f.* spectrum tube, spectral tube. **-tafel,** *f.* spectrum chart, spectral chart.
**Spektren,** *n.pl.* spectrums, spectra.
**spektro-graphisch,** *a.* spectrographic. **-metrisch,** *a.* spectrometric.
**Spektroskop,** *n.* spectroscope.
**Spektroskopie,** *f.* spectroscopy.
**Spektroskopiker,** *m.* spectroscopist.
**spektroskopisch,** *a.* spectroscopic.
**Spelz,** *m.* spelt.
**Spelze,** *f.* chaff, husk, glume (of grains); **awn,** beard.
**Spelzmehl,** *n.* spelt flour.
**spenden,** *v.t.* spend, distribute.

**Spender,** *m.*, **Spenderin,** *f.* giver, donor, distributor, yielder, source.
**Sperbeere,** *f.* service berry.
**Sperma,** *n.* sperm, semen. **-kern,** *m.* sperm nucleus.
**Spermazet, Spermazeti,** *n.* spermaceti. **-öl,** *n.* sperm oil.
**Spermie,** *f.* spermatozoön.
**Spermöl,** *n.* sperm oil.
**Sperrdruck,** *m.* spaced type.
**Sperre,** *f.* shutting, blocking, locking, stoppage; embargo; barrier, obstacle; baffle; seal; wave trap.
**sperren,** *v.t.* shut, shut up, confine, close, seal, stop, stopper, arrest, lock, bar, block, obstruct; exclude; suppress; insulate; open, spread out, space. — *v.r.* resist, struggle, refuse.
**Sperrer,** *m.* shutter, etc. (see sperren); lock, block, trap.
**Sperr-flüssigkeit,** *f.* sealing liquid (to prevent escape of a gas). **-hahn,** *m.* stopcock. **-haken,** *m.* (*Mach.*) catch, pawl, detent. **-holz,** *n.* plywood.
**sperrig,** *a.* bulky, unwieldy; spready; wide open.
**Sperr-klinke,** *f.* catch, pawl, ratchet, detent. **-kreis,** *m.* block circuit, wave trap circuit. **-metall,** *n.* ply metal. **-rad,** *n.* ratchet wheel, cog wheel. **-schichtenzelle,** *f.* solid photovoltaic cell. **-ung,** *f.* shutting, etc. (see sperren). **-ventil,** *n.* stop valve, check valve, shut-off valve. **-waffe,** *f.* defensive weapon. **-wasser,** *n.* sealing water.
**Spesen,** *f.pl.* charges, expenses, costs.
**spez.,** *abbrev.* (spezifisch) specific; (speziell) special(ly).
**Spezerei,** *f.* spices; spicery, grocery.
**spez.Gew.,** *abbrev.* (spezifisches Gewicht) specific gravity.
**spezial,** *a.* special.
**Spezial-benzin,** *n.* special gasoline. **-fall,** *m.* special case. **-gusseisen,** *n.* special cast iron.
**spezialisieren,** *v.i.* specialize.
**spezialistisch,** *a.* specialistic.
**Spezialität,** *f.* specialty.
**Spezial-öl,** *n.* special oil. **-reagens,** *n.* special reagent. **-stahl,** *m.* special steel.
**speziell,** *a.* special, specific.
**Spezies,** *f.* species; specie; (*Pharm.*) simples, herbs, drugs.
**Spezifikum,** *n.* specific.
**spezifisch,** *a.* specific.
**Spezifität,** *f.* specificity.
**spezifizieren,** *v.t.* & *i.* specify.
**sp.G.,** *abbrev.* (spezifisches Gewicht) specific gravity, sp. gr.
**Sphäre,** *f.* sphere, province, range, domain.
**sphärisch,** *a.* spherical.
**Sphäro-kristall,** *m.* spherical crystal, spherocrystal. **-siderit,** *n.* spherosiderite.
**Sphärulith,** *m.* spherulite.
**Sphen,** *m.* sphene, titanite.
**sphenoidisch,** *a.* sphenoid, sphenoidal.
**spicken,** *v.t.* lard; smoke; oil (wool).
**Spicköl,** *n.* wool oil, spinning oil.
**spie,** *pret.* (of speien) spat; vomited.
**Spiegel,** *m.* mirror, speculum, reflector; polished surface; surface (of liquids, fabrics, etc.); level (as in *Biochem.*); specular cast iron, spiegeleisen; stern (of a ship).
**Spiegel-.** mirror, specular, reflected, reflecting. **-ablesung,** *f.* mirror reading. **-beleg,** *m.* mirror coating, reflecting coating. **-bild,** *n.* reflected image, mirror image.
**spiegel-bildisomer,** *a.* showing isomerism characterized by enantiomorphism, enantiomorphic. **-bildlich,** *a.* enantiomorphic; specular. **-blank,** *a.* highly polished.
**Spiegel-ebene,** *f.* reflection plane. **-eisen,** *n.* specular cast iron, spiegeleisen; specular iron (hematite of metallic appearance). **-erz,** *n.* specular iron ore. **-faser,** *f.* medullary ray. **-floss,** *n.* spiegeleisen. **-folie,** *f.* tin foil; silvering (of a mirror). **-giesserei,** *f.* plate-glass factory. **-glanz,** *m.* reflecting luster or surface; (*Min.*) wehrlite. **-glas,** *n.* plate glass.
**spiegelglatt,** *a.* extremely smooth.
**Spiegel-gleichheit,** *f.* mirror symmetry. **-höhe,** *f.* height (or level) of a liquid.
**spiegelig,** *a.* specular, mirror-like.
**Spiegelmetall,** *n.* speculum metal.
**spiegeln,** *v.t.* reflect. — *v.i.* reflect, shine, glitter. — *v.r.* be reflected. — **spiegelnd,** *p.a.* reflecting, specular, shining.
**Spiegelskala,** *f.* mirror scale.
**Spiegelung,** *f.* reflection; mirage.
**Spiegelwelle,** *f.* reflected wave.
**Spiegler,** *m.* reflector.
**Spieke,** *f.* spike, spike lavender.
**Spieköl,** *n.* oil of spike.
**Spiel,** *n.* play, playing; clearance; (*Mach.*) working action; cycle; backlash; game, sport; pack (of cards). **-art,** *f.* variety; variant; (*Biol.*) sport.
**spielen,** *v.i.* play; (of a gem) sparkle; (*Mach.*) work, have play. — *v.t.* play. — **— in,** incline toward, be tinged with (a color).
**Spiel-raum,** *m.* play; latitude, margin, elbowroom; tolerance; backlash. **-waren,** *f.pl.* toys. **-warenlack,** *m.* varnish for toys. **-zeug,** *n.* plaything, toy.
**Spiess,** *m.* spear, lance; spit; (*Cryst.*) long needle.
**spiessen,** *v.t.* spear, spit, pierce.
**spiessförmig,** *a.* spear-shaped, lance-like.
**Spiessglanz,** *m.* antimony; stibnite.

**spiessglanzartig,** *a.* antimonial.

**Spiessglanz-asche,** *f.* antimony ash. **-bleierz,** *n.* bournonite. **-blende,** *f.* antimony blende, kermesite. **-blumen,** *f.pl.* flowers of antimony. **-butter,** *f.* butter of antimony (old name for antimony trichloride). **-erz,** *n.* antimony ore (**graues,** stibnite; **schwarzes,** bournonite; **weisses,** valentinite). **-glas,** *n.* glass of antimony.

**spiessglanzhaltig,** *a.* containing antimony, antimonial.

**Spiessglanz-kermes,** *m.* kermesite; kermes mineral. **-könig,** *m.* regulus of antimony. **-leber,** *f.* liver of antimony, hepar antimonii. **-metall,** *n.* antimony. **-mittel,** *n.* antimonial remedy. **-mohr,** *m.* aethiops antimonialis (old pharmaceutical preparation of mercury and antimony sulfides). **-ocker,** *m.* antimony ocher. **-oxyd,** *n.* antimony trioxide. **-safran,** *m.* crocus of antimony. **-säure,** *f.* antimonic acid. **-schwefel,** *m.* antimony sulfide. **-silber,** *n.* dyscrasite. **-wein,** *m.* antimonial wine. **-weinstein,** *m.* (*Pharm.*) tartrated antimony. **-weiss,** *n.* antimony white (trioxide). **-zinnober,** *m.* kermesite.

**Spiessglas,** *n.* antimony. See also Spiessglanz-. **-erz,** *n.* stibnite. **-weiss,** *n.* antimony white (trioxide).

**spiessig,** *a.* (*Cryst.*) spear-like, lance-like, in long needles; (*Leather*) badly tanned; (*Metal.*) brittle.

**Spiess-kant,** *m.* diamond. **-kobalt,** *m.* smaltite.

**Spik-blüten,** *f.pl.* spike-lavender flowers. **-öl,** *n.* oil of spike, oil of spike lavender.

**Spinat,** *m.* spinach.

**Spinbahn,** *f.* spin orbit.

**Spindel,** *f.* spindle; pivot, axle, arbor. **-baum,** *m.* spindle tree; (*Pharm.*) euonymus. **-faser,** *f.* spindle fiber.

**spindelförmig,** *a.* spindle-shaped, fusiform.

**spindeln,** *v.t.* test with a hydrometer.

**Spindel-öl,** *n.* spindle oil. **-presse,** *f.* screw press. **-wa(a)ge,** *f.* hydrometer. **-zelle,** *f.* fusiform cell.

**Spin-drehimpuls,** *m.* spin angular momentum. **-glied,** *n.* (*Math.*) spin term. **-momentdichte,** *f.* spin momentum density.

**Spinnabfall,** *m.* spinning waste.

**spinnbar,** *a.* spinnable.

**Spinndüse,** *f.* spinneret, spinning nozzle.

**Spinne,** *f.* spider.

**spinnen,** *v.t.* spin; twist (tobacco). — *v.i.* spin; (of oil) thread; purr.

**Spinnengewebe,** *n.* spider web, cobweb.

**Spinnerei,** *f.* spinning; spinning mill.

**spinnfähig,** *a.* suitable for spinning.

**Spinn-faser,** *f.* fiber for spinning, textile fiber; specif., staple rayon. **-fett,** *n.* (*Textiles*) mill oil. **-flüssigkeit,** *f.* spinning solution. spinning dope. **-gewebe,** *n.* cobweb, spider web. **-kerze,** *f.* filter(ing) candle. **-kuchen,** *m.* (*Rayon*) cake. **-lösung,** *f.* spinning solution. **-masse,** *f.* (*Rayon*) spinning solution.

**spinnmattiert,** *a.* delustered during spinning.

**Spinn-öl,** *n.* spinning oil. **-reife,** *f.* ripeness for spinning. **-schmalz,** *n.* spinning lubricant. **-stoff,** *m.* spinning material. **-webe,** *f.* cobweb, spider web.

**spinnwebenartig,** *a.* cobweb-like, arachnoid.

**Spinn-webfaden,** *m.* spider thread; very fine thread. **-wolle,** *f.* wool for spinning, spinning wool.

**Spinrichtung,** *f.* direction of spin.

**Spiräa, Spiräe,** *f.* spiraea, spirea.

**Spiralbohrer,** *m.* (*Mach.*) twist drill.

**Spirale,** *f.* spiral, coil, helix; spiral condenser.

**Spiralfeder,** *f.* spiral spring.

**spiralförmig,** *a.* spiral, helical.

**spiralig,** *a.* spiral. — *adv.* spirally.

**Spiral-kühler,** *m.* spiral condenser; spiral (or coil) cooler. **-linie,** *f.* spiral line, spiral. **-rohr,** *n.*, **-röhre,** *f.* spiral tube or pipe, worm. **-stellung,** *f.* spiral arrangement.

**Spirillose,** *f.* spirillosis.

**Spirituosa, Spirituosen,** *n.pl.* spirituous liquors, alcoholic liquors.

**Spiritus,** *m.* spirit, spirits, specif. alcohol.

**spiritusartig,** *a.* spirituous, alcoholic.

**Spiritus-beize,** *f.* spirit mordant; spirit stain. **-blau,** *n.* spirit blue. **-brenner,** *m.* (spirit) distiller; alcohol burner. **-brennerei,** *f.* distillery. **-dampf,** *m.* alcohol vapor. **-fabrik,** *f.* spirit manufactory, distillery. **-fass,** *n.* spirit cask or barrel. **-geruch,** *m.* odor of spirits. **-industrie,** *f.* spirit industry, distilling industry. **-lack,** *m.* spirit varnish. **-lampe,** *f.* spirit lamp.

**spirituslöslich,** *a.* spirit-soluble.

**Spiritus-messer,** *m.* alcoholometer. **-mischung,** *f.* alcoholic mixture. **-pumpe,** *f.* alcohol pump. **-wa(a)ge,** *f.* alcoholometer; spirit level.

**Spirochäte,** *f.* spirochete.

**Spirochätose,** *f.* spirochetosis.

**spiroylig,** *a.* spiroylous. — **spiroylige Säure,** spiroylous acid (former name for salicylaldehyde).

**Spiroylsäure, Spirsäure,** *f.* salicyclic acid (old names).

**Spital,** *n.* hospital.

**spitz,** *a.* pointed, acute, sharp, acicular.

**Spitz,** *m.* (*Metal.*) paddle. **-becher,** *m.*, **-becherglas,** *n.* sedimenting glass. **-beutel,** *m.* triangular filter bag.

**Spitze,** *f.* point; tip, top, apex, vertex, peak, crest, summit, cusp; lace.

**spitzen,** *v.t.* point, sharpen (to a point); tip. — *v.i.* (of grain), sprout, spire, chit.

**Spitzen-belastung,** *f.* peak load. **-durchmesser,** *m.* over-all diameter. **-elektrode,** *f.* point electrode, needle electrode. **-entladung,** *f.* (*Elec.*) point discharge. **-glas,** *n.* reticulated glass. **-leistung,** *f.* peak output; record performance. **-papier,** *n.* lace paper. **-strom,** *m.* (*Elec.*) peak current. **-wert,** *m.* maximum value, top value. **-zähler,** *m.* needle counter. **-zirkel,** *m.* compasses, dividers.

**Spitz-geschoss,** *n.* pointed bullet. **-glas,** *n.* a glass of tall, conical form; specif., sedimentation glass. **-hacke,** *f.* pickax, pick. **-haufen,** *m.* (*Brewing*) couch.

**spitzig,** *a.* pointed, acute, sharp, tapering; (of colors) mixtury, not uniform.

**spitzkantig,** *a.* acute-angled.

**Spitz-kolben,** *m.* a flask with long, tapering neck; pointed soldering iron. **-malz,** *n.* chit malt. **-maus,** *f.* shrew (*Sorex*). **-röhrchen,** *n.* small pointed tube (as for centrifuges). **-trichter,** *m.* tapering separatory funnel, Squibb funnel.

**spitzwinklig,** *a.* acute-angled.

**spitzzulaufend,** *a.* tapering, tapered.

**Spleisse,** *f.* splint, splinter, shard.

**spleissen,** *v.t.* & *i.* split, cleave; splice.

**Splint,** *m.* sap, sapwood; pin, peg, key; splint.

**splintfrei,** *a.* free from sap, sapless.

**Splint-holz,** *n.* sapwood, sap. **-kohle,** *f.* splint coal.

**spliss,** *pret.* (of spleissen) split; spliced.

**Splitter,** *m.* splinter, splint, chip, scale, fragment.

**splitterbindend,** *a.* shatterproof.

**Splitterbombe,** *f.* fragmentation bomb.

**splitterfrei,** *a.* (of glass) shatterproof; (of paper) free from shives.

**Splittergranate,** *f.* fragmentation shell.

**splitterig,** *a.* splintery; brittle, fragile; (*Paper*) shivy.

**Splitterkohle,** *f.* splint coal.

**splittern,** *v.i.* & *t.* shatter, shiver, splinter, split (up).

**Splitterschutzbrille,** *f.* protective goggles.

**splittersicher,** *a.* splinterproof.

**Splitter-ung,** *f.* shattering, etc. (see splittern). **-wirkung,** *f.* splinter effect, fragmentation effect.

**spönne,** *pret. subj.* of spinnen.

**spontan,** *a.* spontaneous.

**Spor,** *m.* mold, moldiness; mildew. — *n.* spur; spine.

**sporen,** *v.i.* dry up; become moldy.

**sporenbildend,** *p.a.* spore-forming.

**Sporen-bildung,** *f.* formation of spores, sporulation. **-färbung,** *f.* spore staining; spore stain.

**sporenhaltig,** *a.* containing spores.

**Sporenpflanze,** *f.* (*Bot.*) sporophyte.

**Sporfleck,** *m.* mold spot, mold stain.

**sporig,** *a.* moldy, mildewed.

**Sporn,** *m.* spur; spine; spike.

**Sportel,** *f.* fee, perquisite.

**spotten,** *v.i.* mock, scoff, ridicule.

**sprach,** *pret.* (of sprechen) spoke.

**Sprache,** *f.* speech; language; discussion.

**Sprach-eigenheit,** *f.* idiom. **-forschung,** *f.* philology. **-gebrauch,** *m.* colloquial usage. **-lehre,** *f.* grammar.

**sprach-lich,** *a.* lingual; grammatical. **-los,** *a.* speechless, dumb.

**Sprachschatz,** *m.* vocabulary; thesaurus.

**sprachwidrig,** *a.* ungrammatical.

**sprang,** *pret.* (of springen) burst, broke, etc.

**spratzen, spratzeln,** *v.i.* spit, spurt, sputter, splutter, spatter, splash.

**Spratzkupfer,** *n.* = Streukupfer.

**sprechen,** *v.i.* & *t.* speak, talk, say.

**Sprech-maschine,** *f.* talking machine, phonograph. **-saal,** *m.* hall for speaking, forum.

**spreiten,** *v.t.* spread, spread out.

**Spreitung,** *f.* spreading, spreading out.

**Spreize,** *f.* strut, stay, spreader.

**spreizen,** *v.t.* spread; prop up. — *v.r.* strive.

**Spreng-.** explosive, blasting; sprinkling. **-apparat,** *m.* sprinkling apparatus, sprinkler, sparger. **-arbeit,** *f.* blasting. **-bohrloch,** *n.* blast hole. **-bombe,** *f.* high-explosive bomb, demolition bomb. **-brandbombe,** *f.* incendiary-demolition bomb. **-eisen,** *n.* (*Glass*) cracking ring.

**sprengen,** *v.t.* explode, blow up, blast, burst; rupture; sprinkle, spray. — *v.i.* gallop, dash; sprinkle, drizzle.

**sprengfähig,** *a.* explosive.

**Spreng-falle,** *f.* (*Mil.*) booby trap. **-flüssigkeit,** *f.* explosive liquid. **-füllung,** *f.* explosive charge, filler charge. **-gelatine,** *f.* explosive gelatin. **-geschoss,** *n.* explosive missile. **-granate,** *f.* high-explosive grenade or shell, H. E. shell. **-kapsel,** *f.* detonating cap, detonator; booster charge; blasting cap. **-kohle,** *f.* cracking coal (for cracking glass). **-kraft,** *f.* explosive force, explosive power.

**sprengkräftig,** *a.* powerfully explosive.

**Spreng-ladung,** *f.* bursting charge; charge of explosive. **-loch,** *n.* blast hole. **-luft,** *f.* liquid-air explosive, liquid oxygen. **-masse,** *f.* explosive charge. **-mittel,** *n.* explosive; disintegrating agent. **-niet,** *n.*, **-niete,** *f.* explosive rivet. **-öl,** *n.* polyalcohol nitrate, specif. nitroglycerin. **-ölpulver,** *n.* nitroglycerin powder. **-patrone,** *f.* explosive cartridge, blasting cartridge; explosive bullet. **-pulver,** *n.* blasting powder. **-salpeter,** *m.* saltpeter blasting powder, nitrate explosive. **-satz,** *m.* bursting charge. **-schlag,** *m.* explosion. **-schnur,** *f.* fuse. **-schuss,** *m.* shot.

**Sprengstoff,** *m.* explosive. **-füllung,** *f.* explosive filler or charge. **-kammer,** *f.* explosives magazine. **-ladung,** *f.* explosive charge. **-wesen,** *n.* all that concerns explosives, subject of explosives.

**Spreng-stück,** *n.* fragment (from bursting), specif. shell fragment. **-technik,** *f.* technics or manufacture of explosives. **-trichter,** *m.* explosion crater; sprinkling rose.

**Sprengung,** *f.* exploding, explosion, etc. (see sprengen).

**Spreng-wirkung,** *f.* explosive effect, explosive action. **-wolke,** *f.* cloud from an explosion, burst smoke. **-zünder,** *m.* detonating fuse.

**Sprenkel,** *m.* speckle, spot.

**sprenkeln,** *v.t.* sprinkle; speckle, mottle, spot.

**Sprenkler,** *m.* sprinkler, sparger.

**sprenklig,** *a.* speckled, spotted.

**Spreu,** *f.* chaff.

**spricht,** *pr. 3 sing.* (of sprechen) speaks.

**Sprichwort,** *n.* saying, proverb.

**Spriegel,** *m.* hoop; chip; splint; stick.

**spriessen,** *v.i.* sprout, germinate.

**Springbrunnen,** *m.* fountain.

**springen,** *v.i.* burst, break, crack, split; spring, leap, jump, spout.

**Spring-feder,** *f.* (elastic) spring. **-federwa(a)ge,** *f.* spring balance. **-gurke,** *f.* squirting cucumber. **-gurkenextrakt,** *m.* elaterium.

**springhart,** *a.* brittle.

**Spring-kolben,** *m.* Bologna flask. **-kraft,** *f.* springiness, power of recoil, elastic force, elasticity.

**springkräftig,** *a.* springy, elastic.

**Sprit,** *m.* spirit, spirits. **-beize,** *f.* spirit stain. **-blau,** *n.* spirit blue. **-drucken,** *n.* (*Calico*) spirit printing.

**spritecht,** *a.* fast to spirit, insoluble in alcohol.

**Sprit-essig,** *m.* spirit vinegar. **-farbe,** *f.* (*Calico*) spirit color. **-gelb,** *n.* spirit yellow.

**sprithaltig,** *a.* containing spirit, spirituous, (of wine) fortified.

**Spritlack,** *m.* spirit varnish or lacquer.

**sprit-lackecht,** *a.* fast to spirit lacquer. **-löslich,** *a.* spirit-soluble, alcohol-soluble. **-unlöslich,** *a.* insoluble in spirit.

**Spritz-alitieren,** *n.* aluminizing (calorizing) by spraying. **-anlage,** *f.* spraying plant. **-apparat,** *m.* sprayer, sprinkler. **-beton,** *m.* concrete for first coat, rendering concrete; sprayed concrete. **-bewurf,** *m.* rough plastering. **-brenner,** *m.* spray burner. **-druck,** *m.* spray printing. **-düse,** *f.* spray nozzle; injection nozzle; (*Steam*) injector.

**Spritze,** *f.* syringe, squirt, sprayer, gun, injector.

**spritzen,** *v. i. & t.* squirt; spurt, spout, splash, spatter, sputter; spit; spray; atomize; extrude; inject; throw (with a hose).

**spritzfähig,** *a.* suitable for spraying, injecting, etc. (see spritzen).

**Spritz-farbe,** *f.* spray color. **-färbung,** *f.* spray dyeing or coloring. **-flasche,** *f.* washing bottle, wash bottle (for washing precipitates). **-form,** *f.* injection mold; jet mold. **-gummi,** *n.* sealing compound (for cans or tins). **-gurke,** *f.* squirting cucumber. **-guss,** *m.* die casting, injection molding. **-gussmasse,** *f.* injection-molding composition. **-kopf,** *m.* spraying nozzle. **-kork,** *m.* sprinkler stopper. **-kranz,** *m.* (*Brewing*) sparger. **-lack,** *m.* spraying varnish or lacquer.

**spritzlackieren,** *v.t.* varnish by spraying.

**Spritz-ling,** *m.* injection molding. **-masse,** *f.* = Spritzgussmasse. **-mittel,** *n.* remedy administered by injection. **-nudeln,** *f.pl.* vermicelli. **-pistole,** *f.* spray gun. **-probe,** *f.* (*Dyes*) blow test. **-pulver,** *n.* injection molding powder. **-rohr,** *n.*, **-röhre,** *f.* syringe; spray pipe; wash-bottle tube. **-spachtel,** *f.* primer surfacer, spray filler. **-verfahren,** *n.* spraying process. **-vorrichtung,** *f.* spraying device, sprayer.

**sprock,** *a.* brittle, friable.

**spröde,** *a.* brittle, short; friable; shy, prim. **-machen,** *v.t.* make brittle, embrittle.

**Spröd-glanzerz, -glaserz,** *n.* brittle silver ore, stephanite (sometimes, polybasite). **-igkeit,** *f.* brittleness, shortness; friability; reserve, primness. **-metall,** *n.* brittle metal.

**spross,** *pret.* (of spriessen) sprouted.

**Spross,** *m.* shoot, sprout, germ; sprig; scion, offspring.

**Sprosse,** *f.* = Spross; rung, step, bar, spoke, stave.

**sprossen,** *v.i.* sprout, shoot, bud, germinate; spring, descend.

**Sprossen-bier,** *n.* spruce beer. **-extrakt,** *m.* essence of spruce. **-fichte,** *f.* spruce fir, (true) spruce. **-kohl,** *m.* broccoli; **(Brüsseler)** Brussels sprouts. **-tanne,** *f.* hemlock spruce.

**Sprosskeimung,** *f.* sprouting, budding.

**Sprössling,** *m.* = Spross.

**Sprosspilz,** *m.* gemmiparous fungus, budding fungus (specif., yeast fungus, *Saccharomyces*).

**Sprossung,** *f.* sprouting, etc. (see sprossen).

**Sprotte,** *f.* sprat (*Clupea sprattus*).

**Spruch,** *m.* message; sentence, verdict; saying, motto, text.

**Sprudel,** *m.* bubbling spring, hot spring. **-bohrung,** *f.* (*Petroleum*) gusher, spouter.

**sprudeln,** *v.i.* bubble, spout.

**Sprudel-platte,** *f.* bubble tray. **-salz,** *n.* Karlsbad salt. **-stein,** *m.* deposit from hot springs.

**Sprüh-apparat,** *m.* spraying or sprinkling apparatus. **-düse,** *f.* spray nozzle. **-elektrode,** *f.* ionizing electrode.

**sprühen,** *v.i.* spray, spit, scintillate, spark; drizzle. — *v.t.* scatter, sprinkle, emit.
**Sprühentladung,** *f.* spray discharge.
**sprühfest,** *a.* sprayproof.
**Sprüh-flüssigkeit,** *f.* spray liquid, spray. **-ion,** *n.* spray ion. **-kautschuk,** *m. & n.* sprayed rubber. **-kupfer,** *n.* = Streukupfer. **-regen,** *m.* spray; drizzle.
**Sprung,** *m.* crack, chink, fissure; (of strata) fault; jump, spring, bounce, leap; (in a curve) break, discontinuity; (in spectra) transition; (of waves) hop. **-bildung,** *f.* crack formation, fissuring. **-feder,** *f.* (elastic) spring.
**sprunghaft,** *a.* of the nature of a leap or jump, sudden, irregular, spasmodic. — *adv.* by leaps or jumps.
**Sprung-höhe,** *f.* (*Geol.*) throw (of a fault). **-spektrum,** *n.* transition (or jump) spectrum. **-variation,** *f.* (*Biol.*) mutation. **-wahrscheinlichkeit,** *f.* transition probability.
**sprungweise,** *adv.* by leaps or jumps, discontinuously, intermittently.
**Sprung-weite,** *f.* range (as of a water jet); (*Geol.*) shift (of a fault). **-zeit,** *f.* time of transition (of an electron).
**spucken,** *v.t. & i.* spit.
**Spül-.** rinsing, washing, flushing, irrigating. **-bad,** *n.* rinsing bath. **-bottich,** *m.* rinsing tub, rinsing vessel.
**Spule,** *f.* spool; (*Elec.*) coil; bobbin; quill.
**Spüleimer,** *m.* rinsing pail.
**Spüleinrichtung,** *f.* rinsing contrivance.
**spulen,** *v.t.* wind, reel, coil.
**spülen,** *v.t.* rinse, wash, flush, irrigate, scavenge.
**Spulen-galvanometer,** *n.* moving-coil galvanometer. **-lack,** *m.* (*Elec.*) insulating varnish; (*Textiles*) bobbin finish. **-öl,** *n.* spooling oil. **-wicklung,** *f.* (*Elec.*) coil winding. **-widerstand,** *m.* (*Elec.*) coil resistance.
**Spüler,** *m.* rinser, washer.
**Spülerei,** *f.* rinsing; rinsing plant.
**Spül-flüssigkeit,** *f.* rinsing liquid. **-gas,** *n.* rinsing gas, scavenging gas (for sweeping out a tube or the like). **-gefäss,** *n.* rinsing vessel. **-gut,** *n.* flushing material. **-icht,** *n.* dishwater, slop; (*Distilling*) spent wash. **-kasten,** *m.* rinsing box. **-kufe,** *f.* rinsing vat. **-luft,** *f.* scavenging air. **-maschine,** *f.* rinsing machine.
**Spulöl,** *n.* spooling oil.
**Spül-schwelung,** *f.* low-temperature carbonization with gas recirculation. **-topf,** *m.* rinsing pot, rinsing jar. **-trog,** *m.* rinsing trough.
**Spülung,** *f.* rinsing, washing, flushing; drilling mud.
**Spülwasser,** *n.* rinsing water; wash water; flushing water; dishwater.
**Spund,** *m.* stopper, plug, bung; tongue (of a board).
**spunden,** *v.t.* bung (casks); cask (wine, etc.); tongue and groove.
**Spund-gärung,** *f.* bunghole fermentation. **-loch,** *n.* bunghole.
**spundvoll,** *a.* brimful.
**Spur,** *f.* trace; track; trail, scent; mark; gage; gutter, channel, groove; (of a tire) tread. **-arbeit,** *f.* (*Metal.*) concentration.
**spürbar,** *a.* traceable, detectable, sensible.
**Spurelement,** *n.* trace element.
**spuren,** *v.t.* (*Metal.*) concentrate.
**spüren,** *v.t.* track, trace, trail; detect, notice.
**spurenhaft,** *a. & adv.* in traces, sparing(ly).
**Spurensuche,** *f.* search for traces.
**spurenweise,** *adv.* in traces, sparingly.
**Spurgeschoss,** *n.* tracer projectile.
**spurlos,** *a.* traceless; trackless. — *adv.* without a trace.
**Spür-mittel,** *n.* (*Mil.*) gas-detecting means. **-papier,** *n.* (*Mil.*) gas-detection paper. **-pulver,** *n.* (*Mil.*) gas-detection powder.
**Spur-schlacke,** *f.* concentration slag. **-stein,** *m.* concentration metal, concentrated mat(te). **-weite,** *f.* track gage.
**Sr.,** *abbrev.* (Seiner) His (in titles).
**S-Rohr,** *n.*, **S-Röhre,** *f.* S-tube, S-pipe.
**s.S.,** *abbrev.* (siehe Seite) see page . . . .
**S.S.,** *abbrev.* (Schwefelwasserstoffsäure) hydrosulfuric acid ($H_2S$).
**SS.,** *abbrev.* (Säuren) acids.
**s. str.,** *abbrev.* (*sensu stricto*) in a strict sense.
**St.,** *abbrev.* (Stunde) hour; (Sankt) Saint; (Stärke) thickness; (Stück) piece, each.
**St. A.,** *abbrev.* (Stammaktien) shares of common stock.
**Staat,** *m.* state.
**staatlich,** *a.* state, national, government, public.
**Staats-.** state, government, public, political. **-amt,** *n.* public office. **-bürger,** *m.* subject, citizen. **-lehre,** *f.* political science. **-rat,** *m.* council of state, state council; state councilor. **-zeitung,** *f.* (official) gazette.
**Stab,** *m.* rod; stick; bar; staff. **-bakterie,** *f.* bacillus. **-brandbombe,** *f.* stick-type incendiary bomb.
**Stäbchen,** *n.* little rod or stick; rodlet; pin; bacillus.
**stäbchen-artig, -förmig,** *a.* rod-like, rod-shaped.
**Stabeisen,** *n.* bar iron.
**stabförmig,** *a.* rod-shaped, bar-shaped.
**stabil,** *a.* stable; firm, durable, steady.
**Stabilisator,** *m.* stabilizer.
**stabilisieren,** *v.t.* stabilize.
**Stabilisierung,** *f.* stabilization.
**Stabilisierungsmittel,** *n.* stabilizing agent, stabilizer.
**Stabilität,** *f.* stability.

**Stabilitäts-prüfer,** *m.* stability tester. **-prüfung,** *f.* stability test.

**Stab-kranz,** *m.* (*Biol.*) corona radiata. **-kraut,** *n.* = Eberraute. **-magnet,** *m.* bar magnet. **-thermometer,** *n.* & *m.* a thermometer graduated directly on the stem (instead of having a separate scale).

**stach,** *pret.* (of stechen) stuck, pricked, etc.

**Stachel,** *m.* sting, thorn, spine, prickle, prong, point. **-beere,** *f.* gooseberry. **-draht,** *m.* barbed wire.

**stachelig,** *a.* prickly, thorny; pungent, biting.

**stachellos,** *a.* free from thorns or spines.

**Stachelmohn,** *m.* prickly poppy (*Argemone*).

**stacheln,** *v.t.* sting, prick, prod; spur.

**Stachel-schwein,** *n.* porcupine. **-walzwerk,** *n.* (*Mach.*) toothed rolls.

**Stadel,** *m.* shed; (*Metal.*, etc.) open kiln, stall. **-röstung,** *f.* stall roasting.

**Stadien,** *n.pl.* stages, etc. (see Stadium).

**Stadium,** *n.* stage, phase; state; stadium.

**Stadt,** *f.* town; city, municipality. **-haus,** *n.* town house, town hall.

**städtisch,** *a.* town, city, municipal.

**Staffel,** *f.* step; round, rung; stage; squadron.

**staffieren,** *v.t.* trim, equip; prepare (a dye bath).

**stagnieren,** *v.i.* stagnate. — **stagnierend,** *p.a.* stagnating, stagnant.

**stahl,** *pret.* (of stehlen) stole.

**Stahl,** *m.* steel. **-abfall,** *m.* waste steel, steel scrap.

**stahlähnlich,** *a.* steel-like.

**Stahlarbeit,** *f.* steel process; steel work.

**stahlartig,** *a.* steel-like, steely; chalybeate.

**Stahl-arznei,** *f.* medicine containing iron, chalybeate. **-band,** *n.* steel tape; steel strap. **-bereitung,** *f.* steel making. **-beton,** *m.* steel concrete. **-betonbau,** *m.* steel-concrete construction or structure.

**stahlblau,** *a.* steel-blue.

**Stahl-blech,** *n.* steel plate, sheet steel. **-block,** *m.* (*Metal.*) steel ingot. **-bombe,** *f.* steel cylinder; steel bomb, steel shell. **-brunnen,** *m.* chalybeate spring. **-draht,** *m.* steel wire. **-eisen,** *n.* steely iron, steel pig.

**stählen,** *v.t.* steel, harden; convert into steel.

**stählern,** *a.* of steel, steel.

**Stahl-erz,** *n.* steel ore, specif. siderite. **-erzeugung,** *f.* steel production.

**stahlfarbig,** *a.* steel-colored.

**Stahl-feder,** *f.* steel spring; steel pen. **-flasche,** *f.* steel bottle, steel cylinder. **-formguss,** *m.* steel casting. **-frischfeuer,** *n.* steel finery. **-gattung,** *f.* grade of steel. **-gefäss,** *n.* steel vessel, steel receptacle. **-gewinnung,** *f.* steel making. **-giesserei,** *f.* steel founding; steel foundry.

**stahlgrau,** *a.* steel-gray.

**Stahlguss,** *m.* steel casting; cast steel; toughened cast iron.

**Stahlguss-.** cast-steel, steel-cast.

**Stahl-güte,** *f.* quality or grade of steel. **-hahn,** *m.* steel cock. **-hütte,** *f.* steel works. **-kobalt,** *m.* smaltite. **-kohlen,** *n.* conversion of wrought iron into steel by carbonization. **-kraut,** *n.* vervain. **-kugel,** *f.* steel ball. **-legierung,** *f.* steel alloy. **-mittel,** *n.* = Stahlarznei. **-mörser,** *m.* steel mortar. **-ofen,** *m.* steel furnace. **-perle,** *f.* steel bead. **-platte,** *f.* steel plate. **-präparat,** *n.* (*Pharm.*) iron preparation. **-probe,** *f.* steel sample; test of steel. **-puddeln,** *n.* steel puddling. **-quelle,** *f.* chalybeate spring. **-roheisen,** *n.* open-hearth pig iron. **-rohr,** *n.* steel pipe or tube. **-sand,** *m.* steel grit, steel sand. **-säuerling,** *m.* acidulous iron water. **-schmelzen,** *n.* steel melting, steel making. **-schmelzofen,** *m.* steel-melting furnace. **-schrott,** *m.* steel scrap. **-späne,** *m.pl.* steel turnings, steel chips. **-stange,** *f.* steel rod, steel bar. **-stechen,** *n.*, **-stecherei,** *f.* steel engraving. **-stein,** *m.* (*Min.*) siderite. **-stich,** *m.* steel engraving. **-trommel,** *f.* steel drum.

**Stählung,** *f.* steeling, hardening; conversion into steel, acieration.

**Stahl-waren,** *f.pl.* steel articles. **-wasser,** *n.* chalybeate water. **-wein,** *m.* iron wine. **-werk,** *n.* steel mill, steelworks. **-wolle,** *f.* steel wool.

**stak,** *pret.* (of stecken) stuck, etc.

**Staket,** *n.* stockade; railing.

**Stall,** *m.* stable, stall, sty, shed. **-dünger, -mist,** *m.* stable manure.

**Stamm,** *m.* stem; stalk, trunk, stock; staff; breed, race, strain; tribe.

**Stamm-.** parent, original, primary, main, standard, stock. **-aktie,** *f.* share of common stock. **-ansatz,** *m.* (*Dyeing*) stock liquor, stock mixture, stock paste. **-ätze,** *f.* (*Calico*) standard discharge, stock discharge. **-baum,** *m.* flow sheet; pedigree.

**stammeln,** *v.t.* & *i.* stammer.

**Stammemulsion,** *f.* stock emulsion.

**stammen,** *v.i.* spring, descend, originate, come (of or from); date (from).

**Stamm-farbe,** *f.* primary color; = Stammansatz. **-flotte,** *f.* (*Dyeing*) stock liquor, stock solution.

**stämmig,** *a.* robust, strong; stumpy.

**Stamm-körper,** *m.* parent substance (or compound); parent body. **-küpe,** *f.* (*Dyeing*) stock vat. **-leitung,** *f.* (*Elec.*) main circuit, trunk line. **-linie,** *f.* trunk line, main line. **-lösung,** *f.* stock solution. **-reserve,** *f.* (*Calico*) stock resist. **-substanz,** *f.* parent substance. **-tafel,** *f.* flow sheet. **-verdickung,** *f.* stock thickening.

**stammverwandt,** *p.a.* kindred, cognate.

**Stamm-werk,** *n.* parent plant, main plant. **-würze,** *f.* original wort.

**Stampf-asphalt,** *m.* tamped asphalt. **-beton,** *m.* tamped concrete.

**Stampfe,** *f.* stamp, stamper, pestle, punch, rammer, ram, hammer.

**stampfen,** *v.t.* stamp, beat, pound, ram, tamp, punch. — *v.i.* stamp, pitch.

**Stampfer,** *m.* = Stampfe.

**Stampf-futter,** *n.* tamped lining. **-haufen,** *m.* (*Paper*) batch. **-masse,** *f.* tamping mass, ramming mass. **-mörtel,** *m.* tamped mortar. **-werk,** *n.* stamp mill.

**stand,** *pret.* (of stehen) stood, etc.

**Stand,** *m.* position; stand; state, condition, status; stage; height, level (of a liquid); rank, station.

**Standard-abweichung,** *f.* standard deviation. **-einheit,** *f.* standard unit. **-fehler,** *m.* standard error. **-lösung,** *f.* standard solution. **-wert,** *m.* standard value.

**Stand-bild,** *n.* statue. **-bücherei,** *f.* reference library. **-dauer,** *f.* duration (or time) of standing. **-entwicklung,** *f.* (*Photog.*) tank development.

**Ständer,** *m.* stand, standard, support, pillar, post, pedestal; cistern, tank, holder; stator. **-klemme,** *f.* clamp for a stand.

**stand-fähig,** *a.* stable, firm. **-fest,** *a.* stable; rigid, firm.

**Stand-festigkeit,** *f.* stability; rigidity. **-flasche,** *f.* a bottle (or flask) to be stood in a fixed place, as a reagent bottle; flat-bottomed flask. **-gärung,** *f.* standing fermentation. **-gefäss,** *n.* a vessel made to stand in a fixed place, as a museum jar; storage vessel; stock tub. **-glas,** *n.* a glass vessel to be stood in a fixed place, as a reagent bottle; glass cylinder; glass gage.

**stand-haft,** *a.* steady, constant, firm. **-halten,** *v.i.* stand firm, hold out.

**ständig,** *a.* stationary, fixed; constant, permanent, regular.

**-ständig.** in the (given) position.

**Stand-kugel,** *f.* stationary bulb. **-mörser,** *m.* a heavy mortar with a firm base. **-öl,** *n.* stand oil, lithographic oil (made by heating linseed oil). **-ort,** *m.* & *n.* station, stand; location, site; (*Bot.*) habitat. **-punkt,** *m.* standpoint; standard. **-rohr,** *n.* standpipe, vertical pipe. **-sicherheit,** *f.* stability. **-tropfglas,** *n.* dropping bottle. **-verlust,** *m.* storage loss. **-wa(a)ge,** *f.* platform balance or scales. **-zylinder,** *m.* a standing cylindrical vessel, cylinder.

**Stange,** *f.* stick; rod, bar; pole; (of sulfur) roll; (of gold) ingot; (of a valve) stem.

**Stängelchen,** *n.* little stick, small stick.

**Stangen-blei,** *n.* bar lead. **-eisen,** *n.* bar iron, rod iron. **-gold,** *n.* ingot gold. **-kali,** *n.* potash in sticks, stick potash. **-kitt,** *m.* stick cement. **-kupfer,** *n.* bar copper, rod copper. **-lack,** *m.* stick-lac. **-schwefel,** *m.* roll sulfur, stick sulfur, cane brimstone. **-seife,** *f.* bar soap. **-silber,** *n.* ingot silver. **-spat,** *m.* columnar barite. **-stahl,** *m.* bar steel; rod steel. **-stein,** *m.* pycnite (columnar topaz). **-tabak,** *m.* roll tobacco. **-wachs,** *n.* stick wax, stick polish. **-zinn,** *n.* bar tin.

**Staniol,** *f.* tin foil.

**stank,** *pret.* (of stinken) stank.

**stänkern,** *v.i.* stink.

**Stannatlauge,** *f.* stannate liquor.

**Stanni-.** stannic, stanni-, tin(IV). **-azetat,** *n.* stannic acetate, tin(IV) acetate. **-chlorid,** *n.* stannic chloride, tin(IV) chloride. **-chlorwasserstoffsäure,** *f.* chlorostannic acid. **-hydroxyd,** *n.* stannic hydroxide, tin(IV) hydroxide. **-jodid,** *n.* stannic iodide, tin(IV) iodide.

**Stanniol,** *f.* tin foil. **-kapsel,** *f.* tinfoil cap.

**Stanni-oxyd,** *n.* stannic oxide, tin(IV) oxide. **-reihe,** *f.* stannic series, tin(IV) series. **-salz,** *n.* stannic salt, tin(IV) salt. **-sulfozyanid,** *n.* stannic thiocyanate, tin(IV) thiocyanate. **-verbindung,** *f.* stannic compound, tin(IV) compound.

**Stanno-.** stannous, stanno-, tin(II). **-azetat,** *n.* stannous acetate, tin(II) acetate. **-chlorid,** *n.* stannous chloride, tin(II) chloride. **-chlorwasserstoffsäure,** *f.* chlorostannous acid. **-hydroxyd,** *n.* stannous hydroxide, tin(II) hydroxide. **-jodid,** *n.* stannous iodide, tin(II) iodide. **-jodwasserstoffsäure,** *f.* iodostannous acid. **-oxyd,** *n.* stannous oxide, tin(II) oxide. **-salz,** *n.* stannous salt, tin(II) salt. **-sulfid,** *n.* stannous sulfide, tin(II) sulfide. **-verbindung,** *f.* stannous compound, tin(II) compound.

**Stanzabfall,** *m.* stamping, punching (waste).

**Stanze,** *f.* puncher, punch, die; (usually *pl.*) stamping, punching.

**stanzen,** *v.t.* stamp; punch; emboss.

**Stanz-porzellan,** *n.* porcelain for punching. **-presse,** *f.* stamping press.

**Stapel,** *m.* staple; warehouse; pile, heap, stack. **-farbe,** *f.* staple color. **-faser,** *f.* staple fiber (rayon yarn). **-gemüse,** *n.* staple vegetables.

**stapeln,** *v.t.* stack, pile; store.

**Stapelware,** *f.* staple goods.

**Star,** *m.* (*Med.*) cataract; starling.

**starb,** *pret.* (of sterben) died.

**stark,** *a.* strong; powerful, loud, heavy, fat, large, thick. — *adv.* strongly, hard.

**Starkbrenner,** *m.* a kind of burner with self-forced draft.

**Stärke,** *f.* starch; strength; intensity; size; thickness; diameter; corpulency. **-abbau,** *m.* degradation of starch. **-art,** *f.* variety of starch.

**stärkeartig,** *a.* starchy, amylaceous, amyloid.

**Stärke-bildner,** *m.* (*Bot.*) leucoplast. **-bildung,** *f.* formation of starch. **-blau,** *n.* starch blue. **-fabrik,** *f.* starch factory.

**stärkeführend,** *a.* amylaceous.

**Stärke-gehalt,** *m.* starch content. **-grad,** *m.* degree of strength, intensity. **-gummi,** *n.* starch gum, dextrin.

**stärkehaltig,** *a.* containing starch, starchy, amylaceous.

**Stärke-kleister,** *m.* starch paste. **-korn, -körnchen,** *n.* starch granule. **-lösung,** *f.* starch solution. **-mehl,** *n.* starch flour, starch powder, starch.

**stärkemehl-ähnlich,** *a.* amylaceous, amyloid. **-artig,** *a.* starchy, amylaceous. **-haltig,** *a.* containing starch.

**Stärke-mehlkleister,** *m.* starch paste. **-messer,** *m.* amylometer. **-messung,** *f.* measurement of strength or size. **-milch,** *f.* thin starch paste. **-mittel,** *n.* strengthening remedy, tonic, restorative.

**stärken,** *v.t.* starch; strengthen; thicken; refresh; confirm.

**Stärke-papier,** *n.* starch paper. **-pulver,** *n.* starch powder, powdered starch.

**stärkereich,** *a.* rich (or high) in starch.

**Stärke-sirup,** *m.* starch sirup, glucose. **-verhältnis,** *n.* relation as to strength or size. **-wasser,** *n.* starch water. **-weizen,** *m.* starch wheat, emmer. **-wert,** *m.* starch value. **-zucker,** *m.* starch sugar, glucose.

**stark-farbig,** *a.* strongly colored. **-faserig,** *a.* strong-fibered.

**Starkgas,** *n.* rich gas, specif. coal gas.

**starkklopfend,** *a.* strongly knock-producing.

**Starkstrom,** *m.* (*Elec.*) heavy current, power current. **-leitung,** *f.* (*Elec.*) high-tension line.

**Stärkung,** *f.* starching, etc. (see stärken).

**Stärkungsmittel,** *n.* = Stärkemittel.

**starkwandig,** *a.* stout-walled, thick-walled.

**Starkwasser,** *n.* strong ammonia water.

**stark-wirkend,** *p.a.* powerful, efficacious, drastic. **-wirksam,** *a.* highly active, powerful. **-zügig,** *a.* (*Paints*) long-stroke.

**starr,** *a.* rigid, stiff; numb; inflexible.

**Starre,** *f.* = Starrheit.

**starren,** *v.i.* stare; be numb, be stiff, stiffen.

**Starr-heit,** *f.* rigidity, stiffness; rigor; obstinacy. **-krampf,** *m.* tetanus; tonic convulsion. **-krampfserum,** *n.* antitetanus serum. **-leinen,** *n.*, **-leinwand,** *f.* buckram. **-schmiere,** *f.* solid lubricant. **-sucht,** *f.* catalepsy.

**stät, stätig,** *a.* fixed, stable, constant.

**Statik,** *f.* statics.

**stationär,** *a.* stationary; (of flight) steady.

**statisch,** *a.* static.

**statistisch,** *a.* statistical.

**Stativ,** *n.* stand, support; tripod; stage. **-chen,** *n.* small stand or support. **-lupe,** *f.* stand magnifier.

**statt,** *prep.* instead of.

**Statt,** *f.* place, stead.

**Stätte,** *f.* place, room.

**statten.** In the phrases: **von — gehen,** take place, go off, pass off; **zu — kommen,** be of use or advantage.

**stattfinden, statthaben,** *v.i.* take place, occur. — **stattgehabt,** *p.a.* previous.

**statt-haft,** *a.* allowable, permissible; legal. **-lich,** *a.* fine, splendid, stately; portly.

**Stau,** *m.* damming, damming up.

**Staub,** *m.* dust; powder; pollen. **-abscheider,** *m.* dust separator.

**staubartig,** *a.* dust-like, powdery, pulverulent.

**Stäubchen,** *n.* tiny particle, mote.

**staubdicht,** *a.* dust-tight, dustproof.

**stäuben,** *v.t.* dust; powder; spray.

**Staub-fänger,** *m.* dust catcher, dust collector. **-farbe,** *f.* powdered color.

**staubfein,** *a.* fine as dust, very fine.

**Staub-feuerung,** *f.* firing with powdered fuel. **-figuren,** *f.pl.* dust figures, powder pattern.

**staub-förmig,** *a.* in the form of dust, pulverulent. **-frei,** *a.* dust-free, dustless.

**Staub-gefäss,** *n.* (*Bot.*) stamen. **-gehalt,** *m.* dust content.

**staubhaltig,** *a.* containing dust, dust-laden.

**Staubhefe,** *f.* nonflocculating yeast.

**staubig,** *a.* dusty; pulverulent, powdery.

**Staub-kalk,** *m.* air-slaked lime, powdered lime. **-kohle,** *f.* coal dust; powdered coal. **-korn,** *m.* dust particle.

**Staublech,** *n.* baffle plate.

**Staub-luft,** *f.* dust-laden air. **-maske,** *f.* dust mask. **-mehl,** *n.* (flour) mill dust, dustings. **-öl,** *n.* floor oil. **-sand,** *m.* very fine sand, sand dust. **-sauger,** *m.* dust suction apparatus, vacuum cleaner. **-schutzmaske,** *f.* dust mask.

**staubsicher,** *a.* dustproof.

**Staub-sieb,** *n.* dust sieve. **-tee,** *m.* tea dust. **-teilchen,** *n.* dust particle.

**staubtrocken,** *a.* dry as dust; (of varnish) dry so that dust does not stick.

**Staubzähler,** *m.* dust counter.

**Stauch-apparat,** *m.* (*Expl.*) brisance meter. **-druck,** *m.* crushing pressure, compression.

**stauchen,** *v.t.* compress (by a blow); knock, beat; bulge; (*Metals*) upset. — *v.r.* buckle.

**Stauchprobe,** *f.* compression test; bulging test; hammering test.

**Stauchung,** *f.* compression, etc. (see stauchen).

**Stauchzylinder,** *m.* (*Expl.*) crusher gage.

**Staude,** *f.* shrub, bush; perennial herb.
**stauen,** *v.t.* stow; dam up; baffle; choke; congest. — *v.i.* choke.
**Staufferfett,** *n.* Stauffer grease, cup grease.
**staunen,** *v.i.* be astonished, be surprised.
**Staunen,** *n.* astonishment, surprise, wonder.
**staunenswert,** *a.* wonderful, astonishing.
**Stauscheibe,** *f.* baffle plate.
**Stauung,** *f.* obstruction, congestion; damming; rise (of water); stowage.
**Stau-wand,** *f.* baffle plate. **-wirkung,** *f.* damming effect, baffle effect.
**Std.,** *abbrev.* (Stunde, Stunden) hour, hours.
**Stde.,** *abbrev.* (Stunde) hour.
**stdg.,** *abbrev.* (stündig) -hour, -hours.
**Stdn.,** *abbrev.* (Stunden) hours.
**Stearin-kerze,** *f.* stearin candle. **-öl,** *n.* oleic acid. **-pech,** *n.* stearing pitch.
**stearinsauer,** *a.* of or combined with stearic acid, stearate of.
**Stearin-säure,** *f.* stearic acid. **-seife,** *f.* stearin soap, common soap.
**steatinisch,** *a.* tallowy.
**Stechapfel,** *m.* thorn apple (*Datura*, esp. *D. stramonium*); (*Pharm.*) stramonium.
**stechen,** *v.t.* stick, prick, pierce, puncture, stab; sting; tap; turn (malt); cut; engrave. — *v.i.* sting; incline; spout, spire. — **stechend,** *p.a.* stinging, piercing, penetrating, pungent.
**Stecher,** *m.* something that pierces or is stuck in, as a proof stick (for sugar) or a sampler (of various kinds); pin; pricker; engraver.
**Stech-heber,** *m.* plunging siphon, thief tube; pipet(te). **-kolben,** *n.* pipet(te). **-kunst,** *f.* engraving. **-palme,** *f.* holly; Christ's-thorn (*Paliurus*). **-palmenbitter,** *n.* ilicin. **-pipette,** *f.* (ordinary) pipet(te). **-probe,** *f.* touchstone test. **-stock,** *m.* (*Dyeing*) prodding stick.
**Steckdose,** *f.* (*Elec.*) plug socket, receptacle.
**stecken,** *v.i.* stick, stay, remain; hide. — *v.t.* stick, set, fix, put. — **— bleiben,** be stuck, break down, stop.
**Stecker,** *m.* (*Elec.*) plug. **-büchse,** *f.* (*Elec.*) plug socket, plug box.
**Steck-kontakt,** *m.* (*Elec.*) plug connection. **-lot,** *n.* grain spelter (for muffle brazing). **-nadel,** *f.* pin. **-rübe,** *f.* rutabaga.
**Steg,** *m.* path; (small) bridge; crosspiece, stay, strap, bar, web, flange; (*Molding*) gate.
**Steh-bild,** *n.* still picture. **-bolzen,** *m.* stay bolt. **-bütte,** *f.* stock tub.
**stehen,** *v.i.* stand; be; become, fit; be responsible. — **stehend,** *p.a.* standing, stationary, staple, upright, vertical; lasting; (of water) stagnant. — **stehen bleiben,** stand still, stop. — **stehen lassen,** let stand; keep, preserve.
**stehenbleibend,** *a.* stationary; inactive; persistent; remaining.
**Steh-kölbchen,** *n.* small flat-bottomed flask. **-kolben,** *m.* flat-bottomed flask. **-lampe,** *f.* floor lamp.
**stehlen,** *v.t.* steal.
**Stehlstange,** *f.* thief rod.
**steierisch,** *a.* Styrian.
**Steiermark,** *f.* Styria.
**steif,** *a.* stiff, rigid, firm; awkward; formal; precise.
**Steife,** *f.* stiffening (starch, glue, size); consistency; prop, strut, stay; stiffness, rigidity.
**steifen,** *v.t.* stiffen; starch; stay, prop.
**Steifheit,** *f.* stiffness, rigidity.
**Steifigkeit,** *f.* stiffness, rigidity, firmness.
**Steifigkeitszahl,** *f.* coefficient of rigidity.
**Steif-leinen,** *n.*, **-leinwand,** *f.* buckram.
**Steifung,** *f.* stiffening, sizing, starching.
**Steifungsmittel,** *n.* stiffening (agent).
**Steig,** *m.* path; trail. **-brunnen,** *m.* artesian well.
**Steige,** *f.* steps; ladder; trail.
**steigen,** *v.i.* rise, ascend, mount, climb, increase.
**steigern,** *v.t.* raise, increase, augment.
**Steigerohr,** *n.* = Steigrohr.
**Steigerung,** *f.* raising, increase, rise, heightening; raise; increment; comparison (of adjectives, etc.).
**Steig-höhe,** *f.* height of ascent, rise, elevation; pitch (of a screw). **-höhemethode,** *f.* sedimentation-equilibrium method (for determining particle size). **-leitung,** *f.* ascending pipe, rising main. **-raum,** *m.* (*Brewing*) unfilled space above the wort. **-rohr,** *n.*, **-röhre,** *f.* ascending or rising tube or pipe, riser.
**Steigung,** *f.* rising, rise, ascent, increase; incline, pitch, gradient, grade, slope.
**steil,** *a.* steep; precipitous.
**Steile,** *f.* steepness, declivity.
**Steilheit,** *f.* steepness, slope; (*Photog.*) contrast.
**Steilschrauber,** *m.* helicopter.
**Stein,** *m.* stone; rock; brick; (*Metal.*) mat(te); (*Med.*) calculus, concretion. — **— der Weisen,** philosophers' stone.
**Steinabfälle,** *m.pl.* stone chips, spalls.
**steinähnlich,** *a.* stone-like, stony.
**Stein-alaun,** *m.* rock alum. **-arbeit,** *f.* metal smelting; stone work.
**steinartig,** *a.* stone-like, stony.
**Stein-auflösungsmittel,** *n.* solvent for calculus. **-brand,** *m.* (*Bot.*) bunt, stinking smut. **-brech,** *m.* saxifrage. **-brecher,** *m.* stone breaker, stone crusher. **-brechmaschine,** *f.* stone crusher, rock crusher. **-bruch,** *m.* quarry. **-bühlergelb,** *n.* barium yellow (barium chromate). **-butter,** *f.* rock butter.
**Steindruck,** *m.* lithography; lithograph. **-farbe,** *f.* lithographic ink. **-kalkstein,** *m.* lithographic limestone.
**steinern,** *a.* stone, of stone.

**Stein-fänger,** *m.* stone catcher or remover. **-farbe,** *f.* stone color.

**steinfarbig,** *a.* stone-colored.

**Stein-flachs,** *m.* mountain flax, amianthus. **-flasche,** *f.* stoneware bottle. **-frucht,** *f.* stone fruit, drupe. **-glättung,** *f.* (*Paper*) flint glazing. **-grau,** *n.* a gray pigment made from clay slate. **-gries, -griess,** *m.* gravel. **-grün,** *n.* terre verte (pigment made from glauconite or celadonite). **-gut,** *n.* (*Ceram.*) earthenware, specif. white ware (having a white absorbent body and soft glaze). **-gutgeschirr,** *n.* earthenware, specif. white ware (articles).

**steinhart,** *a.* hard as stone.

**Steinholz,** *n.* xylolith (magnesia cement mixed with sawdust or the like).

**steinig,** *a.* stony, of stone, rocky.

**Stein-kern,** *m.* stone (in fruit, in burnt lime). **-kitt,** *m.* cement for stone. **-klee,** *m.* melilot (*Melilotus*, esp. *M. officinalis*); white clover (*Trifolium repens*). **-kohle,** *f.* mineral coal, coal.

**Steinkohlen-asche,** *f.* coal ashes. **-benzin,** *n.* benzene (or benzol(e), the commercial mixture). **-bergwerk,** *n.* coal mine. **-entgasung,** *f.* distillation of coal. **-gas,** *n.* coal gas. **-kampher,** *n.* naphthalene. **-klein,** *n.* slack, culm. **-leuchtgas,** *n.* illuminating gas from coal, coal gas. **-öl,** *n.* coal-tar oil. **-pech,** *n.* coal-tar pitch. **-schicht,** *f.* coal seam, coal measure. **-schiefer,** *m.* coal-bearing shale. **-schlacke,** *f.* (coal) cinders. **-schwelteer,** *m.* low-temperature coal tar. **-schwelung,** *f.* low-temperature carbonization of coal. **-staub,** *m.* coal dust.

**Steinkohlenteer,** *m.* coal tar. **-benzin,** *n.* benzene; benzol(e). **-blase,** *f.* coal-tar still. **-essenz,** *f.* first light oil. **-farbe,** *f.* coal-tar color. **-kampher,** *m.* naphthalene. **-öl,** *n.* coal-tar oil (**leichtes,** light oil; **schweres,** heavy oil). **-pech,** *n.* coal-tar pitch. **-präparat,** *n.* coal-tar preparation, coal-tar product.

**Steinkohlen-verkohlung, -verkokung,** *f.* coking of coal, coking. **-zeit,** *f.* Coal Age, Carboniferous.

**Stein-körper,** *m.* stony body, (*Bot.*) stone cell or cell cluster. **-kraut,** *n.* stonecrop (*Sedum*), also various other plants. **-lager,** *n.* jeweled bearing. **-malz,** *n.* glassy or vitreous malt. **-mark,** *n.* (*Min.*) lithomarge. **-mauer,** *f.* stone wall; brick wall. **-mehl,** *n.* stone powder. **-meissel,** *m.* stone chisel. **-metz,** *m.* stone mason. **-mörtel,** *m.* hard mortar; concrete; (Portland) cement; badigeon. **-nuss,** *f.* ivory nut. **-obst,** *n.* stone fruit. **-öl,** *n.* petroleum.

**steinölhaltig,** *a.* petroliferous, oil-bearing.

**Stein-pappe,** *f.* roofing fabric, roofing paper or board; carton pierre. **-pech,** *n.* stone pitch (hard pitch); (hard) asphalt. **-pilz,** *m.* *Boletus edulis*, an edible mushroom. **-platte,** *f.* stone slab or plate; flagstone. **-porzellan,** *n.* hard porcelain. **-reich,** *n.* mineral kingdom. **-rösten,** *n.* roasting of the regulus or mat(te). **-salz,** *n.* rock salt. **-salzlager,** *n.* rock salt bed. **-säure,** *f.* lithic acid (uric acid). **-schlag,** *m.* broken stone; fall of rock. **-schmelzen,** *n.* (*Metal.*) mat(te) smelting. **-schutt,** *m.* rubble; rock debris. **-staublunge,** *f.* silicosis. **-stopfen,** *n.* stoneware stopper (for carboys). **-waren,** *f.pl.* stoneware. **-zeit,** *f.* Stone Age. **-zelle,** *f.* (*Bot.*) stone cell. **-zement,** *m.* concrete. **-zeug,** *n.* (*Ceram.*) stoneware (having a vitreous gray, yellow or brown body). **-zeuggefäss,** *n.* stoneware vessel. **-zeugrohr,** *n.* stoneware pipe.

**steirisch,** *a.* Styrian.

**Steiss,** *m.* buttock; butt, rump.

**Stell-.** (*Mach.*) stay, set-, adjusting, regulating.

**stellbar,** *a.* adjustable; movable.

**Stellbarkeit,** *f.* adjustability; movability.

**Stellbottich,** *m.* (*Brewing*) fermenting vat; (*Dyeing*) settling vat.

**Stelle,** *f.* place, spot; position, station; office, agency.

**stellen,** *v.t.* place, put, set; regulate, adjust; standardize; stop, check; supply, furnish; shade, blend (colors). — *v.r.* place oneself, stand, appear; prove, be; pretend to be. **-weise,** *adv.* in spots, in places.

**Stellenzahl,** *f.* position number, specif. atomic number; number of places or digits; (*Math.*) index.

**Stell-farbstoff,** *m.* shading dye. **-hahn,** *m.* regulating cock. **-hefe,** *f.* pitching yeast.

**-stellig.** (*Math.*) -place, -figure, -digit.

**stellitieren,** *v.t.* stellite, stellitize.

**Stell-lage,** *f.* rack. **-marke,** *f.* index mark, index. **-mittel,** *n.* diluent, extender; adulterant; standardizing agent. **-mutter,** *f.* adjusting nut. **-öl,** *n.* (*Petroleum*) neutral oil. **-schraube,** *f.* set screw; adjusting screw.

**Stellung,** *f.* placing, etc. (see stellen); position; arrangement; attitude; constellation.

**Stellungsisomerie,** *f.* position isomerism.

**Stell-vertreter,** *m.* deputy, substitute. **-vertretung,** *f.* substitution; proxy. **-vorrichtung,** *f.* adjusting device.

**Stemmeisen,** *n.* chisel; crowbar.

**stemmen,** *v.t.* prop, support; calk; dam up (water); fell (wood).

**Stempel,** *m.* stamp; stamper, die, punch, pestle; piston; brand, mark; pistil; post, prop. **-farbe,** *f.* stamping ink. **-kissen,** *n.* stamp(ing) pad. **-marke,** *f.* stamp.

**stempeln,** *v.t.* stamp; punch; mark; prop.

**Stempelzeichen,** *n.* stamp, mark.
**Stengel,** *m.* stalk, stem; column. **-faser,** *f.* stalk fiber, stem fiber. **-gewebe,** *n.* (*Bot.*) stem tissue.
**stengelig,** *a.* stalked; columnar; (*Metal.*) spiky.
**Stengelkohle,** *f.* columnar coal.
**Stephanskörner,** *n.pl.* stavesacre seeds.
**Steppdecke,** *f.* quilt.
**steppen,** *v.t.* quilt; stitch.
**sterben,** *v.i.* die; die away.
**sterblich,** *a.* mortal.
**Sterblichkeit,** *f.* mortality.
**Sterblingswolle,** *f.* dead wool, fallen wool.
**Stereochemie,** *f.* stereochemistry.
**stereo-chemisch,** *a.* stereochemical. **-isomer,** *a.* stereoisomeric.
**Stereoisomerie,** *f.* stereoisomerism.
**stereometrisch,** *a.* stereometric.
**Stereotypiepapier,** *n.* stereotyping paper, flong.
**stereotypieren,** *v.t.* stereotype.
**Sterilisationsverfahren,** *n.* sterilizing process.
**Sterilisator,** *m.* sterilizer.
**Sterilisierapparat,** *m.* sterilizing apparatus.
**sterilisieren,** *v.t.* sterilize.
**sterilisierfähig,** *a.* capable of being sterilized (esp., without damage).
**Sterilisierung,** *f.* sterilization.
**Sterilität,** *f.* sterility.
**Sterin,** *n.* sterol.
**sterisch,** *a.* steric, spatial.
**Stern,** *m.* star; asterisk; pupil (of the eye). **-anis,** *m.* star anise.
**sternartig,** *a.* star-like, stellar, stellate.
**Stern-bild,** *n.* constellation. **-chen,** *n.* little star; asterisk.
**sternförmig,** *a.* star-shaped, stellate.
**Stern-kunde,** *f.* astronomy. **-leuchtkugel, -leuchtpatrone,** *f.* star shell. **-physik,** *f.* astrophysics. **-rakete,** *f.* star rocket. **-rohr,** *n.* telescope. **-rubin,** *m.* star ruby. **-saphir,** *m.* star sapphire. **-schlacke,** *f.* (*Metal.*) antimony flux. **-schnuppe,** *f.* shooting star, meteor. **-signal,** *n.* (*Mil.*) signal flare. **-tier,** *n.* starfish. **-warte,** *f.* observatory. **-zeit,** *f.* sidereal time.
**Sterrometall,** *n.* sterro metal.
**stet,** *a.* steady, constant, stable, fixed.
**Stete,** *f.* constant.
**stetig,** *a.* continuous; constant; stable.
**stetigen,** *v.t.* stabilize; make constant.
**Stetigkeit,** *f.* continuity; constancy, steadiness; stability.
**stets,** *adv.* continually, ever, always; steadily.
**Steuer,** *f.* tax, duty. — *n.* rudder, helm, control. **-amt,** *n.* revenue board or office; customhouse.
**steuerbar,** *a.* steerable, regulable, controllable, manageable.
**Steuerelektrode,** *f.* control electrode.
**steuerfrei,** *a.* duty-free, exempt from taxes.
**Steuermarke,** *f.* revenue stamp.
**steuern,** *v.t.* steer; regulate, control; pay (taxes), contribute.
**Steuerung,** *f.* steering, etc. (see steuern); (*Mach.*) distribution, distributor (also, steering gear, controls).
**sthenosieren,** *v.t.* (*Textiles*) sthenosize.
**Stibiat,** *n.* antimonate, antimoniate.
**Stich,** *m.* prick, puncture, stab, sting; stitch; engraving; shooting pain; thrust, pass; (of colors) cast, tinge; (*Metal.*) tapping, tapped metal, tap hole, shrink hole. — **im Stiche lassen,** leave in the lurch.
**Stich-auge,** *f.* tap hole. **-eisen,** *n.* (*Metal.*) tapping bar.
**Stichel,** *m.* graver, burin.
**sticheln,** *v.t.* prick, puncture. — *v.i.* stitch; jeer, sneer.
**stichfest,** *a.* punctureproof; compact.
**Stichflamme,** *f.* fine-pointed flame; flareback; jet of flame.
**stichhaltig,** *a.* proof, valid, sound.
**-stichig.** (with names of colors) -tinged, -ish.
**Stich-kultur,** *f.* stab culture. **-loch,** *n.* tap hole. **-pfropf,** *m.* tap-hole plug. **-probe,** *f.* sample at random; sample taken by tapping or piercing; random test, spot check; (*Metal.*) assay of tapped metal; (*Brewing*) pricking test.
**sticht,** *pr. 3 sing.* (of stechen) sticks, etc.
**Stich-tag,** *m.* fixed day, key date, deadline. **-wein,** *m.* sample wine. **-wort,** *n.* heading; catchword; key word; code word; password; cue.
**Stick-dampf, -dunst,** *m.* choke damp; suffocating vapor. **-dioxyd,** *n.* nitrogen dioxide.
**sticken,** *v.i. & t.* choke, suffocate; embroider.
**Stickerei,** *f.* embroidery, fancywork.
**Stickgas,** *n.* suffocating gas, specif. (1) nitrogen gas, nitrogen, (2) carbon dioxide.
**stickig,** *a.* stuffy, close, suffocating.
**Stick-kohlenstoff,** *m.* carbon nitride. **-luft,** *f.* close air; nitrogen. **-oxyd,** *n.* nitric oxide. **-oxydentbindung,** *f.* liberation of nitric oxide. **-oxydul,** *n.* nitrous oxide, dinitrogen oxide. **-stoff,** *m.* nitrogen.
**Stickstoff-.** nitrogen, nitrogenous, nitric, nitrous, nitride of. **-ammonium,** *n.* ammonium nitride.
**stickstoffarm,** *a.* poor in nitrogen.
**Stickstoff-aufnahme,** *f.* absorption of nitrogen. **-ausscheidung,** *f.* nitrogen separation or elimination. **-benzoyl,** *n.* benzoyl nitride (or azide). **-bestimmung,** *f.* determination of nitrogen. **-bor,** *n.* boron nitride. **-brücke,** *f.* nitrogen bridge. **-cyantitan,** *n.* titanium cyanonitride. **-dämpfe,** *m.pl.* nitrous vapors or fumes. **-dioxyd,** *n.* nitrogen dioxide.

**-dünger,** *m.* nitrogenous manure, nitrogenous fertilizer. **-entbindung,** *f.* liberation of nitrogen.
**stickstofffrei,** *a.* nitrogen-free, non-nitrogenous.
**Stickstoff-gas,** *n.* nitrogen gas. **-gehalt,** *m.* nitrogen content. **-gleichgewicht,** *n.* nitrogen equilibrium. **-halogen,** *n.* nitrogen halide.
**stickstoffhaltig,** *a.* containing nitrogen, nitrogenous.
**Stickstoff-kalk,** *m.* = Kalkstickstoff. **-kalomel,** *n.* mercurous azide, mercury(I) azide. **-kalzium,** *n.* calcium nitride. **-kohlenoxyd,** *n.* carbonyl nitride (or azide), carbodiazide. **-lithium,** *n.* lithium nitride. **-lost,** *n.* nitrogen mustard gas. **-magnesium,** *n.* magnesium nitride. **-metall,** *n.* metallic nitride. **-natrium,** *n.* sodium nitride. **-oxyd,** *n.* nitrogen oxide; specif., nitric oxide. **-oxydul,** *n.* nitrous oxide. **-oxydulgas,** *n.* nitrous oxide gas. **-quecksilber,** *n.* mercury nitride. **-quecksilberoxydul,** *n.* mercurous azide, mercury(I) azide.
**stickstoffreich,** *a.* rich in nitrogen, highly nitrogenous.
**Stickstoff-sammler,** *m.* collector of nitrogen, specif. a nitrogen-storing plant (leguminous plant). **-säure,** *f.* nitrogenous acid; specif., hydrazoic acid, hydronitric acid. **-silber,** *n.* silver nitride; fulminating silver. **-silizid,** *n.* nitrogen silicide (silicon nitride). **-titan,** *n.* titanium nitride. **-überschuss,** *m.* excess of nitrogen. **-vanadin,** *n.* vanadium nitride. **-verbindung,** *f.* nitrogen compound. **-wasserstoff,** *m.* hydrogen nitride, nitrogen hydride (specif., the trinitride, $HN_3$).
**stickstoffwasserstoffsauer,** *a.* of or combined with hydrazoic acid, azide (or hydrazoate) of.
**Stickstoffwasserstoffsäure,** *f.* hydrazoic acid, hydronitric acid. **-phenylester,** *m.* phenyl azide (or hydrazoate), azidobenzene.
**Stickstoff-werk,** *n.* nitrogen plant. **-zyantitan,** *n.* titanium cyanonitride.
**stickt,** *pr. 3 sing.* (of stecken) sticks, etc.
**Stickwetter,** *n.pl.* (*Mining*) foul air, choke damp, after-damp, nitrous fumes.
**stieben,** *v.i.* fly about (like dust), be scattered; drizzle.
**Stief-.** step-.
**Stiefel,** *m.* boot; case, barrel, tube. **-lack,** *m.* shoe polish. **-schwärze, -wichse,** *f.* shoe blacking.
**Stiefmütterchen,** *n.* pansy.
**stieg,** *pret.* (of steigen) rose, ascended, etc.
**Stiege,** *f.* stairs; steps; ladder; score.
**stiehlt,** *pr. 3 sing.* (of stehlen) steals.
**Stiel,** *m.* handle, shaft; stem, stalk. **-granate,** *f.* (*Mil.*) stick hand grenade. **-pfeffer,** *m.* cubeb(s). **-zelle,** *f.* stalk cell.

**Stier,** *m.* bull; steer; ox.
**stieren,** *v.i.* stare.
**stiess,** *pret.* (of stossen) pushed, thrust, etc.
**Stift,** *m.* pin, peg, tack, stud, nail, spike; pencil, crayon; tag; snag, stump; apprentice. — *n.* (philanthropic) foundation; monastery; seminary. **-draht,** *m.* wire for making nails.
**stiften,** *v.t.* tack; found, establish, make.
**Stift-farbe,** *f.* pencil color, colored crayon, pastel. **-schraube,** *f.* stud bolt, stud.
**Stiftung,** *f.* foundation, endowment.
**Stil,** *m.*, **Stilart,** *f.* style.
**Stilbenchinon,** *n.* stilbenequinone.
**still, stille,** *a.* still, silent, quiet; inanimate; stagnant, dull. — **stille Entladung,** (*Elec.*) silent discharge. — **das Stille Meer,** the Pacific Ocean.
**Stille,** *f.* stillness, etc. (see still).
**stillen,** *v.t.* still, allay, calm; gratify; stop, stay. — **stillend,** *p.a.* calming, allaying, sedative, lenitive.
**stilllegen,** *v.t.* stop, close, shut down.
**Still-mittel,** *n.* sedative. **-schweigen,** *n.* silence.
**still-schweigend,** *a.* silent; tacit; implied. **-setzen,** *v.t.* stop, close, shut down.
**Stillstand,** *m.* standstill, stop, shutdown; (*Med.*) stasis.
**stillstehen,** *v.i.* stand still, stop. — **stillstehend,** *p.a.* stationary; stagnant.
**stillstellen,** *v.t.* stop.
**Stillung,** *f.* stilling, etc. (see stillen); (*Med.*) lactation.
**Stillungsmittel,** *n.* sedative.
**Stimm-.** of the voice, vocal; tuning; of votes. **-band,** *n.* vocal chord.
**Stimme,** *f.* voice; vote; (musical) part; sound.
**stimmen,** *v.i.* be in tune; accord, agree; vote. — *v.t.* tune; dispose.
**Stimm-gabel,** *f.* tuning fork. **-recht,** *n.* suffrage, franchise.
**Stimmung,** *f.* tuning, tune, key, pitch; mood; morale.
**Stimulantia,** *n.pl.* stimulants.
**stimulieren,** *v.t* stimulate.
**Stimulierung,** *f.* stimulation.
**Stink-.** stinking, fetid. **-asand, -asant,** *m.* asafetida. **-äscher,** *m.* (*Leather*) rotten lime.
**stinken,** *v.i.* stink, smell foul. — **stinkend,** *p.a.* stinking, fetid, ill-smelling.
**Stink-farbe,** *f.* old weak tan liquor. **-fluss, -flussspat,** *m.* fetid fluor spar (bituminous fluorite). **-harz,** *n.* asafetida. **-kalk,** *m.* anthraconite (bituminous limestone). **-kohle,** *f.* fetid coal. **-mergel,** *m.* fetid marl (bituminous marl). **-öl,** *n.* fetid oil, specif. animal oil. **-quarz,** *m.* fetid quartz (bituminous quartz). **-raum,** *m.* gas chamber. **-raumprobe,** *f.* gas-chamber test. **-schiefer,** *m.* fetid shale. **-spat,** *m.* = Stinkfluss. **-stein,**

*m.* stinkstone (any fetid stone, specif. anthraconite).
**Stippe,** *f.* speck, spot; gravy, sauce.
**stippenfrei,** *a.* free from specks or spots.
**stirbt,** *pr. 3 sing.* (of sterben) dies.
**Stirn, Stirne,** *f.* forehead, brow; front, face.
**Stirn-.** frontal, front. **-fläche,** *f.* face, front. **-getriebe,** *n.* spur gear. **-rad,** *n.* spur wheel. **-seite,** *f.* front side, front. **-welle,** *f.* impact wave, bow wave.
**Stirrholz,** *n.* (wooden) stirrer.
**stob,** *pret.* (of stieben) flew about, etc.
**stöbern,** *v.i.* hunt about, rummage; drift; drizzle.
**Stocheisen,** *n.* poker, stoker, stirrer.
**stochen, stochern,** *v.t.* stir, stoke, poke (fire).
**Stöchiometrie,** *f.* stoichiometry.
**stöchiometrisch,** *a.* stoichiometric(al).
**Stock,** *m.* stick, staff; stock; rod, pole; block; trunk, butt, stump; main part, body; story, floor (of a building); mold; (*Brick*) clamp; (*Brewing,* etc.) vat, back.
**stock-.** utterly, entirely. **-blind,** *a.* stone-blind.
**stocken,** *v.i.* stop, slacken, stagnate; curdle; mold; decay; hesitate, falter.
**Stock-ende,** *f.* butt end. **-erz,** *n.* ore in big lumps.
**stockfinster,** *a.* pitch-dark.
**Stock-fisch,** *m.* stockfish (esp., dried codfish). **-fischlebertran,** *m.* cod-liver oil. **-fleck,** *m.* moldy stain, moldy spot, mildew.
**stockfleckig,** *a.* spotted with mold, moldy; stained, foxed.
**Stockholz,** *n.* stump wood.
**stockig, stöckig,** *a.* moldy, musty; stocky, stumpy; stubborn.
**Stock-lack,** *m.* stick-lac. **-lacksäure,** *f.* laccaic acid. **-probe,** *f.* (*Oils*) pour test. **-punkt,** *m.* (*Oils*) solidifying point, setting point, pour point. **-punkterniedriger,** *m.* pour-point depressant. **-schlacke,** *f.* shingling slag.
**Stockung,** *f.* stopping, etc. (see stocken); stoppage; jam, bottleneck; dry rot.
**Stockwerk,** *n.* story, floor (of a building); tier; section; (*Mining*) stockwork.
**Stoff,** *m.* substance; stuff; matter, material; body; cloth, fabric; (*Paper*) stuff, pulp. **-abfall,** *m.* waste, refuse, scrap, chips, parings, shavings, etc. **-ableitung,** *f.* (*Biol.*) translocation. **-ansatz,** *m.* (*Biol.*) anabolism. **-aufnahme,** *f.* absorption of material. **-austausch,** *m.* exchange of material. **-beutel,** *m.* cloth bag. **-bildung,** *f.* formation of a substance. **-brei,** *m.* (*Paper*) pulp (mixed with water). **-bütte,** *f.* (*Paper*) stuff chest. **-dichte,** *f.* (*Paper*) pulp consistency. **-druck,** *m.* calico printing. **-fänger,** *m.* (*Paper*) saveall. **-filter,** *m.* cloth filter. **-flussbild,** *n.* flow sheet. **-gattung,** *f.* kind of material, class of substances. **-haushalt,** *m.* (*Biol.*) metabolism. **-kufe,** *f.* (*Paper*) stuff vat. **-lehre,** *f.* chemistry. **-leimung,** *f.* (*Paper*) pulp sizing, engine sizing.
**stoff-lich,** *a.* material. **-los,** *a.* immaterial, unsubstantial.
**Stoff-menge,** *f.* quantity of a substance; amount of material. **-mischung,** *f.* (*Paper*) pulp mixture. **-mühle,** *f.* (*Paper*) stuff engine, hollander. **-patent,** *n.* patent on a substance. **-rahmen,** *m.* filter disk. **-teilchen,** *n.* particle of matter. **-umsatz,** *m.* change of substance, specif. metabolism. **-verbindung,** *f.* (*Patents*) composition of matter. **-verbrauch,** *m.* consumption of material. **-verwandtschaft,** *f.* chemical affinity.
**Stoffwechsel,** *m.* metabolism; change of substance. **-analyse,** *f.* metabolism analysis. **-beschleunigung,** *f.* acceleration of metabolism. **-gefälle,** *n.* metabolic gradient. **-gleichgewicht,** *n.* metabolic equilibrium. **-grösse,** *f.* metabolic rate. **-krankheit,** *f.* metabolic disorder or disease. **-produkt,** *n.* product of metabolism. **-prozess, -vorgang,** *m.* metabolic process. **-störung,** *f.* disturbance of metabolism.
**Stoff-zahl,** *f.* number of substances. **-zustand,** *m.* state of aggregation.
**stöhle,** *pret. subj.* (of stehlen) would steal.
**Stollen,** *m.* gallery, drift, tunnel; post, prop; cake of butter.
**stolpern,** *v.i.* stumble; trip; blunder.
**stolz,** *a.* proud, lofty.
**Stolz,** *m.* pride, loftiness.
**Stomachale, Stomachalmittel,** *n.* stomachic.
**Stopf-buchse, -büchse,** *f.* (*Mach.*) stuffing box.
**Stöpfel,** *m.* stopper, plug, cork.
**stopfen,** *v.t.* stuff, fill; stop; plug; constipate; darn, mend. — *v.i.* be costive. — **stopfend,** *p.a.* stuffing, etc.; astringent, styptic.
**Stopfen,** *n.* stuffing, etc. (see stopfen); stopper, plug, cork.
**Stopf-mittel,** *n.* (*Med.*) astringent, styptic. **-werg,** *n.* oakum.
**Stoppel,** *f.* stubble.
**Stoppuhr,** *f.* stop watch.
**Stöpsel,** *m.* stopper, plug, cork. **-flasche,** *f.* stoppered bottle (or flask). **-glas,** *n.* stoppered glass. **-hahn,** *m.* stopper cock, cock stopper. **-kasten,** *m.* (*Elec.*) resistance box.
**stöpseln,** *v.t.* stopper, cork, plug; plug in.
**Stöpselsicherung,** *f.* (*Elec.*) plug fuse.
**Stör,** *m.* sturgeon.
**Storaxharz,** *n.* storax resin, storax.
**Storch,** *n.* stork. **-schnabel,** *m.* pantograph; = Storchschnabelkraut. **-schnabelkraut,** *n.* crane's-bill, geranium, esp. herb Robert.
**stören,** *v.t.* disturb; perturb; trouble, de-

range; annoy; interrupt; stir, poke. — *v.i.* stir.

**störr-ig, -isch,** *a.* troublesome, refractory.

**Störstrahlung,** *f.* interfering radiation.

**Störung,** *f.* disturbance; perturbation; interruption; turbulence; (*Geol.*) deformation; trouble, derangement, disorder.

**störungsfrei,** *a.* undisturbed, trouble-free.

**Störungsgleichung,** *f.* perturbation equation.

**Störzel,** *m.* see Kandisstörzel.

**Stoss,** *m.* impulse, thrust, push, blow, stroke; impact, collision, percussion, shock, jolt, bump; recoil; pile, heap, (of papers) file; joint; blast (of a horn).

**stossartig,** *a.* jolting, jerky, intermittent.

**Stossbutter,** *f.* farm butter.

**stossdämpfend,** *a.* shock-absorbing, cushioning.

**Stoss-dämpfer,** *m.* shock absorber; dash pot. **-dauer,** *f.* duration of collision, of impact, etc. (see Stoss).

**Stössel,** *m.* pestle; stamper, rammer; tappet.

**stossempfindlich,** *a.* sensitive to shock.

**stossen,** *v.t.* push, thrust, hit, knock, ram; pound, bray, pulverize; join; slot. — *v.i.* thrust, dash, hit (at, against, or upon); (of boiling liquids) bump, knock; recoil.

**Stösser,** *m.* pestle; rammer, pounder, knocker.

**Stossfänger,** *m.* pressure equalizer, shock absorber.

**stossfest,** *a.* shockproof.

**Stossfestigkeit,** *f.* resistance to shock, impact strength.

**stossfrei,** *a.* free from shocks, smooth, steady.

**Stoss-glanz,** *m.* (*Leather*) friction glaze. **-ionisation,** *f.* ionization by collision. **-kette,** *f.* chain (or succession) of collisions. **-kraft,** *f.* percussive power. **-mine,** *f.* (*Mil.*) contact mine. **-punkt,** *m.* point of impact. **-querschnitt,** *m.* collision area; target area.

**stoss-reizbar,** *a.* sensitive to shock. **-sicher,** *a.* insensitive to shock, shockproof.

**stösst,** *pr. 3 sing.* (of stossen) pushes, etc.

**Stoss-versuch,** *m.* impact test. **-wa(a)ge,** *f.* ballistic pendulum.

**stossweise,** *adv.* by starts or jolts, jerkily; percussively; in batches.

**Stoss-welle,** *f.* percussion wave, impact wave. **-widerstand,** *m.* resistance to shock. **-zahl,** *f.* number of collisions, impact number. **-zünder,** *m.* percussion fuse.

**stottern,** *v.i.* stutter.

**Str.,** *abbrev.* (Strasse) street, St.

**stracks,** *adv.* straightway.

**Strafe,** *f.* punishment; penalty, fine.

**strafen,** *v.t.* punish; fine; rebuke, reprove.

**straff,** *a.* stretched, tight, tense, taut.

**straffen,** *v.t.* tighten, stretch.

**Straffheit,** *f.* tightness, tenseness, tension.

**Strafgeld,** *n.* fine; forfeit.

**sträflich,** *a.* criminal, wrong.

**straflos,** *a.* unpunished, innocent.

**Strahl,** *m.* ray; jet (of liquid or gas); beam; flash (of lightning); (*Geom.*) straight line, radius. — **$\alpha$-—,** $\alpha$-ray, alpha ray. — **$\beta$- —,** $\beta$-ray, beta ray; etc.

**Strahl-antrieb,** *m.* jet propulsion. **-apparat,** *m.* jet apparatus (as steam-jet injector, pump, or blower). **-asbest,** *m.* plumose asbestos. **-baryt,** *m.* radiated barite, Bologna stone. **-blende,** *f.* a variety of sphalerite. **-düse,** *f.* jet nozzle.

**strahlen,** *v.i.* emit rays, radiate. — **strahlend,** *p.a.* radiating, radiant. — **$\beta$-strahlend,** emitting beta rays. — **gestrahlt,** *p.a.* radiated, radiate.

**Strahlen-.** pertaining to rays or radiation; radiated, radiating; (*Anat.*) ciliary. **-art,** *f.* kind of ray or rays.

**strahlen-artig,** *a.* ray-like, radiating. **-brechend,** *p.a.* refracting, refractive.

**Strahlen-brechung,** *f.* refraction. **-brechungsmesser,** *m.* refractometer. **-bündel,** *n.*, **-büschel,** *m.* pencil of rays, beam.

**strahlenempfindlich,** *a.* sensitive to radiation.

**Strahlen-figur,** *f.* radiating figure. **-filter,** *n.* ray filter.

**strahlenförmig,** *a.* radiated, radiate.

**Strahlen-gang,** *m.* path of rays; beam. **-glimmer,** *m.* striated mica. **-härte,** *f.* hardness of radiation. **-kegel,** *m.* cone of rays. **-kunde,** *f.* radiology. **-kupfer,** *n.* clinoclasite. **-messer,** *m.* radiometer; actinometer. **-optik,** *f.* geometrical optics.

**strahlenoptisch,** *a.* of or pertaining to geometrical optics.

**Strahlen-pilz,** *m.* actinomyces. **-schutz,** *m.* protection from radiation, protective screen. **-sonne,** *f.* (*Biol.*) astrosphere. **-stein,** *m.* = Strahlstein. **-werfen,** *n.* radiation.

**Strahler,** *m.* radiator; beacon.

**Strahlerz,** *n.* clinoclasite.

**strahlförmig,** *a.* ray-like.

**Strahlgips,** *m.* fibrous gypsum.

**strahlig,** *a.* radiated, in rays; radiant; fibrous.

**Strahl-keil,** *m.* belemnite. **-kies,** *m.* marcasite. **-kondensator,** *m.* jet condenser. **-körper,** *m.* radiating body, radiator. **-pumpe,** *f.* jet pump, injector. **-punkt,** *m.* radiating point, radiant point. **-quarz,** *m.* fibrous quartz. **-schörl,** *m.* radiated tourmaline. **-stein,** *m.* actinolite; amianthus.

**Strahlung,** *f.* radiation; radiance.

**Strahlungs-druck,** *m.* radiation pressure. **-fläche,** *f.* emitting surface, radiator surface.

**strahlungslos,** *a.* free from radiation, without radiation.

**Strahlungs-vermögen,** *n.* radiating power. **-wärme,** *f.* heat of radiation; radiant heat.

**Strahl-vortrieb,** *m.* jet propulsion. **-wäsche,** *f.* washing with a jet. **-zeolith,** *m.* stilbite.

**Strähne,** *f.* hank, skein; strand.

**stramm,** *a.* tight, tense; (of rubber) snappy; robust; strict.

**Strammheit,** *f.* tightness, etc. (see stramm).

**Strand,** *m.* shore, strand. **-ablagerung,** *f.* (*Geol.*) shore deposit. **-nelke,** *f.* sea lavender (*Limonium*). **-pflanze,** *f.* seaside plant, littoral plant.

**Strang,** *m.* rope, cord; strand; hank, skein; web (of paper).

**Strängchen,** *n.* small rope; small skein.

**Strangfärberei,** *f.* hank dyeing; rope dyeing.

**strangfarbig,** *a.* dyed in the yarn.

**strangförmig,** *a.* cord-like, stringy.

**Strang-gewebe,** *n.* (*Bot.*) vascular tissue. **-presse,** *f.* (*Ceram.*) press for wire cutting; (*Metals*) extruding press. **-pressen,** *n.* (*Metals*) extrusion.

**Strapaze,** *f.* hardship, toil.

**Strasse,** *f.* street; way, road; train (of rolls); strait.

**Strassen-bahn,** *f.* street railway, tramway. **-bau,** *m.* road building. **-bauöl,** *n.* road oil. **-belag, -beleg,** *m.* road surface. **-beleuchtung,** *f.* street lighting. **-decke,** *f.* street (or road) surface. **-kehricht,** *m.* street sweepings; road scrapings. **-material,** *n.* road material.

**stratifizieren,** *v.t.* stratify.

**sträuben,** *v.t.* ruffle up. — *v.r.* bristle up; resist.

**straubig, sträubig,** *a.* (of wool) rough, coarse; rebellious.

**Strauch,** *m.* shrub, bush.

**strauchartig,** *a.* shrub-like, shrubby, frutescent.

**straucheln,** *v.i.* stumble.

**Strauchholz,** *n.* brushwood, underwood.

**Strauss,** *m.* bush; tuft, crest, bunch, bouquet; (*Bot.*) thyrsus; combat, strife; ostrich.

**Strebe,** *f.* stay, strut, brace, prop.

**streben,** *v.i.* strive, struggle, press; tend.

**Streben,** *n.* striving, pressing; tendency.

**strebsam,** *a.* industrious; aspiring, pushing.

**streckbar,** *a.* extensible; ductile; malleable.

**Streckbarkeit,** *f.* extensibility; ductility.

**Strecke,** *f.* distance, space, stretch, extent; gap; (railway) line; (*Mining*) drift, road; (*Metal.*) drawing.

**strecken,** *v.t.* stretch; extend, flatten, spread, draw (metal or thread), roll (metal, glass, etc.); dilute, extend; lay low, lay down. — *v.r.* stretch, spread, extend. — **gestreckt,** *p.a.* stretched, etc.; straight, linear. — **gestrecktes Eisen,** wrought iron. — **gestreckter Winkel,** angle of 180 degrees.

**Strecken-spektrum,** *n.* continuous spectrum. **-teilchen,** *n.* (*Math.*) linear element.

**Strecker,** *m.* stretcher; (*Med.*) extensor; (*Glass*) flattener.

**Streck-festigkeit,** *f.* resistance to stretching, elongation resistance. **-grenze,** *f.* yield point. **-metall,** *n.* expanded metal. **-mittel,** *n.* diluting agent, diluent, extender, filler. **-ofen,** *m.* (*Glass*) flattening furnace. **-stahl,** *m.* rolled steel.

**Streckung,** *f.* stretching, etc. (see strecken); spread.

**Streckungsmittel,** *n.* = Streckmittel.

**Streckwerk,** *n.* (*Metal.*) rolling mill; rolls.

**Streich,** *m.* stroke; blow, stripe; trick, prank.

**streichbar,** *a.* plastic; brushable; (see also streichen and -bar).

**Streich-beize,** *f.* (*Leather*) brush pickle. **-bürste,** *f.* paint brush, varnish brush; (*Paper*) sizing brush.

**Streiche,** *f.* spatula.

**streichen,** *v.t.* stroke, rub, brush; paint, varnish; coat; whet; strike (matches); erase, cancel, knock off; mold (brick or tile); stain or coat (paper); card (wool); scrape (skins); spread (butter). — *v.i.* move, rush, sweep, etc.; rove, roam; (*Mining*) strike, run (in a certain direction).

**streichfähig,** *a.* (of paints, etc.) brushable.

**Streich-fähigkeit,** *f.* (of paints, etc.) brushability, brushing-out property. **-farbe,** *f.* brushing-on color; (*Paper*) staining color.

**streichfertig,** *a.* (*Paint*) ready to brush on.

**Streich-fläche,** *f.* striking surface (for matches), rubber. **-holz, -hölzchen,** *n.* friction match. **-instrument,** *n.* stringed instrument. **-kappe,** *f.* (*Expl.*) friction cap. **-kasten,** *m.* (*Dyeing*) color tub. **-kraut,** *n.* dyer's rocket. **-lack,** *m.* brushing lacquer. **-masse,** *f.* friction composition (for matches). **-mischung,** *f.* coating mixture. **-muster,** *m.* (*Paper*) stained-paper pattern. **-ofen,** *m.* reverberatory furnace. **-papier,** *n.* coated paper. **-stein,** *m.* touchstone; hone. **-torf,** *m.* pressed peat, molded peat. **-zündhölzchen,** *n.* friction match.

**Streif,** *m.* = Streifen.

**streifen,** *v.t.* stripe, streak, striate; graze; channel, flute; strip off; touch on. — *v.i.* graze, glance, touch (on); wander, ramble.

**Streifen,** *m.* band, strip, stripe, stria; streak, vein (in marble, etc.); strap. **-gefüge,** *n.* banded structure. **-kohle,** *f.* banded coal. **-spektrum,** *n.* band spectrum.

**streifenweise,** *adv.* in strips.

**streifig,** *a.* streaked, striated, striped, banded.

**Streifung,** *f.* striping, etc. (see streifen); striation; stria.

**streiken,** *v.i.* (*Labor*) strike.

**Streit,** *m.* contest, combat, strife; debate, dispute.

**streiten,** *v.i & r.* struggle, contend, dispute.
**Streit-fall,** *m.*, **-frage,** *f.* matter in dispute, question at issue, moot point.
**streitig,** *a.* disputed, questionable.
**Streitigkeit,** *f.* contest, dispute.
**streng, strenge,** *a.* severe, rigorous, harsh, strict, hard.
**strengflüssig,** *a.* difficultly fusible, refractory; viscous.
**Strengflüssigkeit,** *f.* difficult fusibility, refractoriness; viscosity.
**strenggenommen,** *adv.* in a strict sense, strictly speaking.
**Strenglot,** *n.* hard solder.
**Streu,** *f.* litter.
**Streu-.** scattering, scattered; strewing; dusting; stray. **-blau,** *n.* powder blue. **-brandbombe,** *f.* (*Mil.*) scatter bomb.
**Streudüse,** *f.* spray nozzle.
**streuen,** *v.t.* scatter; strew; spread; disperse; spray; dust.
**Streu-glanz,** *m.* brass powder. **-gold,** *n.* gold dust. **-gut,** *n.* strewing (or spraying or dusting) material. **-körper,** *m.* scattering body. **-kupfer,** *n.* copper rain (particles of copper thrown from the surface of the molten metal). **-licht,** *n.* scattered light. **-linie,** *f.* scattered line. **-pulver,** *n.* powder for strewing or dusting, as insect powder, lycopodium, or (for use against "mustard gas") bleaching powder. **-spannung,** *f.* (*Elec.*) stray voltage. **-spektrum,** *n.* scattered spectrum. **-strahlung,** *f.* scattered (or stray) radiation. **-strom,** *m.* (*Elec.*) stray current.
**Streuung,** *f.* scattering; dispersion; strewing; dusting; spraying; (*Elec.*) leakage; deviation, variation.
**Streuungswinkel,** *m.* angle of scattering.
**Streu-vermögen,** *n.* scattering power. **-wachs,** *n.* sprinkling wax. **-welle,** *f.* scattered wave. **-wert,** *m.* erratic value; amount of scattering. **-winkel,** *m.* angle of scattering. **-zinn,** *n.* tin dust. **-zucker,** *m.* powdered sugar.
**strich,** *pret.* (of streichen) stroked, etc.
**Strich,** *m.* stroke; streak, stria; line, dash; graduation; mark; prime ($'$); mil; (of wood) grain; train (of powder); batch (of bricks); (of cloth) nap; tract, region; course, direction; flock, brood.
**Strichelchen,** *n.* little stroke or streak.
**stricheln,** *v.t.* streak; shade, hatch; (of lines) break (at short intervals).
**Strich-farbe,** *f.* (*Min.*) streak color, streak. **-formulierung,** *f.* formula writing with lines or dashes (to represent bonds). **-gitter,** *n.* simple line grating. **-kreuz,** *n.* cross hairs, cross wires. **-kultur,** *f.* streak culture.
**strichliert,** *a.* (of a line) broken (- - - -).
**Strich-marke,** *f.* mark, stroke; graduation. **-platte,** *f.* ruled plate; (*Min.*) streak plate. **-punkt,** *m.* semicolon.
**strichpunktiert,** *a.* (of a line) dash-and-dot (—·—·—·).
**Strichzeichnung,** *f.* line drawing.
**Strick,** *m.* cord, string, line, rope; snare.
**stricken,** *v.t.* reticulate, net; knit.
**strickförmig,** *a.* cord-like, rope-like; (*Anat.*) restiform.
**Strick-lava,** *f.* ropy lava. **-waren,** *f.pl.* knitted goods.
**stritt,** *pret.* (of streiten) struggled, etc.
**strittig,** *a.* contested, in dispute; questionable.
**Stroh,** *n.* straw. **-blume,** *f.* everlasting. **-dach,** *n.* thatched roof.
**stroh-farbig, -farben,** *a.* straw-colored.
**Stroh-feile,** *f.* coarse file, rough file. **-flachs,** *m.* raw flax.
**strohgelb,** *a.* straw-yellow.
**Stroh-häcksel,** *m.* chopped straw, chaff. **-halm,** *m.* (a single) straw. **-hülse,** *f.* straw envelope or case.
**strohig,** *a.* strawy, straw-like.
**Stroh-kessel, -kocher,** *m.* (*Paper*) straw boiler. **-papier,** *n.* straw paper. **-pappe,** *f.* straw board. **-ring,** *m.* straw ring. **-stein,** *m.* (*Min.*) carpholite. **-stoff,** *m.* (*Paper*) straw stuff, straw pulp. **-wein,** *m.* straw wine. **-zellstoff,** *m.* (*Paper*) straw pulp. **-zeug,** *n.* = Strohstoff.
**Strom,** *m.* stream, current, flow, flux; (*Elec.*) current. **-abnahme,** *f.* current drop, current fall. **-abnehmer,** *m.* (*Elec.*) brush (also, consumer). **-abweichung,** *f.* variation of current. **-anzeiger,** *m.* current indicator. **-art,** *f.* (*Elec.*) kind of current. **-aufnahme,** *f.* (*Elec.*) charging. **-bahn,** *f.* path of current. **-bild,** *n.* flow sheet. **-dichte, -dichtigkeit,** *f.* current density.
**stromdurchflossen,** *a.* current-carrying, live.
**Strom-durchgang,** *m.* passage of current. **-einheit,** *f.* unit of current.
**strömen,** *v.i.* stream, flow, pour, pass.
**Strom-entnahme,** *f.* (*Elec.*) consumption of current. **-erzeuger,** *m.* current generator. **-feld,** *n.* (*Elec.*) current field.
**stromführend,** *a.* (*Elec.*) current-carrying, live.
**Strom-geschwindigkeit,** *f.* velocity of current. **-indikator,** *m.* current indicator. **-induktion,** *f.* induction of currents, electromagnetic induction. **-kreis,** *m.* (*Elec.*) circuit. **-kreisunterbrecher,** *m.* circuit breaker. **-lauf,** *m.* flow of current. **-leistung,** *f.* (*Elec.*) power, wattage. **-leiter,** *m.* (*Elec.*) conductor. **-leitung,** *f.* (*Elec.*) conduction. **-linie,** *f.* streamline.
**stromlos,** *a.* (*Elec.*) without current, dead.
**Strom-losigkeit,** *f.* (*Elec.*) absence of current. **-menge,** *f.* (*Elec.*) amount of current, current

strength. **-messer,** *m.* current meter; specif., (*Elec.*) ammeter, amperemeter. **-quelle,** *f.* (*Elec.*) source of current. **-regulator,** *m.* current regulator. **-richtung,** *f.* direction of current. **-richtungsanzeiger,** *m.* (*Elec.*) polarity indicator. **-schluss,** *m.* (*Elec.*) circuit closing. **-schlüssel,** *m.* (*Elec.*) key, switch. **-schwankung,** *f.* fluctuation of current. **-spannung,** *f.* current potential, voltage of a current. **-speicher,** *m.* (*Elec.*) accumulator. **-spule,** *f.* (*Elec.*) current coil, solenoid. **-stärke,** *f.* current intensity, current strength, (*Elec.*) amperage. **-stärkemesser,** *m.* (*Elec.*) ammeter, also galvanometer. **-stoss,** *m.* current pulsation, current impulse. **-tor,** *n.* thyratron. **-trenner,** *m.* (*Elec.*) switch. **-umkehrer,** *m.* current reverser, commutator. **-umkehrung,** *f.* reversal of current.

**Strömung,** *f.* streaming, flowing, pouring; current, stream, flow, flood; circulation; transpiration (of gases); (magnetic) flux.

**Strömungsmesser,** *m.* current meter, flow meter.

**Strom-unterbrecher,** *m.* circuit breaker; interrupter. **-verbrauch,** *m.* consumption of current. **-verlust,** *m.* loss of current. **-wandler,** *m.* (*Elec.*) current transformer. **-wärme,** *f.* heat produced by an electric current. **-wechsel,** *m.* (*Elec.*) alternation. **-wechsler,** *m.* (*Elec.*) commutator. **-weg,** *m.* path of current. **-wender,** *m.* (*Elec.*) current reverser; specif., commutator. **-zeiger,** *m.* current indicator; specif., ammeter. **-zelle,** *f.* electric cell. **-zinn,** *n.* stream tin. **-zuführung,** *f.* (*Elec.*) power supply.

**Strontian,** *m.*, **-erde,** *f.* strontia (strontium oxide).

**strontianhaltig,** *a.* containing strontia, strontianiferous.

**Strontian-salpeter,** *m.* strontium nitrate. **-salz,** *n.* strontium salt. **-wasser,** *n.* strontia water. **-weiss,** *n.* strontium white. **-zucker,** *m.* strontium sucrate.

**Strontium-gehalt,** *m.* strontium content. **-jodid,** *n.* strontium iodide. **-oxydhydrat,** *n.* strontium hydroxide. **-salpeter,** *m.* strontium nitrate. **-salz,** *n.* strontium salt. **-wasserstoff,** *m.* strontium hydride.

**Strophant**(h)**-insäure,** *f.* strophanthinic acid. **-säure,** *f.* strophanthic acid.

**strotzen,** *v.i.* swell, swell up, be swollen.

**Strudel,** *m.* whirlpool, eddy, vortex.

**strudellos,** *a.* noneddying, irrotational.

**Struktur,** *f.* structure; (*Petrog.*, etc.) texture. **-änderung,** *f.* change in structure or texture. **-bestandteil,** *m.* structural constituent. **-chemie,** *f.* structural chemistry.

**strukturell,** *a.* structural.

**Struktur-farbe,** *f.* structural color. **-festigkeit,** *f.* resistance to tearing. **-formel,** *f.* structural formula.

**strukturidentisch,** *a.* structurally identical.

**Strukturisomerie,** *f.* structural isomerism.

**strukturlos,** *a.* structureless, amorphous.

**Strukturveränderung,** *f.* change of structure or texture.

**Strumpf,** *m.* stocking, hose; mantle (of a gas burner). **-band,** *n.* garter. **-waren,** *f.pl.* hosiery.

**Strunk,** *m.* stump, trunk, stalk, stock, stem.

**struppig,** *a.* bristly, shaggy, rough.

**Stubbe,** *f.*, **Stubben,** *m.* stump.

**Stubbfett,** *n.* stubb fat. (Cf. Stuppfett.)

**Stube,** *f.* room, apartment.

**Stuccatur,** *f.*, **Stuck,** *m.* = Stukkatur.

**Stück,** *n.* piece; bit, lump, fragment; cake (as of soap); part, element; gun, cannon; (*Metal.*) bloom. **-arbeit,** *f.* piecework.

**Stückchen,** *n.* little piece, bit, particle. **-zucker,** *m.* = Stückenzucker.

**stückeln,** *v.t.* cut into pieces, cut up.

**Stückenzucker,** *m.* crushed sugar; lump sugar.

**Stück-erz,** *n.* lump ore. **-färbekufe,** *f.* piece-dyeing vat. **-färber,** *m.* piece dyer. **-färberei,** *f.* piece dyeing.

**stückfarbig,** *a.* dyed in the piece.

**Stück-färbung,** *f.* piece dyeing; (*Micros.*) staining *in toto*, tissue staining. **-form,** *f.* lump form. **-gewicht,** *n.* (individual) weight.

**Stuckgips,** *m.* plaster of Paris (common grade).

**Stück-grösse,** *f.* size of piece or lump. **-gut,** *n.* gun metal; (*pl.*) piece goods; parcel, bale.

**stückig,** *a.* in pieces, in lumps; lumpy.

**Stück-kohle,** *f.* lump coal. **-koks,** *m.* lump coke. **-lohn,** *m.* piece wages. **-metall,** *n.* gun metal.

**Stuckmörtel,** *m.* stucco; badigeon.

**Stück-ofen,** *m.* high bloomery furnace. **-preis,** *m.* piece price, price by the piece. **-schlacke,** *f.* lump slag. **-waren,** *f.pl.* piece goods. **-wäsche,** *f.* piece scouring or washing.

**stückweise,** *adv.* piece by piece, piecemeal; by retail.

**Studie,** *f.* study.

**studieren,** *v.t. & i.* study.

**Studierende,** *m. & f.pl.* students.

**Studium,** *n.* study.

**Stufe,** *f.* step; stage; degree, rank, grade, gradation. — **Stufen,** *pl.* (*Mercury*) poorest ore.

**stufenartig,** *a.* step-like, stepped, graduated, graded, gradual.

**Stufenfolge,** *f.* succession of steps or stages; gradation.

**stufenförmig,** *a.* = stufenartig.

**Stufen-gesetz,** *n.* law of stages. **-gitter,** *n.* echelon grating. **-heizung,** *f.* heating in

stages; (*Rubber*) step-up cure. **-leiter,** *m.* stepladder; scale. **-linse,** *f.* echelon lens.
**stufenlos,** *a.* without stages, continuous.
**Stufen-photometer,** *m.* step photometer. **-prisma,** *n.* echelon prism. **-rakete,** *f.* step rocket, multistage rocket. **-reaktion,** *f.* reaction in stages, stepwise reaction. **-regel,** *f.* = Stufengesetz. **-trocknen,** *n.* drying with graduated temperature.
**stufenweise,** *adv.* in stages or steps, stepwise; by degrees; gradually.
**Stufenzahl,** *f.* number of stages.
**Stufferz,** *n.* first-class ore.
**stufig,** *a.* stepped, graded, graduated; in stages; sturdy.
**Stuhl,** *m.* chair, stool, seat; loom; (*Med.*) stool.
**Stuhl-.** chair; fecal.
**stuhlbefördernd,** *p.a.* aperient, laxative.
**Stuhl-gang,** *m.* stool, discharge from the bowels. **-zäpfchen,** *n.* suppository. **-züchtung,** *f.* (*Bact.*) culture from feces.
**Stukkatör, Stukkateur,** *m.* stucco worker; plasterer.
**Stukkatur,** *f.* stucco work; plastering.
**stülpen,** *v.t.* turn upside down (or inside out); put (over or upon).
**stumm,** *a.* dumb; mute, speechless, silent.
**Stummel,** *m.* stump, stub, end, snag.
**stumpf,** *a.* blunt; obtuse; flush; (of tools) dull; (of surfaces) dull, mat.
**Stumpf,** *m.* stump; stub; (*Geom.*) frustum.
**stumpf-eckig,** *a.* blunt-cornered. **-kantig,** *a.* blunt-edged; obtuse-angled.
**Stumpf-kegel,** *m.* truncated cone. **-schweissung,** *f.* butt welding; upset welding.
**stumpfwinklig,** *a.* obtuse-angled.
**Stunde,** *f.* hour; lesson.
**stünde,** *pret. subj.* (of stehen) would stand, etc.
**stunden,** *v.t.* suspend, stop. **-lang,** *a.* for hours; by the hour.
**Stunden-leistung,** *f.* hourly output. **-plan,** *m.* timetable; working plan, schedule. **-zeiger,** *m.* hour hand.
**Stunde X.** zero hour.
**stünd-ig,** *a.* of an hour's length, for an hour. **-lich,** *a. & adv.* hourly.
**Stupp,** *f.* stupp, mercurial soot.
**Stuppeasäure,** *f.* stuppeic acid, stuppeaic acid.
**Stuppfett,** *n.* a greasy mixture of hydrocarbons (phenanthrene, pyrene, etc.) obtained in refining stupp.
**stürbe,** *pret. subj.* (of sterben) would die.
**Sturm,** *m.* storm; tumult, alarm, fury; (*Mil.*) assault, also assault company.
**sturmfest,** *a.* stormproof.
**Sturmhut,** *m.* monkshood, aconite.
**stürmisch,** *a.* stormy, turbulent; vigorous (reaction); boiling (fermentation).
**Sturmwagen,** *m.* (*Mil.*) tank.
**Sturz,** *m.* plunge, drop, fall, overthrow; rush, dash; failure (in business); waterfall; (*Iron*) slab, plate. **-acker,** *m.* new-plowed land. **-bomben,** *n.* dive bombing. **-blech,** *n.* thin plate iron, (black) sheet iron.
**Stürze,** *f.* lid, cover.
**stürzen,** *v.t.* hurl, throw, plunge; overturn; (*Math.*) transpose; dump; plow for the first time; overthrow. — *v.r.* rush, plunge, dash. — *v.i.* fall; rush; pour.
**Sturzflamme,** *f.* reverberatory flame.
**Stürzgüter,** *n.pl.* goods loaded in bulk.
**Stürzmühle,** *f.* tumbling mill.
**Stürzung,** *f.* hurling, etc. (see stürzen).
**Stute,** *f.* mare.
**Stutenmilch,** *f.* mare's milk.
**Stützapparat,** *m.* supporting apparatus, support.
**Stütze,** *f.* support, stay, prop.
**stutzen,** *v.t.* clip, top, crop, trim, curtail.
**Stutzen,** *m.* (a short piece of tube or pipe serving as an) opening, connection, socket, nipple, nozzle; a broad cylindrical vessel.
**stützen,** *v.t.* support, prop, stay. — *v.r.* lean, rest, be based.
**Stütz-fläche,** *f.* supporting surface. **-gewebe,** *n.* supporting tissue.
**stutzig,** *a.* startled, perplexed, nonplussed.
**Stütz-mittel,** *n.* supporting medium. **-punkt,** *m.* point of support; base point; bearing surface; fulcrum. **-stoff,** *m.*, **-substanz,** *f.* supporting substance.
**Stutzuhr,** *f.* mantle clock.
**Styphninsäure,** *f.* styphnic acid.
**Styrol,** *n.* styrene.
**s.u.,** *abbrev.* (siehe unten) see below.
**Suakingummi,** *n.* Suakin gum, talha gum.
**subaerisch,** *a.* subaerial.
**subatomar,** *a.* subatomic.
**Subchlorür,** *n.* subchloride.
**Suberinsäure,** *f.* suberic acid.
**Subhaloid,** *n.* subhalide.
**subkutan,** *a.* subcutaneous.
**Sublimat,** *n.* sublimate; specif., corrosive sublimate, mercuric chloride.
**Sublimations-probe,** *f.* sublimation test or sample. **-wärme,** *f.* heat of sublimation.
**Sublimatlösung,** *f.* sublimate solution.
**sublimierbar,** *a.* sublimable.
**Sublimierbarkeit,** *f.* sublimability.
**sublimierecht,** *a.* nonsubliming.
**sublimieren,** *v.t.* sublime, sublimate.
**Sublimier-gefäss,** *n.* sublimation vessel. **-ofen,** *m.* subliming furnace. **-topf,** *m.* subliming pot, aludel.
**Sublimierung,** *f.* sublimation.
**subordinieren,** *v.t.* subordinate.
**Suboxyd,** *n.* suboxide.
**Subphosphorsäure,** *f.* hypophosphoric acid.

**Substantivität,** *f.* substantivity.
**Substanz,** *f.* substance; matter; material. **-fleck,** *m.* (*Dyeing*) dye stain. **-menge,** *f.* amount of substance. **-muster,** *n.* sample in kind. **-verlust,** *m.* loss of material. **-wechsel,** *m.* change of substance.
**Substituent,** *m.* substituent; substitute.
**substituierbar,** *a.* replaceable.
**substituieren,** *v.t.* substitute.
**Substituierung,** *f.* substitution.
**Substrat,** *n.* foundation; base; substratum, substrate.
**subtrahieren,** *v.t.* subtract.
**Suchbuch,** *n.* reference book.
**Suche,** *f.* search.
**suchen,** *v.t. & i.* seek; look for, explore, want, try. — **gesucht,** *p.a.* sought for, in demand.
**Sucher,** *m.* seeker, searcher; detector; (*Optics*) finder; probe.
**Such-geschoss,** *n.* tracer projectile. **-licht,** *n.* searchlight. **-spindel,** *f.* exploring spindle (to indicate which of a set of hydrometer spindles is to be used).
**Sucht,** *f.* disease, sickness; epidemic; mania.
**Sud,** *m.* boiling; brewing, brew, gyle; decoction; (*Dyeing*) mordant.
**Süd,** *m.* south. **-afrika,** *n.* South Africa.
**südafrikanisch,** *a.* South African.
**Südamerika,** *n.* South America.
**Sudan-braun,** *n.* Sudan brown. **-rot,** *n.* Sudan red.
**Süden,** *m.* south.
**Südfrankreich,** *n.* Southern France.
**Sudhaus,** *n.* boiling house (or room); brewing house, brew house.
**südlich,** *a.* south, southern. — *adv.* south.
**Süd-licht,** *n.* aurora australis. **-ost, -osten,** *m.* southeast. **-pol,** *n.* south pole.
**Sud-salz,** *n.* boiled salt (common salt from boiled-down brine). **-seifenbad,** *n.* (*Dyeing*) broken soap bath, broken suds.
**südwärts,** *adv.* southward.
**Sud-werk,** *n.* brew-house outfit, brewing plant. **-wesen,** *n.* brewing.
**süffig,** *a.* palatable, tasty; bibulous.
**Sukzession,** *f.* succession.
**sukzessiv,** *a.* successive.
**Sukzinylsäure,** *f.* succinic acid.
**Sulf-.** sulf-, sulfo-, thio- (see note under Sulfo-). **-amidsäure, -aminsäure,** *f.* sulfamic acid. **-anilsäure,** *f.* sulfanilic acid.
**sulfantimonig,** *a.* thioantimonious.
**Sulfantimonsäure,** *f.* thioantimonic acid.
**sulfarsenig,** *a.* thioarsenious.
**Sulfarsensäure,** *f.* thioarsenic acid.
**Sulfat,** *n.* sulfate. **-ablauge,** *f.* sulfate waste liquor. **-anlage,** *f.* sulfate plant.
**Sulfatation,** *f.* sulfatization.
**sulfat-haltig,** *a.* containing sulfate, sulfatic. **-ieren,** *v.t.* sulfate; sulfatize.
**Sulfat-ierung,** *f.* sulfating; sulfatization. **-ion,** *n.* sulfate ion.
**sulfatisieren,** *v.t.* sulfatize.
**Sulfat-isierung,** *f.* sulfatization. **-isierungsmittel,** *n.* sulfatizing agent. **-kessel,** *m.* (*Paper*) sulfate boiler. **-kocher,** *m.* (*Paper*) sulfate digester. **-papier,** *n.* sulfate paper. **-rest,** *m.* sulfate residue or radical. **-schmelze,** *f.* = Schmelzsoda. **-schwefel,** *m.* sulfur in the form of sulfate, sulfate sulfur. **-see,** *f.* sulfate lake. **-soda,** *f.* sulfate soda, Leblanc soda. **-stoff,** *m.* (*Paper*) sulfate pulp. **-verfahren,** *n.* sulfate process. **-zellstoff,** *m.* sulfate cellulose, sulfate pulp.
**Sulf-carbaminsäure,** *f.* thiocarbamic acid. **-carbanil,** *n.* thiocarbanil (phenyl isothiocyanate).
**Sulfensäure,** *f.* sulfenic acid.
**Sulf-hydrid, -hydrat,** *n.* hydrosulfide. **-hydrit,** *n.* hydrosulfite (dithionite).
**Sulfid,** *n.* sulfide; specif., -ic sulfide (cf. Sulfür). **-erz,** *n.* sulfide ore.
**sulfidieren,** *v.t.* sulfide, sulfidize.
**Sulfidierung,** *f.* sulfiding, sulfidizing.
**sulfidisch,** *a.* sulfidic, pertaining to or containing sulfide(s).
**Sulfidschwefel,** *m.* sulfide sulfur.
**sulfieren,** *v.t.* sulfonate.
**Sulfieren,** *n.*, **Sulfierung,** *f.* sulfonation.
**Sulfin,** *n.* sulfonium, sulfine, $H_3S^+$. **-farbe,** *f.*, **-farbstoff,** *m.* sulfur dye. **-salz,** *n.* sulfonium salt, sulfine salt. **-säure,** *f.* sulfinic acid.
**Sulfit,** *n.* sulfite. **-ablauge,** *f.* sulfite waste liquor. **-ätze,** *f.* sulfite discharge. **-auslauger,** *m.* (*Paper*) sulfite digester. **-cellulose,** *f.* (*Paper*) sulfite pulp.
**sulfitieren,** *v.t.* sulfite.
**Sulfitierung,** *f.* sulfiting, sulfitation.
**Sulfit-kocher,** *m.* (*Paper*) sulfite digester. **-kochung,** *f.* (*Paper*) sulfite cooking or cook. **-lauge,** *f.* sulfite liquor. **-laugenturm,** *m.* sulfite tower. **-pappe,** *f.* sulfite (paper)board. **-reserve,** *f.* sulfite resist or reserve. **-sprit,** *m.* sulfite spirit, alcohol from sulfite liquor. **-stoff,** *m.* (*Paper*) sulfite pulp. **-turm,** *m.* sulfite tower. **-verfahren,** *n.* sulfite process. **-zellstoff,** *m.* sulfite cellulose, sulfite pulp. **-zellstofffabrikation,** *f.* manufacture of sulfite cellulose (or pulp).
**Sulfkohlensäure,** *f.* sulfocarbonic acid (trithiocarbonic acid); thionocarbonic acid (HOCSOH).
**Sulfo-.** sulfo-, thio-. (Preferably, sulfo- is used to designate the sulfonic group, and thio- to denote that sulfur replaces oxygen.) **-azetat,** *n.* sulfoacetate. **-base, -basis,** *f.* sulfur base. **-carbonsäure,** *f.* sulfocarboxylic acid.

**Sulfocyan,** *n.* thiocyanogen, sulfocyanogen. **-eisen,** *n.* iron (esp. ferric) thiocyanate.
**Sulfocyanid,** *n.* thiocyanate.
**Sulfocyankalium,** *n.* potassium thiocyanate.
**sulfocyansauer,** *a.* of or combined with sulfocyanic (thiocyanic) acid, sulfocyanate (thiocyanate) of.
**Sulfocyan-säure,** *f.* sulfocyanic acid (thiocyanic acid). **-verbindung,** *f.* sulfocyanate (thiocyanate).
**Sulfo-fettsäure,** *f.* sulfo fatty acid; sulfosebacic acid (old name). **-gruppe,** *f.* sulfo group, sulfonic group. **-harnstoff,** *m.* sulfourea (thiourea). **-hydrat,** *n.* hydrosulfide. **-karbolsäure,** *f.* sulfocarbolic acid. **-kohlensäure, -karbonsäure,** *f.* sulfocarbonic acid (trithiocarbonic acid, $H_2CS_3$). **-lyse,** *f.* sulfolysis. **-monopersäure,** *f.* monoperoxysulfuric acid ($HOSO_2OOH$).
**Sulfoncarbonsäure,** *f.* sulfonocarboxylic acid, sulfonecarboxylic acid.
**sulfonierbar,** *a.* capable of being sulfonated.
**sulfonieren,** *v.t.* sulfonate.
**Sulfon-ierung,** *f.* sulfonation. **-säure,** *f.* sulfonic acid. **-säurecarbonsäure,** *f.* sulfocarboxylic acid, $R''(SO_3H)CO_2H$.
**Sulfo-ölsäure,** *f.* sulfoöleic acid. **-persäure,** *f.* peroxysulfuric acid, persulfuric acid. **-salz,** *n.* thio salt, sulfo salt.
**sulfosauer,** *a.* of or combined with a sulfo acid; sulfonate of.
**Sulfo-säure,** *f.* sulfo acid (either a sulfonic acid or a sulfacid). **-verbindung,** *f.* sulfo compound.
**Sulfozyan,** *n.* thiocyanogen, sulfocyanogen. (For compounds see Sulfocyan-.)
**Sulfozyanat,** *n.* sulfocyanate (thiocyanate).
**Sulfozyanid,** *n.* sulfocyanide (thiocyanate).
**Sulfthiokohlensäure,** *f.* thiolthionocarbonic acid (HOCSSH).
**Sulfür,** *n.* (lower or -ous) sulfide, (formerly) protosulfide.
**sulfurieren,** *v.t.* sulfonate; sulfurize.
**Sulfuröl,** *n.* sulfocarbon oil (olive oil extracted from marc, esp. with $CS_2$).
**Sulfürschwefel,** *m.* sulfur in the form of sulfide.
**Sulph-.** see Sulf-.
**Sulze, Sülze,** *f.* jelly; gelatin; brine; pickled meat.
**Sulzfleisch,** *f.* pickled meat.
**sulzig, sülzig,** a. gelatinous.
**Sumach-abkochung,** *f.* sumac decoction. **-behandlung,** *f.* (*Leather*) sumacking.
**sumachgar,** *a.* sumac-tanned.
**Sumachgerbung,** *f.* sumac tanning.
**sumachieren,** *v.t.* (*Leather*) sumac.
**Sumbulwurzel,** *f.* sumbul root, musk root.
**Summa,** *f.* sum.
**Summand,** *m.* (*Math.*) term of a sum.
**summarisch,** *a.* summary.
**Summe,** *f.* sum, amount.
**summen,** *v.i.* hum, buzz. — *v.t.* sum up, add.
**Summen-gleichung,** *f.* summation equation. **-regel,** *f.* sum rule, rule of sums. **-satz,** *m.* principle or law of sums. **-wirkung,** *f.* combined action or effect.
**Summer,** *m.* buzzer, vibrator.
**summieren,** *v.t.* sum up, add. — *v.r.* accumulate.
**Sumpf,** *m.* swamp, marsh, bog; (*Tech.*) pit, sump; basin; pool (of mercury); wave absorbent. **-boden,** *m.* marshy or swampy ground or soil. **-eisenstein,** *m.* bog iron ore.
**sümpfen,** *v.t.* drain.
**Sumpf-erz,** *n.* bog ore. **-gas,** *n.* marsh gas.
**sumpfig,** *a.* swampy, marshy, boggy.
**Sumpf-kalk,** *m.* slaked lime. **-luft,** *f.* marsh gas. **-moos,** *n.* swamp moss, sphagnum (moss). **-nelke,** *f.* purple avens (*Geum rivale*). **-öl,** *n.* sump oil. **-pflanze,** *f.* marsh plant. **-porsch, -porst,** *m.* marsh tea (*Ledum palustre*). **-silge,** *f.* marsh parsley (*Peucedanum palustre*).
**Sund,** *m.* sound, strait.
**Sünde,** *f.* sin.
**Superazidität,** *f.* hyperacidity.
**superficiell,** *a.* superficial.
**Super-leitfähigkeit,** *f.* superconductivity. **-oxyd,** *n.* superoxide (peroxide). **-oxydbleiche,** *f.* peroxide bleach.
**superoxydecht,** *a.* fast to peroxide.
**Super-oxydhydrat,** *n.* hydrated peroxide. **-phosphatschlempe,** *f.* a fertilizer made by incorporating superphosphate with molasses residue.
**super-ponieren,** *v.t.* superpose. **-saturieren,** *v.t.* supersaturate.
**Suppe,** *f.* soup.
**Suppen-kraut,** *n.* pot herb. **-würze,** *f.* soup flavoring.
**Supra-leitelektron,** *n.* superconduction electron. **-leiter,** *m.* supraconductor, superconductor. **-leitfähigkeit,** *f.* supraconductivity.
**surren,** *v.i.* hum, whir, buzz.
**Surrogat,** *n.* substitute, surrogate. **-stoff,** *m.* substitute material; (*Paper*) pulp substitute (for rags).
**suspendieren,** *v.t.* suspend.
**Suspensionsmittel,** *n.* dispersing agent.
**süss,** *a.* sweet; (of water) fresh.
**Süssbier,** *n.* sweet beer.
**Süsse,** *f.* sweetness.
**süssen,** *v.t.* sweeten.
**Süsserde,** *f.* beryllia, glucina (BeO).
**Süssholz,** *n.* licorice. **-saft,** *m.* extract of licorice. **-zucker,** *m.* glycyrrhizic acid.
**Süssigkeit,** *f.* sweetness; sweets; suavity.

**süsslich,** *a.* sweetish; mawkish. **-riechend,** *a.* sweet-smelling.
**Süssmandelöl,** *n.* oil of sweet almonds.
**Süssmost,** *m.* (unfermented) grape juice.
**süsssauerlich,** *a.* sourish-sweet.
**Süss-stoff,** *m.* sweet substance; sweetening agent, dulcifier, specif. saccharin. **-waren,** *f.pl.* confectionery, sweets. **-wasser,** *n.* fresh water. **-wasserablagerung,** *f.* fresh-water deposit. **-wein,** *m.* sweet wine.
**Suszeptibilität,** *f.* susceptibility.
**s.W.,** *abbrev.* (spezifische Wärme) specific heat.
**Sweetchrombeize,** *f.* sweet (neutral) chrome mordant.
**swl.,** *abbrev.* (sehr wenig löslich) very difficultly soluble.
**s.w.u.,** *abbrev.* (siehe weiter unten) see below.
**Sylvanerz,** *n.* sylvanite.
**Sylvesterabend,** *m.* New Year's eve.
**Sylvin,** *m.* (*Min.*) sylvite. **-säure,** *f.* sylvic acid (abietic acid).
**Symbasis,** *f.* agreement, correlation; (*Biol.*) symbasis.
**symbat,** *a.* correlative.
**Symbiose,** *f.* symbiosis.
**symbolisieren,** *v.t.* symbolize.
**Symmetrie-achse,** *f.* axis of symmetry. **-ebene,** *f.* plane of symmetry. **-grad,** *m.* degree of symmetry.
**symmetrieren,** *v.t.* symmetrize, balance.
**Symmetriezentrum,** *n.* center of symmetry.
**symmetrisch,** *a.* symmetrical, symmetric.
**Symmetrisierung,** *f.* symmetrization.
**sympathetisch,** *a.* sympathetic.
**Synäresis,** *f.* syneresis.
**synchron,** *a.* synchronous.
**Synchronisator,** *m.* synchronizer.
**synchronisieren,** *v.t.* synchronize.
**synchronistisch,** *a.* synchronous.
**Syndikat,** *n.* syndicate. Cf. Konsortium.
**Synergismus,** *m.* synergism (mutual action).
**syngenetisch,** *a.* syngenetic.
**syntetisch,** *a.* synthetic.
**Synthese,** *f.* synthesis.
**synthesieren,** *v.t.* synthesize.
**synthetisch,** *a.* synthetic.
**synthetisieren,** *v.t.* synthetize, synthesize.
**Syringasäure,** *f.* syringic acid.
**syrisch,** *a.* Syrian.
**syrup-, Syrup-.** see sirup-, Sirup-.
**System,** *n.* system; (atomic) pile.
**systematisch,** *a.* systematic.
**Systemzahl,** *f.* system number; file number.
**s.Z.,** *abbrev.* (seiner Zeit) in his (or its) time, at that time.
**SZ., S.Z.,** *abbrev.* (Säurezahl) acid number; (Sommerzeit) summer time, daylight-saving time.
**szientifisch,** *a.* scientific.
**szintillieren,** *v.i.* scintillate.

# T

**t,** *abbrev.* (Tonne) ton.

**T.,** *abbrev.* (Teil, Teile) part, parts; (Tausend) thousand; (Temperatur) temperature, esp. absolute.

**Tab.,** *abbrev.* (Tabelle) table.

**Tabak,** *m.* tobacco. **-asche,** *f.* tobacco ashes. **-auszug,** *m.* tobacco extract. **-bau,** *m.* tobacco cultivation. **-beize,** *f.* sauce (for tobacco). **-blatt,** *n.* tobacco leaf.

**tabakbraun,** *a.* tobacco-brown.

**Tabak-brühe,** *f.* sauce (for tobacco). **-dampf,** *m.* tobacco smoke. **-fabrik,** *f.* tobacco factory. **-kampher,** *m.* nicotianin. **-rauch,** *m.* tobacco smoke. **-saft,** *m.* tobacco juice.

**Tabaks-asche, -auszug,** etc. See Tabakasche, Tabakauszug, etc.

**Tabaschir, Tabaxir,** *m.* tabasheer, tabashir.

**tabellarisch,** *a.* tabular. — *adv.* in tabular form.

**tabellarisieren,** *v.t.* tabulate, tabularize.

**Tabelle,** *f.* table; chart; schedule; synopsis, summary.

**Tabellenform,** *f.* tabular form.

**tabellisieren,** *v.t.* tabulate, tabularize.

**Tablett,** *n.* tray.

**Tablette,** *f.* tablet, pellet, lozenge; slab; billet; small table.

**Tabletten-form,** *f.* tablet form. **-maschine,** *f.* tablet press.

**tablettieren,** *v.t.* tablet, pellet.

**Tablettiermaschine,** *f.* tablet(ing) or pellet(ing) press.

**Tadel,** *m.* fault; blame; reproof.

**tadel-frei, -los,** *a.* faultless, perfect.

**tadeln,** *v.t.* blame, criticize, reprove.

**Tafel,** *f.* table; plate, slab, tablet; panel; sheet (of metal); cake (of chocolate); pane (of glass); slate; blackboard; chart; index; list.

**tafelartig,** *a.* tabular.

**Tafel-bier,** *n.* table beer. **-blei,** *n.* sheet lead.

**Täfelchen,** *n.* little table, tablet, platelet.

**Tafel-farbe,** *f.* (*Calico*) local color, topical color. **-fett,** *n.* table grease.

**tafelförmig,** *a.* tabular.

**Tafel-geschirr,** *n.* table service, tableware. **-glas,** *n.* sheet glass.

**tafelig,** *a.* tabular.

**Tafel-lack,** *m.* shellac. **-land,** *n.* tableland, plateau. **-leim,** *m.* glue in flat pieces. **-messing,** *n.* sheet brass.

**tafeln,** *v.i.* dine, sup, feast.

**täfeln,** *v.t.* floor; wainscot, panel.

**Tafel-öl,** *n.* salad oil, esp. olive oil. **-paraffin,** *n.* cake paraffin. **-quarz,** *m.* tabular quartz. **-salz,** *n.* table salt. **-schiefer,** *m.* roofing slate; slate in slabs; school slate. **-schmiere,** *f.* table grease. **-spat,** *m.* tabular spar, wollastonite. **-wa(a)ge,** *f.* counter scales; platform scales. **-wasser,** *n.* table water, drinking water. **-wein,** *m.* table wine.

**Taffet, Taft,** *m.* taffeta.

**Taftpapier,** *n.* satin paper.

**Tag,** *m.* day. — **über —,** in the open. — **unter —,** underground.

**Tag-bau,** *m.* open working. **-blatt,** *n.* daily paper. **-buch,** *n.* diary, journal.

**tagelang,** *adv.* the day long, for days.

**Tage-lohn,** *m.* daily wages, day's wages. **-löhner,** *m.* day laborer.

**tagen,** *v.i.* dawn; (of assemblies) sit.

**Tages-.** day; daily, diurnal; surface. **-erz,** *n.* openwork ore. **-frage,** *f.* question of the day, immediate problem. **-leistung,** *f.* daily output. **-licht,** *n.* daylight. **-oberfläche,** *f.* surface of the ground. **-preis,** *m.* current price. **-wasser,** *n.* surface water. **-zeit,** *f.* daytime; hour of the day.

**-tägig.** days, days'.

**täglich,** *a.* daily, diurnal, quotidian.

**tagtäglich,** *a.* daily, everyday.

**Tagung,** *f.* session, sitting.

**Tagwasser,** *n.* surface water.

**Takt,** *m.* (musical) time, measure, rhythm; tact; (*Mach.*) stroke, cycle.

**taktmässig,** *a.* timed, in time.

**Taktstrasse,** *f.* assembly line.

**Tal,** *n.* valley; dip, depression.

**Taler,** *m.* thaler.

**Talg,** *m.* tallow; (solid) fat, grease; suet; (*Anat.*) sebum.

**talgähnlich,** *a.* tallow-like; sebaceous.

**Talgart,** *f.* (variety of) tallow or solid fat.

**talgartig,** *a.* tallowy; (*Anat.*) sebaceous.

**Talg-baum,** *m.* tallow tree. **-brot,** *n.* tallow cake. **-drüse,** f. sebaceous gland. **-einbrennung,** *f.* (*Leather*) hot stuffing.

**talgen,** *v.t.* tallow; grease.

**talggebend,** *a.* yielding tallow or fat, sebiferous.

**Talggrieben,** *f.pl.* tallow cracklings, greaves.

**talghaltig,** *a.* containing tallow or fat, sebaceous.

**talgig,** *a.* tallowy; sebaceous; adipose.

**Talg-kernseife,** *f.* tallow soap. **-kerze,** *f.*, **-licht,** *n.* tallow candle. **-öl,** *n.* tallow oil. **-säure,** *f.* stearic acid. **-schmelzen,** *n.* rendering of suet or tallow. **-seife,** *f.* tallow soap. **-stein,** *m.* soapstone. **-stoff,** *m.* stearin. **-zelle,** *f.* sebaceous cell.

**Talk,** *m.* talc, talcum.

**talkartig,** *a.* talcose, talcous.

**Talk-erde,** *f.* magnesia; magnesite. **-glimmer,** *m.* mica. **-hydrat,** *n.* (*Min.*) brucite.

**talkig,** *a.* talcose, talcous.

**Talk-pulver,** *n.* talcum powder. **-schiefer,** *m.* talc schist, talcose slate, slaty talc. **-spat,** *m.* magnesite. **-stein,** *m.* soapstone, steatite.

**Talkum,** *n.* talc, talcum.

**Tallöl,** *n.* tall oil, talloel (by-product from chemical wood pulp). **-säure,** *f.* talloleic acid.

**Talmi,** *n.* talmi gold (a gold-like brass).

**Taloschleimsäure,** *f.* talomucic acid.

**Talwert,** *m.* minimum (on a curve).

**Tamarindenmus,** *n.* tamarind pulp.

**Tambour,** *m.* drum; drummer.

**Tampon,** *m.* pad, tampon.

**Tang,** *m.* seaweed. **-asche,** *f.* seaweed ashes, kelp.

**Tangens,** *m.*, **Tangente,** *f.* tangent.

**tangieren,** *v.t.* touch, be tangent to.

**Tang-säure,** *f.* tangic acid, tang acid. **-soda,** *f.* kelp.

**tanken,** *v.i.* refuel.

**Tank-farbe,** *f.* tank coating. **-holz,** *n.* wood for producer gas. **-schiff,** *n.* tank ship, tanker. **-wagen,** *m.* tank car; tank wagon.

**Tanne,** *f.* fir, fir tree (*Abies* species); (loosely) pine.

**Tannenbaum,** *m.* fir tree; pine tree.

**tannenbaumartig,** *a.* arborescent, dendritic.

**Tannen-baumkristall,** *m.* arborescent crystal, dendrite. **-harz,** *n.* fir resin. **-harzsäure,** *f.* fir-resin acid, specif. abietic acid. **-holzstoff,** *m.* fir (wood) pulp. **-nadelöl,** *n.* fir-needle oil; (loosely) pine-needle oil. **-zapfen,** *m.* fir cone. **-zapfenöl,** *n.* fir-cone oil; (loosely) pine-cone oil.

**tannieren,** *v.t.* tan; (*Dyeing*) mordant with tannic acid.

**Tannin,** *n.* tannin, tannic acid, specif. gallotannin. **-ätzartikel,** *m.* (*Calico*) tannic-acid resist style. **-bleisalbe,** *f.* tannate of lead ointment. **-buntätzdruck,** *m.* colored tannin discharge printing. **-druck,** *m.* tannic-acid print. **-druckfarbe,** *f.* tannic-acid printing color. **-farblack,** *m.* tannic-acid color lake. **-lösung,** *f.* tannin solution. **-reserve,** *f.* tannic-acid resist. **-salbe,** *f.* tannin ointment. **-säure,** *f.* tannic acid. **-stoff,** *m.* tannic acid, tannin.

**Tantal,** *n.* tantalum. **-erz,** *n.* tantalum ore, specif. tantalite.

**tantalig,** *a.* tantalous.

**tantalisch,** *a.* of tantalum, tantalic.

**Tantal-lampe,** *f.* tantalum lamp. **-oxyd,** *n.* tantalum oxide, specif. tantalum pentoxide. **-säure,** *f.* tantalic acid. **-verbindung,** *f.* tantalum compound.

**Tanz,** *m.* dance; brawl, row.

**tanzen,** *v.i.* dance.

**Tapete,** *f.* tapestry, hanging; wallpaper; (*Anat.*) tapetum.

**Tapeten-druck,** *m.* wallpaper printing. **-papier,** *n.* wallpaper. **-teigfarbe,** *f.* wallpaper pulp (or paste) color.

**tapezieren,** *v.t.* hang with tapestry; paper.

**Tapezierung,** *f.* papering.

**tapfer,** *a.* brave, valiant, bold.

**Tapiokamehl,** *n.* tapioca starch.

**tappen,** *v.i.* grope; tap; tramp.

**täppisch,** *a.* clumsy, awkward.

**Tara,** *f.* tare. **-fläschchen,** *n.* small tare bottle or flask. **-gewicht,** *n.* tare weight.

**Tarierbecher,** *m.* tare cup.

**tarieren,** *v.t.* tare.

**Tarier-granat,** *m.* garnet for taring. **-schrot,** *n.* & *m.* tare shot. **-stück,** *n.* tare. **-wa(a)ge,** *f.* tare balance.

**Tarifsatz,** *m.* tariff rate.

**tarnen,** *v.t.* camouflage.

**Tarnungsfarbe,** *f.* camouflage paint.

**Tarnwort,** *n.* code word.

**tartarisieren,** *v.t.* tartarize.

**Tartronsäure,** *f.* tartronic acid.

**Tasche,** *f.* pocket; pouch; bag; bin; chamber; trap; (*Med.*) bursa.

**Taschen-ausgabe,** *f.* pocket edition. **-buch,** *n.* pocket book. **-filter,** *n.* bag filter. **-format,** *n.* pocket size. **-krebs,** *m.* common crab. **-lampe,** *f.* pocket lamp, (pocket) flashlight. **-lupe,** *f.* pocket lens. **-spiel,** *n.* jugglery. **-tuch,** *n.* pocket handkerchief. **-uhr,** *f.* watch.

**Tasmanien,** *n.* Tasmania.

**Tasse,** *f.* cup; cup and saucer.

**Tastatur,** *f.* keyboard.

**tastbar,** *a.* palpable, tangible.

**Taste,** *f.* (*Mech.*) key.

**tasten,** *v.t.* touch, feel; (*Med.*) palpate. — ***v.i.*** feel, grope, explore; key; tune.

**Taster,** *m.* calipers; key; feeler, antenna. **-zirkel,** *m.* gaging calipers.

**Tast-gefühl,** *n.*, **-sinn,** *m.* sense of touch.

**Tastung,** *f.* touching, etc. (see tasten).

**Tast-versuch,** *m.* tentative experiment, preliminary experiment. **-zirkel,** *m.* calipers.

**tat,** *pret.* (of tun) did, made, put.

**Tat,** *f.* deed, doing, action, act; fact. — **in der —,** in fact, indeed.

**-tät.** A suffix used to form abstract nouns; **-ty,** -ness.

**Tatbestand,** *m.* matter of fact, facts.

**Täter,** *m.* doer, author, perpetrator.

**tätig.** *a.* active; busy.

**Tätigkeit,** *f.* activity; action; occupation; function.
**Tatkraft,** *f.* energy.
**tatkräftig,** *a.* energetic.
**tätlich,** *a.* actual; violent.
**tätowieren,** *v.t.* tattoo.
**Tatsache,** *f.* fact.
**Tatsachenstoff,** *m.* factual material.
**tatsächlich,** *a.* actual, real.
**Tatsächlichkeit,** *f.* actuality, reality.
**Tatze,** *f.* paw; (*Tech.*) cam.
**Tau,** *m.* dew. — *n.* rope, cord, cable.
**taub,** *a.* deaf; numb; empty, barren.
**Taube,** *f.* pigeon, dove.
**Taubengrau,** *n.* dove gray, dove color.
**Taub-glas,** *n.* ground glass, frosted glass. **-heit,** *f.* deafness; numbness; barrenness.
**Taubildung,** *f.* formation of dew.
**Taubkohle,** *f.* anthracite.
**Tauch-alitieren,** *n.* aluminizing (calorizing) by dipping. **-anlage,** *f.* dipping plant; steeping plant. **artikel,** *m.* (*Rubber*) dipping goods. **-bahn,** *f.* dip orbit (of electrons), penetrating orbit. **-batterie,** *f.* plunge battery. **-beize,** *f.* disinfection by immersion; disinfecting steep. **-brenner,** *m.* = Tauchsieder. **-element,** *n.* (*Elec.*) plunge cell. **-emaillelack,** *m.* dipping enamel.
**tauchen,** *v.t.* dip, plunge, immerse, steep, soak; coat (by dipping). — *v.i.* & *r.* dive, dip, plunge.
**Taucherkolben,** *m.* (*Mach.*) plunger.
**Tauch-farbe,** *f.* dipping color. **-färbung,** *f.* dip dyeing; dip coloring. **-filter,** *n.* immersion filter. **-flüssigkeit,** *f.* dipping fluid. **-härten,** *n.*, **-härtung,** *f.* (*Metal.*) hot-bath hardening. **-kolben,** *m.* (*Mach.*) plunger. **-korn,** *n.* (*Brewing*) sinker. **-küpe,** *f.* dipping vat. **-lack,** *m.* dipping varnish or lacquer. **-löten,** *n.* dip brazing. **-mischung,** *f.* dip mixing. **-patentieren,** *n.* (*Wire*) patenting by heating and then immersing in a lead or salt bath (erroneously called "cementation"). **-sieder,** *m.* plunge heater, immersion heater (immersed in the liquid to be heated). **-stange,** *f.* plunger. **-verfahren,** *n.* dipping (or immersion) process. **-wa(a)ge,** *f.* hydrometer. **-zeit,** *f.* time of immersion. **-zylinder,** *m.* plunge cylinder, plunger (of a colorimeter).
**tauen,** *v.t.* taw (hides). — *v.i.* thaw; dew.
**Tauenpapier,** *n.* heavy wrapping paper.
**taugen,** *v.i.* be fit, be good, be of value.
**tauglich,** *a.* good, fit, able, qualified, suited.
**tauig,** *a.* dewy.
**Taumel,** *m.* reeling; giddiness; intoxication; transport, frenzy. **-bewegung,** *f.* (*Mach.*) tumbler motion. **-korn,** *n.* darnel (*Lolium temulentum*).
**taumeln,** *v.i.* reel; be giddy; be intoxicated; wobble.
**Taupunkt,** *m.* dew point; thaw point.
**Taurochol-salz,** *n.* taurocholate. **-säure,** *f* taurocholic acid.
**Tauröste,** *f.* dew retting.
**Tausch,** *m.* exchange; barter
**tauschen,** *v.t.* & *i.* exchange; barter.
**täuschen,** *v.t.* deceive, delude, cheat.
**Täuschung,** *f.* illusion; delusion, deception.
**Tausch-wert,** *m.* exchange value, market value. **-zersetzung,** *f.* double decomposition.
**tausend,** *a.* thousand.
**Tausend-güldenkraut,** *n.* lesser centaury (*Erythraea centaurium*). **-schön,** *n.* daisy.
**Tausendstel,** *n.* thousandth (part).
**tautomer,** *a.* tautomeric.
**Tautomerie,** *f.* tautomerism, tautomery.
**Tautopf,** *m.* condensing pot; steam trap.
**Taxation,** *f.* = Taxierung.
**Taxe,** *f.* tax, duty; set price, rate; taxi(cab).
**taxieren,** *v.t.* value, appraise; assess; tax.
**Taxierung,** *f.* valuation; assessment; taxation.
**Technik,** *f.* technic, technique; technics, arts; technology; engineering.
**Techniker,** *m.* technologist; technicist, technician, engineer.
**Technikum,** *n.* technical institution.
**technisch,** *a.* technical; industrial; commercial. **-chemisch,** *a.* technochemical.
**Technolog, Technologe,** *m.* technologist.
**technologisch,** *a.* technological.
**Tee,** *m.* tea. **-kraut,** *n.* herb used for infusions. **-öl,** *n.* tea oil.
**Teer,** *m.* tar; (sometimes) pitch. **-abscheider,** *m.* tar separator.
**teerartig,** *a.* tarry.
**Teer-asphalt,** *m.* tar asphalt, coal-tar pitch. **-ausscheider,** *m.* tar separator. **-ausschlag,** *m.* tar rash. **-band,** *n.* tarred tape. **-baum,** *m.* Scotch pine (*Pinus sylvestris*). **-benzin,** *n.* benzene, benzol. **-bestandteil,** *m.* constituent of tar. **-bildung,** *f.* formation of tar **-bitter,** *n.* picamar. **-brenner,** *m.* tar burner. **-brennerei,** *f.* tar factory. **-dampf, -dunst,** *m.* tar vapor, tar fumes. **-destillat,** *n.* tar distillate.
**teeren,** *v.t.* tar. — *v.i.* tar, form tarry matter.
**Teer-fabrikation,** *f.* tar manufacture or production. **-farbe,** *f.*, **-farbstoff,** *m.* coal-tar color, coal-tar dye. **-fettöl,** *n.* fatty tar oil (higher-boiling part of anthracene oil). **-feuerung,** *f.* tar furnace.
**teerfrei,** *a.* tar-free.
**Teer-gas,** *n.* tar gas. **-gehalt,** *m.* tar content.
**teerhaltig,** *a.* containing tar, tarry.
**Teerhefe,** *f.* tar dregs.
**teerig,** *a.* tarry.

**Teer-kessel,** *m.* tar kettle. **-kocherei,** *f.* tar boiling; tar-boiling plant. **-nebel,** *m.* tar mist. **-öl,** *n.* tar oil, oil of tar, esp. coal-tar oil. **-papier,** *n.* tarred paper, tar paper. **-pappe,** *f.* tar board. **-pech,** *n.* tar pitch. **-prüfer,** *m.* tar tester.

**teerreich,** *a.* rich in tar.

**Teer-rückstand,** *m.* tarry residue; residue from tar. **-salbe,** *f.* tar ointment. **-satz,** *m.* tar sediment. **-säure,** *f.* tar acid (any phenol from coal tar). **-scheider,** *m.* tar separator. **-schwelapparat,** *m.* apparatus for distilling tar. **-schwelerei,** *f.* tar distillation. **-seife,** *f.* tar soap. **-substanz,** *f.* tar substance; tarry matter. **-tröpfchen,** *n.* tar droplet or globule. **-tuch,** *n.* tarred cloth, tarpaulin. **-überzug,** *m.* tar coating. **-wäsche,** *f.* (*Gas*) tar extraction. **-wäscher,** *m.* tar washer, tar scrubber. **-wasser,** *n.* tar water, specif. (*Gas*) ammoniacal liquor. **-werg,** *n.* tarred oakum. **-zahl,** *f.* tar number.

**Teestück,** *n.* T-piece, T, tee.

**Tegel,** *m.* bluish-green marl.

**Teich,** *m.* pond, pool, tank.

**Teig,** *m.* dough; paste; pulp.

**teigartig,** *a.* doughy, pasty, plastic.

**Teig-farbe,** *f.* paste color. **-form,** *f.* doughy or pasty form, dough, paste.

**teigig,** *a.* doughy, pasty; mellow; overripe.

**Teig-konsistenz,** *f.* doughy or pasty consistency. **-schaber,** *m.* dough scraper. **-ware,** *f.* an article (*e.g.*, a dye) in paste form; alimentary paste.

**Teil,** *m.* part; portion, division; party. — **zwei Teile,** two thirds; **drei Teile,** three fourths; etc.

**Teil-.** partial; divisional, dividing, fractional, component. **-bande,** *f.* component band.

**teilbar,** *a.* divisible.

**Teilbarkeit,** *f.* divisibility.

**Teilchen,** *n.* small part, particle; (*Math.*) element. — *α*- —, alpha particle, *α*-particle. **-grösse,** *f.* particle size. **-ladung,** *f.* particle charge. **-verteilung,** *f.* particle distribution or dispersion.

**Teildruck,** *m.* partial pressure.

**teilen,** *v.t.* divide; graduate; share, participate in. — *v.r.* divide; share.

**Teiler,** *m.* divider; (*Math.*) divisor.

**Teilfehler,** *m.* partial error.

**teilhaben,** *v.i.* share, take part, partake.

**Teilhaber,** *m.* sharer, participator, partner.

**teil-haft, -haftig,** *a.* sharing, participating.

**-teilig.** of . . . parts, -part, -partite.

**Teil-kraft,** *f.* (*Mech.*) component force. **-kreis,** *m.* divided (graduated) circle. **-kurve,** *f.* partial curve. **-nahme,** *f.* participation; sympathy, interest.

**teilnehmen,** *v.i.* take part, participate.

**Teil-nehmer,** *m.* participant; sharer, partner; subscriber. **-niveau,** *n.* partial level. **-platte,** *f.* graduated plate or scale. **-reaktion,** *f.* partial reaction.

**teils,** *adv.* in part, partly.

**Teilstrich,** *m.* graduation mark, graduation.

**Teilung,** *f.* division; graduation, scale; (*Mach.*) pitch; partition; sharing.

**Teilungs-bruch,** *m.* (*Math.*) partial fraction. **-ebene,** *f.* plane of division. **-fläche,** *f.* (*Geol.*) division plane. **-gesetz,** *n.* law of partition. **-koeffizient,** *m.* partition coefficient, distribution coefficient. **-zahl,** *f.* dividend. **-zeichen,** *n.* mark of division; hyphen. **-zustand,** *m.* state of division.

**Teil-verflüssigung,** *f.* partial liquefaction. **-vorgang,** *m.* partial process. **-wand,** *f.* division wall.

**teilweise,** *a.* partial. — *adv.* partially.

**Teilzahl,** *f.* number of divisions; quotient.

**Teïn,** *n.* theine (caffeine).

**Teint,** *m.* complexion.

**Tekholz,** *n.* teakwood.

**Teklubrenner,** *m.* Teclu burner.

**tektonisch,** *a.* tectonic, structural.

**-tel.** part, fraction. (See *Drittel, Viertel,* etc.)

**telefonieren,** *v.i.* telephone.

**telefonisch,** *a.* telephonic.

**Telefunken,** *m.* radio, wireless.

**telegrafieren,** *v.i.* telegraph.

**telegrafisch,** *a.* telegraphic.

**Teleobjektiv,** *n.* telephoto lens.

**teleskopartig,** *a.* telescope-like, telescopic.

**Teller,** *m.* plate (dish); disk; palm (of the hand); seat (of a valve); (*Mil.*) antitank mine, teller mine. **-fuss,** *m.* plate-shaped base. **-kühlung,** *f.* plate cooling. **-mine,** *f.* antitank mine, teller mine. **-trockner,** *m.* disk drier. **-ventil,** *n.* disk valve. **-wäscher,** *m.* plate scrubber. **-zinn,** *n.* plate pewter.

**Tellur,** *n.* tellurium.

**Tellur-.** tellurium, telluric, telluride of. **-alkyl,** *n.* alkyl telluride. **-blei,** *n.* lead telluride, (*Min.*) altaite. **-cyansäure,** *f.* tellurocyanic acid. **-diäthyl,** *n.* diethyl telluride. **-eisen,** *n.* iron telluride; native iron. **-erz,** *n.* tellurium ore.

**tellurführend,** *a.* telluriferous.

**Tellur-glanz,** *m.* tellurium glance (nagyagite). **-gold,** *n.* gold telluride. **-goldsilber,** *n.* gold silver telluride. **-halogen,** *n.* tellurium halide.

**tellurhaltig,** *a.* containing tellurium.

**tellurig,** *a.* tellurous.

**Tellurigsäureanhydrid,** *n.* tellurous anhydride ($TeO_2$).

**tellurisch,** *a.* telluric.

**Tellur-kohlenstoff,** *m.* carbon telluride. **-metall,** *n.* metal(lic) telluride. **-natrium,** *n.* sodium telluride. **-nickel.** *m.* nickel telluride.

-ocker, -ocher, *m.* (*Min.*) tellurite. -oxyd, *n.* tellurium oxide. -salz, *n.* tellurium salt, specif. tellurate.

**tellursauer,** *a.* of or combined with telluric acid, tellurate of.

**Tellur-säure,** *f.* telluric acid. **-schwefelkohlenstoff,** *m.* carbon sulfide telluride, CSTe. **-silber,** *n.* silver telluride. **-silberblei,** *n.* lead silver telluride, (*Min.*) sylvanite. **-silberblende,** *f.* sylvanite; stützite.

**Tellurür,** *n.* (lower or -ous) telluride.

**Tellur-verbindung,** *f.* tellurium compound. **-vorlegierung,** *f.* tellurium prealloy. **-wasserstoff,** *m.* hydrogen telluride. **-wasserstoffsäure,** *f.* hydrotelluric acid (hydrogen telluride). **-wismut,** *n.* bismuth telluride.

**Temp.,** *abbrev.* of Temperatur.

**Tempel,** *m.* temple.

**Temperafarbe,** *f.* tempera color.

**Temperatur-abfall,** *m.* temperature drop. **-änderung,** *f.* change of temperature. **-beobachtung,** *f.* temperature observation. **-bereich,** *m.* temperature range or region.

**temperaturbeständig,** *a.* unaffected by temperature changes.

**Temperatur-einfluss,** *m.* influence of temperature. **-erhöhung,** *f.* temperature rise or raising. **-gefäll, -gefälle,** *n.* temperature drop. **-grad,** *m.* degree of temperature. **-grenze,** *f.* temperature limit. **-leitfähigkeit,** *f.* thermal conductivity. **-messer,** *m.* temperature measurer, thermometer, pyrometer. **-messung,** *f.* temperature measurement. **-mittel,** *n.* mean temperature. **-reg(e)lung,** *f.* temperature regulation. **-regler,** *m.* temperature regulator, thermostat. **-schreiber,** *m.* recording thermometer, thermograph. **-schwankung,** *f.* variation of temperature. **-steigerung,** *f.* rise in temperature. **-strahlung,** *f.* thermactinic radiation. **-überführung,** *f.* heat transfer. **-veränderung,** *f.* change of temperature. **-wechsel,** *m.* temperature change. **-wechsler,** *m.* heat exchanger. **-zahl,** *f.* temperature coefficient. **-zunahme,** *f.* increase of temperature.

**Temper-eisen,** *n.* malleable iron. **-erz,** *n.* annealing ore, iron ore for malleable iron. **-farbe,** *f.* temper(ing) color. **-guss,** *m.* malleable cast iron; (less often) malleable casting. **-gusseisen,** *n.* malleable cast iron. **-ierbad,** *n.* tempering bath.

**temperieren,** *v.t.* temper; give (a certain) temperature to. — **temperiert,** *p.a.* tempered; having (a certain) temperature.

**Temper-kohle,** *f.* temper carbon, graphitic carbon. **-kohlebildung,** *f.* formation of temper carbon, graphitization. **-mittel,** *n.* (*Metal.*) annealing or tempering material, packing.

**tempern,** *v.t.* anneal, malleableize; temper.

**Temper-ofen,** *m.* annealing furnace. **-roheisen,** *n.* malleable pig (iron). **-rohguss,** *m.* unannealed malleable iron. **-schrott,** *m.* (*Metal.*) malleable scrap. **-stahlguss,** *m.* = Temperguss. **-topf,** *m.* annealing pot.

**Temperung,** *f.* annealing, etc. (see tempern).

**temporär,** *a.* temporary.

**Tenacit, Tenazit,** *n.* Tenacit, Tenacite (a phenolformaldehyde plastic). *T.N.*

**Tenakel,** *n.* filtering frame; (*Printing*) copy holder.

**Tenazität,** *f.* tenacity.

**Tendenz,** *f.* tendency.

**Tenne,** *f.* floor.

**Tennenmälzerei,** *f.* floor malting; floor-malting house.

**Teppich,** *m.* carpet; rug; tapestry; (table) cover; blanket.

**Terbinerde,** *f.* terbia, terbium oxide.

**Terebinsäure,** *f.* terebic acid.

**Terephtalsäure,** *f.* terephthalic acid.

**Termfolge,** *f.* sequence of terms.

**Termin,** *m.* term; time; deadline.

**Terminus,** *m.* term, expression.

**Term-schema,** *n.* term diagram. **-verschiebung,** *f.* term shift. **-wert,** *m.* term value.

**ternär,** *a.* ternary.

**Ternärstahl,** *m.* ternary steel, simple alloy steel

**Terneblech,** *n.* terneplate.

**Terpen,** *m.* terpene. **-chemie,** *f.* chemistry of the terpenes.

**terpenfrei,** *a.* terpene-free, terpeneless.

**Terpen-gruppe,** *f.* terpene group. **-kohlenwasserstoff,** *m.* terpene hydrocarbon.

**Terpentin,** *m.* turpentine. **-alkohol,** *m.* spirits (oil) of turpentine. **-art,** *f.* kind or variety of turpentine.

**terpentinartig,** *a.* like turpentine, terebinthine.

**Terpentin-ersatz,** *m.* turpentine substitute, white spirit. **-firnis,** *m.* turpentine varnish. **-geist,** *m.* spirits of turpentine (oil of turpentine).

**terpentinhaltig,** *a.* containing turpentine.

**Terpentin-harz,** *n.* turpentine resin. **-öl,** *n.* (oil of) turpentine; rosin oil. **-ölersatz,** *m.* turpentine substitute. **-ölfirnis,** *m.* turpentine varnish. **-ölseife,** *f.* turpentine-oil soap. **-pech,** *n.* turpentine pitch. **-salbe,** *f.* turpentine ointment. **-spiritus,** *m.* = Terpentingeist.

**Terpin,** *n.* terpinol. **-hydrat,** *n.* terpinol hydrate.

**Terrasse,** *f.* terrace; (*Art*) foreground.

**terrestrisch,** *a.* terrestrial.

**tertiär,** *a.* tertiary.

**Tesseral-kies,** *m.* skutterudite; smaltite. **-system,** *n.* (*Cryst.*) isometric system.

**Test,** *m.* test; cupel; test furnace; cupellation furnace; indicator; graphite; molybdenite. **-asche,** *f.* bone ash. **-benzin,** *n.*

(*Paint*) mineral spirits, white spirit. **-gift,** *n.* test poison, test toxin. **-körper,** *m.* test body, test piece. **-mischung,** *f.* test mixing or mixture. **-platte,** *f.* test plate.

**tetanisieren,** *v.t.* tetanize.

**Tetanthren,** *n.* tetanthrene (tetrahydrophenanthrene).

**Tetanusimpfung,** *f.* tetanus inoculation.

**tetartoedrisch,** *a.* tetartohedral.

**Tetra-borsäure,** *f.* tetraboric acid. **-bromkohlenstoff,** *m.* carbon tetrabromide. **-chlorkohlenstoff,** *m.* carbon tetrachloride. **-chlorzinn,** *n.* tin tetrachloride. **-eder,** *n.* tetrahedron.

**tetraedrisch,** *a.* tetrahedral.

**Tetra-edrit,** *m.* tetrahedrite. **-fluorkohlenstoff,** *m.* carbon tetrafluoride. **-hexaeder,** *m.* tetrahexahedron.

**Tetrajod-.** tetraiodo-; tetraiodide of. **-kohlenstoff,** *m.* carbon tetraiodide.

**Tetra-kontan,** *n.* tetracontane. **-kosan,** *n.* tetracosane. **-oxyd,** *n.* tetroxide.

**Tetraoxy-.** (usually) tetrahydroxy-. See Oxy-.

**Tetra-thionsäure,** *f.* tetrathionic acid. **-vanadinsäure,** *f.* tetravanadic acid.

**Tetrinsäure,** *f.* tetrinic acid.

**teuer,** *a.* dear.

**Teuerung,** *f.* dearth, famine; price increase.

**Teufe,** *f.* depth; (*Mining*) level.

**Teufel,** *m.* devil.

**Teufels-dreck,** *m.* asafetida. **-kirsche,** *f.* belladonna. **-wurz,** *f.* aconite (*Aconitum napellus*).

**teufen,** *v.t.* deepen; sink, bore.

**Teutschschwarz,** *n.* ivory black.

**Textabbildung,** *f.* illustration in the text.

**textilchemisch,** *a.* textile-chemical.

**Textil-faser,** *f.* textile fiber. **-gewerbe,** *n.* textile industry.

**Textilien,** *n.pl.* textiles.

**Textil-seife,** *f.* textile soap. **-veredelung,** *f.* finishing or dressing of textiles. **-waren,** *f.pl.* textile goods.

**Textur,** *f.* texture; (*Petrog.*, etc.) structure.

**Tfl.,** *abbrev.* (Tafel) table.

**T-förmig,** *a.* T-shaped.

**Th-.** see also T-.

**Thal,** *n.* valley.

**Thalleio-chin(in),** *n.* thalleioquin. **-chinolin,** *n.* thalleioquinoline.

**Thalli-.** thallic, thallium(III). **-chlorat,** *n.* thallic chlorate, thallium(III) chlorate. **chlorid,** *n.* thallic chloride, thallium(III) chloride. **-ion,** *n.* thallic ion, thallium(III) ion. **-oxyd,** *n.* thallic oxide, thallium(III) oxide. **-salz,** *n.* thallic salt, thallium(III) salt. **-sulfat,** *n.* thallic sulfate, thallium(III) sulfate.

**Thallium-alaun,** *m.* thallium alum. **-bromür,** *n.* thallous bromide, thallium(I) bromide. **-chlorid,** *n.* thallium chloride, specif. thallic chloride, thallium(III) chloride, **-chlorür,** *n.* thallous chloride, thallium(I) chloride. **-fluorür,** *n.* thallous fluoride, thallium(I) fluoride. **-hydroxyd,** *n.* thallic hydroxide, thallium(III) hydroxide. **-hydroxydul,** *n.* thallous hydroxide, thallium(I) hydroxide. **-jodür,** *n.* thallous iodide, thallium(I) iodide. **-oxyd,** *n.* thallium oxide, specif. thallic oxide, thallium-(III) oxide. **-oxydul,** *n.* thallous oxide, thallium(I) oxide. **-sulfür,** *n.* thallous sulfide, thallium(I) sulfide. **-verbindung,** *f.* thallium compound.

**Thalliverbindung,** *f.* thallic compound, thallium(III) compound.

**Thallo-.** thallous, thallium(I). **-bromid,** *n.* thallous bromide, thallium(I) bromide. **-chlorat,** *n.* thallous chlorate, thallium(I) chlorate. **-chlorid,** *n.* thallous chloride, thallium(I) chloride. **-fluorid,** *n.* thallous fluoride, thallium(I) fluoride. **-ion,** *n.* thallous ion, thallium(I) ion. **-jodat,** *n.* thallous iodate, thallium(I) iodate. **-jodid,** *n.* thallous iodide, thallium(I) iodide. **-salz,** *n.* thallous salt, thallium(I) salt. **-sulfat,** *n.* thallous sulfate, thallium(I) sulfate. **-verbindung,** *f.* thallous compound, thallium(I) compound.

**Thapsiasäure,** *f.* thapsic acid.

**That, Thatsache,** etc. See Tat, Tatsache, etc.

**Thee,** *m.* tea. For compounds see Tee-.

**Theer,** *m.* tar. For compounds see Teer-.

**Theil,** *m.* = Teil.

**Thema,** *n.* theme, subject, topic.

**Thenardsblau,** *n.* Thénard's blue (a cobalt aluminate).

**Thenhydroxamsäure,** *f.* thenohydroxamic (2-thiophenecarbohydroxamic) acid.

**Theoretiker,** *m.* theorist.

**theoretisch,** *a.* theoretical.

**Theorie,** *f.* theory.

**therapeutisch,** *a.* therapeutic.

**Therapie,** *f.* therapeutics.

**Thermalquelle, Therme,** *f.* hot spring, thermal spring.

**Thermik,** *f.* heat (as a branch of knowledge).

**thermionisch,** *a.* thermionic.

**thermisch,** *a.* thermal. **-optisch,** *a.* thermooptical.

**Thermit-bombe,** *f.* thermite bomb. **-brandbombe,** *f.* thermite incendiary bomb. **-füllung,** *f.* thermite filling or charge. **-ladung,** *f.* thermite charge. **-schweissung,** *f.* thermite weld(ing). **-verfahren,** *n.* thermite process.

**Thermo-analyse,** *f.* thermal analysis. **-chemie,** *f.* thermochemistry. **-chemiker,** *m.* thermochemist.

**thermochemisch,** *a.* thermochemical.

**Thermodynamik,** *f.* thermodynamics.

**thermo-dynamisch,** *a.* thermodynamic. **-elektrisch,** *a.* thermoelectric.

**Thermo-elektrizität,** *f.* thermoelectricity. **-farbe,** *f.* thermocolor. **-kauter,** *m.* thermocautery. **-kette,** *f.* thermoelement. **-kraft,** *f.* thermoelectric force or power. **-lyse,** *f.* thermolysis.

**Thermometer-kugel,** *f.* thermometer bulb. **-röhre,** *f.* thermometer tube.

**thermometrisch,** *a.* thermometric.

**Thermopaar,** *n.* thermocouple.

**thermoplastisch,** *a.* thermoplastic.

**Thermo-plastizität,** *f.* thermoplasticity. **-regler,** *m.* thermo-regulator, heat regulator. **-säule,** *f.* thermopile. **-strom,** *m.* thermoelectric current.

**These,** *f.* thesis.

**Thiacetsäure,** *f.* thioacetic acid.

**Thier, Thier-.** see Tier, Tier-.

**Thio-ameisensäure,** *f.* thioformic acid. **-antimonsäure,** *f.* thioantimonic acid. **-arsenigsäure,** *f.* thioarsenious acid. **-arsensäure,** *f.* thioarsenic acid. **-äther,** *m.* thio ether. **-carbaminsäure,** *f.* thiocarbamic acid.

**Thiochin-.** thioquin-.

**Thiocyan,** *n.* thiocyanogen. **-kalium,** *n.* potassium thiocyanate.

**thiocyansauer,** *a.* of or combined with thiocyanic acid, thiocyanate of.

**Thiocyan-säure,** *f.* thiocyanic acid. **-verbindung,** *f.* thiocyanate.

**Thioessigsäure,** *f.* thioacetic acid.

**Thiogenfarbe,** *f.* thiogene dye.

**Thio-germaniumsäure,** *f.* thiogermanic acid. **-harnstoff,** *m.* thiourea. **-kohlensäure,** *f.* thiocarbonic acid, specif. trithiocarbonic acid. $H_2CS_3$.

**Thiolsäure,** *f.* thiolic acid.

**Thiomilchsäure,** *f.* thiolactic acid.

**Thion-carbaminsäure,** *f.* thionocarbamic acid. **-farbe,** *f.* thion dye.

**Thioninlösung,** *f.* thionine solution.

**Thion-kohlensäure,** *f.* thionocarbonic acid. **-kohlenthiolsäure,** *f.* thiolthionocarbonic acid (HOCSSH). **-säure,** *f.* thionic acid.

**Thio-phosphorsäure,** *f.* thiophosphoric acid. **-phtalid,** *n.* thiophthalide.

**Thiophten,** *n.* thiophthene.

**Thio-salz,** *n.* thio salt. **-säure,** *f.* thio acid.

**thioschwefelsauer,** *a.* of or combined with thiosulfuric acid, thiosulfate of.

**Thio-schwefelsäure,** *f.* thiosulfuric acid. **-sulfatlösung,** *f.* thiosulfate solution. **-sulfosäure,** *f.* thiosulfonic acid. **-verbindung,** *f.* thio compound. **-zinnsäure,** *f.* thiostannic acid.

**Thiozyan,** *n.* = Thiocyan.

**thixotrop,** *a.* thixotropic.

**Thl.,** *abbrev.* (Theil) part.

**Thln.,** *abbrev.* (Theilen) parts.

**Thomas-birne,** *f.* (*Metal.*) basic converter. **-eisen,** *n.* Thomas iron, basic iron. **-flusseisen,** *n.* Thomas low-carbon steel. **-mehl,** *n.* Thomas meal (ground basic slag used as a fertilizer). **-roheisen,** *n.* Thomas pig (iron), basic pig (iron). **-schlacke,** *f.* Thomas slag, basic slag. **-schlackenmehl,** *n.* = Thomasmehl. **-stahl,** *m.* Thomas steel, basic steel. **-verfahren,** *n.* (*Iron*) Thomas process, basic process.

**Thon,** *m.* clay. For compounds see ton-, Ton-.

**Thor,** *n.* thorium; gate. — *m.* fool. **-erde,** *f.* thoria (thorium oxide).

**thorieren,** *v.t.* thoriate.

**thoriumhaltig,** *a.* containing thorium, thoriated.

**Thorium-heizfaden,** *m.* thoriated (heating) filament. **-salz,** *n.* thorium salt. **-verbindung,** *f.* thorium compound.

**Thoroxyd,** *n.* thorium oxide.

**Thran,** *m.* = Tran.

**Thräne,** *f.* tear. For compounds see Tränen-.

**Thujaöl,** *n.* thuja oil.

**thun,** *v.t. & i.* = tun.

**Thür, Thüre,** *f.* door.

**thüringisch,** *a.* Thuringian.

**Thurm,** *m.* = Turm.

**thut,** *pr. 3 sing.* of thun. See tun.

**Thymian,** *m.* thyme. **-kampher,** *m.* thymol. **-öl,** *n.* oil of thyme.

**Thymo-chinhydron,** *n.* thymoquinhydrone. **-chinon,** *n.* thymoquinone. **-hydrochinon,** *n.* thymohydroquinone.

**Thymus-drüse,** *f.* thymus gland. **-nucleinsäure,** *f.* thymonucleic acid, thymus nucleic acid.

**Thyrojodin,** *n.* thyroiodin (iodothyrin).

**tief,** *a.* deep; low; (of colors) dark.

**Tief,** *n.* deep, depression; minimum. **-ätzprobe,** *f.* deep-etch test or sample. **-ätzung,** *f.* deep etching. **-bau,** *m.* underground construction or work. **-blick,** *m.* insight, penetration.

**tiefbraun,** *a.* deep brown, dark brown.

**Tief-brunnen,** *m.* deep well. **-druck,** *m.* low pressure; intaglio printing.

**Tiefe,** *f.* depth, deepness; deep.

**Tiefebene,** *f.* low plain, lowland.

**tiefeingreifend,** *a.* penetrating; thoro(ugh).

**tiefen,** *v.t.* deepen; deep-draw, cup.

**Tiefen-gestein,** *n.* plutonic rock. **-lehre,** *f.*, **-messer,** *m.* depth gage. **-schärfe,** *f.* (*Photog.*) depth of focus.

**tief-gehend,** *a.* deep, profound; deep-draft. **-gelb,** *a.* deep yellow. **-greifend,** *a.* penetrating, thorogoing, radical, deep-seated, fundamental. **-grün,** *a.* deep green, dark green. **-gründig,** *a.* deep.

**Tief-gründigkeit,** *f.* deepness, depth. **-kühlung,** *f.* low cooling, intense cooling. **-land,** *n.* lowland.

**tiefliegend,** *a.* deep-lying; deep-seated.
**Tief-ofen,** *m.* (*Metal.*) soaking pit. **-punkt,** *m.* low point, minimum point.
**tief-rot,** *a.* deep red. **-rund,** *a.* concave. **-schmelzend,** *a.* low-melting.
**Tief-schwarz,** *n.* deep black, jet black. **-seeschlamm,** *m.* deep-sea ooze.
**tief-siedend,** *a.* low-boiling. **-sinnig,** *a.* pensive; profound; melancholic. **-stellen,** *v.t.* lower.
**Tiefstwert,** *m.* lowest value, minimum.
**Tieftemperatur-teer,** *m.* low-temperature tar. **-vergasung, -verkokung,** *f.* low-temperature carbonization.
**Tiefung,** *f.* deepening; deep-drawing, cupping; depression.
**tief-wurzelnd,** *a.* deep-rooted; deep-seated. **-ziehen,** *v.t.* deep-draw, cup, dish.
**Tiefziehverfahren,** *n.* deep-drawing, cupping process.
**Tiegel,** *m.* crucible, melting pot; pot, skillet, stewpan; cup; platen. **-boden,** *m.* bottom of a crucible. **-brenner,** *m.* crucible maker. **-brennofen,** *m.* crucible oven. **-deckel,** *m.* crucible cover (or lid). **-einsatz,** *m.* crucible charge. **-flussstahl,** *m.* crucible cast steel. **-form,** *f.* crucible mold. **-formerei,** *f.* crucible molding. **-futter,** *n.* crucible lining. **-giesserei,** *f.*, **-guss,** *m.* casting in crucibles.
**Tiegelgussstahl,** *m.* crucible cast steel, crucible steel. **-giessen,** *n.* casting of crucible steel.
**Tiegel-hohlform,** *f.* crucible mold, pot mold. **-inhalt,** *m.* contents of a (or the) crucible. **-ofen,** *m.* crucible furnace, pot furnace. **-probe,** *f.* crucible test. **-rand,** *m.* rim of a crucible. **-ring,** *m.* crucible ring. **-scherben,** *pl.* crucible shards, broken crucibles. **-schmelzofen,** *m.* crucible melting furnace. **-stahl,** *m.* crucible steel. **-trockner,** *m.* crucible drier. **-untersatz,** *m.* crucible stand (or support). **-verkokung,** *f.* crucible coking (test). **-zange,** *f.* crucible tongs.
**Tiekholz,** *n.* teakwood.
**Tier,** *n.* animal; beast.
**Tier-.** animal; veterinary. **-art,** *f.* species of animal. **-arzneikunde,** *f.* veterinary medicine. **-arzneimittel,** *n.* veterinary remedy. **-arzt,** *m.* veterinary surgeon.
**tierärztlich,** *a.* veterinary.
**Tier-blase,** *f.* bladder of an animal. **-bude,** *f.* menagerie. **-chemie,** *f.* animal chemistry. **-chen,** *n.* animalcule; little animal. **-faser,** *f.* animal fiber. **-fett,** *n.* animal fat. **-fibrin,** *n.* animal fibrin, fibrin. **-garten,** *m.* zoölogical garden. **-gattung,** *f.* genus of animals. **-gift,** *n.* animal poison, venom. **-heilkunde,** *f.* veterinary medicine.
**tierisch,** *a.* animal; brutish, bestial.
**Tier-keim,** *m.* animal germ, animal embryo. **-kenner,** *m.* zoölogist. **-kohle,** *f.* animal charcoal. **-körper,** *n.* animal body; carcass. **-kreis,** *m.* zodiac. **-kunde, -lehre,** *f.* zoölogy. **-leim,** *m.* animal glue (or size). **-mehl,** *n.* meat meal, tankage. **-milch,** *f.* animal milk. **-öl,** *n.* animal oil, specif. bone oil. **-pflanze,** *f.* zoöphyte. **-reich,** *n.* animal kingdom. **-säure,** *f.* zoönic (acetic) acid. *Obs.* **-schutzverein,** *m.* society for the prevention of cruelty to animals. **-schwarz,** *n.* animal black, specif. bone black. **-stoff,** *m.* animal substance. **-versuch,** *m.* experiment on an animal. **-zelle,** *f.* animal cell.
**Tiftikwolle,** *f.* mohair; Spanish moss.
**Tiger-auge,** *f.* tiger-eye. **-sandstein,** *m.* mottled sandstone.
**Tiglin-aldehyd,** *n.* tiglic (or tiglinic) aldehyde, tiglaldehyde. **-säure,** *f.* tiglic (or tiglinic) acid.
**tilgen,** *v.t.* destroy, eradicate, extirpate; cancel, annul; erase, blot out, delete; extinguish (light); pay, amortize (debts).
**Tilgung,** *f.* destruction, etc. (see tilgen).
**tingibel,** *a.* (*Micros.*) stainable.
**tingieren,** *v.t.* dye, stain.
**Tinktion,** *f.* staining or dyeing, tinction.
**tinktoriell,** *a.* tinctorial.
**Tinktur,** *f.* tincture.
**Tinol.** a kind of solder. *T.N.*
**Tinte,** *f.* (writing) ink, tint; pickle, mess.
**tintenartig,** *a.* like ink, inky.
**Tinten-fabrikant,** *m.* ink maker. **-farbe,** *f.* ink color, ink dye. **-fass,** *n.* inkholder. **-fassfeder,** *f.* fountain pen. **-fisch,** *m.* cuttlefish, sepia. **-fischschwarz,** *n.* sepia (the pigment). **-flasche,** *f.* ink bottle. **-fleck,** *m.* ink stain, ink spot. **-gummi,** *n.* (rubber) ink eraser. **-löscher,** *m.* blotter. **-pulver,** *n.* ink powder. **-stein,** *m.* inkstone. **-wein,** *m.* tent (a deep red wine).
**tintig,** *a.* inky.
**tippen,** *v.t.* strike gently, tap, tip; type.
**Tisane,** *f.* ptisan, tisane.
**Tisch,** *m.* table; (of a microscope) stage. **-bier,** *n.* table beer. **-chen,** *n.* little table; bracket; tablet. **-decke,** *f.* table cover, tablecloth. **-gerät, -geschirr,** *n.* tableware. **-leim,** *m.* strong glue.
**Tischler,** *m.* joiner, cabinet maker, carpenter. **-leim,** *m.* joiner's glue, glue.
**Tisch-platte,** *f.* (*Micros.*) stage plate. **-wein,** *m.* table wine.
**Titan,** *n.* titanium. **-chlorid,** *n.* titanium chloride, esp. the tetrachloride.
**Titaneisen,** *n.* titaniferous iron. **-erz,** *n.* titanic iron ore, ilmenite. **-sand,** *m.* titaniferous iron sand (a form of ilmenite). **-stein,** *m.* = Titaneisenerz.
**Titan-erz,** *n.* titanium ore. **-fluorwasserstoffsäure, -flusssäure,** *f.* fluotitanic acid.

**titanführend,** *a.* titaniferous.
**Titan-gehalt,** *m.* titanium content. **-halogen,** *n.* titanium halide.
**titanhaltig,** *a.* containing titanium, titaniferous.
**titanig,** *a.* titanous, titanium(III).
**titanisch,** *a.* titanic.
**Titan-kaliumfluorid,** *n.* potassium fluotitanate. **-karbid,** *n.* titanium carbide. **-metall,** *n.* titanium metal. **-nitrid,** *n.* titanium nitride.
**Titanofluorwasserstoffsäure,** *f.* fluotitanous acid, fluotitanic(III) acid.
**Titanoxyd,** *n.* titanium oxide.
**titanreich,** *a.* rich (or high) in titanium.
**Titansalz,** *n.* titanium salt.
**titansauer,** *a.* of or combined with titanic acid, titanate of.
**Titan-säure,** *f.* titanic acid. **-säureanhydrid,** *n.* titanic anhydride, titanium dioxide ($TiO_2$). **-schwefelsäure,** *f.* titanosulfuric acid. **-stahl,** *m.* titanium steel. **-stickstoff,** *m.* titanium nitride. **-verbindung,** *f.* titanium compound. **-weiss,** *n.* titanium white.
**Titel,** *m.* title. **-bild,** *n.* frontispiece. **-blatt,** *n.* title page.
**Titer,** *n.* titer, titre. **-apparat,** *m.* = Titrierapparat. **-flüssigkeit,** *f.* standard solution.
**titern,** *v.t.* titrate.
**Titerstellung,** *f.* establishment of titer, standardization.
**Titrage,** *f.* titration.
**Titrations-flüssigkeit,** *f.* titration solution. **-verfahren,** *n.* titration method. **-wert,** *m.* titration value.
**Titrier-analyse,** *f.* analysis by titration, volumetric analysis. **-apparat,** *m.* titrating apparatus, volumetric apparatus.
**titrierbar,** *a.* titratable.
**Titrierbecher,** *m.* titrating beaker.
**titrieren,** *v.t.* titrate.
**Titrier-flasche,** *f.* titration bottle (for feeding a buret). **-flüssigkeit,** *f.* titrating solution, standard solution. **-geräte,** *n.pl.* titrating apparatus. **-methode,** *f.* titration method, volumetric method. **-säure,** *f.* titrating acid, standard acid.
**Titrierung,** *f.* titration.
**Titrier-vorrichtung,** *f.* titrating apparatus. **-wa(a)ge,** *f.* (*Textiles*) testing balance.
**titrimetrisch,** *a.* titrimetric.
**Tl.,** *abbrev.* (Teil) part.
**Tle.,** *abbrev.* (Teile) parts.
**Tln.,** *abbrev.* (Teilen) parts.
**Tobsucht,** *f.* delirium, raving, mania.
**Tochter,** *f.* daughter.
**Tochter-.** daughter, filial, subsidiary, secondary.
**Tod,** *m.* death.
**todbringend,** *p.a.* deadly, fatal.
**Todes-dosis, -gabe,** *f.* fatal dose, lethal dose. **-kampf,** *m.* death struggle, agony. **-stoss,** *m.* death blow. **-strafe,** *f.* death penalty; capital punishment. **-strahl,** *m.* death ray. **-ursache,** *f.* cause of death.
**tödlich,** *a.* deadly, fatal, lethal.
**todt, todtbrennen,** etc. See tot, totbrennen, etc.
**Toilette(n)-papier,** *n.* toilet paper. **-seife,** *f.* toilet soap. **-seifenfabrikation,** *f.* toilet soap manufacture.
**Tokaier, Tokaierwein,** *m.* Tokay (wine).
**Tolerierung,** *f.* (*Tech.*) tolerance.
**toll,** *a.* mad; crazy, furious, nonsensical.
**Toll-beere, -kirsche,** *f.* belladonna. **-kraut,** *n.* belladonna; stramonium.
**tollkühn,** *a.* foolhardy.
**Tollwut,** *f.* rabies, hydrophobia. **-gift,** *n.* rabies virus.
**Tolubalsam,** *m.* balsam of Tolu, tolu.
**Toluchin-.** toluquin-.
**Toluchinon,** *n.* toluquinone.
**Toluidinblau,** *n.* toluidine blue.
**Toluol,** *m.* toluene. **-süss,** *n.* saccharin. **-trockenschrank,** *m.* toluene drying closet.
**toluolvergällt,** *a.* denatured with toluene.
**Tolu-sirup,** *m.* sirup of tolu. **-tinktur,** *f.* tincture of tolu.
**Toluylenrot,** *n.* toluylene red.
**Toluylsäure,** *f.* toluic acid.
**Tomate,** *f.* tomato.
**Ton,** *m.* clay; tone; sound; key; tune; accent; fashion. **-art,** *f.* kind of clay; key; tune; (musical) pitch.
**tonartig,** *a.* clayey, argillaceous.
**Ton-aufschluss,** *m.* decomposition of clay. **-aufzeichnung,** *f.* sound recording. **-bad,** *n.* toning bath. **-behälter,** *m.* stoneware container. **-beize,** *f.* (*Dyeing*) red liquor. **-beschlag,** *m.* coat of clay. **-bildnerei,** *f.* ceramics. **-bindemittel,** *n.* clay bond. **-boden,** *m.* clay soil, clay ground. **-brei,** *m.* (*Ceram.*) clay slip. **-decke,** *f.* clay cover. **-dinasstein,** *m.* (clay) Dinas brick. **-dreieck,** *n.* clay triangle.
**toneisenhaltig,** *a.* argilloferruginous.
**Toneisenstein,** *m.* clay ironstone.
**tonen,** *v.t.* (*Photog.*) tone; (*Paper*) tint.
**tönen,** *v.i.* sound, ring. — *v.t.* tone, tint; sound.
**Tonerde,** *f.* alumina; argillaceous earth. **-beize,** *f.* (*Dyeing*) alum mordant, specif. red liquor. **-gehalt,** *m.* alumina content.
**tonerdehaltig,** *a.* containing alumina, aluminiferous.
**Tonerde-hydrat,** *n.* hydrate of alumina (aluminum hydroxide). **-kali,** *n.* potassium aluminate. **-lack,** *m.* alumina lake. **-metall,** *n.* aluminum. **-natron,** *n.* sodium aluminate. **-präparat,** *n.* alumina preparation.
**tonerdereich,** *a.* rich in alumina, aluminous.
**Tonerde-salz,** *n.* aluminum salt. **-stein,** *m.* alumina brick. **-sulfat,** *n.* sulfate of alumina

(aluminum sulfate). **-verbindung,** *f.* compound of alumina, specif. aluminate.

**tönern,** *a.* of clay, clay, clayey, argillaceous.

**Tonfarbe,** *f.* tone color, timbre.

**tonfarbig,** *a.* clay-colored.

**Ton-filter,** *n.* clay filter. **-fixierbad,** *n.* toning and fixing bath. **-fixiersalz,** *n.* toning and fixing salt. **-gefäss,** *n.* clay vessel, earthenware vessel. **-geschirr,** *n.* pottery, earthenware. **-gips,** *m.* argillaceous gypsum.

**ton-gleich,** *a.* alike in tone or shade. **-haltig,** *a.* containing clay, argillaceous.

**Tonhöhe,** *f.* (musical) pitch.

**tonig, tonicht,** *a.* clayey, argillaceous.

**Ton-industrie,** *f.* clay industry. **-industrieller,** *m.* clayworker.

**tonisch,** *a.* tonic.

**Tonkabohne,** *f.* tonka bean.

**Tonkabohnenkampher,** *m.* coumarin.

**Ton-kalk,** *m.* argillaceous limestone, argillocalcite. **-kegel,** *m.* clay cone. **-kerze,** *f.* clay filter candle. **-kühlschlange,** *f.* earthenware cooling coil. **-kunst,** *f.* music; phonetics. **-lager,** *n.* clay bed, stratum of clay. **-masse,** *f.* (*Ceram.*) paste. **-mehl,** *n.* clay dust, ground clay. **-mergel,** *m.* clay marl. **-mörtel,** *m.* clay (esp., fireclay) mortar. **-muffel,** *f.* clay muffle. **-mühle,** *f.* clay mill, pug mill.

**Tönnchen,** *n.* small cask, keg.

**Tonne,** *f.* ton (in Germany now 1000 kilograms); tun, cask, barrel, keg.

**tonnenförmig,** *a.* barrel-shaped.

**Ton-papier,** *n.* tinted paper. **-platte,** *f.* clay plate; earthenware slab. **-prüfung,** *f.* clay testing. **-reiniger,** *m.* (*Ceram.*) stone separator. **-retorte,** *f.* clay retort.

**tonrichtig,** *a.* (*Optics*) orthochromatic.

**Ton-rohr,** *n.*, **-röhre,** *f.* clay tube, clay pipe. **-rohrkrümmer,** *m.* bent clay pipe, clay elbow. **-salz,** *n.* (*Photog.*) toning salt. **-sand,** *m.* argillaceous sand. **-sandstein,** *m.* argillaceous sandstone. **-scherbe,** *f.* clay shard, pottery fragment. **-schicht,** *f.* layer or stratum of clay. **-schiefer,** *m.* clay slate, argillite. **-schlamm,** *m.* clay slip. **-schneider,** *m.* pug mill. **-seife,** *f.* aluminous soap. **-speise,** *f.* tempered clay; clay slip; clay mortar. **-stein,** *m.* clay stone. **-steingut,** *n.* (*Ceram.*) high-clay white ware. **-streifen,** *m.* sound track. **-substanz,** *f.* (*Min.*) clay substance, kaolinite; (*Ceram.*) clay body. **-teller,** *m.* clay plate, clay dish (unglazed). **-tiegel,** *m.* clay crucible. **-topf,** *m.* clay pot, earthenware jar.

**Tönung,** *f.* toning; tone; tinting.

**Ton-verschiebung,** *f.* change in tone or shade. **-waren,** *f.pl.* pottery, earthenware. **-wasser,** *n.* clay water, clay wash. **-zelle,** *f.* clay cell (unglazed). **-zeugwaren,** *f.pl.* crockery. **-ziegel,** *m.* clay tile; clay brick. **-zuschlag,** *m.* (*Metal.*) aluminous flux.

**Topas,** *m.* topaz. **-fluss,** *m.* artificial topaz.

**topasgelb,** *a.* topaz-yellow, topaz.

**Topasschörlit,** *m.* pycnite (columnar topaz).

**Topf,** *m.* pot; jar, crock; top.

**Töpfchen,** *n.* small pot.

**Topfdeckel,** *m.* pot lid.

**Töpfer,** *m.* potter.

**Töpferei,** *f.* ceramics, pottery.

**Töpfer-erde,** *f.* potter's earth, potter's clay. **-erz,** *n.* potter's ore, alquifou. **-farbe,** *f.* pottery color, ceramic color. **-geschirr, -gut,** *n.* pottery.

**töpfern,** *a.* earthen, clay.

**Töpfer-ofen,** *m.* potter's kiln. **-scheibe,** *f.* potter's wheel. **-ton,** *m.* potter's clay. **-ware,** *f.* pottery.

**Topf-giesserei,** *f.* making of crucible steel; casting of pots. **-glasur,** *f.* earthenware glaze, specif. alquifou. **-glühverfahren,** *n.* pot annealing. **-mühle,** *f.* barrel mill. **-rösten,** *n.* pot roasting. **-scherbe,** *f.* potsherd. **-stein,** *m.* potstone, soapstone. **-system,** *n.* (*Dyeing*) pot system. **-versuch,** *m.* pot experiment.

**Topinambur,** *m.* Jerusalem artichoke.

**topisch,** *a.* topical.

**Tor,** *n.* gate. — *m.* fool.

**Tor, tor.** pressure of 1 mm. mercury, 1/760 atmosphere.

**Torf,** *m.* peat.

**torfartig,** *a.* like peat, peaty.

**Torf-asche,** *f.* peat ashes. **-boden,** *m.* peat soil. **-eisenerz,** *n.* bog iron ore. **-erde,** *f.* peaty soil, peat mold. **-faser,** *f.* peat fiber. **-gas,** *n.* peat gas. **-geruch,** *m.* peaty odor. **-geschmack,** *m.* peaty taste, flavor of peat.

**torfhaltig,** *a.* containing peat, peaty.

**torfig,** *a.* peaty.

**Torf-kohle,** *f.* peat charcoal. **-koks,** *m.* peat coke. **-lager,** *n.* peat bed; peat yard. **-masse,** *f.* peat. **-mehl,** *n.* powdered peat. **-moos,** *n.* peat moss, specif. sphagnum moss. **-mull,** *n.* peat dust, peat litter. **-rauchgeschmack,** *m.* flavor of peat smoke. **-staub,** *m.* peat dust. **-teer,** *m.* peat tar. **-verkohlung,** *f.* peat charring. **-watte,** *f.* peat wadding.

**Tor-gummi,** *n.* Bassora gum. **-heit,** *f.* folly, foolishness.

**töricht,** *a.* foolish, silly, absurd.

**torkeln,** *v.i.* wobble, tumble, stagger.

**torkretieren,** *v.t.* plaster pneumatically (cf. Torkretputz).

**Torkretputz,** *m.* (pneumatic) cement-sand plastering, gunite.

**Tornister,** *m.* knapsack, packsack, pack.

**torpedieren,** *v.t.* torpedo; (*Petroleum*) shoot.

**torquieren,** *v.t.* twist.

**Torsions-faden,** *m.* torsion filament or wire. **-festigkeit,** *f.* torsional strength. **-kraft,** *f.* torsional force. **-spannung,** *f.* torsional stress, twisting stress. **-wa(a)ge,** *f.* torsion balance. **-winkel,** *m.* angle of torsion.

**Tort,** *m.* wrong, injury.

**Torte,** *f.* tart; cake.

**tot,** *a.* dead. — **toter Gang,** lost motion, backlash. — **toter Punkt,** dead point, dead center.

**Totalität,** *f.* totality.

**Totalverlust,** *m.* total loss.

**totbrennen,** *v.t.* overburn (gypsum, etc.), deadburn. — **totgebrannt,** *p.a.* overburned, deadburned, dead.

**töten,** *v.t.* kill; deaden; soften (colors).

**Toten-blume,** *f.* marigold. **-farbe,** *f.* livid color. **-fleck,** *m.* (*Med.*) livor, livid spot. **-geruch,** *m.* cadaveric odor. **-kopf,** *m.* caput mortuum, specif. colcothar; death's-head. **-starre, -starrheit,** *f.* rigor mortis.

**Töter,** *m.* killer; murderer; extinguisher.

**tot-gar,** *a.* (*Metal.*) over-refined. **-geboren,** *p.a.* stillborn. **-gebrannt,** *p.a.* see totbrennen. **-gegerbt,** *p.a.* overtanned. **-gekocht,** *p.a.* dead-boiled, overboiled. **-gemahlen,** *p.a.* overground, etc. (see Totmahlen).

**Totgerbung,** *f.* overtanning, casehardening (of leather).

**totgewalzt,** *p. a.* overrolled, overmilled.

**Totlast,** *f.* dead weight.

**tötlich,** *a.* deadly, mortal, lethal, fatal.

**Totmahlen,** *n.* overgrinding, overmilling, (*Paper*) overbeating, dead-grinding; disaggregation by milling, milling to break down structure.

**totpressen,** *v.t.* dead-press.

**Totpunkt,** *m.* dead point, dead center.

**tot-reif,** *a.* dead ripe. **-rösten,** *v.t.* dead-roast, dead-burn. **-sicher,** *a.* dead sure, cocksure.

**Totspülen,** *n.* (*Petroleum*) mudding off, watering off.

**Tötung,** *f.* killing, destruction; deadening (of colors).

**touchieren,** *v.t.* touch; corrode slightly.

**Tour,** *f.* turn; revolution, round; tour.

**Touren-zahl,** *f.* number of turns or revolutions. **-zähler,** *m.* revolution counter, speed counter, speed indicator.

**Tourill,** *m.* bombonne, tourie (Woulfe bottle used in distilling acids). — *pl.* **Tourills.**

**Tournantöl,** *n.* rank (rancid) olive oil.

**Tournesol,** *m.* litmus.

**Toxämie,** *f.* toxemia.

**Toxicität,** *f.* toxicity.

**toxikologisch,** *a.* toxicological. **-chemisch,** *a.* toxicological-chemical.

**toxinbindend,** *a.* toxin-binding.

**toxisch,** *a.* toxic.

**Toxizität,** *f.* toxicity.

**Trabant,** *m.* attendant; (*Astron.*) satellite; (*Spect.*) attendant line, satellite.

**Tracht,** *f.* load; pregnancy; litter (of kittens, etc.); crop; course; costume; fashion.

**trachten,** *v.i.* try, attempt, strive.

**trächtig,** *a.* pregnant.

**Trächtigkeit,** *f.* pregnancy, gestation.

**traf,** *pret.* (of treffen) hit, struck, etc.

**Trafo,** *abbrev.* (Transformator) transformer.

**Tragant,** *m.* tragacanth. **-gummi,** *n.* gum tragacanth. **-schleim,** *m.* tragacanth mucilage. **-stoff,** *m.* bassorin.

**Trag-bahre,** *f.* handbarrow; stretcher, litter. **-band,** *n.* strap, sling, suspenders, suspensory.

**tragbar,** *a.* portable; bearing, productive; wearable; (*Dyeing*) fast to wearing; practicable.

**träge,** *a.* inert; inactive, sluggish, idle, lazy, slow, dull.

**Trag(e)büchse,** *f.* carrying case or can.

**tragecht,** *a.* fast to wearing.

**tragen,** *v.t.* bear, carry, support; yield, produce; endure; wear. — *v.r.* wear; dress. — *v.i.* carry; be pregnant.

**Träger,** *m.* carrier; bearer, supporter, support; vehicle: girder; wearer. **-gestein,** *n.* (*Petroleum*) reservoir rock. **-metall,** *n.* (*Metal.*) cementing material, binder. **-schaft,** *f.* responsibility.

**Trag-fähigkeit,** *f.* buoyancy; bearing strength; capacity; productiveness. **-gas,** *n.* buoyant gas, supporting gas, lifting gas.

**Trägheit,** *f.* inertia, inertness; laziness, idleness, slowness.

**Trägheits-kraft,** *f.* force of inertia. **-mittelpunkt,** *m.* center of inertia. **-moment,** *n.* moment of inertia.

**Trag-kraft,** *f.* supporting power, carrying capacity; lifting force; productiveness. **-lager,** *n.* journal bearing. **-last,** *f.* load, burden.

**Tragödie,** *f.* tragedy.

**trägt,** *pr. 3 sing.* (of tragen) bears, etc.

**Trag-vermögen,** *n.* carrying or supporting power; buoyancy. **-weite,** *f.* range; significance. **-zapfenreibung,** *f.* journal-bearing friction.

**Traktat,** *m.* treatise; tract; treaty.

**traktieren,** *v.t.* treat.

**Trambahn,** *f.* tramway.

**Tran,** *m.* train oil (from any marine animal), fish oil; (with a prefix) oil; blubber. **-brennerei,** *f.* = Transiederei.

**Träne,** *f.* tear.

**tranen,** *v.t.* oil.

**Tränen-.** of tears, lacrimal. **-drüse,** *f.* lacrimal gland.

**tränenerregend,** *a.* tear-exciting, lacrimatory.

**Tränen-feuchtigkeit, -flüssigkeit,** *f.* lacrimal fluid. **-fliessen,** *n.*, **-fluss,** *m.* flow of tears.

**-gas,** *n.* tear gas, lacrimator. **-gaskerze,** *f.* tear-gas candle. **-reiz,** *m.* lacrimatory irritation. **-stoff,** *m.* tear gas, lacrimator. **-stoffkerze,** *f.* tear-gas candle. **-wasser,** *n.* lacrimal fluid, tears.
**Tran-füllung,** *f.* (*Leather*) train stuffing. **-gerbung,** *f.* fish oil tannage. **-geruch,** *m.* odor of train oil.
**tranhaltig,** *a.* containing train oil, oily.
**tranig,** *a.* like train oil; greasy.
**trank,** *pret.* (of trinken) drank.
**Trank,** *m.* drink, beverage, potion.
**Tränkbad,** *n.* impregnating bath.
**Tränkchen,** *n.* draft, physic.
**Tränke,** *f.* watering, water.
**tränken,** *v.t.* steep, soak, saturate, impregnate; water; suckle; give to drink.
**Tränk-gefäss,** *n.* drinking vessel. **-harz,** *n.* impregnating resin. **-kessel,** *m.* steeping vessel, impregnating vessel. **-masse,** *f.* impregnating material. **-stoff,** *m.* impregnating agent.
**Tränkung,** *f.* steeping, etc. (see tränken).
**Tränkungs-mittel,** *n.* steeping agent, steep, impregnating agent. **-stoff,** *m.* impregnating agent.
**Tran-leder,** *n.* leather dressed with train oil. **-schmiere,** *f.* (*Leather*) daubing. **-seife,** *f.* train-oil soap.
**Transformator,** *m.* (*Elec.*) transformer.
**Transformatorenöl,** *n.* transformer oil.
**transformieren,** *v.t.* transform.
**Transiederei,** *f.* train-oil boilery, blubber boilery.
**Transkörper,** *m.* trans substance.
**transkristallisieren,** *v.i.* transcrystallize.
**translatorisch,** *a.* translational.
**Transparenz,** *f.* transparency.
**Transpeck,** *m.* blubber.
**trans-plantieren,** *v.t.* transplant; graft. **-ponieren,** *v.t.* transpose. **-portabel,** *a.* transportable.
**Transporteur,** *m.* transporter, conveyor; protractor.
**transportfähig,** *a.* transportable.
**Transportflasche,** *f.* carboy; cylinder.
**transportieren,** *v.t.* transport, carry; transfer.
**Trans-stellung,** *f.* trans position. **-versalschwingung,** *f.* transverse vibration or oscillation.
**Trantrester,** *m.pl.* blubber residue.
**Trapez,** *n.* trapezium; trapeze.
**Trapezoeder,** *n.* trapezohedron.
**Trapp,** *m.* trap (rock).
**trappartig,** *a.* of the nature of trap, trappean.
**Trappe,** *f.* footstep, footprint; trap; bustard.
**trappeln, trappen,** *v.i.* trample, stamp, patter.
**Trassbeton,** *m.* trass concrete.
**trassieren,** *v.t.* trace, mark out.
**Trassmörtel,** *m.* trass mortar.
**trat,** *pret.* (of treten) trod, stepped, etc.
**Tratte,** *f.* draft, bill of exchange.
**Traube,** *f.* bunch of grapes; grape; cluster, (*Bot.*) raceme.
**Traubenabfall,** *m.* husks or marc of grapes.
**trauben-ähnlich, -artig,** *a.* like grapes or a bunch of grapes, botryoidal; in clusters, racemose.
**Trauben-beere,** *f.* grape. **-blei,** *n.* mimetite; pyromorphite. **-dicksaft,** *m.* concentrated grape juice. **-essig,** *m.* grape vinegar.
**traubenförmig,** *a.* of the form of a grape or bunch of grapes, grape-like, botryoidal; (*Bot.*) aciniform, racemose.
**Trauben-gärung,** *f.* fermentation of grapes. **-kern,** *m.* grape seed, grapestone. **-kernöl,** *n.* grapeseed oil. **-kraut,** *n.* sea wormwood; (**mexikanisches**) Mexican tea. **-lese,** *f.* vintage. **-most,** *m.* grape must, must. **-öl,** *n.* grape(seed) oil. **-saft,** *m.* grape juice.
**traubensauer,** *a.* of or combined with racemic acid, racemate of.
**Trauben-säure,** *f.* racemic acid. **-süssmost,** *m.* unfermented grape juice. **-trester,** *m.pl.* marc of grapes. **-vitriol,** *m.* copperas ($FeSO_4 \cdot 7H_2O$). **-zucker,** *m.* grape sugar (dextrose, D-glucose). **-zuckeragar,** *m.* glucose agar. **-zuckerlösung,** *f.* glucose solution.
**traubig,** *a.* = traubenähnlich; grape-laden.
**trauen,** *v.i.* trust, rely. — *v.t.* marry.
**Trauer,** *f.* mourning; sorrow. **-birke,** *f.* weeping birch. **-buche,** *f.* weeping beech.
**trauern,** *v.t.* mourn.
**Trauer-spiel,** *n.* tragedy. **-weide,** *f.* weeping willow.
**Traufe,** *f.* drip; eaves; gutter, trough.
**träufeln,** *v.i.* drip, drop, trickle. — *v.t.* drop, add dropwise.
**Traufwasser,** *n.* rainwater.
**traulich,** *a.* intimate, cordial; cozy, snug.
**Traum,** *m.* dream.
**traumatisch,** *a.* traumatic.
**träumen,** *v.t. & i.* dream.
**Träumerei,** *f.* dreaming; reverie; fancy.
**traurig,** *a.* sad; melancholy; wretched.
**Treber,** *pl.* spent residue, draff (as the marc of grapes or spent malt); (*Brewing*) grains. **-branntwein,** *m.* marc brandy. **-wasser,** *n* (*Brewing*) grains water.
**Trecker,** *m.* tractor.
**treffen,** *v.t.* hit, strike; find, meet with; take, provide. — *v.r.* happen. — *v.i.* hit, take effect. — **treffend,** *p.a.* striking, appropriate.
**Treffen,** *n.* engagement, combat, battle.
**Treffer,** *m.* hit; impact; prize. **-zahl,** *f.* number of impacts or hits.
**trefflich,** *a.* excellent, choice, admirable.
**Treffpunkt,** *m.* point of impact or of meeting.

**Treib-alkohol,** *m.* power alcohol. **-arbeit,** *f.* cupellation. **-asche,** *f.* cupel ashes, bone ash. **-brühe,** *f.* (*Tech.*) old liquor. **-eisen,** *n.* white pig iron.

**treiben,** *v.t.* drive, propel, impel; cupel; sublime; refine; raise (dough or hides); work, hammer, chase or emboss (metal); force (plants); put forth (leaves); (of occupations) practice, carry on, work at; stimulate, promote. — *v.i.* drive, drift; shoot, sprout; circulate; ferment; act as a diuretic; (*Cement*) blow. — **getriebenes Eisen,** wrought iron.

**Treibeofen,** *m.* = Treibofen.

**Treiber,** *m.* driver; propeller; beater; (*Metal.*) refiner.

**Treib-gas,** *n.* propellent gas; fuel gas, power gas. **-haus,** *n.* hothouse. **-herd,** *m.* refining hearth or furnace, cupellation furnace. **-holz,** *n.* driftwood. **-kraft,** *f.* motive power; moving force. **-ladung,** *f.* propelling charge. **-mine,** *f.* floating mine, drifting mine. **-mittel,** *m.* propellant; motor fuel; leavening agent (as baking powder); (*Med.*) purgative. **-ofen,** *m.* refining furnace; cupelling furnace. **-öl,** *n.* motor (fuel) oil. **-pflanze,** *f.* forcing (or forced) plant. **-prozess,** *m.* cupellation. **-riemen,** *m.* driving belt. **-riss,** *m.* expansion crack. **-satz,** *m.* propelling composition. **-scherben,** *m.* cupel. **-schwefel,** *m.* native sulfur. **-sitz,** *m.* (*Mach.*) drive fit, driving fit. **-sprengstoff,** *m.* (*Expl.*) propellant.

**Treibstoff,** *m.* motor fuel; propellant. **-alkoholgemisch,** *n.* alcoholic motor-fuel mixture. **-tank,** *m.* motor fuel tank, "gas" tank, petrol tank.

**Treib-strahl,** *m.* propulsive jet. **-verfahren,** *n.* (*Metal.*) cupellation process.

**Tremie,** *f.* hopper, funnel.

**trennbar,** *a.* separable; divisible.

**trennen,** *v.t.* separate; sever, sunder, divide; resolve, decompose; sort; (*Elec.*) disconnect. — **getrennt,** *p.a.* separated, etc., separate.

**Trenner,** *m.* separator, etc. (see trennen).

**Trennmittel,** *n.* (*Plastics*) parting compound.

**trennscharf,** *a.* (*Physics*) selective.

**Trenn-schärfe,** *f.* (*Physics*) selectivity. **-schicht,** *f.* = Trennungsschicht.

**Trennung,** *f.* separation, etc. (see trennen).

**Trennungs-fläche,** *f.* parting plane; cleavage plane; surface of separation. **-flüssigkeit,** *f.* separating liquid. **-gang,** *m.* course or procedure of separation or analysis. **-grad,** *m.* degree of separation. **-linie,** *f.* line of demarcation, dividing line. **-methode,** *f.* method of separation. **-mittel,** *n.* means of separation. **-schicht,** *f.* separating layer; (*Bot.*) absciss layer. **-strich,** *m.* line of separation; hyphen. **-verfahren,** *n.*, **-vorgang,** *m.* separation process. **-vorrichtung,** *f.* separator. **-wand,** *f.* dividing wall, partition, septum, diaphragm. **-wärme,** *f.* heat of separation or decomposition.

**Trennwand,** *f.* = Trennungswand.

**Treppe,** *f.* staircase, stairs.

**Treppenabsatz,** *m.* landing.

**treppenförmig,** *a.* in the form of stairs, stepped.

**Treppen-rost,** *m.* step grate. **-stufe,** *f.* step, stair.

**treppenweise,** *adv.* stepwise, by stages, by degrees.

**Tresor,** *m.* treasury; safe; strong room. **-stahl,** *m.* a kind of steel for safes.

**Trespe,** *f.* brome grass.

**Trester,** *m.pl.* residue (as the marc of grapes, the husks of olives, or the remains of blubber after the making of train oil). **-branntwein,** *m.* brandy made from the marc of grapes. **-wein,** *m.* wine made from the marc of grapes, piquette.

**Tret-.** treading, tread.

**treten,** *v.i.* tread, step, go, pass, enter. — *v.t.* tread; trample.

**Tret-gebläse,** *n.* foot bellows, foot blower. **-mine,** *f.* (*Mil.*) tread mine, antipersonnel mine.

**treu,** *a.* true, faithful, loyal.

**Treue,** *f.* faithfulness, fidelity; faith; sincerity; loyalty; uniformity.

**Triakis-oktaeder,** *n.* triakisoctahedron (trigonal trisoctahedron). **-tetraeder,** *n.* triakistetrahedron.

**Triakontan,** *n.* triacontane.

**Triamido-.** triamino-, triamido-. (See Amido-.)

**Triäthanolamin,** *n.* triethanolamine.

**Triazetat,** *n.* triacetate.

**Triazojodid,** *n.* triazoiodide (iodine azide, $N_3I$).

**tribasisch,** *a.* tribasic.

**Tribolumineszenz,** *f.* triboluminescence.

**Tribüne,** *f.* platform, rostrum; gallery.

**Tricarbonsäure,** *f.* tricarboxylic acid.

**Trichinoyl,** *n.* triquinoyl.

**Trichloressigsäure,** *f.* trichloroacetic acid.

**trichroitisch,** *a.* trichroic.

**Trichromsäure,** *f.* trichromic acid.

**Trichter,** *m.* funnel; hopper; crater; (hollow) cone; horn; (*Biol.*) infundibulum; (*Founding*) gate.

**trichterartig,** *a.* = trichterförmig.

**Trichter-chen,** *n.* small funnel; small hopper. **-einlage,** *f.* filter cone. **-falte,** *f.* funnel fold.

**trichterförmig,** *a.* funnel-shaped, infundibular, infundibuliform.

**Trichter-gestell,** *n.* funnel stand. **-hals,** *m.* neck of a funnel. **-halter,** *m.* funnel holder. **-kolben,** *m.* funnel flask. **-lunker,** *n.* (*Metal.*) pipe, cavity. **-mühle,** *f.* funnel mill, cone mill.

**trichtern,** *v.t.* pour thru a funnel.

**Trichter-rohr,** *n.*, **-röhre,** *f.* funnel tube, tube funnel; funnel pipe. **-stativ,** *n.* funnel stand. **-stiel,** *m.* funnel stem. **-wandungen,** *f.pl.* funnel walls.

**Tricyan,** *n.* tricyanogen. **-chlorid,** *n.* tricyanyl chloride (cyanuryl chloride). **-säure,** *f.* tricyanic acid (cyanuric acid).

**trieb,** *pret.* (of treiben) drove, propelled, etc.

**Trieb,** *m.* driving force, impetus; drive; (of beer) life; impulse, inclination; instinct; shoot, sprout; driving, drifting; drift; drove. **-gas,** *n.* = Treibgas. **-kraft,** *f.* motive power, moving force. **-malz,** *n.* leavening malt. **-mittel,** *n.* propellant; motor fuel; leavening agent. **-rad,** *n.* driving wheel. **-rinde,** *f.* (*Bot.*) cambium. **-salz,** *n.* leavening salt. **-schraube,** *f.* (*Micros.*) coarse adjustment. **-stahl,** *m.* pinion steel. **-stoff,** *m.* motor fuel; propellant. **-welle,** *f.* driving shaft, drive shaft. **-werk,** *n.* driving mechanism, drive; motor, engine; machine, machinery, gearing, gear; transmission, drive; power plant.

**triefen,** *v.i.* drop, drip, trickle, water.

**Trieur,** *m.* sorter, separator, classifier.

**trifft,** *pr. 3 sing.* (of treffen) hits, strikes, etc.

**Trift,** *f.* drift; pasture; drove, herd.

**triften,** *v.i.* drift, float.

**Triftholz,** *n.* driftwood.

**triftig,** *a.* weighty, sound, valid; adrift.

**Triftrohr,** *n.* (*Physics*) klystron.

**trigonometrisch,** *a.* trigonometric.

**Trijod-.** triiodo-; triiodide of.

**Trikaliumphosphat,** *n.* tripotassium phosphate.

**triklin, triklinisch,** *a.* triclinic.

**Trikosan,** *n.* tricosane.

**Trikotfärberei,** *f.* dyeing of knitted goods.

**Trilit,** *n.* (*Expl.*) "trilit" (trinitrotoluene).

**Trimellit(h)säure,** *f.* trimellitic acid.

**Trimesinsäure,** *f.* trimesic acid.

**trimetrisch,** *a.* trimetric.

**Trimolybdänsäure,** *f.* trimolybdic acid.

**trimorph,** *a.* trimorphous, trimorphic.

**Trimorphie,** *f.* trimorphism.

**Trinatriumphosphat,** *n.* trisodium phosphate.

**trinkbar,** *a.* drinkable, potable.

**Trink-becher,** *m.* drinking cup (or glass). **-branntwein,** *m.* potable spirits.

**trinken,** *v.t. & i.* drink.

**Trink-gefäss,** *n.* drinking vessel. **-glas,** *n.* drinking glass. **-wasser,** *n.* drinking water, potable water.

**Trioxy-.** trihydroxy-, trioxy- (see Oxy-).

**Tripel,** *n.* triplet. — *m.* tripoli.

**Tripel-.** triple; tripoli.

**tripelartig,** *a.* like tripoli, tripoline.

**Tripel-erde,** *f.* tripoli. **-phosphat,** *n.* triple phospate. **-punkt,** *m.* triple point. **-salz,** *n.* triple salt. **-stein,** *m.* tripoli stone

**Triphenylsiliziumchlorid,** *n.* triphenylsilicon chloride (chlorotriphenylsilane).

**triplieren,** *v.t.* triple, treble.

**Trippel,** *m.* tripoli. See Tripel-.

**Tripper,** *m.* clap, gonorrhea. **-gift,** *n.* gonorrheal virus.

**Trisulfaminsäure,** *f.* trisulfamic acid.

**Trithionsäure,** *f.* trithionic acid.

**Tritol,** *n.* trinitrotoluene, TNT.

**tritt,** *pr. 3 sing.* (of treten) treads, steps, etc.

**Tritt,** *m.* tread, step; footprint, track. **-gebläse,** *n.* foot bellows, foot blower. **-leiter,** *m.* stepladder.

**trivial,** *a.* trivial; trite.

**Trivial-bezeichnung,** *f.* common (or popular) designation. **-name,** *f.* trivial name, common (or nonsystematic) name.

**Trizyan-.** see Tricyan-.

**trocken,** *a.* dry. — **auf trockenem Wege,** in the dry way.

**Trocken-.** dry; drying. **-anlage,** *f.* drying establishment or plant. **-apparat,** *m.* drying apparatus, drier, desiccator. **-batterie,** *f.* dry battery. **-beerwein,** *m.* straw wine. **-beize,** *f.* dry disinfection (as of seeds); dry disinfectant. **-bestimmung,** *f.* dry determination. **-blech,** *n.* drying plate or sheet. **-bleiche,** *f.* dry bleaching. **-boden,** *m.* drying loft, drying room. **-brett,** *n.* drying board. **-brikett,** *n.* dry-pressed briquet. **-chlor,** *n.* (*Bleaching*) dry-chemicking. **-dampf,** *m.* dry steam. **-darre,** *f.* drying kiln. **-dauer,** *f.* duration of drying, drying time.

**trockendekatieren,** *v.t.* decatize with dry steam.

**Trocken-dekatur,** *f.* dry decatizing. **-destillation,** *f.* dry distillation.

**Trockene,** *f.* dryness.

**Trocken-element,** *n.* dry cell. **-entgasung,** *f.* dry distillation. **-extrakt,** *m.* dry extract. **-farbe,** *f.* dry color, pigment; pastel color.

**Trockenfäule,** *f.* dry rot.

**trockenfest,** *a.* resistant to dryness or drying.

**Trocken-festigkeit,** *f.* strength when dry; resistance to dryness. **-filter,** *n.* (*Optics*) dry filter. **-filz,** *m.* drying felt. **-firnis,** *m.* siccative varnish, japan; drying oil. **-flasche,** *f.* drying bottle; drying flask. **-frucht,** *f.* dried fruit; dry fruit. **-füllung,** *f.* dry filling, specif. (*Elec.*) solid electrolyte. **-gas,** *n.* dry gas, specif. (*Petroleum*) gas free from condensable hydrocarbons. **-gefäss,** *n.* drying vessel. **-gehalt,** *m.* dry content, content of solid material. **-gehaltsbestimmung,** *f.* determination of dry content. **-gemüse,** *n.* dried (or dehydrated) vegetables. **-gerüst,** *n.* drying frame or rack, hack. **-geschwindigkeit,** *f.* drying speed. **-gestell,** *n.* drying frame, drying stand, drain board. **-gewicht,** *n* dry weight. **-glas,** *n.* drying glass.

-**gummi,** *n.* dry gum; dry rubber. -**guss,** *m.* dry sand casting. -**gut,** *n.* material to be dried. -**haus,** *n.* drying house. -**hefe,** *f.* dry yeast. -**heit,** *f.* dryness; drought. -**heitsgrad,** *m.* degree of dryness. -**kalk,** *m.* dry lime. -**kammer,** *f.* drying chamber, drying room. -**kasten,** *m.* = Trockenschrank. -**kohle,** *f.* dry coal (coal containing little volatile matter). -**legen,** *n.*, -**legung,** *f.* drainage.

**trockenliebend,** *a.* (*Bot.*) xerophilous.

**Trocken-malerei,** *f.* pastel painting. -**maschine,** *f.* drying machine, drier. -**mass,** *n.* dry measure. -**milch,** *f.* dried milk, powdered milk. -**mittel,** *n.* drying agent, drier, siccative, desiccative. -**nährboden,** *m.* (*Bact.*) desiccated nutrient medium. -**ofen,** *m.* drying oven, drying kiln, dry kiln, drying stove. -**öl,** *n.* drying oil; siccative oil, drier. -**pflanze,** *f.* (*Bot.*) xerophyte. -**pistole,** *f.* drying pistol. -**platte,** *f.* drying plate; (*Photog.*) dry plate. -**präparat,** *n.* dry preparation. -**probe,** *f.* dry test, dry assay. -**puddeln,** *n.* dry puddling. -**pulver,** *n.* drying powder. -**rahmen,** *m.* drying frame. -**raum,** *m.* drying room, drying space, drier. -**reinigung,** *f.* dry cleaning. -**riss,** *m.* check, crack (due to drying). -**rohr,** *n.*, -**röhre,** *f.* drying tube. -**rückstand,** *m.* dry residue. -**schälchen,** *n.* drying capsule. -**schale,** *f.* drying dish. -**scheibe,** *f.* drying plate. -**schlamm,** *m.* (*Sewage*) dry sludge. -**schleuder,** *f.* centrifugal drier. -**schliff,** *m.* dry grinding. -**schrank,** *m.* drying closet, drying oven, drying chamber, drier. -**schwindung,** *f.*, -**schwund,** *m.* shrinkage in drying. -**ständer,** *m.* drying stand or rack. -**stoff,** *m.* drying substance, drier; dry substance. -**stofflösung,** *f.* liquid drier. -**stube,** *f.* drying room, drying stove. -**substanz,** *f.* dry substance, solid matter; drying agent. -**teller,** *m.* drying plate, drying dish. -**temperatur,** *f.* temperature of drying. -**torf,** *f.* dry peat, dried peat. -**treber,** *f.* (*Brewing*) dried grains. -**trommel,** *f.* drying drum, rotary drier. -**tunnel,** *m.* tunnel drier. -**turm,** *m.* drying tower; (*Leather*) turret drier. -**verfahren,** *n.* drying process; dry process. -**verlust,** *m.* loss on drying. -**vorgang,** *m.* drying process. -**vorrichtung,** *f.* drying apparatus or contrivance. -**walze,** *f.* drying roll, drying roller. -**wäsche,** *f.* dry cleaning; dry scrubbing. -**wirkung,** *f.* drying action or effect. -**zeit,** *f.* drying time. -**zylinder,** *m.* drying cylinder.

**Trockne,** *f.* dryness.

**trocknen,** *v.t.* & *i.* dry, desiccate; season (wood). — **trocknend,** *p.a.* drying, siccative, desiccative. — **trocknendes Öl,** drying oil, boiled oil.

**Trockner,** *m.* drier.

**Trocknerei,** *f.* drying plant.

**Trocknis,** *f.* dryness.

**Trocknung,** *f.* drying, desiccation; seasoning.

**Trocknungs-.** see also Trocken-. -**anlage,** *f.* drying plant. -**beschleuniger,** *m.* drying accelerator. -**grad,** *m.* degree of dryness. -**gut,** *n.* material to be dried. -**mittel,** *n.* drying agent, drying medium. -**ofen,** *m.* = Trockenofen. -**vorlage,** *f.* drying device (placed before or in front).

**troff,** *pret.* (of triefen) dropped, dripped, etc.

**trog,** *pret.* (of trügen) deceived, cheated.

**Trog,** *m.* trough; vat; tank; pan; hod. -**apparat,** *m.* trough apparatus, specif. (*Elec.*) trough battery. -**batterie,** *f.* trough battery.

**Trögelchen,** *n.* little trough.

**trogförmig,** *a.* trough-shaped.

**Trogstecher,** *m.* (*Sugar*) stirrer.

**T-Rohr,** *n.* T-tube, T-pipe.

**Trommel,** *f.* drum; barrel, cylinder; tumbler, (*Anat.*) tympanum. -**darre,** *f.* drum kiln. -**fell,** *n.*, -**haut,** *f.* drumhead; (*Anat.*) tympanic membrane. -**filter,** *n.* drum filter or strainer. -**mälzerei,** *f.* drum malting. -**mischer,** *m.* drum mixer. -**mühle,** *f.* drum mill, (*Ceram.*) Alsing cylinder.

**trommeln,** *v.t.* & *i.* drum; screen (with a drum sieve); tumble; (*Coke*) rattle.

**Trommel-ofen,** *m.* rotary furnace or oven; cylinder roaster. -**probe,** *f.* (*Coke, Ceram.*) rattler test. -**sieb,** *n.* drum sieve, cylindrical screen, trommel. -**trockner,** *m.* drum drier, rotary drier. -**versuch,** *m.* = Trommelprobe.

**Trompete,** *f.* trumpet; (*Anat.*) tube.

**Trona,** *f.*, **Tronasalz,** *n.* trona.

**troostitisch,** *a.* (*Metal.*) troostitic.

**Tropäolin,** *n.* (*Dyes*) tropeolin, tropaeolin.

**Tropasäure,** *f.* tropic acid.

**Tropen,** *f.pl.* tropics.

**tropenbeständig,** *a.* stable under tropical conditions.

**Tropen-frucht,** *f.* tropical fruit. -**gewächs,** *n.*, -**pflanze,** *f.* tropical plant. -**kraftstoff,** *m.* tropical motor fuel.

**tropfbar,** *a.* capable of forming drops, liquid. -**flüssig,** *a.* liquid.

**Tropf-barkeit,** *f.* capability of forming drops, liquidity. -**behälter,** *m.* dripping pan, dripping cup, etc. -**bernstein,** *m.* liquidambar. -**bier,** *n.* = Trubbier. -**blech,** *n.* drip pan, drain pan. -**brett,** *n.* dripping board, draining board.

**Tröpfchen,** *n.* little drop, droplet; globule; small bead. -**kultur,** *f.* hanging-drop culture.

**Tropfdüse,** *f.* dripping (or dropping) nozzle.

**Tröpfel,** *m.* drippings, drips.

**Tropfelektrode,** *f.* dropping electrode.
**Tröpfelfett,** *n.* drippings.
**tröpfeln,** *v.i.* drop, drip, trickle.
**Tröpfel-pfanne,** *f.* dripping pan, dripper. **-werk,** *n.* (*Salt*) graduation house, drying house.
**tropfen,** *v.i.* drop; drip, trickle.
**Tropfen,** *m.* drop. **-bildung,** *f.* drop formation. **-flasche,** *f.* dropping bottle.
**tropfenförmig,** *a.* drop-shaped, guttiform.
**Tropfen-glas,** *n.* dropping glass, dropping tube. **-messer,** *m.* drop counter, dropper, stalagmometer, stactometer; buret(te). **-mixtur,** *f.* (*Med.*) drops. **-probe,** *f.* drop test, spot test. **-wasser,** *n.* drip water.
**tropfenweise,** *adv.* dropwise, drop by drop.
**Tropfenzähler,** *m.* dropping bottle; drop counter, dropper, stalagmometer, stactometer.
**Tropf-fallpumpe,** *f.* (*Physics*) Sprengel pump. **-fläschchen,** *n.* (small) dropping bottle. **-flasche,** *f.* dropping bottle. **-gefäss,** *n.* dropping (or dripping) vessel. **-gewichtmethode,** *f.* drop-weight method. **-glas,** *n.* dropping glass (a pipet or a dropping bottle). **-gläschen,** *n.* small dropping bottle or pipet(te). **-hahn,** *m.* dropping cock; drip cock. **-harz,** *n.* resin exuded in drops. **-kante,** *f.* (*Tin Plate*) list. **-kasten,** *m.* (*Paper*) save-all. **-körper,** *m.* (*Sewage*) trickling filter. **-pipette,** *f.* dropping pipet(te). **-probe,** *f.* dropping test; pour test. **-punkt,** *m.* dropping point, drop-forming temperature. **-rohr,** *n.* dropping tube. **-schale,** *f.* dripping dish or basin, drip tray, drip pan. **-schwefel,** *m.* drop sulfur. **-stein,** *m.* dripstone.
**tropfsteinartig,** *a.* of or like dripstone, stalactitic, stalagmitic.
**Tropf-trichter,** *m.* dropping funnel. **-wasser,** *n.* drip water. **-wässer,** *n.pl.* (*Med.*) drops. **-wein,** *m.* wine leakings, droppings. **-zink,** *n.* drop zinc. **-zinn,** *n.* drop tin, granulated tin.
**tropisch,** *a.* tropical.
**trösten,** *v.t.* comfort, console.
**Trotte,** *f.* wine press; bruising mill.
**Trottoir,** *n.* sidewalk.
**Trotyl,** *n.* trotyl (trinitrotoluene).
**trotz,** *pret.* in spite of.
**Trotz,** *m.* defiance, insolence, scorn, spite.
**trotzdem,** *adv.* nevertheless, after all. — *conj.* notwithstanding, even tho.
**trotzen,** *v.i.* bid defiance (to); be obstinate; be sulky; presume, boast (of).
**trüb,** *a.* = trübe.
**Trub,** *m.* sediment, dregs; (*Wine*) cloudiness.
**Trubbier, Trübbier,** *n.* beer from the sediment bag.
**trübe,** *a.* turbid; muddy, cloudy, dull, (of wine) thick; (of colors) dull, dead; gloomy, sad.
**Trübe,** *f.* turbidity, etc. (see trübe); turbid liquid; sludge, slime, mud; (*Metal.*) pulp; dross. **-dichte,** *f.* (*Metal.*) pulp density.
**trüben,** *v.t.* render turbid, trouble; dull, dim, cloud; make gloomy, sadden. — **getrübt,** *p.a.* troubled, etc., turbid, cloudy, dull, dim, opaque.
**Trübe-punkt,** *m.* (*Petroleum*) cloud point. **-verdicker,** *m.* (*Metal.*) pulp thickener.
**Trübglas,** *n.* translucent glass (frosted glass, opal glass, etc.).
**Trubsack,** *m.* (*Brewing*) sediment bag, filter bag.
**Trübung,** *f.* rendering turbid, etc. (see trüben); turbidity; blushing (of lacquer); haze (in plastics); tarnish(ing).
**Trübungs-grad,** *m.* degree of turbidity. **-messer,** *m.* turbidimeter; nephelometer; opacimeter. **-punkt,** *m.* turbidity point. **-stoff,** *m.* substance causing turbidity.
**trudeln,** *v. t. & i.* spin; roll.
**Trüffel,** *f.* truffle.
**trug,** *pret.* (of tragen) bore, carried, etc.
**Trug,** *m.* deception, fraud. **-bild,** *n.* phantom, illusion.
**trügen,** *v.i.* be deceitful or deceptive. — *v.t.* deceive, cheat.
**trügerisch,** *a.* deceptive; deceitful; treacherous.
**Trugschluss,** *m.* false conclusion, fallacy, sophism.
**Truhe,** *f.* trunk, chest.
**Trum,** *n.*, **Trumm,** *m.* vein, lode; way; track; strand; strip (of film).
**Trümmer,** *n.pl.* fragments; fission products; remains; debris; wreck, ruin. **-achat,** *m.* brecciated agate. **-gestein,** *n.* breccia; conglomerate; rubble. **-masse,** *f.* debris, detritus.
**Trunk,** *m.* drink, potion; liquor; draft; drinking.
**Trupp,** *m.* troop, band, set, group, flock, etc.
**Truppe,** *f.* troop, body; company, troupe.
**Truthahn,** *m.* turkey cock, turkey.
**Trutz,** *m.* offensive, offense.
**Truxinsäure,** *f.* truxinic acid.
**Trypan-blau,** *n.* trypan blue. **-rot,** *n.* trypan red.
**tryptisch,** *a.* tryptic.
**tschechisch,** *a.* Czechic, Czechish.
**Tschecho-Slowakei,** *f.* Czechoslovakia.
**tschecho-slowakisch,** *a.* Czechoslovakian.
**T-Stoff,** *m.* (Tränenstoff) tear gas, lacrimator; hydrogen peroxide.
**T-Stück,** *n.* T-piece, T, tee.
**Tubasäure,** *f.* tubaic acid.
**Tube, Tübe,** *f.* tube.

**Tuben-.** tubular, tube. **-creme,** *f.* tube cream. **-emaille,** *f.* enamel for tubes. **-lack,** *m.* tube lacquer or varnish.
**Tuberkel,** *f.* tubercle.
**Tuberkel-.** tubercle, tubercular.
**tuberkulös,** *a.* tuberculous, tubercular.
**Tuberkulose,** *f.* tuberculosis.
**Tubulator,** *m.* tubulure, tubulation.
**tubuliert,** *p.a.* tubulated.
**tubulös,** *a.* tubulous, tubular.
**Tubulus,** *m.* tubulure, tubulation; tubule.
**Tubus,** *m.* tube; tubulure. **-aufsatz,** *m.* tube attachment. **-auszug,** *m.* drawtube. **-röhre,** *f.* (*Micros.*) drawtube. **-schlitten,** *m.* tube slide. **-träger,** *m.* tube support.
**Tuch,** *n.* cloth; fabric; handkerchief; shawl.
**tuchartig,** *a.* of or like cloth.
**Tuch-fabrik,** *f.* cloth factory, cloth mill. **-färberei,** *f.* cloth dyeing. **-rot,** *n.* cloth red.
**tüchtig,** *a.* capable, skilful, effective, efficient; strong, sound, able.
**Tücke,** *f.* malice, spite.
**tückisch,** *a.* malignant; insidious; tricky.
**Tuff,** *m.* tuff, tufa; dust.
**tuffartig,** *a.* tufaceous.
**Tuff-erde,** *f.* tufaceous earth. **-kalk,** *m.* tufaceous limestone. **-stein,** *m.* tufa, tuff.
**tuffsteinartig,** *a.* tufaceous.
**Tuffwacke,** *f.* decomposed trap (rock).
**Tugend,** *f.* virtue.
**tugendhaft,** *a.* virtuous.
**Tülle,** *f.* nozzle, spout; socket.
**Tulpe,** *f.* tulip.
**Tulpenbaum,** *m.* tulip tree.
**tumeszieren,** *v.i.* tumefy, swell.
**tummeln,** *v.t.* exercise, keep moving. — *v.r.* bestir oneself.
**Tummler, Tümmler,** *m.* porpoise; dolphin; tumbler.
**Tümpel,** *m.* pool; sump; (*Metal.*) tymp.
**tun,** *v.t.* do; make, perform, effect; put. — **zu wissen —,** give notice.
**Tun,** *n.* doing, action, conduct.
**Tünche,** *f.* whitewash, parget, plaster.
**tünchen,** *v.t.* whitewash; rough-cast, plaster.
**Tünch-farbe,** *f.* plastering color; water color. **-kalk,** *m.* lime for whitewashing. **-schicht,** *f.* finishing coat (in plastering). **-werk,** *n.* whitewashing, pargeting.
**Tungöl,** *n.* tung oil.
**Tungstein,** *m.* scheelite. **-säure,** *f.* tungstic acid.
**tunken,** *v.t.* dip, steep, soak.
**Tunkverfahren,** *n.* dipping or soaking process.
**tunlich,** *a.* practicable, feasible; convenient.
**Tunlichkeit,** *f.* practicability, feasibility; convenience.
**Tunnelofen,** *m.* tunnel kiln.
**Tupf,** *m.* spot, dot, point, speck.
**Tüpfel,** *m.* spot, dot, point, speck; pit. **-analyse,** *f.* spot analysis, drop analysis. **-gewebe,** *n.* pitted tissue.
**tüpfelig,** *a.* speckled, spotted, dotted, mottled.
**Tüpfelmethode,** *f.* spot method, drop method.
**tüpfeln,** *v.t.* spot, dot, speckle, mottle, stipple; pit; test by the spot method.
**Tüpfel-probe,** *f.* spot test, drop test. **-reaktion,** *f.* spot reaction, drop reaction. **-zelle,** *f.* pitted cell.
**tupfen,** *v.t.* touch, dab, tip, spot, dot.
**Tupfer,** *m.* pledget, tampon; swab.
**Tupf-probe,** *f.* spot test, drop test. **-reaktion,** *f.* spot reaction.
**Tür,** *f.* door.
**Turbinenschaufel,** *f.* turbine vane or blade.
**turbinieren,** *v.t.* centrifuge.
**Turbo-brenner,** *m.* turboburner. **-gebläse,** *n.* turboblower. **-läufer,** *m.* turborotor, turbine rotor. **-mischer,** *m.* turbomixer. **-verdichter,** *m.* turbocompressor. **-zerstäuber,** *m.* turbopulverizer.
**Türe,** *f.* door.
**Turil(l),** *m.* = Tourill.
**Türkei,** *f.* Turkey.
**Türkis,** *m.* turquoise. **-blau,** *n.* turquoise blue.
**türkisch,** *a.* Turkish. — **türkische Bohne,** scarlet runner. — **türkischer Weizen,** maize.
**Türkischrot,** *n.* Turkey red. **-artikel,** *m.* Turkey-red style. **-bleiche,** *f.* Turkey-red bleaching, madder bleaching. **-öl,** *n.* Turkey-red oil.
**Türkisgrün,** *n.* turquoise green.
**Turm,** *m.* tower; derrick; turret.
**Turmalin,** *m.* tourmaline. **-zange,** *f.* tourmaline tongs.
**türmen,** *v.t.* pile up. — *v.r.* tower.
**turmförmig,** *a.* tower-like; turreted.
**Turmlauge,** *f.* (*Paper*) tower liquor.
**Turnbullblau,** *n.* Turnbull blue.
**turnen,** *v.i.* practice gymnastics.
**Turnus,** *m.* turn, rotation; cycle.
**Tusch,** *m.*, **Tusche,** *f.* India ink.
**Tuschen,** *n.* painting with India ink; painting with water colors.
**Tuscheverfahren,** *n.* (*Micros.*) India ink method, negative staining.
**Tuschfarbe,** *f.* water color.
**tuschieren,** *v.t.* paint with India ink or water color; ink in; touch.
**tut,** *pr. 3 sing.* (of tun) does, makes, etc.
**Tute, Tüte,** *f.* assay crucible (usually a little lead or iron cup with foot); (*Glass*) glass cylinder; (*Metal.*) prolong, also pipe; paper bag.
**tuten,** *v.i.* toot.
**tütenförmig,** *a.* (paper)bag-shaped, bag-like.
**Tütenpapier,** *n.* bag paper.
**Tutia,** *f.* (*Zinc*) tutty.

**Tutte,** *f.* = Tute.
**T.W.,** *abbrev.* (Teile(n) Wasser), parts of water.
**Tyndallkegel,** *m.* Tyndall cone.
**Typ,** *m.* type, standard.
**Typen-druck,** *m.* type printing. **-metall,** *m.* type metal. **-molekül,** *n.* type molecule. **-muster,** *n.* standard sample. **-theorie,** *f.* type theory.
**Typfärbung,** *f.* standard dyeing.
**typhös,** *a.* typhoid; typhous.
**Typhus-.** typhus, typhous; typhoid. **-gift,** *n.* typhus (or typhoid) virus.
**typisch,** *a.* typical.
**typisieren,** *v.t.* standardize.
**Typlösung,** *f.* type (or reference) solution.
**Typus,** *m.* type, standard.

# U

**u,** *abbrev.* (Undichtigkeitsgrad) degree of porosity.

**u.,** *abbrev.* (und) and; (unter) under, among, etc.; (unten) below.

**U,** *abbrev.* (Umdrehung) revolution.

**u.a.,** *abbrev.* (unter anderen) among others; (und andere) and others.

**u.ä.,** *abbrev.* (und ähnliche) and similar ones.

**u.a.a.O.,** *abbrev.* (und an anderen Orten) and elsewhere.

**u.a.m.,** *abbrev.* (und andere mehr) and others; (und anderes mehr) and so forth, and so on.

**u.ä.m.,** *abbrev.* (und ähnliches mehr) and the like.

**u.a.O.,** *abbrev.* (und andere Orten) and elsewhere; (unter andere Orten) among other places.

**üb.,** *abbrev.* (über) over.

**übel,** *a.* evil, ill, bad. — *adv.* ill, badly.

**Übel,** *n.* evil, ill; disease; injury; misfortune. **-keit,** *f.* nausea. **-klang,** *m.* dissonance.

**übelriechend,** *p.a.* ill-smelling, foul, fetid.

**Übelstand,** *m.* disadvantage, drawback; inconvenience, nuisance.

**üben,** *v.t.* practice, exercise, exert. — **geübt,** *p.a.* practiced, experienced, skilled.

**über,** *prep.* over, above, on, upon; across, beyond, by way of; about, concerning. — *adv.* over. — **— und hinaus,** over and above.

**über-.** per-; over-, super-, hyper-, supra-.

**überall,** *adv.* everywhere, all over; universally.

**über-anstrengen,** *v.t.* overexert, strain. **-antworten,** *v.t.* deliver, consign. **-arbeiten,** *v.t.* work over; revise; retouch. — *v.i.* overwork; work overtime. **-äschern,** *v.t.* (*Leather*) overlime. **-ätzen,** *v.t.* overetch.

**überaus,** *adv.* exceedingly, extremely.

**über-basisch,** *a.* superbasic. **-beizen,** *v.t.* (*Leather*) overbate.

**Über-belichtung,** *f.* (*Photog.*) overexposure. **-besserung,** *f.* overcorrection, overcompensation.

**über-bieten,** *v.t.* outbid; outdo, surpass. **-blasen,** *v.t.* overblow.

**Über-bleibsel,** *n.* residue, residuum, remainder, remnant. **-bleiche,** *f.* overbleaching.

**überbleichen,** *v.t.* overbleach.

**Überblick,** *m.* survey, general view, synopsis, review.

**überborsauer,** *a.* of or combined with perboric acid, perborate of.

**Überborsäure,** *f.* perboric acid.

**über-brennen,** *v.t.* overburn, etc. (see **brennen**). **-bringen,** *v.t.* deliver, transmit.

**Überbromsäure,** *f.* perbromic acid.

**über-brücken,** *v.t.* bridge over, bridge, span. **-chlorsauer,** *a.* of or combined with perchloric acid, perchlorate of.

**Über-chlorsäure,** *f.* perchloric acid. **-chromsäure,** *f.* perchromic acid.

**über-dampfen,** *v.i.* distil. **-dauern,** *v.t.* outlast, survive. **-decken,** *v.t.* cover over, spread over; overlap; mask.

**überdem,** *adv.* besides, moreover.

**überdestillieren,** *v.i.* distil over.

**überdies,** *adv.* besides, moreover.

**Überdruck,** *m.* excess pressure; overprint; (*Calico*) cover printing. **-artikel,** *m.* (*Calico*) cover-print style. **-behälter,** *m.* pressure tank.

**überdruckecht,** *a.* (*Calico*) fast to overprinting.

**überdrucken,** *v.t.* overprint, cover-print.

**Überdruck-farbe,** *f.* (*Calico*) cover-print paste. **-hahn,** *m.* high-pressure cock. **-pumpe,** *f.* booster pump. **-regler,** *m.* excess-pressure regulator.

**übereilt,** *p.a.* precipitate, premature.

**überein,** *adv.* in agreement, conformably.

**übereinander,** *adv.* one upon another. **-fallen, -greifen,** *v.i.* overlap.

**Übereinanderlagerung,** *f.* superposition.

**übereinanderliegend,** *a.* superjacent.

**Übereinanderschweissung,** *f.* lap weld.

**übereinkommen,** *v.i.* agree.

**Überein-kommen,** *n.*, **-kunft,** *f.* agreement.

**übereinstimmen,** *v.i.* agree; harmonize, correspond. — *v.t.* (*Dyeing*) dye to pattern. — **übereinstimmend,** *p.a.* agreeing, consistent, concordant, corresponding.

**Übereinstimmung,** *f.* agreement, conformity, correspondence, harmony.

**überelastisch,** *a.* hyperelastic.

**Überempfindlichkeit,** *f.* hypersensitiveness.

**überendlich,** *a.* transfinite.

**Überentwicklung,** *f.* overdevelopment; (*Biol.*) hypertrophy.

**übererregen,** *v.t.* overexcite.

**Übererzeugung,** *f.* overproduction.

**über-eutektisch,** *a.* hypereutectic. **-eutektoid,** *a.* hypereutectoid. **-exponiert,** *a.* overexposed.

**Überexposition,** *f.* overexposure.

**Überf.**, *abbrev.* (Überführung) conversion.
**überfahren,** *v.i.* drive over, pass over. — *v.t.* convey over, take across; cover.
**Überfall,** *m.* overflow.
**über-fallen,** *v.t.* fall upon, surprise, overtake. — *v.i.* overflow; be superposed. **-fällig,** *a.* overdue.
**Überfall-rohr,** *n.*, **-röhre,** *f.* overflow tube or pipe.
**überfangen,** *v.t.* (*Glass*) flash, case, plate.
**Überfärbeartikel,** *m.* (*Calico*) cross-dyed style.
**über-färbeecht,** *a.* fast to cross-dyeing. **-färben,** *v.t.* overcolor, overdye, overstain; cross-dye; top; fill up, pad (cotton warp); dye on a mordant.
**Überfärbung,** *f.* overdyeing, etc. (see überfärben).
**über-faulen,** *v.i.* overferment. **-fein,** *a.* overfine, over-refined; (of structure) hyperfine. **-fetten,** *v.t.* (*Soap*) superfat; (*Leather*) overstuff.
**Überfettung,** *f.* superfatting; (*Leather*) overstuffing.
**über-feuern,** *v.t.* overfire. overheat. **-firnissen,** *v.t.* varnish over. **-fliessen,** *v.i.* overflow. **-flügeln,** *v.t.* outflank.
**Überfluss,** *m.* abundance, plenty; superfluity, surplus; overflow.
**über-flüssig,** *a.* overflowing, waste (water); in excess; superfluous; abundant, plentiful. **-fluten,** *v.t.* overflow, flood. **-formen,** *v.t.* (*Ceram.*) mold on an inside mold. **-führbar,** *a.* convertible, etc. (see überführen). **-führen,** *v.t.* convert; transport, transfer, convey; convince, convict.
**Über-führung,** *f.* conversion, etc. (see überführen); transport, transfer; overpass. **-führungszahl,** *f.* transference number, transport number. **-führungszeit,** *f.* conversion period. **-fülle,** *f.* excess, repletion, plethora. **-fütterung,** *f.* overfeeding, forced alimentation. **-gabe,** *f.* surrender; delivery. **-gang,** *m.* transition; passage, crossing; (of colors) blending, shading off.
**Übergangs-bogen,** *m.* transition curve; reducing elbow. **-eisen,** *n.* off-grade iron. **-element,** *n.* transition element. **-farbe,** *f.* transition color. **-gebiet,** *n.* transitional region. **-punkt,** *m.* transition point. **-rohr,** *n.*, **-röhre,** *f.* reducing tube or pipe. **-schicht,** *f.* transition layer. **-stadium,** *n.* transition stage. **-stahl,** *m.* borderline steel. **-stelle,** *f.* place of transition, transition point. **-stück,** *n.* reducing piece, reducer. **-stufe,** *f.* transition stage. **-temperatur,** *f.* transition temperature. **-wahrscheinlichkeit,** *f.* transition probability. **-zeit,** *f.* time of transition. **-zustand,** *m.* transition state.
**übergar,** *a.* overdone; overfermented; (*Metal.*) over-refined; (of copper) dry; (of the state of a furnace) too hot.
**über-gären,** *v.i.* overferment; ferment over, run over in fermenting. **-geben,** *v.t.* deliver, surrender, commit. — *v.r.* vomit; surrender. **-gehen,** *v.i.* go over, pass over; change, turn; (of colors) shade; overflow. — *v.t.* pass over, overlook, omit.
**Über-gemengteil,** *m.* minor constituent. **-gewicht,** *n.* overweight, excess weight; preponderance.
**über-giessen,** *v.t.* cover (by pouring); (*Med.*) irrigate, douche; transfer (by pouring), transfuse; spill. **-gipsen,** *v.t.* plaster, parget. **-glasen,** *v.t.* overglaze, glaze over, glaze.
**Über-glasung,** *f.* overglazing, overglaze, glazing, glaze. **-glasur,** *f.* overglaze.
**übergolden,** *v.t.* gild.
**Übergoldung,** *f.* gilding.
**übergreifen,** *v.i.* overlap; encroach, infringe.
**Überguss,** *m.* covering, etc. (see übergiessen); that which is poured over; (of sugar) crust, icing.
**übergut,** *a.* above standard; too good.
**Überhand-nahme,** *f.*, **-nehmen,** *n.* prevalence, too great increase, becoming too powerful.
**über-hängen,** *v.i.* overhang, project. **-häufen,** *v.t.* overload, overstock.
**überhaupt,** *adv.* in general, on the whole, at all.
**über-heben,** *v.t.* pull over; exempt, excuse. — *v.r.* overstrain; be conceited, boast. **-heizen,** *v.t.* overheat; superheat.
**Überhitze,** *f.* excess heat; waste heat; superheat.
**überhitzen,** *v.t.* overheat, superheat.
**Überhitzer,** *m.* superheater. **-dampf,** *m.* superheated steam.
**Überhitzung,** *f.* overheating, superheating.
**überholen,** *v.t.* overtake, outstrip, pass; supersede; overhaul. — **überholt,** *p.a.* superseded, antiquated.
**Über-holungsgebiet,** *n.* overtake range, bunching range (of electrons). **-holz,** *n.* transmuted (resin-impregnated) wood. **-hörfrequenz,** *f.* supersonic (or ultrasonic) frequency.
**über-impfen,** *v.t.* inoculate, vaccinate (from one to another). **-irdisch,** *a.* superterrestrial, heavenly.
**Über-jodid,** *n.* periodide. **-jodsäure,** *f.* periodic acid.
**über-kalken, -kälken,** *v.t.* overlime. **-kalten,** *v.t.* supercool, undercool.
**Über-kaltung,** *f.* supercooling, undercooling. **-kieselung,** *f.* silicification.
**überkippen,** *v.t.* tip over, overturn.
**Überkiste,** *f.* outside box or case.
**über-klotzen,** *v.t.* (*Calico*) slop-pad. **-kochen,** *v.i.* boil over. — *v.t.* overboil.

**Überkoch-rohr,** *n.*, **-röhre,** *f.* overflow tube or pipe.
**überkohlensauer,** *a.* per(oxy)carbonate of; (formerly) bicarbonate of.
**Über-kohlensäure,** *f.* peroxycarbonic acid, percarbonic acid. **-kohlung,** *f.* (*Metal.*) supercarbonization.
**über-kommen,** *v.t.* receive, get; attack, seize. **-kompensieren,** *v.t.* overcompensate.
**Über-korn,** *n.* oversize (grain). **-korrektur,** *f.* overcorrection, overcompensation. **-kreuzung,** *f.* crossing over, crossover.
**über-kriechen,** *v.i.* creep over. **-kritisch,** *a.* above-critical (temperature, speed, etc.).
**Überkrümmung,** *f.* excessive curvature.
**überkrusten,** *v.t.* incrust.
**Überkrustung,** *f.* incrustation.
**über-kühlen,** *v.t.* overcool, supercool. **-lackierecht,** *a.* fast to overvarnishing. **-laden,** *v.t.* overload, overcharge; supercharge; transship. **-lagern,** *v.t.* superpose, superimpose, overlay. — *v.i.* overlie; overlap; (of waves) interfere.
**Überlagerung,** *f.* superposition, etc. (see überlagern).
**überlappen,** *v.t.* overlap. — **überlappte Schweissung,** lap welding.
**Überlappung,** *f.* overlapping, overlap.
**überlassen,** *v.t.* leave, give up, abandon, relinquish; let pass.
**Überlast,** *f.* overload, excess load. **-barkeit,** *f.* overload capacity.
**überlasten,** *v.t.* overload, overburden, overcharge; supercharge; overtax.
**Überlauf,** *m.* overflow; net profit.
**überlaufen,** *v.i.* run over, overflow; desert. — *v.t.* run over; annoy.
**Überlauf-gefäss,** *n.* overflow vessel. **-pipette,** *f.* overflow pipet(te). **-rohr,** *n.* overflow tube (or pipe). **-stutzen,** *m.* overflow tube (or pipe).
**über-leben,** *v.t.* outlive, survive. **-legen,** *v.t.* reflect, consider; lay over. — *p.a.* superior; prevalent.
**Über-legenheit,** *f.* superiority. **-legung,** *f.* consideration, reflection, deliberation.
**über-leiten,** *v.t.* lead over, conduct over, pass over; transfuse (blood). **-leitfähig,** *a.* superconductive.
**Überleitfähigkeit,** *f.* superconductivity.
**überlichten,** *v.t.* overexpose (to light).
**Über-lichtgeschwindigkeit,** *f.* velocity greater than that of light. **-lichtung,** *f.* overexposure (to light). **-lieferung,** *f.* delivery, transmission; surrender; tradition.
**überlöst,** *a.* overgrown (malt).
**Übermacht,** *f.* superior force, predominance.
**übermangansauer,** *a.* of or combined with permanganic acid, permanganate of.
**Über-mangansäure,** *f.* permanganic acid. **-mass,** *n.* excess; allowance (in press fits); oversize.
**über-mässig,** *a.* excessive. **-mastiziert,** *a.* (*Rubber*) overmasticated, dead-rolled.
**Übermatrix,** *f.* (*pl.* **Übermatrizen**) (*Math.*) matrix of matrices.
**übermenschlich,** *a.* superhuman.
**Über-mikrometer,** *n.* ultramicrometer. **-mikroskop,** *n.* supermicroscope, electronic microscope. **-mikroskopie,** *f.* supermicroscopy.
**über-mikroskopisch,** *a.* supermicroscopic. **-mitteln,** *v.t.* transmit, forward.
**Über-mut,** *m.* arrogance; exuberance. **-nahme,** *f.* acceptance, etc. (see übernehmen).
**über-nähren,** *v.t.* overfeed. **-nehmen,** *v.t.* accept, receive; take charge of, enter upon; overcharge. — *v.r.* overdo; overeat. **-normal,** *a.* supernormal.
**Über-osmiumsäure,** *f.* perosmic acid. **-oxyd,** *n.* peroxide. **-oxydation,** *f.* = Überoxydierung.
**überoxydieren,** *v.t.* peroxidize; overoxidize.
**Über-oxydierung,** *f.* peroxidation; overoxidation. **-pflanze,** *f.* (*Bot.*) epiphyte. **-pflanzung,** *f.* transplanting; grafting.
**über-pflatschen,** *v.t.* (*Calico*) pad. **-phosphorsauer,** *a.* of or combined with perphosphoric acid, perphosphate of.
**Überphosphorsäure,** *f.* perphosphoric acid (specif., peroxydiphosphoric acid, $H_4P_2O_8$).
**überpolen,** *v.t.* overpole.
**Über-probe,** *f.*, **-probeweingeist,** *m.* overproof spirit. **-produkt,** *n.* residual product, by-product. **-produktion,** *f.* surplus production; overproduction.
**über-prüfen,** *v.t.* check, review, revise. **-raffinieren,** *v.t.* overrefine. **-ragen,** *v.t.* surpass, excel; overtop. — **überragend,** *p.a.* surpassing, excelling, outstanding, transcendent; overtowering.
**überraschen,** *v.t.* surprise. — **überraschend,** *p.a.* astonishing, surprising.
**überreden,** *v.t.* talk over, persuade.
**Überreduktion,** *f.* overreduction.
**über-reichen,** *v.t.* hand over, present, deliver. **-reichlich,** *a.* superabundant. **-reif,** *a.* overripe. **-reissen,** *v.t.* carry over, entrain.
**Überrest,** *m.* residue, remainder; (*pl.*) remains, scraps, waste.
**überrieseln,** *v.t.* irrigate.
**Überröste,** *f.* overroasting; overretting.
**über-rosten,** *v.i.* become covered with rust. **-rösten,** *v.t.* overroast, burn; overret (flax or hemp). **-rot,** *a.* infra-red, ultra-red.
**Überrutheniumsäure,** *f.* perruthenic acid.
**übersäen,** *v.t.* strew, sow over.
**Übersalpetersäure,** *f.* pernitric acid.
**übersättigen,** *v.t.* supersaturate; surfeit.
**Übersättigung,** *f.* supersaturation; satiety.

**übersauer,** *a.* too acid, too sour; (of salts) containing more than two equivalents of acid to one of base, as **übersaures oxalsaures Kali,** potassium tetroxalate.

**übersäuern,** *v.t.* overacidify; peroxidize.

**Übersäuerung,** *f.* overacidification; peroxidation.

**Überschall,** *m.* (*Physics*) supersonics.

**Überschall-,** supersonic, ultrasonic. **-welle,** *f.* supersonic wave. **-zelle,** *f.* supersonic light relay or valve.

**über-schärfen,** *v.t.* oversharpen; overstrengthen (a solution). **-schatten,** *v.t.* overshadow, overshade. **-schätzen,** *v.t.* overvalue, overrate. **-schäumen,** *v.i.* foam over, froth over.

**Überschein,** *m.* reflected color, overtone.

**überschichten,** *v.t.* cover with a layer (as of another liquid); arrange in layers, stratify.

**Über-schiebung,** *f.* shoving over; (*Math.*) transvection; (*Geol.*) overthrust. **-schlag,** *m.* estimate, (rough) calculation; covering, coating; (*Elec.*) flashover.

**über-schlagen,** *v.t.* pass over, omit; throw over; cover; estimate, compute. — *v.i.* become lukewarm; fall over; turn. **-schlägig,** *a.* roughly estimated.

**Überschlags-länge,** *f.* (*Expl.*) propagation distance. **-probe,** *f.* (*Expl.*) gap test. **-rechnung,** *f.* approximate calculation, estimate.

**überschmelzen,** *v.t.* superfuse; enamel.

**Überschmelzung,** *f.* superfusion; enameling.

**überschmieren,** *v.t.* smear, daub.

**Überschneidung,** *f.* overcutting; overlapping (of lines); intersection.

**über-schreiben,** *v.t.* inscribe, head; address (a letter, parcel, etc.). **-schreiten,** *v.t.* go beyond, overstep; exceed; transgress.

**Über-schreitung,** *f.* overstepping, exceeding (of a limit or normal point); transgression. **-schrift,** *f.* inscription, heading, title; address (of a letter). **-schuss,** *m.* excess; surplus.

**über-schüssig,** *a.* excess, in excess, excess of; surplus, remaining. **-schwänzen,** *v.t.* (*Brewing*) sparge.

**Überschwefelblei,** *n.* lead persulfide.

**überschwefelsauer,** *a.* of or combined with persulfuric acid, persulfate of.

**Überschwefelsäure,** *f.* persulfuric acid (peroxydisulfuric acid, $H_2S_2O_8$).

**über-schwellen,** *v.t.* (*Leather*) overplump. **-schwemmen,** *v.t.* overflow, flood. **-schwenglich,** *a.* exuberant, excessive. **-schwer,** *a.* too heavy; too difficult. **-schwimmend,** *a.* supernatant. **-seeisch,** *a.* oversea, transocean, transmarine. **-sehen,** *v.t.* oversee; overlook; look over. **-setzen,** *v.t.* translate; transport; transform; overcharge; (*Dyeing*) top.

**Über-setzung,** *f.* translation, etc. (see übersetzen); (*Mach.*) transmission, gearing. **-sicht,** *f.* survey, review; synopsis, summary, abstract; view; insight; (*Dyeing*) overtone.

**übersichtlich,** *a.* easily visible, clear.

**Übersichts-bild,** *n.* general view, over-all picture. **-spektrum,** *n.* general spectrum. **-tabelle,** *f.* tabular summary.

**übersieden,** *v.t. & i.* boil over, distil.

**Übersieden,** *n.* boiling over; (*Brewing*) extra brew.

**über-silbern,** *v.t.* silver, silver-plate. **-sinnlich,** *n.* metaphysical, abstract, supersensible.

**Übersinterung,** *f.* incrustation.

**über-spannen,** *v.t.* overstrain, force; (over)-spread; cover; span. **-spannt,** *p.a.* overstrained; exaggerated; eccentric.

**Überspannung,** *f.* overstraining, etc. (see überspannen); (*Elec.*) overvoltage.

**über-spinnen,** *v.t.* spin over, cover. **-sponnen,** *p.a.* (of wire, etc.) covered. **-springen,** *v.i.* jump over, jump across; pass abruptly. — *v.t.* skip, omit; jump over. **-spritzen,** *v.i.* spurt over. — *v.t.* spray, overspray.

**Überspritzfarbe,** *f.* overspraying color.

**über-sprudeln,** *v.i.* bubble over, gush over. **-spülen,** *v.t.* wash, drench; overflow. **-ständig,** *a.* stale, flat; overripe; (of ores) weathered. **-stark,** *a.* overstrong, too strong, too much. **-stehen,** *v.t.* endure, overcome; survive. — *v.i.* stand over; project, stand out. **-stehend,** *p.a.* standing over, overlying, (of liquids) supernatant; projecting. **-steigen,** *v.t.* exceed; surmount. — *v.i.* overflow; mount or step over.

**Über-steiger,** *m.* overflow (device); siphon. **-steiggefäss,** *n.* overflow vessel.

**überstrahlen,** *v.t.* illuminate, irradiate; outshine.

**Überstrahlung,** *f.* overradiation, overexposure (to radiation).

**über-streichen,** *v.t.* paint over, coat; apply (color); overspread; sweep over. **-streuen,** *v.t.* strew over.

**Überstrom,** *m.* (*Elec.*) excess current, overload.

**überströmen,** *v.i.* flow over, overflow.

**Über-struktur,** *f.* (*Cryst.*) overstructure. **-stunden,** *f.pl.* extra hours, overtime.

**über-stürzen,** *v.t. & i.* overturn. — *v.r.* hurry; act rashly. **-stürzt,** *p.a.* precipitate, hasty.

**Über-sud,** *m.* boiled-over material; distillate. **-sulfid,** *n.* persulfide.

**Übertage-.** above-ground, surface.

**übert. an,** *abbrev.* (übertragen an) assignor to.

**über-täuben,** *v.t.* deafen; drown (a sound). **-teuern,** *v.t.* overcharge. **-tragbar,** *a.* transferable, etc. (see übertragen); infectious (disease). **-tragen,** *v.t.* transfer; carry (oxygen, etc.); transmit; propagate (waves);

transport; translate; transcribe; assign (patents, etc.).

**Über-trager, -träger,** *m.* carrier; transferrer; transmitter; transporter; translator; transcriber; (*Elec.*) transformer. **-tragung,** *f.* transference, transfer, etc. (see übertragen); convection.

**Übertragungs-frequenz,** *f.* transmission frequency. **-körper,** *m.* (*Expl.*) induced-detonation charge. **-ladung,** *f.* (*Expl.*) propagation charge, primer charge.

**über-treffen,** *v.t.* surpass, exceed, excel. **-treiben,** *v.t.* drive over; distil; sublimate; overdo, exaggerate.

**Übertreibkühler,** *m.* = Abflusskühler.

**über-treten,** *v.t.* overstep, transgress, infringe. —*v.i.* step over, go over. **-trieben,** *p.a.* excessive; exaggerated.

**Übertritt,** *m.* going over, passage.

**über-trocknen,** *v.t.* overdry. **-tünchen,** *v.t.* whitewash; plaster; gloss over. **-verdichten,** *v.t.* supercompress, supercharge.

**Über-verdichter,** *m.* supercharger. **-vergrösserung,** *f.* supplementary magnification; overmagnification. **-vulkanisation,** *f.* overvulcanization, overcure.

**über-wachen,** *v.t.* supervise, superintend, inspect, control. **-wachsen,** *v.t. & i.* overgrow.

**Über-wachsung,** *f.* overgrowth. **-wachung,** *f.* control; supervision; control device.

**über-wallen,** *v.i.* boil over, overflow; heal over. **-wältigen,** *v.t.* overpower, overcome.

**Überwärme,** *f.* excess heat; overheating.

**über-wiegen,** *v.t.* outweigh, overbalance. **-wiegend,** *p.a.* preponderant; overpowering. — *adv.* preponderantly. **-winden,** *v.t.* overcome; surmount. **-wintern,** *v.t.* winter, keep thru the winter. **-wuchern,** *v.i. & t.* overgrow, (*Biol.*) hypertrophy.

**Über-wucht,** *f.* unbalance, imbalance; overweight. **-wurf,** *m.* overgarment; roughcast. **-wurfmutter,** *f.* coupling nut, union nut; cap nut, screw cap; lock nut. **-zahl,** *f.* greater number; surplus; excess; odds.

**über-zählig,** *a.* supernumerary, surplus. **-zeugen,** *v.t.* persuade, convince.

**Über-zeugung,** *f.* persuasion, conviction. **-zeugungskraft,** *f.* persuasive power.

**überziehen,** *v.t.* cover, coat, line, plate, overlay, incrust; put on, put over. — *v.r.* become covered or coated.

**Über-zug,** *m.* coating, coat, covering, cover, crust, incrustation, plating, skin, lining, flashing. **-zugslack,** *m.* coating varnish; finishing varnish coat, finishing.

**Übf.,** *abbrev.* (Überführung) conversion, etc.

**Übg.,** *abbrev.* (Übung) exercise.

**üblich,** *a.* customary, usual, ordinary.

**üblicherweise,** *adv.* customarily, commonly.

**U-Boot,** *abbrev.* (Unterseeboot) U-boat, submarine.

**übrig,** *a.* over, left, remaining, to spare; superfluous. — **im übrigen,** = übrigens.

**übrigbleiben,** *v.i.* remain (over); survive.

**übrigens,** *adv.* as for the rest; besides; however, after all.

**übriggeblieben,** *p.a.* residual, remaining.

**Übung,** *f.* practice; exercise, use; drill; dexterity; routine; discipline.

**Übungs-beispiel,** *n.* example (for practice). **-bombe,** *f.* practice bomb. **-ladung,** *f.* practice powder charge. **-reizstoff,** *m.* (*Mil.*) irritant training agent. **-riechstoff,** *m.* (*Mil.*) odor-detection training agent.

**Uchatiusstahl,** *m.* Uchatius steel, direct steel.

**u.dergl.,** *abbrev.* (und dergleichen) and the like.

**u.d.f.,** *abbrev.* (und die folgende) and those following.

**u.dgl.,** *abbrev.* (und dergleichen) and the like.

**u.dgl.m.,** *abbrev.* (und dergleichen mehr) and the like, and so forth.

**u.d.M.,** *abbrev.* (unter dem Mikroskop) under the microscope.

**u.E.,** *abbrev.* (unseres Erachtens) in our opinion.

**Ue-.** see Ü-.

**u.e.a.,** *abbrev.* (und einige andere) and some others.

**Ueb-.** see Üb-.

**U-Eisen,** *n.* channel iron.

**u.f.,** *abbrev.* (und folgende) and following, *et seq.*

**U.F.,** *abbrev.* (Unterfamilie) subfamily.

**Ufa,** *abbrev.* of *U*niversum *F*ilm *A*ktiengesellschaft.

**Ufer,** *n.* bank, shore, coast, beach.

**u.ff., uff.,** *abbrev.* = u.f.

**U-förmig,** *a.* U-shaped.

**Uhr,** *f.* watch; clock; meter; hour, o'clock.

**Uhrenöl,** *n.* watch oil, clock oil.

**Uhr-feder,** *f.* watch spring; clock spring. **-glas,** *n.* watch glass, (of large sizes) clock glass. **-macheröl,** *n.* watchmaker's oil. **-werk,** *n.* clockwork. **-zeiger,** *m.* watch hand; clock hand. **-zeigergegensinn,** *m.* counterclockwise direction. **-zeigersinn,** *m.* clockwise direction.

**UKW,** *abbrev.* (Ultrakurzwellen ultrashort (radio) waves.

**Ulme,** *f.* elm.

**Ulmenrinde,** *f.* elm bark.

**Ulminsäure,** *f.* ulmic acid.

**ultrabasisch,** *a.* ultrabasic.

**Ultra-beschleuniger,** *m.* ultra-accelerator. **-hochfrequenz,** *f.* ultrahigh frequency.

**ultrakurz,** *a.* ultrashort, (of waves) ultrahigh-frequency.

**Ultra-lampe,** *f.* ultraviolet lamp. **-marinfarbe,** *f.* ultramarine color.

**ultra-mikroskopisch,** *a.* ultramicroscopic. **-rot,** *a.* ultrared, infrared. **-rotdurchlässig,** *a.* diathermanous. **-rotundurchlässig,** *a.* athermanous.
**Ultraschall,** *m.* (*Physics*) supersonant. **-welle,** *f.* supersonic wave. **-zelle,** *f.* supersonic light valve.
**Ultra-strahlung,** *f.* ultraradiation, specif. cosmic rays. **-wage, -waage,** *f.* ultrabalance. **-wasser,** *n.* optically empty water.
**um,** *prep.* round, about, at, for, by. — *adv.* about, over, up, in order to, to. — **einen Tag — den andern,** every other day.
**um-.** round, about, over, up, re-, inversely.
**umändern,** *v.t.* convert, change, alter.
**Umänderung,** *f.* conversion, change.
**umarbeiten,** *v.t.* work over, recast; convert; rewrite, revise; work up.
**Umbau,** *m.* rebuilding, reconstruction.
**Umbenennung,** *f.* renaming.
**Umber,** *m.*, **Umbererde,** *f.* umber.
**umbiegen,** *v.t.* bend round, double back.
**umbilden,** *v.t.* remodel; transform; re-form; alter.
**Umbildung,** *f.* remodeling, etc. (see umbilden).
**umblasen,** *v.t.* blow down.
**umbördeln, umbörteln,** *v.t.* turn, turn over (all around); edge, flange, border.
**Umbra, Umbraerde,** *f.* umber.
**umbringen,** *v.t.* kill, destroy.
**umdefinieren,** *v.t.* redefine.
**Umdestillation,** *f.* redistillation.
**umdestillieren,** *v.t.* redistil, rectify.
**Umdeutung,** *f.* reinterpretation.
**umdrehbar,** *a.* reversible; turning, revolving.
**umdrehen,** *v.t.* & *r.* turn round, rotate, twirl, twist, revolve. — **umdrehend,** *p.a.* rotatory; revolving.
**Umdrehung,** *f.* rotation; revolution; turn.
**Umdrehungs-achse,** *f.* axis of rotation (or revolution). **-bewegung,** *f.* rotatory motion. **-geschwindigkeit,** *f.* speed of rotation (or revolution). **-punkt,** *m.* center of rotation (or revolution). **-richtung,** *f.* direction of rotation (or revolution). **-zahl,** *f.* number of revolutions, r.p.m. **-zähler,** *m.* revolution counter.
**Umdruck,** *m.* reprint; reprinting. **-farbe,** *f.* reprinting ink. **-papier,** *n.* transfer paper.
**Umesterung,** *f.* interchange of ester radicals.
**umfällen,** *v.t.* dissolve and reprecipitate.
**Umfang,** *m.* circumference; periphery; circuit, extent, range, compass, radius, scope.
**umfangen,** *v.t.* embrace; surround.
**umfangreich,** *a.* extensive, ample, wide.
**Umfangs-geschwindigkeit,** *f.* peripheral (or circumferential) velocity. **-kraft,** *f.* circumferential force.
**umfärben,** *v.t.* redye.
**umfassen,** *v.t.* embrace; comprise; span. — **umfassend,** *p.a.* comprehensive, extensive.
**umflechten,** *v.t.* twist or weave about, braid.
**umformen,** *v.t* transform; convert; remodel.
**Umformer,** *m.* (*Elec.*) converter, transformer; (*Steam*) desuperheater.
**Umformung,** *f.* transformation, deformation, change.
**Umfrage,** *f.* inquiry.
**umfüllen,** *v.t.* transfer (liquids or gases); decant; refill, recharge; (*Brewing*) re-rack.
**Umfüllung,** *f.* transfer(ring); decantation.
**Umgang,** *m.* round, circuit, turn, rotation; convolution; by-pass; intercourse; society.
**umgänglich,** *a.* sociable.
**umgearbeitet,** *p.a.* worked over, etc. (see umarbeiten).
**umgeben,** *v.t.* surround; inclose.
**Umgebung,** *f.* surrounding(s), environment.
**Umgebungsflüssigkeit,** *f.* enveloping fluid.
**Umgegend,** *f.* surroundings, vicinity.
**umgehen,** *v.i.* go round, go about; work, be in action; associate; manage, deal. — *v.t.* go round; by-pass; avoid, evade.
**umgekehrt,** *p.a.* see umkehren.
**umgelegt,** *p.p.* of umlegen. — **umgelegter Hals,** ring neck.
**umgeschmolzen,** *p.a.* see umschmelzen.
**umgestalten,** *v.t.* change, transform; recast, remodel.
**Umgestaltung,** *f.* change, transformation, metamorphosis; reform.
**umgestülpt,** *p.a.* overturned, inverted.
**umgewandelt,** *p.a.* see umwandeln.
**umgibt,** *pr. 3 sing.* (of umgeben) surrounds.
**umgiessen,** *v.t.* transfer (by pouring); decant; pour around; recast; cast around.
**Umgrenzung,** *f.* bounding, boundary; limitation.
**umgrössern,** *v.t.* change in size, enlarge, reduce.
**umgruppieren,** *v.t.* regroup, rearrange.
**Umguss,** *m.* transfer (by pouring); decantation; recasting, recast.
**umher,** *adv.* around, about, here and there.
**umhin,** *adv.* otherwise, but.
**umhüllen,** *v.t.* wrap up, envelop, cover, case.
**Umhüllung,** *f.* covering, wrapping, casing, sheathing, jacket, envelope.
**U/Min.,** *abbrev.* (Umdrehungen in der Minute) revolutions per minute, r.p.m.
**u.Mk.,** *abbrev.* (unter dem Mikroskop) under the miscroscope.
**Umkehr,** *f.* reversal; return; sudden change.
**Umkehrbad,** *n.* (*Photog.*) reversing bath.
**umkehrbar,** *a.* reversible, invertible, capable of being turned about, over, or inside out.
**Umkehrbarkeit,** *f.* reversibility, invertibility.
**umkehren,** *v.t.* turn round, about, over, or inside out; invert; reverse. — *v.i.* turn round

or back, return. — **umgekehrt,** *p.a.* inverted, inverse, reverse, converse; (*adv.*) inversely, conversely, vice versa. — **umgekehrte Fällung,** reverse precipitation.

**Umkehr-entwicklung,** *f.* (*Photog.*) reversal development. **-erscheinung,** *f.* reversal phenomenon. **-funktion,** *f.* inverse function.

**Umkehrung,** *f.* inversion; turning about, etc. (see umkehren).

**umkippen,** *v.t.* tip over, overturn, upset, dump.

**umklappen,** *v.i.* fall, drop, collapse. — *v.t.* double up, double back.

**umkleiden,** *v.t.* coat; case, jacket, line; clothe.

**umkochen,** *v.t.* boil.

**umkommen,** *v.i.* perish; spoil.

**Umkreis,** *m.* = Umfang.

**umkreisen,** *v.t.* turn, circle, or revolve around.

**Umkreisgeschwindigkeit,** *f.* peripheral velocity.

**Umkristallisation,** *f.* = Umkristallisierung.

**umkristallisieren,** *v.t.* (dissolve and) recrystallize.

**Umkristallisierung,** *f.* (dissolving and) recrystallization.

**umkrücken,** *v.t.* rake, rabble; (*Brewing*) mash.

**umladen,** *v.t.* reload; (*Elec.*) change the potential of, also reverse the charge of.

**Umladung,** *f.* reloading; (*Elec.*) change in potential, also reversal of sign.

**umlagern,** *v.t.* rearrange; transpose; re-store; surround.

**Umlagerung,** *f.* rearrangement; transposition; re-storing; surrounding, besieging.

**Umlauf,** *m.* revolution; rotation; circulation; cycle; recycling.

**umlaufen,** *v.i.* revolve; rotate; run around; circulate. — *v.t.* run over.

**Umlauf-gebläse,** *n.* centrifugal blower. **-geschwindigkeit,** *f.* speed of rotation or revolution. **-pumpe,** *f.* circulation pump. **-trocknung,** *f.* drying with circulating air. **-zahl,** *f.* rotation number, number of revolutions. **-zeit,** *f.* time of rotation, revolution period.

**umlegbar,** *a.* reversible; inclinable; hinged.

**umlegen,** *v.t.* change, shift; turn (malt); put round, put on; turn down.

**Umleitung,** *f.* turning aside, diversion.

**umlenken,** *v.t.* & *i.* turn round or off, turn.

**umlernen,** *v.t.* learn anew, relearn.

**umliegend,** *p.a.* surrounding.

**umlösen,** *v.t.* dissolve and allow to crystallize (without filtration).

**Ummagnetisierung,** *f.* reversal of magnetism; (magnetic) hysteresis.

**ummanteln,** *v.t.* jacket, sheathe, case, incase.

**umpacken,** *v.t.* repack; pack all around.

**Umpolung,** *f.* pole reversal.

**Umrahmung,** *f.* framing, frame, (*Printing*) box.

**umrechnen,** *v.t.* convert (into), reduce (to).

**Umrechnung,** *f.* conversion, reduction.

**Umrechnungs-faktor,** *m.* conversion factor. **-tabelle, -tafel,** *f.* conversion table.

**umreissen,** *v.t.* outline, sketch; tear down.

**umringen,** *v.t.* encircle, surround.

**Umriss,** *m.* outline, contour; sketch.

**umrühren,** *v.t.* stir, stir up, agitate, work (with some implement).

**Umrühren,** *n.* stirring, stirring up, specif. (*Iron*) puddling, (*Copper*) poling.

**Umrührstab,** *m.* stirring rod, stirrer.

**Umsatz,** *m.* exchange; change, transformation; sale, business. **-produkt,** *n.* product of exchange, specif. metabolism product.

**Umschaltbrett,** *n.* switchboard.

**umschalten,** *v.t.* (also *Elec.*) reverse; (*Elec.*) commutate.

**Umschalter,** *m.* reverser; commutator; switchboard.

**Umschaltfeuerung,** *f.* regenerative furnace.

**Umschau,** *f.* survey, review.

**umschaufeln,** *v.t.* turn (as with a shovel), stir.

**umschichtig,** *adv.* in layers; alternately.

**Umschlag,** *m.* cover, covering, wrapper, envelope; sudden change, turn, turning; cataplasm, poultice; transshipment; sale; hem, facing, collar.

**umschlagen,** *v.t.* wrap about; apply (a poultice); turn over, up, or down; knock down. — *v.i.* turn, change; decompose; overturn, upset.

**Umschlagpapier,** *n.* wrapping paper.

**Umschlags-punkt,** *m.* transition point; (in titration) end point. **-zahl,** *f.* titration value.

**umschliessen,** *v.t.* surround, enclose, include.

**umschlingen,** *v.t.* wind around, clasp, cling to.

**umschmelzen,** *v.t.* remelt, recast, refound.

**Umschmelzofen,** *m.* remelting furnace.

**Umschmelzung,** *f.* remelting, recasting, refounding.

**umschreiben,** *v.t.* rewrite, transcribe; circumscribe; paraphrase; (*Math.*) describe.

**umschütteln,** *v.t.* shake, shake up, agitate.

**umschütten,** *v.t.* transfer (by pouring); decant.

**Umschweif,** *m.* roundabout way; digression.

**umschwenken,** *v.t.* turn round, rotate.

**Umschwung,** *m.* rotation, revolution.

**umsetzbar,** *a.* transposable, etc. (see umsetzen).

**umsetzen,** *v.t.* transpose; change the position of; change, convert; transform; reverse; cause to react; transplant; exchange, sell. — *v.r.* change; react.

**Umsetzung,** *f.* transposition; double decomposition; conversion, change; transformation; reversal; reaction; transplantation; exchange, sale, business.

**Umsetzungsgeschwindigkeit,** *f.* velocity of transformation, reaction rate.

**Umsicht,** *f.* prospect; panorama; circumspection.

**umsieden,** *v.t. & i.* distil.
**umsomehr,** *adv.* so much the more, the more.
**umsonst,** *adv.* for nothing, gratis; in vain; aimlessly; causelessly.
**umspannen,** *v.t.* surround; (*Elec.*) transform.
**Umspanner,** *m.* (*Elec.*) transformer.
**umspülen,** *v.t.* wash, wash round, flow around.
**Umstand,** *m.* circumstance; condition; (*pl.*) ceremonies. — **unter Umständen,** under certain circumstances, on occasion.
**umständlich,** *a.* circumstantial; ceremonious; bothersome, troublesome, cumbersome.
**Umstandswort,** *n.* adverb.
**umstechen,** *v.t.* turn, stir up; re-engrave.
**umstehend,** *p.a.* next, following; standing about; surrounding.
**umstellbar,** *a.* reversible, invertible, transposable.
**umstellen,** *v.t.* reverse, transpose, invert; surround; readjust; adapt.
**Umstellung,** *f.* reversal, etc. (see umstellen); change-over, conversion.
**Umstellwerkstoff,** *m.* substitute material.
**umsteuerbar,** *a.* reversible; revertible.
**umsteuern,** *v.t.* (*Mach.*) reverse.
**Umstimmungsmittel,** *n.* alterative.
**umstossen,** *v.t.* throw down, overthrow; abolish, cancel.
**umstrahlen,** *v.t. & i.* irradiate, radiate.
**Umstrahlung,** *f.* irradiation, radiation.
**umstritten,** *p.a.* disputed, debated.
**umstülpen,** *v.t.* overturn, invert.
**umstürzen,** *v.t.* overthrow, upset, dump. — *v.i.* fall down.
**Umsud,** *m.* distillate.
**umtauschen,** *v.t.* exchange.
**umtun,** *v.t.* put on, put around. — *v.r.* seek, inquire.
**umwälzen,** *v.t.* roll or turn round; stir up; revolutionize. — *v.r.* revolve, rotate.
**umwandelbar,** *a.* convertible, transformable.
**Umwandelbarkeit,** *f.* convertibility, transformability.
**umwandeln,** *v.t.* convert, transform, change; (*Grammar*) inflect. — *v.r.* become converted or changed.
**Umwandler,** *m.* converter; transducer; (*Elec.*) transformer.
**Umwandlung,** *f.* conversion, transformation, change; transmutation; metamorphosis; (*Grammar*) inflection.
**Umwandlungsartikel,** *m.* (*Calico*) conversion style.
**umwandlungsfähig,** *a.* capable of being converted, etc. (see umwandeln), convertible, transformable.
**Umwandlungs-produkt,** *n.* transformation product. **-punkt,** *m.* transformation point, transition point. **-spannung,** *f.* (*Elec.*) transformation potential. **-theorie,** *f.* transformation theory. **-wärme,** *f.* heat of transformation.
**Umweg,** *m.* roundabout way, detour.
**Umwelt,** *f.* world about us, environment. **-einfluss,** *m.* environmental influence.
**umwenden,** *v.t.* turn over, about, or upside down, invert, reverse.
**umwerten,** *v.t.* convert; revalue.
**umwickeln,** *v.t.* wrap round, cover, envelop.
**Umwick(e)lung,** *f.* wrapping, covering, casing.
**umziehen,** *v.t.* draw round, cover, wrap; turn, manipulate; pull down. — *v.i.* change, move.
**Umzug,** *m.* wandering; moving; procession; removal, change.
**umzüngeln,** *v.t.* (of flames) play about, envelop.
**un-.** A prefix used like English un-, but even more widely, to give a reverse meaning; also to denote immensity. Equivalents: un-, non-, not, in-, il-, im-, ir-, an-, dis-, de-, mis-; prodigious, countless, etc.
**un-abänderlich,** *a.* unchangeable, invariable. **-abhängig,** *a.* independent.
**Unabhängigkeit,** *f.* independence.
**un-abkömmlich,** *a.* indispensable. **-ablässig,** *a.* incessant, uninterrupted. **-absehbar,** *a.* unbounded, incalculable, immense. **-absichtlich,** *a.* unintentional. **-ächt,** *a.* not genuine, false. **-achtsam,** *a.* inadvertent, negligent. **-ähnlich,** *a.* unlike, dissimilar. **-aktinisch,** *a.* nonactinic. **-anfechtbar,** *a.* indisputable, incontestable. **-angegriffen,** *a.* unattacked, unaffected. **-angelassen,** *a.* untempered, unannealed. **-angemessen,** *p.a.* unsuitable, inadequate. **-angenehm,** *a.* unpleasant, disagreeable. **-angeregt,** *a.* unexcited, in the normal state. **-angreifbar,** *a.* unattackable.
**Unannehmlichkeit,** *f.* inconvenience, annoyance.
**un-ansehnlich,** *a.* unattractive; insignificant. **-anwendbar,** *a.* inapplicable, unsuitable. **-atembar,** *a.* irrespirable. **-auffällig,** *a.* inconspicuous. **-aufgelöst,** *a.* undissolved; unresolved. **-aufhaltsam,** *a.* irresistible. **-aufhörlich,** *a.* incessant, continual, perpetual. **-auflösbar,** *a.* insoluble.
**Unauflösbarkeit,** *f.* insolubility.
**unauflöslich,** *a.* insoluble.
**Unauflöslichkeit,** *f.* insolubility.
**un-ausdehnbar,** *a.* inexpansible; nonductile. **-ausführbar,** *a.* impracticable, unfeasible. **-ausgefällt,** *a.* unprecipitated. **-ausgeglichen,** *p.a.* uncompensated, unbalanced.
**Unausgeglichenheit,** *f.* uncompensated state.
**un-ausgemacht,** *p.a.* undecided, uncertain. **-ausgesetzt,** *p.a.* uninterrupted. **-auslöschbar, -auslöschlich,** *a.* indelible (ink); inextinguishable. **-aussprechlich,** *a.* inexpressible, unspeakable. **-auswaschbar,** *a.* in-

capable of being washed out. **-beachtet,** *a.* unnoticed. **-bearbeitet,** *p.a* unwrought, raw; unmachined; unfinished; (of hides) undressed; (of land) untilled. **-bedeckt,** *p.a.* uncovered. **-bedenklich,** *a.* unobjectionable; unhesitating. **-bedeutend,** *p.a.* insignificant, unimportant. **-bedingt,** *a.* unconditional; unlimited. — *adv.* unconditionally, absolutely. **-beeinflusst,** *a.* uninfluenced, unaffected. **-befangen,** *p.a* unprejudiced; unconcerned. **-befleckt,** *a.* unspotted, spotless. **-befriedigend,** *a.* unsatisfactory. **-befugt,** *a.* unauthorized; unwarranted. **-begreiflich,** *a.* incomprehensible. **-begrenzt,** *a.* unlimited, boundless.

**Unbehagen,** *n.* uneasiness, discomfort.

**un-behandelt,** *p.a.* untreated; unworked. **-bekannt,** *p.a.* unknown; unacquainted. **-belebt,** *p.a.* inanimate, lifeless. **-belichtet,** *a.* unexposed (to light). **-bemerkt,** *p.a.* unnoticed, unobserved. **-benannt,** *p.a.* unnamed, anonymous; (*Math.*) indefinite, indeterminate; (*Anat.*) innominate. **-benutzbar,** *a.* unusable, unserviceable. **-bequem,** *a.* inconvenient, unpleasant.

**Unbequemlichkeit,** *f.* inconvenience.

**un-berechenbar,** *a.* incalculable. **-berechtigt,** *p.a.* unauthorized; unjustified. **-berücksichtigt,** *a.* unconsidered, disregarded.

**unberuhigt,** *a.* unquieted; unstabilized; (*Metal.*) unkilled. — **unberuhigter Stahl,** rimming steel, rimmed steel.

**un-berührt,** *a.* untouched. **-beschädigt,** *p.a.* undamaged, intact. **-beschränkt,** *p.a.* unlimited; uncontrolled. **-beschwert,** *a.* unloaded, unfilled. **-besetzt,** *p.a.* (of positions) unoccupied; unset, etc. (see besetzen). **-beständig,** *a.* unstable, labile, inconstant.

**Unbeständigkeit,** *f.* instability; inconstancy.

**unbestimmt,** *p.a.* undetermined; indeterminate, indefinite.

**Unbestimmtheit,** *f.* indeterminacy, uncertainty, indefiniteness.

**un-bestritten,** *a.* undisputed. **-beteiligt,** *p.a.* not concerned, non-participating. **-beugsam,** *a.* inflexible. **-bewaffnet,** *p.a.* unarmed; (of the eye) unaided, naked. **-beweglich,** *a.* immovable, fixed. **-bewusst,** *p.a.* unknown; ignorant (of); unaware; involuntary. **-bezogen,** *a.* unrelated, etc. (see beziehen). **-biegsam,** *a.* inflexible. **-brauchbar,** *a.* useless, unserviceable. **-brennbar,** *a.* noncombustible.

**Unbrennbarmachung,** *f.* fireproofing.

**und,** *conj.* and.

**undefinierbar,** *a.* undefinable.

**Undefiniertheit,** *f.* indefiniteness.

**un-dehnbar,** *a.* inextensible, nonductile. **-denkbar,** *a.* unthinkable, inconceivable. **-deutlich,** *a.* indistinct, blurred. **-dicht,** *a.* not tight, pervious.

**Undicht-heit, -igkeit,** *f.* leakiness, perviousness; porosity; leak. **-igkeitsgrad,** *m.* degree of perviousness or porosity.

**Unding,** *n.* absurdity; nonentity.

**undissoziiert,** *a.* undissociated.

**undulatorisch,** *a.* undulatory.

**undulieren,** *v.i.* undulate. — **undulierend,** *p.a.* undulatory.

**undulös,** *a.* undulous, undulatory.

**un-durchdringlich,** *a.* impermeable, impervious; impenetrable. **-durchforscht,** *a.* unexplored. **-durchführbar,** *a.* impracticable, unfeasible. **-durchgängig,** *a.* impenetrable, impermeable. **-durchlässig,** *a.* impermeable, impervious. **-durchscheinend,** *a.* nontranslucent, opaque. **-durchsichtig,** *a.* nontransparent, opaque, obscure.

**Undurchsichtigkeit,** *f.* opacity; obscureness.

**uneben,** *a.* uneven.

**Unebenheit,** *f.* unevenness, inequality.

**un-echt,** *a.* not genuine, false, pseudo, counterfeit, artificial; (of colors) not fast, fugitive, loose. **-edel,** *a.* not noble, base. **-egal,** *a.* unequal; uneven.

**Unegalität,** *f.* inequality; unevenness.

**un-eigentlich,** *a.* not true or real or proper, not in a strict sense; not literal, figurative. **-einheitlich,** *a.* nonuniform, inhomogeneous. **-elastisch,** *a.* inelastic, unelastic. **-elektrisch,** *a.* unelectrified, uncharged. **-empfänglich,** *a.* unreceptive, insusceptible. **-empfindlich,** *a.* insensitive, insensible, insusceptible.

**unendlich,** *a* infinite; endless. — **ins Unendliche,** to infinity, ad infinitum.

**un-entbehrlich,** *a.* indispensable. **-entdeckt,** *a.* undiscovered; undisclosed. **-entflammbar,** *a.* nonflammable, uninflammable. **-entgeltlich,** *a.* gratuitous, free. **-entschieden,** *a.* undecided; uncertain. **-entwickelt,** *p.a.* undeveloped; (*Math.*) implicit. **-entwirrbar,** *a.* inextricable. **-entzündbar, -entzündlich,** *a.* nonflammable, uninflammable. **-erbittlich,** *a.* inexorable. **-erfahren,** *p.a.* inexperienced. **-erforschlich,** *a.* inscrutable. **-erforscht,** *a.* unexplored. **-erheblich,** *a.* insignificant, unimportant. **-erhört,** *p.a.* unheard of; ungranted. **-erklärbar, -erklärlich,** *a.* unexplainable, inexplicable. **-erlässlich,** *a.* indispensable. **-erlaubt,** *a.* forbidden, unpermitted. **-ermesslich,** *a.* immeasurable, immense. **-ermüdlich,** *a.* untiring, indefatigable. **-erregt,** *a.* unexcited. **-erreichbar,** *a.* unattainable. **-erschöpflich,** *a.* inexhaustible. **-ersetzbar,** *a.* irreplaceable, irreparable. **-erträglich,** *a.* intolerable, insupportable. **-erwähnt,** *p.a.* unmentioned. **-erwartet,** *p.a.* unexpected. **-erwünscht,** *a.* undesired, undesirable. **-explodierbar,** *a.* inexplosive. **-fähig,** *a.* incapable, unable.

**Unfähigkeit,** *f.* incapability, incapacity, inability.

**Unfall,** *m.* accident; mishap, misfortune.

**un-fallsicher,** *a.* accidentproof. **-fassbar, -fasslich,** *a.* incomprehensible. **-fehlbar,** *a.* infallible, unfailing. **-fern,** *a. & prep.* near. **-fertig,** *a.* unfinished; unready. **-frei,** *a.* unfree; constrained; (of equilibrium) nonvariant, invariant. **-freiwillig,** *a.* unintentional, involuntary. **-fruchtbar,** *a.* unfruitful, infertile, sterile, barren.

**Unfug,** *m.* disorder, mischief.

**unfühlbar,** *a.* impalpable; imperceptible.

**ung.,** *abbrev.* (ungefähr) about, approximately.

**-ung.** A suffix attached to verb roots to form nouns denoting the action or an effect of it; -ing, -tion, -sion, etc.; as, *Verbrennung,* combustion, *Bindung,* binding, union, bond.

**unganz,** *a.* unsound, defective.

**Ungänze,** *f.* defect, flaw.

**ungar,** *a.* not done, etc. (see gar); underdone; (*Leather*) undertanned.

**ungarisch,** *a.* Hungarian.

**Ungarn,** *n.* Hungary.

**un-geachtet,** *prep.* notwithstanding. — *conj.* altho. **-geahnt,** *a.* unexpected, unsuspected. **-gealtert,** *a.* unaged. **-gebleicht,** *p.a.* unbleached. **-gebrannt,** *p.a.* unburnt. **-gebührlich,** *a.* indecent, improper, undue. **-gebunden,** unbound, (of elements) uncombined, free; dissolute; prose. **-gedämpft,** *p.a.* undamped, etc. (see dämpfen).

**Ungeduld,** *f.* impatience.

**ungedüngt,** *a.* (*Agric.*) unfertilized.

**ungeeignet,** *a.* unsuited, unfit.

**ungefähr,** *adv.* about. — *a.* approximate.

**Ungefähr,** *n.* chance, hazard.

**un-gefährlich,** *a.* harmless, inoffensive. **-gefällig,** *a.* disagreeable. **-gefärbt,** *p.a.* undyed; uncolored; unstained. **-gefrierbar,** *a.* nonfreezing. **-gegerbt,** *p.a.* untanned. **-gegoren,** *p.a.* unfermented. **-gehärtet,** *a.* unhardened, soft. **-geheissen,** *p.a.* unasked; spontaneous. **-geheizt,** *p.a.* unheated; unfired. **-geheuer,** *a.* enormous, huge; amazing. **-gehörig,** *a.* improper, undue. **-gekocht,** *p.a.* unboiled, raw. **-gekränkt,** *p.a.* uninjured. **-geladen,** *p.a.* unloaded; uninvited. **-geläutert,** *p.a.* unpurified, unrefined. **-gelegen,** *p.a.* inconvenient, inopportune. **-gelehrt,** *p.a.* unlearned. **-geleimt,** *p.a.* unglued; (*Paper*) unsized. **-gelernt,** *a.* unskilled. **-gelöscht,** *p.a.* unquenched; unslaked. **-gelöst,** *p.a.* undissolved; unsolved. **-gemein,** *a.* uncommon. **-gemessen,** *p.a.* unmeasured; boundless. **-gemischt,** *p.a.* unmixed. **-gemünzt,** *p.a.* uncoined. **-gemütlich,** *a.* uncomfortable, unpleasant. **-genannt,** *p.a.* unnamed, anonymous; (*Anat.*) innominate. **-genau,** *a.* inexact, inaccurate.

**Ungenauigkeit,** *f.* inaccuracy; uncertainty; lack of sharpness (of definition).

**un-geneigt,** *p.a.* disinclined; unfriendly. **-geniessbar,** *a.* uneatable, unpalatable. **-genügend,** *p.a.* insufficient. **-genügsam,** *a.* insatiable. **-genutzt,** *p.a.* unused. **-geordnet,** *a.* disordered, confused, unregulated. **-geprüft,** *p.a.* unexamined, untried. **-gequantelt,** *a.* unquantized. **-gerade,** *a.* uneven, odd; not straight.

**ungerad-wertig,** *a.* of odd valence. **-zahlig,** *a.* (*Math.*) uneven, odd.

**un-gerechnet,** *p.a.* not counted. **-gereinigt,** *p.a.* unpurified. **-gerinnbar,** *a.* incoagulable. **-gern,** *adv.* unwillingly. **-geröstet,** *p.a.* unroasted, not calcined. **-gerufen,** *p.a.* uncalled.

**unges.,** *abbrev.* (ungesättigt) unsaturated.

**un-gesalzen,** *p.a.* unsalted, fresh; insipid. **-gesättigt,** *p.a.* unsaturated; not satiated. **-gesäuert,** *p.a.* not acidified; (*Baking*) unleavened. **-gesäumt,** *p.a.* immediate; seamless. **-geschält,** *p.a.* unhusked, unpeeled. **-geschehen,** *a.* undone. **-geschichtet,** *p.a.* unstratified. **-geschickt,** *a.* awkward. **-geschliffen,** *p.a.* unground; unpolished. **-geschlossen,** *a.* unclosed, open. **-geschmolzen,** *a.* unmelted, unfused. **-geschützt,** *a.* unprotected. **-gespalten,** *a.* unsplit, uncleaved. **-gestalt, -gestaltet,** *a.* deformed, misshapen. **-gestört,** *a.* undisturbed. **-gesucht,** *p.a.* unsought; unaffected. **-gesund,** *a.* unhealthy; unhealthful. **-geteilt,** *p.a.* undivided; ungraduated. **-geübt,** *a.* unpracticed, inexperienced. **-gewaschen,** *p.a.* unwashed. **-gewiss,** *a.* uncertain.

**Ungewissheit,** *f.* uncertainty.

**Ungewissheitsprinzip,** *n.* uncertainty principle.

**Ungewitter,** *n.* thunderstorm.

**un-gewöhnlich,** *a.* unusual, extraordinary, abnormal. **-gewohnt,** *p.a.* unaccustomed; unusual.

**Ungeziefer,** *n.* vermin. **-bekämpfung,** *f.* vermin destruction.

**un-gezwungen,** *p.a.* unconstrained, unforced. **-giftig,** *a.* nonpoisonous, nontoxic.

**Ungiftigkeit,** *f.* nonpoisonousness, nontoxicity.

**unglasiert,** *a.* unglazed; unvarnished.

**Unglaube,** *m.* incredulity; unbelief.

**unglaublich,** *a.* incredible.

**ungleich,** *a.* unequal; unlike, dissimilar; uneven, (of numbers) odd; not uniform; different. — *adv.* incomparably, far, by far. **-artig,** *a.* dissimilar; heterogeneous.

**Ungleichartigkeit,** *f.* dissimilarity; heterogeneity.

**ungleichförmig,** *a.* not uniform, unsymmetrical, unconformable, heterogeneous, irregular.

**Ungleich-gewicht,** *n.* disequilibrium, unbalance. **-heit,** *f.* inequality; dissimilarity; unevenness.

**ungleich-mässig,** *a.* not uniform; disproportionate, unsymmetrical, irregular. **-namig,** *a.* (of poles) unlike, opposite. **-seitig,** *a.* scalene (triangle). **-stoffig,** *a.* inhomogeneous.

**Ungleich-stoffigkeit,** *f.* inhomogeneity. **-ung,** *f.* (*Math.*) inequality, inequation.

**ungleichwertig,** *a.* of unlike valence; of unequal value.

**Unglück,** *n.* misfortune, bad luck; disaster.

**unglücklich,** *a.* unfortunate, unlucky, ill-fated. **-erweise,** *adv.* unfortunately.

**Unglücksfall,** *m.* disaster, accident.

**ungreifbar,** *a.* impalpable, imperceptible.

**ungültig,** *a.* not valid, void.

**Ungunst,** *f.* disfavor; unfavorableness.

**un-günstig,** *a.* unfavorable, detrimental. **-gut,** *adv.* ill, amiss. **-haltbar,** *a.* not durable; untenable. **-haltig,** *a.* (*Mining*) containing no metal.

**Unhaltiges,** *n.* waste, refuse, tailings.

**un-hämmerbar,** *a.* not malleable. **-handlich,** *a.* unhandy, unwieldy.

**Unheil,** *n.* harm, trouble, evil.

**un-heilbar,** *a.* incurable. **-heilsam,** *a.* unwholesome, noxious. **-heizbar,** *a.* that cannot be heated.

**Unhomogenität,** *f.* inhomogeneity.

**unhörbar,** *a.* inaudible.

**Uniartikel,** *m.* (*Calico*) solid style.

**uniert,** *p.a.* united.

**Unifarbe,** *f.* (*Dyeing*) self color, uniform color, plain color, solid color.

**uni-färben,** *v.t.* dye a self (uniform) shade, dye solid. **-farbig,** *a.* self-colored, plain, solid.

**Uniongerbung,** *f.* union tannage.

**Unistückware,** *f.* plain-shade piece goods.

**unitär, unitarisch,** *a.* unitary.

**Uniton,** *m.* plain shade, solid shade.

**Universal-arznei,** *f.* universal remedy, cure-all. **-gelenk,** *n.* universal joint. **-mittel,** *n.* = Universalarznei.

**Universität,** *f.* university.

**unk.,** *abbrev.* (unkorrigiert) uncorrected.

**un-kennbar, -kenntlich,** *a.* undiscernible, unrecognizable.

**Unkenntnis,** *f.* ignorance.

**un-klar,** *a.* not clear; indistinct; turbid; confused. **-kondensierbar,** *a.* uncondensable. **-kontrollierbar,** *a.* uncontrollable. **-korrigiert,** *p.a.* uncorrected. **-korrodierbar,** *a.* noncorrodible.

**Un-kosten,** *f.pl.* expenses, charges. **-kraut,** *n.* weed, weeds.

**un-kristallinisch,** *a.* noncrystalline, amorphous. **-kristallisierbar,** *a.* uncrystallizable.

**unl.,** *abbrev.* (unlöslich) insoluble.

**un-längst,** *adv.* of late, recently. **-lauter,** *a.* impure; unfair; sordid. **-legiert,** *a.* unalloyed. **-leidlich,** *a.* insufferable, intolerable. **-lesbar, -leserlich,** *a.* illegible. **-leugbar,** *a.* undeniable, indisputable. **-lieb, -liebsam,** *a.* unpleasant, objectionable. **-lösbar,** *a.* undetachable; indissoluble; not solvable. **-löschbar,** *a.* slakeless; unquenchable. **-löslich,** *a.* insoluble.

**Un-lösliches,** *n.* insoluble matter. **-löslichkeit,** *f.* insolubility. **-lust,** *f.* dislike, displeasure.

**unmagnetisch,** *a.* nonmagnetic.

**Unmasse,** *f.* great quantity.

**un-massgeblich,** *a.* unauthoritative. **-mässig,** *a.* immoderate, intemperate. **-menschlich,** *a.* inhuman; superhuman. **-merklich,** *a.* imperceptible. **-messbar,** *a.* immeasurable; (*Math.*) incommensurable. **-mischbar,** *a.* immiscible.

**Unmischbarkeit,** *f.* immiscibility.

**un-mittelbar,** *a.* immediate, direct. — *adv.* immediately, directly. **-möbliert,** *p.a.* unfurnished. **-modern,** *a.* not in fashion, old-fashioned. **-möglich,** *a.* impossible. — *adv.* impossibly.

**Unmöglichkeit,** *f.* impossibility.

**un-nachahmlich,** *a.* inimitable. **-nachgiebig,** *a.* unyielding, inflexible. **-nahbar,** *a.* inaccessible. **-nennbar,** *a.* unutterable, inexpressible. **-nötig,** *a.* unnecessary. **-nütz, -nützlich,** *a.* useless, unprofitable; naughty. — *adv.* uselessly, vainly. **-okular,** *a.* monocular. **-ordentlich,** *a.* disorderly, irregular.

**Unordnung,** *f.* disorder; litter.

**un-organisch,** *a.* inorganic. **-oxydierbar,** *a.* inoxidizable. **-paarwertig,** *a.* of odd valence. **-parteiisch,** *a.* impartial, unprejudiced. **-pass,** *a.* unwell. **-passend,** *p.a.* unfit, unsuitable. **-pässlich,** *a.* unwell, indisposed. **-periodisch,** *a.* aperiodic, nonperiodic. **-plastisch,** *a.* nonplastic. **-polarisierbar,** *a.* unpolarizable, nonpolarizing. **-pressbar,** *a.* incompressible.

**Un-pressbarkeit,** *f.* incompressibility. **-rat,** *m.* dirt, trash, refuse, offal, garbage; (*Metal.*) dross.

**unrecht,** *a.* wrong; false, unfair, undue.

**Unrecht,** *n.* wrong, injustice; fault, error. — **— haben,** be wrong.

**un-rechtmässig,** *a.* unlawful, illegal. **-regelmässig,** *a.* irregular; abnormal, anomalous.

**Unregelmässigkeit,** *f.* irregularity; abnormality, anomaly.

**un-reif,** *a.* unripe; immature. **-rein,** *a.* impure; unclean.

**Un-reinheit, -reinigkeit,** *f.* impurity.

**un-reinlich,** *a.* uncleanly. **-reizbar,** *a.* nonirritable, not sensitive. **-rettbar,** *a.* irrecoverable, past help. **-richtig,** *a.* wrong, false, erroneous, inaccurate, unjust.

**Unruhe,** *f.* disquiet, uneasiness, trouble, commotion; irregularity, fluctuation; balance (of a watch).

**unruhig,** *a.* unquiet, restless, troubled, irregular, fluctuating: (of steel) effervescent, unkilled (cf. unberuhigt).

**uns,** *pron.* us, to us, ourselves, to ourselves.

**uns.,** *abbrev.* (unsymmetrisch) unsymmetrical.

**un-sachgemäss,** *a.* inappropriate, unsuitable. **-sagbar, -säglich,** *a.* unspeakable. **-sanft,** *a.* harsh, rough. **-sauber,** *a.* unclean, dirty, foul. **-schädlich,** *a.* harmless, innocuous. **-scharf,** *a.* not sharp; blurred; indefinite.

**Unschärfe,** *f.* lack of sharpness.

**un-schätzbar,** *a.* invaluable, inestimable. **-scheidbar,** *a.* inseparable; undecomposable. **-scheinbar,** *a.* not showy, plain; (of colors) dull, pale.

**Unschlitt,** *n.* tallow, suet. **-seife,** *f.* tallow soap.

**un-schlüssig,** *a.* undecided, irresolute. **-schmackhaft,** *a.* insipid, unpalatable. **-schmelzbar,** *a.* infusible.

**Unschmelzbarkeit,** *f.* infusibility.

**un-schuldig,** *a.* innocent. **-schweissbar,** *a.* unweldable. **-schwer,** *a.* not difficult, easy. **-selbständig,** *a.* dependent, requiring assistance.

**unser,** *pron.* our, ours; of us.

**unsicher,** *a.* uncertain, unsteady, insecure, unsafe; (*Mach.*) unsteady.

**Unsicherheit,** *f.* uncertainty; insecurity.

**unsichtbar,** *a.* invisible.

**Unsinn,** *m.* nonsense, absurdity.

**un-sinnig,** *a.* nonsensical; irrational; insane. **-spaltbar,** *a.* uncleavable. **-stabil,** *a.* unstable. **-stät, -stätig,** etc., see unstet, unstetig, etc. **-statthaft,** *a.* inadmissible; illicit. **-stet, -stetig,** *a.* unsteady, unstable, variable, discontinuous.

**Unstetigkeit,** *f.* unsteadiness, instability, variableness, variation; discontinuity.

**Unstimmigkeit,** *f.* lack of agreement.

**un-sträflich,** *a.* blameless, irreproachable. **-streckbar,** *a.* not extensible, nonductile, nonmalleable. **-streitig,** *a.* indisputable, unquestionable. **-studiert,** *p.a.* unstudied; unlettered. **-sulfiert,** *p.a.* unsulfonated.

**Unsumme,** *f.* immense sum.

**Unsymmetrie,** *f.* asymmetry, dissymetry.

**unsymmetrisch,** *a.* unsymmetrical.

**unt.,** *abbrev.* of unter.

**untätig,** *a.* inactive, inert; idle; unproductive; dormant; indolent.

**Untätigkeit,** *f.* inactivity, etc. (see untätig).

**un-tauglich,** *a.* unfit, unsuitable, useless. **-teilbar,** *a.* indivisible.

**Unteilbarkeit,** *f.* indivisibility.

**unteilhaftig,** *a.* not sharing, nonparticipating.

**unten,** *adv.* below, beneath, underneath, at the bottom.

**unter,** *prep.* under, below, beneath; during; among, amidst, between, with.

**Unter-.** hypo-; under, inferior, lower, partial, sub-, infra-. **-abschnitt,** *m.* subsection.

**unterabteilen,** *v.t.* subdivide.

**Unter-abteilung,** *f.* subdivision. **-arm,** *m.* forearm. **-art,** *f.* subspecies, variety.

**Unteraugenhöhlen-.** infra-orbital.

**Unter-bau,** *m.* substructure, foundation. **-bauch,** *m.* hypogastrium. **-beamter,** *m.* inferior officer, subordinate official.

**unterbelichten,** *v.t.* underexpose (to light).

**Unterbelichtung,** *f.* (*Photog.*) underexposure.

**unterbewusst,** *a.* subconscious.

**Unter-bewusstsein,** *n.* subconsciousness. **-bilanz,** *f.* deficit.

**unterbinden,** *v.t.* stop; tie up, ligature.

**Unterbindung,** *f.* ligature; ligation.

**unterbleiben,** *v.i.* not occur, be left undone; cease.

**Unterboden,** *m.* subsoil.

**unterbrechen,** *v.t.* interrupt; discontinue; disconnect; break, stop. — **unterbrochen,** *p.a.* interrupted, discontinuous, intermittent.

**Unter-brecher,** *m.* interrupter; contact breaker. **-brechung,** *f.* interruption; break, stop; intermission. **-brechungsstrom,** *m.* interrupted current.

**unter-breiten,** *v.t.* submit. **-bringen,** *v.t.* provide for; accommodate; dispose of, sell; invest. **-brochen,** *p.a.* see unterbrechen.

**unterbromig,** *a.* hypobromous. — **unterbromige Säure,** hypobromous acid.

**unterbromigsauer,** *a.* of or combined with hypobromous acid, hypobromite of.

**unterchlorig,** *a.* hypochlorous. — **unterchlorige Säure,** hypochlorous acid.

**unterchlorigsauer,** *a.* of or combined with hypochlorous acid, hypochlorite of.

**Unter-chlorigsäure,** *f.* hypochlorous acid. **-chlorsäure,** *f.* hypochloric acid (formerly applied to chlorine dioxide).

**unterdes, unterdessen,** *adv.* meanwhile.

**Unterdruck,** *m.* diminished pressure, (partial) vacuum.

**Unterdruck-.** low-pressure; vacuum.

**unterdrücken,** *v.t.* suppress; repress; oppress.

**Unterdruck-kessel,** *m.* low-pressure boiler or tank. **-messer,** *m.* vacuometer, vacuum gage.

**Unterdrückung,** *f.* suppression; repression.

**untere,** *a.* low, lower, under, inferior.

**untereinander,** *adv.* among one another, together, mutually; confusedly.
**Unter-einheit,** *f.* subunit. **-einteilung,** *f.* subdivision. **-ernährung,** *f.* undernourishment, undernutrition.
**unter-essigsauer,** *a.* subacetate of. **-eutektisch,** *a.* hypoeutectic. **-eutektoid,** *a.* hypoeutectoid. **-exponiert,** *a.* underexposed.
**Unterfamilie,** *f.* subfamily.
**unter-fangen,** *v.r.* dare, venture. **-feuern,** *v.t.* underfire.
**Unterfläche,** *f.* under surface, base.
**Unterflur-.** underground, below ground.
**Unter-form,** *f.* subvariety, subspecies. **-futter,** *n.* lining. **-gang,** *m.* going down, (of the sun) setting; fall, ruin.
**untergärig,** *a.* fermented from below, bottom-fermenting. — **untergärige Hefe,** bottom yeast.
**Unter-gärung,** *f.* bottom fermentation. **-gattung,** *f.* subgenus.
**unter-geben,** *v.t.* place under; subject, submit. — *p.a.* inferior, subordinate. **-gehen,** *v.i.* go down; (of the sun, etc.) set; perish; become extinct. **-geordnet,** *p.a.* subordinate, secondary, minor. **-geschoben,** *p.a.* substituted, spurious.
**Unter-geschoss,** *n.* ground floor. **-gestell,** *n.* underframe, substructure. **-gewicht,** *n.* underweight, short weight. **-glasur,** *f.* underglaze. **-glasurfarbe,** *f.* under-glaze color.
**unter-graben,** *v.t.* undermine; dig (something) in. **-grädig,** *a.* underproof.
**Untergräten-.** (*Anat.*) infraspinous.
**Untergrund,** *m.* subsoil; underground; (*Geol.*) underlying strata, bedrock; background; (*Paint*) ground, priming coat, undercoat; (*Dyeing*) bottom; (*Calico*) bottom print, first print. **-farbe,** *f.* (*Dyeing*) bottom color.
**Unter-gruppe,** *f.* subgroup; subordinate group. **-guss,** *m.* (*Photog.*) substratum.
**unter-halb,** *prep.* below, beyond, under. **-halogenig,** *a.* hypohal(ogen)ous.
**Unterhalt,** *m.* upkeep, maintenance, support.
**unterhalten,** *v.t.* support; maintain, keep up, keep; entertain. — *v.r.* discourse; amuse oneself.
**Unterhaltung,** *f.* support, maintenance; entertainment; conversation.
**unterhandeln,** *v.i.* treat, negotiate.
**Unterhaut,** *f.* under skin, derma, hypodermis.
**Unterhaut-.** subcutaneous.
**Unterhefe,** *f.* bottom yeast.
**Unterhirn,** *n.* (*Anat.*) subencephalon.
**unter-irdisch,** *a.* subterranean, underground. **-jochen,** *v.t.* subjugate, subdue. **-jodig,** *a.* hypoiodous. **-jodigsauer,** *a.* of or combined with hypoiodous acid, hypoiodite of.
**Unterjodigsäure,** *f.* hypoiodous acid.
**Unterkiefer-.** lower-jaw, submaxillary, mandibular.
**unterkommen,** *v.i.* find shelter, find employment.
**Unter-korn,** *n.* undersize (grain). **-korrektur,** *f.* undercorrection, undercompensation. **-kreide,** *f.* (*Geol.*) Lower Cretaceous.
**unter-kriechen,** *v.i.* crawl under. **-kriegen,** *v.t.* get the better of. **-kritisch,** *a.* below-critical (temperature, speed, etc.). **-kühlen,** *v.t.* supercool, undercool.
**Unter-kühlung,** *f.* supercooling, undercooling. **-lage,** *f.* support, base, bed, foundation, stand; basis; substratum; subsoil; lining; parent stock; (supporting) document; *pl.* **Unterlagen,** data, notes, record. **-lagegestein,** *n.* underlying rock.
**unterlagert,** *a.* underlying, subjacent
**Unter-lagsring,** *m.* supporting ring. **-lass,** *m.* intermission, cessation.
**unterlassen,** *v.t.* leave off, discontinue; omit, fail.
**Unterlauf,** *m.* lower course, lower side.
**unterlaufen,** *v.i.* run under; slip in, creep in. — *p.a.* extravasated, bloodshot.
**Unterlauge,** *f.* (*Soap*) underlye, spent lye.
**unterlegen,** *v.t.* lay under, put under, underlay.
**Unterleg-ring,** *m.* supporting ring. **-scheibe,** *f.* supporting disk; washer.
**Unterleib,** *m.* abdomen, belly.
**Unterleibs-.** abdominal. **-entzündung,** *f.* peritonitis.
**unter-liegen,** *v.i.* lie under; succumb; be liable, be subject. **-liegend,** *p.a.* underlying, subjacent; subject, liable. **-löst,** *a.* insufficiently grown (malt). **-meerisch,** *a.* submarine. **-mengen, -mischen,** *v.t.* intermix, mix; adulterate. **-nahm,** *pret.* (of unternehmen) undertook.
**unternehmen,** *v.t.* undertake. — **unternehmend,** *p.a.* enterprising.
**Unternehmung,** *f.* undertaking, enterprise, venture.
**Unternehmverband,** *m.* combination (of any kind in business), syndicate, trust, pool, etc.
**unter-normal,** *a.* subnormal. **-ordnen,** *v.t.* subordinate. — **untergeordnet,** *p.a.* subordinate, secondary, minor.
**Unter-ordnung,** *f.* subordination; subdivision; (*Biol.*) suborder; subordinate position. **-fand,** *n.* pledge, security, mortgage.
**unter-phosphorig,** *a.* hypophosphorous. **-phosphorigsauer,** *a.* of or combined with hypophosphorous acid, hypophosphite of. — **phosphorsauer,** *a.* of or combined with hypophosphoric acid, hypophosphate of.
**Unter-phosphorsäure,** *f.* hypophosphoric acid. **-probe,** *f.*, **-probeweingeist,** *m.* underproof

spirit. **-redung,** *f.* conference, conversation, interview. **-richt,** *m.* instruction, teaching.

**unterrichten,** *v.t.* teach, instruct; inform.

**Unter-richtsanstalt,** *f.* school, academy. **-rinde,** *f.* under bark; under crust.

**Unters.,** *abbrev.* (Untersuchung) investigation, examination.

**untersagen,** *v.t.* forbid, prohibit.

**Untersalpetersäure,** *f.* hyponitric acid (old name for nitrogen peroxide).

**unter-salpetrig,** *a.* hyponitrous. **-salpetrigsauer,** *a.* of or combined with hyponitrous acid, hyponitrite of. **-sättigen,** *v.t.* undersaturate.

**Untersatz,** *m.* support, stand, base; stay; saucer; assumption. **-schale,** *f.* supporting dish; subshell (of electrons). **-schall,** *m.* (*Physics*) subsonics.

**Unterschall-.** subsonic, infrasonic.

**unter-schätzen,** *v.t.* undervalue, underrate. **-scheidbar,** *a.* distinguishable, discernible. **-scheiden,** *v.t.* distinguish; discriminate, differentiate; discern.

**Unterscheidung,** *f.* distinction, etc. (see unterscheiden).

**Unter-scheidungsmarkierung,** *f.* distinctive marking. **-scheidungsmerkmal,** *n.* distinguishing characteristic. **-schicht,** *f.* under layer, under stratum.

**unterschieben,** *v.t.* push under; substitute; forge. — **untergeschoben,** *p.a.* substituted, spurious.

**Unterschied,** *m.* difference; distinction; partition; interval.

**unter-schiedlich,** *a.* different, distinct; differential; variable. **-schiedslos,** *a.* indiscriminate. **-schneiden,** *v.t.* undercut. **-schreiben,** *v.t.* sign; subscribe. **-schreiten,** *v.t.* go below, fall below, keep within.

**Unterschrift,** *f.* signature; subscription.

**unterschwefelsauer,** *a.* of or combined with hyposulfuric acid, hyposulfate of (dithionate of).

**Unterschwefelsäure,** *f.* hyposulfuric acid (dithionic acid).

**unterschweflig,** *a.* hyposulfurous. — **unterschweflige Säure,** hyposulfurous acid (formerly, thiosulfuric acid, $H_2S_2O_3$; now, dithionous acid, $H_2S_2O_4$).

**unterschwefligsauer,** *a.* of or combined with hyposulfurous acid, hyposulfite of (thiosulfate of, or dithionite of; cf. unterschweflige Säure).

**unterschwellig,** *a.* subliminal.

**Unterschwingung,** *f.* (*Physics*) subharmonic oscillation.

**Unterseeboot,** *n.* undersea boat, submarine.

**unterseeisch,** *a.* submarine.

**Unterseite,** *f.* under (or lower) side, bottom; (of cloth, etc.) wrong side.

**untersetzen,** *v.t.* put under; scale down, reduce.

**Untersetzer,** *m.* stand; mat.

**Untersetzscherbe,** *f.* plate or saucer set under something, (for crucibles) crucible stand.

**Unterspannung,** *f.* (*Elec.*) undervoltage, low tension.

**unterst,** *a.* lowest, undermost.

**unter-stecken,** *v.t.* immerse, submerge. **-stehen,** *v.i.* stand under; pertain. — *v.r.* dare, venture. — *v.t.* undertake. **-stellen,** *v.t.* place under; store, park; assume; impute.

**Unterstock,** *m.* (*Brewing*) underback.

**unterstreichen,** *v.t.* underline.

**Unterstufe,** *f.* substage.

**unterstützen,** *v.t.* support; assist.

**Unterstützung,** *f.* support.

**unter-suchbar,** *a.* capable of being investigated or inspected. **-suchen,** *v.t.* investigate; examine; inspect; probe.

**Untersuchung,** *f.* investigation, research; examination, inquiry.

**Untersuchungs-arbeit,** *f.* research work. **-chemiker,** *m.* research chemist. **-laboratorium,** *n.* research laboratory. **-material,** *n.* material for investigation or under investigation. **-methode,** *f.* investigational method, research method. **-mittel,** *n.* means of research or examination; indicator. **-raum,** *m.* laboratory. **-richtung,** *f.* line or direction of investigation.

**Untertage-.** below-ground, underground.

**unter-tan,** *a.* subject, dependent (on). **-tänig,** *a.* subject; submissive, obedient.

**Untertasse,** *f.* saucer.

**unter-tauchbar,** *a.* immersible, submersible. **-tauchen,** *v.t.* immerse, submerge.

**Unter-tauchung,** *f.* immersion, submersion. **-teig,** *m.* (*Brewing*) underdough. **-teil,** *m.* under part, lower part.

**unter-teilbar,** *a.* divisible. **-teilen,** *v.t.* subdivide; partition.

**Unter-teilung,** *f.* subdivision; breakdown, split-up; partitioning. **-ton,** *m.* undertone. **-wald,** *m.* underbrush. **-walze,** *f.* under roll, bottom roll.

**unterwärts,** *adv.* downward, underneath.

**Unterwäsche,** *f.* underlinen, underwear.

**Unterwasser-anstrich,** *m.* underwater (antifouling) painting. **-bombe,** *f.* depth bomb. **-farbe,** *f.* underwater paint, bottom paint (for ships).

**unter-wegs,** *adv.* on the way, en route. **-weichen,** *v.t.* understeep. **-weisen,** *v.t.* instruct, teach. **-werfen,** *v.t.* subject. **-wühlen,** *v.t.* undermine. **-zeichnen,** *v.t.* sign; underwrite.

**Unterzeug,** *n.* underclothing.

**unterziehen,** *v.t.* draw or lay under; put on underneath. — *v.r.* undergo; undertake.

**Unterzungen-.** sublingual.

**unthätig,** *a.* = untätig.

**Untier,** *n.* monster.

**un-tilgbar,** *a.* indelible; irredeemable. **-trennbar,** *a.* inseparable; indivisible; undetachable.

**Untrennbarkeit,** *f.* inseparability, etc. (see untrennbar).

**un-trinkbar,** *a.* undrinkable. **-trüglich,** *a.* infallible, unerring, unmistakable. **-tunlich,** *a.* impossible, impracticable.

**unt.Zers.,** *abbrev.* (unter Zersetzung) with decomposition.

**un-übersehbar,** *a.* impossible (or difficult) to inspect or control, intricate; boundless. **-übersichtlich,** *a.* unclear; of indefinite extent; vague; unpredictable. **-übersteiglich,** *a.* insurmountable. **-übertrefflich,** *a.* unsurpassable, unrivaled. **-überwindlich,** *a.* invincible. **-umgänglich,** *a.* indispensable, unavoidable. **-umschränkt,** *p.a.* unlimited. **-umstösslich,** *a.* irrefutable. **-umwunden,** *p.a.* frank, plain. **-unterbrochen,** *p.a.* uninterrupted, unbroken, continuous. **-unterscheidbar,** *a.* indistinguishable. **-untersucht,** *p.a.* uninvestigated.

**unv.,** *abbrev.* (unveröffentlicht) unpublished.

**un-veränderlich,** *a.* invariable, unchangeable, constant. **-verändert,** *p.a.* unchanged, unaltered. **-verantwortlich,** *a.* inexcusable; irresponsible. **-verarbeitet,** *p.a.* unwrought, not made up. **-veräusserlich,** *a.* inalienable. **-verbesserlich,** *a.* unimprovable; incorrigible. **-verbindlich,** *a.* not binding; disobliging. **-verblümt,** *p.a.* plain. **-verbrannt,** *p.a.* unburned. **-verbrennbar, -verbrennlich,** *a.* incombustible, (often in practice) slow-burning.

**Unverbrennbarkeit,** *f.* incombustibility.

**un-verbrüchlich,** *a.* inviolable. **-verbunden,** *p.a.* uncombined; unconnected; unbound. **-verbürgt,** *p.a.* unwarranted, unconfirmed. **-verdaulich,** *a.* indigestible.

**Unverdauung,** *f.* indigestion.

**unverdichtbar,** *a.* incondensable; incompressible.

**Unverdichtbarkeit,** *f.* incondensability; incompressibility.

**un-verdient,** *p.a.* undeserved. **-verdrossen,** *a.* unwearied, patient. **-verdünnt,** *a.* undiluted. **-vereinbar,** *a.* incompatible, irreconcilable, inconsistent. **-verestert,** *a.* unesterified. **-verfälscht,** *p.a.* unadulterated. **-verfaulbar,** *a.* unputrefiable, imputrescible. **-verflüchtigt,** *a.* unvolatilized. **-vergänglich,** *a.* not perishable, imperishable. **-vergärbar,** *a.* unfermentable. **-vergasbar,** *a.* ungasifiable. **-vergesslich,** *a.* unforgettable. **-verglast,** *p.a.* unvitrified. **-vergleichbar, -vergleichlich,** *a.* incomparable. **-vergrünbar, -vergrünlich,** *a.* ungreenable. **-verhältnismässig,** *a.* disproportionate. **-verhofft,** *a.* unhoped for. **-verhohlen,** *p.a.* unconcealed, open. **-verholzt,** *p.a.* unlignified. **-verhüttbar,** *a.* unsmeltable, unworkable. **-verkäuflich,** *a.* unsalable, unmarketable. **-verkennbar,** *a.* unmistakable. **-verkittet,** *a.* uncemented, unluted. **-verkürzt,** *p.a.* unabridged. **-verletzt,** *p.a.* unimpaired, intact. **-vermeidbar, -vermeidlich,** *a.* unavoidable, inevitable. **-vermengt,** *p.a.* unmixed. **-vermerkt,** *p.a.* unperceived, imperceptible. **-vermindert,** *p.a.* undiminished. **-vermischbar,** *a.* immiscible. **-vermischt,** *p.a.* unmixed, unalloyed, pure. **-vermittelt,** *a.* sudden; unassisted. — *adv.* suddenly.

**Unvermögen,** *n.* inability, impotence.

**unvermutet,** *p.a.* unexpected.

**Unvernunft,** *f.* unreasonableness, absurdity.

**un-veröffentlicht,** *p.a.* unpublished. **-verrichtet,** *p.a.* unperformed. **-verrostbar,** *a.* nonrusting, stainless. **-verschnitten,** *a.* uncut; unblended; unadulterated. **-verschuldet,** *p.a.* not in debt; unmerited. **-versehens,** *adv.* unexpectedly. **-versehrt,** *p.a.* uninjured, undamaged. **-verseifbar,** *a.* unsaponifiable.

**Unverseifbares,** *n.* unsaponifiable matter.

**un-versiegbar,** *a.* inexhaustible. **-versorgt,** *p.a.* unprovided for. **-verständig,** *a.* unwise, imprudent. **-verständlich,** *a.* unintelligible. **-versteuert,** *p.a.* duty unpaid. **-versucht,** *p.a.* untried. **-vertilgbar,** *a.* ineradicable; indelible. **-verträglich,** *a.* incompatible; inconsistent; unsociable.

**Unverträglichkeit,** *f.* incompatibility; inconsistency; unsociability.

**un-verwandt,** *p.a.* unrelated; unmoved. **-verweilt,** *adv.* without delay. **-verweslich,** *a.* imputrescible, undecaying. **-verwittert,** *a.* unweathered. **-verwüstlich,** *a.* indestructible. **-verzeihlich,** *a.* unpardonable. **-verzerrt,** *a.* undistorted, undeformed. **-verzollt,** *p.a.* duty unpaid. **-verzüglich,** *a.* immediate, instant. **-verzweigt,** *p.a.* unbranched. **-vollendet,** *a.* unfinished, incomplete. **-vollkommen,** *a.* imperfect, incomplete.

**Unvollkommenheit,** *f.* imperfection, incompleteness

**unvollständig,** *a.* incomplete, imperfect.

**Unvollständigkeit,** *f.* incompleteness, imperfection.

**un-vorbereitet,** *p.a.* unprepared. **-vorhergesehen,** *p.a.* unforeseen. **-vorsätzlich,** *a.* unpremeditated. **-vorsichtig,** *a.* incautious, careless. **-vorteilhaft,** *a.* disadvantageous unprofitable. **-wägbar,** *a.* unweighable; imponderable.

**Unwägbarkeit,** *f.* unweighability; imponderability.

**un-wahr,** *a.* untrue, false. **-wahrscheinlich,** *a.* improbable. **-wandelbar,** *a.* unchangeable, invariable. **-wegsam,** *a.* impassable; impervious; pathless. **-weit,** *adv.* not far. — *prep.* not far from.

**Unwesen,** *n.* disorder; nuisance; monster.

**unwesentlich,** *a.* unessential, immaterial, accidental.

**Unwetter,** *n.* bad weather, storm.

**un-wichtig,** *a.* unimportant. **-widerlegbar, -widerleglich,** *a.* irrefutable. **-widerstehlich,** *a.* irresistible. **-willkürlich,** *a.* involuntary. **-wirksam,** *a.* inactive; ineffective, inefficient; void.

**Unwirksamkeit,** *f.* inactivity; ineffectiveness.

**unwirtschaftlich,** *a.* uneconomical.

**Un-wucht,** *f.* unbalance, imbalance, disequilibrium. **-zahl,** *f.* immense number.

**unzählbar, unzählig,** *a.* innumerable.

**Unze,** *f.* ounce.

**Unzeit,** *f.* wrong time.

**un-zeitgemäss, -zeitig,** *a.* untimely; premature; immature; out of date. **-zerbrechlich,** *a.* unbreakable. **-zerfressbar,** *a.* incorrodible. **-zerlegbar,** *a.* indecomposable; indivisible. **-zerlegt,** *a.* undecomposed, etc. (see zerlegen). **-zerreissbar,** *a.* untearable, indestructible. **-zersetzbar,** *a.* indecomposable. **-zersetzt,** *p.a.* undecomposed. — *adv.* without decomposition. **-zerstörbar,** *a.* indestructible.

**Unzerstörbarkeit,** *f.* indestructibility.

**un-zerstört,** *p.a.* undestroyed. **-zertrennbar,** *a.* inseparable. **-ziehbar,** *a.* not ductile. **-zufrieden,** *p.a.* discontented, dissatisfied. **-zugänglich,** *a.* inaccessible. **-zulänglich,** *a.* insufficient, inadequate. **-zulässig,** *a.* inadmissible. **-zureichend,** *a.* insufficient. **-zusammendrückbar,** *a.* incompressible.

**Unzusammendrückbarkeit,** *f.* incompressibility.

**un-zuträglich,** *a.* disadvantageous; unhealthy. **-zutreffend,** *a.* incorrect. **-zuverlässig,** *a.* unreliable, uncertain. **-zweckmässig,** *a.* unsuitable, inexpedient. **-zweideutig,** *a.* unequivocal, unambiguous. **-zweifelhaft,** *a.* indubitable, undoubted. — *adv.* undoubtedly.

**U.P.,** *abbrev.* (ungarisches Patent) Hungarian patent.

**Upas-baum,** *m.* upas tree, upas. **-gift,** *n.* upas poison, upas.

**U.p.M., Upm.,** *abbrev.* (Umlaufungen pro Minute) revolutions per minute, r.p.m.

**üppig,** *a.* luxuriant, rich, rank.

**-ür.** -ide (for "ous" compounds. See Chlorür).

**Ur-.** primitive, original, primordial, primary, master, standard, proto-. **-ahn,** *m.* original ancestor; great grandfather.

**Uralitisierung,** *f.* (*Min.*) uralitization.

**uralt,** *a.* very old, ancient.

**Urämie,** *f.* uremia.

**Uran,** *n.* uranium. **-blei,** *n.* uranium lead. **-brenner,** *m.* uranium pile. **-carbid,** *n.* uranium carbide. **-erz,** *n.* uranium ore.

**Uranfang,** *m.* origin, very beginning.

**Uran-gehalt,** *m.* uranium content. **-gelb,** *n.* uranium yellow. **-glas,** *n.* uranium glass. **-glimmer,** *m.* (*Min.*) torbernite. **-grün,** *n.* (*Min.*) uranochalcite. **-gummi,** *n.* (*Min.*) gummite.

**uranhaltig,** *a.* containing uranium, uraniferous.

**Urani-.** uranic, specif. uranium(VI).

**uranig,** *a.* uranous, specif. uranium(IV).

**Urani-nitrat,** *n.* uranic nitrate (uranyl nitrate). **-oxyd,** *n.* uranic oxide, uranium(VI) oxide, $UO_3$. **-verbindung,** *f.* uranic compound (uranyl compound).

**Uran-metall,** *n.* uranium metal. **-nitrat,** *n.* uranium nitrate.

**Urano-.** uranous, uranoso-, specif. uranium(IV).

**Uranocker,** *m.* uranium ocher, uraconite (variety of uranopilite).

**Urano-hydroxyd,** *n.* uranous hydroxide, uranium(IV) hydroxide. **-reihe,** *f.* uranous series. **-salz,** *n.* uranous salt. **-uranat,** *n.* uranous uranate, uranium(IV,VI) oxide, $U_3O_8$. **-verbindung,** *f.* uranous compound.

**Uran-oxyd,** *n.* uranium oxide, specif. uranic oxide, uranium(VI) oxide, $UO_3$. **-oxydhydrat,** *n.* uranium hydroxide. **-oxydoxydul,** *n.* = Uranoxyduloxyd. **-oxydrot,** *n.* uranium oxide red. **-oxydul,** *n.* uranous oxide, uranium(IV) oxide, $UO_2$. **-oxyduloxyd,** *n.* uranoso-uranic oxide, uranium(IV,VI) oxide, $U_3O_8$. **-oxydulsalz,** *n.* uranous salt, uranium(IV) salt. **-pechblende,** *f.*, **-pecherz,** *n.* pitchblende. **-phosphat,** *n.* uranium phosphate. **-rot,** *n.* uranium red. **-salz,** *n.* uranium salt.

**uransauer,** *a.* of or combined with uranic acid, uranate of.

**Uran-säure,** *f.* uranic acid. **-strahlen,** *m.pl.* uranium rays. **-tonbad,** *n.* (*Photog.*) uranium toning bath. **-tönung,** *f.* uranium toning.

**uranuranig,** *a.* uranoso-uranic, uranium(IV,VI).

**Uran-verbindung,** *f.* uranium compound. **-verstärker,** *m.* uranium intensifier. **-vitriol,** *n.* (*Min.*) johannite.

**Urat,** *n.* urate.

**Uratom,** *n.* primordial atom.

**urbar,** *a.* arable, tillable.

**urbaren,** *v.t.* (*Agric.*) cultivate, till.

**Ur-baustein,** *m.* basic (or primary) building material. **-bestandteil,** *m.* ultimate constituent. **-bewohner,** *m.* original inhabitant.

**-bild,** *n.* prototype, original. **-boden,** *m.* original soil, virgin soil. **-destillation,** *f.* low-temperature distillation. **-farbe,** *f.* primary color. **-fels,** *m.* primitive rock. **-form,** *f.* original form, prototype. **-gebirge,** *n.* (*Geol.*) primitive rock(s).

**urgeschichtlich,** *a.* prehistoric.

**Ur-gestein,** *n.* primitive rock; parent rock; (*Ceram.*) native kaolinic rock (from which kaolin is obtained by elutriation). **-gewicht,** *n.* standard weight. **-granit,** *m.* primitive granite. **-heber,** *m.* author; inventor; originator, founder.

**Urin-absatz,** *m.* urinary sediment. **-küpe,** *f.* (*Wool*) urine vat. **-stein,** *m.* urinary calculus.

**Ur-kalk,** *m.* primitive limestone. **-koks,** *m.* low-temperature coke, semicoke.

**urkräftig,** *a.* very powerful, hearty.

**Ur-kunde,** *f.* document, record, voucher, diploma. **-kundenpapier,** *n.* document paper. **-laub,** *m.* leave of absence. **-läuter,** *m.* (*Leather*) sod oil. **-lehre,** *f.* master gage. **-lösung,** *f.* original solution. **-mass,** *n.* standard measure, master gage. **-muster,** *n.* prototype, standard.

**Urne,** *f.* urn.

**U-Rohr,** *n.*, **U-Röhre,** *f.* U-tube.

**urplötzlich,** *a.* very sudden. — *adv.* very suddenly.

**Ur-preis,** *m.* original price, manufacturer's price. **-quell,** *m.* fountain head, origin. **-sache,** *f.* cause, reason.

**ursächlich,** *a.* causal, causative.

**Ursäure,** *f.* a ureide of acid character, as barbituric or oxaluric acid, a "-uric" acid.

**Ur-schleim,** *m.* protoplasm. **-schrift,** *f.* original copy, original. **-sprung,** *m.* origin, source.

**ursprünglich,** *a.* original, primitive, first.

**Urstoff,** *m.* primary matter; (formerly) element; initial material. **-lehre,** *f.* the theory of a primary matter of which the elements are composed; atomism, atomic theory.

**urstofflich,** *a.* elementary.

**Ur-stoffteilchen,** *n.* primordial particle. **-substanz,** *f.* original substance; primary matter. **-teer,** *m.* low-temperature tar; original tar crude tar.

**Urteil,** *n.* judgment, decision, opinion, verdict (*Logic*) proposition. **-chen,** *n.* primary (or primordial) particle; (formerly) atom.

**urteilen,** *v.i.* judge, form an opinion; decide, pass sentence.

**Ur-tier, -tierchen,** *n.* protozoön. **-tinktur,** *f.* mother tincture. **-titer,** *m.* original titer, titrimetric standard. **-titersubstanz,** *f.* standard titrimetric substance. **-verkokung,** *f.* low-temperature coking (or carbonization). **-verschwelung,** *f.* low-temperature distillation (or carbonization). **-wald,** *m.* virgin (or primeval) forest; jungle. **-wasser,** *n.* primordial water.

**urwellen,** *v.t.* (*Metal.*) double.

**Urwelt,** *f.* primeval world.

**urwüchsig,** *a.* original, native; rough, blunt.

**Ur-zelle,** *f.* primitive cell, ovum. **-zeugung,** *f.* abiogenesis. **-zustand,** *m.* original (or primitive) state.

**u.s.f.,** *abbrev.* (und so fort) and so on, etc.

**Usnet-insäure,** *f.* usnetinic acid. **-säure,** *f.* usnetic acid.

**Usninsäure,** *f.* usnic acid.

**u.s.w., usw.,** *abbrev.* (und so weiter) and so forth, and so on, etc.

**Utensilien,** *n.pl.* utensils, implements.

**u.U.,** *abbrev.* (unter Umständen) under certain circumstances.

**u.ü.V.,** *abbrev.* (unter üblichen Vorbehalt) with the usual reservations.

**u.v.a.m.,** *abbrev.* (und viele andere mehr) and many others.

**Uvinsäure,** *f.* uvic acid, pyrotritaric acid.

**Uviollicht,** *n.* ultraviolet light.

**Uvitinsäure,** *f.* uvitic acid.

**Uwarowit,** *m.* uvarovite.

**Uwp.,** *abbrev.* (Umwandlungspunkt) transformation point, transition point.

**u.Z., u.Zers.,** *abbrev.* (unter Zersetzung) with decomposition.

**u.zw.,** *abbrev.* (und zwar) namely, that is, i.e.

# V

**v.,** *abbrev.* vicinal; (von) of, from, etc., (in titles) von; (vorig) preceding, last; volt.

**V.,** *abbrev.* (Vormittags) in the forenoon, A.M.; (Vorkommen) occurrence, presence; (Verein) union, society.

**vaccinieren,** *v.t.* vaccinate.

**Vacheleder,** *n.* neat's leather.

**vagabundieren,** *v.i.* rove, wander. — **vagabundierend,** *p.a.* vagrant, roving, stray.

**Vagusstoff,** *m.* vagus substance, acetylcholine or (**2.Vagusstoff**) thiamine.

**Vakanz,** *f.* vacancy; (*pl.*) vacation, holidays.

**Vakuomesser,** *m.* vacuum gage.

**Vakuumbirne,** *f.* vacuum bulb.

**vakuumdicht,** *a.* vacuum-tight, airtight.

**Vakuum-dichtung,** *f.* vacuum sealing or packing. **-fett,** *n.* vacuum grease. **-förderer,** *m.* vacuum conveyor. **-gärung,** *f.* vacuum fermentation. **-glocke,** *f.* vacuum bell jar. **-glühlampe,** *f.* vacuum incandescent lamp. **-hahn,** *m.* vacuum cock, vacuum tap. **-kitt,** *m.* vacuum cement. **-kolben,** *m.* vacuum flask. **-kühler,** *m.* vacuum cooler. **-lichtbogen,** *m.* (*Elec.*) vacuum arc. **-mantelgefäss,** *n.* vacuum-jacketed vessel, Dewar vessel. **-meter,** *n.* vacuum gage, vacuometer. **-öl,** *n.* vacuum oil. **-pfanne,** *f.* vacuum pan. **-prüfrohr,** *n.*, **-prüfröhre,** *f.* vacuum testing tube. **-pumpe,** *f.* vacuum pump. **-rohr,** *n.*, **-röhre,** *f.* vacuum tube. **-schlauch,** *m.* vacuum hose, vacuum tubing. **-teer,** *m.* vacuum tar. **-trockenofen,** *m.* vacuum drying oven. **-trockner,** *m.* vacuum drier. **-verdampfer,** *m.* vacuum evaporator. **-verdampfung,** *f.* vacuum evaporation. **-zelle,** *f.* vacuum cell.

**Vakzine,** *f.* vaccine.

**vakzinieren,** *v.t.* vaccinate.

**Valenz,** *f.* valence, valency. **-betätigung,** *f.* valence activity. **-einheit,** *f.* valence unit, valence. **-kraft,** *f.* valence (or valency) force. **-lehre,** *f.* doctrine of valence. **-richtung,** *f.* valence direction. **-strich,** *m.* valence line or dash. **-stufe,** *f.* valence stage.

**Valerian-öl,** *n.* valerian oil. **-säure,** *f.* valeric acid, valerianic acid. **-säureamyläther,** *m.* amyl valerate. **-säuresalz,** *n.* salt of valeric acid, valerate.

**Valet,** *n.* farewell.

**Valone,** *f.* valonia.

**Valuta,** *f.* value; standard; rate, equivalent. **-aufschlag,** *m.* increase or advance in value or price due to exchange.

**Vanadatbeize,** *f.* (*Dyeing*) vanadete mordant.

**Vanadin, Vanad,** *n.* vanadium.

**Vanadinat,** *n.* vanadate.

**Vanadin-bleierz,** *n.*, **-bleispat,** *m.* vanadinite. **-chlorid,** *n.* = Vanadiumchlorid. **-eisen,** *n.* ferrovanadium.

**vanadin-enthaltend, -haltig,** *a.* containing vanadium, vanadiferous. **-ig,** *a.* vanadous.

**Vanadinsalz,** *n.* vanadium salt.

**vanadinsauer,** *a.* of or combined with vanadic acid, vanadate of.

**Vanadin-säure,** *f.* vanadic acid. **-säureanhydrid,** *n.* vanadic anhydride, vanadium pentoxide, vanadium(V) oxide, $V_2O_5$. **-stahl,** *m.* vanadium steel. **-stickstoff,** *m.* vanadium nitride. **-sulfat,** *n.* vanadium sulfate. **-verbindung,** *f.* vanadium compound.

**Vanadium-chlorid,** *n.* vanadium chloride, specif. vanadium(III) chloride, $VCl_3$. **-chlorür,** *n.* vanadous chloride, vanadium(II) chloride, $VCl_2$. **-eisen,** *n.* ferrovanadium.

**vanadiumenthaltend,** *a.* = vanadinenthaltend.

**Vanadium-säure,** *f.* vanadium acid, specif. vanadic acid. **-stahl,** *m.* vanadium steel.

**Vanadosulfat,** *n.* vanadous sulfate, vanadium(II) sulfate.

**Vanadschwarz,** *n.* vanadium black.

**Vanille,** *f.* vanilla.

**Vanillen-kampfer,** *m.* vanillin. **-pflanze,** *f.* vanilla plant.

**variabel,** *a.* variable.

**Variabilität,** *f.* variability.

**Variationsbreite,** *f.* range (or amplitude) of variation.

**variationsfähig,** *a.* variable.

**Variations-fähigkeit,** *f.* variability. **-kurve,** *f.* curve of variations, frequency curve. **-rechnung,** *f.* calculus of variations.

**Varietät,** *f.* variety.

**variieren,** *v.t. & i.* vary.

**Variierung,** *f.* variation.

**Vaselin,** *n.* petroleum jelly, petrolatum, (*T.N.*) Vaseline. **-öl,** *n.* paraffin oil.

**vaskularisieren,** *v.t.* vascularize.

**Vater,** *m.* father, sire. **-land,** *n.* native land; Germany.

**vaterländisch,** *a.* native, national.

**väterlich,** *a.* fatherly, paternal.

**Vb.,** *abbrev.* (Verbindung) compound.

**Vbb.,** *abbrev.* (Verbindungen) compounds.

**v.Chr.,** *abbrev.* (vor Christus) before Christ, B.C.
**V.d.E.,** *abbrev.* (Verein deutscher Eisenhüttenleute) Association of German Metallurgists.
**V.d.I., VDI,** *abbrev.* (Verein deutscher Ingenieure) Association of German Engineers.
**v.d.L.,** *abbrev.* (vor dem Lötrohr) before the blowpipe, B.B.
**Vegetabilien,** *pl.* vegetables; botanical drugs.
**vegetabilisch,** *a.* vegetable.
**Vegetationskasten,** *m.* plant incubator.
**vegetieren,** *v.i.* vegetate.
**Veilchen,** *n.* violet; (**dreifarbiges**) pansy.
**veilchen-blau,** *a.* violet. **-farben,** *a.* violet-colored.
**Veilchen-holz,** *n.* violet wood. **-keton,** *n.* ionone. **-öl,** *n.* violet oil. **-stein,** *m.* iolite. **-wurzel, -wurz,** *f.* orris root.
**Veitsbohne,** *f.* kidney bean.
**Veitstanz,** *m.* St. Vitus's dance, chorea.
**Vektorengleichung,** *f.* vector equation.
**Vektorgerüst,** *n.* vector diagram.
**vektoriell,** *a.* vectorial.
**Velin,** *n.* vellum.
**velinartig,** *a.* like vellum, vellumy.
**Velin-form,** *f.* (*Paper*) wove mold. **-papier,** *n.* vellum paper; wove paper.
**Velour(s)-leder,** *n.* suède leather, suède. **-tapete,** *f.* flock wallpaper.
**veloutieren,** *v.t.* flock (paper).
**Velozität,** *f.* velocity.
**Vene,** *f.* vein.
**Venedig,** *n.* Venice.
**Venen-blut,** *n.* venous blood. **-häutchen,** *n.* choroid membrane. **-stein,** *m.* vein stone, phlebolite.
**Venerie,** *f.* venereal disease, specif. syphilis.
**venerisch,** *a.* syphilitic.
**Venet-.** see Venez-.
**Venezianer-seife,** *f.* Venetian soap. **-weiss,** *n.* Venetian white.
**venezianisch,** *a.* Venetian.
**Venezianischrot,** *n.* Venetian red.
**venieren,** *v.t.* veneer.
**venös,** *a.* venous.
**Ventil,** *n.* valve.
**Ventilator,** *m.* ventilator, fan, blower.
**Ventil-deckel,** *m.* valve lid, valve cover. **-eimer,** *m.* **-eimerchen,** *n.* valved container (for viscous liquids). **-gehäuse,** *n.* valve chamber.
**ventilieren,** *v.t.* ventilate.
**Ventil-küken,** *m.* valve plug. **-öl,** *n.* valve oil. **-schlauch,** *m.* valve tubing. **-sitz,** *m.* valve seat. **-stahl,** *m.* valve steel. **-stopfen,** *n.* stopper with a valve, valve stopper. **-zelle,** *f.* (*Elec.*) valve cell.
**Venturi-messer,** *m.* Venturi meter. **-rohr,** *n.* Venturi tube.
**venturisch,** *a.* Venturi.
**ver.,** *abbrev.* (vereinigt) united.
**Ver.,** *abbrev.* (Verein) union, association, society.
**ver-.** A verbal prefix meaning: (1) Forth, away, out, either in the sense of removal, as *vertreiben,* drive away, dispel; or of the perfecting of an action, as *verschliessen,* close up, *verblühen,* cease blooming, fade. (2) A reversal of meaning, as *verbieten,* forbid (from *bieten,* offer). (3) Wrongly, too much, mis-, as *versalzen,* oversalt. (4) Make, convert into, or become, as *vergrössern,* make larger, magnify, *verkalken,* calcine, calcify, *verkäsen,* become cheesy.
**verab-folgen,** *v.t.* deliver, hand over, surrender. **-reden,** *v.t.* agree upon, appoint. **-reichen,** *v.t.* deliver, dispense. **-schieden,** *v.t.* dismiss, discharge. — *v.r.* take leave.
**verachten,** *v.t.* despise, scorn.
**verallgemeinern,** *v.t.* generalize.
**Verallgemeinerung,** *f.* generalization.
**veralmen,** *v.t.* (proposed term for) aluminize, plate with aluminum.
**veralten,** *v.i.* grow old or obsolete. — **veraltet,** *p.a.* obsolete, antiquated, out of date.
**veraluminieren,** *v.t.* (*Metal.*) aluminize, calorize.
**veränderlich,** *a.* variable; changeable, fluctuating, unstable, unsteady.
**Veränderliche,** *f.* variable.
**Veränderlichkeit,** *f.* variability, etc. (see veränderlich).
**verändern,** *v.t.* alter, change, vary; modify; concentrate (ore). — *v.r.* vary; change.
**Veränderung,** *f.* variation; change, alteration, modification.
**verankern,** *v.t.* anchor, make fast, fasten.
**veranlassen,** *v.t.* occasion, cause, give rise to; induce.
**Veranlassung,** *f.* occasion, cause; motive, inducement.
**veranschaulichen,** *v.t.* illustrate, make clear.
**Veranschaulichung,** *f.* illustration; viewpoint.
**veran-schlagen,** *v.t.* estimate, value. **-stalten,** *v.t.* arrange, manage, prepare, organize.
**verantworten,** *v.t.* answer for, justify.
**verantwortlich,** *a.* answerable, responsible.
**Verantwortung,** *f.* responsibility; justification.
**verarbeitbar,** *a.* workable, machinable.
**verarbeiten,** *v.t.* work, work up, treat, process, fabricate, manufacture.
**Verarbeitung,** *f.* working, working up, treatment, processing, manufacture.
**verarbeitungsfähig,** *a.* workable, machinable.
**Verarbeitungsfähigkeit,** *f.* workability, machinability.
**verarmen,** *v.i.* become poor. — *v.t.* reduce in strength, weaken; impoverish.
**verarten,** *v.i.* & *t.* degenerate.
**veraschen,** *v.t.* ash, incinerate.
**Veraschung,** *f.* ashing, incineration.

**Veraschungs-probe,** *f.* incineration test. **-schale,** *f.* incinerating dish.
**verästelt,** *a.* ramified; (*Metal.*) feathery.
**Verästelung, Verästung,** *f.* ramification.
**verastet,** *a.* branched, ramified.
**veräthern,** *v.t.* etherify.
**Verätherung,** *f.* etherification.
**veratmen,** *v.t.* breathe; use up by breathing, (of yeast) consume in respiration.
**Veratmung,** *f.* breathing, etc. (see veratmen).
**Veratrinsäure,** *f.* veratric acid.
**Veratrum-aldehyd,** *n.* veratraldehyde. **-alkohol,** *m.* veratric alcohol. **-säure,** *f.* veratric acid.
**verätzen,** *v.t.* corrode; cauterize.
**verausgaben,** *v.t.* spend, expend, pay; issue.
**verb.,** *abbrev.* (of books, verbessert) revised.
**Verb.,** *abbrev.* (Verbindung) compound; (Verband) association, union.
**Verband,** *m.* binding, fastening; bandaging, bandage; association, union; (*Masonry*) bond. **-päckchen,** *n.* first-aid packet. **-stoff,** *m.* fastening (or bandaging) material. **-watte,** *f.* absorbent cotton. **-zeug,** *m.* first-aid kit.
**verbannen,** *v.t.* banish.
**verbaumwollen,** *v.t.* cottonize.
**Verbb.,** *abbrev.* (Verbindungen) compounds.
**verbeissen,** *v.t.* suppress, stifle.
**verbeizen,** *v.t.* (*Leather*) overbate.
**Verbene,** *f.* vervain.
**verbergen,** *v.t. & r.* hide, conceal, mask. — **verborgen,** *p.a.* latent; hidden, secret.
**verbessern,** *v.t.* better, improve; correct, revise (books).
**Verbesserung,** *f.* improvement, betterment; correction; revision; reform.
**Verbesserungs-mittel, -produkt,** *n.* corrective, ameliorant. **-wert,** *m.* correction factor.
**verbeugen,** *v.r.* bow.
**Verbeulung,** *f.* bulging, swelling.
**verbiegen,** *v.t.* bend wrong, strain, distort, twist. — *v.r.* warp, buckle. — **verbogen,** *p.a.* crooked; warped; twisted.
**verbieten,** *v.t.* forbid, prohibit.
**verbilligen,** *v.t.* cheapen, reduce in price.
**verbinden,** *v.t.* combine; bind, bind up, join, link, connect; oblige. — *v.r.* combine, unite.
**verbindlich,** *a.* obliging; binding, obligatory; obliged.
**Verbindlichkeit,** *f.* civility, kindness; obligation; liability; obligatoriness.
**Verbindung,** *f.* compound; combining, combination, union; connection; blending (of colors); joining, fastening, binding; joint, bond; tie, link; communication; union, alliance, society.
**Verbindungs-draht,** *m.* connecting wire. **-fähigkeit,** *f.* combining ability. **-form,** *f.* form of combination. **-gang,** *m.* connecting passage. **-gewebe,** *n.* connective tissue. **-gewicht,** *n.* combining weight. **-gleichung,** *f.* equation of combination. **-glied,** *n.* connecting link. **-hahn,** *m.* connecting cock. **-kitt,** *m.* cement or lute for joints. **-klammer,** *f.* brace; (*Elec.*) clip connector. **-klemme,** *f.* (*Elec.*) connector, also binding post. **-kraft,** *f.* combining power. **-linie,** *f.* line of union; connecting line; line of communication. **-molekül,** *n.* molecule of a compound. **-punkt,** *m.* juncture, junction. **-rohr,** *n.*, **-röhre,** *f.* connecting tube or pipe. **-schlauch,** *m.* connecting tube or tubing. **-schliff,** *m.* ground joint. **-stelle,** *f.* juncture, junction. **-streben,** *n.* (chemical) affinity. **-strich,** *m.* hyphen. **-stück,** *n.* connecting piece, fitting. **-stufe,** *f.* stage of combination. **-verhältnis,** *n.* combining proportion. **-volumen,** *n.* combining volume. **-wärme,** *f.* heat of combination. **-wert,** *m.* combining value. **-zeichen,** *n.* hyphen.
**verbitten,** *v.t.* object, to, decline; deprecate.
**verblasen,** *v.t.* blow (glass or metal); dilute (colors).
**Verblase-ofen,** *m.* blast furnace. **-röstung,** *f.* (*Metal.*) blast roasting.
**verblassen,** *v.i.* fade; pale.
**Verbleib,** *m.* location, whereabouts; abode.
**verbleiben,** *v.i.* remain, continue, stay.
**verbleichen,** *v.i.* fade; grow pale; expire.
**verbleien,** *v.t.* (coat or line or treat with) lead.
**Verbleiung,** *f.* leading; lead lining.
**verblenden,** *v.t.* blind, dazzle; dim, black out; face (with some material); delude.
**Verblender,** *m.* (*Ceram.*) face brick.
**verblüffen,** *v.t.* amaze, astound, startle.
**verblühen,** *v.i.* fade, wither; cease blooming.
**verblümen,** *v.t.* disguise. — **verblümt,** *p.a.* figurative.
**verbluten,** *v. i & r.* bleed to death; cease bleeding.
**verbogen,** *p.p. & p.a.* see verbiegen.
**verborgen,** *v.t.* lend; sell on credit. — *p.a.* (from verbergen) latent; hidden, secret.
**Verbot,** *n.* prohibition.
**verboten,** *p.p.* (of verbieten) forbidden.
**verbr.,** *abbrev.* (verbraucht) consumed, used.
**verbrämen,** *v.t.* trim, border, adorn.
**verbrannt,** *p.p.* (of verbrennen) burnt, etc.
**Verbrauch,** *m.* consumption, use.
**verbrauchbar,** *a.* consumable; expendable.
**verbrauchen,** *v.t.* consume, use up. — **verbraucht,** *p.a.* spent, exhausted, used up, worn out, stale (air).
**Verbraucher,** *m.* consumer.
**Verbrauchs-gegenstand,** *m.* article of consumption, commodity. **-güter,** *n.pl.* consumer goods. **-messer,** *m.* meter (for gas, etc.). **-stelle,** *f.* place of consumption, place of use.

**-stoff,** *m.* article of consumption. **-zähler,** *m.* meter (for gas, etc.).
**verbrausen,** *v.i.* cease fermenting; subside.
**Verbrechen,** *n.* crime, offense, guilt.
**verbreiten,** *v.t.* spread, disseminate, diffuse, distribute. — *v.r.* spread. — **verbreitet,** *p.a.* widespread, widely distributed.
**verbreitern,** *v.t.* widen, broaden, spread.
**Verbreiterung,** *f.* widening, broadening.
**verbreitet,** *p.a.* see verbreiten.
**Verbreitung,** *f.* spreading, dissemination, distribution; circulation (of journals); range.
**Verbreitungsmittel,** *n.* means of dissemination or distribution.
**verbrennbar,** *a.* combustible.
**Verbrennbarkeit,** *f.* combustibility.
**verbrennen,** *v.t.* burn; scorch, tan, scald; bake.
**verbrennlich,** *a.* combustible; (in)flammable. — **verbrennliche Luft,** inflammable air (old name for hydrogen).
**Verbrennlichkeit,** *f.* combustibility; inflammability.
**Verbrennung,** *f.* combustion; burning; incineration; cremation.
**Verbrennungs-analyse,** *f.* combustion analysis, analysis by combustion. **-bombe,** *f.* combustion bomb. **-ergebnis,** *n.* product of combustion. **-gase,** *n.pl.* gases of combustion; flue gases. **-geschwindigkeit,** *f.* rate of combustion. **-glas,** *n.* combustion glass. **-hilfstoff,** *m.* aid to combustion, burning agent. **-intensität,** *f.* intensity of combustion. **-kammer,** *f.* combustion chamber. **-kapillare,** *f.* capillary combustion tube. **-kraftmaschine,** *f.* (internal) combustion engine. **-löffel,** *m.* combustion spoon. **-luft,** *f.* air for combustion. **-motor,** *m.* internal-combustion engine. **-narbe,** *f.* scar due to a burn. **-ofen,** *m.* combustion furnace. **-probe,** *f.* combustion test, ignition test. **-produkt,** *n.* product of combustion, combustion product. **-raum,** *m.* combustion chamber, fire chamber; combustion space. **-rohr,** *n.*, **-röhre,** *f.* combustion tube. **-rückstand,** *m.* residue on ignition (or combustion). **-schälchen,** *n.* combustion capsule or boat. **-schiffchen,** *n.* combustion boat. **-versuch,** *m.* combustion experiment. **-vorgang,** *m.* process of combustion. **-wärme,** *f.* heat of combustion. **-wert,** *m.* combustion value, specif. calorific power. **-zone,** *f.* zone of combustion.
**verbriefen,** *v.t.* confirm or secure by writing.
**verbringen,** *v.t.* spend, pass, waste; remove.
**verbrühen,** *v.t.* scald.
**Verbund,** *m.* joining, connection, union.
**Verbund-.** (*Mach.*, etc.) compound; joint. **-block,** *m.* (*Metal.*) compound ingot.
**verbunden,** *p.p.* (of verbinden) combined, etc.
**Verbund-glas,** *n.* laminated glass, compound glass (consisting of layers). **-guss,** *m.* compound casting. **-maschine,** *f.* compound engine. **-pressstoff,** *m.* composite plastic. **-stahl,** *m.* compound steel. **-stoff,** *m.* compounding material. **-stück,** *n.* fitting, coupling, connector. **-werkstoff,** *m.* compound material; bimetal, clad metal; duplex alloy. **-wirkung,** *f.* compound action or effect; mutual action or effect.
**verbürgen,** *v.t.* warrant, guarantee.
**verchloren,** *v.t.* chlorinate.
**Verchlorung,** *f.* chlorination.
**verchromen,** *v.t.* chrome; plate with chromium.
**Verchromung,** *f.* chroming; chromium plating.
**vercoken,** *v.t.* coke.
**verd.,** *abbrev.* (verdünnt) diluted, dilute.
**Verd.,** *abbrev.* (Verdünnung) dilution.
**Verdacht,** *m.* suspicion, distrust.
**verdächtig,** *a.* suspicious, suspected.
**verdämmen,** *v.t.* tamp, dam; check; stunt.
**Verdampfapparat,** *m.* evaporating apparatus, evaporator; vaporizer; carburetor.
**verdampfbar,** *a.* vaporizable; volatile.
**Verdampf-barkeit,** *f.* vaporizability, volatility. **-becken,** *n.* evaporating dish or basin.
**verdampfen,** *v.t.* evaporate (either vaporize or concentrate by evaporation). — *v.i.* evaporate, vaporize.
**Verdampfer,** *m.* evaporator; vaporizer; carburetor. **-kolonne,** *f.* evaporating column; evaporator tower.
**Verdampf-oberfläche,** *f.* evaporating surface. **-pfanne,** *f.* evaporating pan. **-schale,** *f.* evaporating dish or basin. **-turm,** *m.* evaporator tower.
**Verdampfung,** *f.* evaporation, evaporating; vaporization. — **— durch Entspannung,** flash evaporation.
**Verdampfungs-druck,** *m.* evaporation pressure. **-ente,** *f.* duck-shaped evaporating vessel.
**verdampfungsfähig,** *a.* capable of evaporation.
**Verdampfungs-fähigkeit,** *f.* evaporative capacity; volatility. **-geschwindigkeit,** *f.* rate of evaporation or vaporization. **-kolben,** *m.* evaporating flask. **-kühlung,** *f.* evaporative cooling. **-messer,** *m.* evaporimeter. **-pfanne,** *f.* evaporating pan, boiling-down pan. **-punkt,** *m.* vaporization point. **-röstung,** *f.* volatilization roasting. **-rückstand,** *m.* residue on evaporation. **-schale,** *f.* evaporating dish or basin. **-verlust,** *m.* loss from evaporation or volatilization. **-vermögen,** *n.* evaporating power. **-wärme,** *f.* heat of vaporization or evaporation. **-wert,** *m.* evaporating value. **-zahl, -ziffer,** *f.* coefficient of evaporation.
**verdanken,** *v.t.* owe, have to thank.
**verdarb,** *pret.* (of verderben) spoiled, etc.
**verdauen,** *v.t.* digest. — *v.r.* be digested, be digestible.

**verdaulich,** *a.* digestible.
**Verdaulichkeit,** *f.* digestibility.
**Verdauung,** *f.* digestion.
**Verdauungs-apparat,** *m.* digestive apparatus. **-dauer,** *f.* duration of digestion. **-eingeweide,** *n.* digestive tract.
**verdauungsfähig,** *a.* digestible.
**Verdauungs-fähigkeit,** *f.* digestibility. **-flüssigkeit,** *f.* digestive fluid, specif. gastric juice. **-geschäft,** *n.* digestive process. **-kanal,** *m.* alimentary canal. **-mittel,** *n.* digestive remedy. **-ofen,** *m.* digesting oven. **-rohr,** *n.* alimentary canal. **-saft,** *m.* = Verdauungsflüssigkeit. **-störung,** *f.* indigestion. **-tractus,** *m.* digestive tract. **-vorgang,** *m.* digestive process.
**Verdeck,** *n.* cover; (automobile) hood; deck.
**verdecken,** *v.t.* cover, conceal, mask.
**verdenken,** *v.t.* find fault with.
**Verderb,** *m.* waste; decay; corrosion; ruin.
**verderben,** *v.t.* spoil, damage; ruin, corrupt. — *v.i.* be spoiled, spoil, decay. — **verdorben,** *p.a.* spoiled, damaged, foul, rotten.
**verderblich,** *a.* perishable; destructive, injurious.
**Verderbnis,** *n.* spoiling, decay, damage.
**verdeutlichen,** *v.t.* elucidate; illustrate.
**verdeutschen,** *v.t.* translate into German; Germanize.
**verdichtbar,** *a.* condensable; compressible.
**Verdichtbarkeit,** *f.* condensability; compressibility.
**verdichten,** *v.t.* condense; compress; pack; seal; consolidate; concentrate.
**Verdichter,** *m.* condenser; compressor.
**Verdichtung,** *f.* condensation, etc. (see verdichten).
**Verdichtungs-apparat,** *m.* condensing apparatus, condenser. **-druck,** *m.* compression pressure. **-grad,** *m.* degree of condensation or compression (or concentration). **-hub,** *m.* compression stroke. **-ring,** *m.* packing ring. **-stosswelle,** *f.* (*Expl.*) compression wave. **-wärme,** *f.* heat of condensation or compression. **-welle,** *f.* compression wave. **-zündung,** *f.* compression ignition.
**verdicken,** *v.t.* thicken, concentrate, inspissate; coagulate, curdle. — *v.r.* thicken; jell; become viscous; coagulate, curd.
**Verdicker,** *m.* thickener, etc. (see verdicken).
**Verdickung,** *f.* thickening, etc. (see verdicken); (*Calico*) paste.
**Verdickungsmittel,** *n.* thickening agent, thickener.
**verdienen,** *v.t.* deserve; gain, earn, make.
**Verdienst,** *n.* merit, deserts; earnings, profit.
**verdoppeln,** *v.t.* double; duplicate.
**Verdopp(e)lung,** *f.* doubling; duplication.
**verdorben,** *p.p.* & *p.a.* see verderben.
**verdorren,** *v.i.* dry up, dry; wither.
**verdrahten,** *v.t.* wire.
**Verdrahtung,** *f.* wiring.
**Verdrang,** *m.* displacement.
**verdrängbar,** *a.* displaceable.
**verdrängen,** *v.t.* displace; drive out, expel, remove; dislodge.
**Verdrängung,** *f.* displacement; removal, dispossession.
**Verdrängungs-messer,** *m.* displacement meter. **-mittel,** *n.* displacing agent.
**verdrehen,** *v.t.* twist; distort, wrench.
**Verdrehschwingung,** *f.* torsional vibration.
**Verdrehung,** *f.* twisting, torsion; distortion.
**Verdrehungs-kraft,** *f.* torsional force. **-wage,** *f.* torsion balance. **-winkel,** *m.* angle of torsion.
**verdreifachen,** *v.t.* triple, treble.
**Verdreifachung,** *f.* tripling, trebling.
**verdriessen,** *v.t.* grieve, vex, annoy. — **verdrossen,** *p.a.* grieved, etc.; loath, indolent.
**verdrillen.** *v.t.* twist.
**Verdrillung,** *f.* twisting, torsion.
**verdrosseln,** *v.t.* throttle, choke.
**verdrucken,** *v.t.* misprint; use up in printing.
**verdrücken,** *v.t.* mash, crush, crumple, pinch, squeeze, overpress.
**Verdruss,** *m.* ill will; trouble, annoyance.
**verduften,** *v.i.* evaporate.
**verdunkeln,** *v.t.* darken, obscure, dim.
**verdünnbar,** *a.* capable of dilution; rarefiable.
**verdünnen,** *v.t.* dilute (liquids); rarefy (gases); attenuate (wort); thin; extend, weaken; dim (light). — **verdünnt,** *p.a.* diluted, etc., dilute, rare, thin.
**Verdünner,** *m.* diluter, thinner.
**Verdünnung,** *f.* dilution; rarefaction; thinning; extending; (*Brewing,* etc.) attenuation.
**Verdünnungs-gesetz,** *n.* dilution law. **-grad,** *m.* degree of dilution. **-mittel,** *n.* diluent; extender, reducer, thinner; (*Med.*) attenuant. **-wärme,** *f.* heat of dilution.
**verdunstbar,** *a.* evaporable, vaporizable.
**verdunsten,** *v.i.* & *t.* evaporate, vaporize.
**Verdunsten,** *n.* evaporation, vaporization.
**verdünsten,** *v.t.* evaporate.
**Verdunster,** *m.* evaporator.
**Verdunstung, Verdünstung,** *f.* evaporation, vaporization.
**Verdunstungs-gefäss,** *n.* evaporating vessel; evaporimeter. **-geschwindigkeit,** *f.* rate of evaporation. **-kälte,** *f.* cold due to evaporation. **-kühlung,** *f.* cooling by evaporation. **-messer,** *m.* evaporimeter. **-verlust,** *m.* loss by evaporation or vaporization. **-wärme,** *f.* heat of vaporization.
**verdutzen,** *v.t.* nonplus.
**veredeln,** *v.t.* improve; purify, refine; enrich; plate with a nobler metal; cultivate (plants);

graft; finish, dress, process (textiles); ennoble.

**Vered(e)lung,** *f.* improvement, etc. (see veredeln).

**Veredelungs-bad,** *n.* (*Textiles*) processing bath. **-mittel,** *n.* (*Textiles*) processing agent. **-produkt,** *n.* finishing (or processing) agent.

**verehren,** *v.t.* revere, adore, admire.

**Verein,** *m.* union, association, society, club, company.

**verein-bar,** *a.* combinable; compatible. **-baren,** *v.t.* reconcile, agree upon. **-bart,** *p.a.* agreed on, conventional.

**Vereinbarung,** *f.* agreement, reconcilement.

**vereinen,** *v.t. & r.* = vereinigen. — **die Vereinte Nationen,** the United Nations.

**vereinfachen,** *v.t.* simplify; (*Math.*) reduce.

**Vereinfachung,** *f.* simplification; (*Math.*) reduction.

**vereinheitlichen,** *v.t.* standardize, normalize; render uniform, unify.

**vereinigen,** *v.t. & r.* unite, combine; collect; make agree, agree; (of colors) blend. — **vereinigt,** *p.a.* united, etc. — **die Vereinigten Staaten,** the United States.

**Vereinigung,** *f.* union, combination; association, society, club; agreement.

**Vereinigungs-haut,** *f.* (*Anat.*) conjunctiva. **-stelle,** *f.* place of union; junction.

**vereinzeln,** *v.t.* isolate, detach, separate. — **vereinzelt,** *a.* isolated, solitary, sporadic. — *adv.* sporadically.

**vereisen,** *v.t. & i.* ice, freeze, freeze up, frost.

**Vereisung,** *f.* icing, etc. (see vereisen); (*Geol.*) glaciation.

**Vereisungsschutzflüssigkeit,** *f.* anti-icing fluid.

**vereiteln,** *v.t.* balk, thwart, defeat, nullify.

**vereitern,** *v.i.* suppurate.

**Vereiterung,** *f.* suppuration.

**verengen, verengern,** *v.t. & r.* narrow, contract, constrict.

**Verengung,** *f.* contraction, constriction.

**vererben,** *v.t.* transmit, hand down, bequeath. — **vererbt,** *p.a.* hereditary, inherited.

**Vererbung,** *f.* inheritance; transmission.

**Vererbungs-forschung, -lehre,** *f.* genetics. **-substanz,** *f.* (*Biol.*) idioplasm.

**vererden,** *v.t. & i.* turn to earth, specif. oxidize.

**vererzbar,** *a.* mineralizable.

**vererzen,** *v.t.* mineralize; encase in ore.

**Vererzung,** *f.* mineralization.

**Vererzungsmittel,** *n.* mineralizer.

**veresterbar,** *a.* esterifiable.

**verestern,** *v.t.* esterify.

**Veresterung,** *f.* esterification.

**verewigen,** *v.t.* perpetuate; immortalize. — **verewigt,** *p.a.* late, deceased.

**Verf.,** *abbrev.* (Verfasser) author; (Verfahren) process, method.

**verfahren,** *v.i.* proceed; act, manage, deal. — *v.t.* transport; work; muddle. — *v.r.* blunder.

**Verfahren,** *n.* process, method, procedure, proceeding, mode, technique; operation; conduct; management.

**Verfahrungs-art, -weise,** *f.* mode of proceeding, process, method.

**Verfall,** *m.* decay, decline, deterioration, ruin; expiration, lapse.

**verfallen,** *v.i.* decay, decline; degenerate; fall; chance, hit; (of time) expire.

**verfälschen,** *v.t.* adulterate; debase (coins); falsify, counterfeit.

**Verfälscher,** *m.* adulterator; falsifier, forger.

**Verfälschung,** *f.* adulteration; falsification, forgery.

**Verfälschungsmittel,** *n.* adulterant.

**verfangen,** *v.i.* operate, have effect, be of avail. — *v.r.* be caught.

**verfänglich,** *a.* insidious, deceitful.

**verfärben,** *v.r.* change color; discolor; fade. — *v.t.* use up (in dyeing); dye poorly.

**Verfärbung,** *f.* discoloration; fading.

**verfassen,** *v.t.* compose, write.

**Verfasser,** *m.*, **Verfasserin,** *f.* author, writer.

**Verfassung,** *f.* composition, writing; constitution; condition.

**verfaulbar,** *a.* putrescible.

**verfaulen,** *v.i.* putrefy, rot, decompose.

**Verfaulung,** *f.* putrefaction, rotting, decaying.

**verfechten,** *v.t.* defend, advocate.

**verfehlen,** *v.t.* miss. — *v.i.* fail. — **verfehlt,** *p.a.* unsuccessful, misplaced.

**verfeinern,** *v.t.* refine, purify; improve.

**Verfeinerung,** *f.* refinement; improvement.

**verfertigen,** *v.t.* make, prepare, construct, manufacture; compose.

**Verfertigung,** *f.* making, etc. (see verfertigen); make, manufacture.

**verfestigen,** *v.t.* fasten; make firm, strengthen, consolidate, solidify, harden.

**Verfestigung,** *f.* fastening, etc. (see verfestigen).

**Verfestigungszeit,** *f.* (of gels) setting time.

**Verfettung,** *f.* fatty degeneration.

**verfeuern,** *v.t.* burn up, burn, fire.

**verfilzen,** *v.t. & i.* felt, mat; clog up.

**Verfilzung,** *f.* felting, matting.

**Verfilzungsfähigkeit,** *f.* felting or matting property.

**verfinstern,** *v.t.* darken, obscure.

**Verfinsterung,** *f.* darkening; eclipse.

**verfitzen,** *v.t.* entangle, tangle.

**verflachen,** *v.t.* flatten, level, smooth. — *v.r. & i.* become flat or level, level off.

**verflechten,** *v.t.* interlace, interweave, involve.

**Verflechtung,** *f.* interweaving; complexity, complication, entanglement.

**verfliegen,** *v.i.* volatilize; fly away, vanish. — **verfliegend,** *p.a.* volatile; evanescent.

**verfliessen,** *v.i.* blend; flow away; (of time) pass, elapse.
**verflochten,** *p.a.* (from verflechten) interwoven; complicated; entangled.
**verflüchtigbar,** *a.* volatilizable.
**verflüchtigen,** *v.t.* & *r.* volatilize, evaporate.
**Verflüchtigung,** *f.* volatilization.
**Verflüchtigungs-fähigkeit,** *f.* volatility. **-probe,** *f.* volatility test. **-verlust,** *m.* loss by volatilization.
**verflüssigen,** *v.t.* & *r.* liquefy; (*Metal.*) thin, dilute. — **verflüssigt,** *p.a.* liquefied, liquid.
**Verflüssiger,** *m.* liquefier, condenser.
**Verflüssigung,** *f.* liquefaction; (*Metal.*) thinning.
**Verflüssigungs-druck,** *m.* liquefying pressure. **-mittel,** *n.* liquefacient; (*Metal.*) thinning agent.
**verfolgen,** *v.t.* pursue; prosecute, carry on; follow (up); persecute.
**Verfolgung,** *f.* pursuit; prosecution; persecution.
**verformbar,** *a.* deformable, moldable, plastic.
**Verformbarkeit,** *f.* deformability, plasticity, workability, malleability.
**verformen,** *v.t.* deform; form, shape, work.
**Verformung,** *f.* deformation; working; shaping; strain.
**verfrischen,** *v.t.* (*Metal.*) refine.
**verfrüht,** *p.a.* premature.
**verfügbar,** *a.* at disposal, available.
**Verfügbarkeit,** *f.* availability.
**verfügen,** *v.i.* (with **über**) have at one's disposal, dispose (of). — *v.t.* order, arrange.
**Verfügung,** *f.* disposal, disposition; order. — **zur —,** available.
**verführen,** *v.t.* transport; mislead; corrupt, seduce.
**verfüllen,** *v.t.* fill.
**verfuttern, verfüttern,** *v.t.* feed (something); overfeed.
**Verfutterung, Verfütterung,** *f.* feeding; overfeeding.
**Verfütterungsversuch,** *m.* feeding experiment.
**vergällen,** *v.t.* denature; embitter.
**Vergällung,** *f.* denaturing.
**Vergällungsmittel,** *n.* denaturant.
**vergangen,** *p.a.* gone, past.
**Vergangenheit,** *f.* the past; prior treatment.
**vergänglich,** *a.* transient, perishable.
**vergärbar,** *a.* fermentable, attenuable.
**Vergärbarkeit,** *f.* fermentability.
**vergären,** *v.t.* ferment; attenuate (wort). — **vergoren,** *p.a.* fermented, (*Brewing*) finished.
**Vergärung,** *f.* fermentation; attenuation (of wort).
**Vergärungs-fähigkeit,** *f.* fermentability. **-grad,** *m.* degree of fermentation or attenuation **-messer,** *m.* zymometer.
**vergasbar,** *a.* gasifiable; vaporizable.
**vergasen,** *v.t.* gasify; vaporize; gas. — **vergast,** *p.a.* gasified; vaporized; (*Mil.*) gassed, contaminated by gas.
**Vergaser,** *m.* gasifier; vaporizer; carburetor. **-graphit,** *m.* retort graphite.
**vergass,** *pret.* (of vergessen) forgot.
**Vergasung,** *f.* gasification; vaporization; destructive distillation; carburetion; gassing.
**Vergasungs-gas,** *n.* manufactured gas. **-mittel,** *n.* gasifying agent. **-öl,** *n.* oil for gasification.
**vergeben,** *v.t.* give, bestow, confer; forgive.
**vergebens,** *adv.* in vain.
**vergeblich,** *a.* vain, futile.
**vergegenwärtigen,** *v.t.* represent, figure. — *v.r.* imagine, realize.
**vergehen,** *v.i.* vanish, perish, cease, (of time) pass, elapse. — *v.r.* transgress; exercise.
**Vergeilen,** *n.* (*Bot.*) etiolation.
**vergelben,** *v.i.* turn yellow; etiolate.
**vergelten,** *v.t.* reward, repay, return.
**Vergeltung,** *f.* reward, remuneration; retaliation, reprisal.
**Vergesellschaftung,** *f.* association.
**vergessen,** *v.t.* forget.
**Vergessenheit,** *f.* forgetfulness, oblivion.
**vergesslich,** *a.* forgetful, oblivious.
**vergeuden,** *v.t.* squander, waste.
**vergewissern,** *v.t.* convince, assure, confirm.
**vergiessbar,** *a.* castable, ready to cast.
**Vergiessbarkeit,** *f.* castability, coulability.
**vergiessen,** *v.t.* cast in, run in; fill in, fill up; cast badly; spill, shed.
**Vergiesstemperatur,** *f.* casting (or pouring) temperature.
**vergiften,** *v.t.* poison; contaminate.
**Vergiftung,** *f.* poisoning, intoxication; contamination.
**Vergiftungserscheinung,** *f.* symptom of poisoning.
**vergilben,** *v.t.* & *i.* turn yellow, yellow; etiolate. — **vergilbt,** *p.a.* yellowed; etiolated.
**vergipsen,** *v.t.* plaster.
**vergisst,** *pr. 2 & 3 sing.* (of vergessen) forgets.
**vergittern,** *v.t.* grate, lattice, screen.
**Vergitterung,** *f.* grating, lattice, grid, grill(e).
**vergl.,** *abbrev.* (vergleiche) compare, cf.
**Vergl.,** *abbrev.* (Vergleich) comparison.
**verglasbar,** *a.* vitrifiable.
**verglasen,** *v.t.* vitrify; glaze. — *v.i.* & *r.* vitrify.
**Verglasung,** *f.* vitrification; glaze; glazing.
**Vergleich,** *m.* comparison; agreement, arrangement, contract.
**vergleichbar,** *a.* comparable.
**Vergleichbarkeit,** *f.* comparability.
**vergleichen,** *v.t.* compare; check; equalize,

adjust. — *v.r.* agree, come to terms. — **vergleichend,** *p.a.* comparative.
**vergleichlos,** *a.* unparalleled, matchless.
**Vergleichprisma,** *n.* comparison prism.
**Vergleichs-ausfärbung,** *f.* comparative dyeing. **-fähigkeit,** *f.* comparability. **-feld,** *n.* (*Photometry*) matching field. **-flüssigkeit,** *f.* comparison liquid. **-kraftstoff,** *m.* standard motor fuel. **-linie,** *f.* standard line, comparison line. **-lösung,** *f.* comparison solution, standard solution. **-mas(s)stab,** *m.* standard of comparison. **-pflanze,** *f.* control plant. **-präparat,** *n.* comparison preparation. **-substanz,** *f.* comparison substance, standard. **-tier,** *n.* control animal. **-verfahren,** *n.* comparison method. **-versuch,** *m.* comparative experiment, comparison test.
**vergleichsweise,** *adv.* by way of comparison, comparably.
**Vergleichs-wert,** *m.* comparative value. **-zahl,** *f.* comparative figure.
**Vergleichung,** *f.* comparison; parallel.
**Vergleichunterlage,** *f.* basis for comparison.
**verglichen,** *p.p.* (of vergleichen) compared, etc.
**verglimmen,** *v.i. & r.* cease glowing, die out; smolder.
**Verglühbrand,** *m.* (*Ceram.*) biscuit baking.
**verglühen,** *v.t.* bake, fire, give the biscuit fire to (porcelain); anneal poorly. — *v.i.* cease glowing, cool down; burn out.
**Verglühen,** *n.* (*Ceram.*) biscuit baking; (*Metal.*) faulty annealing.
**Verglühofen,** *m.* (*Ceram.*) biscuit kiln.
**Verglühung,** *f.* = Verglühen.
**vergnügen,** *v.t.* please, gratify. — *v.r.* enjoy oneself, be delighted. — **vergnügt,** *p.a.* pleased, delighted; cheerful, gay.
**Vergnügung,** *f.* pleasure, amusement, sport.
**vergolden,** *v.t.* gild; plate with gold. — **vergoldet,** *p.a.* gilded, gilt; gold-plated.
**Vergolder-masse,** *f.* gilding. **-wachs,** *n.* gilder's wax.
**Vergoldung,** *f.* gilding; gold plating.
**Vergoldungs-wachs,** *n.* gilder's wax. **-wasser,** *n.* quickening liquid.
**vergönnen,** *v.t.* permit, grant.
**vergoren,** *p.a.* see vergären.
**vergossen,** *p.p.* (of vergiessen) cast in, etc.
**Vergr.,** *abbrev.* (Vergrösserung) magnification.
**vergraben,** *v.t.* bury; intrench.
**vergreifen,** *v.r.* mistake; attack, violate; steal, embezzle. — *v.t.* buy up, buy out. — **vergriffen,** *p.a.* sold out; exhausted; out of print.
**Vergreisenung,** *f.* (*Petrog.*) greisenization.
**vergröbern,** *v.t.* make coarser, coarsen.
**vergrössern,** *v.t.* increase, enlarge; magnify; exaggerate. — *v.r.* grow larger.
**Vergrösserung,** *f.* increase, enlargement; magnification; exaggeration.
**Vergrösserungs-glas,** *n.* magnifying glass. **-kraft,** *f.* magnifying power. **-linse,** *f.* magnifying lens.
**vergrünen,** *v.i.* turn green; lose green color, fade.
**vergrünlich,** *a.* (*Dyeing*) greenable.
**Verguss,** *m.* pouring, casting, filling, seal. **-harz,** *n.* casting resin. **-masse,** *f.* sealing compound, filler.
**vergütbar,** *a.* improvable; (*Metal.*) heat-treatable, temperable.
**Vergütbarkeit,** *f.* improvability; (*Metal.*) tempering quality.
**vergüten,** *v.t.* make good; improve; (*Metal.*) heat-treat, temper; coat (a lens); compensate, allow.
**Vergüten,** *n.*, **Vergütung,** *f.* improvement; (*Metal.*) heat treatment, tempering; allowance.
**Vergüterei,** *f.* (*Metal.*) heat-treating plant.
**Vergütungsstahl,** *m.* heat-treated (or heat-treatable) steel.
**Verh.,** *abbrev.* (Verhalten) behavior; (Verhältnis) proportion, ratio.
**verhaften,** *v.t.* arrest, apprehend.
**verhagern,** *v.i.* become lean or thin. — **verhagert,** *p.a.* lean, thin, poor.
**verhaken,** *v.t. & r.* hook together, hook on; interlock.
**Verhalt,** *m.* state, condition.
**verhalten,** *v.r.* behave, act, be. — *v.t.* hold (back), retain.
**Verhalten,** *n.* behavior; conduct; character, quality; retention, suppression.
**Verhältnis,** *n.* proportion; ratio, rate; relation; situation, connection, circumstance; condition, consistency. **-anzeiger,** *m.* (*Math.*) exponent. **-gleichheit,** *f.* proportion.
**verhältnis-mässig,** *a.* proportional, proportionate; relative; commensurable, commensurate. — *adv.* proportionately, relatively. **-widrig,** *a.* disproportionate.
**Verhältniszahl,** *f.* proportional number.
**Verhaltung,** *f.* = Verhalten.
**verhandeln,** *v.t.* transact; try; sell. — *v.i.* treat, negotiate.
**Verhandlung,** *f.* transaction; proceeding; deliberation; debate.
**verhängen,** *v.t.* hang; curtain off; hang in the air, air; decree, proclaim; impose.
**Verhängnis,** *n.* destiny, fate.
**verharren,** *v.i.* remain, persist.
**verhärten,** *v.t. & i.* harden, indurate.
**Verhärtung,** *f.* hardening, induration.
**verharzen,** *v. i. & r.* become resinous, resinify, gum; blur (as in X-ray pictures). — *v.t.* resin; convert into resin.

**Verharzen,** *n.*, **Verharzung,** *f.* resinification; resining; gumming; blurring.
**verhauen,** *v.t.* cut up, hack, prune.
**verhehlen,** *v.t.* hide, conceal; (*Warfare*) camouflage.
**verheilen,** *v.t., i. & r.* heal.
**verheimlichen,** *v.t.* keep secret, disguise, conceal.
**verheiraten,** *v.t.* give in marriage, marry.
**verheissen,** *v.t.* promise.
**verhelfen,** *v.t.* help, assist.
**verhindern,** *v.t.* hinder, prevent.
**Verhinderung,** *f.* hindrance, obstacle.
**Verhinderungsmittel,** *n.* preventive.
**verholzen,** *v.i.* lignify, become wood.
**Verholzung,** *f.* lignification.
**Verhör,** *n.* hearing; trial.
**verhornen,** *v.i.* become horny.
**Verhornung,** *f.* cornification.
**verhüllen,** *v.t.* wrap up, cover; veil, conceal.
**verhungern,** *v.i.* starve.
**Verhungerung,** *f.* starvation.
**verhunzen,** *v.t.* botch, bungle.
**verhüten,** *v.t.* avert, prevent; inhibit. — **verhütend,** *p.a.* preventive.
**verhüttbar,** *a.* smeltable.
**verhütten,** *v.t.* work, smelt (ores).
**Verhüttung,** *f.* (*Metal.*) working (off), smelting.
**Verhütung,** *f.* prevention, (*Med.*) prophylaxis.
**Verhütungsmittel,** *n.* preventive, prophylactic; inhibitor.
**verifizieren,** *v.t.* verify.
**verimpfen,** *v.t.* transmit (by inoculation or contagion).
**verirren,** *v.r.* err, go astray.
**verjagen,** *v.t.* drive out, drive off, expel.
**verjähren,** *v.i.* grow old (or obsolete); lapse.
**verjauchen,** *v.i.* putrefy.
**Verjauchung,** *f.* putrefaction.
**verjüngen,** *v.t.* reduce, diminish, contract, constrict, narrow; taper; rejuvenate, renew.
**Verjüngung,** *f.* diminution, reduction, taper, (of a tube) constriction; rejuvenation, regeneration.
**verk.,** *abbrev.* (verkürzt) abbreviated.
**verkadmen, verkadminieren, verkadmiumen, verkadmiumieren,** *v.t.* plate with cadmium.
**verkalkbar,** *a.* calcinable.
**verkalken,** *v.t. & i.* calcine; calcify; lime.
**Verkalkung,** *f.* calcination; calcification; liming.
**verkannt,** *p.p.* (of verkennen) mistaken; misunderstood.
**verkanten,** *v.t.* tilt, cant, tip.
**verkappen,** *v.t.* mask, disguise.
**verkäsen,** *v.i.* (*Med.*) become caseous, or cheesy.
**Verkäsung,** *f.* caseation.
**verkauen, verkäuen,** *v.t.* chew, chew up. — *v.r.* be chewed up.
**Verkauf,** *m.* sale.
**verkaufen,** *v.t. & r.* sell.
**verkäuflich, verkaufsfähig,** *a.* salable, marketable.
**Verkehr,** *m.* traffic, commerce, trade; communication, intercourse.
**verkehren,** *v.t.* invert, reverse; pervert. — *v.i.* visit, associate. — **verkehrt,** *p.a.* inverted, reversed; wrong; absurd; perverted, perverse. — *adv.* inversely; wrongly, wrong.
**verkehrssicher,** *a.* safe for commerce. — **-Sprengstoff,** safety explosive.
**verkehrt,** *p.a.* see verkehren.
**verkennen,** *v.t.* mistake; misunderstand.
**Verkernung,** *f.* conversion to heartwood.
**verketten,** *v.t.* link (together), form into a chain.
**Verkettung,** *f.* linking, linkage.
**Verkettungsfähigkeit,** *f.* linking capacity, ability to form chains.
**verkienen,** *v.t.* saturate with resin.
**verkieseln,** *v.t.* silicify.
**Verkieselung,** *f.* silicification.
**verkiesen,** *v.t.* gravel, ballast; pyritize.
**verkitten,** *v.t.* cement, lute; seal.
**Verkittung,** *f.* cementing, luting.
**Verkittungsfähigkeit,** *f.* cementing property.
**verklammern,** *v.t.* clamp; (*Printing*) brace.
**verkleben,** *v.t.* cement, lute; plaster (over), glue (over), paste (over); gum up; agglutinate.
**Verklebung,** *f.* cementing, luting; covering or closing with an adhesive; agglutination.
**Verklebungsstoff,** *m.* agglutinative substance.
**verkleiden,** *v.t.* face, case, line; disguise, mask.
**Verkleidung,** *f.* facing, casing, lining; disguise.
**verkleinern,** *v.t.* diminish, reduce; disparage.
**Verkleinerung,** *f.* diminution, reduction; detraction.
**verkleistern,** *v.t.* paste up; make into paste; clog. — **verkleistert,** *p.a.* pasty.
**Verkleisterung,** *f.* conversion into paste; pasting; glutinization; (so-called) gelatinization; clogging.
**verklingen,** *v.i.* (of waves, etc.) die out, decay.
**verknallen,** *v.t. & r.* detonate.
**verkneten,** *v.t.* knead, work.
**verknistern,** *v.i.* decrepitate.
**Verknisterung,** *f.* decrepitation.
**Verknisterungswasser,** *n.* water of decrepitation.
**verknittern,** *v.t.* crease, crumple.
**verknöchern,** *v.i.* ossify.
**Verknöcherung,** *f.* ossification.
**verknorpeln,** *v.i.* become cartilaginous. — **verknorpelt,** *p.a.* cartilaginous.
**Verknorpelung,** *f.* chondrification.
**verknoten, verknotigen,** *v.t.* snarl, tangle.
**verknüpfen,** *v.t.* tie, bind, connect, join, link.
**Verknüpfung,** *f.* connection; linkage; union.

**verkobalten,** *v.t.* plate with cobalt.
**Verkobaltung,** *f.* cobalt plating.
**verkochbar,** *a.* (*Varnish*) compatible with drying oil on boiling.
**verkochen,** *v.t.* boil down, concentrate; injure by boiling, overheat. — *v.i.* be injured by boiling.
**verkohlen,** *v.t. & i.* char, carbonize.
**Verkohlung,** *f.* charring, carbonization.
**Verkohlungsvorgang,** *m.* carbonization process.
**verkoken,** *v.t.* coke.
**Verkokung,** *f.* coking.
**verkokungsfähig,** *a.* capable of coking.
**Verkokungs-kammer,** *f.* coking chamber. **-ofen,** *m.* coke oven. **-probe,** *f.* coking test or sample. **-vorgang,** *m.* coking process. **-zeit,** *f.* coking time.
**verkommen,** *v.i.* decay, degenerate; die.
**verkoppeln,** *v.t.* couple, link, join.
**verkorken,** *v.t.* cork; convert into cork.
**Verkorkung,** *f.* corking; suberification.
**verkörnen,** *v.t.* granulate.
**verkörpern,** *v.t.* embody.
**Verkörperung,** *f.* embodiment.
**verkracken,** *v.t.* crack.
**Verkrackung,** *f.* cracking.
**verkraften,** *v.t.* strengthen; reinforce; (*Mil.*, etc.) mechanize.
**verkreiden,** *v.t.* calcify.
**Verkreidung,** *f.* calcification.
**verkrümmen,** *v.t.* crook, curve, bend, warp.
**Verkrümmung,** *f.* crookedness; curvature; warping; curling.
**verkrusten,** *v.i.* become incrusted, form a crust.
**Verkrustung,** *f.* incrustation.
**verkühlen,** *v.t. & r.* cool down.
**verkümmern,** *v.t.* stunt; interfere with, spoil. — *v.i.* be stunted; languish.
**verkünden, verkündigen,** *v.t.* announce, proclaim, publish.
**verküpbar,** *a.* capable of use as a vat dye.
**Verküpbarkeit,** *f.* (*Dyeing*) vatting property.
**verküpen,** *v.t.* vat, reduce (a vat dye) preparatory to dyeing.
**verkupfern,** *v.t.* copper, copperplate.
**Verkupferung,** *f.* coppering, copper plating.
**verkuppeln,** *v.t.* couple.
**Verküpung,** *f.* vatting (see verküpen).
**Verküpungsdauer,** *f.* (*Dyeing*) vatting time.
**verkürzen,** *v.t.* shorten, abridge, abbreviate, curtail, contract, shrink.
**Verkürzung,** *f.* shortening, etc. (see verkürzen).
**Verl.,** *abbrev.* (Verlag) publishing house.
**verlacken,** *v.t.* lake, convert into a lake.
**Verlackungs-verfahren,** *n.* laking process or procedure. **-vorschrift,** *f.* laking recipe.
**verladen,** *v.t* load; ship.
**Verlag,** *m.* publication; publishing house.
**Verlagerung,** *f.* displacement; shift.
**Verlags-buchhändler,** *m.* publisher. **-buchhandlung,** *f.* publishing house. **-recht,** *n.* copyright.
**verlangen,** *v.t.* ask, demand, require; long for, want. — *v.i.* long, wish (for).
**verlängern,** *v.t.* lengthen, prolong, extend; replenish (dye liquor); (*Math.*) produce. — **verlängertes Mark,** medulla oblongata.
**Verlängerung,** *f.* prolongation, elongation, extension; (*Math.*) production.
**Verlängerungsstück,** *n.* extension piece.
**verlangsamen,** *v.t.* retard, slow down, slacken.
**Verlangsamung,** *f.* retardation.
**Verlass,** *m.* trust, reliance.
**verlassen,** *v.t.* leave, give up, abandon. — *v.r.* depend, rely. — *p.a.* abandoned, forsaken.
**verlässig, verlässlich,** *a.* reliable, dependable.
**Verlaub,** *m.* permission.
**Verlauf,** *m.* course; progress; lapse (of time); flowing, flow; running; trend; pattern.
**verlaufen,** *v.i & r.* follow a course, proceed; run; (of time) pass; be scattered; run off; (of colors) blend.
**verlauten,** *v.i.* be heard, be reported.
**verleben,** *v.t.* live, pass (time). — **verlebt,** *p.a.* used up, decrepit.
**verlegen,** *v.t.* lay; mislay; transport, transfer, shift; delay; obstruct; publish (books); misplace. — *p.a.* spoiled, stale; embarrassed, confused.
**Verlegenheit,** *f.* perplexity, difficulty.
**Verleger,** *m.* publisher.
**Verlegung,** *f.* laying, etc. (see verlegen).
**verleihen,** *v.t.* lend; bestow, grant; impart.
**verleimen,** *v.t.* cement, glue.
**verlernen,** *v.t.* unlearn, forget.
**verlesen,** *v.t.* pick; sort; read aloud. — *v.r* read wrong.
**verletzbar,** *a.* easily injured, frail, vulnerable.
**verletzen,** *v.t.* injure, damage, offend, infringe.
**Verletzung,** *f.* injury, damage; offense.
**verleugnen,** *v.t.* deny, disavow.
**verlieh,** *pret.* (of verleihen) lent, etc.
**verlieren,** *v.t. & i.* lose. — *v.r.* get lost; disappear. — **verlorener Kopf,** (*Metal.*) feedhead, dead head, top end.
**verlohnen,** *v.r.* be worth.
**verlor, verloren,** *pret. & p.p.* (of verlieren) lost
**verlöschen,** *v.i.* go out, be extinguished. — *v.t.* overburn (lime). — **verloschen,** *p.a.* gone out, dead.
**verlöten,** *v.t.* solder, solder up; (*Med.*) close by adhesion.
**verlüften,** *v.t.* air, ventilate.
**Verlust,** *m.* loss; waste, escape; damage, detriment.
**verlust-arm,** *a.* low-loss. **-los,** *a. & adv.* without loss, lossless, without waste, nondissipative.

**Verlust-quelle,** *f.* source of loss. **-winkel,** *m.* loss angle, phase angle (difference).
**verm.,** *abbrev.* (vermehrt) enlarged; (vermindert) diminished, reduced.
**vermag,** *pr. 1 & 3 sing.* of vermögen.
**vermahlen,** *v.t.* grind, mill; spoil in grinding.
**vermanteln,** *v.t.* cover, sheathe, case, jacket.
**vermaschen,** *v.t.* mesh, connect.
**vermehren,** *v.t.* increase; enlarge; multiply; propagate.
**Vermehrung,** *f.* increase; enlargement; propagation.
**vermeidbar,** *a.* avoidable.
**vermeiden,** *v.t.* avoid; evade, elude, shirk.
**Vermeidung,** *f.* avoidance; evasion.
**vermeinen,** *v.t.* think, suppose; mean.
**vermeintlich,** *a.* supposed; pretended, supposititious.
**vermengen,** *v.t.* mix, mingle, blend; confuse.
**Vermengung,** *f.* mixing, mixture, blending; confusion.
**Vermerk,** *m.* remark, note, notation.
**vermessen,** *v.t.* measure; survey (land). — *v.r.* mismeasure; venture. — *p.a.* bold, presumptuous.
**vermessingen,** *v.t.* (*Metal.*) brass, brass-plate.
**Vermessingung,** *f.* brassing, brass plating.
**Vermessung,** *f.* measuring, measurement; surveying; (of ships) tonnage.
**vermieten,** *v.t.* let, hire out, lease.
**vermilchen,** *v.t.* emulsify.
**Vermillon,** *m.* vermilion.
**vermindern,** *v.t.* diminish, lessen, reduce. — *v.r.* decline, diminish.
**Verminderung,** *f.* decrease, reduction, diminution, decline.
**vermischbar,** *a.* miscible; adulteratable.
**vermischen,** *v.t.* mix; adulterate; mingle, blend, compound, alloy. — **vermischt,** *p.a.* mixed, miscellaneous; adulterated.
**Vermischung,** *f.* mixing, mixture; adulteration; alloy; medley.
**vermissen,** *v.t.* miss.
**vermitteln,** *v.t.* facilitate; mediate; adjust, arrange, bring about. — *v.i.* mediate.
**vermittelst,** *prep.* by means of, by help of.
**Vermittelung,** *f.* agency, means; mediation, interposition; adjustment; conveyance.
**vermochte,** *pret.* (of vermögen) was able, etc.
**vermodern,** *v.i.* molder, decay, rot. — **vermodert,** *p.a.* moldy, decayed, rotten.
**Vermoderung,** *f.* decay, rotting, moldering.
**vermöge,** *prep.* by virtue of, according to.
**vermögen,** *v.t.* be able, have power, have influence; induce. — **vermögend,** *p.a.* propertied, wealthy.
**Vermögen,** *n.* ability, power, capacity; property.
**vermuten,** *v.t.* suppose, think, conjecture, imagine, suspect.
**vermutlich,** *a.* supposed; probable. — *adv.* supposedly; probably.
**Vermutung,** *f.* supposition, conjecture, surmise.
**vernachlässigbar,** *a.* negligible.
**vernachlässigen,** *v.t.* neglect, disregard.
**vernarben,** *v.i.* scar, be cicatrized.
**Vernarbungsgewebe,** *n.* scar tissue.
**vernebeln,** *v.t.* convert into mist or fog, atomize, cloud. screen.
**Vernebelung,** *f.* atomizing; smoke screen(ing).
**Vernebelungsapparat,** *m.* atomizer; (*Mil.*) smoke generator.
**Vernebler,** *m.* atomizer.
**vernehmen,** *v.t.* perceive, distinguish; hear, learn.
**Vernehmen,** *n.* perception; hearing, report; understanding.
**vernehmlich,** *a.* perceptible; audible; distinct.
**verneinen,** *v.t.* deny, disavow, contradict. — **verneinend,** *p.a.* negative.
**vernetzen,** *v.t.* (make into a) net, cross-link, interlace.
**Vernetzung,** *f.* cross-linking; network.
**vernichten,** *v.t.* destroy, annihilate, annul.
**Vernichtung,** *f.* destruction, annihilation.
**Vernichtungsbombe,** *f.* demolition bomb.
**vernickeln,** *v.t.* nickel, nickel-plate.
**Vernickelung,** *f.* nickeling, nickel plating.
**vernieten,** *v.t.* rivet.
**Vernunft,** *f.* reason, intellect, intelligence, judgment.
**vernünftig,** *a.* rational, reasonable, sensible.
**veröden,** *v.i.* become waste. — *v.t.* lay waste.
**veröffentlichen,** *v.t.* publish; advertise.
**Veröffentlichung,** *f.* publication; announcement; advertisement.
**verölen,** *v.t.* oil.
**Veroneser-erde,** *f.* Verona earth. **-gelb,** *n.* Verona yellow. **-grün,** *n.* Verona green (Verona earth).
**verordnen,** *v.t.* order, prescribe, decree; appoint.
**Verordnung,** *f.* order, decree, regulation, ordinance; appointment; (*Med.*) prescription.
**verpacken,** *v.t.* pack, pack up, wrap up.
**Verpackflasche,** *f.* packing bottle (ordinary round bottle, with or without glass stopper).
**Verpackung,** *f.* packing; bagging, casking, etc.; casing, lining; package.
**verpassen,** *v.t.* lose, miss.
**verpechen,** *v.t.* pitch, treat with pitch.
**verpesten,** *v.t.* infect, poison, taint.
**verpflanzen,** *v.t.* transplant; transmit.
**Verpflanzung,** *f.* transplantation; transmission; parallel displacement.

**verpflegen,** *v.t.* take care of, nurse, tend; feed.
**Verpflegung,** *f.* care, nursing; feeding, food, rations, board.
**verpflichten,** *v.t.* oblige; obligate; bind.
**Verpflichtung,** *f.* obligation, duty.
**verpfuschen,** *v.t.* bungle, botch, spoil.
**verpichen,** *v.t.* pitch, treat with pitch.
**Verpichung,** *f.* pitching; pitch formation.
**verplatinieren,** *v.t.* platinize.
**Verplatinierung,** *f.* platinization.
**verpönen,** *v.t.* forbid.
**verpuddeln,** *v.t.* puddle.
**verpuffen,** *v.i.* puff off, deflagrate; explode, detonate, fulminate.
**Verpuffung,** *f.* deflagration; explosion, detonation, fulmination.
**Verpuffungs-apparat,** *m.* explosion apparatus. **-motor,** *m.* explosion engine, internal-combustion engine. **-probe,** *f.* deflagration test. **-röhre,** *f.* explosion tube.
**Verputz,** *m.* plastering, plaster.
**verputzen,** *v.t.* plaster; dress, clean, polish.
**verquellen,** *v.i.* swell, swell up; warp; flow away.
**verquicken,** *v.t.* quicken, amalgamate.
**verraten,** *v.t.* betray.
**verrauchen,** *v.i.* evaporate; escape as smoke or fumes.
**verräuchern,** *v.t.* smoke, cure; fumigate. — *v.i.* become smoky.
**verrechnen,** *v.t.* reckon. — *v.r.* be mistaken, miscalculate.
**verreiben,** *v.t.* grind fine, triturate; spread by rubbing; rub down.
**verrenken,** *v.t.* sprain, dislocate.
**verrichten,** *v.t.* do, perform, execute.
**Verrichtung,** *f.* performance, execution, action; business, affair, function.
**verrieseln,** *v.t.* irrigate. — *v.i.* trickle away.
**verringern,** *v.t.* diminish, lessen, decrease, reduce, attenuate.
**Verringerung,** *f.* diminution, decrease, reduction, attenuation.
**verrinnen,** *v.i.* run off; (of time) pass.
**Verrohrung,** *f.* (well) casing; (shaft) tubbing.
**verrosten,** *v.i.* rust. — **verrostet,** *p.a.* rusted, rusty.
**Verrostung,** *f.* rusting.
**verrotten,** *v.i.* rot. — **verrottet,** *p.a.* rotten.
**verrucht,** *p.a.* infamous, nefarious.
**verrücken,** *v.t.* displace, shift, disturb, derange. —**verrückt,** *p.a.* deranged, insane, crazy.
**Verrückung,** *f.* displacement, shift; (*Geol.*) slip; derangement.
**verrühren,** *v.t.* stir up, mix up (by stirring).
**verrussen,** *v.t.* foul with soot, smoke; Russianize. — *v.i.* become sooty or smoked.
**Vers.,** *abbrev.* (Versuch) experiment, test, effort; (Versammlung) meeting.
**versagen,** *v.t.* deny, refuse; promise. — *v.i.* fail to work, miss.
**Versager,** *m.* failure; (*Expl.*) misfire.
**versalzen,** *v.t.* oversalt; mar, spoil.
**versammeln,** *v.t.* & *r.* assemble.
**Versammlung,** *f.* assembly, meeting, convention, congress.
**Versand,** *m.* shipping, dispatch; exportation. **-bier,** *n.* export beer.
**versandfähig,** *a.* fit for shipment.
**Versand-fass,** *n.* shipping cask (barrel, keg). **-schachtel,** *f.* shipping case.
**Versatz,** *m.* mixing, etc. (see versetzen); packing; (*Ceram.*) batch; (*Leather*) layer (also, lay-away); (*Mining*) gobbing. **-grube,** *f.* (*Leather*) lay-away vat.
**versauern,** *v.i.* turn sour.
**versäuern,** *v.t.* acidify, make sour.
**Versäuerung,** *f.* acidification; souring.
**versäumen,** *v.t.* miss, fail, neglect.
**verschachteln,** *v.t.* nest, insert into one another.
**verschaffen,** *v.t.* procure, supply, secure, get.
**verschalen,** *v.t.* board, plank, case, lag.
**verschärfen,** *v.t.* sharpen, intensify, strengthen.
**verschäumen,** *v.i.* cease foaming; foam away.
**verscheiden,** *v.i.* expire, die.
**verschenken,** *v.t.* give away; retail.
**verschiebbar,** *a.* displaceable; movable, sliding; adjustable.
**verschieben,** *v.t.* displace; shift, move, remove; postpone.
**Verschiebung,** *f.* displacement, etc. (see verschieben); shift; (*Geol.*) dislocation, slip; (*Elec.*) lag.
**Verschiebungs-gesetz,** *n.* displacement law. **-satz,** *m.* displacement principle. **-strom,** *m.* displacement current.
**verschieden,** *a.* different, differing, various; deceased. **-artig,** *a.* different, unlike, various, heterogeneous. **-farbig,** *a.* of different colors, varicolored.
**Verschiedenheit,** *f.* difference, variety, variation, diversity.
**verschiedentlich,** *a.* different. — *adv.* differently, variously, at different times.
**verschiedenwertig,** *a.* of different valences.
**verschiessen,** *v.i.* fade, discolor; shoot away. — *v.t.* shoot off, discharge; shade off (colors).
**verschimmeln,** *v.i.* mold, grow moldy. — **verschimmelt,** *p.a.* moldy.
**verschlacken,** *v.t.* scorify. — *v.i.* be reduced to scoria, slag, scale, clinker.
**Verschlackung,** *f.* scorification; slagging.
**Verschlackungs-fähigkeit,** *f.* slaggability, fluxing property. **-probe,** *f.* scorification assay. **-vermögen,** *n.* slaggability, fluxing power.
**verschlafen,** *v.t.* sleep away, sleep off, oversleep. — *p.a.* sleepy.
**Verschlag,** *m.* partition; compartment.

**verschlagen,** *v.i.* warm a little, grow lukewarm; matter, make a difference. — *v.t.* take the chill off; board up, close up; partition; lose or spoil by striking; recoin; drive away. — *p.a.* slightly warmed, tepid; cunning, wily.

**verschlammen, verschlämmen,** *v.t.* clog with mud or slime, silt up, mud up.

**verschlechtern,** *v.r.* deteriorate, spoil. — *v.t.* make worse, impair, debase.

**Verschlechterung,** *f.* deterioration; degeneration; debasement.

**verschleiern,** *v.t.* veil; cloud; dull. — **verschleiert,** *p.a.* (of beer, etc.) hazy, slightly cloudy.

**verschleimen,** *v.t.* choke up with mucus or slime, foul. — **verschleimt,** *p.a.* slimy.

**Verschleimung,** *f.* choking with slime or mucus; (of guns, etc.) fouling.

**Verschleiss,** *m.* wear (and tear); retail, sale.

**verschleissen,** *v.t.* wear out; retail.

**verschleissfest,** *a.* resistant to wear.

**Verschleissfestigkeit,** *f.* resistance to wear, wearing quality.

**verschleppen,** *v.t.* misplace; carry off; spread (a disease); protract; delay.

**verschleudern,** *v.t.* squander; sell very cheap.

**verschliessbar,** *a.* capable of being closed (or locked).

**verschliessen,** *v.t.* close, stop; stopper; shut; occlude; seal; lute; lock; reserve; protect.

**Verschliessung,** *f.* closing, etc. (see verschliessen).

**verschlimmern,** *v.t.* make worse, aggravate.

**verschlingen,** *v.t.* twist, entangle; intertwine, interweave; devour, swallow.

**verschlossen,** *p.p.* (of verschliessen) closed, etc.

**verschlucken,** *v.t.* absorb; swallow.

**verschlungen,** *p.p.* (of verschlingen) twisted, etc.

**Verschluss,** *m.* closing, closure, stopping, sealing; occlusion; fastening; shutting; locking; fastener, stopper, seal, lock, clasp, snap; trap (for water, etc.); (*Photog.*) shutter; breechblock; (of dutiable goods) bond.

**verschlüsseln,** *v.t.* put into code, code.

**Verschluss-flüssigkeit,** *f.* sealing liquid. **-hahn,** *m.* stopcock. **-kölbchen,** *n.* a small flask with a special fastening, pressure flask. **-stück,** *n.* plug, stopper; seal; lid.

**verschmälern,** *v.t.* narrow, diminish, constrict.

**verschmelzen,** *v.t.* melt, smelt, fuse; melt together; alloy; solder; blend (colors). — *v.i.* melt, melt away; blend, merge, coalesce.

**Verschmelzung,** *f.* melting, smelting, fusion; alloy; blending, coalescence; merger.

**Verschmelzungs-körper,** *m.* alloy constituent. **-wärme,** *f.* heat of fusion.

**Verschmiedbarkeit,** *f.* forgeability.

**verschmieren,** *v.t.* smear, daub, lute; soil; blur. — *v.r.* clog; fog; blur.

**Verschmierung,** *f.* smearing, etc. (see verschmieren).

**verschmitzt,** *p.a.* artful, subtle, cunning.

**verschmolzen,** *p.p.* (of verschmelzen) melted, etc.

**verschmoren,** *v.t.* scorch, char; overcook.

**verschmutzen,** *v.t.* soil, foul, pollute.

**verschneiden,** *v.t.* cut; clip, prune; dilute, reduce; blend; adulterate; castrate.

**Verschnitt,** *m.* cuttings, chips; cutting, etc. (see verschneiden); blend. **-ansatz,** *m.* (*Calico*) reduction paste.

**verschnitten,** *p.a.* cut, clipped, etc. (see verschneiden).

**verschnittfähig,** *a.* cuttable, clippable, etc. (see verschneiden); specif., capable of dilution.

**Verschnitt-fähigkeit,** *f.* cuttability; (of lacquers, etc.) dilution value. **-mittel,** *n.* cutting agent; (of lacquers, etc.) diluent, extender, filler. **-wein,** *m.* adulterated wine, blended wine.

**verschoben,** *p.p.* (of verschieben) displaced, etc.

**verschollen,** *p.a.* missing, lost.

**verschonen,** *v.t.* spare, excuse.

**verschönern,** *v.t.* beautify; refine.

**verschossen,** *p.p.* (of verschiessen) faded, etc.

**verschränken,** *v.t.* cross, interlace.

**verschrauben,** *v.t.* screw up; screw wrong; bolt. — **verschroben,** *p.a.* distorted, tangled; eccentric, queer.

**Verschraubung,** *f.* screwing; screw cap; screw joint.

**verschreiben,** *v.t.* prescribe; order; transfer in writing; miswrite; use up (paper) in writing.

**Verschreibung,** *f.* prescription; order; assignment, note, bond.

**verschroben,** *p.a.* see verschrauben.

**verschrotten,** *v.t.* scrap, convert into scrap.

**verschrumpfen,** *v.i.* shrink, contract, shrivel.

**verschuldet,** *p.a.* indebted, in debt; merited.

**verschütten,** *v.t.* spill, shed; fill up, choke, bury.

**Verschwächung,** *f.* weakening.

**verschwand,** *pret.* (of verschwinden) disappeared.

**verschweigen,** *v.t.* keep secret, suppress.

**Verschweissung,** *f.* welding, bonding.

**verschwelen,** *v.t. & i.* = schwelen.

**verschwellen,** *v.i.* swell, swell up, swell shut.

**Verschwelung,** *f.* = Schwelung.

**verschwenden,** *v.t.* waste, squander.

**verschwenken,** *v.t.* tilt, incline.

**verschwimmen,** *v.i.* (of colors) blend; blur; dissolve, vanish. — **verschwommen,** *p.a.* indistinct, indefinite, blurred.

**verschwinden,** *v.i.* disappear, vanish.

**verschwommen,** *p.a.* see verschwimmen.
**versehen,** *v.t.* provide, supply, furnish; perform, conduct, attend to; be mistaken in. — *v.r.* be aware, expect; provide oneself; make a mistake, be in error. — *p.a.* provided, furnished, supplied.
**Versehen,** *n.* oversight, error.
**versehentlich,** *adv.* erroneously, by mistake.
**versehren,** *v.t.* injure, disable, damage.
**verseifbar,** *a.* saponifiable.
**Verseifbarkeit,** *f.* saponifiability.
**verseifen,** *v.t.* saponify.
**Verseifung,** *f.* saponification.
**Verseifungs-fass,** *n.* saponifying tun. **-mittel,** *n.* saponifying agent. **-vorgang,** *m.* saponification process. **-zahl,** *f.* saponification number or value.
**verselben,** *v.t.* make automatic, automatize.
**versenden,** *v.t.* send, transmit, forward, export.
**Versender,** *m.* sender, shipper, consigner.
**versengen,** *v.t.* singe, scorch, parch.
**versenken,** *v.t.* sink, lower, submerge; countersink.
**Versenkgrube,** *f.* (*Leather*) tan pit.
**Versenkung,** *f.* sinking, etc. (see versenken); subsidence.
**versetzbar,** *a.* capable of being mixed, treated, etc. (see versetzen); movable, portable.
**versetzen,** *v.t.* mix, treat, compound (**— A mit B,** add B to A); alloy (metals); handle (hides); stop, tamp, obstruct; transfer, transpose, transplant; stagger; displace, shift; dislocate; misplace; pledge, mortgage. — *v.r.* change course; be stopped up.
**Versetzgrube,** *f.* (*Leather*) tan pit.
**Versetzung,** *f.* mixing, etc. (see versetzen); (*Med.*) retention; (*Math.*) permutation; alligation.
**verseuchen,** *v.t.* infect; poison, vitiate.
**versichern,** *v.t.* insure; assure, assert. — *v.r.* make sure (of)
**Versicherung,** *f.* insurance; assurance, affirmation.
**Versicherungsschein,** *m.* insurance policy; bond.
**versickern,** *v.i.* ooze away, seep away, percolate.
**Versickerung,** *f.* seepage, percolation.
**versiegeln,** *v.t.* seal, seal up.
**versiegen,** *v.i.* dry up, be exhausted.
**versilbern,** *v.t.* silver, silver-plate.
**Versilberung,** *f.* silvering, silver plating.
**Versilberungsbad,** *n.* silver bath.
**versinken,** *v.i.* sink.
**versinn-bilden, -bildlichen,** *v.t.* symbolize, represent.
**versintern,** *v.i.* sinter.
**Versinterung,** *f.* sintering.
**versorgen,** *v.t.* provide for, provide, supply.
**Versorgung,** *f.* provision, maintenance, supply; situation.
**verspannen,** *v.t.* brace, stay, guy.
**Verspannungsfaktor,** *m.* (*Expl.*) loading factor.
**Verspanung,** *f.* removal of material as chips, shavings, borings, etc.
**verspäten,** *v.t.* retard, delay. — *v.r.* be late.
**versperren,** *v.t.* obstruct, block, lock, seal.
**verspiegeln,** *v.t.* coat with metal, metalize.
**verspratzen,** *v.i.* spatter, splash.
**versprechen,** *v.t.* promise. — *v.r.* make a slip; be engaged.
**verspritzen,** *v.t.* spurt, squirt, spill, spatter; mold by injection.
**Versprödung,** *f.* embrittling, embrittlement.
**versprühen,** *v.i.* fly away in spray or sparks.
**verspüren,** *v.t.* perceive, feel.
**Verss.,** *abbrev.* (Versuche) experiments, trials.
**verstaatlichen,** *v.t.* take over by the government, nationalize.
**Verstaatlichung,** *f.* nationalization.
**verstählen,** *v.t.* convert into steel; face or edge or point with steel, steel.
**Verstand,** *m.* understanding, intelligence, sense, judgment.
**verstanden,** *p.p.* (of verstehen) understood.
**verständig,** *a.* intelligent, reasonable, sensible.
**verständigen,** *v.t.* inform. — *v.r.* agree, arrange.
**Verständigung,** *f.* information; explanation; understanding.
**verständlich,** *a.* intelligible, comprehensible.
**Verständnis,** *n.* comprehension, intelligence.
**verstärken,** *v.t.* strengthen, increase, reinforce, fortify, concentrate, intensify, amplify.
**Verstärker,** *m.* intensifier; amplifier; activator; reinforcing agent.
**Verstärkung,** *f.* strengthening, etc. (see verstärken).
**Verstärkungskolonne,** *f.* concentrating column.
**verstatten,** *v.t.* permit, allow.
**verstauben,** *v.i.* become dusty.
**verstäuben,** *v.t.* convert into dust; scatter as dust, atomize; cover with dust.
**Verstäuber,** *m.* atomizer, sprayer; duster.
**verstauchen,** *v.t.* sprain, strain.
**verstechen,** *v.t.* blend; adulterate; exchange.
**verstecken,** *v.t.* hide, conceal. — *v.r.* hide, lurk. — **versteckt,** *p.a.* hidden; latent; insincere.
**verstehen,** *v.t.* understand; mean. — *v.r.* agree, consent; be good or skilled (at); have an understanding; be understood.
**versteifen,** *v.i.* & *r.* stiffen; reinforce.
**Versteifer,** *m.* stiffener, stiffening agent.
**Versteifung,** *f.* stiffening; reinforcement.
**versteigern,** *v.t.* sell at auction.
**versteinern,** *v.t.* petrify.
**Versteinerung,** *f.* petrifaction; fossil.
**Versteinerungs-kunde,** *f.* paleontology. **-mittel,** *n.* (*Min.*) mineralizing agent.

**Versteinung,** *f.* (*Metal.*) devitrification; petrifaction.
**verstellbar,** *a.* movable, adjustable.
**verstellen,** *v.t.* shift, move; transpose; adjust; misplace; obstruct; disguise. — *v.r.* dissemble. — **verstellt,** *p.a.* feigned, fictitious.
**Verstellvorrichtung,** *f.* adjusting device.
**verstemmen,** *v.t.* calk.
**versteuern,** *v.t.* pay duty on. — **versteuert,** *p.a.* duty-paid.
**versticken,** *v.t.* nitrogenize, nitride.
**Versticksthal,** *m.* nitrided steel.
**verstocken,** *v.t.* harden. — *v.i.* mold, rot; grow stubborn.
**verstopfen,** *v.t.* stop, stop up, choke, clog, obstruct; (*Med.*) constipate.
**Verstopfung,** *f.* stopping up, clogging, obstruction; (*Med.*) constipation.
**Verstopfungsmittel,** *n.* (*Med.*) astringent.
**verstöpseln,** *v.t.* stopper.
**verstorben,** *p.a.* deceased, late.
**verstören,** *v.t.* disturb, confuse, trouble.
**verstossen,** *v.t.* cast off, repel, reject. — *v.i.* blunder, offend.
**verstrammen,** *v.t.* tighten; strengthen.
**Verstrammungsmittel,** *n.* strengthening agent.
**verstreichen,** *v.t.* fill up, stop up, spread over, level. — *v.i.* elapse, expire.
**verstreuen,** *v.t.* disperse, scatter.
**verstricken,** *v.t.* entangle.
**verstümmeln,** *v.t.* mutilate, maim; curtail.
**verstummen,** *v.i.* become dumb or silent.
**Versuch,** *m.* experiment; assay, trial, test; attempt, effort.
**versuchen,** *v.t.* try, test; taste, sample (liquors, etc.); attempt. — *v.i.* experiment.
**Versuchs-anlage,** *f.* testing plant; experimental plant; pilot plant. **-anordnung,** *f.* mode of (experimental) procedure. **-anstalt,** *f.* research institute or institution; experimental plant. **-arbeit,** *f.* experimental work. **-bedingung,** *f.* experimental condition(s). **-bohrung,** *f.* test boring; test well. **-dauer,** *f.* duration of experiment, time of experimentation. **-ergebnis,** *n.* result of experiment or test. **-fehler,** *m.* experimental error. **-feld,** *n.* field for experiment; experimental field or plat; proving ground. **-flamme,** *f.* test flame. **-folge,** *f.* set or series of experiments or tests. **-gefäss,** *n.* experimental vessel (in which an experiment is conducted). **-gegenstand,** *m.* experimental object, test piece. **-grundlage,** *f.* basis of experiment. **-körper,** *m.* experimental object, test piece. **-laboratorium,** *n.* experimental laboratory. **-ladung,** *f.* (*Expl.*) test charge. **-lauf,** *m.* test run, trial run.
**versuchsmässig,** *a.* experimental.
**Versuchs-material,** *n.* experimental material. **-methode,** *f.* experimental method; tentative method. **-muster,** *n.* = Gebrauchsmuster. **-raum,** *m.* laboratory; research space. **-reihe,** *f.* series of experiments or tests. **-resultat,** *n.* result of experiment or trial. **-rohr,** *n.*, **-röhre,** *f.* experimental tube. **-serie,** *f.* = Versuchsreihe. **-stab,** *m.* test rod or bar. **-stadium,** *n.* experimental stage. **-stand,** *m.* testing stand. **-station, -stelle,** *f.* experiment station. **-stück,** *n.* test piece. **-tier,** *n.* experimental animal. **-träger,** *m.* test stand. **-vorschrift,** *f.* experimental directions.
**versuchsweise,** *adv.* by way of experiment, experimentally, tentatively; on approval.
**Versuchs-wert,** *m.* experimental value or datum. **-wesen,** *n.* research. **-zweck,** *m.* experimental purpose.
**Versuchtier,** *n.* experimental animal.
**Versuchung,** *f.* experimenting, experiment; research; temptation.
**versumpft,** *a.* swampy, boggy.
**versüssen,** *v.t.* sweeten; purify by washing, edulcorate; oversweeten. — **versüsster Salpetergeist,** (*Pharm.*) sweet spirit of niter, spirit of nitrous ether. — **versüsster Salzgeist,** sweet spirit of salt (alcoholic solution of ethyl chloride).
**Versüssung,** *f.* sweetening, etc. (see versüssen).
**Versüssungsmittel,** *n.* sweetening agent, sweetener.
**vertagen,** *v.t.* adjourn; postpone.
**vertauschbar,** *a.* exchangeable; interchangeable.
**Vertauschbarkeit,** *f.* exchangeability; interchangeability.
**vertauschen,** *v.t.* exchange, change.
**Vertauschung,** *f.* exchange, interchange; (*Math.*) permutation.
**verte,** *v. imperative.* turn over, turn the leaf.
**verteeren,** *v.t.* tar.
**verteidigen,** *v.t.* defend, maintain, uphold.
**Verteidigung,** *f.* defense, advocacy; protection.
**Verteidigungswaffe,** *f.* defensive weapon.
**verteilen,** *v.t.* distribute; divide; disperse; disseminate, diffuse, spread; dispense, apportion, assign, allot.
**Verteiler,** *m.* distributor. **-leitung,** *f.* distributing line or main.
**Verteiltrichter,** *m.* distributing funnel or hopper, distributor.
**Verteilung,** *f.* distribution, etc. (see verteilen); division; partition.
**Verteilungs-gesetz,** *n.* law of distribution. **-grad,** *m.* degree of dispersion or distribution. **-koeffizient,** *m.* partition coefficient, distribution coefficient. **-kurve,** *f.* distribution curve. **-mittel,** *n.* distributing agent. **-rohr,** *n.*, **-röhre,** *f.* distributing tube or pipe; (of a

blast furnace) blast main. **-satz,** *m.* principle of distribution, distribution law. **-stand, -zustand,** *m.* state of division.
**verteuern,** *v.t.* raise in price.
**Vertheil-.** see Verteil-.
**vertiefen,** *v.t.* deepen. — *v.r.* be deeply engaged.
**Vertiefung,** *f.* deepening; depression, cavity, hollow, recess, indentation.
**Vertikal-achse,** *f.* vertical axis. **-bewegung,** *f.* vertical motion. **-ebene,** *f.* vertical plane. **-lage,** *f.* vertical position. **-schnitt,** *m.* vertical section.
**vertilgbar,** *a.* eradicable, exterminable.
**vertilgen,** *v.t.* extirpate, eradicate, exterminate, destroy.
**Vertilgungsmittel,** *n.* eradicator, destroyer.
**vertorft,** *a.* converted into peat, peaty.
**Vertorfung,** *f.* peat formation, peatification.
**Vertrag,** *m.* contract, agreement, bargain, treaty.
**vertragen,** *v.t.* bear, endure, tolerate. — *v.r.* be compatible, be consistent, agree, harmonize.
**vertraglich,** *a.* contractual.
**verträglich,** *a.* compatible, consistent, amicable, friendly.
**Verträglichkeit,** *f.* compatibility; tolerance; peaceableness; friendliness.
**vertrauen,** *v.t. & i.* trust, confide. — **vertraut,** *p.a.* intimate, conversant, familiar.
**vertrauenswürdig,** *a.* trustworthy.
**vertraulich,** *a.* confidential, intimate.
**vertraut,** *p.a.* see vertrauen.
**vertreiben,** *v.t.* drive away, dispel, expel, disperse; propel; sell; soften (colors).
**vertretbar,** *a.* replaceable; capable of being attended to, or represented, by deputy.
**Vertretbarkeit,** *f.* replaceability, etc. (see vertretbar).
**vertreten,** *v.t.* replace, take the place of; represent; stretch, strain; obstruct.
**Vertreter,** *m.* substituent; representative; substitute, deputy: intercessor.
**Vertretung,** *f.* displacement, etc. (see vertreten).
**Vertrieb,** *m.* sale, market.
**vertrocknen,** *v.i.* dry up, wither.
**Vertrocknung,** *f.* drying up, desiccation.
**vertun,** *v.t.* waste, lavish, squander.
**verunglücken,** *v.i.* come to grief.
**verunkrautet,** *a.* overgrown with weeds.
**verunreinigen,** *v.t.* render impure, contaminate, soil, vitiate, pollute; adulterate.
**Verunreinigung,** *f.* impurity; contamination, pollution; adulteration.
**verunstalten,** *v.t.* deform, disfigure.
**verunzieren,** *v.t.* deface, disfigure, mar.
**verursachen,** *v.t.* cause, produce, occasion.
**verurteilen,** *v.t.* condemn, sentence.
**verviel-fachen, -fältigen,** *v.t.* multiply; duplicate, copy.
**Verviel-facher, -fältiger,** *m.* multiplier.
**vervierfachen,** *v.t.* quadruple.
**vervoll-kommen,** *v.t.* perfect, improve. **-ständigen,** *v.t.* complete.
**Vervollständigung,** *f.* completion.
**verw.,** *abbrev.* (verwandt) related.
**verwachsen,** *v.i.* grow together, coalesce; grow crooked; be overgrown. — *v.t.* outgrow. — *p.a.* grown together, intergrown; deformed.
**Verwachsung,** *f.* growing together, intergrowth; coalescence; overgrowth.
**Verwachsungsfläche,** *f.* (*Cryst.*) composition plane.
**verwägen,** *v.t.* weigh.
**verwahren,** *v.t.* keep, guard, preserve.
**verwahrlosen,** *v.t.* neglect, slight.
**Verwahrung,** *f.* keeping, preservation; custody; protest.
**verwalten,** *v.t.* manage, administer, supervise.
**Verwaltung,** *f.* administration; management.
**verwalzen,** *v.t.* roll.
**verwandelbar,** *a.* transformable, convertible.
**Verwandelbarkeit,** *f.* transformability, convertibility.
**verwandeln,** *v.t.* transform, convert, turn. change; transmute; metamorphose.
**Verwandlung,** *f.* transformation, etc. (see verwandeln).
**verwandt,** *p.a.* related; allied, cognate; analogous.
**Verwandte,** *m. & f.* relative, relation.
**Verwandtschaft,** *f.* affinity; relationship; kindred; congeniality.
**Verwandtschafts-einheit,** *f.* unit of affinity, valence. **-lehre,** *f.* doctrine of affinity.
**Verwärmung,** *f.* absorption (of heat).
**verwaschen,** *v.t.* wash, wash out. — *p.a.* washed out, faded; indistinct, blurred, vague. — **verwaschenes Gut,** (*Mining*) middlings.
**Verwaschenheit,** *f.* washed-out or faded state, indistinctness.
**verwässern,** *v.t.* water; dilute, weaken; flood, drown.
**verweben,** *v.t.* weave, interweave. — *v.r.* interlace, intermingle.
**verwechseln,** *v.t.* exchange; mix up, confound, confuse.
**verwehen,** *v.t.* blow away. — *v.i.* blow over.
**verwehren,** *v.t.* prevent, forbid, refuse.
**Verwehung,** *f.* blowing (away); draft; wind.
**verweigern,** *v.t.* refuse, decline.
**verweilen,** *v.i.* stay, tarry.
**Verweil-weg,** *n.* tarrying path. **-zeit,** *f.* duration, time of stay.
**verweisen,** *v.t.* refer; expel, banish; rebuke.
**Verweisung,** *f.* reference; banishment; reproof.
**verwelken,** *v.i.* fade, wither, wilt.
**verwendbar,** *a.* available, applicable.

**verwenden,** *v.t.* employ, apply, use; invest; turn away. — *v.r.* intercede.
**Verwendung,** *f.* application, use; appropriation; intercession.
**verwendungsfähig,** *a.* applicable, usable.
**Verwendungs-fähigkeit,** *f.* applicability, usability. **-gebiet,** *n.* field of application. **-stoffwechsel,** *m.* catabolism. **-zweck,** *m.* intended use.
**verwerfen,** *v.t.* reject, repudiate, abandon; misplace; (*Mining*) dislocate; distort. — *v.r.* warp; misthrow.
**Verwerfung,** *f.* rejection; (*Mining*) dislocation, throw, slip, fault, faulting.
**Verwerfungs-fläche,** *f.* (*Geol.*) fault plane. **-lette,** *f.* (*Mining*) gouge, flucan.
**verwertbar,** *a.* utilizable; realizable.
**Verwertbarkeit,** *f.* utilizability; salability.
**verwerten,** *v.t.* utilize; evaluate; sell.
**Verwertung,** *f.* utilization; evaluation; sale.
**verwesen,** *v.i.* rot, decay, decompose. — *v.t.* administer, manage.
**verweslich,** *a.* liable to decay.
**Verwesung,** *f.* decay, (slow) decomposition; administration.
**Verwesungs-pilz,** *m.* (*Bot.*) saprophyte. **-prozess,** *m.* process of decay or decomposition.
**verwettern,** *v.i.* = verwittern.
**verwichen,** *p.a.* past, former.
**verwickeln,** *v.t.* complicate, involve, entangle. — **verwickelt,** *p.a.* complicated, involved.
**Verwickelung,** *f.* complication; complexity; plot.
**verwiegen,** *v.t.* weigh, weigh out. — *v.r.* weigh wrong.
**Verwiegung,** *f.* weighing.
**verwiesen,** *p.p.* (of verweisen) referred, etc.
**verwinden,** *v.t.* twist; get over, recover from.
**Verwindung,** *f.* twisting, twist; recovery.
**verwirklichen,** *v.t.* realize, accomplish.
**verwirren,** *v.t.* tangle; perplex, embarrass. — **verworren, verwirrt,** *p.a.* complicated, complex; confused; puzzled, distracted.
**Verwirrung,** *f.* tangle; perplexity; (*Mining*) dislocation.
**verwischen,** *v.t.* blot out, efface; smudge; blur, obscure.
**verwittern,** *v.i.* effloresce; disintegrate; (of rocks, etc.) weather; (of lime) air-slake.
**Verwitterung,** *f.* efflorescence; weathering; disintegration.
**verworfen,** *p.p.* (of verwerfen) rejected, etc.
**verworren,** *p.a.* see verwirren.
**verworrenfas(e)rig,** *a.* reticulate-fibrous.
**verwunden,** *v.t.* wound; scarify. — *p.a.* twisted.
**verwunderlich,** *a.* astonishing, surprising.
**verwundern,** *v.t.* astonish, surprise. — *v.r.* wonder.
**Verwundung,** *f.* wounding, wound, injury; scarification.
**Verwurf,** *m.* = Verwerfung.
**verwüsten,** *v.t.* lay waste, devastate.
**verzählen,** *v.t.* miscount, miscalculate.
**verzahnen,** *v.t.* tooth, cog, indent, notch.
**Verzahnung,** *f.* gearing, gear; indentation.
**verzapfen,** *v.t.* join, mortise; retail (liquors).
**verzehren,** *v.t.* consume; spend; waste.
**verzeichnen,** *v.t.* note down, record, register, catalog, specify; misdraw; (*Optics*) distort.
**Verzeichnis,** *n.* list, register, index, table, catalog, inventory, invoice.
**Verzeichnung,** *f.* listing, etc. (see verzeichnen).
**verzeihen,** *v.t.* pardon, excuse.
**verzerren,** *v.t.* distort, deform, strain.
**Verzerrung,** *f.* distortion, deformation.
**verzerrungsfrei,** *a.* distortion-free, distortionless.
**Verzicht,** *m.* renunciation; waiver. — **auf . . . — leisten,** relinquish, give up, waive.
**verzichten,** *v.i.* (with auf) relinquish, give up.
**verziehen,** *v.t.* distort, strain — *v.r.* warp; buckle; withdraw, disappear. — *v.i.* stay; move. — *p.p.* (of verzeihen) pardoned.
**verzieren,** *v.t.* decorate, ornament, illustrate (books).
**Verzierung,** *f.* decoration, ornamentation.
**verzinken,** *v.t.* coat with zinc, galvanize, zinc.
**Verzinken,** *n.*, **Verzinkung,** *f.* zincking, galvanizing.
**Verzinkerei,** *f.* galvanizing plant.
**Verzinkungs-anlage,** *f.* galvanizing plant. **-bad,** *n.* galvanizing bath.
**verzinnen,** *v.t.* tin, tin-plate; line with tin. — **verzinntes Eisenblech,** tin plate.
**Verzinnen,** *n.*, **Verzinnung,** *f.* tinning.
**Verzinnerei,** *f.* tinning plant.
**verzinsen,** *v.t.* pay interest on. — *v.r.* yield interest, pay.
**verzogen,** *p.p.* (of verziehen) distorted, etc.
**Verzögerer,** *m.* retarder, retarding agent; (*Photog.*) restrainer; (*Varnish*) reducer.
**verzögern,** *v.t.* retard; delay, postpone.
**Verzögerung,** *f.* retardation; delay, postponement; lag.
**Verzögerungs-bad,** *n.* (*Photog.*) restraining bath. **-mine,** *f.* delayed-action mine. **-mittel,** *n.* retarding agent, retarder, delayer. **-satz,** *m.* (*Expl.*) delay composition. **-zünder,** *m.* delayed-action fuse.
**verzollen,** *v.t.* pay duty on. — **verzollt,** *p.a.* duty paid.
**verzuckern,** *v.t.* saccharify; sugar, candy.
**Verzuckerung,** *f.* saccharification; sugaring, candying.
**Verzuckung,** *f.* convulsion.
**Verzug,** *m.* delay; lag; distortion, deformation; sheathing, lagging.

**Verzugszünder,** *m.* delay fuse.
**Verzunderung,** *f.* (*Metal.*) scaling.
**verzunderungsbeständig,** *a.* resistant to scaling, nonscaling.
**verzweifeln,** *v.i.* despair.
**verzweigen,** *v.t.* branch, ramify.
**Verzweigung,** *f.* branching, ramification.
**Verweigungspunkt,** *m.* branching point, branch point.
**verzwillingt,** *p.a.* twinned.
**Verzwillingung,** *f.* twinning.
**vexieren,** *v.t.* vex, puzzle.
**Vf.,** *abbrev.* (Verfasser) author.
**Vff.,** *abbrev.* (Verfasser) authors.
**V-förmig,** *a.* V-shaped.
**vgl.,** *abbrev.* (vergleiche) compare, see, cf.
**vgl.a.,** *abbrev.* (vergleiche auch) see also.
**v.H.,** *abbrev.* (vom Hundert) per hundred, per cent.
**Vhdl.,** *abbrev.* (Verhandlung, -lungen) transaction(s).
**vibrieren,** *v.i.* vibrate.
**Vidalschwarz,** *n.* Vidal black.
**Vieh,** *n.* cattle; beast, brute. **-arzt,** *m.* veterinarian. **-dünger,** *m.* stable manure. **-futter,** *n.* fodder, forage. **-salz,** *n.* cattle salt, cattle lick, salt for animals. **-waschmittel,** *n.* dip (for animals).
**viel,** *a.* much; (*pl.*) many. — *adv.* much.
**viel-.** much, many, multi-, poly-. **-atomig,** *a.* polyatomic. **-deutig,** *a.* ambiguous.
**Vieleck,** *n.* polygon.
**viel-eckig,** *a.* polygonal. multangular. **-erlei,** *a.* various, multifarious. **-fach,** *a.* manifold, various; multiple; frequent.
**Vielfach, Vielfache,** *n.* multiple.
**vielfältig,** *a.* manifold, various; frequent.
**Vielfältigkeit,** *f.* multiplicity, variety.
**vielfarbig,** *a.* many-colored, variegated, polychromatic.
**Vielflach,** *n.* polyhedron.
**vielflächig,** *a.* polyhedral.
**Vielflächner,** *m.* polyhedron.
**viel-förmig,** *a.* multiform, polymorphous. **-genannt,** *a.* oft-mentioned. **-gestaltig,** *a.* multiform, polymorphic; manifold, diverse. **-gliederig,** *a.* many-membered; (*Math.*) polynomial.
**Vielheit,** *f.* multiplicity; multitude.
**viel-kantig,** *a.* many-edged, polygonal. **-kernig,** *a.* polycyclic; multinuclear, polynuclear.
**vielleicht,** *adv.* perhaps, possibly.
**Vielling,** *m.* (*Cryst.*) multiple twin.
**Viellinienspektrum,** *n.* many-line spectrum.
**viellinig,** *a.* many-line, multilinear.
**viel-mal,** *adv.* many times. **-mehr,** *adv.* much more, more. — *conj.* rather. **-phasig,** *a.* polyphase, multiphase. **-polig,** *a.* multipolar. **-sagend,** *p.a.* expressive, significant. **-säurig,** *a.* polyacid.
**Vielseit,** *n.* polyhedron.
**viel-seitig,** *a.* many-sided; versatile; (*Geom.*) polyhedral. **-stufig,** *a.* multiple-stage. **-teilig,** *a.* of many parts; (*Math.*) polynomial. **-versprechend,** *a.* very promising.
**Vielwegehahn,** *m.* multiple-way stopcock.
**vielwertig,** *a.* multivalent, polyvalent.
**Vielwertigkeit,** *f.* multivalence, polyvalence.
**Vielzahl,** *f.* large number; plurality; plural.
**vielzellig,** *a.* multicellular.
**vier,** *a.* four.
**vier-, Vier-.** four-, tetra-, quadri-, quadruple.
**vier-atomig,** *a.* tetratomic. **-basisch,** *a.* tetrabasic, quadribasic.
**vierdrittel,** *a.* designating a salt which contains four units of base to three of acid; as, — **kohlensaures Natrium,** $Na_2CO_3 \cdot 2NaHCO_3 \cdot 3H_2O$ (trona).
**Viereck,** *n.* quadrangle.
**viereckig,** *a.* four-cornered, quadrangular (specif., square).
**viererlei,** *a.* of four kinds.
**Vierervektor,** *m.* four-component vector, four-vector.
**vierfach,** *a.* fourfold, quadruple, quadruplex; quaternary.
**vierfach-.** (in old names) tetra-, quadri-. — **-Chlorkohlenstoff,** carbon tetrachloride.
**vierfältig,** *a.* = vierfach.
**Vierfarbendruck,** *m.* four-color printing.
**Vier-flach,** *n.*, **-flächner,** *m.* tetrahedron.
**vierflächig,** *a.* four-faced, tetrahedral.
**Vierfuss,** *m.* four-footed stand.
**vier-gliedrig,** *a.* four-membered; (*Cryst.*) tetragonal; (*Math.*) quadrinomial. **-jährig,** *a.* quadrennial.
**Vierkant-.** square.
**vierkantig,** *a.* = viereckig.
**Vierkantstöpsel,** *m.* square-headed stopper or plug.
**vier-komponentig,** *a.* four-component. **-phasig,** *a.* four-phase.
**Vierpol,** *m.* quadrupole, quadripole.
**vier-polig,** *a.* four-pole; quadrupole. **-quantig,** *a.* of four quanta, 4-quantum. **-reihig,** *a.* of four series, four-series.
**Vierring,** *m.* four-membered ring.
**viersäurig,** *a.* tetracid.
**Vierseit,** *n.* quadrilateral.
**vier-seitig,** *a.* four-sided, quadrilateral (specif., square). **-stellig,** *a.* four-place.
**Vierstoffsystem,** *n.* quaternary system.
**vierstufig,** *a.* four-stage.
**Vierstundenlack,** *m.* four-hour varnish.
**Viertakt,** *m.* (*Mach.*) four-stroke cycle.
**vierte,** *a.* fourth.
**vierteilen,** *v.t.* quarter.

**Vierteilung,** *f.* quartering, quadripartition.
**Viertel,** *n.* fourth, quarter. **-drehung,** *f.* quarter turn.
**viertelgeleimt,** *a.* (*Paper*) quarter-sized.
**Viertel-jahr,** *n.* quarter (of a year), three months. **-jahresschrift,** *f.* quarterly.
**vierteljährlich,** *a.* quarterly.
**Viertel-kreis,** *m.* quarter circle, quadrant. **-stunde,** *f.* quarter of an hour. **-wellenlänge,** *f.* quarter wavelength.
**viertens,** *adv.* fourthly, in the fourth place.
**Vierundzwanzigflächner,** *m.* icositetrahedron.
**vierwandig,** *a.* four-walled.
**Vierweg(e)hahn,** *m.* four-way cock.
**vierwertig,** *a.* quadrivalent, tetravalent.
**Vierwertigkeit,** *f.* quadrivalence, tetravalence.
**vierzählig,** *a.* fourfold.
**vierzehn,** *a.* fourteen.
**vierzig,** *a.* forty.
**Viktoriablau,** *n.* Victoria blue.
**Vinyl-benzol,** *n.* vinylbenzene. **-cyanür,** *n.* vinyl cyanide, acrylonitrile. **-harz,** *n.* vinyl resin.
**Viole,** *f.* violet; viol.
**Violenwurzel,** *f.* orris root.
**Violettschwarz,** *n.* violet black.
**violettstichig,** *a.* violet-tinged.
**virginisch,** *a.* Virginian.
**Virialsatz,** *m.* virial principle.
**virtuell,** *a.* virtual.
**Virus-forschung,** *f.* virus research. **-krankheit,** *f.* virus disease.
**visc-, Visc-.** see visk-, Visk-.
**Visetholz,** *n.* fustet, young fustic.
**Visier,** *n.* sight; visor.
**visieren,** *v.t.* sight; align; gage; aim; visé.
**Visierlupe,** *f.* magnifying sight lens.
**Visitenkarte,** *f.* visiting card.
**visitieren,** *v.t.* visit; search; inspect.
**viskos, viskös,** *a.* viscous.
**Viskose-kunstseide,** *f.* viscose rayon. **-verfahren,** *n.* viscose process.
**Viskosität,** *f.* viscosity.
**Viskositäts-messer,** *m.* viscosimeter, viscometer. **-zahl,** *f.* viscosity number or value.
**Vistra.** Vistra (an acetate rayon). *T.N.*
**visuell,** *a.* visual.
**Vitalfärbung,** *f.* vital staining, *intra-vitam* staining.
**Vitalität,** *f.* vitality.
**Vitaminmangel,** *m.* vitamin deficiency.
**vitrifizieren,** *v.t.* vitrify.
**vitriolartig,** *a.* vitriolic, like vitriol.
**Vitriol-bildung,** *f.* vitriolation. **-blei,** *n.* lead vitriol ($PbSO_4$). **-bleierz,** *n.*, **-bleispat,** *m.* anglesite. **-erz,** *n.* vitriol(ic) ore. **-fabrik,** *f.* vitriol (sulfuric acid) works. **-flasche,** *f.* carboy. **-gelb,** *n.* (*Min.*) jarosite.
**vitriolhaltig,** *a.* containing vitriol, vitriolic.
**Vitriolhütte,** *f.* = Vitriolfabrik.
**vitriolisch, vitriolig,** *a.* vitriolic.
**vitriolisieren,** *v.t.* vitriolate.
**Vitriol-kies,** *m.* marcasite. **-küpe,** *f.* blue vat, copperas vat. **-öl,** *n.* oil of vitriol (sulfuric acid). **-säure,** *f.* vitriolic acid (sulfuric acid). **-schiefer,** *m.* pyritic shale or schist; alum shale. **-siederei,** *f.* = Vitriolfabrik.
**vitrophyrisch,** *a.* (*Petrog.*) vitrophyric.
**Vitsbohne,** *f.* kidney bean.
**vizinal,** *a.* vicinal, neighboring.
**v.J., v.Jr.,** *abbrev.* (vorigen Jahres) of last year; (vom Jahre) of the year.
**Vlies, Vliess,** *n.* fleece.
**vm.,** *abbrev.* (vormittags) in the morning, A.M.
**v.M.,** *abbrev.* (vorigen Monats) last month.
**v.o.,** *abbrev.* (von oben) from above, from the top.
**Vogel,** *m.* bird. **-amber,** *m.* spermaceti. **-beerbaum,** *m.* mountain ash, service tree. **-beere,** *f.* berry of the mountain ash, service berry. **-beersäure,** *f.* sorbic acid. **-dünger,** *m.* bird dung, guano. **-dunst,** *m.* fine bird shot, dust shot. **-ei,** *n.* bird's egg. **-kirsche,** *f.* bird cherry. **-kunde,** *f.* ornithology. **-leim,** *m.* birdlime, bird glue. **-mist,** *m.* bird dung. **-mistbeize,** *f.* (*Leather*) bird dung bate. **-perspektive,** *f.* bird's-eye (view).
**Vogt,** *m.* magistrate (of various kinds, as bailiff, judge, governor, etc.); steward.
**Vokal,** *m.* vowel.
**Vol.,** *abbrev.* (Volumen, Volum-) volume.
**Vol-.Gew.,** *abbrev.* (Volumgewicht) volume weight.
**Volk,** *m.* people; nation; forces, men; flock, herd.
**Völkerbund,** *m.* League of Nations.
**volkreich,** *a.* populous.
**volks-, Volks-.** popular, people's, public, national.
**volkstümlich,** *a.* popular, national.
**Volkswirtschaft,** *f.* political economy.
**voll,** *a.* full; (of leather) compact, plump; massive, solid; whole, entire, complete; gross (price).
**Voll-analyse,** *f.* complete analysis. **-appretur,** *f.* full finish.
**vollauf,** *adv.* in abundance, plentifully.
**Voll-bau,** *m.* solid construction or structure. **-bleiche,** *f.* full bleach.
**voll-blütig,** *a.* plethoric. **-bringen,** *v.t.* accomplish, execute, achieve.
**Voll-draht,** *m.* solid wire. **-druck,** *m.* full pressure; (*Calico*) full print.
**vollenden,** *v.t.* finish, terminate, complete, perfect. — **vollendet,** *p.a.* accomplished, perfect.
**vollends,** *adv.* wholly, altogether; besides.
**Vollendung,** *f.* completion; accomplishment.
**voll-entwickelt,** *a.* fully developed. **-farbig,** *a.*

of full (or saturated) color. **-fett,** *a.* (of cheese) full-fat, rich.
**Vollfeuer,** *n.* full fire, full heat.
**vollflächig,** *a.* (*Cryst.*) holohedral.
**Vollflächner,** *m.* (*Cryst.*) holohedron.
**vollfüllen,** *v.t.* fill (full).
**Vollgehalt,** *m.* full value.
**vollgesogen,** *p.a.* sucked full.
**Voll-gummi,** *n.* solid rubber. **-gummireifen,** *m.* solid rubber tire.
**vollhaltig,** *a.* of full value, standard.
**Vollheit,** *f.* fullness.
**völlig,** *a.* full, entire, complete, total. — *adv.* fully, completely.
**Völligkeit,** *f.* fulness, completeness; solidity.
**voll-jährig,** *a.* of age. **-kommen,** *a.* complete, entire, perfect.
**Voll-kommenheit,** *f.* completeness; perfection. **-kornmehl,** *n.* whole-meal flour. **-körper,** *m.* solid body. **-kraft,** *f.* vigor, energy.
**vollkristallin,** *a.* holocrystalline.
**Voll-last,** *f.* full load. **-macht,** *f.* full power, power of attorney. **-milch,** *f.* whole milk.
**vollmundig,** *a.* (of beer, etc.) full, having good body.
**Voll-mundigkeit,** *f.* (of liquors) body, palate fullness. **-pipette,** *f.* a pipet(te) delivering a single definite amount, without a graduated scale; transfer pipet. Cf. Messpipette. **-reife,** *f.* full ripeness. **-reifen,** *m.* (*Rubber*) solid tire.
**voll-saugen,** *v.t.* suck full. **-ständig,** *a.* complete; entire, total; integral. — *adv.* completely, fully. **-strecken,** *v.t.* execute, carry out.
**Voll-ton,** *m.* full tone, full shade, mass tone. **-versatz,** *m.* solid packing.
**voll-wertig,** *a.* full-value, superior, up to standard. **-wichtig,** *a.* of full weight; weighty. **-zählig,** *a.* complete.
**Vollziegel,** *m.* solid brick or tile.
**vollziehen,** *v.t.* execute, consummate, put into effect, carry out, accomplish.
**Vollziehung,** *f.* execution, consummation.
**vollzogen,** *p.p.* (of vollziehen) executed, etc.
**Vollzug,** *m.* = Vollziehung.
**Vol.T.,** *abbrev.* (Volumenteil) part by volume.
**voltaisch,** *a.* voltaic.
**Voltasche Säule.** voltaic pile.
**Volt-messer,** *m.* voltmeter. **-spannung,** *f.* (*Elec.*) voltage.
**Volum,** *n.* volume. **-abnahme,** *f.* decrease in volume. **-änderung,** *f.* change of volume, alteration in volume. **-dichte,** *f.* density by volume. **-einheit,** *f.* unit of volume.
**Volumen,** *n.* volume. For compounds see Volum-.
**volumetrisch,** *a.* volumetric.
**Volum-gesetz,** *n.* law of volumes. **-gewicht,** *n.* volume weight, weight of unit volume.
**Volumina,** *n.pl.* volumes.
**voluminös,** *a.* voluminous.
**Volum-messer,** *m.* volumeter. **-minderung,** *f.* decrease in volume. **-prozent,** *n.* per cent by volume. **-prozentgehalt,** *m.* volume-per-cent content.
**volumprozentig,** *a.* per cent by volume.
**Volum-teil,** *m.* part by volume. **-veränderung,** *f.* change in volume. **-vergrösserung,** *f.* increase in volume. **-verhältnis,** *n.* volume relation; proportion by volume. **-verlust,** *m.* loss in volume. **-vermehrung,** *f.* increase in volume. **-verminderung,** *f.* decrease in volume. **-zunahme,** *f.*, **-zuwachs,** *m.* increase in volume.
**vom,** *abbrev.* (von dem) of the, from the.
**Vomhundert-gehalt,** *m.* percentage content. **-satz,** *m.* percentage.
**vomieren,** *v.i.* vomit.
**von,** *prep.* from, of, about, by, on.
**voneinander,** *adv.* of or from one another.
**vonnöten,** *adv.* in need, necessary.
**vor,** *prep.* before; for, from, of. — *adv.* forward, on; before, formerly. — **— allem,** above all. — **— einem Jahre,** a year ago.
**vor.,** *abbrev.* (vorig) former, preceding.
**Vor-.** fore-, pre-, pro-, preliminary, previous, prior, first.
**vorab,** *adv.* above all, especially.
**Vor-abend,** *m.* eve. **-ahnung,** *f.* presentiment.
**voran,** *adv.* before, on.
**vorangehen,** *v.i.* lead the way, precede. — **vorangehend,** *p.a.* preceding, antecedent.
**voranschicken,** *v.t.* premise, observe beforehand; send before.
**Vor-anschlag,** *m.* (provisional) estimate. **-anzeige,** *f.* preliminary notice; previous announcement. **-appretur,** *f.* preliminary finishing or processing. **-arbeit,** *f.* preliminary work, preparation.
**vorauf,** *adv.* before, on.
**voraus,** *adv.* beforehand, in advance, previously. **-berechnet,** *a.* (previously) calculated. **-bezahlen,** *v.t.* pay in advance, prepay. **-gegangen,** *p.a.* previous, preliminary. **-gehen,** *v.i.* go before, go ahead. **-gehend,** *p.a.* preceding, previous; leading. **-haben,** *v.t.* have the better of. **-nehmen,** *v.t.* anticipate. **-sagen,** *v.t.* predict, foretell, forecast. **-schikken,** *v.t.* = voranschicken. **-sehen,** *v.t.* foresee, anticipate. **-setzen,** *v.t.* suppose, presuppose, assume.
**Voraus-setzung,** *f.* hypothesis, assumption, postulate, supposition, provision, prerequisite. **-sicht,** *f.* foresight, forethought.
**voraussichtlich,** *a.* probable, expected, prospective. — *adv.* presumably, most probably.

**vorbauen,** *v.i.* guard against, prevent.
**Vor-bauung,** *f.* = Vorbeugung. **-bauungsmittel,** *n.* (*Med.*) prophylactic. **-bearbeitung,** *f.* preliminary working or treatment. **-bedacht,** *m.* forethought. **-bedingung,** *f.* preliminary condition, precondition, prerequisite. **-behalt,** *m.* reservation, proviso.
**vorbehalten,** *v.t.* reserve, stipulate for.
**vorbe-haltlich, -hältlich,** *prep.* with reservation as to, conditioned on, subject to.
**Vorbehandlung,** *f.* preliminary (or previous) treatment, preparation, preconditioning, prefabrication, etc.
**vorbei,** *adv.* by, past, over, gone, done. **-fliegen,** *v.i.* fly by, fly past. **-führen,** *v.t.* lead past; (of gas, etc.) furnish, pass. **-streichen,** *v.i.* sweep by, sweep past. **-streifen,** *v.i.* brush (against), graze, glance.
**Vorbeize,** *f.* (*Dyeing*) bottom mordant, preliminary mordant.
**vorbeizen,** *v.t.* (*Dyeing*) mordant previously; (*Metal.*) black-pickle.
**Vor-belichtung,** *f.* preliminary illumination, preliminary exposure. **-bemerkung,** *f.* preliminary remark; preface; preamble. **-benutzung,** *f.* prior use. **-berechnung,** *f.* preliminary calculation.
**vorbereiten,** *v.t. & r.* prepare. — **vorbereitend,** *p.a.* preparatory.
**Vor-bereitung,** *f.* preparation, readying. **-bericht,** *m.* preface, introduction; preliminary report. **-besprechung,** *f.* previous discussion, preliminary discussion.
**vor-beugen,** *v.t.* guard against, prevent; bend forward. **-beugend,** *p.a.* preventive, precautionary, prophylactic.
**Vor-beugung,** *f.* prevention; (*Med.*) prophylaxis. **-beugungsmassnahme,** *f.* preventive (or prophylactic) measure. **-beugungsmittel,** *n.* preservative; preventive; (*Med.*) prophylactic. **-bild,** *n.* pattern, model, standard; prototype, type.
**vorbilden,** *v.t.* represent, typify; prepare, school.
**Vorbildung,** *f.* preparation.
**vorbinden,** *v.t.* tie on, put on.
**Vorbleiche,** *f.* preliminary bleach.
**Vorblick,** *m.* look forward.
**vor-bringen,** *v.t.* bring forward, produce, utter, adduce. **-datieren,** *v.t.* antedate. **-decken,** *v.t.* (*Dyeing*) ground.
**vordem,** *adv.* formerly.
**vorder,** *a.* fore, front, anterior.
**Vorder-ansicht,** *f.* front view. **-arm,** *m.* forearm. **-ende,** *f.* front end, fore end. **-finger,** *m.* forefinger. **-glied,** *n.* antecedent; front rank; front limb. **-grund,** *m.* foreground.
**vorderhand,** *adv.* for the present, provisionally.
**Vorder-herd,** *m.* forehearth. **-hirn,** *n.* (*Anat.*) forebrain. **-satz,** *m.* antecedent, premise. **-seite,** *f.* front side, front, obverse, face.
**vorderseitig,** *a.* on the front side, front.
**vorderst,** *a.* foremost.
**Vorder-teil,** *m.* front part, front. **-wand,** *f.* front wall, front, (of a blast furnace) breast. **-würze,** *f.* first wort.
**vor-drängen,** *v.t. & r.* press forward, push forward. **-dringen,** *v.i.* push on, advance.
**Vordruck,** *m.* first impression, proof; form, blank; (*Calico*) first or bottom printing.
**vordrucken,** *v.t.* prefix.
**Vordruckreserve,** *f.* (*Calico*) preprinted resist.
**voreilen,** *v.i.* hasten, anticipate; lead.
**Vor-eilen,** *n.*, **-eilung,** *f.* advance; (*Mach.*) lead. **-eilungswinkel,** *m.* angle of lead.
**voreingenommen,** *p.a.* prepossessed, prejudiced
**Voreltern,** *pl.* ancestors.
**vorenthalten,** *v.t.* withhold.
**Vor-erhitzer,** *m.* preheater. **-erhitzung,** *f.* preheating.
**vorerst,** *adv.* first of all; for the present.
**vorerwähnt,** *p.a.* aforementioned.
**Vor-erzeugnis,** *n.* semifinished product, crude product. **-fahr,** *m.* ancestor; predecessor. **-fahrt,** *f.* right of way; priority. **-fall,** *m.* occurrence, event; incident; (*Med.*) prolapse.
**vorfallen,** *v.i.* happen, occur; prolapse.
**vorfärben,** *v.t.* color preliminarily; (*Dyeing*) predye, ground, bottom.
**Vor-färbung,** *f.* preliminary dyeing or staining; specif., (*Dyeing*) grounding, bottoming. **-faulbecken,** *n.* (*Sewage*) primary digestion tank. **-fechter,** *m.* champion. **-feile,** *f.* bastard file. **-filter,** *m.* first filter, coarse filter. **-filtern,** *n.* preliminary filtering.
**vorfinden,** *v.t.* come upon, find. — *v.r.* be found, be forthcoming.
**Vorflut,** *f.* drainage; tide rise.
**vorformen,** *v.t.* preform.
**Vor-formling,** *m.* (*Plastics*) preform. **-frischen,** *n.* preliminary refining.
**vorführen,** *v.t.* bring out, produce, present; display; demonstrate; project (film).
**Vor-führung,** *f.* presentation; production; demonstration. **-gang,** *m.* process; (chemical) reaction; proceeding, procedure; operation; action; occurrence, event; transaction; priority, precedence; precedent, example; (*Distilling*) first runnings. **-gänger,** *m.* predecessor; antecedent.
**vorgängig,** *a.* foregoing, previous; preliminary.
**Vorgärung,** *f.* preliminary fermentation.
**vorgeben,** *v.t.* give in advance; pretend; suggest; give (odds).
**Vorgebirge,** *n.* headland, promontory; foothill.
**vor-geblich,** *a.* pretended, would-be, so-called.

-geburtlich, *a.* prenatal. **-gefasst,** *p.a.* preconceived. **-geformt,** *p.a.* preformed. **-gefrischt,** *a.* semirefined, semipurified. **-gehen,** *v.i.* go before, precede; proceed; advance; go on, happen; (of a watch) be fast.
**Vorgelege,** *n.* connecting gearing.
**vorgerben,** *v.t.* pretan.
**Vorgerbung,** *f.* preliminary tanning, pretannage.
**vorgeschichtlich,** *a.* prehistoric.
**vorgeschritten,** *p.a.* see vorschreiten.
**vorgesehen,** *p.a.* see vorsehen.
**Vorgesetzte,** *m.* superior, head.
**vorgestern,** *adv.* day before yesterday.
**Vor-glühen,** *n.* preliminary heating; (*Metal.*) annealing. **-glühofen,** *m.* annealing oven or furnace; (*Ceram.*) biscuit kiln.
**vor-greifen,** *v.t.* anticipate. **-grundieren,** *v.t.* (*Dyeing*) ground. **-haben,** *v.t.* intend, purpose; be engaged in; have on, wear; reprimand.
**Vorhaben,** *n.* intention, purpose; plan, project.
**vor-halten,** *v.t.* hold before; reproach. — *v.i.* hold out, last. **-handen,** *adv.* & *a.* at hand, on hand, ready, available, present, existing.
**Vor-handensein,** *n.* presence, existence. **-hang,** *m.* curtain, drop. **-haupt,** *n.* forehead.
**vorher,** *adv.* previously, before. **-bedenken,** *v.t.* premeditate. **-bestimmen,** *v.t.* predetermine, predestine.
**Vorherd,** *m.* forehearth.
**vorher-gehen,** *v.i.* go before, precede. **-gehend,** *p.a.* preceding, previous, prior.
**vorherig,** *a.* previous, preceding.
**vorherrschen,** *v.i.* predominate, prevail.
**Vorhersage,** *f.* prediction, forecast, prophecy.
**vorhersagen,** *v.t.* predict, forecast, prophesy.
**vorhin,** *adv.* before, heretofore, lately.
**Vorhut,** *f.* vanguard, van.
**vorig,** *a.* former, preceding, last.
**vorionisiert,** *a.* pre-ionized.
**Vorjahr,** *n.* preceding year.
**Vork,** *abbrev.* (Vorkommen) occurrence.
**vorkalkulieren,** *v.t.* precalculate.
**Vor-kammer,** *f.* antechamber; (*Anat.*) auricle. **-kehr, -kehrung,** *f.* precaution, provision. **-kenntnis,** *n.* preliminary knowledge; (*pl.*) rudiments, elements. **-klärbecken,** *n.* preliminary sedimentation tank. **-klotzung,** *f.* (*Calico*) pad ground.
**vorkommen,** *v.i.* occur, be found; happen; appear, seem; be admitted, be presented, come up; come sooner.
**Vorkommen,** *n.* occurrence, etc. (see vorkommen); presence, existence; (of ores) deposit.
**Vor-kondensator,** *m.* preliminary condenser. **-kost,** *f.* provisions; first course. **-kracken,** *n.*, **-krackung,** *f.* (*Petroleum*) primary cracking.
**Vorkriegs-.** pre-war.
**vorkühlen,** *v.t.* forecool, precool.
**Vor-kühler,** *m.* forecooler, primary cooler. **-kühlung,** *f.* forecooling, precooling. **-kultur,** *f.* preliminary culture.
**vorküpen,** *v.t.* bottom with a vat dye.
**Vorlack,** *m.* priming lacquer, primer.
**vorladen,** *v.t.* summon.
**Vorlage,** *f.* something put before or in front; specif., receiver; absorption bulb; (*Zinc*) condenser; (*Gas*) collector main; (*Expl.*) antiflash bag; matter, proposal, bill; text, copy; pattern.
**vorlagern,** *v.r.* & *i.* extend in front of or before; protrude.
**Vorlass,** *m.* = Vorlauf.
**vorlassen,** *v.t.* admit, give access to; give precedence to.
**Vor-lauf,** *m.* first runnings; specif., (*Whisky*) foreshot, (*Coal Tar*) first light oil. **-läufer,** *m.* forerunner, precursor, sign, indication; (mountain) spur.
**vorläufig,** *a.* preliminary, previous, provisional, tentative. — *adv.* previously, meantime, for the present.
**Vorlaugung,** *f.* preliminary leaching.
**vorlegen,** *v.t.* put on, apply; lay before, place before, submit, propose; display, exhibit.
**Vorlegierung,** *f.* key alloy, prealloy.
**vorlesen,** *v.t.* read aloud, recite.
**Vorlesung,** *f.* lecture, discourse; reading.
**Vorlesungstisch,** *m.* lecture table.
**vorletzt,** *a.* next to last, penultimate.
**Vor-licht,** *n.* priming illumination. **-lickerung,** *f.* (*Leather*) preliminary fat-liquoring. **-liebe,** *f.* preference, fondness.
**vorliegen,** *v.i.* lie before, be in hand or at hand, be under consideration, be present, exist.
**Vorliegen,** *n.* presence, existence.
**vorm.,** *abbrev.* (vormals) formerly; (vormittags) A.M.
**Vor-mahlen,** *n.* preliminary grinding. **-maischapparat,** *m.* foremashing apparatus. **-maischbottich,** *m.* foremashing vat. **-maischen,** *n.* (*Brewing*) foremashing (soaking of the grist before mashing). **-maischer,** *m.* foremasher, premasher, pony masher.
**vormals,** *adv.* formerly.
**Vormann,** *m.* foreman.
**Vormaterial,** *n.* initial material.
**vormerken,** *v.t.* note, note down; reserve.
**Vor-merkung,** *f.* note, memorandum; notice; reservation. **-milch,** *f.* colostrum, foremilk. **-mischung,** *f.* premixing; (*Rubber*) master batch. **-mittag,** *m.* forenoon, morning. **-mund,** *m.* guardian, trustee.
**vorn, vorne,** *adv.* in front, before, ahead. — **von —,** from before; from the beginning. — **von — herein,** from the first, at first, to begin with.

**Vorname,** *m.* first name, given name.
**vornehm,** *a.* noble, aristocratic; distinguished; (of luster) subdued.
**vor-nehmen,** *v.t.* take, take up, undertake; intend. **-nehmlich,** *adv.* chiefly, especially. **-nehmste,** *f.* chief, foremost, principal.
**Vornetzbad,** *n.* (*Textiles*) wetting-out bath.
**vornetzen,** *v.t.* (*Textiles*) wet out.
**vornherein,** *adv.* — **von —, im —,** from the outset, from the first, to begin with.
**Vorniere,** *f.* head kidney, pronephros.
**Vornierengang,** *m.* Wolffian duct.
**Vor-norm,** *f.* tentative standard. **-oxydation,** *f.* previous oxidation. **-polieren,** *n.* rough-polishing, first polishing. **-posten,** *m.* outpost. **-präparation,** *f.* previous or preliminary preparation or treatment. **-probe,** *f.* preliminary test. **-produkt,** *n.* initial (or primary) product; crude product, specif. crude benzol; intermediate. **-produktkühler,** *m.* (*Coal Tar*) crude benzol condenser. **-prüfung,** *f.* previous or preliminary examination. **-pumpe,** *f.* auxiliary pump (as for vacuum); (*Brewing*) circulator, wort pump.
**vorquellen,** *v.t.* presoak, presteep.
**Vorr.,** *abbrev.* of Vorrichtung.
**Vorraffination,** *f.* prerefining; (*Lead*) softening, improving.
**vor-raffinieren,** *v.t.* prerefine; (*Lead*) soften, improve. **-ragen,** *v.i.* stand out, project, be prominent. — **-ragend,** *p.a.* prominent, outstanding.
**Vorrang,** *m.* precedence, priority, superiority.
**Vorrat,** *m.* stock, store, supply, reserve. **-flasche,** *f.* stock bottle. **-gefäss,** *n.* stock vessel, reservoir.
**vorrätig,** *a.* in stock, on hand.
**Vorratlösung,** *f.* stock solution.
**Vorrats-behälter,** *m.* storage container (storage tank, storage bin, etc.). **-bottich,** *m.* storage vat or vessel. **-eiweiss,** *n.* supply protein, circulating protein. **-fass,** *n.* storage vessel (barrel, tank, etc.). **-flasche,** *f.* stock bottle. **-gefäss,** *n.* supply vessel, reservoir. **-lösung,** *f.* stock solution. **-raum,** *m.* stock room, storeroom. **-tank,** *m.* storage (or stock) tank. **-teil,** *m.* spare part.
**Vor-reaktion,** *f.* preliminary reaction. **-rechnung,** *f.* calculation; counting up. **-recht,** *n.* privilege. **-rede,** *f.* preface; preamble. **-reduktion,** *f.* prereduction; previous reduction. **-reduktionsansatz,** *m.* (*Calico*) prereduction paste.
**vor-reduzieren,** *v.t.* prereduce. **-reiben,** *v.t.* grind beforehand. **-reinigen,** *v.t.* purify in a preliminary way.
**Vorreinigung,** *f.* preliminary purification.
**vorrichten,** *v.t.* prepare, develop, open up.
**Vorrichtung,** *f.* contrivance, device, appliance, instrument, apparatus, arrangement; preparation, dressing.
**Vorröste,** *f.* preroasting; preretting.
**Vorrösten,** *n.*, **Vorröstung,** *f.* preliminary roasting, preroasting.
**Vorröstofen,** *m.* preroasting furnace.
**vorrucken,** *v.i.* advance, progress. — *v.t.* advance; reproach.
**Vorsatz,** *m.* something put before, or in front (*e.g.*, screen); attached device; design, intention.
**vorsätzlich,** *a.* intentional, willful.
**Vorsatz-linse,** *f.* lens placed in front. **-papier,** *n.* book lining paper, flyleaf paper.
**vorschalten,** *v.t.* (*Elec.*) introduce (into a circuit), cut in, connect, connect in series.
**Vorschaltwiderstand,** *m.* (*Elec.*) (rheostatic) resistance, series resistance.
**vorschärfen,** *v.t.* sharpen (or strengthen) previously.
**Vorschein,** *m.* appearance.
**vor-schieben,** *v.t.* push forward, advance; (*Mach.*) feed. **-schiessen,** *v.i.* shoot forward. — *v.t.* circulate (wort, etc.); advance (money).
**Vorschlag,** *m.* proposal, proposition; (*Metal.*) fusion, flux; blank space on the first page of a book.
**vorschlagen,** *v.t.* propose, suggest, move; overcharge; put on before, prefix.
**Vor-schlichten,** *n.* (*Metal.*) = Vorpolieren. **-schliff,** *m.* rough grinding. **-schmack,** *m.* foretaste; predominant taste.
**vor-schmecken,** *v.i.* (of a flavor) predominate. **-schmelzen,** *v.t.* premelt, prefuse.
**Vorschmelzofen,** *m.* premelting furnace.
**vor-schnell,** *a.* hasty, rash. **-schreiben,** *v.t.* prescribe, dictate, direct, specify.
**vorschreiten,** *v.i.* step forward, progress, advance. — **vorgeschritten,** *p.a.* advanced.
**Vorschrift,** *f.* prescription; recipe; directions, instructions; specification(s); order, command; rule, precept; copy; decree.
**vorschriftsmässig,** *adv.* as prescribed, as directed.
**Vor-schub,** *m.* assistance, furtherance; (*Mech.*) feed, feeding; advance, lead. **-schuh,** *m.* upper leather, vamp. **-schule,** *f.* preparatory school; primer. **-schuss,** *m.* advance (of money).
**vorschützen,** *v.t.* pretend, allege. **-schweben,** *v.i.* float; be in one's mind. **-sehen,** *v.t.* foresee; provide for. — *v.r.* take care; provide. — **vorgesehen,** *p.a.* foreseen; provided for; intentional.
**Vor-sehung,** *f.* providence. **-setzblatt,** *n.* flyleaf.
**vorsetzen,** *v.t.* set before, put before, prefix; advance; propose (to oneself).

**Vorsetzer,** *m.* something put in front, specif. fire screen.
**Vorsicht,** *f.* foresight, caution, prudence; precaution, care; providence; take care!
**vorsichterweise,** *adv.* by way of precaution.
**vorsichtig,** *a.* cautious, careful, prudent, provident. — *adv.* cautiously, carefully.
**Vorsichts-massnahme, -massregel,** *f.* precaution, precautionary measure.
**Vor-sieden,** *n.* preliminary boiling. **-silbe,** *f.* prefixed syllable, prefix.
**vorsintern,** *v.t.* presinter, semisinter.
**Vor-sitz,** *m.* presidency, chair. **-sitzend, -sitzender,** *m.* chairman, president. **-sorge,** *f.* precaution, care, forethought. **-sortierung,** *f.* preliminary sorting. **-spannung,** *f.* initial tension, prestress. **-spektrum,** *n.* preliminary spectrum (applied by Goldstein to certain low-temperature spectra).
**vorspiegeln,** *v.t.* exhibit in a false light, pretend, simulate.
**Vorspiel,** *n.* prelude.
**vorspringen,** *v.i.* project, protrude, be prominent; leap out. — **vorspringend,** *p.a.* projecting, prominent, (of colors) glaring.
**Vor-sprung,** *m.* projection, prominence; protrusion; salient; advantage. **-stabilisator,** *m.* prestabilizer. **-stadt,** *f.* suburb. **-stand,** *m.* directory, executive committee, board of management; director, head.
**vor-stecken,** *v.t.* put, stick or fasten before; prefix; mark out, propose. **-stehen,** *v.i.* stand before, precede; stand out, project; be prominent; direct, preside (over).
**Vorsteher,** *m.* director, manager, superintendent, etc. **-drüse,** *f.* prostate gland, prostate.
**vorstellbar,** *a.* imaginable; presentable.
**vorstellen,** *v.t.* represent; imagine; demonstrate; personate, play; introduce, present; put before, put ahead, advance.
**Vorstellung,** *f.* conception, idea, notion; representation, performance; introduction; review (of troops); remonstrance.
**Vorstellungsfähigkeit,** *f.* conceptual (or imaginative) power.
**Vorstoss,** *m.* adapter; lap (of a tile); edging; stop; projection; attack, advance.
**vorstossen,** *v.t. & i.* push forward; advance; protrude.
**Vorstudie,** *f.* preliminary study.
**Vor-stufe,** *f.* first step; first (or preliminary) stage; primer. **-sud,** *m.* first boiling.
**vortäuschen,** *v.t.* simulate; delude, deceive.
**Vorteil,** *m.* advantage, profit, benefit; knack.
**vorteilhaft,** *a.* advantageous, profitable, favorable.
**Vor-tiegel,** *m.* (*Lead*) outer basin, lead pot; (*Tin*) forehearth. **-trag,** *m.* discourse, lecture, address, recital; report; exposition; delivery, enunciation; (*Com.*) balance.
**vortragen,** *v.t.* carry before; report on; deliver; lecture on.
**Vortragstisch,** *m.* lecture table.
**vor-trefflich,** *a.* excellent, superior, prime. **-treiben,** *v.t.* drive forward, propel. **-treten,** *v.i.* step forward, stand out; advance.
**Vor-trieb,** *m.* driving forward, propulsion; advance. **-tritt,** *m.* precedence.
**vortrocknen,** *v.t.* dry beforehand, predry.
**Vortrockner,** *m.* predrier, (*Paper*) receiving drier.
**vorüber,** *adv.* past, gone, over, done. **-gehen,** *v.i.* pass, pass by, pass away. **-gehend,** *p.a.* temporary, transient.
**Vor-untersuchung,** *f.* preliminary investigation. **-urteil,** *n.* prejudice, bias. **-vakuum,** *n.* preliminary vacuum. **-verbrennung,** *f.* precombustion. **-verdampfer,** *m.* pre-evaporator.
**vorverdampft,** *p.a.* pre-evaporated.
**Vorverdauung,** *f.* predigestion.
**vorverdichten,** *v.t.* precompress; supercharge.
**Vor-verfahren,** *n.* preliminary procedure. **-veröffentlichung,** *f.* prior publication. **-versuch,** *m.* preliminary experiment or test. **-vulkanisation,** *f.* prevulcanizing.
**vorvulkanisieren,** *v.t.* prevulcanize.
**Vorwachs,** *n.* bee glue, propolis.
**vor-walken,** *v.t.* scour (cloth). **-walten,** *v.i.* prevail, predominate. **-walzen,** *v.t.* (*Metal.*) rough down (blooms).
**Vor-walzwerk,** *n.* (*Metal.*) roughing rolls. **-wand,** *m.* pretext, pretense. **-wärmapparat,** *m.* preheating apparatus, forewarming apparatus.
**vorwärmen,** *v.t.* heat (beforehand), preheat, (fore)warm, anneal.
**Vor-wärmer,** *m.* (pre)heater, (fore)warmer, economizer. **-wärmerohr,** *n.* preheating tube or pipe. **-wärmofen,** *m.* preheating oven, annealing oven (or furnace). **-wärmschrank,** *m.* preheating cabinet. **-wärmung,** *f.* forewarming, preheating. **-wärmzone,** *f.* zone of preparatory heating.
**vorwärts,** *adv.* forward, onward, on, ahead.
**Vorwärtsgang,** *m.* forward movement.
**vorwärtstreiben,** *v.t.* drive forward, propel.
**Vorwäsche,** *f.*, **Vorwaschen,** *n.* preliminary washing.
**vorweg,** *adv.* before, beforehand. **-nehmen,** *v.t.* take beforehand, anticipate.
**Vor-wein,** *m.* (*Wine*) first runnings. **-welt,** *f.* prehistoric world; antiquity.
**vor-weltlich,** *a.* prehistoric, primeval. **-werfen,** *v.t.* throw before; reproach with.
**Vorwiderstand,** *m.* (*Elec.*) series resistance.
**vor-wiegen,** *v.i.* outweigh, preponderate. **-wie-**

gend, *p.a.* preponderant, predominant, major, chief. — *adv.* preponderantly, chiefly.

**Vor-wissen,** *n.* foreknowledge. **-wort,** *n.* foreword, preface; preposition. **-wurf,** *m.* subject, object; reproach, blame. **-zählung,** *f.* enumeration. **-zeichen,** *n.* indication, symptom, omen; (*Math.*) sign. **-zeichenwechsel,** *m.* (*Math.*) change of sign.

**vorzeigen,** *v.t.* show, exhibit; present.

**Vor-zeiger,** *m.* pointer, indicator; bearer. **-zeit,** *f.* ancient times, past ages, antiquity.

**vorzeitig,** *a.* premature, untimely.

**Vor-zerkleinerung,** *f.* preliminary crushing. **-zerlegung,** *f.* preliminary decomposition; crude fractionation.

**vor-ziehbar,** *a.* preferable. **-ziehen,** *v.t.* prefer; draw forth.

**Vorzug,** *m.* advantage, merit, virtue; preference; precedence, priority, superiority, privilege.

**vorzüglich,** *a.* preferable; excellent, superior, choice; distinguished. — *adv.* preferably; chiefly, especially.

**Vorzugs-.** preferred, preferential. **-aktien,** *f.pl.* (shares of) preferred stock. **-milch,** *f.* special milk. **-richtung,** *f.* preferred direction.

**vorzugsweise,** *adv.* preferably, especially, preëminently.

**Vorzündung,** *f.* early ignition; pre-ignition.

**V.St.,** *abbrev.* (Vereinigte Staaten) United States.

**v.T.,** *abbrev.* (von Tausend) per thousand, per mille.

**V.T.,** *abbrev.* (Volumenteil) part by volume.

**v.u.,** *abbrev.* (von unten) from below, from beneath, from the bottom.

**Vulkan,** *m.* volcano; Vulcan. **-asbest,** *m.* vulcanized asbestos. **-fiber,** *f.* Vulcanized Fiber. *T.N.* **-gas,** *n.* volcanic gas. **-glas,** *n.* volcanic glass; tempered glass.

**Vulkanisat,** *n.* vulcanizate.

**Vulkanisations-agens,** *n.* vulcanizing agent. **-artikel,** *m.* (*Dyeing*) vulcanizing style. **-bereich,** *m.* (*Rubber*) curing range. **-beschleuniger,** *m.* vulcanization accelerator. **-einsatz,** *m.* (*Rubber*) start of the cure.

**vulkanisationshemmend,** *a.* retarding vulcanization.

**Vulkanisations-mittel,** *n.* vulcanizing agent. **-probe,** *f.* vulcanizing test or sample. **-verzögerung,** *f.* retardation of vulcanization.

**Vulkanisator,** *m.* vulcanizer.

**vulkanisch,** *a.* volcanic.

**vulkanisierecht,** *a.* fast to vulcanizing.

**vulkanisieren,** *v.t.* vulcanize, (*Rubber*) cure. ("Curing" is vulcanizing to the desired degree.)

**Vulkanisierer,** *m.* vulcanizer.

**Vulkanisier-presser,** *m.* vulcanizer. **-trog,** *m.* (*Rubber*) curing trough.

**Vulkanisierung,** *f.* vulcanization.

**Vulkanismus,** *m.* (*Geol.*) volcanism.

**Vulkanöl,** *n.* mineral lubricating oil.

**Vuzin,** *n.* vuzine, vuzin.

**VZ.,** *abbrev.* (Verseifungszahl) saponification number.

# W

**w.,** *abbrev.* warm; watt.
**W,** symbol for Wolfram (tungsten).
**W.,** *abbrev.* (Wasser) water.
**Waag-, Waage,** *f.* = Wag-, Wage.
**Waare,** *f.* = Ware.
**Wabe,** *f.* honeycomb.
**wabenartig,** *a.* honeycombed, alveolar.
**Waben-honig,** *m.* comb honey. **-theorie,** *f.* alveolar theory (of protoplasm).
**wach,** *a.* awake, waking.
**Wache,** *f.* watch, watching; guardhouse.
**wachen,** *v.i.* be awake, wake; watch.
**Wachmittel,** *n.* antisoporific.
**Wacholder,** *m.* juniper. **-beere,** *f.* juniper berry. **-branntwein, -geist,** *m.* (Holland) gin. **-harz,** *n.* juniper resin; gum juniper (sandarac). **-öl,** *n.* juniper oil; (**brenzliches**) oil of cade. **-spiritus,** *m.* (*Pharm.*) spirit of juniper. **-teer,** *m.* juniper tar, oil of cade.
**Wachs,** *n.* wax.
**Wachs-.** wax, waxen; growing, sprouting. **-abdruck,** *m.* impression in wax.
**wachsähnlich,** *a.* like wax, waxy.
**Wachsalaun,** *m.* crystallized alum.
**wachsam,** *a.* watchful, vigilant.
**Wachsappretur,** *f.* wax finish.
**Wachsart,** *f.* (variety of) wax.
**wachsartig,** *a.* waxy, wax-like.
**Wachs-ausscheidung,** *f.* secretion of wax. **-baum,** *m.* wax myrtle, bayberry tree. **-beize,** *f.* wax stain. **-bildnerei,** *f.* modeling in wax. **-bleiche,** *f.*, **-bleichen,** *n.* wax bleaching. **-boden,** *m.* wax cake. **-bohnermasse,** *f.* polishing wax. **-bottich,** *m.* (*Alum*) roching cask. **-draht,** *m.* wax-insulated wire. **-drüse,** *f.* ceruminous gland.
**wachsen,** *v.i.* grow; increase; crystallize; (*Malting*) sprout; (of lime) swell. — *v.t.* wax. — **gewachsen,** *p.a.* grown, etc.; native; equal (to).
**wächsen,** *v.t.* wax.
**wächsern,** *a.* waxen, wax.
**Wachsfarbe,** *f.* wax color.
**wachs-farben, -farbig,** *a.* wax-colored.
**Wachs-firnis,** *m.* wax varnish. **-gagel,** *m. & f.* wax myrtle. **-gehalt,** *m.* wax content.
**wachsgelb,** *a.* wax-yellow.
**Wachsglanz,** *m.* waxy luster.
**wachsglänzend,** *a.* of waxy luster.
**Wachs-handel,** *m.* wax trade. **-harzreserve,** *f.* wax-resin resist. **-kerzchen,** *n.* wax match. **-kerze,** *f.* wax candle. **-kitt,** *m.* wax cement; luting wax. **-kohle,** *f.* paraffin coal. **-kuchen,** *m.* cake of wax. **-leim,** *m.* wax glue. **-leinen,** *n.*, **-leinwand,** *f.* = Wachstuch. **-machen,** *n.* roching (crystallization) of alum. **-malerei,** *f.* encaustic painting. **-masse,** *f.* wax composition. **-myrte,** *f.* wax myrtle. **-öl,** *n.* wax oil. **-opal,** *m.* wax opal. **-palme,** *f.* wax palm. **-papier,** *n.* wax paper. **-paste,** *f.* wax paste; cerate. **-pauspapier,** *n.* waxed tracing paper. **-pflaster,** *n.* cerate. **-präparat,** *n.* preparation in wax. **-raum,** *m.* growing space. **-reserve,** *f.* (*Calico*) wax resist. **-salbe,** *f.* cerate; ointment. **-schmelze,** *f.* wax-melting house. **-seife,** *f.* wax soap. **-sonde,** *f.* (*Med.*) wax bougie. **-stock,** *m.* wax candle.
**wächst,** *pr. 3 sing.* (of wachsen) grows, etc.
**Wachs-tafel,** *f.* tablet of wax. **-taffet,** *m.* oiled silk; waxed silk. **-tuch,** *n.* oilcloth; leather cloth; (formerly) cerecloth. **-tuchlack,** *m.* oilcloth varnish.
**Wachstum,** *n.* growth; increase; accretion.
**wachstum-fördernd,** *a.* growth-promoting. **-hemmend,** *a.* growth-checking, growth-inhibiting.
**wachstumsfähig,** *a.* capable of growth.
**Wachstums-geschwindigkeit,** *f.* rate of growth; rate of increase. **-kurve,** *f.* growth curve. **-schicht,** *f.* growth layer, (of woody plants) cambium. **-vorgang,** *m.* growth process. **-zentrum,** *n.* center of growth, nucleus.
**Wachsüberzug,** *m.* wax(y) coating.
**wachsweich,** *a.* soft like wax.
**Wachszündholz,** *n.* wax match, vesta.
**Wacht,** *f.* guard, watch.
**Wächter,** *m.* watchman; (*Elec.*) controller.
**wackelig,** *a.* shaky, rickety, wabbly, loose.
**wackeln,** *v.i.* shake, totter, wabble, rock.
**wacker,** *a.* stout, brave, good.
**Wade,** *f.* calf (of the leg).
**Wadenbein,** *n.* fibula.
**Waderz,** *n.* wad (the mineral).
**Waffe,** *f.* weapon, (*pl.*) arms, force.
**Waffen-dienst,** *m.* military service. **-fabrik,** *f.* arms factory. **-fett,** *n.* gun grease, rifle grease. **-haus,** *n.* arsenal, armory.
**waffenlos,** *a.* unarmed.
**Waffen-rüstung,** *f.* armor; arming; armament.
**waffnen,** *v.t.* arm.
**Wagbalken,** *m.* balance beam, scale beam.
**wägbar,** *a.* weighable, ponderable.
**Wägbarkeit,** *f.* weighableness, ponderability.

**Wage,** *f.* balance, scales, weighing machine; hydrometer; weigh-house; level (the instrument). **-arm,** *m.* arm of a balance. **-balken,** *m.* beam of a balance, scale beam.
**Wäge-bühne,** *f.* weighing platform. **-bürette,** *f.* weighing buret(te). **-fläschchen,** *n.* weighing bottle. **-garnitur,** *f.* weighing set. **-gegengewicht,** *n.* counterpoise.
**Wagegehäuse,** *n.* balance case.
**Wäge-glas, -gläschen,** *n.* weighing glass.
**Wagekasten,** *m.* balance case.
**wagen,** *v.t.* venture, risk, hazard.
**Wagen,** *m.* vehicle, conveyance (carriage, wagon, cart, truck, car, etc.).
**wägen,** *v.t.* weigh; poise, balance; ponder.
**Wagen-fett,** *n.* wagon grease, axle grease. **-lack,** *m.* carriage varnish, coach varnish; automobile varnish. **-lastung,** *f.* carload; truck load; wagon load. **-öl,** *n.* car oil, (railway) carriage oil. **-schmiere,** *f.* wagon grease, axle grease.
**Wägepipette,** *f.* weighing pipet(te).
**Wäger,** *m.* weigher.
**wagerecht,** *a.* horizontal, level.
**Wäge-röhrchen,** *n.*, **-röhre,** *f.* weighing tube.
**Wageschale,** *f.* balance pan, scale pan.
**Wäge-schale,** *f.* weighing dish. **-schiffchen,** *n.* weighing boat. **-substanz,** *f.* substance to be weighed. **-vorrichtung,** *f.* weighing device. **-zimmer,** *n.* weighing room, balance room.
**Waggon,** *m.* car, (railway) carriage. **-ladung,** *f.* (railway) carload.
**Wagnis,** *n.* hazard, hazardous affair.
**wagrecht,** *a.* horizontal, level.
**Wagschale,** *f.* balance pan, scale pan.
**Wägung,** *f.* weighing.
**Wagzimmer,** *n.* weighing room, balance room.
**Wahl,** *f.* choice, selection; option; election.
**wählbar,** *a.* eligible.
**Wählbarkeit,** *f.* eligibility.
**wählen,** *v.t.* choose, select; elect.
**Wähler,** *m.* chooser; selector; elector, voter.
**wählerisch,** *a.* particular, fastidious.
**wahl-frei,** *a.* optional. **-los,** *a.* nonselective, random.
**Wahl-recht,** *n.* suffrage, franchise. **-spruch,** *m.* motto, device. **-verwandtschaft,** *f.* elective affinity; congeniality.
**wahlweise,** *adv.* as one chooses; at will, selectively.
**Wahn,** *m.* illusion, delusion; fancy; folly. **-bild,** *n.* phantom, illusion, delusion.
**wähnen,** *v.i.* fancy, imagine, suppose.
**Wahnsinn,** *m.* insanity; delirium; frenzy.
**wahnsinnig,** *a.* insane, mad; frantic.
**wahr,** *a.* true, real, genuine. — *adv.* truly.
**wahren,** *v.t.* keep, preserve; guard, look after.
**währen,** *v.i.* last, continue, endure.
**während,** *prep.* during, for. — *conj.* while; whereas.
**wahr-genommen,** *p.p.* (of wahrnehmen) perceived, etc. **-haft,** *a.* true, genuine; truthful, sincere; sure; regular. **-haftig,** *a.* true; truthful. — *adv.* truly, verily, really.
**Wahrheit,** *f.* truth; truthfulness; reality, fact.
**wahr-lich,** *adv.* surely, really, truly, verily. **-nehmbar,** *a.* perceptible, noticeable, discernible.
**Wahrnehmbarkeit,** *f.* perceptibility, noticeability, discernibility.
**wahrnehmen,** *v.t.* perceive, notice, observe; attend to, profit by.
**Wahrnehmung,** *f.* perception; observation; attention.
**wahr-sagen,** *v.t. & i.* prophesy, divine, predict. **-scheinlich,** *a.* probable, likely; plausible.
**Wahrscheinlichkeit,** *f.* probability; plausibility.
**Wahrscheinlichkeits-gesetz,** *n.* probability law. **-kurve,** *f.* probability curve. **-rechnung,** *f.* calculus of probabilities. **-wert,** *m.* probable value.
**Wahrspruch,** *m.* verdict.
**Wahrung,** *f.* support, vindication; preservation.
**Währung,** *f.* standard, value, currency; duration.
**Wahrzeichen,** *n.* distinctive mark, sign.
**Waid,** *m.* woad. **-blau,** *n.* woad blue, woad. **-färber,** *m.* woad dyer. **-küpe,** *f.* woad vat. **-küpenschwarz,** *n.* woaded logwood black.
**Wal,** *m.* whale.
**Wald,** *m.* wood(s), forest.
**Wald-.** wood, forest, wild. **-ahorn,** *m.* sycamore. **-bau,** *n.* silviculture, forestry. **-baum,** *m.* forest tree. **-boden,** *m.* forest soil.
**Walden'sche Umkehrung.** Walden inversion.
**Wald-gewächs,** *n.* forest plant. **-humus,** *m.* forest humus, leaf mold.
**waldig,** *a.* wooded, woody, woodland.
**Wald-kirsche,** *f.* wild cherry. **-malve,** *f.* mallow (*Malva sylvestris*). **-meister,** *m.* woodruff (*Asperula odorata*). **-rebe,** *f.* clematis.
**Waldung,** *f.* woods, forest, woodland.
**Wald-wolle,** *f.* pine wool, pine-needle wool. **-wollöl,** *n.* pine-needle oil.
**Walfisch,** *m.* whale. **-öl,** *n.* whale oil. **-speck,** *m.* whale blubber. **-tran,** *m.* whale oil, train oil.
**Walk-.** fuller's, fulling; felting, felted. **-brühe,** *f.* (*Textiles*) milling liquor.
**Walke,** *f.* fulling, milling (of cloth); fulling machine; fulling mill.
**walkecht,** *a.* fast to fulling.
**Walkechtheit,** *f.* fastness to fulling.
**walken,** *v.t.* full, mill (cloth); beat, mill (leather); felt; press, squeeze.

**Walker,** *m.* fuller.
**Walkerde, Walkererde,** *f.* fuller's earth.
**Walker-distel,** *f.* fuller's teasel. **-seife,** *f.* fuller's soap, milling soap. **-ton,** *m.* fuller's earth.
**Walk-fähigkeit,** *f.* fulling (or milling) property; felting property. **-fass,** *n.* (*Leather*) drum, tumbler. **-fett,** *n.* fulling fat, milling fat; (*Leather*) dressing grease. **-flüssigkeit,** *f.* (*Textiles*) milling liquor. **-mittel,** *n.* fulling (or milling) agent. **-probe,** *f.* fulling (or milling) test. **-seife,** *f.* fuller's soap. **-ton,** *n.* fuller's earth.
**Wall,** *m.* rampart; dam, bank; coast.
**Wallach,** *m.* gelding; Wallachian.
**wallen,** *v.i.* bubble, boil up, simmer; wave, heave, undulate.
**wällen,** *v.t.* boil, simmer.
**wallisisch,** *a.* Welsh; Valaisan.
**Wallnuss,** *f.* walnut. See Walnuss-.
**Wallonen-arbeit,** *f.*, **-frischen,** *n.*, **-schmiede,** *f.* Walloon process. **-eisen,** *n.* Walloon iron.
**Wallrat, Wallross.** = Walrat, Walross.
**Wallstein,** *m.* dam (of a blast furnace), damstone. **-platte,** *f.* (*Metal.*) dam plate.
**Wallung,** *f.* boiling, ebullition; simmering; undulation; excitement.
**Walnuss,** *f.* walnut. **-baum,** *m.* walnut tree (*Juglans* species, esp. *J. regia*); (**grauer**) butternut tree (*J. cinerea*); (**weisser**) hickory (*Hicoria* sp.).
**walnussgross,** *a.* walnut-sized, nut-sized.
**Walnuss-grösse,** *f.* size of walnuts, nut size. **-öl,** *n.* walnut oil.
**Walrat,** *m.* spermaceti. **-öl,** *n.* sperm oil.
**Walross,** *n.* walrus.
**Wälschkorn,** *n.* maize, corn.
**walten,** *v.i.* dispose, manage, govern, rule.
**Wal-tier,** *n.* cetacean. **-tran,** *m.* whale oil.
**walzbar,** *a.* capable of being rolled, rollable.
**Walz-barkeit,** *f.* rollability, rolling property. **-blech,** *n.* rolled plate. **-blei,** *n.* sheet lead. **-draht,** *m.* rod wire; wire rod.
**Walze,** *f.* roller, roll; cylinder, drum.
**Walzeisen,** *n.* rolled iron, drawn iron; pin, axle.
**walzen,** *v.t.* roll; mill. — *v.i.* waltz.
**wälzen,** *v.t.* roll, turn (over). — *v.r.* roll, revolve. — **wälzende Reibung,** rolling friction.
**Walzen-apparat,** *m.* (*Dyeing*) rolling frame. **-drehzahl,** *f.* roll (or roller) velocity, roll r.p.m. **-druck,** *m.* cylinder printing; roller pressure. **-druckfarbe,** *f.* roller printing color.
**walzenförmig,** *a.* cylindrical.
**Walzen-glas,** *n.* cylinder glass. **-glättwerk,** *n.* (*Paper*) calender. **-kessel,** *m.* cylinder boiler, cylindrical boiler. **-lager,** *m.* roller bearing. **-mühle,** *f.* roller mill, roll crusher. **-satz,** *m.* set of rolls, roll train. **-sinter,** *m.* mill scale. **-strasse, -strecke,** *f.* roll train. **-vorschub,** *m.* (*Mach.*) roller feed.
**Walzer,** *m.* waltz.
**Walz-erz,** *n.* ore for crushing. **-erzeugnis,** *n.* rolled product. **-fehler,** *m.* rolling defect. **-gut,** *n.* material for rolling or roll-crushing. **-gutwerkstoff,** *m.* (industrial) rolling material. **-haut,** *f.* mill scale, mill cinder. **-hitze,** *f.* (*Metal.*) rolling heat.
**walzig,** *a.* cylindrical.
**Walz-kupfer,** *m.* sheet copper. **-messing,** *n.* sheet brass, rolled brass. **-normale,** *f.* normal to the plane of rolling. **-produkt,** *n.* rolled product, sheet, plate. **-reibung,** *f.* rolling friction. **-schlacke,** *f.* mill scale, mill cinder. **-sinter,** *m.* mill scale, mill cinder. **-stahl,** *m.* rolled steel. **-strasse, -strecke,** *f.* roll train.
**Wälzverfahren,** *n.* rotary process.
**Walzung,** *f.* rolling; milling.
**Walz-werk,** *n.* rolls, roll train, rolling mill, blooming mill, crushing mill, etc. **-zink,** *n.* rolled zinc, sheet zinc. **-zinn,** *n.* rolled tin, sheet tin. **-zunder,** *m.* mill scale, mill cinder. **-zustand,** *m.* rolled state.
**wand,** *pret.* (of winden) wound, coiled.
**Wand,** *f.* wall; partition, septum; coat; (*Tech.*) side, cheek, panel, screen, baffle. **-bekleidung,** *f.* wall covering. **-bewurf,** *m.* plastering. **-dicke,** *f.* thickness of wall (as of a tube).
**Wände,** *pl.* walls, etc. (see Wand); lump ore.
**Wandel,** *m.* change, variation; mutation; conduct, life; trade, traffic.
**wandelbar,** *a.* changeable, convertible, variable; perishable.
**Wandelbarkeit,** *f.* changeableness, etc. (see wandelbar).
**wandellos,** *a.* unalterable.
**wandeln,** *v.i.* walk, travel, wander; trade. — *v.t.* change, convert. — *v.r.* change; vary.
**Wandelstern,** *m.* planet.
**Wandelung,** *f.* transformation, change.
**Wander-.** migratory, wandering, movable. **-block,** *m.* (*Geol.*) erratic block.
**wandern,** *v.i.* migrate; wander; creep; diffuse; travel, walk, go.
**Wander-rost,** *m.* traveling grate. **-sand,** *m.* shifting sand. **-schaft,** *f.* traveling, travels, tour. **-stärke,** *f.* translocatory starch. **-tier,** *n.* migratory animal.
**Wanderung,** *f.* migration; creeping; diffusion; traveling, travels, walking, walking trip.
**Wanderungs-geschwindigkeit,** *f.* migration velocity. **-sinn,** *m.* direction of migration (of ions). **-zahl,** *f.* transport number.
**Wander-welle,** *f.* traveling wave. **-zelle,** *f.* migratory cell.
**Wandkatalyse,** *f.* wall catalysis.

**Wandler,** *m.* transformer; converter.
**Wandlung,** *f.* transformation, change, metamorphosis.
**Wand-malerei,** *f.* house painting; mural painting. **-putz,** *m.* plastering.
**wandständig,** *a.* parietal, marginal.
**Wand-stärke,** *f.* thickness of wall. **-tafel,** *f.* wall chart; blackboard.
**wandte,** *pret.* (of wenden) turned.
**Wandtisch,** *m.* table attached to a wall.
**Wandung,** *f.* wall; partition.
**Wandungs-schicht,** *f.* (*Biol.*) parietal layer. **-zelle, Wandzelle,** *f.* (*Biol.*) parietal cell.
**Wange,** *f.* cheek; side piece, end piece.
**Wangendrüse,** *f.* buccal gland.
**wankelhaft,** *a.* unsteady, inconstant.
**wanken,** *v.i.* totter, stagger, waver.
**wann,** *adv.* when, then. — *conj.* when.
**Wanne,** *f.* trough; tub; vat; tank; case.
**Wannen-färberei,** *f.* dyeing in open vat. **-ofen,** *m.* (*Glass*) tank furnace.
**Wanze,** *f.* bug (specif., bedbug).
**Wanzenkraut,** *n.* marsh tea; cimicifuga.
**war,** *pret.* (of sein) was.
**warb,** *pret.* (of werben) advertised, etc.
**ward,** *pret.* (of werden) became, etc.
**Wardein,** *m.* mint warden, assay master.
**Ware,** *f.* ware, article, manufacture; specif., textile fabric; (*pl.*) goods, merchandise.
**Waren-haus, -lager,** *n.* warehouse. **-probe,** *f.* sample (of goods). **-stempel,** *m.*, **-zeichen,** *n.* trademark.
**warf,** *pret.* (of werfen) threw, etc.
**Wa.Rk.,** *abbrev.* of Wassermannsche Reaktion.
**warm,** *a.* warm; hot. — **— laufen,** (of moving parts) heat up.
**Wärmaushärtung,** *f.* (*Metal.*) age hardening at higher than room temperature.
**Warmbad-härten,** *n.*, **-härtung,** *f.* (*Metal.*) hot-bath hardening, martempering.
**Warm-bearbeitung,** *f.* hot-working. **-behandlung,** *f.* heat treatment.
**warmbildsam,** *a.* thermoplastic; forgeable.
**Warmbildsamkeit,** *f.* thermoplasticity; (*Metal.*) forgeability.
**Warmblase-.** hot-blast.
**Warmblasen,** *n.* hot blow; (*Water Gas*) air blow.
**Warmblüter,** *m.pl.* warm-blooded animals.
**warm-blütig,** *a.* warm-blooded, hematothermal. **-brüchig,** *a.* (*Metal.*) hot-short, brittle when hot.
**Warmbrunnen,** *m.* hot spring, thermal spring.
**warmdehnbar,** *a.* (*Metal.*) hot-ductile.
**Wärme,** *f.* heat; warmth, warmness.
**Wärme-.** heat, thermal, thermo-, calori-. **-abgabe,** *f.* loss of heat.
**wärmeabgebend,** *a.* exothermic.
**Wärme-alterung,** *f.* heat aging **-änderung,** *f.* change of temperature. **-arbeitswert,** *m.* mechanical equivalent of heat. **-aufnahme,** *f.* absorption of heat. **-aufspeicherung,** *f.* heat storage. **-ausdehnung,** *f.* thermal expansion. **-ausnutzung,** *f.* heat efficiency. **-ausstrahlung,** *f.* radiation of heat. **-austausch,** *m.* heat exchange. **-austauscher,** *m.* heat exchanger. **-behandlung,** *f.* heat treatment.
**wärmebeständig,** *a.* resistant to heat, heatproof, stable on heating, thermostable; of constant temperature.
**Wärme-beständigkeit,** *f.* resistance to heat. **-bewegung,** *f.* heat motion, thermal agitation. **-bilanz,** *f.* heat balance. **-bildner,** *m.* heat producer. **-bildung,** *f.* production of heat. **-bindung,** *f.* absorption of heat.
**wärme-durchlassend, -durchlässig,** *a.* diathermic; heat-conducting.
**Wärme-durchlässigkeit,** *f.* diathermancy; heat conductance. **-dynamik,** *f.* thermodynamics. **-effekt,** *m.* heat effect. **-einfluss,** *m.* influence of heat; heat influx. **-einheit,** *f.* heat unit, thermal unit.
**wärmeelektrisch,** *a.* thermo-electric.
**Wärmeelektrizität,** *f.* thermo-electricity.
**wärmeempfindlich,** *a.* sensitive to heat.
**Wärme-empfindung,** *f.* sensation of heat. **-entbindung,** *f.* disengagement of heat. **-entwickelung,** *f.* evolution of heat.
**wärmeerzeugend,** *p.a.* heat-producing.
**Wärme-erzeuger,** *m.* heat producer, heat-producing substance. **-erzeugung,** *f.* heat production. **-festigkeit,** *f.* heat resistance. **-fluss,** *m.* heat flow, thermal flux.
**wärmegebend,** *a.* heat-yielding, specif. exothermic.
**Wärme-gehalt,** *m.* heat content, enthalpy. **-gewicht,** *n.* heat weight, entropy.
**wärmegleich,** *a.* isothermal.
**Wärme-gleiche,** *f.* isothermal line, isotherm. **-gleichgewicht,** *n.* thermal equilibrium. **-grad,** *m.* degree of heat; temperature. **-gradmesser,** *m.* thermometer. **-grösse,** *f.* specific heat. **-inhalt,** *m.* heat content, enthalpy. **-ionisation,** *f.* thermal ionization. **-isolator,** *m.* heat insulator. **-isolierung,** *f.* heat insulation. **-kapazität,** *f.* heat capacity, thermal capacity. **-kraftlehre,** *f.* thermodynamics. **-kraftmaschine,** *f.* heat engine. **-lehre,** *f.* (science of) heat, theory of heat.
**wärmeleitend,** *p.a.* heat-conducting.
**Wärme-leiter,** *m.* conductor of heat. **-leitfähigkeit,** *f.* thermal conductivity, heat conductance. **-leitung,** *f.* conduction of heat. **-leitvermögen,** *n.*, **-leitzahl,** *f.* thermal conductivity.
**wärmeliefernd,** *a.* furnishing heat; exothermal.
**Wärmemechanik,** *f.* thermodynamics.

**wärmemechanisch,** *a.* thermodynamic.
**Wärme-menge,** *f.* amount or quantity of heat. **-mengenmessung,** *f.* calorimetry.
**wärmemessend,** *a.* calorimetric; thermometric.
**Wärme-messer,** *m.* calorimeter; thermometer; pyrometer. **-messung,** *f.* measurement of heat, calorimetry, thermometry, pyrometry.
**wärmen,** *v.t.* warm; heat. — *v.r.* warm oneself, become warm.
**Wärme-platte,** *f.* warming plate. **-quantum,** *n.* quantity of heat; heat quantum. **-quelle,** *f.* source of heat.
**Wärmer,** *m.* heater.
**Wärme-regler,** *m.* thermoregulator, thermostat. **-sammler,** *m.* heat accumulator. **-schrank,** *m.* warming cabinet. **-schutz,** *m.*, **-schutzmittel,** *n.* heat insulator (or insulation), protection against heat. **-schwankung,** *f.* heat fluctuation. **-schwingung,** *f.* heat vibration.
**wärmesicher,** *a.* heatproof.
**Wärme-speicher,** *m.* heat accumulator, regenerator. **-speicherung,** *f.* heat storage. **-spektrum,** *n.* heat spectrum, thermal spectrum. **-stich,** *m.* fever-producing puncture. **-stoff,** *m.* caloric, thermogen. **-strahl,** *m.* heat ray. **-strahlung,** *f.* heat radiation. **-strömung,** *f.* heat convection. **-summe,** *f.* heat sum. **-technik,** *f.* heat technology.
**wärmetechnisch,** *a.* pertaining to heat engineering.
**Wärme-theorie,** *f.* theory of heat. **-tisch,** *m.* warming table. **-tönung,** *f.* heat effect (of a reaction), heat of reaction, heat change, heat tone. **-übergang,** *m.* passage of heat, heat transmission, heat transfer. **-übertragung,** *f.* heat transfer.
**wärme-unbeständig,** *a.* unstable to heat, thermolabile. **-undurchlässig,** *a.* impervious to heat, athermanous. **-verbrauchend,** *a.* heat-consuming, specif. endothermic.
**Wärme-vergangenheit,** *f.* prior heat treatment. **-vergütung,** *f.* (*Metal.*) heat treatment. **-verlust,** *m.* loss of heat, heat loss. **-vermögen,** *n.* heat capacity. **-vorgang,** *m.* thermal process or phenomenon. **-wert,** *m.* heat value, calorific value.
**wärmewiderstehend,** *a.* heat-resistant.
**Wärme-wirkung,** *f.* effect or action of heat, thermal effect. **-wirkungsgrad,** *m.* thermal efficiency. **-wirtschaft,** *f.* heat economy. **-zahl,** *f.* temperature coefficient.
**wärmezehrend,** *a.* heat-consuming, specif. endothermic.
**Wärme-zerreissversuch,** *m.* heat tensile test. **-zufuhr,** *f.* addition (or supplying) of heat. **-zustand,** *m.* thermal condition.
**warmfest,** *a.* heat-resistant, (of steel) high-temperature.
**Warmfestigkeit,** *f.* heat resistance, (of steel) resistance to deformation at high temperatures.
**Wärmflasche,** *f.* hot-water bottle.
**warmgepresst,** *p.a.* hot-pressed.
**Warm-haus,** *n.* hothouse. **-heit,** *f.* hotness; warmness; temperature. **-lack,** *m.* lacquer applied warm or hot.
**warmlaufen,** *v.i.* (*Mach.*) run hot.
**Warmluft-.** hot-air.
**Wärm-ofen,** *m.* heating furnace; reheating furnace. **-platte,** *f.* warming plate.
**Warm-pressstahl,** *m.* hot-pressing steel. **-probe,** *f.* hot test. **-riss,** *m.* (*Metal.*) heating crack. **-rissigkeit,** *f.* hot-shortness; heat checking. **-sprödigkeit,** *f.* hot-shortness.
**Wärmung,** *f.* warming; heating.
**Warm-versprödung,** *f.* embrittlement by heat. **-vulkanisation,** *f.* (*Rubber*) hot cure.
**Warmwasser-.** hot-water. **-bad,** *m.* hot-water bath. **-speicher,** *m.* hot-water tank.
**Warmwind,** *m.* (*Metal.*) hot blast.
**warnen,** *v.t.* warn, caution.
**Warner,** *m.*, **Warnvorrichtung,** *f.* alarm.
**Warte,** *f.* observatory; lookout.
**warten,** *v.i.* wait; attend (to). — *v.t.* take care of, nurse.
**-wärts.** -ward, -wards.
**Wartung,** *f.* attendance, attention; maintenance, upkeep; nursing.
**warum,** *adv.* why?
**Warze,** *f.* wart; nipple, teat; mastoid; pin, knob, boss, excrescence, tubercle.
**warzen-ähnlich, -artig,** *a.* wart-like, mammillary, (*Biol.*) papillary. **-förmig,** *a.* wart-shaped, wart-like, mammillary, (*Biol.*) papillary.
**Warzenkraut,** *n.* warty plant, specif. marigold.
**warzig,** *a.* warty, verrucose.
**was,** *pron.* what?; that, which; something. — **— für,** what?; what a; what sort of?
**Wasch-anlage,** *f.* washing plant. **-anstalt,** *f.* laundry. **-apparat,** *m.* washing apparatus, washer. **-aufsatz,** *m.* washing attachment. **-bad,** *n.* washing bath, washing liquor.
**waschbar,** *a.* washable, fast (color).
**Wasch-bär,** *m.* raccoon, coon. **-barkeit,** *f.* washability. **-behälter,** *m.* washing tank. **-benzin,** *n.* gasoline for cleaning. **-benzol,** *n.* commercial benzene for cleaning.
**waschbeständig,** *a.* resistant to washing, washproof.
**Wasch-blau,** *n.* bluing, laundry blue. **-bottich,** *m.* washing vat (tub, etc.). **-bürste,** *f.* washing brush, cleaning brush. **-bütte,** *f.* washing tank, purification tub.
**Wäsche,** *f.* washing, wash; washery; clothes, linen.
**waschecht,** *a.* fast to washing.
**waschen,** *v.t.* & *i.* wash; scrub, clean, scour.

**Wascher, Wäscher,** *m.* washer; scrubber.

**Wascherde,** *f.* fuller's earth.

**Wäscherei,** *f.* washing; washhouse, laundry; gossip.

**Wasch-fass,** *n.* washing vat. **-flasche,** *f.* washing bottle, wash bottle. **-flotte, -flüssigkeit,** *f.* wash(ing) liquid. **-gefäss,** *n.* washing vessel. **-gold,** *n.* placer gold. **-gut,** *n.* material (as coal) to be washed. **-holländer,** *m.* (*Paper*) washing engine. **-kristall,** *n.* washing crystals, soda crystals ($Na_2CO_3 \cdot 10H_2O$). **-lauge,** *f.* washing liquor. **-leder,** *n.* wash leather. **-lösung,** *f.* wash(ing) solution. **-maschine,** *f.* washing machine, washer. **-mittel,** *n.* washing agent, detergent; (*Med.*) lotion. **-mittelfabrikation,** *f.* manufacture of detergents. **-öl,** *n.* (*Gas,* etc.) washing oil, wash oil, absorption oil. **-probe,** *f.* washing test; assay of washed (buddled) ore. **-pulver,** *n.* washing powder. **-seife,** *f.* washing soap. **-soda,** *f.* washing soda.

**wäscht,** *pr. 3 sing.* (of waschen) washes.

**Wasch-trommel,** *f.* washing drum, drum washer, washing cylinder. **-turm,** *m.* washing tower.

**Waschung,** *f.* washing; lotion, wash.

**Wasch-verfahren,** *n.*, **-vorgang,** *m.* washing process. **-vorrichtung,** *f.* washing apparatus or device. **-wasser,** *n.* wash water. **-wirkung,** *f.* cleansing action (or effect). **-wurzel,** *f.* soapwort. **-zinn,** *n.* stream tin.

**Wasen,** *m.* vapor, exhalation; lawn, turf.

**Wasser,** *n.* water.

**wasser-, Wasser-.** water, watery, aqueous, hydro-, hygro-, hydraulic. **-abgabe,** *f.* giving off (or elimination) of water, water loss.

**wasserabhaltend,** *a.* waterproof.

**Wasser-ablass,** *m.*, **ableitung,** *f.* drainage, draining. **-abscheidung,** *f.* separation of water; secretion or excretion of water. **-abspaltung,** *f.* splitting off of water, dehydration.

**wasser-abstossend,** *p.a.* repelling water, water-repellent. **-ähnlich,** *a.* like water, watery.

**Wasseranalyse,** *f.* water analysis.

**wasser-anziehend,** *p.a.* attracting moisture, hygroscopic. **-arm,** *a.* having little water; of low humidity. **-artig,** *a.* like water, watery, aqueous.

**Wasser-aufbereitung,** *f.* water treatment. **-aufnahme,** *f.* absorption of water.

**wasser-aufnahmefähig,** *a.* capable of absorbing water. **-aufsaugend,** *a.* absorbing water.

**Wasser-ausscheidung,** *f.* = Wasserabscheidung. **-ausspülung,** *f.* rinsing with water. **-austritt,** *m.* elimination of water. **-auszug,** *m.* water extract, aqueous extract. **-bad,** *n.* water bath. **-balg,** *m.* (*Med.*) serous cyst. **-ballon,** *m.* water carboy. **-baukunst,** *f.* hydraulic engineering. **-bedarf,** *m.* water requirement.

**wasserbegierig,** *a.* readily absorbing, or combining with, water.

**Wasser-behälter,** *m.* (water) reservoir, tank, cistern; (*Brewing*) water back. **-behandlung,** *f.* water treatment. **-beize,** *f.* water stain. **-berieselung,** *v.* water spraying; irrigation.

**wasserbeständig,** *a.* stable in water; resistant to water, waterproof.

**Wasserbestimmung,** *f.* water determination.

**wasserbewohnend,** *f.* (*Biol.*) aquatic.

**Wasserbildung,** *f.* formation of water.

**wasserbindend,** *a.* combining with water; (loosely) absorbing water.

**Wasser-bindung.** *f.* combination of or with water. **-bindungsvermögen,** *n.* water-binding power. **-blase,** *f.* bubble; (*Med.*) vesicle; vessel for heating water; water-storage cell.

**wasserblau,** *a.* blue like water, sea-blue.

**Wasser-blau,** *n.* water blue. **-blei,** *n.* molybdenite; graphite. **-bleiocker,** *m.* molybdic ocher, molybdite. **-bleisäure,** *f.* molybdic acid. **-bombe,** *f.* depth bomb, depth charge. **-bruch,** *m.* hydrocele.

**Wasserdampf,** *m.* water vapor, steam. **-bad,** *n.* steam bath; (*Med.*) vapor bath. **-destillation,** *f.* distillation with steam. **-entwickler, -erzeuger,** *m.* (steam) boiler. **-gehalt,** *m.* steam content.

**Wasserdeckfarbe,** *f.* water pigment color.

**wasserdicht,** *a.* waterproof, water-tight.

**Wasser-dichte, -dichtheit, -dichtigkeit,** *f.* imperviousness to water, waterproofness. **-dichtmachen,** *n.* waterproofing. **-dichtmachungsmittel,** *n.* waterproofing agent. **-druck,** *m.* water pressure; hydraulic pressure. **-drucklehre,** *f.* hydrodynamics. **-dunst,** *m.* water vapor.

**wasserdurchlässig,** *a.* permeable to water.

**Wasserdurchlässigkeit,** *f.* permeability to water.

**wasserecht,** *a.* fast to water.

**Wasserechtmachungsmittel,** *n.* water-resisting agent.

**wasserempfindlich,** *a.* sensitive to water.

**Wasser-enteisenung,** *f.* removal of iron from water. **-enthärtung,** *f.* water softening.

**wasserentziehend,** *a.* removing water, dehydrating, desiccating.

**Wasser-entzieher,** *m.* (*Textiles,* etc.) hydroextractor. **-entziehung,** *f.* removal of water, dehydration; desiccation; hydroextraction. **-entziehungsmittel,** *n.* dehydrating agent. **-erguss,** *m.* watery effusion, edema. **-farbe,** *f.* water color; color of water. **-fass,** *n.* water cask, water tub. **-fenchel,** *m.* water fennel.

**wasserfest,** *a.* water-tight, waterproof.

**Wasser-festigkeit,** *f.* waterproofness. **-fläche,** *f.* water level; surface of water; sheet of water. **-flasche,** *f.* water bottle. **-fleck,** *m.* water stain.

**wasser-förmig,** *a.* like water, watery. **-frei,** *a.* anhydrous, free from water. **-führend,** *p.a.* water-bearing.

**Wasser-gang,** *m.* aqueduct; drain; waterway. **-gas,** *n.* water gas. **-gasteer,** *m.* water-gas tar. **-gebläse,** *n.* water blast. **-gefäss,** *n.* water vessel; (*Med.*) lymphatic vessel. **-gehalt,** *m.* water content, moisture content.

**wassergekühlt,** *p.a.* water-cooled.

**Wasser-geschwulst,** *f.* edema; hygroma. **-gewächs,** *n.* aquatic plant. **-gier,** *f.* hygroscopicity.

**wassergierig,** *a.* hygroscopic; hydrophilic.

**Wasser-glanz,** *m.* moiré. **-glas,** *n.* water glass; glass for water; water gage. **-glaskitt,** *m.* water-glass cement.

**wassergleich,** *a.* like water, watery; level.

**Wassergrün,** *n.* water green (a finely ground green verditer).

**wasserhaft,** *a.* aqueous.

**Wasserhahn,** *m.* water cock, water tap.

**wasser-haltend,** *p.a.* containing water; water-retaining. **-haltig,** *a.* hydrous, hydrated, containing water, aqueous.

**Wasserhaltung,** *f.* drainage.

**wasserhart,** *a.* (*Ceram.*) air-dried, half-dry.

**Wasser-härten,** *n.*, **-härtung,** *f.* water hardening. **-härtungsstahl,** *m.* water-hardening steel. **-harz,** *n.* Burgundy pitch. **-haut,** *f.* water film; hyaloid membrane; amnion. **-heilkunde,** *f.* hydropathy. **-heizung,** *f.* hot-water heating.

**wasserhell,** *a.* clear as water, transparent, water-white.

**Wasserhöhe,** *f.* water level, height (or depth) of water.

**wässerig,** *a.* watery, aqueous, hydrous, (*Med.*) serous.

**Wässerigkeit,** *f.* wateriness; serosity.

**Wasser-kalk,** *m.* hydraulic lime, water lime. **-kasten,** *m.* water tank. **-kessel,** *m.* water boiler, tank or kettle. **-kies,** *m.* (*Min.*) marcasite. **-kitt,** *m.* hydraulic cement.

**wasserklar,** *a.* clear as water, water-white.

**Wasser-kläranlage,** *f.* water-purification plant. **-klee,** *m.* buck bean, bog bean. **-kopf,** *m.* hydrocephalus. **-kraft,** *f.* water power. **-kraftlehre,** *f.* hydrodynamics. **-kran, -krahn,** *m.* water faucet. **-kreislauf,** *m.* water circulation. **-kristall,** *m.* rock crystal. **-kühler,** *m.* water cooler. **-kühlkasten,** *m.* water block. **-kühlung,** *f.* water cooling. **-kunst,** *f.* hydraulics; hydraulic engine; fountain; pumping engine.

**wasserl.,** *abbrev.* (wasserlöslich) water-soluble.

**wasserlässig,** *a.* admitting water, leaky.

**Wasserlauf,** *m.* watercourse, stream.

**wasserleer,** *a.* free from water, anhydrous.

**Wasserleitung,** *f.* water pipes, water piping, water main, (also *Anat.*) aqueduct.

**Wasserleitungs-rohr,** *n.*, **-röhre,** *f.* water pipe, water tube. **-wasser,** *n.* tap water, city water.

**Wasserlinie,** *f.* water line.

**wasser-los,** *a.* waterless, without water, anhydrous. **-löslich,** *a.* water-soluble.

**Wasser-luftpumpe,** *f.* water vacuum pump. **-maische,** *f.* (aqueous) infusion; mash. **-malerei,** *f.* water-color painting. **-mangel,** *m.* lack (or scarcity) of water. **-mantel,** *m.* water jacket. **-mass,** *n.* water gage. **-menge,** *f.* amount of water.

**Wassermess-.** hydrometric.

**Wasser-messer,** *m.* water meter, water gage; hydrometer. **-messkunst,** *f.* hydrometry. **-moos,** *n.* alga; seaweed. **-mörtel,** *m.* hydraulic mortar.

**wässern,** *v.t.* water; soak; hydrate; dilute; irrigate. — *v.i.* water.

**Wasser-nabel,** *m.* marsh pennywort (*Hydrocotyle*). **-niederschlag,** *m.* deposit of moisture. **-opal,** *m.* water opal, hyalite; hydrophane. **-papier,** *n.* (*Paper*) waterleaf. **-pflanze,** *f.* aquatic plant, hydrophyte. **-presse,** *f.* hydraulic press. **-probe,** *f.* water test; sample of water. **-prüfer,** *m.* water tester. **-prüfung,** *f.* water testing, water analysis. **-pumpe,** *f.* water pump.

**wasserreich,** *a.* rich in water; of high humidity.

**Wasser-reinigung,** *f.* purification of water. **-reinigungsanlage,** *f.* water-purification plant. **-reinigungsmittel,** *n.* water-purifying agent. **-rest,** *m.* water residue, hydroxyl. **-rohr,** *n.*, **-röhre,** *f.* water pipe, water tube. **-rohrkessel, -röhrenkessel,** *m.* water-tube boiler. **-röste,** *f.* water retting.

**wassersatt,** *a.* water-saturated.

**wassersaugend,** *a.* water-absorbing.

**Wasser-säule,** *f.* water column. **-scheide,** *f.* water parting, watershed. **-scheu,** *f.* fear of water; (*Med.*) hydrophobia. **-schierling,** *m.* water hemlock (*Cicuta virosa*). **-schlag,** *m.* water hammer. **-schlange,** *f.* water hose; water snake; bladderwort. **-schlauch,** *m.* water hose, (flexible) water tubing; bladderwort. **-schluss,** *m.* water seal, trap. **-siedemesser,** *m.* hypsometer. **-speisung,** *f.* water feed, water supply. **-spiegel,** *m.* water surface, water level. **-spritze,** *f.* syringe; water sprinkler. **-stand,** *m.* height of water, water level; constant (water) level device. **-standsglas,** *n.* gage glass. **-standshahn,** *m.* gage cock. **-stein,** *m.* scale (from water);

whetstone. **-steinansatz,** *m.* deposit of scale.

**Wasserstoff,** *m.* hydrogen (in combination often best translated hydride, *e.g. Äthylwasserstoff*, ethyl hydride).

**wasserstoff-ähnlich,** *a.* resembling hydrogen. **-arm,** *a.* poor in hydrogen.

**Wasserstoffelektrode,** *f.* hydrogen electrode.

**wasserstoffenthaltend,** *a.* = wasserstoffhaltig.

**Wasserstoff-entwickelung,** *f.* evolution of hydrogen. **-entwickler,** *m.* hydrogen generator.

**wasserstoffentziehend,** *a.* abstracting hydrogen, dehydrogenating.

**Wasserstoff-erzeuger,** *m.* hydrogen generator. **-flamme,** *f.* hydrogen flame. **-flasche,** *f.* hydrogen cylinder.

**wasserstofffrei,** *a.* free from hydrogen.

**Wasserstoff-gas,** *n.* hydrogen gas. **-gehalt,** *m.* hydrogen content.

**wasserstoffhaltig,** *a.* containing hydrogen, hydrogenous.

**Wasserstoff-hyperoxyd,** *n.* hydrogen peroxide. **-ion,** *n.* hydrogen ion. **-kalium,** *n.* potassium hydride. **-knallgas,** *n.* detonating gas (explosive mixture of hydrogen and oxygen). **-lötung,** *f.* hydrogen soldering. **-palladium,** *n.* palladium hydride. **-peroxyd,** *n.* hydrogen peroxide.

**wasserstoffreich,** *a.* rich in hydrogen.

**Wasserstoffsalz,** *n.* hydrogen salt.

**wasserstoffsauer,** *a.* of, or combined with, a hydracid.

**Wasserstoff-säure,** *f.* hydracid. **-strom,** *m.* current of hydrogen. **-sulfid,** *n.* hydrogen sulfide. **-superoxyd,** *n.* hydrogen superoxide (hydrogen peroxide). **-verbindung,** *f.* hydrogen compound. **-wertigkeit,** *f.* hydrogen valence. **-zahl,** *f.* hydrogen-ion concentration, *p*H. **-zündmaschine,** *f.* hydrogen lamp, Döbereiner's lamp.

**Wasserstrahl,** *m.* jet of water, water jet. **-gebläse,** *n.* water-jet blast. **-luftpumpe,** **-pumpe,** *f.* water-jet vacuum pump.

**Wasser-strasse,** *f.* waterway. **-strom,** *m.* stream or current of water. **-sturz,** *m.* waterfall. **-sucht,** *f.* dropsy.

**wassersüchtig,** *a.* (*Med.*) dropsical.

**Wasser-suppe,** *f.* water gruel. **-talk,** *m.* brucite. **-teilchen,** *n.* water particle. **-tiefe,** *f.* depth of water; draft (of ships). **-tier,** *n.* water animal, aquatic animal.

**wassertreibend,** *p.a.* (*Med.*) hydragog.

**Wasser-trockenschrank,** *m.* water-jacketed drying closet. **-trommelgebläse,** *n.* water-drum blast, trompe. **-tröpfchen,** *n.* water droplet. **-tropfen,** *n.* drop of water. **-umlauf,** *m.* water circulation.

**wasserundurchlässig,** *a.* impervious to water, water-tight.

**Wässerung,** *f.* watering (specif., irrigation); soaking; purification (with water); hydration.

**wasserunlöslich,** *a.* insoluble in water.

**Wasser-untersuchung,** *f.* investigation of water, specif. water analysis. **-verbrauch,** *m.* consumption of water. **-verdampfung,** *f.* evaporation of water. **-vergoldung,** *f.* water gilding. **-vergüten,** *n.*, **-vergütung,** *f.* (*Metal.*) heat treatment using water. **-verlust,** *m.* loss of water. **-vermögen,** *n.* (*Ceram.*) water-holding ability. **-verschluss,** *m.* water seal. **-versorgung,** *f.* water supply; waterworks. **-verträglichkeit,** *f.* compatibility with water. **-verunreinigung,** *f.* impurity in water; contamination of water. **-vorrat,** *m.* water supply. **-wa(a)ge,** *f.* water level (the instrument); hydrostatic balance. **-wanne,** *f.* water trough, pneumatic trough. **-werk,** *n.* waterworks. **-wert,** *m.* water equivalent. **-zeichen,** *n.* (*Paper*) watermark. **-zement,** *m.* hydraulic cement. **-zersetzung,** *f.* decomposition of water.

**wasserziehend,** *p.a.* attracting water; hydrophilic.

**Wasser-zufluss,** *m.*, **-zufuhr,** *f.* water supply, water feed. **-zusatz,** *m.* addition of water.

**wässrig,** *a.* = wässerig.

**Watte,** *f.* wadding (as of cotton or glass wool), wad, padding, pad; cotton wool. **-bausch,** *m.* cotton plug or pad. **-filter,** *n.* cotton-wool strainer. **-pfropf,** *m.* plug of wadding, wad. **-schicht,** *f.* layer of wadding. **-verschluss,** *m.* plug of wadding (esp., cotton).

**wattieren,** *v.t.* wad; pad.

**Wattleistung,** *f.* power in watts.

**wattlos,** *a.* (*Elec.*) wattless.

**Watt-messer,** *m.* (*Elec.*) wattmeter. **-stunde,** *f.* (*Elec.*) watt-hour. **-zahl,** *f.* (*Elec.*) number of watts, wattage.

**Wau,** *m.* weld, dyer's weed (*Reseda luteola*). **-gelb,** *n.* luteolin.

**W.E., WE.,** *abbrev.* (Wärmeeinheit) heat unit.

**weben,** *v.t.* weave.

**Weber,** *m.* weaver. **-distel,** *f.* fuller's teasel (*Dipsacus*).

**Weberei,** *f.* weaving; texture, tissue; weaving mill.

**Weber-glas,** *n.* thread counter; web glass. **-zettel,** *m.* warp.

**Webstuhl,** *m.* loom. **-öl,** *n.* loom oil.

**Webware,** *f.* woven goods.

**Wechsel,** *m.* change, shifting; alternation; cycle; variation; exchange; cock, tap; joint, junction; rotation (of crops); bill (of exchange), draft.

**wechselbar,** *a.* changeable.

**Wechsel-bewegung,** *f.* reciprocating motion. **-beziehung,** *f.* correlation; interrelation;

(*Com.*) drawing. **-fall,** *m.* vicissitude; alternative, dilemma.
**wechselfarbig,** *a.* changing color, iridescent.
**Wechsel-feld,** *n.* (*Elec.*) alternating field. **-fieber,** *n.* intermittent fever. **-gespräch,** *n.* dialog. **-hahn,** *m.* change cock. **-handel,** *m.* banking. **-kontakt,** *m.* (*Elec.*) make and break. **-kraft,** *f.* variable force; periodic force. **-kurs,** *m.* rate of exchange.
**wechsellagern,** *v.i.* be interbedded or interstratified.
**wechseln,** *v.t.* change; vary; exchange; interchange; reverse. — *v.i.* alternate; change places. — **wechselnd,** *p.a.* varying, variable; alternating.
**Wechselsatz,** *m.* exchange principle.
**wechselseitig,** *a.* reciprocal; mutual; interchangeable; alternate; alternating.
**Wechsel-spannung,** *f.* alternation of stress; (*Elec.*) alternating(-current) voltage. **-spiel,** *n.* alternation, fluctuation.
**wechselständig,** *a.* alternate.
**Wechsel-stein,** *m.* glazed tile, glazed brick. **-strom,** *m.* alternating current.
**wechselsweise,** *adv.* = wechselweise.
**Wechsel-ventil,** *n.* change-over valve. **-verhältnis,** *n.* reciprocal relation; reciprocal proportion.
**wechselweise,** *adv.* alternately; reciprocally; mutually; interchangeably.
**Wechsel-winkel,** *m.pl.* alternate angles. **-wirkung,** *f.* reciprocal action or effect. **-zahl,** *f.* number of changes or alternations, cycle number, frequency. **-zersetzung,** *f.* double (or mutual) decomposition.
**Wechsler,** *m.* changer; (*Com.*) money changer.
**Wechslung,** *f.* changing, etc. (see wechseln).
**Weck, Wecken,** *m.*, **Wecke,** *f.* roll, small loaf.
**wecken,** *v.t.* wake, waken, rouse.
**Wecker,** *m.* alarm; bell.
**Wedel,** *m.* fan; brush; (*Bot.*) frond.
**weder,** *conj.* neither. — **— . . . noch,** neither . . . nor.
**weg,** *adv.* away, off, gone.
**Weg,** *m.* way; passage, route, road, street, path, course; manner; means; (*Mech.*) displacement.
**weg-.** away, off, a-, ab-. **-ätzen,** *v.t.* remove by caustics, etch away. **-begeben,** *v.r.* go away, withdraw. **-beizen,** *v.t.* = wegätzen. **-bekommen,** *v.t.* get, catch; get away; get the knack of. **-brennen,** *v.t.* burn away, burn off. **-bringen,** *v.t.* carry or take away, remove. **-denken,** *v.t.* imagine to be absent. **-diffundieren,** *v.i.* diffuse away.
**Wege-bau,** *m.* road making. **-dorn,** *m.* purging buckthorn (*Rhamnus cathartica*).
**wegen,** *prep. with gen.* (sometimes following its object). on account of, regarding.
**Wegerich,** *m.* plantain.
**Wegfall,** *m.* omission; suppression. — **in — kommen,** be omitted or suppressed.
**wegfallen,** *v.i.* fall off, drop; be omitted, cease.
**Wegfiltern,** *n.* filtering off or away.
**weg-gehen,** *v.i.* go away, go off, escape. **-giessen,** *v.t.* pour away, pour off. **-glühen,** *v.t.* drive off by ignition. **-kochen,** *v.t. & i.* boil away, boil off. **-kommen,** *v.i.* get away; come off; get lost. **-kratzen,** *v.t.* scratch out.
**Weglänge,** *f.* (length of) path. — **mittlere freie —,** mean free path.
**weg-lassen,** *v.t.* leave out, omit; let go, release. **-leitend,** *p.a* efferent. **-machen,** *v.t.* remove. — *v.r.* make off.
**Wegnahme,** *f.* taking away, removal; seizure; (*Physiol.*) elimination.
**weg-nehmen,** *v.t.* take away, remove. **-oxydieren,** *v.t.* oxidize away or off. **-radieren,** *v.t.* erase; scratch out. **-räumen,** *v.t.* remove, clear away.
**wegsam,** *a.* pervious, penetrable, passable.
**Wegsamkeit,** *f.* perviousness, penetrability.
**weg-saugen,** *v.t.* suck away, remove by suction. **-schaben,** *v.t.* scrape off. **-schaffen,** *v.t.* remove, eliminate. **-schmelzen,** *v.t.* melt away, melt off, remove by fusion. **-schütten,** *v.t.* pour off, run off. **-sein,** *v.i.* be away, be gone; be faint. **-setzen,** *v.t.* put away. — *v.i.* leap. **-sickern,** *v.i.* ooze away, trickle away. **-sieden,** *v.t.* boil away, boil off. **-spülen,** *v.t.* rinse away, wash away.
**Wegstrecke,** *f.* distance, stretch.
**weg-streichen,** *v.t.* strike out; stroke away. **-tun,** *v.t.* put away, remove, dismiss.
**Wegwart,** *m.* chicory. **-wurzel,** *f.* chicory root.
**weg-waschbar,** *a.* removable by washing. **-waschen,** *v.t.* wash away.
**Wegweiser,** *m.* guide; sign post; directory.
**weg-werfen,** *v.t.* throw away; reject. **-werfend,** *p.a.* disparaging. **-wischen,** *v.t.* wipe away. **-ziehen,** *v.t.* draw away, pull away. — *v.i.* depart, move.
**weh,** *interj.* woe. — *a.* sore, painful, aching. — **— tun,** ache, give pain.
**Weh, Wehe,** *n.* woe, pain, grief, ache.
**Wehe,** *f.* (snow) drift.
**wehen,** *v.i.* blow; (of a flag) wave.
**Wehenmittel,** *n.* ecbolic.
**Wehr,** *n. & f.* weir, dam; dike.
**Wehr, Wehre,** *f.* defense.
**Wehrdrüse,** *f.* defensive scent gland.
**wehren,** *v.t.* check, keep, restrain, prevent. — *v.r.* resist.
**wehrlos,** *a.* unarmed, unprotected.
**Wehrmacht,** *f.* armed forces.
**Weib,** *n.* woman; wife.
**weiblich,** *a.* female; feminine; womanly; womanish.

**weich,** *a.* soft; plastic; (*Leather*) limp; tender, weak, gentle, mild.

**Weichblei,** *n.* soft lead, refined lead.

**weichbleibend,** *p.a.* remaining soft, non-hardening.

**Weich-bottich,** *m.* steeping tub. **-brand,** *m.* soft brick, place brick. **-braunstein,** *m.* pyrolusite. **-bütte,** *f.* (*Brewing*) steep tank, cistern. **-dauer,** *f.* time of steeping or soaking.

**Weiche,** *f.* softness; side, (*pl.*) groin; siding, switch; soaking vessel; (*Leather*) soak pit, soak.

**Weicheisen,** *n.* soft iron. **-kies,** *m.* (*Min.*) marcasite.

**weichen,** *v.t.* soften; soak, steep. — *v.i.* yield, give way, retreat, recede.

**Weichen-.** inguinal; switch.

**Weichfass,** *n.* steeping tub.

**weichfeuern,** *v.t.* (*Puddling*) melt down.

**Weich-fleckigkeit,** *f.* (*Metal.*) liability to soft spots. **-floss,** *n.* (*Metal.*) porous white pig. **-glühen,** *n.*, **-glühung,** *f.* soft annealing, spheroidizing anneal. **-gummi,** *n.* soft rubber. **-guss,** *m.* malleable cast iron, malleable iron. **-haltungsmittel,** *n.* softening agent, softener, plasticizer. **-harz,** *n.* soft resin, oleoresin. **-heit,** *f.* softness, etc. (see weich). **-holz,** *n.* soft wood. **-käse,** *f.* soft cheese. **-kautschuk,** *m.* soft rubber. **-kohle,** *f.* soft coal. **-kopal,** *m.* soft copal. **-kufe,** *f.* steeping vat, soaking tub, etc. **-kupfer,** *n.* soft copper. **-leder,** *n.* soft leather.

**weichlich,** *a.* soft, tender, delicate, weak.

**Weichlot,** *n.* soft solder.

**weichlöten,** *v.t.* soft-solder.

**Weich-machen,** *n.* softening; plasticizing. **-macher,** *m.* softener; plasticizer. **-machungsmittel,** *n.* softening agent, softener, plasticizer. **-mangan, -manganerz,** *n.* pyrolusite. **-metall,** *n.* soft metal. **-paraffin,** *n.* soft paraffin. **-pech,** *n.* soft pitch. **-porzellan,** *n.* soft porcelain.

**Weichselkirsche,** *f.* mahaleb; morello.

**Weich-stahl,** *m.* milk steel, soft steel. **-stelle,** *f.* soft place, soft spot. **-stock,** *m.* steeping tub; (*Brewing*) steep tank, cistern. **-teil,** *m.* soft part. **-tier,** *n.* mollusk. **-wasser,** *n.* steeping water, steep water, soak liquor. **-werden,** *n.* softening.

**Weid,** *m.* woad. — *f.* hunting.

**Weide,** *f.* willow; pasture, pasturage.

**weiden,** *v.t. & i.* pasture, feed.

**Weiden-bitter,** *n.* salicin. **-geflecht,** *n.* wickerwork. **-kohle,** *f.* willow charcoal.

**weidlich,** *adv.* soundly, thoroly.

**Weife,** *f.* reel.

**weifen,** *v.t.* reel, wind.

**weigern,** *v.t. & r.* refuse, decline.

**Weihe,** *f.* consecration; sanction; kite (the bird).

**weihen,** *v.t.* consecrate, ordain, devote.

**Weiher,** *m.* pond, pool.

**Weihnachten,** *f.pl.* Christmas.

**Weihnachtswurzel,** *f.* black hellebore.

**Weihrauch,** *m.* incense; specif., frankincense, olibanum. **-harz,** *n.* incense resin; specif., frankincense.

**weil,** *conj.* because, since; while.

**Weilchen,** *n.* little while.

**Weile,** *f.* while, time; leisure.

**weilen,** *v.i.* tarry, stay.

**Wein,** *m.* wine; vine.

**weinähnlich,** *a.* like wine, vinaceous.

**Weinart,** *f.* kind of wine.

**weinartig,** *a.* vinous, winy.

**Wein-bau,** *m.* viniculture, viticulture. **-bauer,** *m.* wine grower, grape grower. **-beere,** *f.* grape. **-beeröl,** *n.* oil of wine, enanthic ether. **-berg,** *m.* vineyard. **-blau,** *n.* wine blue (enocyanin). **-blume,** *f.* bouquet (of wine); enanthic ether (as an artificial flavoring). **-blüte,** *f.* vine blossom. **-brand, -branntwein,** *m.* brandy made from wine.

**weinen,** *v.i.* weep, cry.

**Weinernte,** *f.* vintage.

**weinerzeugend,** *p.a.* wine-producing.

**Wein-essig,** *m.* wine vinegar. **-fabrik,** *f.* winery. **-farbe,** *f.* wine color.

**weinfarben, weinfarbig,** *a.* wine-colored.

**Wein-farbstoff,** *m.* coloring matter of wine. **-fass,** *n.* wine cask. **-flasche,** *f.* wine bottle.

**weingar,** *a.* fermented. — **weingare Maische,** (*Distilling*) wash.

**Wein-garten,** *m.* vineyard. **-gärung,** *f.* vinous fermentation. **-gegend,** *f.* wine district. **-gehalt,** *m.* wine content, vinosity.

**Weingeist,** *m.* (ethyl) alcohol, spirit of wine. — **versüsster —,** (*Pharm.*) spirit of nitrous ether.

**weingeistartig,** *a.* alcoholic.

**Weingeistfirnis,** *m.* spirit varnish.

**weingeisthaltig,** *a.* alcoholic.

**weingeistig,** *a.* spirituous, alcoholic. — **weingeistiges Ammoniak,** spirit of ammonia.

**Weingeist-lack,** *m.* spirit varnish. **-lampe,** *f.* spirit lamp, alcohol lamp. **-messer,** *m.* alcoholometer.

**wein-gelb,** *a.* wine-yellow. **-haltig,** *a.* containing wine.

**Wein-handel,** *m.* wine trade. **-hefe,** *f.* wine lees; wine yeast. **-honig,** *m.* wine and honey, oenomel.

**weinig,** *a.* vinous.

**Wein-kamm,** *m.* grape pomace, rape. **-kernöl,** *n.* grape-seed oil. **-lese,** *f.* vintage. **-messer,** *m.* vinometer, enometer. **-most,** *m.* grape must, grape juice. **-öl,** *n.* oil of wine, enanthic ether; **(schweres)** heavy oil of wine (oily residue from preparation of ether). **-probe,** *f.* sample of wine; sampling of wine. **-prüfung,** *f.* wine testing. **-raute,** *f.* (common) rue. **-rebe,** *f.* grapevine. **-rebenschwarz,** *n.* Frankfort black.

**wein-rot,** *a.* wine-red, claret. **-sauer,** *a.* of or combined with tartaric acid, tartrate of. **-säuerlich,** *a.* sourish (like some wine).

**Wein-säure,** *f.* tartaric acid; acidity of wine. **-schöne,** *f.* fining for wine. **-sprit,** *m.* spirit of wine, (ethyl) alcohol. **-stärkemesser,** *m.* wine hydrometer, enometer. **-stein,** *m.* tartar. — **roher —,** crude tartar, wine stone, argol. — **gereinigter —,** purified tartar, cream of tartar.

**weinsteinartig,** *a.* tartar-like, tartareous.

**Weinstein-bildung,** *f.* tartar formation, tartarization. **-ersatz,** *m.* (*Dyeing*) tartar substitute, specif. sodium hydrogen sulfate. **-kohle,** *f.* black flux. **-präparat,** *n.* (*Dyeing*) sodium hydrogen sulfate. **-rahm,** *m.* cream of tartar. **-salz,** *n.* salt of tartar (potassium carbonate).

**weinsteinsauer,** *a.* = weinsauer.

**Wein-steinsäure,** *f.* tartaric acid. **-stock,** *m.* grapevine. **-traube,** *f.* grape, bunch of grapes. **-treber,** *f.pl.*, **-trester,** *m.pl.* marc of grapes. **-untersuchung,** *f.* examination (or investigation) of wine. **-verfälschung,** *f.* adulteration of wine. **-wa(a)ge,** *f.* vinometer, enometer.

**weise,** *a.* wise, prudent.

**Weise,** *f.* manner, custom, way; (*Gram.*) mood; melody. — *m.* sage, philosopher.

**-weise.** in . . . manner, by . . . , -ly.

**weisen,** *v.t.* show; indicate, point out, direct, send, teach. — *v.i.* point.

**Weiser,** *m.* pointer, indicator, hand; sign post; guide, teacher.

**Weisheit,** *f.* wisdom, knowledge.

**weiss,** *pr. 1 & 3 sing.* (of wissen) know(s).

**weiss,** *a.* white; blank; clean. — **weisser Amber,** spermaceti. — **weiss ätzbar,** (*Dyeing*) dischargeable to white. — **weisses Eisenblech,** tin plate. — **weisser Elektronenstrahl,** heterogeneous beam of electrons. — **weisser Fluss,** leucorrhea. — **weiss gerben,** taw. — **weisse Glut,** white heat. — **weisser Kupferstein,** (*Copper*) white metal. — **weisser Leim,** gelatin. — **weisse Magnesia,** magnesia alba (basic magnesium carbonate). — **weisses Nichts,** nihil album (zinc oxide). — **weiss sieden,** blanch. — **weisser Vitriol,** white vitriol (zinc sulfate). — **weiss werden,** become white; (of varnish) blush, chalk.

**Weiss,** *n.* white.

**weissagen,** *v.t. & i.* predict, prophesy.

**Weiss-anlaufen,** *n.* (of varnish) blushing, chalking. **-äscher,** *m.* (*Leather*) white lime, fresh lime. **-ätze, -ätzung,** *f.* (*Calico*) white discharge. **-bad,** *n.* whitening bath, (in Turkey-red dyeing) white liquor bath. **-baumöl,** *n.* cajuput oil. **-bier,** *n.* pale beer; specif., weiss beer.

**weissblau,** *a.* whitish-blue.

**Weiss-blech,** *n.* tin plate. **-blechdose,** *f.* tin can, tin box, tin. **-blechwaren,** *f.pl.* tinware. **-blei,** *n.* tin. **-bleiche,** *f.* bleaching, full bleach. **-bleierz,** *n.* white lead ore, cerussite. **-blütigkeit,** *f.* leukemia, leucocythemia. **-boden,** *m.* (*Tech.*) white ground. **-brennen,** *n.* calcining at white heat. **-brot,** *n.* white bread, wheat bread.

**weissbrüchig,** *a.* of white or pale fracture.

**Weiss-brühe,** *f.* (*Leather*) tawing liquor. **-buche,** *f.* hornbeam. **-dorn,** *m.* hawthorn.

**Weisse,** *m. & f.* white person, white. — *f.* whiteness; white; whitewash; pale beer.

**Weiss-eisen,** *n.* white iron. **-emaille,** *f.* white enamel.

**weissen,** *v.t.* whiten, bleach; whitewash; (*Iron*) refine.

**Weiss-erde,** *f.* white earth, terra alba, specif. white clay. **-erz,** *n.* arsenopyrite; siderite; krennerite; an impure marcasite. **-farbe,** *f.* white color, white pigment.

**weissfärben,** *v.t.* bleach (and blue); color white, whiten.

**Weiss-färber,** *m.* bleacher. **-fäule,** *f.* (*Bot.*) white rot. **-feuer,** *n.* white fire. **-föhre,** *f.* Scotch pine (*Pinus sylvestris*).

**weiss-gar,** *a.* tawed. **-gelb,** *a.* pale yellow. **-gerben,** *v.t.* taw.

**Weiss-gerber,** *m.* tawer. **-gerberdegras,** *n.* (*Leather*) sod oil. **-gerberei,** *f.* tawing, alum tanning; tawery, alum tannery. **-gerberfett,** *n.* (*Leather*) sod oil. **-gerbung,** *f.* tawing, alum tannage. **-glühen,** *n.* incandescence.

**weiss-glühen,** *v.t.* raise to white heat. **-glühend,** *p.a.* white-hot, incandescent.

**Weiss-glühhitze, -glut,** *f.* white heat, incandescence. **-gold,** *n.* platinum; white gold. **-golderz,** *n.* sylvanite.

**weissgrau,** *a.* light gray, pale gray.

**Weiss-güldenerz, -gültigerz,** *n.* argentiferous tetrahedrite. **-guss,** *m.* white metal; white malleable cast iron. **-hitze,** *f.* white heat. **-kalk,** *m.* pyrolignite of lime (crude calcium acetate); fat lime, white lime. **-kernguss,** *m.* white-heart malleable iron.

**weisskernig,** *a.* (*Iron*) white-heart.

**Weiss-kies,** *m.* arsenopyrite. **-klee,** *m.* white clover.

**weisskochen,** *v.t.* degum (silk).

**Weiss-kohl,** *m.* white cabbage, common cabbage. **-kreuz,** *n.* (*Mil.*) white cross (German marking for a lacrimator). **-kupfer,** *n.* native copper arsenide, domeykite; white copper (paktong, nickel silver, etc.). **-kupfererz,** *n.* cubanite; an impure marcasite. **-lauge,** *f.* white liquor. **-leder,** *n.* white leather, tawed leather.

**weisslich,** *a.* whitish. **-grau,** *a.* whitish-gray.

**Weisslot,** *n.* soft solder, tin solder.

**weissmachen,** *v.t.* make white, bleach.

**Weiss-mehl,** *n.* white flour, wheat flour. **-messing,** *n.* white brass. **-metall,** *n.* white metal. **-nickelerz,** *n.*, **-nickelkies,** *m.* white nickel ore, chloanthite. **-ofen,** *m.* (*Metal.*) refining furnace. **-papp,** *m.* (*Calico*) white resist. **-produkt,** *n.* white product, (*Petroleum*) refined product. **-reserve,** *f.* (*Calico*) white resist.

**weissrot,** *a.* whitish red.

**Weiss-schliff,** *m.* white ground wood, (*Paper*) white mechanical pulp. **-siedekessel,** *m.* blanching copper.

**weis(s)sieden,** *v.t.* blanch.

**Weiss-siedlauge,** *f.* blanching liquor. **-spiessglanz,** *m.*, **-spiessglanzerz,** *n.* white antimony, valentinite. **-stein,** *m.* white stone or rock; (*Copper*) white metal. **-strahl,** *m.*, **-strahleisen,** *n.* white pig iron resembling spiegeleisen.

**weis(s)strahlig,** *a.* white-radiated.

**Weiss-stuck,** *m.* white stucco. **-sud,** *m.* blanching; blanching solution. **-sylvanerz,** *n.* sylvanite. **-tanne,** *f.* silver fir (*Abies alba* and *A. pectinata*). **-tellur,** *n.* sylvanite. **-tönung,** *f.* white tint. **-trockner,** *m.* (*Paints*) white drier. **-verdünnung,** *f.*, **-verschnitt,** *m.* dilution (or reduction) with white. **-vitriol,** *n.* white vitriol (zinc sulfate). **-waren,** *f.pl.* white goods, linen goods.

**weisswarm,** *a* white-hot.

**Weiss-wäsche,** *f.* white laundry goods. **-wäscherei,** *f.* laundry (for white goods). **-wein,** *m.* white wine. **-werden,** *n.* whitening; (of lacquers, etc.) blushing, chalking. **-wurzel,** *f.* Solomon's seal. **-zeug,** *n.* & *m.* white material or goods. **-zucker,** *m.* white sugar.

**Weisung,** *f.* order, direction, instructions, assignment; direction finding.

**weit,** *a.* far, distant; long, great; wide, extended; loose. — *adv.* far, much. — **bei weitem,** by far.

**weitaus,** *adv.* by far. **-gebreitet,** *a.* widespread, extended, expanded.

**Weite,** *f.* distance; wideness, width; diameter; amplitude; extent, length, range.

**weiten,** *v.t.* & *r.* widen; extend; expand.

**weiter,** *a.* farther; wider; further, additional. — *adv.* farther, forward, on.

**Weiter-bearbeitung, -behandlung,** *f.* further or subsequent treatment. **-entwickeln,** *n.*, **-entwickelung,** *f.* further development.

**Weiteres,** *n.* remainder, rest. — **ohne —, ohne weiteres,** without more ado, directly.

**weiter-färben,** *v.t.* dye further, continue dyeing. **-gerben,** *v.t.* re-tan. **-hin,** *adv.* furthermore, in addition. **-oxydieren,** *v.t.* oxidize further.

**Weiterung,** *f.* complication, formality, (*pl.* **Weiterungen**) red tape.

**Weiter-verarbeitung,** *f.* further working or manufacture, subsequent treatment. **-wirkung,** *f.* further action, continued action.

**weitgehend,** *p.a.* far-reaching, extensive; excessive. — *adv.* extensively, largely.

**Weithalsflasche,** *f.* wide-necked bottle.

**weithalsig,** *a.* wide-necked.

**Weithals-kölbchen,** *n.* small wide-necked flask. **-kolben,** *m.* wide-necked flask.

**weit-hin,** *adv.* far off, in wide extent. **-läufig,** *a.* wide, large, roomy; distant; widespread, scattered, straggling, diffuse, detailed. **-lochig,** *a.* large-holed, large-pored. **-maschig,** *a.* wide-meshed, coarse-meshed. **-mündig,** *a.* wide-mouthed. **-sichtig,** *a.* far-sighted. **-tragend,** *p.a.* carrying a great distance; important. **-umfassend,** *a.* comprehensive, extensive.

**Weitung,** *f.* widening; width; space.

**weit-verbreitet,** *a.* widespread, extended. **-winklig,** *a.* wide-angle(d).

**Weizen,** *m.* wheat. — **türkischer —,** maize.

**Weizen-brot,** *m.* wheat bread; wheaten loaf. **-griess,** *m.* wheat grits. **-griesskleie,** *f.* middlings. **-keim,** *m.* wheat germ. **-kleie,** *f.* wheat bran. **-kleienbeize,** *f.* (*Leather*) bran drench. **-malz,** *n.* wheat malt. **-mehl,** *n.* wheat flour. **-schrot,** *n.* coarse ground wheat. **-stärke,** *f.*, **-stärkemehl,** *n.* wheat starch. **-stärkekleister,** *m.* wheat starch paste. **-stroh,** *n.* wheat straw.

**welch,** *pron.* which? what?; who, which, that; some, any. — **welcher auch,** whosoever; **welches auch,** whatosever.

**welcherlei,** *a.* of what kind.

**Weldonschlamm,** *m.* Weldon mud.

**welk,** *a.* withered, faded; flaccid; languid.

**Welkboden,** *m.* (*Brewing*) withering floor.

**welken,** *v.i.* wither, wilt, fade, decay. — *v.t.* wither, wilt, dry.

**Welkmalz,** *n.* withered malt, air-dried malt.

**Well-baum,** *m.* arbor, shaft, axletree. **-blech,** *n.* corrugated plate or sheet, specif. corrugated iron.

**Welle,** *f.* wave; shaft, arbor, axle, spindle; roller, roll; stria (in glass); fagot, bundle.

**wellen,** *v.t.* boil, simmer; roll; wave; corrugate; wield. — **gewellt,** *p.a.* wavy; corrugated.

**Wellen-änderung,** *f.* (wave) frequency shift. **-anzeiger,** *m.* wave detector, cymoscope.

**wellenartig,** *a.* wave-like, wavy, undulatory.

**Wellen-ausbreitung,** *f.* wave propagation. **-bereich,** *m.* wave band. **-berg,** *m.* wave crest, wave peak. **-bewegung,** *f.* wave motion, undulatory motion. **-bild,** *n.* wave form; wave image; oscillogram. **-bündel,** *n.* wave packet. **-bündelung,** *f.* beaming. **-filter,** *n.* wave filter. **-fläche,** *f.* wave surface.

**wellenförmig,** *a.* undulatory, wavy; corrugated.

**Wellen-front,** *f.* wave front, wave head. **-gipfel,** *m.* wave crest, wave peak. **-gleichung,** *f.* wave equation. **-kopf,** *m.* wave front. **-lager,** *n.* (*Mach.*) bearing, carriage. **-länge,** *f.* wave length. **-leitung,** *f.* wave guide; shafting. **-linie,** *f.* wavy line. **-mechanik,** *f.* wave mechanics.

**wellenmechanisch,** *a.* wave-mechanical.

**Wellen-messer,** *m.* wavemeter, ondometer, cymometer. **-optik,** *f.* wave optics.

**wellenoptisch,** *a.* of or pertaining to wave optics.

**Wellen-paket,** *n.* wave packet. **-papier,** *n.* corrugated paper. **-rückstrahlung,** *f.* wave reflection. **-sauger, -schlucker,** *m.* wave trap. **-schreiber,** *m.* oscillograph. **-schwingung,** *f.* undulation. **-spannung,** *f.* wave potential. **-stirn,** *f.* wave face, wave front. **-strom,** *m.* (*Elec.*) pulsating current, undulatory current. **-stromlichtbogen,** *m.* pulsating-current arc. **-tal,** *n.* wave trough, wave valley. **-theorie,** *f.* wave theory, undulatory theory. **-weite,** *f.* amplitude. **-zahl,** *f.* wave number. **-zug,** *m.* wave train.

**Weller,** *m.* loam, clay, mud.

**wellig,** *a.* undulating, wavy.

**Welligkeit,** *f.* undulating property, waviness.

**Well-packpapier, -papier,** *n.* corrugated paper. **-pappe,** *f.* corrugated (paper)board. **-rad,** *n.* wheel and axle; arbor wheel. **-rohr,** *n.* corrugated tube or pipe.

**Wellung,** *f.* waving, undulation; corrugation.

**Wellwurzel,** *f.* (*Pharm.*) symphytum.

**welsch,** *a.* foreign (specif., Italian or French); Welsh.

**Welschkorn,** *n.* maize, corn.

**Welt,** *f.* world; good breeding. **-all,** *n.* universe. **-alter,** *n.* age of the world; age. **-anschauung,** *f.* view of the world or of life, ideology. **-auge,** *f.* hydrophane. **-ausstellung,** *f.* world's fair. **-beschreibung,** *f.* cosmography.

**weltbürgerlich,** *a.* cosmopolitan.

**Weltenraum,** *m.* universal space, interstellar space.

**Welt-gegend,** *f.* quarter of the world. **-gürtel,** *m.* zone. **-handel,** *m.* world commerce. **-körper,** *m.* heavenly body. **-krieg,** *m.* world war. **-kugel,** *f.* globe.

**weltlich,** *a.* worldly, mundane; secular, temporal, civil, profane.

**Welt-meer,** *n.* ocean. **-postverein,** *m.* Postal Union. **-raum,** *m.* = Weltenraum. **-sprache,** *f.* universal language. **-stadt,** *f.* metropolis. **-teil,** *m.* continent; part of the world.

**weltweit,** *a.* worldwide.

**wem,** *pron.* (dative of wer) whom, to whom.

**wen,** *pron.* whom, which.

**Wende,** *f.* turning, turning point, turn; change; epoch, era. **-kreis,** *m.* tropic; turning radius.

**Wendel,** *f.* helix, coil, (screw-like) spiral.

**wendeln,** *v.i.* wind, spiral (like a screw thread).

**wenden,** *v.t., i. & r.* turn; (*Elec.*) reverse. — **gewandt,** *p.a.* versed, skilled, clever, quick.

**Wendepunkt,** *m.* turning point, point of inflection.

**Wender,** *m.* turner, rotator, rotor; (*Elec.*) reverser.

**Wendestelle,** *f.* turning place.

**Wendigkeit,** *f.* manageableness, maneuverability; mobility; turning radius.

**Wendung,** *f.* turning, turn; (*Elec.*) reversal.

**wenig,** *a.* little; (*pl.*) few. — *adv.* little.

**weniger,** *a.* less, fewer. — *adv.* less.

**Wenigkeit,** *f.* littleness, small amount, small number; trifle.

**wenigslöslich,** *a.* little (or difficultly) soluble.

**wenigste,** *a.* least, fewest.

**wenigstens,** *adv.* at least.

**wenn,** *adv.* when. — *conj.* when; if. — **— auch, — gleich, — schon,** altho, even if.

**wer,** *pron.* who? which?; who, he who. — **— . . . nur, — . . . auch,** whoever.

**Werbe-.** advertising, publicity, propaganda.

**werben,** *v.i.* advertise; carry on propaganda; strive; sue, court. — *v.t.* levy, recruit.

**Werbeschrift,** *f.* advertising publication; propaganda article or pamphlet.

**Werdegang,** *m.* development.

**werden,** *v.i.* become; turn; fall (to one's lot). — *v. aux.* shall, will, be, am, etc. — **es wird mir,** I feel.

**werfen,** *v.t.* throw; cast, fling, project. — *v.i.* bring forth young. — *v.r.* throw oneself, apply oneself; warp; (of beer) become turbid.

**Werfer,** *m.* projector; thrower. **-geschoss,** *n.* projector missile. **-rahmen,** *m.* projector frame; frame-type rocket projector.

**Werft,** *f.* wharf, dock; weft.

**Werg,** *n.* tow, oakum.

**Werk,** *n.* work; works; apparatus, mechanism; (*Salt*) brine evaporated at one time; (*Metal.*) pig of raw lead; (*Paper*) stuff. **-anlage,** *f.* plant, works; work equipment. **-blei,** *n.* raw lead (usually containing silver). **-bottich,** *m.*, **-bütte,** *f.* (*Paper*) stuff vat. **-führer,** *m.* foreman. **-leitung,** *f.* management. **-leute,** *pl.* workmen, hands. **-meister,** *m.* foreman. **-probe,** *f.* (*Metal.*) sample of metal. **-silber,** *n.* silver extracted from lead ore. **-statt, -stätte,** *f.* (work)shop, workroom, laboratory, studio. **-stein,** *m.* freestone, quarry stone. **-stoff,** *m.* (industrial) material. **-stof(f)forschung,** *f.* materials research. **-stoffprüfung,** *f.* testing of materials. **-stück,** *n.* piece of metal (to be machined), work piece; working part; hewn stone block. **-stufe,** *f.* stage of work or operation.

**werk-tägig,** *a.* workaday, commonplace. **-tätig,** *a.* working, active, operative; practical.

**Werkzeug,** *n.* tool, instrument, implement; organ. **-maschine,** *f.* machine tool. **-stahl,** *m.* tool steel.

**Werk-zink,** *n.* raw zinc. **-zinn,** *n.* raw tin.

**Wermut,** *m.* wormwood; vermuth. **-bitter,** *m.* absinthin. **-öl,** *n.* oil of wormwood. **-schnaps,** *m.* vermuth.

**wert,** *a.* worth; worthy; dear, valued, respected.

**Wert,** *m.* value; valence; worth, merit. **-angabe,** *f.* statement of value. **-bestimmung,** *f.* determination of value, valuation; determination of valence.

**werten,** *v.t.* value, appraise.

**Wertepaar,** *n.* pair of values.

**Wertersatz,** *m.* equivalent.

**wertgeschätzt,** *p.a.* valued, esteemed.

**Wertgut,** *n.* article of value.

**-wertig.** -valent.

**Wertigkeit,** *f.* valence, valency.

**Wertigkeits-einheit,** *f.* unit of valence. **-formel,** *f.* valence formula, linkage formula. **-stufe,** *f.* valence stage, valence.

**wertlos,** *a.* worthless, valueless.

**Wert-papier,** *n.* valuable paper, security. **-sachen,** *f.pl.* valuables.

**wertschaffend,** *a.* productive.

**wertschätzen,** *v.t.* value, esteem highly.

**Wertstoff,** *m.* valuable substance.

**Wertung,** *f.* valuation, appraisal.

**Wertverhältnis,** *n.* relative value.

**wertvoll,** *a.* valuable.

**Wesen,** *n.* being, essence, substance; nature, character, condition, manner; affairs, concerns, matters; means, property.

**wesenhaft,** *a.* (proposed term for) schematic.

**Wesenriss,** *m.* (proposed term for) schematic diagram.

**wesentlich,** *a.* essential; real, intrinsic; substantial. — **im wesentlichen,** essentially.

**weshalb,** *adv.* why, wherefore.

**Wespe,** *f.* wasp.

**Wespen-.** (*Anat.*) sphenoid.

**wessen,** *pron.* whose, of which.

**Westag, West-AG,** *abbrev.* of *West*fälisch-Anhaltische Sprengstoff-*A*ktien-*G*esellschaft.

**westeuropäisch,** *a.* Western European.

**Westfalen,** *n.* Westphalia.

**west-fälisch,** *a.* Westphalian. **-indisch,** *a.* West India, West Indian. **-lich,** *a.* west, western, occidental.

**weswegen,** *adv.* why?

**wett,** *adv.* even, quits.

**Wettbewerb,** *m.* competition, rivalry.

**Wette,** *f.* bet, wager; rivalry, competition.

**Wetteifer,** *m.* emulation, competition.

**wetteifern,** *v.i.* vie, contend, compete.

**Wetter,** *n.* weather; storm; (*Mining*) damp, also air or ventilation.

**wetterbeständig,** *a.* weatherproof.

**Wetter-beständigkeit,** *f.* weather resistance. **-dynamit,** *n.* (*Mining*) permissible dynamite, wetterdynamite.

**wetterecht,** *a.* fast to exposure.

**Wettereintritt,** *m.* (*Mining*) air inlet.

**wetterfest,** *a.* resistant to weather, weatherproof.

**Wetter-fulminit,** *n.* wetterfulminite (an explosive). **-kunde,** *f.* meteorology. **-leitung,** *f.* (*Mining*) air channel.

**wettern,** *v.i.* thunder and lighten; storm.

**Wetter-probe,** *f.* (*Mining*) air sample or test. **-prüfung,** *f.* weathering test; (*Mining*) air testing.

**wettersicher,** *a.* (*Mining*) dampproof, flameproof.

**Wetter-sprengstoff,** *m.* (*Mining*) permissible explosive. **-stein,** *m.* belemnite. **-strom,** *m.* (*Mining*) air current. **-voraussage,** *f.* weather forecast. **-zünder,** *m.* (*Mining*) electric fuse.

**Wett-kampf,** *m.* contest. **-lauf,** *m.* race.

**wettmachen,** *v.t.* make good, compensate for.

**Wettstreit,** *m.* contest.

**wetzen,** *v.t.* whet, sharpen.

**Wetz-schiefer,** *m.* (*Petrog.*) novaculite. **-stein,** *m.* whetstone, hone; grindstone.

**wf.,** *abbrev.* (wasserfrei) anhydrous, free from water.

**wich,** *pret.* (of weichen) softened, etc.

**Wichse,** *f.* (polishing) wax, polish, blacking; drubbing.

**wichsen,** *v.t.* wax, polish; glaze; clean.

**Wichte,** *f.* unit of weight; specific gravity.

**wichtig,** *n.* important, weighty; serious.

**Wichtigkeit,** *f.* importance; important matter.

**Wicke,** *f.* vetch.

**Wickel,** *m.* roll; coil; ball (of yarn); wrapper, wrapping; filler (of a cigar).

**wickeln,** *v.t.* wind, coil, roll, wrap, twist.

**Wickelung,** *f.* winding; wrapping, casing.

**Wickenstroh,** *n.* vetch straw.

**Wicklung,** *f.* winding; wrapping, casing.

**Widder,** *m.* ram.

**widdern,** *v.t.* turn (malt).

**wider,** *prep.* against, contrary to.
**Wider-.** counter-, contra-, re-, anti-, with-, gain-. **-druck,** *m.* counterpressure, reaction.
**wider-fahren,** *v.i.* happen, befall. **-haarig,** *a.* cross-grained, perverse.
**Wider-haken,** *m.* barb. **-hall,** *m.* echo, reverberation.
**wider-legbar,** *a.* refutable. **-legen,** *v.t.* refute, disprove. **-lich,** *a.* repugnant, repulsive, disagreeable. **-natürlich,** *a.* unnatural, preternatural. **-rechtlich,** *a.* illegal, unlawful.
**Widerrede,** *f.* contradiction, objection.
**widerrufen,** *v.t.* recall, revoke.
**Wider-sacher,** *m.* adversary, opponent. **-schein,** *m.* reflection.
**wider-setzen,** *v.t.* resist, oppose. **-sinnig,** *a.* of opposite sense or direction, reversed; anticlinal; contradictory, nonsensical. **-spenstig,** *a.* refractory, stubborn. **-spiegeln,** *v.t.* reflect.
**Widerspiel,** *n.* contrary, opposition.
**widersprechen,** *v.i.* contradict. — **widersprechend,** *p.a.* contradictory.
**Widerspruch,** *m.* contradiction, opposition, variance.
**widerspruchslos,** *adv.* without contradiction, without question.
**Widerstand,** *m.* resistance.
**Widerstands-brücke,** *f.* (*Elec.*) resistance bridge. **-büchse,** *f.* resistance box. **-draht,** *m.* (*Elec.*) resistance wire. **-einheit,** *f.* resistance unit.
**widerstandsfähig,** *a.* resistant, capable of resistance, refractory.
**Widerstands-fähigkeit,** *f.* capability of resisting, resistivity. **-heizung,** *f.* resistance heating. **-kasten,** *m.* (*Elec.*) resistance box. **-kraft,** *f.* power of resistance. **-legierung,** *f.* resistance alloy. **-messer,** *m.* resistance meter, ohmmeter. **-messung,** *f.* measurement of resistance. **-moment,** *n.* moment of resistance. **-ofen,** *m.* resistance furnace or oven. **-satz,** *m.* (*Elec.*) resistance set, resistance box. **-schaltung,** *f.* rheostat. **-spule,** *f.* (*Elec.*) resistance coil. **-vermögen,** *n.* resisting power, resistance. **-verschiebung,** *f.* variation of resistance. **-wert,** *m.* coefficient of resistance.
**widerstehen,** *v.i.* resist, withstand; be repugnant.
**Widerstoss,** *m.* countershock.
**wider-strahlen,** *v.i.* reradiate, reflect. **-streben,** *v.i.* oppose, resist. **-strebend,** *p.a.* resistant; refractory; reluctant. **-streiten,** *v.i.* conflict (with), be contrary (to). — **widerstreitend,** *p.a.* conflicting, contrary. **-wärtig,** *a.* repugnant, disagreeable; adverse.
**Widerwille,** *f.* aversion, antipathy.
**widerwillig,** *a.* reluctant, unwilling.
**widmen,** *v.t.* dedicate, devote.
**Widmung,** *f.* dedication; devotion.
**widrig,** *a.* contrary, adverse; repugnant; (as a suffix) opposing, anti-, as *fäulniswidrig,* antiseptic.
**widrigenfalls, widrigens,** *adv.* failing which, otherwise.
**wie,** *adv.* how. — *conj.* as, like. — **— . . . auch,** however.
**Wiebel,** *m.* weevil.
**Wied,** *m.* woad.
**wieder,** *adv.* again, anew, re-; back, in return. **-abdrucken,** *v.t.* reprint, republish.
**Wieder-anmeldung,** *f.* (*Patents*) reapplication. **-anreicherung,** *f.* reconcentration.
**wieder-anwärmen,** *v.t.* reheat. **-aufarbeiten,** *v.t.* rework, recondition.
**Wiederaufbau,** *m.* reconstruction.
**wieder-auffüllen,** *v.t.* refill. **-aufladen,** *v.t.* (*Elec.*) recharge. **-auflösen,** *v.t.* & *r.* redissolve. **-aufnehmen,** *v.t.* take up again; redissolve; resume. **-aufsaugen,** *v.t.* reabsorb. **-ausfällen,** *v.i.* reprecipitate, redeposit.
**Wiederausfällung,** *f.* reprecipitation, redeposition.
**wieder-auskristallisieren,** *v.t.* & *i.* recrystallize. **-ausrichten,** *v.t.* realign; readjust. **-beleben,** *v.t.* revive, revivify, reactivate, regenerate; (*Sugar*) reburn (char); (*Med.*) resuscitate.
**Wieder-belebung,** *f.* revival, etc. (see wiederbeleben). **-belebungsmittel,** *n.* (*Med.*) restorative.
**wiederbelüften,** *v.t.* re-aerate, reventilate.
**Wiederbenutzung,** *f.* reutilization.
**wieder-beschicken,** *v.t.* reload, recharge. **-bilden,** *v.t.* form again.
**Wieder-brauchbarmachen,** *n.* regeneration. **-druck,** *m.* reprint. **-einschmelzen,** *n.* remelting.
**wieder-erhitzen,** *v.t.* reheat. **-erkennen,** *v.t.* recognize. **-erwärmen,** *v.t.* rewarm, reheat. **-erzeugen,** *v.t.* reproduce, regenerate.
**Wiedererzeugung,** *f.* reproduction, regeneration.
**wieder-fällen,** *v.t.* reprecipitate. **-färben,** *v.t.* recolor, redye.
**Wiedergabe,** *f.* reproduction; return; response; version.
**wieder-gebbar,** *a.* translatable; returnable; reproducible. **-geben,** *v.t.* translate, render; represent; return; reproduce.
**Wiedergebrauch,** *m.* reuse.
**wieder-gewinnbar,** *a.* recoverable. **-gewinnen,** *v.t.* recover, reclaim.
**Wiedergewinnung,** *f.* recovery.
**wiedergewonnen,** *p.a.* recovered, reclaimed.
**Wiederhall,** *m.* echo, reverberation, resonance.
**wiederherstellen,** *v.t.* reprepare; reproduce; restore, revive; readjust.

**Wiederherstellung,** *f.* repreparation, etc. (see wiederherstellen).
**wieder-hervorbringen,** *v.t.* = wiedererzeugen. **-holbar,** *a.* capable of being repeated, reproducible. **-holen,** *v.t.* repeat. — *v.r.* repeat oneself; recur. **-holt,** *p.a.* repeated. — *adv.* repeatedly.
**Wieder-holung,** *f.* repetition. **-instandsetzung,** *f.* reconditioning.
**wiederkäuen,** *v.t.* ruminate; go over and over.
**Wieder-käuer,** *m.* ruminant. **-kehr,** *f.* return, recurrence.
**wiederkehren,** *v.i.* return, recur.
**Wiederkehrspannung,** *f.* (*Elec.*) recovery voltage.
**wiederkristallisieren,** *v.t.* recrystallize.
**Wieder-kristallisierung,** *f.* recrystallization. **-oxydation,** *f.* reoxidation. **-schein,** *m.* reflection, reflex.
**wiederschmelzen,** *v.t.* remelt, re-fuse.
**Wiedersehen,** *n.* meeting again. — **auf —,** au revoir.
**wiederspiegeln,** *v.t.* reflect.
**Wieder-stoss,** *m.* countershock. **-strahl,** *m.* reflected ray.
**wieder-strahlen,** *v.t.* reflect. **-um,** *adv.* again, in return. **-vereinigen,** *v.t.* reunite; reconcile.
**Wiedervereinigung,** *f.* reunion, recombination; focusing (of rays or particles).
**wieder-verstärken,** *v.t.* strengthen again; replenish. **-verwandeln,** *v.t.* reconvert.
**Wieder-verwendung,** *f.* reuse. **-verwertung,** *f.* reutilization. **-wässerung,** *f.* watering or soaking again; rehydration. **-zündung,** *f.* reignition.
**Wiege,** *f.* cradle; rocker.
**Wiegegläschen,** *n.* weighing glass.
**wiegen,** *v.t.* weigh; rock. — *v.i.* weigh. — **gewogen,** *p.a.* weighed; well disposed, favorable. — **gewiegt,** *p.a.* skilled, experienced; rocked.
**Wiege-schale,** *f.* scale pan. **-vorrichtung,** *f.* weighing device.
**Wiegung,** *f.* weighing; rocking.
**Wieke,** *f.* pledget.
**Wien,** *n.* Vienna.
**Wiener, wienerisch,** *a.* Vienna, Viennese. — **Wiener Ätzpulver,** Vienna paste, Vienna caustic. — **Wiener Grün,** Vienna green. — **Wiener Kalk,** Vienna lime, Vienna white. — **Wiener Lack,** Vienna lake. — **Wiener Metall,** Vienna metal (a white copper-antimony alloy).
**wies,** *pret.* (of weisen) showed, indicated, etc.
**Wiese,** *f.* meadow.
**Wiesen-erz,** *n.* meadow ore, bog iron ore. **-flachs,** *m.* purging flax. **-heu,** *n.* meadow hay. **-kalk,** *m.* limestone from springs, freshwater limestone. **-klee,** *m.* red clover. **-knöterich,** *m.* bistort (*Polygonum bistorta*). **-lein,** *m.* purging flax. **-torf,** *m.* meadow peat.
**wieviel,** *adv.* how much, how many.
**wiewohl,** *conj.* altho.
**wild,** *a.* wild; savage, fierce, unruly. — **wildes Fleisch,** proud flesh. — **wildes Gestein,** rock containing no metal. — **wilder Stahl,** wild steel.
**Wild,** *n.* game.
**Wilde,** *m. & f.* savage; wildness; wilderness.
**Wildgeschmack,** *m.* gamy taste.
**wildgewachsen,** *a.* grown wild, run wild.
**Wild-hefe,** *f.* wild yeast. **-kirschenrinde,** *f.* wild cherry bark. **-leder,** *n.* buckskin, deerskin; chamois; suède.
**Wildnis,** *f.* wilderness.
**will,** *pr. 1 & 3 sing.* (of wollen) will, wish(es).
**Wille,** *f.*, **Willen,** *m.* will, volition; design, intent; permission.
**willfahren,** *v.i.* yield to, comply with.
**willig,** *a.* willing, ready.
**willkommen,** *a. & adv.* welcome.
**Willkür,** *f.* free will, option; arbitrariness.
**willkürlich,** *a.* arbitrary; random; voluntary. **-verteilt,** *a.* randomly distributed.
**Wilson-kammer,** *f.* Wilson cloud (or fog) chamber, expansion chamber. **-nebelspur,** *f.* Wilson cloud track.
**wimmeln,** *v.i.* swarm, teem.
**wimmerig,** *a.* wavy-fibered, crossgrained.
**Wimper,** *f.* eyelash; cilium.
**wimperig,** *a.* ciliated, ciliary.
**Wimperinfusorien,** *f.pl.* (*Zoöl.*) Ciliata.
**wimpernd,** *p.a.* ciliated, ciliary; winking.
**Wind,** *m.* wind, breeze; air; blast. **-bläser,** *m.* blower, blast apparatus. **-darm,** *m.* colon.
**winddicht,** *a.* airtight.
**Wind-druck,** *m.* (*Metal.*) blast pressure; wind pressure. **-düse,** *f.* blast nozzle, twyer, tuyère.
**Winde,** *f.* windlass, winch; jack; hoist; worm (screw); bindweed; (*Glass*) stria.
**winden,** *v.t.* wind, coil, reel, roll, twist. — *v.r.* wind, coil, wriggle. — **gewunden,** *p.a.* wound, coiled, rolled, twisted, spiral.
**Wind-erhitzer,** *m.* = Winderhitzungsapparat. **-erhitzung,** *f.* blast heating. **-erhitzungsapparat,** *m.* hot blast stove; regenerator. **-erzeuger,** *m.* blast apparatus, blower, fan. **-fahne,** *f.* vane. **-flügel,** *m.* (ventilator) fan; fan blade. **-form,** *f.* (*Metal.*) twyer, tuyère. **-frischapparat,** *m.* (*Metal.*) converter. **-frischen,** *n.* (*Metal.*) blast purifying, converting. **-frischverfahren,** *n.* (*Steel*) converter process, Bessemer process. **-geschwulst,** *f.* emphysema.
**windgetragen,** *a.* wind-borne.
**windig,** *a.* windy, breezy; visionary, shaky.

**Wind-kanal,** *m.* air passage, air duct. **-kasten,** *m.* wind chest, air chamber; (*Metal.*) twyer box. **-kessel,** *m.* blast pressure tank, blast box; air chamber. **-leitung,** *f.* (*Metal.*) blast main. **-leitungsrohr,** *n.* (*Metal.*) blast pipe. **-messer,** *m.* wind meter, anemometer; blast gage. **-mühle,** *f.* windmill. **-ofen,** *m.* wind furnace, air furnace. **-pocken,** *f.pl.* chicken pox. **-pressung,** *f.* (*Metal.*) blast pressure. **-rohr,** *n.* (*Metal.*) blast pipe, twyer pipe. **-sammler,** *m.* air reservoir, compressed-air tank.

**windschnittig,** *a.* streamlined.

**Windsichter, Windsortierer,** *m.* air separator; aspirator.

**windstill,** *a.* calm.

**Wind-strom,** *m.* air current, blast current. **-strömung,** *f.* air flow, air current.

**wind-treibend,** *p.a.* carminative. **-trocken,** *a.* wind-dried, air-dry.

**Wind-trocknung,** *f.* wind drying; blast drying; air drying. **-trocknungsverfahren,** *n.* dry-blast process.

**Windung,** *f.* winding, etc. (see winden); convolution, turn; spiral; torsion; (screw) thread.

**Windungszahl,** *f.* number of turns.

**Wind-werk,** *n.* winding gear, hoisting gear. **-zufuhr, -zuführung,** *f.* air (or blast) supply. **-zug,** *m.* air current; ventilator.

**Wink,** *m.* wink; beckoning; nod; hint, suggestion.

**Wink-.** signaling, signal.

**Winkel,** *m.* angle; corner. **-abstand,** *m.* angular distance. **-abweichung,** *f.* angular deviation. **-beschleunigung,** *f.* angular acceleration. **-bewegung,** *f.* angular motion. **-eisen,** *n.* angle iron.

**winkelförmig,** *a.* angular.

**Winkel-frequenz,** *f.* angular frequency. **-geschwindigkeit,** *f.* angular velocity.

**winkelig,** *a.* angular, -angled, -cornered.

**Winkel-linie,** *f.* diagonal. **-mass,** *n.*, **-messung,** *f.* angular measurement, goniometry. **-messer,** *m.* angle measurer (goniometer, protractor, theodolite, etc.).

**winkelrecht,** *a.* right-angled, rectangular.

**Winkel-stück,** *n.* elbow piece, elbow, angle piece. **-thermometer,** *n.* bent-tube thermometer. **-verschiebung,** *f.* angular displacement. **-zug,** *m.* shift, pretext.

**winken,** *v.i.* wink; beckon; nod; signal.

**winklig,** *a.* = winkelig.

**Winkzeichen,** *n.* signal.

**winterfest,** *a.* (of plants) hardy.

**Winter-grün,** *n.* wintergreen; oil of wintergreen; ivy; myrtle, periwinkle. **-kresse,** *f.* winter cress (*Barbarea*). **-spritzung,** *f.* (*Agric.*) dormant spray.

**Wintersrinde,** *f.* Winter's bark.

**Winterweizen,** *m.* winter wheat.

**winzig,** *a.* minute, tiny; mean, petty.

**Wipfel,** *m.* top (of a tree).

**Wippe,** *f.* balancing; balancer, equalizer; counterpoise; rocker; clipping (from coins); seesaw; tilting table; (*Elec.*) tumbler switch.

**wir,** *pron.* we.

**Wirbel,** *m.* whirl, vortex, eddy; whirlwind; whorl; spiral; vertebra; (*Tech.*) spigot, button, collar, swivel, sheave, etc.; vertigo; intoxication; crown (of the head); warbling.

**Wirbel-.** whirl-, vortical; vertebral, vertebrate. **-bein,** *n.* vertebra. **-bewegung,** *f.* vortex motion, eddying.

**wirbelfrei,** *a.* (*Physics*) irrotational, free from turbulence.

**Wirbeligkeit,** *f.* vorticity.

**Wirbel-knochen,** *m.* vertebra. **-lehre,** *f.* vortex theory.

**wirbellos,** *a.* invertebrate; free from eddies, nonvortical.

**wirbeln,** *v.i.* whirl, spin; eddy; spiral; warble; (of a drum) roll. — **gewirbelt,** *p.a.* whirled, etc.; vertebrate.

**Wirbel-säule,** *f.* vertebral column. **-strom,** *m.* whirlpool; (*Elec.*) eddy current. **-strömung,** *f.* vortex motion, turbulent flow. **-sturm,** *m.* tornado; cyclone. **-tier,** *n.* vertebrate.

**Wirbelung,** *f.* whirling, etc. (see wirbeln); vortex motion.

**Wirbelwirkung,** *f.* whirling effect.

**wirbt,** *pr. 3 sing.* (of werben) advertises, etc.

**wird,** *pr. 3 sing.* (of werden) becomes; will; is.

**wirft,** *pr. 3 sing.* (of werfen) throws, etc.

**Wirk.,** *abbrev.* of Wirkung.

**wirken,** *v.i.* act, work, operate, have an effect, function. — *v.t.* work, effect, produce, perform, specif. boil (salt); knead (dough); knit; weave. — **wirkend,** *p.a.* acting, working, operative. — **wirkendes Mittel,** agent.

**Wirkleistung,** *f.* actual (or real) power or efficiency, effective output.

**wirklich,** *a.* real, actual, acting, true. — *adv.* really, actually, truly.

**Wirklichkeit,** *f.* reality, actuality.

**wirksam,** *a.* active; effective; efficient, efficacious.

**Wirksamkeit,** *f.* activity; agency; effectiveness, efficacy, efficiency; strength (of acids, etc.); operation. — **in — setzen,** set going, start; (*Mach.*) throw into gear.

**Wirk-spannung,** *f.* (*Elec.*) active voltage. **-stoff,** *m.* active material or substance, specif. a vitamin or hormone. **-strom,** *m.* (*Elec.*) actual current, active current.

**Wirkung,** *f.* action; effect; result; reaction; working, operation, agency; efficacy.

**Wirkungs-art,** *f.* kind of action; mode of acting; mode of operation. **-bereich,** *m.* range of action or effect, effective range. **-bombe,** *f.* demolition bomb, high-capacity bomb. **-dauer,** *f.* period (or duration) of action or effect.

**wirkungsfähig,** *a.* capable of acting, active, effective, efficient.

**Wirkungs-fähigkeit,** *f.* activity, effectiveness, efficiency. **-faktor,** *m.* effective (or responsible) factor. **-gehalt,** *m.* active content. **-geschwindigkeit,** *f.* rapidity of action. **-grad,** *m.* efficiency, effect; strength (of a reagent). **-kraft,** *f.* effective force, working power, efficiency, efficacy. **-kreis,** *m.* sphere of action, sphere of activity.

**wirkungslos,** *a.* inactive, ineffectual, inefficient, inert.

**Wirkungs-losigkeit,** *f.* inactivity, ineffectiveness, inefficiency. **-möglichkeit,** *f.* possible effect. **-quant, -quantum,** *n.* quantum of action, effective quantum. **-querschnitt,** *m.* effective cross section. **-sphäre,** *f.* sphere of action. **-variabel,** *n.* action variable. **-vermögen,** *n.* power of action, working power.

**wirkungsvoll,** *a.* effective, efficacious.

**Wirkungs-weise,** *f.* mode of acting, mode of operation, action. **-wert,** *m.* effective value; (of an acid, etc.) strength; efficacy.

**Wirk-waren,** *f.pl.* knitted goods. **-zeit,** *f.* reaction time.

**wirr,** *a.* confused, tangled, disordered.

**Wirre,** *f.* confusion, disorder.

**Wirr-seide,** *f.* silk waste. **-warr,** *m.* confusion, disorder.

**Wirt,** *m.* host, landlord.

**Wirtel,** *m.* whorl.

**Wirtschaft,** *f.* economy, management; industry; housekeeping; household; farm; hotel, inn.

**wirt-schaften,** *v.i.* keep house; keep an inn; run a farm; manage, go. **-schaftlich,** *a.* household; economic; industrial; economical, thrifty. — *adv.* economically.

**Wirtschaftlichkeit,** *f.* economy, thrift; industrial efficiency.

**Wirtschafts-.** economic, industrial, business, commercial. **-betrieb,** *m.* household management; farm management. **-krieg,** *m.* economic warfare. **-lehre,** *f* economics.

**Wisch,** *m.* rag; mop; whisk; piece of waste paper.

**wischecht,** *a.* fast to wiping.

**wischen,** *v.t.* wipe. — *v.i.* whisk, slip (away).

**Wischer,** *m.* wiper; rubber, duster, swab, sponge, (drawing) stump.

**Wisch-gold,** *n.* gold leaf. **-gummi,** *n.* rubber wiper. **-kontakt,** *m.* wiping contact. **-lappen,** *m.* wiping or cleaning rag. **-tuch,** *n.* wiping or dusting cloth.

**Wismut, Wismuth,** *n. & m.* bismuth.

**wismutartig,** *a.* bismuthal.

**Wismut-bleierz,** *n.* schapbachite. **-blende,** *f.* bismuth blende, eulytite. **-blüte,** *f.* bismuth ocher, bismite. **-bromid,** *n.* bismuth bromide. **-butter,** *f.* (*Old Chem.*) butter of bismuth (bismuth trichloride). **-chlorid,** *n.* bismuth chloride, bismuth trichloride.

**wismuten,** *v.t.* solder with bismuth or bismuth solder.

**Wismut-erz,** *n.* bismuth ore. **-gehalt,** *m.* bismuth content. **-glanz,** *m.* bismuth glance, bismuthinite; (**prismatischer**), aikinite. **-glätte,** *f.* bismuth litharge, bismuth oxide.

**wismuthaltig,** *a.* bismuthiferous.

**Wismut-jodid,** *n.* bismuth iodide. **-kupfererz,** *n.* emplectite; klaprotholite; wittichenite. **-legierung,** *f.* bismuth alloy. **-lot,** *n.* bismuth solder (a fusible bismuth alloy). **-metall,** *n.* bismuth metal. **-nickel(kobalt)kies,** *m.* grunauite. **-niederschlag,** *m.* bismuth precipitate; specif., bismuth oxynitrate. **-nitrat,** *n.* bismuth nitrate. **-ocker,** *m.* bismuth ocher, bismite ($Bi_2O_3$). **-oxyd,** *n.* bismuth oxide; specif., bismuth trioxide. **-oxyjodid,** *n.* bismuth oxyiodide. **-raffination,** *f.* bismuth refining. **-salz,** *n.* bismuth salt.

**wismutsauer,** *a.* of or relating to bismuthic acid, bismuthate of.

**Wismut-säure,** *f.* bismuthic acid. **-säureanhydrid,** *n.* bismuthic anhydride (dibismuth pentoxide, $Bi_2O_5$). **-schwamm,** *m.* bismuth sponge. **-silber,** *n.* chilenite; schapbachite. **-spat,** *m.* bismutite. **-subjodid,** *n.* bismuth subiodide ($BiI_2$ or BiI, existence not confirmed). **-sulfid,** *n.* bismuth sulfide. **-tellur,** *n.* tetradymite, telluric bismuth. **-verbindung,** *f.* bismuth compound. **-wasserstoff,** *m.* bismuth hydride. **-weiss,** *n.* bismuth white.

**wiss.,** *abbrev.* (wissenschaftlich) scientific.

**wissbegierig,** *a.* inquisitive, curious.

**wissen,** *v.t. & i.* know; know how.

**Wissen,** *n.* knowledge; learning. **-schaft,** *f.* science; learning, knowledge, intelligence. **-schaftler,** *m.* scientist; scholar.

**wissenschaftlich,** *a.* scientific.

**Wissen-schaftlichkeit,** *f.* scientific nature or quality, scientific or scholarly method. **-schaftslehre,** *f.* theory of science; economics, economy.

**Wissens-gebiet,** *n.* department of knowledge. **-zweig,** *m.* branch of knowledge.

**wissentlich,** *a.* knowing, conscious, deliberate.

**Wissmut,** *n. & m.* = Wismut.

**Witol,** *n.* a synthetic toluene. *T.N.*

**Witterung,** *f.* weather; scent, trail.

**Witterungsbedingung,** *f.* atmospheric condition.

**witterungsbeständig,** *a.* fast to weathering, (of steel) rust-resistant.

**Witterungs-beständigkeit,** *f.* resistance to weathering. **-einfluss,** *m.* atmospheric influence. **-kunde, -lehre,** *f.* meteorology. **-schutz,** *m.* protection against weather. **-verhältnisse,** *n.pl.* atmospheric conditions.
**Wittsche Scheibe.** Witt plate.
**Witz,** *m.* wit; joke; sense.
**Witzelei,** *f.* witticism; quibble, quibbling.
**wl.,** *abbrev.* (wenig löslich) difficultly soluble.
**wlösl.,** *abbrev.* (wasserlöslich) soluble in water.
**wo,** *adv.* where; somewhere. — *conj.* if.
**w.o.,** *abbrev.* (weiter oben) above.
**wob,** *pret.* (of weben) wove.
**wobbeln,** *v.i.* wobble.
**wobei,** *adv.* whereby, whereat.
**Woche,** *f.* week; (*pl.*) lying-in, confinement.
**Wochen-.** weekly; lying-in, obstetric, puerperal, maternity. **-bett,** *n.* childbed. **-binde,** *f.* sanitary napkin. **-fluss,** *m.* lochia.
**wochenlang,** *adv.* for weeks.
**Wochenschrift,** *f.* weekly.
**wöchentlich,** *a.* weekly, week's. — *adv.* weekly.
**-wöchig.** -weekly, of . . . weeks' duration.
**Wöchnerin,** *f.* lying-in woman.
**wodurch,** *adv.* whereby, by what, by which.
**wofern,** *conj.* so far as, provided, in case.
**wofür,** *adv.* for what, for which.
**wog,** *pret.* (of wägen and of wiegen) weighed.
**wogegen,** *adv.* & *conj.* against what, against which; for what, for which; whereas, while.
**woher,** *adv.* whence, from where.
**wohin,** *adv.* whither, where. **-gegen,** *conj.* whereas, while.
**wohl,** *adv.* well; perhaps, probably; indeed. — **so — als,** as well as.
**Wohl,** *n.* weal, health, benefit, good.
**wohl-, Wohl-.** well, good.
**wohl-angebracht,** *p.a.* well-timed. **-auf,** *adv.* well. — *interj.* come on! now then! **-ausgebildet,** *a.* well-developed. **-bedacht,** *p.a.* well-considered.
**Wohlbefinden,** *n.* good health.
**wohl-begründet,** *p.a.* well-founded. **-behalten,** *p.a.* in good condition. **-bekannt,** *p.a.* well-known. **-beleibt,** *p.a.* corpulent.
**Wohlbeleibtheit,** *f.* corpulence.
**wohl-belesen,** *p.a.* well-read. **-besetzt,** *p.a.* well-filled. **-bewusst,** *p.a.* well-known; conscious. **-definiert,** *p.a.* well-defined. **-erfahren,** *p.a.* experienced.
**Wohlergehen,** *n.* welfare, prosperity.
**wohl-erhalten,** *p.a.* well-preserved, in good condition. **-erwogen,** *p.a.* well-considered.
**Wohlfahrt,** *f.* welfare; charity.
**wohlfeil,** *a.* cheap.
**Wohlfeilheit,** *f.* cheapness.
**wohl-gebaut,** *p.a.* well-built. **-gebildet,** *p.a.* well-formed; well-bred.
**wohlgeboren,** *p.a.* well-born; Esquire. — **wohlgeborener Herr!** dear Sir.
**Wohlgefallen,** *n.* liking, pleasure, delight.
**wohl-gefällig,** *a.* pleasant, pleasing, pleased. **-gehärtet,** *a.* well-hardened; well-tempered. **-gelitten,** *p.a.* popular. **-gemeint,** *p.a.* well-meant. **-gemut,** *a.* cheery, cheerful, merry. **-genährt,** *p.a.* well-nourished. **-geordnet,** *p.a.* well-arranged, well-ordered. **-geraten,** *p.a.* well-done, perfect; well-bred.
**Wohl-geruch,** *m.* agreeable odor, fragrance. **-geschmack,** *m.* agreeable taste or flavor.
**wohl-gesinnt,** *p.a.* well-disposed. **-geübt,** *p.a.* practised, skilled. **-gewogen,** *p.a.* well-inclined. **-habend,** *p.a.* well-to-do, well-off.
**Wohlklang,** *m.* euphony; harmony.
**wohlklingend,** *a.* melodious; harmonious.
**Wohl-laut,** *m.* euphony; harmony. **-leben,** *n.* high living, luxury.
**wohl-redend,** *p.a.* eloquent, well-spoken. **-riechend,** *p.a.* fragrant, sweet-smelling, aromatic. **-schmeckend,** *p.a.* savory, palatable.
**Wohl-sein,** *n.* good health, well-being. **-stand,** *m.* welfare, prosperity. **-tat,** *f.* good deed; benefit, kindness, blessing. **-täter,** *m.* benefactor.
**wohltätig,** *a.* beneficent, benevolent; charitable; beneficial, wholesome.
**Wohltätigkeit,** *f.* beneficence, etc. (see wohltätig); charity.
**wohltun,** *v.i.* do good, benefit, give pleasure.
**Wohlverlei,** *m.* arnica (*Arnica montana*). **-wurzel,** *f.* arnica root.
**wohl-verschlossen,** *p.a.* well-closed. **-versehen,** *p.a.* well-provided. **-weislich,** *adv.* very wisely. **-wollen,** *v.i.* wish well, be well-disposed.
**Wohlwollen,** *n.* good will, kind feeling, favor.
**wohnen,** *v.i.* live, dwell.
**wohnhaft,** *a.* dwelling, residing, resident.
**wohnlich,** *a.* habitable; comfortable.
**Wohn-ort, -platz,** *m.* dwelling place, residence. **-sitz,** *m.* domicile, residence. **-stube,** *f.* living room, sitting room.
**Wohnung,** *f.* dwelling, residence, housing.
**Wohnungs-anzeiger,** *m.* directory. **-bombe,** *f.* incendiary bomb.
**wölben,** *v.t.* curve, vault, arch. — *v.r.* curve, arch.
**Wölbung,** *f.* curvature; camber; vault, vaulting, crown.
**wölbungsfrei,** *a.* free from curving or buckling, flat.
**Wolf,** *m.* wolf; (*Iron*) lump, ball, bloom; (*Textiles*) willow; (*Med.*) lupus; chafing.
**Wolfram,** *m.* & *n.* tungsten, wolfram; wolframite.
**Wolframat,** *n.* tungstate, wolframate.
**Wolfram-blau,** *n.* wolfram blue, mineral blue

(a tungsten oxide, $W_3O_8$?). **-bleierz,** *n.* stolzite. **-chlorid,** *n.* (any) tungsten chloride. **-draht,** *m.* tungsten wire. **-erz,** *n.* tungsten ore. **-faden,** *m.* tungsten filament. **-gelb,** *n.* a yellow variety of tungsten bronze.

**wolframhaltig,** *a.* tungsteniferous.

**Wolframid,** *n.* tungstide.

**Wolframit,** *n.* (*Min.*) wolframite.

**Wolfram-lampe,** *f.* tungsten lamp. **-metall,** *n.* metallic tungsten. **-ocker,** *m.* tungstic ocher, tungstite. **-oxyd,** *n.* tungsten oxide. **-salz,** *n.* tungsten salt.

**wolframsauer,** *a.* of or combined with tungstic acid, tungstate of.

**Wolframsäure,** *f.* tungstic acid, wolframic acid. **-anhydrid,** *n.* tungstic anhydride. **-salz,** *n.* salt of tungstic acid, tungstate.

**Wolfram-stahl,** *m.* tungsten steel. **-stickstoff,** *m.* tungsten nitride. **-sulfid,** *n.* tungsten sulfide.

**Wolfs-bohne,** *f.* lupine. **-kirsche,** *f.* belladonna. **-milch,** *f.* wolf's milk, spurge (*Euphorbia* sp.).

**wolfsmilchartig,** *a.* (*Bot.*) euphorbiaceous.

**Wolfs-stahl,** *m.* natural steel. **-wurz,** *f.* baneberry.

**Wolke,** *f.* cloud; (*Warfare*) cloud, wave (of gas); flaw (in a gem stone).

**Wolken-achat,** *m.* clouded agate. **-angriff,** *m.* wave attack, cloud gas attack.

**wolkenartig,** *a.* cloud-like, cloudy, clouded.

**Wolkenbildung,** *f.* cloud formation, clouding.

**wolkig,** *a.* cloudy, clouded.

**Wolkigkeit,** *f.* cloudiness.

**Woll-abgang,** *m.*, **-abfälle,** *m.pl.* wool waste, waste wool.

**woll-ähnlich, -artig,** *a.* wool-like, woolly.

**Woll-asche,** *f.* wool ashes. **-blumen,** *f.pl.* (*Pharm.*) mullen flowers. **-druck,** *m.* wool printing.

**Wolle,** *f.* wool. — **philosophische —,** philosopher's wool (zinc oxide).

**wollen,** *v.i. & t.* will, be willing, choose, intend, mean, wish, want; be about, be going (to do something). — *a.* woolen.

**Wollen-,** wool, woolen, worsted.

**Woll-entfettung, -entschweissung,** *f.* degreasing of wool. **-färber,** *m.* wool dyer.

**wollfarbig,** *a.* dyed in the wool.

**Woll-faser,** *f.* wool fiber. **-fett,** *n.* wool fat, wool grease. **-fettsäure,** *f.* wool fat acid. **-filz,** *m.* wool felt. **-garn,** *n.* woolen yarn. **-garnfett,** *n.* wool yarn grease. **-grün,** *n.* wool green.

**wollig,** *a.* woolly.

**Woll-kraut,** *n.* mullen. **-öl,** *n.* wool oil. **-pulver,** *n.* wool flock, wool powder. **-schmiere,** *f.* (wool) yolk, suint; wool softener. **-schwarz,** *n.* wool black.

**Wollschweiss,** *m.* (wool) yolk, suint. **-asche,** *f.* potash from suint. **-fett,** *n.* wool grease. **-küpe,** *f.* suint vat. **-salz,** *n.* suint salt.

**Wollspicköl,** *n.* wool (lubricating) oil.

**Wollstaub,** *m.* wool flock, wool powder.

**Wollstra.** Woolstra, Wollstra (a fiber made from wood). *T.N.*

**Woll-veredelung,** *f.* wool processing. **-wachs,** *n.* wool wax. **-wäsche,** *f.* wool scouring.

**womit,** *adv.* wherewith.

**womöglich,** *adv.* if possible.

**wonach,** *adv.* whereupon, after which, after what.

**Wonne,** *f.* bliss, delight, pleasure.

**wonnereich,** *a.* delightful, delicious.

**Woodöl,** *n.* wood oil.

**Wootzstahl,** *m.* wootz steel, wootz.

**woran,** *adv.* whereon, whereat, by what.

**worauf,** *adv.* whereon, whereupon, on what.

**woraus,** *adv.* from what, from which, by which.

**worein,** *adv.* into which, into what.

**worfeln,** *v.t.* winnow, fan.

**worin,** *adv.* wherein, in which, in what.

**Wort,** *n.* word; term, expression. **-ableitung,** *f.* etymology, derivation. **-ausdruck,** *m.* phraseology.

**Wörterbuch,** *n.* dictionary; glossary.

**Wort-folge,** *f.* order of words. **-fügung,** *f.* sentence structure, syntax. **-führer,** *m.* spokesman, speaker.

**wortgetreu,** *a.* literal.

**Wort-kunde,** *f.* etymology. **-laut,** *m.* wording, text.

**wörtlich,** *a.* verbal, literal. — *adv.* verbatim, literally.

**Wort-register,** *n.* index of words, vocabulary, concordance. **-schatz,** *m.* vocabulary; thesaurus. **-verbindung,** *f.* connection of words, context. **-zeichen,** *n.* trade name; trademark; catchword.

**worüber,** *adv.* whereat, whereof, over, at, about or on which or what.

**worum,** *adv.* for which, for what, about what.

**worunter,** *adv.* under what, under which, among which.

**woselbst,** *adv.* where.

**Woulfische Flasche.** Woulfe bottle.

**wovon,** *adv.* whereof, of what, which or whom.

**wovor,** *adv.* before what, before which, of which.

**wozu,** *adv.* whereto, whereat, to what, why.

**Wrack,** *n.* wreck; refuse, waste.

**Wrasen,** *m.* vapor; air.

**wringen,** *v.t.* wring.

**Wrkg.,** *abbrev.* (Wirkung) action, effect.

**Ws.,** *abbrev.* (Wasser) water.

**W.-S.,** *abbrev.* (Wassersäule) water column.

**wss.,** *abbrev.* (wässerig) aqueous, hydrous.

**wuchern,** *v.i.* grow rapidly, (*Biol.*) proliferate; practise usury.

**Wucherung,** *f.* (*Biol.*) proliferation.

**wuchs,** *pret.* (of wachsen) grew.

**Wuchs,** *m.* growth; grain (of wood); form, stature.

**Wucht,** *f.* weight, burden; force; pressure; (*Mech.*) kinetic energy; fulcrum.

**wühlen,** *v.i.* rake, rummage, dig, root; agitate.

**Wulst,** *n.* pad, padding, roll; swelling, enlargement, elevation; bead; bulb; collar.

**wulstförmig,** *a.* roll-shaped; doughnut-shaped, toroidal.

**wulstig,** *a.* padded, stuffed, swelled, tumid.

**Wulstnaht,** *f.* reinforced weld.

**wund,** *a.* wounded, sore, chafed; defective; difficult. — **wunder Punkt,** difficulty, snag.

**Wundarzt,** *m.* surgeon.

**wundärztlich,** *a.* surgical.

**Wundbalsam,** *m.* vulnerary balsam.

**Wunde,** *f.* wound; injury.

**Wunder,** *n.* wonder, marvel; miracle.

**wunderbar,** *a.* wonderful, marvelous, strange.

**Wunder-baum,** *m.* castor-oil plant; locust tree. **-baumöl,** *n.* castor oil. **-erde,** *f.* lithomarge. **-erscheinung,** *f.* miraculous phenomenon. **-kerze,** *f.* (*Pyro.*) sparkler.

**wunderlich,** *a.* strange, singular, peculiar, odd, whimsical.

**wundern,** *v.t.* surprise, astonish. — *v.r.* wonder.

**Wunder-pfeffer,** *m.* allspice. **-salz,** *n.* sal mirabile, Glauber's salt.

**wunder-schön,** *a.* very beautiful. **-voll,** *a.* wonderful.

**Wunderwasser,** *n.* aqua mirabilis.

**Wund-klee,** *m.* kidney vetch. **-kraut,** *n.* vulnerary plant. **-pulver,** *n.* vulnerary powder. **-saft,** *m.* wound exudate. **-schwamm,** *m.* surgeon's agaric. **-stein,** *m.* copper aluminate.

**Wunsch,** *m.* wish, desire.

**Wünschelrute,** *f.* divining (or dowsing) rod.

**wünschen,** *v.t.* wish, wish for, desire.

**wünschenswert,** *a.* desirable.

**würbe,** *pret. subj.* of werben.

**wurde,** *pret.* (of werden) became; was.

**Würde,** *f.* dignity; honor, preferment.

**würde-los,** *a.* undignified. **-voll,** *a.* dignified.

**würdig,** *a.* worthy, deserving, deserved.

**würdigen,** *v.t.* value, prize, appreciate; consider worthy.

**Wurf,** *m.* throw, cast; litter, brood; (*Mech.*) projection.

**würfe,** *pret. subj.* (of werfen) would throw.

**Würfel,** *m.* cube; die (*pl.* dice). **-alaun,** *m.* cubic alum. **-brikett,** *n.* cubical briquet(te). **-eck,** *n.*, **-ecke,** *f.* corner of a cube, cubic summit. **-erz,** *n.* cube ore, pharmacosiderite. **-festigkeit,** *f.* crushing strength of a cube.

**würfelförmig,** *a.* cubic, cubical, diced.

**Würfel-gambir,** *n.* cube gambier. **-gips,** *m.* anhydrite.

**würfelig,** *a.* cubic, cubical; checkered.

**Würfel-inhalt,** *m.* cubic contents. **-kohle,** *f.* cob coal, cobbles.

**würfeln,** *v.i.* play at dice. — *v.t.* checker. — **gewürfelt,** *p.a.* checked, checkered.

**Würfel-nickel,** *m.* & *n.* cube nickel, nickel in cubes. **-pulver,** *n.* (*Expl.*) cube-cut powder. **-salpeter,** *m.* cubic niter, cubic saltpeter (sodium nitrate). **-schiefer,** *m.* clay slate, argillite. **-spaltbarkeit,** *f.* (*Cryst.*) cubic cleavage. **-spat,** *m.* anhydrite. **-stein,** *m.* boracite. **-werk,** *n.* checkerwork. **-zahl,** *f.* (*Math.*) cube. **-zeolith,** *m.* analcite. **-zucker,** *m.* cube sugar.

**Wurf-geschoss,** *n.* missile, projectile. **-granate,** *f.* mortar shell. **-granatzünder,** *m.* mortar-shell fuse. **-körper,** *m.* projectile. **-kraft,** *f.* projectile force. **-ladung,** *f.* propellent charge. **-lehre,** *f.* ballistics.

**würflig,** *a.* cubic, cubical; checkered.

**Wurf-linie,** *f.* line or curve of projection. **-maschine,** *f.* launcher, projector. **-mine,** *f.* trench-mortar shell or bomb. **-rauchkörper,** *n.* smoke maroon. **-schaufel,** *f.* shovel, scoop. **-weite,** *f.* range.

**würgeln,** *v.t.* roll, roll flat.

**Würgelpumpe,** *f.* rotary pump.

**würgen,** *v.t.* choke; strangle; destroy; gulp. — *v.i.* choke; retch.

**Wurm,** *m.* worm; vermin; reptile, snake; vermiform process.

**wurm-abtreibend,** *p.a.* vermifuge, anthelmintic. **-ähnlich, -artig,** *a.* wormlike, vermicular, vermiform.

**Wurm-arznei,** *f.* anthelmintic. **-farn,** *m.* male fern.

**wurmförmig,** *a.* worm-shaped, vermicular, vermiform.

**Wurm-fortsatz,** *m.* vermiform process. **-getriebe,** *n.* worm gearing, worm gear. **-kraut,** *n.* anthelmintic herb, specif. (1) tansy, (2) (amerikanisches) pinkroot. **-loch,** *n.* wormhole; (*pl.*, **Wurmlöcher**) wormy surface (on castings). **-mehl,** *n.* worm(hole) dust. **-mittel,** *n.* anthelmintic. **-moos,** *n.* worm moss, Corsican moss. **-pulver,** *n.* worm powder. **-rad,** *n.* worm wheel, worm gear. **-rinde,** *f.* worm bark. **-samen,** *m.* wormseed. **-samenöl,** *n.* wormseed oil.

**wurmstichig,** *a.* worm-eaten.

**Wurmtang,** *m.* = Wurmmoos.

**wurm-treibend, -vertilgend, -vertreibend, -widrig,** *a.* anthelmintic.

**Wurst,** *f.* sausage; (black) pudding; roll, pad, padding. **-darm,** *m.* skin for sausages. **-fleisch,** *n.* sausage meat.

**wurstförmig,** *a.* sausage-shaped; toroidal.

**Wurst-gift,** *n.* sausage poison. **-hülle,** *f.* sausage casing. **-kraut,** *n.* savory; marjoram.

**-kunstpapier,** *n.* synthetic sausage casing. **-stein,** *m.* pudding stone. **-vergiftung,** *f.* sausage poisoning.

**Wurz,** *f.* (in combination) -wort, herb.

**Würze,** *f.* spice, seasoning, flavoring, condiment; (*Brewing*) wort. **-brechen,** *n.* breaking of the wort. **-kühler,** *m.* wort cooler.

**Wurzel,** *f.* root.

**Würzelchen,** *n.* rootlet, radicle.

**Wurzel-faser,** *f.* root fiber. **-fäule,** *f.* root rot. **-gemüse,** *n.* root vegetable. **-gerbstoff,** *m.* root tannin. **-gewächs,** *n.* (*Agric.*) root plant, root crop. **-grösse,** *f.* (*Math.*) radical quantity. **-gummi,** *n.* root rubber. **-haar,** *n.* (*Bot.*) root hair. **-kautschuk,** *m.* & *n.* root rubber. **-keim,** *m.* (*Bot.*) radicle. **-knöllchen,** *n.* root nodule. **-knolle,** *f.*, **-knollen,** *m.* tuber, bulb.

**wurzeln,** *v.i.* root, take root, be rooted.

**Wurzel-stock,** *m.* rootstock, rhizome. **-stoff,** *m.* (*Old Chem.*) radical principle. **-werk,** *n.* root system. **-zeichen,** *n.* radical sign.

**würzen,** *v.t.* spice, season. — **gewürzt,** *p.a.* spiced, aromatic.

**Würze-pfanne,** *f.* wort kettle. **-siedepfanne,** *f.* wort boiler, brewing copper. **-vorwärmer,** *m.* wort preheater.

**Würz-geruch,** *m.* odor of spices, spicy odor. **-geschmack,** *m.* spicy taste.

**würzig,** *a.* spicy, aromatic.

**würzlos,** *a.* unspiced, unseasoned, flat.

**Würz-mittel,** *n.* condiment. **-nägelein,** *n.*, **-nelke,** *f.* clove. **-stoff,** *m.* aromatic essence. **-wein,** *m.* spiced wine.

**wusch,** *pret.* (of waschen) washed.

**wusste,** *pret.* (of wissen) knew.

**Wust,** *m.* confused mass, mess, jumble; rubbish.

**wüst,** *a.* waste; desert; wild.

**Wüste,** *f.* waste, desert, wilderness.

**wüsten,** *v.i.* waste.

**Wüstenlack,** *m.* (*Geol.*) desert varnish.

**Wut,** *f.* rage, fury, madness; mania; rabies.

**wüten,** *v.i.* rage; fume, rave. — **wütend,** *p.a.* raging, furious.

**Wutgift,** *n.* rabies virus.

**wütig,** *a.* raging, furious, mad.

**Wut-seuche, -krankheit,** *f.* rabies.

**Wutz, -stahl,** *m.* wootz steel, wootz.

# X

**X-Achse,** *f.* X axis.
**Xanthanwasserstoff,** *m.* xanthan hydride (perthiocyanic acid, $C_2H_2N_2S_3$).
**xanthisch,** *a.* xanthic.
**xanthogensauer,** *a.* of or relating to xanthic acid, xanthate of.
**Xantho-gensäure,** *f.* xanthogenic acid, xanthic acid. **-kobaltchlorid,** *n.* xanthocobaltic chloride, nitropentamminecobalt(III) chloride. **-proteinsäure,** *f.* xanthoproteic acid.
**x-beliebig,** *a.* any.
**X-Einheit,** *f.* X-ray unit (of wave length).
**Xeres, Xereswein,** *m.* sherry.
**x-geschnitten,** *a.* x-cut. **-mal,** *adv.* *x* times.
**X-Stoss,** *m.* double V joint.
**X-Strahlen,** *m.pl.* X-rays, Röntgen rays.
**Xylidinrot,** *n.* xylidine red.
**Xylo-chinol,** *n.* xyloquinol. **-chinon,** *n.* xyloquinone.
**Xylol,** *n.* xylene.
**Xylorcin,** *n.* xylorcinol, xylorcin.
**Xylylsäure,** *f.* xylic acid.
**X-Zeit,** *f.* zero hour.

# Y

**Y-Achse,** *f.* Y axis.
**Yachtfarbe,** *f.* yacht paint, racing paint.
**Yamwurzel,** *f.* yam.
**Yerbastrauch,** *m.* maté, Paraguay tea.
**Y-förmig,** *a.* Y-shaped.
**y-geschnitten,** *a.* y-cut.
**Y-Legierung,** *f.*, **Y-Metall,** *n.* Y alloy, Y metal.
**Yohimboasäure,** *f.* yohimboaic acid (yohimbic acid).
**Y-Rohr,** *n.*, **Y-Röhre,** *f.* Y-tube.
**Ysop,** *m.* hyssop. **-öl,** *n.* oil of hyssop.
**Ytter-.** yttrium.
**Ytterbin,** *n.*, **-erde,** *f.* ytterbia.
**Ytter-erde,** *f.* yttria; (as class name) yttrium earth. **-flussspat,** *m.* yttrocerite.
**ytterhaltig,** *a.* containing yttrium, yttriferous, yttric.
**Ytter-oxyd,** *n.* ytterbium oxide. **-salz,** *n.* ytterbium salt. **-spat,** *m.* xenotime.
**Yttriumerde,** *f.* yttrium earth, specif. yttria (yttrium oxide).
**yttriumhaltig,** *a.* containing yttrium, yttriferous.

# Z

(See also under C)

**z.,** *abbrev.* (zu, zum, zur) to, at, for, by; (ziemlich) rather.

**Z,** *abbrev.* (Zähigkeit) toughness.

**Z.,** *abbrev.* (Zeitschrift) periodical, journal; (Zahl) number; (Zeile) line; (Zeit) time; (Zoll) inch.

**za.,** *abbrev.* (zirka) about, approximately.

**Z-Achse,** *f.* Z axis.

**Zachunöl, Zachäusöl,** *n.* bito oil, zachun (from *Balanites aegyptiaca*).

**Zacke,** *f.*, **Zacken,** *m.* prong, tooth, jag; twig, bough; scallop, edging; (*Metal.*) plate.

**Zackelwolle,** *f.* refuse wool.

**zacken,** *v.t.* jag, tooth, indent, notch; scallop.

**zackig,** *a.* jagged, toothed, indented, serrated, (of a fracture) hackly.

**Zaffer,** *m.* zaffer, zaffre (impure oxide of cobalt).

**Zaffetika,** *f.* asafetida.

**Zageleisen,** *n.* slab iron.

**Zaggel,** *m.* & *f.* (*Metal.*) billet.

**zäh, zähe,** *a.* tough, tenacious; ductile; (of liquids) viscous, viscid, stringy; stingy.

**Zähe,** *f.* = Zähigkeit.

**Zähegrad,** *m.* (degree of) viscosity.

**Zäheisen,** *n.* toughened iron.

**Zäheit,** *f.* = Zähigkeit.

**zähfestig,** *a.* tenacious; tough.

**Zäh-festigkeit,** *f.* tenacity, toughness. **-fluss,** *m.* viscosity, viscidity.

**zähflüssig,** *a.* thickly liquid, viscous; difficultly fusible, refractory.

**Zähflüssigkeit,** *f.* viscosity; refractoriness.

**Zähflüssigkeitsmesser,** *m.* viscosimeter, viscometer.

**zähhart,** *a.* tough.

**zähig,** *a.* tough, tenacious; viscous, viscid.

**Zähigkeit,** *f.* viscosity, viscidity; toughness, tenacity; ductility.

**Zähigkeits-einheit,** *f.* unit of viscosity (or tenacity or ductility). **-grad,** *m.* (degree of) viscosity or ductility or tenacity. **-mass,** *n.* measure of ductility (or tenacity or viscosity). **-messer,** *m.* viscosimeter. **-probe,** *f.* toughness (or ductility or viscosity) test or sample.

**Zähkupfer,** *n.* tough-pitch copper, tough pitch.

**Zahl,** *f.* number; numeral; (numerical) value.

**Zählapparat,** *m.* counting apparatus, counter.

**zahlbar,** *a.* payable, due.

**zahlen,** *v.t.* & *i.* pay.

**zählen,** *v.t.* & *i.* number, count, reckon, calculate.

**Zahlen-angaben,** *f. pl.* numerical data. **-folge,** *f.* numerical order. **-grösse,** *f.* numerical quantity. **-index,** *m.* numerical index or suffix.

**zahlenmässig,** *a.* numerical; quantitative.

**Zahlen-reihe,** *f.* numerical series. **-tafel,** *f.* table of figures, numerical table. **-verhältnis,** *n.* numerical relation or ratio. **-wert,** *m.* numerical value.

**Zähler,** *m.* numerator; counter, marker; meter.

**Zähleröl,** *n.* counter oil, meter oil.

**Zählflasche,** *f.* counting bottle.

**-zählig.** -fold, -nary, -ple.

**Zähligkeit,** *f.* multiplicity.

**Zählkammer,** *f.* counting chamber.

**zahllos,** *a.* numberless, countless.

**zahlr.,** *abbrev.* (zahlreich) numerous.

**zahlreich,** *a.* numerous.

**Zählrohr,** *n.* counting tube, tube counter.

**Zahlung,** *f.* payment.

**Zählung,** *f.* counting, count, enumeration; calculation, computation.

**zahlungsfähig,** *a.* (*Com.*) solvent.

**Zahlungsschein,** *m.* receipt.

**zahlungsunfähig,** *a.* insolvent.

**Zählvorrichtung,** *f.* counting device.

**Zählwerk,** *n.* counting (or calculating) device.

**Zahl-wert,** *m.* numerical value. **-wort,** *n.* numeral. **-zeichen,** *n.* figure, numeral.

**zahm,** *a.* tame, gentle, domestic, cultivated.

**zähmen,** *v.t.* tame, domesticate; restrain, control.

**Zahn,** *m.* tooth; cog. — **— und Trieb,** rack and pinion.

**Zahn-.** tooth, dental, odonto-, toothed, notched.

**zahnähnlich,** *a.* toothlike, (*Anat.*) odontoid.

**Zahnarzt,** *m.* dentist.

**zahnärztlich,** *a.* dentist's, dental.

**Zahn-bein,** *n.* dentine. **-blei,** *n.* (*Bot.*) leadwort. **-bürste,** *f.* tooth brush.

**Zähne,** *m. pl.* teeth.

**zähneln,** *v.t.* tooth, indent, denticulate.

**Zähnelung,** *f.* toothing, indentation, serration.

**Zahnemail,** *n.* dental enamel.

**zahnen,** *v.t.* tooth, indent. — *v.i.* teeth. — **gezahnt,** *p.a.* toothed, dentate, dentated, indented.

**Zahn-fäule,** *f.* tooth decay, (dental) caries.

**-fleisch,** *n.* gum, gums. **-formel,** *f.* dental formula.

**zahnförmig,** *a.* tooth-shaped, dentiform.

**Zahn-gewebe,** *n.* dental tissue. **-gummi,** *n.* dental rubber. **-heilkunde,** *f.* dentistry.

**zahnig, zähnig,** *a.* toothed, dentate, indented, jagged.

**Zahn-keim,** *m.* dental pulp. **-kitt,** *m.* dental cement. **-knorpel,** *m.* dental cartilage. **-latwerge, -paste, -pasta,** *f.* tooth paste. **-plombe,** *f.* tooth filling, dental filling. **-pulpa,** *f.* dental pulp. **-pulver,** *n.* tooth powder. **-rad,** *n.* cog wheel, gear; pinion. **-radfett,** *n.* gear grease; pinion grease. **-reinigungsmittel,** *n.* dentifrice. **-schmelz,** *m.* dental enamel. **-schmerz,** *m.* toothache. **-stange,** *f.* (*Mach.*) rack. **-stein,** *n.* tartar (on the teeth). **-substanz,** *f.* tooth substance, dentine. **-trieb,** *m.* rack and pinion.

**Zahnung,** *f.* toothing; indentation, serration; dentition.

**Zahn-wasser,** *n.* tooth wash, dental lotion. **-weh,** *n.* toothache. **-wehholz,** *n.* prickly ash (*Zanthoxylum*). **-weinstein,** *m.* tartar (on the teeth). **-werk,** *n.* gearing. **-zement,** *m.* dental cement.

**zäh-polen,** *v.t.* (*Metal.*) toughen by poling. **-schlackig,** *a.* of or forming tough clinker or slag. **-schleimig,** *a.* mucous.

**Zain,** *m.* ingot, bar, rod, pig.

**zainen,** *v.t.* make into ingots or bars; draw out, stretch (iron, etc.).

**Zainform,** *f.* ingot mold.

**Zängchen,** *n.* small forceps or tweezers.

**Zange,** *f.* (pair of) tongs; pincers, nippers, forceps, pliers, tweezers.

**Zänge-.** (*Metal.*) shingling. **-arbeit,** *f.* (*Metal.*) shingling.

**Zängelchen,** *n.* pincers, nippers, tweezers.

**zängen,** *v.t.* (*Metal.*) shingle.

**Zangengriff,** *m.* handle of tongs, forceps, etc.

**Zänger,** *m.* shingler.

**Zänge-schlacke,** *f.* shingling slag. **-walzen,** *f. pl.* shingling rolls.

**Zäpfchen,** *n.* small pin, peg or plug; (*Anat.*) uvula.

**Zäpfchen-.** (*Anat.*) uvular.

**zapfen,** *v.t.* tap, draw (liquids).

**Zapfen,** *m.* peg, pin, plug, stud, pivot; tap, spigot, bung; journal, trunnion; tenon; cone.

**zapfenartig,** *a.* plug-shaped, cone-shaped.

**Zapfenbaum,** *m.* conifer.

**zapfenförmig,** *a.* peg-shaped, cone-shaped, conical, (*Bot.*) strobiliform.

**Zapfen-korn,** *n.* ergot. **-lager,** *n.* (*Mach.*) bearing, socket, bush, collar. **-loch,** *n.* peg hole, pivot hole; (in casks) bung hole, tap hole.

**zapfentragend,** *p.a.* (*Bot.*) coniferous.

**Zapfen-träger,** *m.pl.* (*Bot.*) Coniferae, Pinales. **-wein,** *m.* leaked wine.

**Zapf-hahn,** *m.* drain cock, tap. **-kolophonium,** *n.* gum rosin. **-loch,** *n.* = Zapfenloch. **-stelle,** *f.* tapping point; gasoline station.

**Zapfung,** *f.* tapping, drawing (of liquids).

**Zapon,** *m.* varnish.

**zaponieren,** *v.t.* varnish with Zaponlack.

**Zapon-lack,** *m.* cellulose ester (nitrate, acetate, etc.) varnish, zapon, zapon varnish. **-verdünnung,** *f.* zapon thinner.

**zappeln,** *v.i.* struggle, flounder, writhe, fidget.

**Zarge,** *f.* border, rim, edge.

**zart,** *a.* tender; delicate; fragile, soft, fine.

**Zartheit,** *f.* tenderness, etc. (see zart).

**zartrosa,** *a.* pale pink.

**Zärul-, zärul-.** cerul-.

**Zaser,** *f.* fiber, filament.

**Zäserchen,** *n.* fine fiber, fibril, filament.

**zaserig,** *a.* fibrous, filamentous.

**Zäsium,** *n.* cesium. For compounds see Cäsium-.

**Zaspel,** *f.* skein, hank.

**Zauber,** *m.* charm, spell; magic, witchcraft.

**Zauber-.** magic, fairy.

**Zauberei,** *f.* magic, sorcery.

**Zauberer,** *m.* magician, wizard.

**zauberhaft, zauberisch,** *a.* magic, enchanting.

**Zauber-hasel,** *f.* witch-hazel. **-laterne,** *f.* magic lantern. **-wurzel,** *f.* mandrake.

**zaudern,** *v.i.* delay, hesitate, waver.

**Zaum,** *m.* bridle, rein, check.

**Zaun,** *m.* fence, fencing; hedge. **-draht,** *m.* fence wire. **-gitter,** *n.* fence netting, wire fencing. **-rübe,** *f.* bryony.

**zausen, zauseln,** *v.t.* pull, pick, drag.

**z.B.,** *abbrev.* (zum Beispiel) for example, *e.g.*

**z.E.,** *abbrev.* (zum Exempel) for example, *e.g.*

**Zeche,** *f.* mine, mining company; score, bill.

**Zechen-kohle,** *f.* mine coal, mineral coal. **-koks,** *m.* furnace coke. **-teer,** *m.* coke tar.

**zechfrei,** *a.* scot-free.

**Zechstein,** *m.* (*Geol.*) Zechstein, Thuringian.

**Zecke,** *f.* (*Zoöl.*) tick.

**Zeder,** *f.* cedar.

**Zeder(n)-harz,** *n.* cedar resin. **-holzöl,** *n.* cedar-wood oil. **-öl,** *n.* cedar oil.

**zedieren,** *v.t.* cede, transfer, assign.

**Zedratöl, Zedroöl,** *n.* citron oil.

**Zehe,** *f.*, **Zeh,** *m.* toe; clove (of garlic); **knot,** stick (of ginger).

**Zehen-.** digital, toe.

**zehn,** *a.* ten. **-basisch,** *a.* decabasic.

**Zehneck,** *n.* decagon.

**Zehner-logarithmus,** *m.* logarithm to the base 10, common logarithm. **-potenz,** *f.* power of ten; tenth power. **-stein,** *m.* hollow concrete block. **-stelle,** *f.* decimal place. **-system,** *n.*

decimal system. **-wa(a)ge,** *f.* decimal balance.

**zehn-fach, -fältig,** *a.* tenfold. **-fachnormal,** *a.* decanormal, 10 *N*-. **-lötig,** *a.* weighing 100 grams, etc. (see lötig). **-prozentig,** *a.* 10 per cent.

**zehnte,** *a.* tenth.

**Zehntel,** *n.* tenth. **-grad,** *m.* tenth of a degree. **-lösung,** *f.* tenth-normal solution.

**zehntelnormal,** *a.* tenth-normal.

**Zehntelsilberlösung,** *f.* tenth-normal silver solution.

**zehren,** *v.i.* consume, waste; live, feed.

**Zehrung,** *f.* consumption; provisions, expenses; waste, loss (of wine, etc.); (*Explosives*) priming.

**Zeichen,** *n.* symbol; sign; mark, stamp, brand; signal; symptom; token.

**Zeichen-.** symbolic, sign; drawing, marking. **-brett,** *n.* drawing board. **-ebene,** *f.* plane of the drawing, plane of the paper. **-erklärung,** *f.* explanation of symbols, marks or signs. **-farbe,** *f.* drawing (or marking) color. **-kreide,** *f.* crayon, marking chalk. **-papier,** *n.* drawing paper.

**zeichenrechtlich geschützt.** protected by registration, registered (said of trademarks).

**Zeichen-regel,** *f.* rule for drawing, construction rule. **-setzung,** *f.* punctuation. **-sprache,** *f.* symbolic notation, sign language. **-stab,** *m.* rule (for drawing). **-stift,** *m.* drawing pencil. **-tinte,** *f.* drawing ink, marking ink.

**zeichnen,** *v.t. & i.* draw, design; plot, map; mark, brand, label; sign, subscribe.

**Zeichner,** *m.* drawer, draftsman, designer; signer, subscriber.

**zeichnerisch,** *a.* pertaining to drawing, graphic, diagrammatic. — *adv.* graphically.

**Zeichnung,** *f.* drawing, diagram, sketch, design, plan, pattern; illustration, cut; marking, marks; signature, subscription.

**Zeigefinger,** *m.* forefinger, index.

**zeigen,** *v.t.* show, exhibit; point out, indicate. — *v.r.* appear, show oneself, become evident; turn out, prove. — *v.i.* point.

**Zeiger,** *m.* pointer, indicator, hand, index, needle; (*Math.*) index; index finger; one that shows, presenter, bearer. **-ablesung,** *f.* pointer reading. **-ausschlag,** *m.* pointer deflection. **-diagramm,** *n.* vector diagram. **-galvanometer,** *n.* needle galvanometer. **-hebel,** *m.* pointing lever, pointer. **-platte, -scheibe,** *f.* dial plate, dial.

**Zeile,** *f.* line; row; streak, band.

**Zeilen-folge,** *f.* series (or sequence) of lines. **-struktur,** *f.* banded structure.

**Zein,** *m.* ingot, bar, rod, pig. — *n.* zein.

**Zeisig,** *m.* siskin.

**zeisig-gelb,** *a.* siskin-yellow, light greenish-yellow. **-grün,** *a.* siskin-green, light yellowish-green.

**Zeit,** *f.* time; period; epoch, era, season; tense; tide. — **zur —,** at the time; at present. — **vor kurzer —,** a short time ago.

**Zeit-abschnitt,** *m.* period, interval. **-abstand,** *m.* time interval. **-alter,** *n.* age, period. **-angabe,** *f.* date. **-aufnahme,** *f.* (*Photog.*) time exposure. **-aufwand,** *m.* loss of time. **-bombe,** *f.* time bomb. **-dauer,** *f.* duration, period of time. **-einheit,** *f.* unit of time.

**zeiten,** *v.t.* time.

**Zeit-ersparnis,** *f.* time saving, economy of time. **-faktor,** *m.* time factor. **-festigkeit,** *f.* prolonged strength or stability. **-folge,** *f.* chronological order or succession, time sequence. **-frage,** *f.* topic of the day. **-geist,** *m.* spirit of the age.

**zeitgemäss,** *a.* timely, seasonable; up-to-date.

**Zeitgenoss,** *m.* contemporary.

**zeitgeordnet,** *p.a.* chronological.

**Zeit-gleichung,** *f.* time equation. **-härtung,** *f.* age-hardening.

**zeither,** *adv.* hitherto, ever since.

**zeitig,** *a.* early, timely; ripe, mature.

**zeitigen,** *v.t.* mature, ripen.

**Zeitigung,** *f.* maturation, maturity.

**Zeitlang,** *f.* time. — **eine —,** for some time.

**Zeitlauf,** *m.* lapse (or course) of time.

**zeit-lebens,** *adv.* for life, forever. **-lich,** *a.* temporary; temporal; transient; periodic; timely; chronological.

**Zeit-lose,** *f.* colchicum. **-mass,** *n.* measure of time; (*Music*) time, rhythm; (*Gram.*) quantity. **-massstab,** *m.* time scale. **-messer,** *m.* chronometer, time piece, watch, clock. **-messung,** *f.* time measurement; timing. **-punkt,** *m.* point of time, moment.

**zeitraubend,** *p.a.* time-consuming.

**Zeit-raum,** *m.* time interval, period. **-rechnung,** *f.* chronology. **-schnur,** *f.* time fuse.

**Zeitschr.,** *abbrev.* of Zeitschrift.

**Zeit-schreiber,** *m.* chronograph. **-schrift,** *f.* periodical, journal, magazine. **-schriftenliteratur,** *f.* journal literature. **-spanne, -strecke,** *f.* length of time, time.

**zeitunabhängig,** *a.* independent of time.

**Zeitung,** *f.* newspaper, paper; news.

**Zeitungs-ausgabe,** *f.* issue of a newspaper. ... newspaper office. **-druckfarbe,** *f.* newsp... color. **-papier,** *n.* (*Paper*) newsprint, ne... old newspapers. **-wesen,** *n.* newspaper bu... ness; journalism.

**Zeit-verhältnis,** *n.* time relation. **-verlauf,** *m.* lapse (or course) of time. **-verlust,** *m.* loss of time. **-verschiebung,** *f.* time shift; time lag. **-vertreib,** *m.* pastime.

**zeit-weilig,** *a.* temporary; periodic; present,

n.
spar,
ub, m.
dust
-ver-
zinc
eiss,
zinc
inc
.

actual. **-weise,** *adv.* temporarily; periodically; occasionally, at times.

**Zeit-wort,** *n.* verb. **-zünder,** *m.* time fuse; delay-action cap, delay igniter. **-zündung,** *f.* delayed ignition. **-zwischenraum,** *m.* time interval.

**zelebrieren,** *v.t.* celebrate.

**zellähnlich,** *a.* cell-like, celloid, cytoid.

**Zell-bestandteil,** *m.* cell constituent. **-bildung,** *f.* cell formation.

**Zellchen,** *n.* cellule, small cell.

**Zelldehydrase,** *f.* cellular dehydrogenase.

**Zelle,** *f.* cell; booth.

**Zellen-.** cell, cellular.

**zellenähnlich,** *a.* cell-like.

**Zellenart,** *f.* kind of cell.

**zellenartig,** *a.* cell-like, cellular.

**Zellenaufbau,** *m.* cell(ular) structure.

**zellenbildend,** *p.a.* cell-forming.

**Zellen-bildung,** *f.* cell formation. **-faser,** *f.* cell fiber. **-faserstoff,** *m.* cellulose. **-filter,** *n.* revolving filter. **-flüssigkeit,** *f.* cell fluid, cell sap.

**zellenförmig,** *a.* in the form of cells, cellular.

**zellenfrei,** *a.* cell-free.

**Zellen-gehalt,** *m.* cell contents. **-gewebe,** *n.* cellular tissue.

**zellenhaltig,** *a.* containing cells, cellular.

**Zellen-haut,** *f.* cell membrane. **-inhalt,** *m.* cell contents. **-keim,** *m.* cell germ. **-kern,** *m.* cell nucleus. **-kies,** *m.* cellular pyrites. **-körper,** *m.* cellular body; body of a cell. **-rad,** *n.* bucket wheel. **-saft,** *m.* cell fluid, cell sap. **-schale,** *f.* cell membrane. **-schalter,** *m.* (*Elec.*) battery switch. **-spannung,** *f.* (*Elec.*) cell voltage. **-stoff,** *m.* cellulose; gas cell fabric. **-struktur,** *f.* cellular structure. **-teilung,** *f.* cell division. **-tiefofen,** *m.* soaking-pit furnace. **-wand, -wandung,** *f.* cell wall. **-zwischensubstanz,** *f.* intercellular substance.

**Zellfaserstoff,** *m.* cellulose.

**zellförmig,** *a.* cellular.

**Zell-gewebe,** *n.* cellular tissue. **-gift,** *n.* intracellular toxin. **-glas,** *n.* a product similar to cellophane, cellulose glass. *T.N.* **-haut,** *f.* a product similar to cellophane (*T.N.*); (*Biol.*) cell membrane. **-horn,** *n.* celluloid or a similar product.

**zellig,** *a.* cellular, celled; honeycombed, vesicular.

**Zell-kern,** *n.* cell nucleus. **-kernteilung,** *f.* (*Biol.*) nuclear division. **-körper,** *m.* cellular body or substance. **-masse,** *f.* cellular substance.

**Zelloidinembettung,** *f.* celloidin embedding.

**Zellonlack,** *m.* a cellulose acetate lacquer. *T.N.*

**Zellophan,** *n.* cellophane.

**Zell-pech,** *n.* cellulose pitch, cell pitch (a pitchy product from the evaporation of sulfite liquor). **-saft,** *m.* cell sap, cell fluid.

**Zellstoff,** *n.* cellulose; (*Paper*) pulp. **-ausbeute,** *f.* (*Paper*) yield of pulp. **-chemie,** *f.* cellulose chemistry. **-fabrik,** *f.* (*Paper*) pulp factory, pulp mill. **-fabrikation,** *f.* cellulose manufacture; (*Paper*) pulp making. **-faser,** *f.* cellulose fiber. **-flocken,** *f.pl.* loose (paper) pulp. **-glashaut,** *f.* transparent cellulose film. **-holz,** *n.* pulpwood. **-karton,** *m.* paperboard, pulpboard. **-kocher,** *m.* cellulose digester. **-pappe,** *f.* paperboard, pulpboard. **-prüfung,** *f.* cellulose testing, specif. pulp testing. **-schleifer,** *m.* (*Paper*) pulp grinder. **-schleim,** *m.* cellulose slime, pulp slime. **-seide,** *f.* cellulose silk, rayon. **-trockner,** *m.* (*Paper*) pulp drier. **-verbindung,** *f.* cellulose compound. **-watte,** *f.* cellulose wadding, specif. cellucotton. **-wechsel,** *m.* cell metabolism.

**Zellteilung,** *f.* cell division.

**Zelluloid,** *n.* celluloid. **-lack,** *m.* celluloid varnish.

**Zellulose,** *f.* cellulose. (For compounds see Cellulose-.)

**Zell-verschmelzung,** *f.* cell fusion. **-wand,** *f.* cell wall. **-wolle,** *f.* staple fiber, staple rayon; artificial wool.

**Zelt,** *n.* tent; awning; pavilion.

**Zeltchen,** *n.* lozenge, tablet.

**Zeltstoff,** *m.* tent cloth, awning.

**Zement,** *m.* & *n.* cement.

**zementartig,** *a.* cement-like.

**Zementation,** *f.* cementation.

**Zement-beton,** *m.* cement concrete. **-brei,** *m.* cement slurry. **-brennofen,** *m.* cement kiln.

**zementecht,** *a.* (of colors) stable in cement.

**Zement-fabrik,** *f.* cement factory. **-gerbstahl,** *m.* shear steel.

**zementieren,** *v.t.* cement; subject to cementation, carburize.

**Zementieren,** *n.* = Zementierung.

**Zementier-fass,** *n.* precipitation vat. **-mittel,** *n.* cementing agent, cement. **-often,** *m.* cementation furnace.

**Zementierung,** *f.* cementing; cementation, carburization.

**Zementierungs-ofen,** *m.* cementing furnace. **-pulver,** *n.* cementing powder.

**Zementierverfahren,** *n.* cementation process.

**Zementit,** *n.* cementite.

**Zement-kalk,** *m.* hydraulic lime. **-kalkmörtel,** *m.* lime-and-cement mortar. **-kalkstein,** *m.* hydraulic limestone. **-kohle,** *f.* cementation carbon. **-kufe, -küpe,** *f.* cement (or concrete) vat. **-kupfer,** *m.* cement copper. **-mastix,** *m.* mastic cement. **-metall,** *n.* metal precipitated by the cementation process. **-milch,** *f.* thin cement mortar, grout. **-mörtel,** *m.* cement mortar. **-mörtelbrei,** *m.* grout. **-ofen,** *m.* cement kiln. **-prüfung,** *f.* cement testing. **-pulver,** *n.* cement powder; (*Metal.*) cementing powder. **-putz,** *m.* cement plaster. **-schlacke,** *f.* cement clinker. **-silber,** *n.* precipitated silver. **-stahl,** *m.* cementation steel, cemented steel. **-stein,** *m.* cement stone. **-tiegel,** *m.* cementation crucible. **-wasser,** *n.* cement(ing) water. **-werk,** *n.* cement plant.

**zensieren,** *v.t.* criticize.

**Zensur,** *f.* censorship; report.

**Zenti-.** centi-. **-gramm,** *n.* centigram. **-liter,** *n.* centiliter. **-meter,** *n.* centimeter.

**Zentner,** *m.* hundredweight; quintal.

**zentral,** *a.* central.

**Zentralblatt,** *n.* central journal or paper (a name used by periodicals).

**Zentrale,** *f.* central office, center; central station; median (line); line joining centers.

**Zentral-gruppe,** *f.* central group. **-heizung,** *f.* central heating.

**zentralisieren,** *v.t.* centralize.

**Zentral-körperchen,** *n.* (*Biol.*) centrosome. **-kraftsystem,** *n.* central force system. **-lager,** *n.* (*Com.*) central store or stock. **-stelle,** *f.* central place, office or station. **-strahl,** *n.* central ray.

**zentralsymmetrisch,** *a.* centrosymmetric.

**Zentralverein,** *m.* central union or association.

**Zentren,** *pl.* of Zentrum.

**zentrieren,** *v.t.* center.

**Zentrifugal-abscheider,** *m.* centrifugal separator. **-gebläse,** *n.* centrifugal blower or fan. **-kraft,** *f.* centrifugal force. **-stoffmühle,** *f.* (*Paper*) centrifugal beater.

**Zentrifuge,** *f.* centrifuge; sling.

**zentrifugieren,** *v.t.* centrifuge, centrifugalize.

**zentrisch,** *a.* centric; central; concentric.

**Zentrizität,** *f.* centricity.

**Zentrum,** *n.* center; bull's-eye.

**Zeolith,** *m.* zeolite.

**zeolithisch,** *a.* zeolitic.

**Zer,** *n.* cerium.

**zer-.** apart, asunder, in pieces, dis-.

**zerarbeiten,** *v.t.* work, prepare by working; destroy by working, crumble; overwork.

**Zerasin,** *n.* cerasin.

**Zerat,** *n.* cerate.

**zerätzen,** *v.t.* destroy with caustics.

**zerbomben,** *v.t.* destroy with bombs.

**zerbrechen,** *v.t.* break (in pieces), shatter; break down (an emulsion). — **zerbrechend,** *p.a.* shattering, disruptive, brisant.

**zerbrechlich,** *a.* breakable, fragile; brittle.

**Zerbrechlichkeit,** *f.* fragility; brittleness.

**Zerbrechungsfestigkeit,** *f.* resistance to breaking stress, breaking strength.

**zerbrochen,** *p.a.* broken, shattered.

**zerbröckeln,** *v.t. & i.* crumble. — **zerbröckelnd,** *p.a.* crumbling, friable.

**Zerbröck(e)lung,** *f.* crumbling.

**Zerdehnung,** *f.* radial distortion.

**Zerdrehung,** *f.* rotational distortion, torsion, twist.

**zerdrückbar,** *a.* friable, brittle.

**zerdrücken,** *v.t.* crush; crumple.

**Zerdrück(ungs)festigkeit,** *f.* resistance to crushing stress, crush strength.

**Zerealien,** *pl.* cereals.

**zerebral,** *a.* cerebral.

**Zeremonie,** *f.* ceremony.

**zeremoniell,** *a.* ceremonial.

**Zeresin,** *n.* ceresin.

**zerfahren,** *v.t.* injure (by driving over, as roads). — *p.a.* unsteady, inattentive, thoughtless.

**Zerfall,** *m.* decomposition; dissociation; disintegration; decay; ruin.

**zerfallbar,** *a.* decomposable, etc. (see zerfallen).

**Zerfall-barkeit,** *f.* decomposability, disintegrability. **-elektron,** *n.* decay electron (resulting from disintegration).

**zerfallen,** *v.i.* decompose; dissociate; divide; break down, disintegrate, crumble, fall to pieces; quarrel. — *v.t.* injure by falling.

**Zerfall-geschwindigkeit,** *f.* velocity of decomposition. **-grad,** *m.* degree of decomposition (or dissociation). **-grenze,** *f.* limit of dissociation or decomposition. **-kurve,** *f.* decay (or disintegration) curve. **-produkt,** *m.* = Zerfallsprodukt. **-prozess,** *m.* decomposition process. **-schlacke,** *f.* disintegrating slag.

**Zerfalls-elektron,** *n.* = Zerfallelektron. **-konstante,** *f.* (nuclear) disintegration constant, decay coefficient; dissociation constant. **-leuchten,** *n.* decomposition luminescence. **-produkt,** *m.* decomposition (or dissociation or disintegration) product. **-reihe,** *f.* disintegration series.

**Zerfall-wärme,** *f.* heat of decomposition or dissociation. **-zeit,** *f.* (nuclear) disintegration time, decay time.

**Zerfaserer,** *m.* (*Paper*) stuff grinder, pulper, disintegrator.

**zerfasern,** *v.t.* separate into fibers, rag, pulp, unravel.

**zerfetzen,** *v.t.* cut in pieces, shred; slash.

**zerfl.,** *abbrev.* (zerfliesslich) deliquescent.

**zerfleischen,** *v.t.* lacerate.

**zerfliessbar,** *a.* deliquescent.

**Zerfliessbarkeit,** *f.* deliquescence.

**zerfliessen,** *v.i.* deliquesce, melt, be dissolved; (of colors) run. — **zerfliessend,** *p.a.* deliquescent.

**zerfliesslich,** *a.* deliquescent.

**Zerfliesslichkeit,** *f.* deliquescent property.

**Zerfliessung,** *f.* deliquescence.

**Zerfluor,** *m.* cerium fluoride.

**zerfressen,** *v.t.* eat away, corrode; cauterize. — **zerfressend,** *p.a.* corrosive.
**Zerfressung,** *f.* corrosion; cauterization.
**zerfrieren,** *v.i.* break (up) through freezing.
**zergehen,** *v.i.* deliquesce; disperse, dissolve, dwindle.
**zergliedern,** *v.t.* decompose, analyze; dismember; (*Med.*) dissect.
**Zergliederung,** *f.* decomposition, analysis; dissection; dismemberment.
**Zergliederungs-kunde, -kunst,** *f.* anatomy.
**zerhacken,** *v.t.* cut to pieces, chop up, mince.
**Zerhacker,** *m.* chopper; (*Elec.*) vibrator.
**Zerin,** *n.* cerin.
**Zerit,** *m.* cerite. **-erde,** *f.* cerite earth.
**Zerium,** *n.* cerium.
**Zerkleinerer,** *m.* comminuter, etc. (see zerkleinern).
**zerkleinern,** *v.t.* reduce to small pieces, comminute, disintegrate, crush, pulverize.
**Zerkleinerung,** *f.* comminution, etc. (see zerkleinern).
**Zerkleinerungsmaschine,** *f.* crusher, pulverizer.
**zerklüften,** *v.t.* cleave, split, fissure, divide, segment, separate.
**Zerklüftung,** *f.* cleavage, etc. (see zerklüften).
**Zerknall,** *m.* explosion, detonation.
**zerknallen,** *v.i.* explode, detonate.
**Zerknallstoss,** *m.* shock of explosion.
**zerknicken,** *v.t.* crack (esp. by bending).
**zerknistern,** *v.i.* decrepitate.
**zerknittern, zerknullen,** *v.t.* crumple, rumple; corrugate.
**zerkochen,** *v.t.* boil (or cook) to pieces, (*Paper*) pulp.
**zerkörnen,** *v.t.* granulate.
**zerkratzen,** *v.t.* scratch, mar by scratching.
**zerkrümeln,** *v.t.* crumble, pulverize; fritter away. — *v.i.* & *r.* crumple away, vanish.
**zerlassen,** *v.t.* melt, liquefy, dissolve.
**zerlegbar,** *a.* decomposable, etc. (see zerlegen); detachable.
**Zerlegbarkeit,** *f.* decomposability, etc. (see zerlegen).
**zerlegen,** *v.t.* decompose; dissociate; split up, take apart, cut up, dissect, analyze, resolve, divide; (*Mach.*) dismount; (*Optics*) disperse or diffract; (*Elec.*) scan.
**Zerlegung,** *f.* decomposition, etc. (see zerlegen).
**Zerlegungswärme,** *f.* heat of decomposition or dissociation.
**zerlöchern,** *v.t.* perforate, punch.
**zermahlen,** *v.t.* grind fine, pulverize, triturate.
**zermalmen,** *v.t.* bruise, crush, grind.
**Zermalmung,** *f.* bruising, crushing, grinding, attrition.
**Zermetall,** *n.* cerium metal.
**zermürben,** *v.t.* crush; wear down; rot (as fabrics).
**Zermürb-erscheinung,** *f.* fatigue. **-ung,** *f.* crushing; wearing down, attrition; rotting (of fabrics). **-versuch,** *m.* fatigue test. **-widerstand,** *m.* (*Mech.*) fatigue resistance.
**zernagen,** *v.t.* eat away, erode, corrode.
**Zernitrat,** *n.* cerium nitrate.
**zerpflücken,** *v.t.* pull apart, pick apart, pick to pieces.
**Zerplatzdruck,** *m.* burst(ing) pressure.
**zerplatzen,** *v.i.* burst, explode, disintegrate (violently).
**Zerplatzprobe,** *f.* bursting test.
**zerpulvern,** *v.t.* pulverize.
**zerquetschen,** *v.t.* crush, mash, bruise.
**Zerrbild,** *n.* distorted picture; caricature.
**zerreibbar,** *a.* friable, triturable.
**zerreiben,** *v.t.* pulverize, powder, triturate, grind.
**zerreiblich,** *a.* friable, crumbly, triturable.
**Zerreiblichkeit,** *f.* friability.
**Zerreibung,** *f.* pulverization, trituration.
**zerreissbar,** *a.* capable of being torn or rent.
**zerreissen,** *v.t.* tear, lacerate, break, rend, rupture; wear out.
**Zerreiss-festigkeit,** *f.* resistance to tearing or breaking, tensile strength. **-grenze,** *f.* breaking point. **-maschine,** *f.* tensile-test machine. **-probe,** *f.* rending or breaking test; sample for tensile test. **-versuch,** *m.* tensile test.
**zerren,** *v.t.* & *i.* pull, tug, drag, tear.
**Zerrennboden,** *m.* (*Metal.*) slag bottom.
**zerrennen,** *v.t.* (*Metal.*) refine, fine.
**Zerrenner,** *m.* refiner.
**Zerrenn-feuer,** *n.* (*Metal.*) refining fire. **-herd,** *m.* (*Metal.*) refining hearth.
**zerrieben,** *p.p.* (of zerreiben) pulverized, etc.
**zerrieseln,** *v.i.* (of slag) disintegrate.
**zerrinnen,** *v.i.* melt away, vanish.
**zerrissen,** *p.p.* (of zerreissen) torn, etc.
**zerrühren,** *v.t.* mix by stirring, beat up.
**Zerrung,** *f.* pulling, etc. (see zerren); tensile stress.
**zerrütten,** *v.t.* disturb, disorder, disorganize, derange, destroy.
**zers.,** *abbrev.* (zersetzend) decomposing; (zersetzt) decomposed; (zersetzbar) decomposable.
**Zers.,** *abbrev.* (Zersetzung) decomposition.
**zerschellen,** *v.t.* smash, shatter, shiver.
**zerschlagen,** *v.t.* break in pieces, smash, shatter, crush, batter.
**zerschmelzen,** *v.t.* & *i.* melt.
**zerschmettern,** *v.t.* shatter, smash, crush.
**zerschneiden,** *v.t.* cut up; mince, shred; dissect. — **zerschnitten,** *p.p.* cut up, minced, etc.
**zerschnitzeln,** *v.t.* cut into small pieces, shred.
**zersetzbar,** *a.* decomposable.
**Zersetzbarkeit,** *f.* decomposability.

**zersetzen,** *v.t. & r.* decompose; disintegrate.
**Zersetzer,** *m.* decomposer, decomposing agent.
**zersetzlich,** *a.* liable to decompose, unstable.
**Zersetzlichkeit,** *f.* liability to decomposition, instability.
**Zersetzung,** *f.* decomposition; disintegration.
**Zersetzungs-destillation,** *f.* destructive distillation. **-erscheinung,** *f.* phenomenon of decomposition or disintegration. **-erzeugnis,** *f.* decomposition product.
**zersetzungsfähig,** *a.* capable of decomposition.
**Zersetzungs-gas,** *n.* gaseous decomposition product. **-gefäss,** *n.* decomposition vessel. **-geruch,** *m.* odor of decomposition. **-geschwindigkeit,** *f.* rate of decomposition. **-kolben,** *m.* decomposition flask, reaction flask. **-kunst,** *f.* analysis. **-mittel,** *n.* decomposing agent. **-pfanne,** *f.* decomposing pan. **-produkt,** *n.* decomposition product. **-punkt,** *m.* decomposition point. **-spannung,** *f.* (*Elec.*) decomposition voltage. **-vorgang,** *m.* process of decomposition. **-wärme,** *f.* heat of decomposition. **-widerstand,** *m.* (*Elec.*) electrolytic resistance.
**zerspalten,** *v.t. & i.* cleave, split (up).
**zerspanbar,** *a.* cuttable, machinable.
**Zerspanbarkeit,** *f.* machinability.
**zerspanen,** *v.t.* remove by cutting, chip off; machine.
**Zerspanung,** *f.* removal by cutting or boring or the like, machining.
**Zerspanungseigenschaft,** *f.* cutting or machining property.
**zersplittern,** *v.t. & i.* shiver, splinter, split up, break up, shatter, scatter.
**Zersplitterung,** *f.* shivering, etc. (see zersplittern).
**zersprengen,** *v.t.* burst, blow up, shatter, snap; disperse. — **zersprengend,** *p.a.* bursting, shattering, explosive.
**zerspringen,** *v.t.* burst, explode, shiver, break, crack.
**zerstampfen,** *v.t.* pound, bray; break (emulsions).
**zerstäubbar,** *a.* comminutable, etc. (see zerstäuben).
**zerstäuben,** *v.t.* reduce to dust, comminute, (of liquids) atomize, (of mercury) flour; scatter as dust, spatter, disperse, (of liquids) spray.
**Zerstäuber,** *m.* atomizer, sprayer, etc. (see zerstäuben). **-brenner,** *m.* atomizing burner. **-rohr,** *n.* atomizer pipe or tube.
**Zerstäubung,** *f.* comminution, fine disintegration, atomization; spattering, scattering; dispersion; spraying, spray; (of mercury) flouring; (cathode) sputtering.
**Zerstäubungs-apparat,** *m.* spray apparatus, atomizer. **-mittel,** *n.* atomizing agent. **-trockner,** *m.* atomizing (or spraying) drier. **-verfahren,** *n.* atomizing or spraying process.
**zerstieben,** *v.i.* scatter as dust, spray, disperse; vanish.
**zerstörbar,** *a.* destructible.
**Zerstörbarkeit,** *f.* destructibility.
**zerstören,** *v.t.* destroy; break down, ruin.
**Zerstörladung,** *f.* demolition charge.
**Zerstörung,** *f.* destruction; overthrow, ruin.
**Zerstörungsbombe,** *f.* demolition bomb.
**zerstörungsfrei,** *a.* nondestructive.
**zerstossen,** *v.t.* pound (to pieces), bray, bruise, crush, powder, pulverize.
**Zerstrahlung,** *f.* annihilation radiation.
**zerstreuen,** *v.t.* disperse, scatter, disseminate, dissipate, diffuse; divert, distract. — **zerstreut,** *p.a.* dispersed, etc.; diffuse; disperse; abstracted, distracted.
**zerstreutporig,** *a.* diffuse-porous.
**Zerstreuung,** *f.* dispersion, etc. (see zerstreuen); (*Optics*) dispersion (sometimes, divergence); diversion, amusement.
**Zerstreuungs-linse,** *f.* dispersing (or diverging) lens. **-vermögen,** *n.* (*Optics*) dispersive power. **-wirkung,** *f.* (of electrons, etc.) scattering.
**zerstückeln, zerstücken,** *v.t.* divide into small pieces, cut up, parcel out, dismember; spall (ore).
**zerteilbar,** *a.* divisible.
**zerteilen,** *v.t.* divide; split, dissever, separate, resolve. — *v.r.* divide; disperse.
**Zerteilung,** *f.* division; separation, dissolution, resolution, dispersion.
**Zerteilungs-grad,** *m.* degree of division or dispersion, fineness. **-kraft,** *f.* (*Expl.*) fragmentation power. **-mittel,** *n.* (*Med.*) resolvent.
**zertrennen,** *v.t.* separate, etc. ( = trennen).
**Zertrennung,** *f.* separation, etc. (see trennen).
**zertrümmerbar,** *a.* demolishable, disruptable, (of atomic nuclei) fissionable.
**zertrümmern,** *v.t.* shatter, demolish, disrupt, destroy, wreck.
**Zertrümmerung,** *f.* shattering, demolition, fragmentation, destruction.
**Zerussit,** *m.* cerussite.
**Zervelatwurst,** *f.* saveloy.
**zerzupfen,** *v.t.* pick or pull to pieces.
**zessieren,** *v.i.* cease.
**Zettel,** *m.* slip (of paper), card, ticket, label, check, placard, handbill, note; warp. **-katalog,** *m.* card catalog.
**Zeug,** *n. & m.* stuff, material(s); tools, implements, equipment; mortar; harness; rigging; trash; (*Paper*) stuff, pulp; (*Brewing*) yeast; (*Metal.*) metal; (*Fireworks*) composition; (*Weaving*) stuff, cloth, fabric. **-bütte,** *f.* (*Paper*) stuff chest, pulp vat. **-druck,** *m.* cloth printing, calico printing. **-drucker,** *m.*

cloth printer, calico printer. **-druckerei,** *f.* calico printing; print works.

**Zeuge,** *m.* witness. **-linie,** *f.* generating line, generatrix.

**zeugen,** *v.t.* beget, procreate, generate, reproduce; produce; demonstrate, prove. — *v.i.* testify, give evidence.

**Zeugen-.** of a witness, of testimony.

**Zeug-fabrik,** *f.* cloth factory, specif. woolen mill. **-fänger,** *m.* (*Paper*) stuff catcher. **-färberei,** *f.* dyeing; dye works. **-festigkeit,** *f.* (*Paper*) pulp strength. **-geben,** *n.* (*Brewing*) adding the yeast, pitching the wort. **-haus,** *n.* arsenal, armory. **-kasten,** *m.* (*Paper*) stuff chest; tool chest. **-lumpen,** *m.pl.* (*Paper*) cloth rags. **-nis,** *n.* testimony, witness, evidence; testimonial; certificate. **-sichter,** *m.* (*Paper*) pulp strainer.

**Zeugung,** *f.* procreation, generation, reproduction, breeding; production.

**Zeugungs-.** generative, procreative. **-flüssigkeit,** *f.* seminal fluid. **-mittel,** *n.* aphrodisiac. **-stoff,** *m.* semen.

**zeugungsunfähig,** *a.* impotent, sterile.

**Zeugwanne,** *f.* (*Brewing*) yeast tub.

**Zibebe,** *f.* cubeb; (large) raisin.

**Zibet, Zibeth,** *m.* civet.

**Zibeton,** *n.* civetone.

**Zichorie,** *f.* chicory.

**Zichorienwurzel,** *f.* chicory root.

**Zickel-fell, -leder,** *n.* kid (leather).

**Zickzack,** *m.* zigzag. **-bewegung,** *f.* zigzag motion.

**zickzackförmig,** *a.* zigzag, staggered.

**Zickzacklinie,** *f.* zigzag line.

**Zider,** *m.* cider. For compounds see Cider-.

**Ziege,** *f.* goat, she-goat.

**Ziegel,** *m.* brick; tile; briquet(te). **-backstein,** *m.* (burnt) brick. **-brand,** *m.* brick burning, tile burning; batch of brick or tile. **-brennen,** *n.* brick burning, tile burning. **-brenner,** *m.* brick (or tile) burner (or maker). **-brennerei,** *f.* brick (or tile) burning; brick (or tile) factory. **-brennofen,** *m.* brick kiln, tile kiln.

**Ziegelei,** *f.* brickyard, tile works; brick kiln, tile kiln. **-ofen,** *m.* brick (or tile) kiln.

**Ziegel-erde,** *f.* brick earth, brick clay. **-erz,** *n.* tile ore. **-fachwerk,** *n.* brick checkerwork. **-be,** *f.* brick color, brick-red. **arbig, -farben,** *a.* brick (or tile)-colored, k-red. **-förmig,** *a.* brick-shaped, in brick n. **l-hütte,** *f.* brick kiln, tile kiln. **-mehl,** *n.* ck dust. **-ofen,** *m.* brick kiln, tile kiln.

**elrot,** *a.* brick-red.

**gel-sorte,** *f.* grade or sort of brick or tile. **-stein,** *m.* brick. **-ton,** *f.* brick clay, tile clay.

**egen-.** goat's, goat. **-butter,** *f.* goat's butter. **-fell,** *n.* goat skin. **-käse,** *m.* goat's-milk cheese. **-lab,** *n.* goat rennet. **-leder,** *n.* goatskin or kid (leather). **-milch,** *f.* goat's milk. **-peter,** *m.* mumps. **-stein,** *m.* bezoar. **-talg,** *m.* goat tallow.

**Ziegler,** *m.* brickmaker, tile maker.

**Zieh-.** drawing, draw-, towing, tow-; moving; foster. **-arm,** *m.* arm, handle, crank.

**ziehbar,** *a.* ductile.

**Ziehbarkeit,** *f.* ductility.

**ziehen,** *v.t.* draw; pull, tug, haul, drag; suck; draw out, remove; raise, breed; cultivate; rear, train, educate; extract (drugs); (*Math.*) extract (roots); couch, floor (grain); dip, mold (candles), rifle (guns, etc.). — *v.r.* stretch; soak, penetrate; be ropy; warp; move. — *v.i.* draw; pull, etc.; have effect; move, go; (of colors) incline. — **Fäden —,** string, be ropy.

**Ziehen,** *n.* drawing, etc. (see ziehen); draft, traction; (of liquids) ropiness; move; twinge, twitch. **-lassen,** *n.* drawing, infusion (as of tea); allowing (a vessel) to fill, filling.

**Zieh-fähigkeit,** *f.* capability of being drawn, pulled, etc. (see ziehen); (*Metal.*) drawability, ductility. **-feder,** *f.* drawing pen. **-fett,** *n.* (*Metal.*) drawing compound. **-grad,** *m.* (*Metal.*) ductility. **-haken,** *m.* draw hook, drag hook, rake. **-hitze,** *f.* (*Metal.*) drawing heat. **-kraft,** *f.* drawing power, tractive power. **-pappe,** *f.* molded (paper)board. **-presse,** *f.* drawing press, extruding press. **-probe,** *f.* sample drawn (or to be drawn) out; tensile test. **-schnur,** *f.* pull cord, draw cord. **-spachtel,** *f.* glazing filler.

**Ziehung,** *f.* drawing, etc. (see ziehen); draft.

**Zieh-vermögen,** *n.* (*Dyeing*) affinity. **-wert,** *m.* (*Metal.*) ductility value.

**Ziel,** *n.* goal, aim, object, objective, end; limit, boundary; mark, target; term, time.

**zielbewusst,** *a.* clear-sighted, discerning.

**zielen,** *v.i.* aim (at), strive (for); tend (to). — **zielendes Zeitwort,** transitive verb.

**ziellos,** *a.* aimless.

**Ziel-punkt,** *m.* aim, mark, bull's-eye. **-scheibe,** *f.* mark, target.

**zielstrebig,** *a.* purposeful, purposive.

**Zielsucher,** *m.* radar; sonar.

**ziemen,** *v.i.* become, be fitting, suit.

**ziemlich,** *a.* seemly, suitable; fair, moderate; considerable, rather large. — *adv.* fairly, tolerably, rather.

**Zier,** *f.* ornament, grace.

**Zier-.** ornamental, decorative, fancy.

**Zierat,** *m.* ornament, decoration, finery; foil.

**Zierde,** *f.* ornament, honor.

**zieren,** *v.t.* adorn, ornament, decorate. — *v.r.* be affected, coy, or prim. — **geziert,** *p.a.* adorned, etc.; affected, finical.

**Zierlack,** *m.* decorative varnish.

**zierlich,** *a.* elegant, graceful, pretty, dainty, smart.

**Zierpflanze,** *f.* ornamental plant.

**Ziffer,** *f.* figure, digit, numeral, number, cipher; cryptograph. **-blatt,** *n.* graduated face, dial.

**Zigarre,** *f.* cigar.

**zigarrenförmig,** *a.* cigar-shaped.

**Zigorie,** *f.* chicory ( = Zichorie).

**Zimmer,** *n.* room, chamber, apartment.

**Zimmer-.** room, house, home; carpenter's. **-decke,** *f.* ceiling. **-gerät,** *n.* furniture, furnishings. **-holz,** *n.* timber, lumber. **-mann,** *m.* carpenter.

**zimmern,** *v.t.* frame, timber, build of wood; fabricate.

**Zimmer-temperatur, -wärme,** *f.* room temperature.

**Zimmet, Zimmt,** *m.* = Zimt.

**zimolisch,** *a.* = cimolisch.

**Zimt,** *m.* cinnamon. — **weisser —,** canella bark, canella. — **chinesischer —,** cassia bark.

**Zimt-.** cinnamic; cinnamon. **-aldehyd,** *n.* cinnamaldehyde, cinnamic aldehyde. **-alkohol,** *m.* cinnamic alcohol. **-blüte,** *f.* cinnamon flower, cassia bud. **-blütenöl,** *n.* cassia oil.

**zimtbraun,** *a.* cinnamon-brown.

**Zimtcarbonsäure,** *f.* carboxycinnamic acid.

**zimt-farbig, -farben,** *a.* cinnamon-colored.

**Zimt-kaneel,** *m.* canella bark, canella. **-kassia,** *f.* cassia bark, cassia. **-kassienöl,** *n.* oil of cassia.

**Zimtöl,** *n.* oil of cinnamon. — **chinesisches —,** cassia oil.

**Zimtrinde,** *f.* cinnamon bark.

**zimtsauer,** *a.* of or combined with cinnamic acid, cinnamate of.

**Zimt-säure,** *f.* cinnamic acid. **-stein,** *m.* cinnamon stone, essonite. **-wasser,** *n.* cinnamon water.

**Zinder,** *m.* cinder.

**Zink,** *n.* & *m.* zinc.

**zinkartig,** *a.* zincky.

**Zinkasche,** *f.* zinc ash, zinc dross (oxide of zinc).

**Zinkat,** *n.* zincate.

**Zink-äthyl,** *n.* zinc ethyl, diethylzinc. **-ätze,** *f.* zinc-etching solution. **-ätzung,** *f.* zinc etching. **-auflage,** *f.* zinc coating or layer. **-azetat,** *n.* zinc acetate. **-bad,** *n.* zinc bath. **-becher,** *m.* zinc case (of a dry cell). **-beize,** *f.* zinc mordant. **-blech,** *n.* sheet zinc, zinc plate. **-blende,** *f.* zinc blende, sphalerite. **-blumen,** *f.pl.* flowers of zinc (zinc oxide). **-blüte,** *f.* zinc bloom, hydrozincite. **-butter,** *f.* (*Old Chem.*) butter of zinc (zinc chloride). **-chromgelb,** *n.* zinc chrome, zinc yellow. **-dampf,** *m.* zinc vapor, zinc fume. **-destillierofen,** *m.* zinc-distillation furnace, zinc furnace. **-draht,** *m.* zinc wire. **-druck,** *m.* zinc printing.

**Zinke,** *f.* prong, spike, tooth, lug; proboscis.

**Zinkeisen-erz,** *n.*, **-stein,** *m.* franklinite. **-spat,** *m.* ferriferous smithsonite.

**Zinkelectrolysenanlage,** *f.* electrolytic zinc plant.

**Zinken,** *m.* tine, prong, tooth, jag, lug.

**Zink-entsilberung,** *f.* desilverizing of zinc. **-entsilberungsanlage,** *f.* zinc-desilverizing plant.

**Zinkerz,** *n.* zinc ore. — **rotes —,** zincite.

**Zink-fahlerz,** *n.* tennantite. **-farbe,** *f.* zinc paint. **-feile,** *f.*, **-feilspäne,** *m.pl.* zinc filings. **-folie,** *f.* zinc foil. **-formiat,** *n.* zinc formate.

**zinkführend,** *a.* zinc-bearing, zinciferous.

**Zink-gehalt,** *m.* zinc content. **-gekrätz,** *n.* zinc dross (oxide). **-gelb,** *n.* zinc yellow (zinc chromate). **-gewinnung,** *f.* extraction of zinc, zinc production. **-glas, -glaserz,** *n.* (siliceous) calamine. **-granalien,** *f.pl.* granulated zinc. **-grau,** *n.* zinc gray. **-grün,** *n.* zinc green.

**zinkhaltig,** *a.* containing zinc, zinciferous.

**Zink-harz,** *n.* zinc blende, sphalerite. **-hütte,** *f.* zinc works, zinc smeltery. **-hüttenrauch,** *m.* zinc (smelter) fume.

**zinkisch,** *a.* zincky, of zinc.

**Zink-jodid,** *n.* zinc iodide. **-kalk,** *m.* zinc calx, zinc ash. **-kasten,** *m.* zinc case; zinc tank. **-kiesel,** *m.*, **-kieselerz,** *n.* (siliceous) calamine. **-kitt,** *m.* zinc cement. **-kohlenbatterie,** *f.* zinc-carbon battery. **-legierung,** *f.* zinc alloy. **-lösung,** *f.* zinc solution. **-mehl,** *n.* zinc powder, zinc dust. **-nebel,** *m.* (*Mil.*) zinc smoke mixture. **-ofen,** *m.* zinc furnace. **-ofenbruch,** *m.* tutty, cadmia.

**zinkorganisch,** *a.* zinc-organic, organozinc.

**Zinkoxyd,** *n.* zinc oxide. — **rotes —,** zincite.

**Zink-oxydnitrat,** *n.* zinc nitrate. **-pecherz,** *n.* sphalerite. **-pol,** *m.* zinc pole, cathode. **-pulver,** *n.* zinc powder. **-raffinerie,** *f.* zinc refinery. **-rauch,** *m.* zinc fume. **-salbe,** *f.* zinc ointment. **-salz,** *n.* zinc salt.

**zinksauer,** *a.* zincate of.

**Zink-schale,** *f.* zinc dish or basin. **-schaum,** *m.* (*Metal.*) zinc scum. **-schlicker,** *m.* zinc dross. **-schnitzel,** *n.* zinc cutting or filing. **-schwamm,** *m.* tutty, cadmia. **-span,** [illegible] zinc shaving or chip. **-spat,** *m.* zinc [illegible] smithsonite. **-stab,** *m.* zinc rod. **-st**[illegible] zinc dust. **-staubätze,** *f.* (*Calico*) zin[illegible] discharge. **-überzug,** *m.* zinc coating. [illegible] **bindung,** *f.* zinc compound. **-vitriol,** *n.* [illegible] vitriol, white vitriol ($ZnSO_4 \cdot 7H_2O$). **-w**[illegible] *n.* zinc white (zinc oxide). **-werk,** *n.* [illegible] works. **-wolle,** *f.* flowers of zinc; mossy z[illegible] metal. **-zyanid,** *n.* zinc cyanide.

**Zinn,** *n.* tin. **-abstrich,** *m.* tin scum, tin dross

**-ader,** *f.* tin lode, tin vein. **-after,** *m.* tin (ore) refuse.

**zinnähnlich,** *a.* tin-like.

**Zinnammoniumchlorid,** *n.* ammonium chlorostannate.

**zinn-arm,** *a.* poor (or low) in tin. **-artig,** *a.* tin-like, tinny.

**Zinn-asche,** *f.* tin ashes, stannic oxide. **-ätzfarbe,** *f.* (*Calico*) tin discharge paste. **-bad,** *n.* tin bath. **-beize,** *f.* tin mordant, tin spirit. **-beizendruck,** *m.* tin-mordant printing. **-bergwerk,** *n.* tin mine. **-blatt,** *n.* tin foil. **-blech,** *n.* tin plate, sheet tin. **-bleilegierung,** *f.* tin-lead alloy. **-bleilot,** *n.* tin-lead solder. **-bromid,** *n.* tin bromide, specif. stannic bromide, tin(IV) bromide. **-bromür,** *n.* stannous bromide, tin(II) bromide.

**zinnbromwasserstoffsauer,** *a.* of or combined with bromostannic acid, bromostannate of.

**Zinn-bromwasserstoffsäure,** *f.* bromostannic acid. **-butter,** *f.* (*Old Chem.*) butter of tin (stannic chloride). **-charge,** *f.* (*Textiles*) tin weighting. **-chlorammonium,** *n.* ammonium chlorostannate, (*Dyeing*) pink salt. **-chlorid,** *n.* tin chloride, specif. stannic chloride, tin (IV) chloride. **-chlorür,** *n.* stannous chloride, tin(II) chloride.

**zinnchlorwasserstoffsauer,** *a.* of or combined with chlorostannic acid, chlorostannate of.

**Zinn-chlorwasserstoffsäure,** *f.* chlorostannic acid. **-diphenylchlorid,** *n.* diphenyltin chloride. **-draht,** *m.* tin wire.

**Zinne,** *f.* pinnacle.

**zinnen,** *v.t.* tin.

**zinnen, zinnern,** *a.* of tin, tin, pewter.

**Zinn-erschwerung,** *f.* (*Textiles*) tin weighting. **-erz,** *n.* tin ore, cassiterite. **-erzseife,** *f.* tin placer deposit. **-farbe,** *f.* (*Dyeing*) tin-mordant color. **-feilicht,** *n.*, **-feilspäne,** *m.pl.* tin filings. **-flammofen,** *m.* reverberatory tin furnace. **-folie,** *f.* tin foil.

**zinnführend,** *a.* tin-bearing, stanniferous.

**Zinn-gehalt,** *m.* tin content. **-gekrätz,** *n.* tin refuse, tin sweepings. **-gerät, -geschirr,** *n.* tin vessels, pewter. **-geschrei,** *n.* tin cry, crackling of tin. **-giesser,** *m.* tin founder.

**zinnglasiert,** *p.a.* tin-glazed.

**Zinn-glasur,** *f.* tin glazing, tin glaze. **-granalien,** *f.pl.* granulated tin. **-graupen,** *f.pl.* (*Mining*) cassiterite in twin crystals. **-grube,** *f.* tin mine. **-grundierung,** *f.* (*Dyeing*) bottoming (or grounding) with tin.

**zinnhaltig,** *a.* containing tin, stanniferous.

**Zinn-hütte,** *f.* tin smeltery, tin works. **-hydrat,** *n.* tin hydroxide. **-hydroxyd,** *n.* tin hydroxide, specif. stannic hydroxide, tin(IV) hydroxide. **-hydroxydul,** *n.* stannous hydroxide, tin(II) hydroxide. **-jodid,** *n.* tin iodide, specif. stannic iodide, tin(IV) iodide. **-jodür,** *n.* stannous iodide, tin(II) iodide. **-kalk,** *m.* tin calx, stannic oxide, tin(IV) oxide. **-kapsel,** *f.* tin capsule; tin case; tin cap. **-kies,** *m.* tin pyrites, stannite. **-knirschen, -kreischen,** *n.* = Zinngeschrei. **-krätze,** *f.* tin dross, tin waste. **-lagerstätte,** *f.* tin deposit. **-legierung,** *f.* tin alloy. **-lösung,** *f.* tin solution; (*Dyeing*) tin spirit. **-lot,** *n.*, **-löte,** *f.* tin solder.

**Zinnober,** *m.* cinnabar, (also, when used as a pigment) vermilion. **-ersatz,** *m.* vermilion substitute. **-farbe,** *f.* vermilion (color).

**zinnober-farbig,** *a.* vermilion. **-grün,** *a.* cinnabar-green.

**Zinnober-rot,** *n.* vermilion. **-salz,** *n.* vermilion substitute. **-spat,** *m.* crystallized cinnabar.

**Zinnofen,** *m.* tin furnace.

**Zinnoxyd,** *n.* tin oxide, specif. stannic oxide, tin(IV) oxide. **-chlorid,** *n.* stannic chloride, tin(IV) chloride. **-hydrat,** *n.* stannic hydroxide, tin(IV) hydroxide. **-natron,** *n.* sodium stannate. **-salz,** *n.* stannic salt, tin(IV) salt.

**Zinnoxydul,** *n.* stannous oxide, tin(II) oxide. **-chlorid,** *n.* stannous chloride, tin(II) chloride. **-hydrat,** *n.* stannous hydroxide, tin(II) hydroxide. **-natron,** *n.* sodium stannite. **-reserve,** *f.* stannous oxide resist. **-salz,** *n.* stannous salt, tin(II) salt. **-verbindung,** *f.* stannous compound, tin(II) compound.

**Zinn-oxydverbindung,** *f.* stannic compound, tin(IV) compound. **-pest,** *f.* tin plague, tin pest. **-pfanne,** *f.* (*Tinning*) tin pot. **-platte,** *f.* tin plate, sheet of tin (plate).

**zinnplattiert,** *a.* tin-plated.

**Zinn-probe,** *f.* sample, test, or assay of tin. **-puder,** *m.* powdery tin dross. **-pulver,** *n.* powdered tin, grain tin. **-raffination,** *f.* tin refining or refinery.

**zinnreich,** *a.* rich in tin.

**Zinn-rohr,** *n.*, **-röhre,** *f.* tin pipe. **-rückstände,** *m.pl.* tin residues, tin refuse. **-salmiak,** *n.* ammonium chlorostannate, pink salt. **-salz,** *n.* tin salt; specif. (*Dyeing*) stannous chloride, $SnCl_2 \cdot 2H_2O$, called also tin crystals. **-salzätze,** *f.* (*Dyeing*) tin crystal discharge. **-sand,** *m.* (*Mining*) grain tin.

**zinnsauer,** *a.* of or combined with stannic acid, stannate of.

**Zinn-saum,** *m.* list of tin, selvedge. **-säure,** *f.* stannic acid. **-säureanhydrid,** *n.* stannic anhydride, tin dioxide. **-schlich,** *m.* (*Ores*) tin slimes, fine tin. **-schrei,** *m.* = Zinngeschrei. **-seife,** *f.* (*Mining*) stream tin. **-soda,** *f.* sodium stannate. **-staub,** *m.* tin dust. **-stein,** *m.* tinstone, cassiterite. **-sulfid,** *n.* tin sulfide, specif. stannic sulfide, tin(IV) sulfide. **-sulfocyanid,** *n.* tin thiocyanate, specif.

stannic, or tin(IV), thiocyanate. **-sulfür,** *n.* stannous sulfide, tin(II) sulfide. **-verbindung,** *f.* tin compound. **-weiss,** *n.* tin white. **-wolle,** *f.* mossy tin.
**Zins,** *m.* rent; (*pl.*) interest; tribute.
**zinsen,** *v.t. & i.* pay rent, interest, or tribute.
**Zipfel,** *m.* tip, point, end, summit; lobe, ear.
**Zirbel-.** (*Anat.*) pineal. **-drüse,** *f.* pineal gland, pineal body. **-fichte, -kiefer,** *f.* Swiss pine (*Pinus cembra*). **-nuss,** *f.* cedar nut (from *Pinus cembra*).
**zirka,** *adv.* about, approximately.
**zirkassisch,** *a.* Circassian.
**Zirkel,** *m.* circle; (pair of) compasses.
**Zirkel-.** circular; compass.
**Zirkon,** *n.* zirconium; zircon. **-brenner,** *m.* zirconium (incandescent) filament. **-erde,** *f.* zirconia, zirconium oxide. **-glas,** *n.* zirconium glass.
**Zirkonium-stahl,** *m.* zirconium steel. **-verbindung,** *f.* zirconium compound.
**Zirkon-lampe,** *f.* zirconium lamp. **-licht,** *n.* zircon light. **-oxyd,** *n.* zirconium oxide. **-präparat,** *n.* zirconium preparation. **-säure,** *f.* zirconic acid. **-stahl,** *m.* zirconium steel.
**Zirkulante,** *f.* (*Math.*) circulant.
**Zirkular,** *n.* circular.
**Zirkulationstrocknung,** *f.* drying by circulation (of a gas, usually air).
**zirkulieren,** *v.i.* circulate.
**Zirkuliergefäss,** *n.* circulating vessel.
**Zisch,** *m.* hiss, sizz, fizz, sizzle, whiz.
**zischen,** *v.i.* hiss, sizz, fizz, sizzle, whiz.
**Zissoide,** *f.* cissoid.
**Zisterne,** *f.* cistern; tank.
**Zisternenwagen,** *m.* tank car.
**Zitat,** *n.* citation, quotation.
**zitieren,** *v.t.* quote, cite; summon.
**Zitr-, zitr-.** citr-.
**Zitrat,** *n.* citrate.
**zitratlöslich,** *a.* citrate-soluble.
**Zitraweinsäure,** *f.* citratartaric acid.
**Zitrin,** *n.* citrine.
**Zitronat,** *n.* candied lemon peel.
**Zitronbartgras,** *n.* lemon grass.
**Zitrone,** *f.* lemon; citron.
**Zitronell-al,** *n.* citronellal. **-asäure,** *f.* citronellic acid. **-ol,** *n.* citronellol. **-öl,** *n.* citronella oil. **-säure,** *f.* citronellic acid.
**Zitronen-äther,** *m.* citric ester. **-farbe,** *f.* lemon color, citron color.
**zitronen-farben, -farbig,** *a.* lemon-colored, lemon-yellow. **-gelb,** *a.* lemon-yellow, citrine.
**Zitronengras,** *n.* lemon grass. **-öl,** *n.* lemongrass oil.
**zitronenlöslich,** *a.* citrate-soluble.
**Zitronen-melisse,** *f.* balm, balm mint (*Melissa officinalis*). **-öl,** *n.* lemon oil. **-saft,** *m.* lemon juice. **-salz,** *n.* citrate.
**zitronensauer,** *a.* = zitronsauer.
**Zitronen-säure,** *f.* citric acid. **-schale,** *f.* lemon peel. **-wasser,** *n.* lemonade.
**zitronsauer,** *a.* of or combined with citric acid, citrate of.
**Zitronsäure,** *f.* citric acid.
**Zitrulle,** *f.* watermelon.
**Zitrusöl,** *n.* citrus oil, specif. shaddock oil.
**Zitter-bewegung,** *f.* variable motion; trembling; (of light) twinkling. **-elektrode,** *f.* vibrating electrode.
**zittern,** *v.i.* tremble, shake, quiver, vibrate.
**Zitter-sieb,** *n.* vibrating screen. **-wurzel,** *f.* zedoary.
**Zitwer,** *m.* zedoary; aconite; sweet flag; ginger. **-kraut,** *m.* tarragon. **-samen,** *m.* wormseed, esp. santonica; zedoary seed. **-wurzel,** *f.* zedoary.
**Zitz,** *m.* chintz.
**Zitze,** *f.* nipple, teat, dug.
**zitzenförmig,** *a.* mammillary; mastoid.
**Zitzentier,** *n.* mammal.
**zivil,** *a.* civil; moderate (price).
**zl.,** *abbrev.* (ziemlich löslich) fairly soluble.
**Zle.,** *abbrev.* (Zeile) line.
**Zobel,** *m.* sable.
**Zober,** *m.* tub.
**zog,** *pret.* (of ziehen) drew, pulled, etc.
**zögern,** *v.i.* tarry, linger, lag, delay; hesitate.
**Zögling,** *m.* pupil.
**Zölestin,** *n.* celestite.
**Zoll,** *m.* duty, custom, toll; inch. **-amt,** *n.* customhouse; board of customs.
**zollbar,** *a.* dutiable.
**Zoll-beamte, -beamter,** *m.* customhouse officer, revenue officer.
**zollen,** *v.t.* pay, render.
**zollfrei,** *a.* duty-free.
**Zoll-freiheit,** *f.* exemption from duty. **-haus,** *n.* customhouse. **-mass,** *m.* measure(ment) in inches.
**zollpflichtig,** *a.* dutiable.
**Zoll-satz,** *m.* tariff rate. **-teilung,** *f.* division in inches. **-verein,** *m.* tariff union. **-verschluss,** *m.* bond.
**Zone,** *f.* zone; region, district.
**zonenförmig,** *a.* zonal.
**Zoochemie,** *f.* zoöchemistry.
**zoochemisch,** *a.* zoöchemical.
**Zoo-log,** *m.* zoölogist. **-logie,** *f.* zoölogy.
**zoologisch,** *a.* zoölogical.
**Zootinsalz,** *n.* Chile saltpeter.
**Zopf,** *m.* tuft; tress, plait; top (of a tree); red tape; pedantry.
**Zorn,** *m.* anger, wrath, rage, passion.
**Zotte, Zottel,** *f.* tuft, tangle; (*Anat.*) villus.
**Zottelwolle,** *f.* shaggy wool.

**Zottenhaut,** *f.* chorion.
**zottig,** *a.* shaggy, matted, (*Bot.*) villous.
**Zp.,** *abbrev.* (Zersetzungspunkt) decomposition point.
**z.T., z.Th.,** *abbrev.* (zum Teil, zum Theil) in part.
**Ztg.,** *abbrev.* (Zeitung) newspaper, paper.
**Ztschr.,** *abbrev.* (Zeitschrift) journal, periodical.
**zu,** *prep.* to, at, in, for. — *adv.* toward, on, too, closed; (on instruments, etc.) on.
**Zubehör,** *n.* belongings, accessories, fittings. **-teil,** *m.* accessory, fitting.
**zubekommen,** *v.t.* get in addition; get closed.
**zubenannt,** *p.a.* surnamed.
**Zuber,** *m.* tub.
**zubereiten,** *v.t.* prepare, dress, finish, cook.
**Zubereitung,** *f.* preparation, dressing, finishing, cooking.
**zubessern,** *v.t.* improve; feed up, strengthen (a bath).
**Zubesserung,** *f.* improvement; feeding addition.
**zubilligen,** *v.t.* grant, allow.
**zubrennen,** *v.t.* roast, calcine; cauterize; close by heating.
**zubringen,** *v.t.* bring; convey; spend.
**Zubringer,** *m.* conveyor, carrier; feeder.
**Zubrühen,** *n.* (*Brewing*) addition of boiling water in mashing.
**Zubusse,** *f.* supply, contribution.
**Zucht,** *f.* breeding, rearing; cultivation, culture; breed, race; education; propriety; discipline.
**züchten,** *v.t.* breed, rear, grow, cultivate.
**Züchter,** *m.* breeder, raiser, grower.
**Züchtung,** *f.* breeding, growing, culture.
**Züchtungsgefäss,** *n.* growing vessel (for crystals); culture vessel.
**Zuchtwahl,** *f.* (*Biol.*) selection.
**Zuckanzeige,** *f.* ballistic (or kick or flash) reading or indication.
**zucken,** *v.i.* twitch, jerk, kick, palpitate; flicker, flash. — **zuckend,** *p.a.* convulsive, spasmodic.
**Zucker,** *m.* sugar. **-abbau,** *m.* sugar degradation.
**zuckerähnlich,** *a.* like sugar, saccharoid.
**Zucker-ahorn,** *m.* sugar maple. **-art,** *f.* kind or variety of sugar; (*pl.*) sugars.
**zuckerartig,** *a.* sugar-like, saccharine, saccharoid, sugary.
**Zucker-ausbeute,** *f.* yield of sugar, rendement. **-bäcker,** *m.* confectioner. **-baryt,** *n.* barium sucrate. **-beschwerung,** *f.* weighting with sugar. **-bestimmung,** *f.* determination of sugar. **-bildung,** *f.* formation of sugar, saccharification, (*Physiol.*) glycogenesis. **-branntwein,** *m.* sugared spirit. **-brot,** *n.* sugar loaf; sweet bread. **-busch,** *m.* sugar bush, honey flower (*Protea mellifera*). **-couleur,** *f.* caramel. **-dicksaft,** *m.* molasses, treacle. **-erde,** *f.* animal charcoal for refining sugar; clay for refining sugar. **-fabrik,** *f.* sugar factory. **-fabrikation,** *f.* sugar manufacture. **-farbe,** *f.* confectionery color. **-form,** *f.* sugar mold. **-gärung,** *f.* fermentation of sugar, saccharine fermentation. **-gehalt,** *m.* sugar content. **-gehaltmesser,** *m.* saccharimeter. **-geist,** *m.* rum. **-geschmack,** *m.* sugary taste. **-gewinnung,** *f.* extraction of sugar, sugar manufacture.
**zuckerhaltig,** *a.* containing sugar, sugary, saccharine, saccharated, sacchariferous.
**Zucker-harnen,** *n.* glycosuria. **-harnruhr,** *f.* diabetes mellitus. **-hirse,** *f.* sorghum. **-honig,** *m.* molasses, treacle; crystallized honey. **-hut,** *m.* sugar loaf.
**zuckerig,** *a.* sugary, saccharine.
**Zuckerin,** *n.* saccharin.
**Zucker-industrie,** *f.* sugar industry. **-kalk,** *m.* calcium sucrate, sugar-lime. **-kand, -kandis,** *m.* sugar candy. **-kessel,** *m.* sugar kettle, sugar boiler. **-kiefer,** *f.* sugar pine (*Pinus lambertiana*). **-kohle,** *f.* charcoal from sugar. **-korn,** *n.* grain of sugar; sugar plum. **-kranker,** *m.* diabetic. **-krankheit,** *f.* diabetes mellitus. **-küpe,** *f.* (*Wool*) glucose vat. **-lauge,** *f.* (*Sugar*) limewater. **-lösung,** *f.* sugar solution; sirup. **-mais,** *m.* sweet corn, sugar corn. **-mehl,** *n.* powdered sugar. **-melasse,** *f.* molasses (in Germany chiefly beet molasses). **-messer,** *m.* saccharimeter. **-messkunst, -messung,** *f.* saccharimetry. **-mühle,** *f.* sugar mill.
**zuckern,** *v.t.* sugar, sweeten.
**Zucker-palme,** *f.* sugar palm, specif. gomuti palm (*Arenga saccharifera*). **-pflanzung, -plantage,** *f.* sugar plantation. **-probe,** *f.* sample of sugar; sugar test. **-raffinerie,** *f.* sugar refinery.
**Zuckerrohr,** *n.* sugar cane. — **chinesisches —,** sorghum.
**Zuckerröhrchen,** *n.* sugar tube (small cylindrical funnel for sugar determinations).
**Zuckerrohr-faser,** *f.* sugarcane fiber, bagasse fiber. **-melasse,** *f.* cane molasses. **-rückstände,** *m.pl.* bagasse. **-saft,** *m.* cane juice.
**Zucker-rose,** *f.* red rose. **-rübe,** *f.* sugar beet.
**Zuckerrüben-essig,** *m.* sugar-beet vinegar, beetroot vinegar. **-melasse,** *f.* beet molasses, beetroot molasses. **-saft,** *m.* sugarbeet juice. **-schnitzel,** *n.* beet chip, cossette. **-zucker,** *m.* beet sugar, beetroot sugar.
**Zucker-ruhr,** *f.* diabetes mellitus. **-saft,** *m.* saccharine juice. **-satz,** *m.* molasses.
**zuckersauer,** *a.* of or combined with saccharic acid, saccharate of.
**Zucker-säure,** *f.* saccharic acid; (*Old Chem.*) oxalic acid. **-schaum,** *m.* powdered animal charcoal. **-schlamm,** *m.* (*Beet Sugar*) lime

scum. **-schleuder,** *f.* sugar centrifugal. **-schotenbaum,** *m.* honey locust. **-sieden,** *n.* sugar boiling, sugar refining. **-siederei,** *f.* sugar refinery, sugar house. **-sirup,** *m.* sugar sirup; molasses. **-spaltung,** *f.* sugar cleavage. **-stein,** *m.* finely granular albite. **-stoff,** *m.* saccharine matter.

**zuckerstoffhaltig,** *a.* saccharine.

**Zuckerstrontian,** *m.* strontium sucrate.

**zuckersüss,** *a.* sweet as sugar, saccharine.

**Zucker-umwandlung,** *f.* sugar conversion, specif. sugar metabolism. **-untersuchung,** *f.* examination (or investigation) of sugar. **-verbindung,** *f.* compound of sugar, specif. sucrate. **-waren,** *f.pl.*, **-werk,** *n.* confectionery, sweets.

**Zuckung,** *f.* twitching, etc. (see zucken); twitch, quiver; convulsion, spasm.

**zudem,** *adv.* besides.

**zudrängen,** *v.r.* throng, crowd, intrude.

**zudrehen,** *v.t.* turn off, shut off.

**zudringlich,** *a.* intrusive, intruding.

**zudrücken,** *v.t.* shut, close.

**zueignen,** *v.t.* dedicate; attribute; appropriate.

**zueinander,** *adv.* to one another or each other.

**zuerkennen,** *v.t.* adjudge, award; admit, allow.

**zuerst,** *adv.* at first, first, above all.

**zuerteilen,** *v.t.* allot, assign, award.

**Zufall,** *m.* chance, accident; casualty; incident; occurrence; attack.

**zufällig,** *a.* accidental, incidental, casual, chance, random.

**Zufälligkeitsfehler,** *m.* accidental error.

**Zufalls-ergebnis,** *n.* fortuitous result. **-gesetz,** *n.* law of chance or probability. **-kurve,** *f.* probability curve. **-wert,** *m.* chance value, freak value.

**zufliessen,** *v.i.* flow in.

**Zuflucht,** *f.* refuge, recourse.

**Zufluss,** *m.* flow, flux, afflux, influx, inflow; (*Tech.*) feed; resources; (of a stream) tributary. **-behälter,** *m.* feed tank, feed vessel. **-rohr,** *n.* supply tube or pipe, feed pipe.

**zufolge,** *prep.* according to, owing to.

**zufrieden,** *a.* contented, satisfied, pleased. **-stellend,** *p.a.* satisfactory.

**zufrieren,** *v.i.* freeze up or over.

**zufügen,** *v.t.* add; inflict, cause (an injury).

**Zufügung,** *f.* addition; infliction.

**Zufuhr,** *f.* addition; supply, supplies; (*Tech.*) feed; conveyance; importation; administration (of medicines).

**zuführen,** *v.t.* add, supply, feed; admit; bring, conduct, convey; import.

**Zuführer,** *m.* adder, etc. (see zuführen); feeder, feeding apparatus.

**Zuführung,** *f.* (*Tech.*) supply, feed; importation; conveyance; inlet.

**Zuführungs-draht,** *m.* (*Elec.*) lead wire. **-rohr,** *n.* supply pipe, feed pipe, supply tube. **-vorrichtung,** *f.* feeding device. **-walze,** *f.* feed(ing) roller, feed roll.

**zufüllen,** *v.t.* pour in, add; fill up.

**Zug,** *m.* drawing, pulling, pull, traction, tug; draw; tension; stretch (of leather); motion, move; passage, progress; pass; impulse, disposition; draft; current; train; procession, flock, team, etc.; range (of mountains); stroke, line; feature, trait; trend; flue; pulley; piston; drawtube (of a microscope); groove, (*pl.* **Züge**) rifling; (*Dyeing*) dip; etc.

**Zug-.** drawing, draw, pulling, traction, tractive, tensile, tension, extension; draft; train.

**Zugabe,** *f.* addition; extra, surplus; supplement; filler; (*Mach.*) tolerance. **-material,** *n.* added material, filler.

**Zugang,** *m.* admittance, access.

**zugängig, zugänglich,** *a.* accessible, approachable.

**Zugänglichkeit,** *f.* accessibility.

**Zug-beanspruchung,** *f.* tensile stress. **-dauer,** *f.* (*Dyeing*) duration of the dip. **-druckversuch,** *m.* tensile-compression test.

**zugeben,** *v.t.* add; charge, feed; permit, allow.

**zugebracht,** *p.p.* (of zubringen) brought, etc.

**zugegen,** *adv.* & *a.* present.

**zugehen,** *v.i.* go up (to), approach, go on; come, arrive; close, meet; happen, come to pass.

**zugehören,** *v.i.* belong.

**zugehörig,** *a.* belonging, pertinent, appropriate, proper; respective; accompanying, allied.

**zugemischt,** *p.a.* admixed.

**zugeschliffen,** *p.p.* (of zuschleifen) ground, etc.

**zugeschmolzen,** *p.p.* (of zuschmelzen) sealed.

**zugespitzt,** *p.a.* see zuspitzen.

**zugestandenermassen,** *adv.* admittedly.

**zugestehen,** *v.t.* concede, admit, permit.

**zugetan,** *p.a.* see zutun.

**Zugfeder,** *f.* tension spring.

**Zugfestigkeit,** *f.* tensile strength, tenacity.

**zugfrei,** *a.* free from drafts.

**zugiessen,** *v.t.* fill up by pouring; pour to, pour in.

**zügig,** *a.* (of leather) flexible, pliant; ductile; tensile, stressed.

**Zügigkeit,** *f.* pliability; ductility.

**Zug-kanal,** *m.* flue. **-klappe,** *f.* (flue) damper. **-kraft,** *f.* tractive force, traction; tension; attraction.

**zugleich,** *adv.* at the same time, at once, together.

**Zug-leistung,** *f.* tractive output or power. **linie,** *f.* (*Geom.*) tractrix. **-loch,** *n.* draft hole, air hole, vent hole. **-luft,** *f.* air current, draft. **-messer,** *m.* tensometer; draft gage; draw knife. **-mittel,** *n.* tension medium; attraction; (*Med.*) vesicant; tractor. **-muf-**

fel, *f.* (*Ceram.*) continuous muffle. **-ofen,** *m.* wind furnace, draft furnace. **-pflaster,** *n.* blistering plaster, vesicatory. **-probe,** *f.* tensile test.

**zugreifen,** *v.i.* lay hold, seize.

**Zug-rohr,** *n.*, **-röhre,** *f.* air pipe, vent pipe.

**zugrunde,** *adv.* = zu Grunde. (See Grund.)

**Zugrundelegung,** *f.* (*lit.*) foundation laying. — **unter —,** on the basis (of).

**Zug-salbe,** *f.* (*Pharm.*) rosin cerate. **-spannung,** *f.* tensile stress.

**zugunsten,** *prep. with gen.* in favor of, for the sake of.

**Zuguss,** *m.* infusion; addition (of liquid).

**zugutemachen,** *v.t.* work up, work (ores, etc.).

**zuguterletzt,** *adv.* last, finally.

**Zug-verformung,** *f.* tensile deformation. **-versuch,** *m.* tensile test, tension test. **-wagen,** *m.* tractor. **-wirkung,** *f.* pulling effect, pull.

**zuheilen,** *v.i.* heal up.

**Zuhilfenahme,** *f.* utilization, aid, recourse.

**zuhören,** *v.i.* listen, attend.

**Zuhörer,** *m.* hearer, auditor. **-schaft,** *f.* audience.

**zuinnerst,** *adv.* innermost, deep inside.

**zukitten,** *v.t.* cement up.

**zukleben, zukleistern,** *v.t.* paste up, glue up, stick together.

**zukommen,** *v.i.* come up, come to, be due, belong; get on, manage.

**zukorken,** *v.t.* cork up, stopper up.

**Zukunft,** *f.* future.

**zukünftig,** *a.* future, to come. — **zukünftige Woche,** next week.

**Zulage,** *f.* addition, increase (in pay), allowance.

**zulangen,** *v.i.* help oneself; suffice.

**zulänglich,** *a.* sufficient, adequate.

**Zulass,** *m.* admission; access; (*Mach.*) tolerance.

**zulassen,** *v.t.* admit; permit; turn on (steam, etc.); leave closed.

**zulässig,** *a.* admissible, permissible.

**Zulauf,** *m.* influx; supply, feed; inlet; rush; crowd, throng; vogue.

**zulaufen,** *v.i.* run, crowd, flock; run on; run in. — *v.t.* run in, add.

**Zulauf-flotte,** *f.* feeding (or replenishing) liquor. **-temperatur,** *f.* temperature on admission.

**zulegen,** *v.t.* add; procure, get, take; cover. — *v.i.* gain flesh.

**zulegieren,** *v.t.* alloy.

**zuleimen,** *v.t.* glue up, cement.

**zuleiten,** *v.t.* lead, conduct (in or to), let in.

**Zuleitung,** *f.* leading in or on; feed pipe, feed line, feed wire, lead wire, etc.

**Zuleitungs-rohr,** *n.*, **-röhre,** *f.* inlet tube or pipe, feed pipe.

**zuletzt,** *adv.* at last, last, finally.

**Zulieferung,** *f.* supplying; supply.

**zulöten,** *v.t.* solder up.

**zum,** *abbrev.* (zu dem) to the, at the.

**zumachen,** *v.t.* shut, close, seal. — *v.i.* be quick.

**zumal,** *adv.* chiefly, especially; all together.

**zumeist,** *adv.* for the most part, generally.

**zumessen,** *v.t.* measure out, apportion, allot.

**zumindest,** *adv.* at least.

**zumischen,** *v.t.* mix with, admix, add.

**Zumisch-pulver,** *n.* admixed powder; (for dynamite) dope. **-stoff,** *m.* admixed material, admixture.

**Zumischung,** *f.* admixture.

**zumuten,** *v.t.* expect, require.

**zunächst,** *adv.* nearest, next; first, above all.

**Zunahme,** *f.* increase; increment; growth; progress.

**Zuname,** *f.* surname, family name.

**Zünd-.** ignition, lighting, priming. **-apparat,** *m.* ignition apparatus, igniter; priming apparatus, primer.

**zündbar,** *a.* flammable, inflammable, ignitible.

**Zünd-barkeit,** *f.* flammability, inflammability, ignitibility. **-draht,** *m.* ignition wire. **-einrichtung,** *f.* ignition device. **-elektrode,** *f.* igniting electrode, igniter. **-empfindlichkeit,** *f.* ignition sensibility.

**zünden,** *v.i.* take fire, ignite. — *v.t.* set fire to, ignite, kindle, fire.

**Zunder,** *m.* tinder; forge scale, cinder; cause, occasion.

**Zünder,** *m.* lighter, igniter; fuse; fusee; cinder.

**zunderbeständig,** *a.* (*Metal.*) nonscaling.

**Zunder-beständigkeit,** *f.* nonscaling property. **-bildung,** *f.* (forge) scale formation.

**zunder-fest,** *a.* tinderproof; (*Metal.*) nonscaling. **-frei,** *a.* free from (forge) scale.

**Zunderfreiglühen,** *n.* scale-free annealing.

**Zünderfüllmasse,** *f.*, **Zündersatz,** *m.* fuse composition.

**Zunderpapier,** *n.* touch paper.

**Zunderung,** *f.* (*Metal.*) scaling.

**zündfähig,** *a.* = zündbar.

**Zünd-fähigkeit,** *f.* = Zündbarkeit. **-flämmchen,** *n.*, **-flamme,** *f.* igniting flame, pilot flame. **-funke,** *f.*, **-funken,** *m.* ignition spark. **-gas,** *n.* fuse gas. **-gerät,** *n.* = Zündapparat. **-geschwindigkeit,** *f.* ignition velocity. **-holz, -hölzchen,** *n.* match. — **schwedisches Zündhölzchen,** safety match.

**Zündholz-draht,** *m.* match splint. **-fabrik,** *f.* match factory. **-masse,** *f.* match composition. **-papier,** *n.* match paper. **-satz,** *m.* match composition.

**Zündhütchen,** *n.* percussion cap, detonating cap, blasting cap, detonator, primer. **-satz,** *m.* priming composition, priming.

**Zünd-kapsel,** *f.* = Zündhütchen. **-kerze,** *f.* spark plug; vesta, wax match. **-kerzenspannung,** *f.* spark plug voltage. **-kirsche,** *f.*

ignition pellet. **-ladung,** *f.* priming charge. **-magnet,** *m.* magneto. **-maschine,** *f.* (*Expl.*) blasting machine, priming machine, exploder. **-masse,** *f.* igniting composition, ignition mixture. **-metall,** *n.* (in)flammable metal. **-mittel,** *n.* igniting agent, priming medium, primer. **-papier,** *n.* ignition paper, touch paper. **-patrone,** *f.* priming cartridge, primer. **-pille,** *f.* pellet primer, priming drop. **-pulver,** *n.* priming powder, priming. **-punkt,** *m.* ignition point. **-satz,** *m.* priming composition, detonator. **-schnur,** *f.* fuse, match cord, match; lanyard. **-schwamm,** *m.* German tinder, punk. **-spannung,** *f.* (*Expl.*) firing voltage, ignition tension; striking potential (of an arc lamp, etc.); glow potential (in a glow tube). **-spule,** *f.* ignition coil. **-stelle,** *f.* place of ignition. **-stoff,** *m.* (in)-flammable material; igniting agent, primer.

**Zündung,** *f.* ignition; priming, primer; fuse.

**Zündungstemperatur,** *f.* temperature of ignition.

**Zünd-vorrichtung,** *f.* ignition device, igniter. **-waren,** *f.pl.* (in)flammable goods, (in)flammables. **-wärme,** *f.* heat of ignition.

**zunehmen,** *v.i.* increase, grow; grow larger, swell; advance, improve; prosper. — *v.t.* take (more).

**Zuneigung,** *f.* inclination; attachment.

**Zunft,** *f.* guild, corporation, profession, fraternity. — **-gelehrter,** *m.* professional man.

**Zunge,** *f.* tongue; blade; reed; (of a balance) pointer, needle; (of a magnet) keeper.

**züngeln,** *v.i.* (of flames) shoot out, lick. — **züngelnd,** *p.a.* lambent.

**Zungen-.** tongue, lingual, hyoid, glosso-, gloss-.

**zungenförmig,** *a.* tongue-shaped.

**Zungenzäpfchen,** *n.* epiglottis.

**zunutze machen.** make use of, put to use.

**zuoberst,** *adv.* uppermost.

**zuordnen,** *v.t.* coördinate; correlate; assign, allot.

**Zuordnung,** *f.* coördination; correlation; assignment, allotment.

**zupassen,** *v.t.* fit, adjust.

**zupfen,** *v.t.* pick, pluck, tug, pull; pick apart, tease, unravel.

**Zupf-leinwand,** *f.* lint. **-nadel,** *f.* dissecting needle. **-präparat,** *n.* teased-out preparation.

**zupichen,** *v.t.* pitch, pitch up.

**zupropfen,** *v.t.* cork up, stop up, plug up.

**zur,** *abbrev.* (zu der) to the, at the.

**zuraten,** *v.i.* advise in favor.

**Zürbelkiefer,** *f.* Swiss pine (*Pinus cembra*).

**zurechnen,** *v.t.* add, include; attribute.

**zurechnungsfähig,** *a.* accountable, responsible.

**zurecht,** *adv.* right, in order, in time. **-legen,** *v.t.* put right, arrange. **-machen,** *v.t.* get ready, prepare, adjust, line up.

**zureden,** *v.i.* speak (to), encourage, persuade.

**zureichen,** *v.i.* suffice. — *v.t.* hand (to).

**Zurichtdeckfarbe,** *f.* (*Leather*) coating color.

**zurichten,** *v.t.* prepare, make ready, dress, finish; adjust; curry (leather); leaven (dough); condition (air); size (textiles); maltreat.

**Zurichtmasse,** *f.* (*Textiles*) sizing material.

**Zurichtmittel,** *n.* (*Leather*) dressing agent.

**Zurichtung,** *f.* preparation, etc. (see zurichten).

**zurück,** *adv.* back, backward, behind. **-behalten,** *v.t.* = zurückhalten. **-bilden,** *v.t.* form again, re-form. **-bleiben,** *v.i.* remain behind; be late; be slow; fall short, be inferior; survive. **-bleibend,** *p.a.* remaining behind, etc., residual. **-bringen,** *v.t.* bring back, restore; reduce. **-drängen,** *v.t.* push or drive or force back; repress, restrain. **-erhalten,** *v.t.* recover. **-fallen,** *v.i.* fall back, be reflected, revert, relapse. **-fliessen,** *v.i.* flow back; recede, ebb. **-führbar,** *a.* traceable; reducible. **-führen,** *v.t.* trace (back); lead back, reconvey; reduce; restore; refer. **-gehen,** *v.i.* go back, return, revert; decline, deteriorate; fail.

**Zurückgehen,** *n.* return; reversion; decline; drop; failure.

**zurück-gelangen,** *v.i.* arrive back, return. **-gewinnbar,** *a.* recoverable. **-gewinnen,** *v.t.* win back, recover, reclaim. **-geworfen,** *p.a.* reflected; thrown back. **-halten,** *v.t.* keep back, retain, detain, repress, retard, stop. **-haltend,** *p.a.* reserved, shy. **-kehren,** *v.i.* return; revert. **-knallen,** *v.i.* backfire. **-kommen,** *v.i.* return, come back; decline. **-lassen,** *v.t.* leave behind, leave. **-laufen,** *v.i.* run back; recur; retrograde; recoil. **-legen,** *v.t.* put by; shelve; travel, go, live. **-nehmen,** *v.t.* take back, recall, retract. **-prallen,** *v.i.* rebound, recoil, be reflected; reverberate. **-saugen,** *v.t.* suck back, draw back (by suction). **-schlagen,** *v.i.* (of burners) strike back, flash back, backfire. **-setzen,** *v.t.* set back, put back; reduce; neglect, slight. **-spiegeln,** *v.t.* reflect. **-springen,** *v.i.* spring back, rebound, recoil; (of angles) re-enter. **-spülen,** *v.t.* rinse back, wash back. **-steigen,** *v.i.* rise back, mount back. **-stossen,** *v.t.* repel; push back.

**Zurückstossung,** *f.* repulsion; pushing back.

**Zurückstossungskraft,** *f.* repulsive force.

**zurück-strahlen,** *v.t.* & *i.* reflect. **-titrieren,** *v.t.* titrate back.

**Zurück-titrieren,** *n.*, **-titrierung,** *f.* return titration, back titration.

**zurück-treiben,** *v.t.* drive back, check. **-treten,** *v.i.* go back, recede, retire. **-verwandeln,** *v.t.* change back, reconvert. **-weichen,** *v.i.* recede, retreat, yield. **-weisen,** *v.t.* send back, decline, refuse. **-werfen,** *v.t.* reflect; throw back. **-wiegen,** *v.t.* reweigh. **-ziehen,** *v.t.* draw back, withdraw. — *v.r.* retire. — *v.i.* return.

**zurunden,** *v.t.* round, round off.

**zurüsten,** *v.t.* prepare, fit out, equip.

**zurzeit,** *adv.* at the time, for the time being.

**zus.,** *abbrev.* (zusammen) together.

**Zus.,** *abbrev.* (Zusammensetzung) composition; (Zusatz) addition

**zusagen,** *v.i.* agree, suit, please; consent, accept. — *v.t.* promise; assert.

**zusammen,** *adv.* together; altogether. **-arbeiten,** *v.i.* work together, coöperate, collaborate. **-backen,** *v.t.* & *i.* stick together, cake, agglomerate. **-ballen,** *v.t.* & *r.* agglomerate, conglomerate, ball, bunch, coagulate.

**Zusammen-ballung,** *f.* agglomeration, balling, bunching, coagulation. **-bau,** *m.* assembly, assemblage, erection.

**zusammen-bauen,** *v.t.* assemble, erect. **-binden,** *v.t.* tie (or fasten) together. **-brechen,** *v.i.* break down, collapse. **-brennen,** *v.t.* & *i.* burn together.

**Zusammenbruch,** *m.* breakdown, collapse.

**zusammendrängen,** *v.t.* press together, compress, condense.

**Zusammendrehung,** *f.* twisting, torsion.

**zusammendrückbar,** *a.* compressible.

**Zusammendrückbarkeit,** *f.* compressibility.

**zusammendrücken,** *v.t.* compress; compact.

**Zusammen-drücker,** *m.* compressor. **-drückung,** *f.* compression. **-drückungsmesser,** *m.* compressometer.

**zusammen-fallen,** *v.i.* fall (in), collapse; converge; coincide. **-falten,** *v.t.* fold together, fold up. **-fassen,** *v.t.* grasp, comprehend; comprize; collect, summarize.

**Zusammenfassung,** *f.* summary, résumé; compilation; comprehension.

**zusammen-fliessen,** *v.i.* flow together; coalesce. **-frieren,** *v.i.* freeze together; freeze with contraction. **-fügen,** *v.t.* join, unite, combine. **-gehörig,** *a.* belonging together, corresponding, correlated, (*Biol.*) homologous.

**Zusammengehörigkeit,** *f.* correlation.

**zusammen-geschliffen,** *p.p.* (of zusammenschleifen) ground together. **-gesetzt,** *p.a.* see zusammensetzen. **-gewachsen,** *p.p.* (of zusammenwachsen) grown together. **-gezogen,** *p.p.* (of zusammenziehen) drawn together, etc. **-giessen,** *v.t.* pour together.

**Zusammenhalt,** *m.* cohesion; consistency; unity.

**zusammen-haltbar,** *a.* capable of holding together, cohesive; comparable; (formerly, of gases) coercible. **-halten,** *v.i.* cohere, hold together. — *v.t.* hold together; compare.

**Zusammenhang,** *m.* coherence, cohesion; relationship, connection, correlation; consistency.

**zusammen-hangen, -hängen,** *v.i.* cohere; be connected. **-hangend, -hängend,** *p.a.* cohesive; coherent; connected. **-häufen,** *v.t.* heap up, accumulate, aggregate. **-kitten,** *v.t.* cement (or bond) together. **-klappbar,** *a.* collapsible, folding. **-kleben,** *v.t.* & *i.* stick together, agglutinate.

**Zusammen-klebung,** *f.* adhesion; agglutination. **-kunft,** *f.* convention, assembly; conference. **-lagerung,** *f.* assemblage.

**zusammen-laufen,** *v.i.* run together, converge, blend, coagulate; concur. **-legen,** *v.t.* put together, collect; fold, fold up. **-leimen,** *v.t.* agglutinate; glue together.

**Zusammenleimung,** *f.* agglutination; gluing together.

**zusammenlöten,** *v.t.* solder (together).

**Zusammenmündung,** *f.* (*Biol.*) anastomosis.

**zusammen-prallen,** *v.i.* bounce together, collide. **-pressbar,** *a.* compressible. **-pressen,** *v.t.* compress. **-reiben,** *v.t.* rub or grind together. **-rücken,** *v.t.* push together, crowd. **-rühren,** *v.t.* stir together, mix by stirring. **-schiebbar,** *a.* capable of being shoved together, collapsible. **-schleifen,** *v.t.* grind together.

**Zusammenschluss,** *m.* consolidation, combination.

**zusammen-schmelzen,** *v.t.* melt together, fuse. — *v.i.* melt, melt down; melt away, vanish **-schrumpfen,** *v.i.* shrink, shrink up; wrinkle. **-schütteln,** *v.t.* shake together; shake down. **-schütten,** *v.t.* pour together, mix. **-schweissen,** *v.t.* weld together.

**zusammensetzen,** *v.t.* compose; combine; put together; set up, construct; compound; laminate (glass). — *v.r.* be composed, consist; combine; sit together. — **zusammensetzend,** *p.a.* component, constituent. — **zusammengesetzt,** *p.a.* compound; composite; complex, complicated; (of glass) laminated.

**Zusammensetzung,** *f.* composition; synthesis; combination; construction; structure; compound: complication.

**zusammensintern,** *v.t.* & *i.* sinter together, agglomerate.

**Zusammenspiel,** *n.* interplay.

**zusammenstellen,** *v.t.* put together, join, unite, group, compile, collate, summarize.

**Zusammenstellung,** *f.* putting together, grouping, classification, combination, compilation, juxtaposition, association, assembly; summary.

**zusammenstimmen,** *v.i.* agree, accord, harmonize; vote together.

**Zusammenstoss,** *m.* collision, encounter, impact.

**zusammen-stossen,** *v.i.* come together, meet; collide; adjoin. — *v.t.* knock together; crush. **-stossend,** *p.a.* adjacent, contiguous. **-tragen,** *v.t.* collect; compile. **-treffen,** *v.i.* meet; coincide, concur.

**zusammentreten,** *v.i* go (or come) together; meet.

**zusammen-trocknen,** *v.i.* dry up, shrivel. **-wachsen,** *v.i.* grow together, concrete, coalesce, unite. **-wirken,** *v.i.* act together, coöperate; interact; synchronize. **-ziehbar,** *a.* contractible; contractile. **-ziehen,** *v.t.* draw together, contract, abridge; tighten; assemble. — *v.r.* contract, shrink; gather. **-ziehend,** *p.a.* contractive; astringent.

**Zusammenziehung,** *f.* contraction, shrinking, etc. (see zusammenziehen).

**Zusatz,** *m.* addition; admixture; supplement, appendix; corollary.

**Zusatz-.** additional, supplementary, auxiliary; admixed, added; additive. **-element,** *n.* (*Metal.*) alloying element. **-feld,** *n.* additional field, supplementary field. **-gerät,** *n.* supplementary apparatus, attachment. **-glied,** *n.* additional term, supplementary term. **-lack,** *m.* blending varnish.

**zusätzlich,** *a.* additional; additive; supplementary, auxiliary.

**Zusatz-linse,** *f.* supplementary lens. **-luft,** *f.* additional (or supplementary) air. **-material,** *n.* = Zusatzstoff. **-metall,** *n.* alloy. **-mittel,** *n.* addition agent, supplementary agent (something added to assist a reaction), admixed substance, substance used for admixture. **-patent,** *n.* patent of addition, addition patent. **-spannung,** *f.* (*Elec.*) boosting voltage. **-stoff,** *m.* admixed material; material for admixing; filler. **-waschmittel,** *n.* supplementary detergent; soap substitute. **-wasser,** *n.* added water, make-up water.

**zuschalten,** *v.t.* (*Elec.*) synchronize, also connect to.

**zuschärfen,** *v.t.* sharpen, point; (*Cryst.*) bevel.

**Zuschauer,** *m.* spectator, onlooker.

**zuschieben,** *v.t.* push to, shut; shift (to someone else).

**Zuschlag,** *m.* addition; admixture; (*Metal.*) flux; increase; extra charge.

**zuschlagen,** *v.t.* add (as, a flux); hit hard, slam, bang; close up (casks).

**Zuschlag-erz,** *n.* fluxing ore. **-kalkstein,** *m.* limestone for flux.

**zuschleifen,** *v.t.* grind, cut, polish.

**zuschmelzen,** *v.t.* close by melting, seal.

**zuschmieren,** *v.t.* gum up, clog; smear over.

**zuschneiden,** *v.t.* cut out, cut; trim.

**zuschreiben,** *v.t.* dedicate; credit; attribute; assign; add.

**Zuschrift,** *f.* letter, writing; dedication.

**Zuschuss,** *m.* extra sheet; addition; contribution; allowance.

**zuschütten,** *v.t.* fill up, fill in, add (to).

**zusehen,** *v.i.* look (at, on or upon); witness.

**zusehends, zusehens,** *adv.* visibly, noticeably.

**zusetzen,** *v.t.* add; mix; alloy; adulterate; replenish; contribute; stop up; obstruct, bar; lose (money, etc.).

**Zusetzmittel,** *n.* reagent.

**zusichern,** *v.t.* assure, promise.

**Zus.-P.,** *abbrev.* (Zusatzpatent) addition to a patent.

**zuspitzen,** *v.t.* point, sharpen or taper to a point. — *v.r.* taper to a point; come to a crisis. — **zugespitzt,** *p.a.* tapering to a point, pointed, acuminate.

**Zuspitzung,** *f.* pointing, tapering to a point, acumination; point.

**zusprechen,** *v.t.* impart by speaking; adjudicate; attribute. — *v.i.* speak (to); cheer; call (on); agree (with), suit.

**Zuspruch,** *m.* encouragement; address; call.

**Zustand,** *m.* state; condition; phase; stage; status; situation, circumstances.

**zustande bringen.** carry thru, accomplish.

**zustande kommen.** come about, take place.

**zuständig,** *a.* appropriate; competent.

**Zuständigkeit,** *f.* competence; jurisdiction.

**Zustands-änderung,** *f.* change of state. **-diagramm,** *n.* phase diagram. **-formel,** *f.* state formula. **-gebiet,** *n.* phase region. **-gleichung,** *f.* equation of state. **-grösse,** *f.* variable of state, variable quantity; specif., entropy. **-kurve,** *f.* curve of state. **-schaubild,** *n.* phase diagram. **-summe,** *f.* partial function. **-verschiebung,** *f.* displacement of state, change in state.

**zustecken,** *v.t.* pin together; convey secretly.

**zustehen,** *v.i.* pertain, belong; be incumbent (on), become, suit.

**zustellen,** *v.t.* block up, close; line (a furnace); deliver.

**Zustellungsmasse,** *f.* (*Metal.*) lining mass.

**zustimmen,** *v.i.* agree, consent, assent.

**Zustimmung,** *f.* agreement, consent, assent.

**zustopfen,** *v.t.* stop up.

**zustöpseln,** *v.t.* stopper, cork.

**Zustrebekraft,** *f.* centripetal force.

**zustreben,** *v.i.* strive (for); tend (toward).

**Zustrom,** *m.* inflow, influx.

**zuströmen,** *v.i.* flow in, stream in.

**zutage,** *adv.* to light, to or on the surface. — **— bringen,** bring to light, reveal. — **— kommen, — treten,** come to light, appear, become evident. — **— liegen,** be on the surface, be obvious.

**Zutat,** *f.* ingredient; addition, complement, trimming, furniture.
**zuteilen,** *v.t.* assign, allot, distribute, ration; (*Tech.*) feed, supply; award.
**zuträglich,** *a.* good, profitable, beneficial.
**zutrauen,** *v.t.* credit (with), expect (of); confide (in).
**zutraulich,** *a.* confiding, confidential.
**zutreffen,** *v.i.* agree, correspond, prove correct, come true. — **zutreffend,** *p.a.* agreeing, corresponding, concordant; conclusive.
**Zutritt,** *m.* access, admittance, admission.
**zutröpfeln, zutropfen,** *v.i.* drop in, drip in. — **— lassen,** add drop by drop.
**zutun,** *v.t.* close, shut; add, furnish. — **zugetan,** *p.a.* attached, devoted.
**Zutun,** *n.* coöperation, aid.
**zuverlässig,** *a.* reliable; certain, authentic.
**Zuverlässigkeit,** *f.* reliability, trustworthiness.
**Zuversicht,** *f.* reliance, confidence, certainty.
**zuversichtlich,** *a.* confident, positive, certain.
**zuviel,** *adv.* too much, too many.
**Zuviel,** *n.* too much, excess.
**zuvor,** *adv.* before, beforehand, previously.
**zuvörderst,** *adv.* first of all; previously.
**zuvor-kommend,** *p.a.* anticipating; obliging. **-tun,** *v.t.* surpass, outdo.
**Zuwachs,** *m.* increase, increment, growth, accretion.
**zuwachsen,** *v.i.* grow together; clog up; accrue.
**zuwege bringen.** bring about, bring to pass.
**zuweilen,** *adv.* sometimes, at times.
**zuweisen,** *v.t.* allot, assign; refer to.
**zuwenden,** *v.t. & r.* turn.
**zuwider,** *prep. & adv.* against, contrary (to), repugnant (to). **-handeln,** *v.i.* act against, counteract.
**zuziehen,** *v.t.* draw shut or together; tighten; call in, invite, incur. — *v.i.* pull; move in, enter.
**zuzüglich,** *prep. with gen.* with addition of, including.
**zw.,** *abbrev.* (zwischen) between; (zwar) indeed, to be sure; (zwecks) for the purpose of.
**Zwackeisen,** *n.* pincers.
**zwacken,** *v.t.* pinch; tease.
**zwang,** *pret.* (of zwingen) forced, etc.
**Zwang,** *m.* stress, constraint; compulsion, coercion, force, pressure.
**zwängen,** *v.t.* force, press, coerce.
**Zwanglauflehre,** *f.* kinematics.
**zwanglos,** *a.* unrestrained, unrestricted, free; (of periodicals) irregular in appearance.
**Zwangs-.** forced, coercive, compulsory.
**zwang(s)läufig,** *a.* guided, restricted, (en)forced; (*Mach.*) positive.
**Zwang(s)-läufigkeit,** *f.* guided motion, forced motion. **-syndikat,** *n.* compulsory syndicate.
**zwangsweise,** *adv.* by force, by compulsion. — *a.* compulsory, forcible.
**zwanzig,** *a.* twenty.
**Zwanzigflächner,** *m.* icosahedron.
**zwanzigste,** *a.* twentieth.
**zwar,** *adv.* indeed, to be sure, truly. — **und —,** namely, that is.
**Zweck,** *m.* object, end, aim, goal, purpose; tack, pin, peg.
**zweckdienlich,** *a.* appropriate, serviceable, suitable, efficient, useful.
**Zwecke,** *f.* tack, pin, peg.
**zweck-entsprechend, -haft,** *a.* = zweckmässig.
**Zweckforschung,** *f.* practical research.
**zweck-los,** *a.* aimless, useless. **-mässig,** *a.* suitable, appropriate, expedient.
**Zweckmässigkeit,** *f.* suitability, expediency.
**zwecks,** *prep. with gen.* for the purpose of.
**zweckwidrig,** *a.* inappropriate, unsuitable, inexpedient.
**zwei,** *a.* two.
**zwei-, Zwei-.** two-, di-, bi-, double.
**zwei-achsig,** *a.* biaxial. **-armig,** *a.* two-armed. **-atomig,** *a.* diatomic. **-äugig,** *a.* binocular. **-badig,** *a.* two-bath.
**Zweibadverfahren,** *n.* two-bath process.
**zwei-basisch,** *a.* dibasic. **-deutig,** *a.* ambiguous, equivocal. **-einhalbfach,** *a.* two-and-a-half-fold. **-einhalbmal,** *adv.* two and a half times.
**zweierlei,** *a.* of two kinds, different; twofold. **-wertig,** *a.* having two valencies.
**Zweierschale,** *f.* duplet shell or ring.
**Zweierstoss,** *m.* collision of two bodies.
**zweifach,** *a.* twofold, double, dual, bi-. — **— chromsaures Kali,** potassium dichromate. — **— kohlensaures Natron,** sodium bicarbonate.
**zweifach-basisch,** *a.* dibasic. **-frei,** *a.* having two degrees of freedom, bivariant.
**Zweifachschwefeleisen,** *n.* iron disulfide.
**zweifachschwefelsauer,** *a.* bisulfate of.
**Zweifachschwefelzinn,** *n.* tin disulfide.
**zweifachungesättigt,** *a.* doubly unsaturated.
**Zweifachverbindung,** *f.* binary compound.
**zweifädig,** *a.* two-threaded, bifilar.
**Zweifarbendruck,** *m.* two-color print(ing).
**zweifarbig,** *a.* two-colored, two-color, bicolored, dichromatic, dichroic.
**Zweifarbigkeit,** *f.* dichroism.
**Zweifel,** *m.* doubt, question, uncertainty.
**zweifel-haft,** *a.* doubtful, dubious. **-los,** *a.* doubtless, indubitable.
**zweifeln,** *v.i.* doubt; hesitate.
**zweifelsohne,** *adv.* without doubt, doubtless.
**zweiflächig,** *a.* two-faced, dihedral.
**Zweig,** *m.* twig, sprig; branch; (mountain) spur; (*Tech.*) branch, leg, arm, etc.
**zweigängig,** *a.* (*Mach.*) double-thread.

**zweigestaltig,** *a.* dimorphous, dimorphic.
**Zweigestaltung,** *f.* dimorphism.
**zweigipfelig,** *a.* two-peaked, double-peaked.
**Zweigleitung,** *f.* branch line.
**zweigliedrig,** *a.* two-membered; binary; (*Math.*) binomial.
**Zweig-rohr,** *n.*, **-röhre,** *f.* branch tube or pipe, lateral. **-strom,** *m.* branch current.
**zweihalsig,** *a.* two-necked.
**Zweiheit,** *f.* duality, dualism; couple.
**zwei-höck(e)rig,** *a.* two-humped, double-hump. **-jährig,** *a.* of two years, biennial.
**Zweikern-.** binuclear; as, **Zweikernchinon,** binuclear quinone.
**zwei-kernig,** *a.* binuclear. **-lebig,** *a.* amphibious.
**zweimal,** *adv.* twice.
**zweimalig,** *a.* done twice, double, repeated.
**Zweimalschmelzerei,** *f.* (*Metal.*) two-stage melting process, specif. Walloon process.
**Zweimetall,** *n.* bimetal.
**zweimonatlich,** *a. & adv.* bimonthly, every two months.
**Zweiphasen-.** (*Elec.*) two-phase.
**zwei-phasig,** *a.* two-phase, diphase. **-polig,** *a.* bipolar, dipole, double-pole. **-quantig,** *a.* of two quanta, 2-quantum.
**Zweirad,** *n.* bicycle.
**zwei-reihig,** *a.* two-series; double-row, two-rowed. **-säurig,** *a.* diacid. **-schalig,** *a.* bivalve, bivalvular. **-schenkelig, -schenklig,** *a.* having two legs or branches. **-schichtig,** *a.* two-layer; two-shift.
**Zweischlangendurchfluss,** *m.* two-coil flow.
**zwei-schneidig,** *a.* two-edged, double-edged. **-seitig,** *a.* two-sided, bilateral; double-face, duplex. **-spitzig,** *a.* (of curves) two-peaked.
**Zweistoff-.** two-component, binary. **-legierung,** *f.* two-component alloy, binary alloy.
**zwei-stufig,** *a.* two-stage. **-stündig,** *a.* lasting two hours.
**Zweitaktverfahren,** *n.* two-stroke cycle.
**zweite,** *a.* second.
**zweiteilig,** *a.* two-part, bipartite, two-piece.
**Zweiteilung,** *f.* bipartition, bisection; binary fission; dichotomy; bifurcation.
**zweitens,** *adv.* secondly.
**zweitklassig,** *a.* second-class, second-rate.
**Zweiunddreissigerschale,** *f.* shell of thirty-two (electrons).
**zweiwandig,** *a.* two-walled, double-walled.
**Zweiweg(e)-hahn,** *m.* two-way cock. **-ventil,** *n.* two-way valve.
**zweiwellig,** *a.* two-wave, (of a curve) double-hump.
**Zweiwelligkeit,** *f.* two-wave property.
**zweiwertig,** *a.* bivalent, divalent.
**Zweiwertigkeit,** *f.* bivalence.
**zweizählig,** *a.* twofold, double, binary, (*Bot.*) binate.
**Zweizweck-.** dual-purpose.
**Zwerchfell,** *n.* (*Anat.*) diaphragm.
**Zwerg,** *m.* dwarf. **-welle,** *f.* midget wave, dwarf wave, microwave.
**Zwetsche, Zwetschge, Zwetschke,** *f.* plum.
**zwetschgenblau,** *a.* plum-blue, plum.
**Zwickel,** *m.* wedge; try cock, proof cock.
**zwicken,** *v.t.* pinch, nip; gripe; worry.
**Zwickzange,** *f.* pincers.
**Zwieback,** *m.* biscuit, specif. rusk, zwieback.
**Zwiebel,** *f. & m.* bulb, specif. onion.
**zwiebelartig,** *a.* bulbous; alliaceous.
**zwiebelförmig,** *a.* bulbshaped, bulbar.
**Zwiebel-gewächs,** *n.* bulbous plant. **-linse,** *f.* biconvex lens. **-marmor,** *m.* cipolin. **-öl,** *n.* onion oil.
**zwiebelrot,** *a.* onion-red.
**Zwiebelsaft,** *m.* onion juice.
**zwiefach,** *a.* twofold, double.
**Zwie-licht,** *n.* twilight. **-metall,** *n.* bimetal, clad metal.
**zwiespaltig,** *a.* split, forked, bifid; divided, disunited.
**Zwilling,** *m.* twin.
**Zwillingsachse,** *f.* twinning axis.
**zwillingsartig,** *a. & adv.* in the form of twins, of the nature of twins.
**Zwillings-bildung,** *f.* twin formation, twinning. **-doppelverbindung,** *f.* conjugated double linkage. **-ebene, -fläche,** *f.* twinning plane. **-kerne,** *m.pl.* twin nuclei. **-kristall,** *m.* twin crystal. **-prisma,** *n.* biprism. **-salz,** *n.* double salt.
**Zwinge,** *f.* clamp, cramp; vise; ferrule, hoop.
**zwingen,** *v.t.* force, compel, constrain; subdue, conquer. — **zwingend,** *p.a.* cogent, compelling.
**Zwinger,** *m.* wedge; enclosure, keep; coercer.
**Zwirn,** *m.* twine, twist, thread. **-band,** *n.* tape.
**zwirnen,** *v.t.* twist, twine, throw (silk).
**Zwirnfaden,** *m.* (twisted) thread.
**zwischen,** *prep.* between, among.
**zwischen-.** inter-, intermediate, middle, mid-.
**Zwischen-bad,** *n.* intermediate bath. **-behälter,** *m.* intermediate container, (*Petroleum*) surge tank. **-bild,** *n.* intermediate image. **-boden,** *m.* intermediate bottom; diaphragm.
**zwischendurch,** *adv.* thru; at intervals.
**Zwischen-erzeugnis,** *f.* intermediate product, intermediate. **-fall,** *m.* incident, episode. **-farbe,** *f.* intermediate color; (*Leather*) intermediate pit. **-ferment,** *n.* intermediate enzyme. **-form,** *f.* intermediate form. **-frequenz,** *f.* intermediate frequency. **-gefäss,** *n.* intermediate vessel or receptacle. **-gerbung,** *f.* intermediate tannage.

**zwischengeschichtet,** *a.* interstratified.

**Zwischen-gewebe,** *n.* interstitial tissue. **-gewebesubstanz,** *f.* intercellular substance. **-glasurmalerei,** *f.* (*Ceram.*) painting between glazes. **-glied,** *n.* intermediate or connecting member, intermediate. **-glühen,** *n.*, **-glühung,** *f.* (*Metal.*) intermediate anneal(ing). **-händler,** *m.* middleman, commission man; mediator. **-klemmungsmasse,** *f.* = Zwischenmasse. **-körper,** *m.* intermediate body (or substance). **-kühler,** *m.* intercooler. **-kühlung,** *f.* intercooling. **-lage,** *f.* intermediate layer; intermediate position; interposition. **-lagerung,** *f.* interstratification.

**zwischen-legen,** *v.t.* interpose, insert. **-liegend,** *a.* intermediate.

**Zwischen-mass,** *n.* intermediate size. **-masse,** *f.* ground substance; interstitial matter.

**zwischenmolekular,** *a.* intermolecular.

**Zwischen-niveau,** *n.* intermediate level; interface. **-optik,** *f.* intermediate optical device or apparatus. **-produkt,** *n.* intermediate product, intermediate; (*Ores,* etc.) middlings; interposition. **-raum,** *m.* intermediate space; interstice, interspace, gap; interval. **-reaktion,** *f.* intermediate reaction.

**zwischenschalten,** *v.t.* insert, interpose, intercalate, (*Elec.*) cut in.

**Zwischen-schicht,** *f.* intermediate layer or stratum, interlayer. **-sorte,** *f.* intermediate sort or quality. **-spülung,** *f.* intermediate rinsing.

**zwischenstaatlich,** *a.* international.

**Zwischenstadium,** *n.* intermediate stage.

**zwischenständig,** *a.* intermediate.

**Zwischen-stein,** *m.* (*Copper*) blue metal. **-stellung,** *f.* intermediate (or middle) position. **-stück,** *n.* intermediate piece or part; connecting piece; insert. **-stufe,** *f.* intermediate stage. **-stufenvergüten,** *n.* (*Metal.*) austempering. **-substanz,** *f.* interstitial substance, ground substance. **-ton,** *m.* (of colors) medium or intermediate tone or shade. **-träger,** *m.* intermediate carrier or support; intermediary. **-trocknung,** *f.* intermediate drying. **-verbindung,** *f.* intermediate compound. **-vergütung,** *f.* (*Metal.*) austempering. **-wand,** *f.* partition; diaphragm; baffle; septum; shelf; (*Paper*) midfeather (of a beater). **-wärmung,** *f.* intermediate heating. **-weite,** *f.* distance between, interval. **-wirbel-.** (*Anat.*) intervertebral. **-zeit,** *f.* interval, interim.

**zwischenzellig,** *a.* intercellular.

**Zwischen-zellraum,** *m.* intercellular space. **-zünder,** *m.* (*Expl.*) intermediate charge, booster. **-zustand,** *m.* intermediate state.

**zwistig,** *a.* disputing; in dispute.

**Zwistigkeit,** *f.* difference, dispute, discord.

**Zwitter,** *m.* hermaphrodite; hybrid; bastard; mongrel; (*Petrog.*) zwitter. **-ion,** *n.* hybrid ion, amphoteric ion.

**zwl.,** *abbrev.* (ziemlich wenig löslich) rather difficultly soluble.

**zwo,** *a.* = zwei, two.

**zwölf,** *a.* twelve.

**Zwölf-eck,** *n.* dodecagon. **-fingerdarm,** *m.* duodenum. **-flach,** *n.* dodecahedron.

**zwölfflächig,** *a.* dodecahedral.

**Zwölfflächner,** *m.* dodecahedron.

**zwölfseitig,** *a.* twelve-sided, dodecahedral; dodecagonal.

**zwölfte,** *a.* twelfth.

**Zyan,** *n.* cyanogen. For compounds see Cyan-.

**zygotisch,** *a.* (*Biol.*) zygotic.

**zyklisch,** *a.* cyclic.

**Zyklisieren,** *n.* cyclization.

**Zykloide,** *f.* cycloid.

**zykloidisch,** *a.* cycloidal.

**Zyklon,** *m.* cyclone.

**Zyklus,** *m.* cycle, circle.

**Zylinder,** *m.* cylinder. **-chen,** *n.* small cylinder.

**Zylinderdämpfer,** *m.* cylinder steamer.

**zylinderförmig,** *a.* cylinder-shaped, cylindrical

**zylindern, zylindrieren,** *v.t.* calender.

**Zylinderöl,** *n.* cylinder oil.

**zylindrisch,** *a.* cylindrical.

**Zymotechnik, Zymotechnie,** *f.* zymotechnics.

**zymotechnisch,** *a.* zymotechnic(al).

**Zyper-.** Cyprus, Cyprian; cypress. **-vitriol,** *n.* blue vitriol, copper sulfate. **-wein,** *m.* Cyprus wine.

**Zypresse,** *f.* cypress.

**Zypressen-.** see Cypressen-.

**Zyst-.** see also Cyst-.

**Zyste,** *f.* cyst.

**Zyt-.** cyt-.

**Zytolyse,** *f.* cytolysis.

**z.Z., z.Zt.,** *abbrev.* (zur Zeit) at the time; **at** present; acting.